cried with a curiously happy laugh. "Wait; do not believe me a madman. I have more riddles to elucidate if you can spare me the patience."

"I have a fabulous appetite for old wives' tales," Gozzi admitted rudely, and Peter Innocent was quiet and kind in his silence.

"Good," said the Chevalier. "We were at Soissons, were we not? At Soissons in a cold December, with a northeast wind and seventy miles dividing it from the classic gayety of Versailles. Here, among Gothic churches and darker mediæval memories of Saint Crispin the Shoemaker and Louis the Pious, here where Becket prayed and Abélard despaired, Bernis came alone and sorrowful, having put his trust in princes, and served his country better than his King's mistress.

"Imagine, if you are something kindlier than stone, the desolation of that Christmas season, when in Soissons the Gothic roses of Notre Dame were carved in snow, and the Cardinal de Bernis sat alone in his vast apartment. He had caused no fire to be lighted, no supper to be laid, and when the chimes, like stars made audible, began to pierce the midnight with rejoicing, he stopped his ears against their voices and wept the burning tears of Lucifer fallen from heaven.

"At that moment, out of the darkness, upon the wings of the bells as it were, and feathered with snow like a little bird, Caterina came to him."

"Thank God!" said Carlo Gozzi, fervently. Peter Innocent said nothing.

"She folded him in her gray cloak, that was all feathered and furred with the snow, and she kissed his beautiful cold hands. It was the first kiss she had ever given him; she gave it to the lion who had delivered her from the power of the dog, at Venice, in the room of mirrors, on an evening of full carnival, when she was only fourteen years old."

"I am glad she came," said Carlo Gozzi, adding, after he had cleared his throat, "I suppose, then, that we are to understand that Rosalba Berni is the offspring of this interesting union!"

"Yes, you are to understand precisely that, my dear Count; I fear you are incapable of fully appreciating the poignancy of the

situation, but the bare facts you are at liberty to understand,"
answered the Chevalier with impudent urbanity. He finished the
tale, turning his blazing eyes towards Peter Innocent, who continued to say nothing.

"When Caterina came to Soissons on Christmas Eve, she was
seventeen years old and a widow. At the time Bernis was past
forty, and tired by the vanities of a Dead Sea dream, an ashy-
flavored world. Six years later, when Rosalba was born in the
South, her father could laugh very lightly as he sprinkled her
with almond blossoms and peach blossoms and cherry blossoms
or tickled her lips with a pigeon's feather. Perhaps he was happy
because he had been recalled to court, where he had magnificently
rejected the seals of office; perhaps he was happy because he was
Archbishop of Albi. Perhaps, on the other hand, he was happy
because of Rosalba, who had been born in happiness in the South,
in a farmhouse whose outer walls were covered with espaliered
peach trees, and whose windows were fringed with climbing roses.
Upon the day of her birth a golden peach knocked at the door
and a white rose flew into the window. Bernis ate the peach and
gave the rose to Caterina. To the child they gave the name Rosalba.

"At Albi, the Archbishop's palace is a fortified castle of the
Middle Ages, and perhaps it is not strange that Bernis loved better
the farmhouse with the espaliered fruit-trees. Here for five years
a golden age endured; a little world existed for a time, round and
smooth and perfect as a peach. A bitter stone was hidden in its
heart, but before Bernis set his teeth to that his felicity was absolute. Then, in the plenitude of summer, Caterina died.

"Bernis gave every rose in the garden to Caterina; she clasped
them with gentle indifference. In this same manner she accepted
his last kiss; he was glad enough to go to Rome, to assist at the
conclave which elected Lorenzo Ganganelli. He had a chill conviction of her forgetfulness.

"Rosalba was conveyed to Paris in the care of an impoverished
cousin of her father's; this gentlewoman was amiable, but frivolous and injudicious. Having acquired a little wealth through the
generosity of her kinsman Bernis, she repaired to Versailles, taking
the child with her. There, in the midst of that sumptuous, but
effete, civilization, Rosalba was remarked by Madame Necker for

THE

BORZOI

READER

EDITED WITH AN INTRODUCTION AND NOTES BY
CARL VAN DOREN

1936
NEW YORK
ALFRED A KNOPF

CONTENTS

[iii]

THE BORZOI READER

Contents

Introduction

I F there has ever been another anthology like this I do not know it. Talking with Alfred Knopf about the books his house had published over twenty-one years, I said that the total list made up a kind of work of art, and that a rigorous selection from it in a single volume might be, still more strictly, a work of art too. Some editorial instinct in me suddenly thought, and said, that I myself should enjoy selecting such a book. Alfred Knopf said at once that if I would do that he would give me a free hand. He has done it. The choices which have gone into the anthology are all mine, all but one my first choices. I have excluded long novels, notably the viking-sized *Kristin Lavransdatter*, *Growth of the Soil*, and *The Magic Mountain*, and have given room that any one of them would have more than taken up to five short novels. I have excluded longer works not fiction. Since space is arbitrary, I had to be. There is only one excerpt from a longer work: Mencken on the nature of slang, which without its footnotes may be read as an independent essay although it is a chapter out of *The American Language*. On other grounds I have confined myself to what was written, or translated, in the twentieth century. As most of the book would be in this century's special idiom, it seemed better to admit nothing which, coming from another age, might be discordant to the general tone.

While the volume is in a sense a memorial, I have tried to avoid being merely historical or representative. No writer has been included only because he stood for something or other, no writing only because it illustrated some type. I have asked of everything selected whether it seemed to me excellent in itself.

Excellence is a term which is nearly as vague as taste. We say that a thing is excellent with a kind of condescending approval, and we think of taste as concerned with petty, pretty matters. By excellent I mean, literally, surpassing, and I think that taste is the man as truly as style is. This is what makes it so hard and so unsatisfying to argue about tastes. Each debater is really talking about himself, about his whole conscious and unconscious history, and about the point of opinion at which he has arrived. I know well enough that my taste in literature is not what it was forty years ago, or thirty, or twenty, or ten. Decade after decade I have found myself growing out of one set of perceptions and judgments and into another. Experience changes even a critic. I remember that when I was fifteen I copied Longfellow's *Psalm of Life* on my first typewriter, framed it with my own hands, and hung it on the wall over my desk. I then thought it profound and original. Not till I had met all these maxims in dozens of other writers, often more powerfully stated, did it strike me that the *Psalm* was melodious commonplaces and little more. When I was twenty I thought Ibsen's *Ghosts* as lofty and shattering as any tragedy of the Greeks. I went on thinking of it as that until a few years ago when I read it again and incredulously discovered that it now seemed to be mere Scandinavian melodrama. After every important experience of my life I have been a different reader as well as a different man, my eyes newly opened by my experience to similar experiences in books. The process is as continuous as life itself, except where, as sometimes happens, a rigor sets in and growth stops. What has seemed elevated may come to seem toplofty. What has seemed

finely constructed may come to seem machine-made. What has
seemed true may come to seem trite. Or the changes may be in the
other direction. Young readers may be cold to dramas which in
their later years will move them. Again and again I have, rereading some book which I thought I had read carefully, been surprised
by what I did not know was there. I read Montaigne through after
a quarter of a century, and I could hardly believe that it was the
same book. Not only did I recognize as arrestingly true many observations which I should once have passed over, but I also noted
in the expression many turns of language, wisdom happily compacted in a phrase, proud and stirring reticence, insinuating candor, which formerly I had not had enough knowledge to have a
taste for. If I had that vanity which makes some men want to appear always consistent I should be a good deal embarrassed by the
thought of some books I have at one time or another admired.
Since taste is the man, and every man has been several men, every
man must have had several tastes. But as the several men in every
man have a strong line of kinship running through them, so have
his several tastes.

When I was a boy I read as most boys do: for the stories and the
music. When I was a scholar in a university I read with historical
and technical considerations in mind. When I became a journalist
I had to learn to read no longer as a specialist but as a whole man.
Criticism, I then reflected, might be said to have three dimensions
in that it was concerned with the good, the true, and the beautiful
in literature. These dimensions did not satisfy me. A masterpiece
might have all of them and still not be alive. Literature, I then
wrote, " may represent the good, may speak the truth, may use the
modes of beauty — any one or all of these things. Call the good the
bow which lends the power; call the truth the string which fixes
the direction; call the beautiful the arrow which wings and stings.
But there is still the arm in which the true life of the process lies.
Or, to change the figure, one of those gods who in the mythologies
model men out of clay may have good clay and a true purpose and
may shape his figure beautifully; but there is still the indispensable
task of breathing the breath of life into it before it will wake and
go its own course and continue its breed to other generations." I
had just been reading James Branch Cabell's *Figures of Earth* and

I took this image from Manuel. " Life," I went on, " is obviously
what makes the difference between human sculpture and divine
creation; it is the same element which makes the difference between good literature and dead literature."

This seems to me now to be metaphorical and inexact, but it
does make a point which I think is fundamental and without which
taste in literature becomes dilettantism. Any sound taste must demand that literature shall deal with something that is alive and
shall scrutinize it, at least with the imagination, at first hand. Take
almost any one of the common run of novels. The story goes its
course with little reference to what you know perfectly well would
happen in such a case. The characters are not like the people you
know, do not think, feel, act, or talk like them — now that you
come to study them as compared with your experience. They and
their behavior are not drawn from flesh and blood but from the
conventions of this kind of literature. So many novels of the inferior sort have been written that they make a separate universe,
a stream of fiction flowing like a mist across the face of reality
without touching it or being touched by it. In all the popular forms
of literature the same thing happens. They seem to escape from
fact and float with a soft momentum of their own. Nor is this true
only of infantile romances. The recent gangster novels and plays
and films at first seemed as true as murder, but they soon were as
conventional as saints' lives. Good literature always has to struggle
against this tendency in literary tradition. That is why most good
writers try to get back to nature and why at the beginning they
often meet with resistance from a public taste which has half forgotten what nature is like.

A strong, sure taste can always feel the difference in a given piece
of writing between what has been seen or understood or imagined
at first hand — and so remains alive — and what is mere literary
echo — and so is soon dead. The difference does not lie in surface
realism. For example the play which I have here included, *Of Thee
I Sing*, is hilarious foolery. But beneath the plot, showing through
in every line, is evidence that the playwrights had looked intently
and critically at American political life, had come to conclusions
about it, and had burlesqued and parodied it with satiric accuracy.
Enoch Soames tells the story of a man who sold himself to the

devil, but tells it so circumstantially that it brings the old story home to familiar life. Soames, foolish Faust, is the essence of all silly poets studied from that life. Though almost half of *This Simian World* is taken up with fancies of what life on the earth would be like if some other race besides mankind had risen to dominion, every fancy suggests a fact of human experience, seen with alert and speculative eyes. And so fantastic a fable as that in *The Venetian Glass Nephew* is grounded in the most realistic perception of the incompatibility between such a husband as Virginio and such a wife as Rosalba, or — the hint cannot be missed — between any ideal man and any real woman. Here is a fairy-tale based upon irony, and irony based upon the closest observation.

There is a kind of downright taste which can find reality only in the blunter forms of realism. But, though this may sound like a paradox, reality is not always realistic. Many things happen that do not seem credible. Timid people somehow manage to disregard them. Bolder minds accept them, knowing that life is large and varied and unexpected. And so is literature, " which collects, transmutes, and utters life." In spite of all that may be done to press literature into this or that useful service — and useful service is one of its functions — it often eludes the regimenting will and works waywardly and indirectly. For literature is produced always by individuals. Undistinguished literature is all more or less alike because the undistinguished producers of it are. Distinguished literature, like its producers, is highly differentiated. Taste too must be capable of variety. Of course there is no taste which embraces every mode of excellence with equal understanding and judgment. But it is possible for one critic to feel many kinds of excellence and to interpret them to readers of many tastes.

I here present a miscellany as varied as my taste and the available materials permit. The selections can speak for themselves. As for my taste, I should perhaps explain that I am usually indifferent to writers unless I feel in their work that they have experienced or imagined life closely and accurately, have found something important to say, and have, with whatever devices, known how to say it with effective art. I leave the sweet, the quaint, the well-intentioned, the voluble, the improvisatory to other tastes.

C.V.D.

Novels

THE SHORT novel is the true pocket theater. It takes about as long to read one as to go to a play, and it calls for something like the same attention. If the play has the advantage that it is acted out to the life, the short novel has the counter-advantage that it may be enjoyed at the most convenient time in the least distracting circumstances. There are persons to whom the ceremony of the theater means so much — the audience ready and anxious to be held together in a general pleasure, the regulated tempo of the performance, the statutory intermissions, the mounting excitement, and the resolving climax — that they prefer almost any play to almost any short novel. Persons who do not need these helps to their imaginations, and who do not particularly value the ceremony for itself, are likely to find a purer pleasure in reading. As they visualize the action, none of the actors is miscast or unconvincing, nothing merely theatrical creeps in as stage business, no moment in the story is drawn out for effect or hurried over. In the theater there can be only one timing for everybody. The action must move at a pace which will keep the entire audience, whatever their natural speeds, from either lagging behind and being lost or from running ahead and having to stop and think while events catch up with them. The reader of a short novel can set his own pace. If he wants to race he may, or linger over a scene or sentence, or even turn back to confirm his memory and strengthen his perception of what is happening.

If the reader of a short novel is freer than the spectator of a play, so is the novelist freer than the dramatist in the choice and handling of his theme. In a play the action must be visible or audible and, though time may be supposed to have passed during the intermissions, must be compressed to the two hours or so in which it is represented. A short novel may be a whole chronicle in essence, the outline of a complete life-story, as in Willa Cather's *My Mortal Enemy*. Like *A Lost Lady*, this companion to it is studied from an actual person and closely follows her history. The method of the narrative is as natural as the experience of the girl, later woman, who remembers. She tells about her first meeting with Myra, recalls what had gone before in Myra's life and now came to have some meaning for the girl, shows Myra living in New York, where she might have been happy but was not, and then skips, as the narrator's experience did, through ten years to the Pacific coast, where Myra appears with her dissatisfactions grown to desperate rebellion and her native violence out of control. No play, I think, could have done what this novel does. In a play the character of Myra would have had to be established from the first and to be presented in full view of the audience. In the novel Myra emerges gradually through the medium of Nellie's comprehension of her and reveals herself only at the cumulative end, when she cries out: " Why must I die like this, alone with my mortal enemy? " — the husband with whom she romantically ran away from the life which she was meant to lead and which she now unavailingly regrets. It would have been difficult in a play to show how violent the nature of Myra was without exhibiting it in spectacular detail. In a novel, which has no machinery but the voice of the story-teller, the story is free to confine itself largely to a single character and to reveal that step by step until the final secret comes out like the simple conclusion to which a scientist arrives after piecemeal research.

Nor could any playwright translate into visible and audible drama the story of Thomas Mann's *Death in Venice*. Hardly a thing that Gustave Aschenbach outwardly does or says is of real importance in the narrative. All the action takes place within his spirit, invaded at the height of its powers by an overwhelming attraction toward something beautiful, disruptive, and fatal. In a sense, the novel has no scenes at all. The story lies in the cells of a silent brain, along the nerves of a solitary man. It would be as hard to dramatize as the story of healthy tissue set upon by cancer. Yet the novelist can follow the ins and outs of the disease and pour light upon the invisible, give voice to the inaudible.

The Venetian Glass Nephew by Elinor Wylie might of course be made into an opera, but I am sure I should still prefer it as a novel. When, on the stage, after the hocus-pocus of manufacturing the cardinal a nephew out of glass, some actor got up and walked, I should know he was flesh and blood and had been from his cradle. And to see the actress who had been playing Rosalba for three acts, now entering the furnace to be baked into porcelain, would be fearful if it were not funny. Such symbolisms I can easily imagine when nothing but the imagination is involved, not when I am half imagining and half seeing. In a short novel symbolism may be powerful. In a play it is dangerous.

The range of the short novel may be seen in a comparison of *The Venetian Glass Nephew* with *The Sailor's Return* by David Garnett. They are both stories of badly-matched marriages: the abstract Virginio and his concrete Rosalba, the English William and his African Tulip. With a bold and cynical irony Elinor Wylie implies that nothing human can be done. Rosalba has to be turned into a formal work of art to be happy with her husband. David Garnett is realistic in another fashion. There is no true incompatibility in the hero and heroine themselves, and left alone they might have been happy. They are not left alone. The society in which they live is certain that they are badly matched, resents their marriage across the barriers of race, and manages to destroy them. Only in the imagination can such conflicts be quieted, Elinor Wylie seems to say, and she impatiently cuts the knot by a magic which is an arraignment of all Virginios and their makers. In fact, David Garnett hints, these conflicts drag out and end miserably. He refuses to cut the knot, and lets a narrow-minded society furnish its own arraignment. Two very different methods, the same moral.

My Mortal Enemy evokes an intricate character from old memories, fits the parts delicately together, and shapes a living woman. *Death in Venice* profoundly and beautifully examines a tragic spiritual crisis in a noble mind. *The Venetian Glass Nephew* is a glittering episode, an ironical fairy-tale. *The Sailor's Return* and Joseph Hergesheimer's *Tubal Cain* are nearer in form and procedure to the usual long novel, and are made short only by the precision with which their stories are told and by the exclusion of all matters not relevant to the central characters and situations. Here are theaters for many pockets. Immediately following them I have put the lively play *Of Thee I Sing*, which would illustrate all the advantages the stage gives to a story if I could reproduce the music by George Gershwin, the dancing, the costumes, and the scenery.

C.V.D.

Willa Cather

MY MORTAL ENEMY

PART I

1

I FIRST met Myra Henshawe when I was fifteen, but I had known about her ever since I could remember anything at all. She and her runaway marriage were the theme of the most interesting, indeed the only interesting, stories that were told in our family, on holidays or at family dinners. My mother and aunts still heard from Myra Driscoll, as they called her, and Aunt Lydia occasionally went to New York to visit her. She had been the brilliant and attractive figure among the friends of their girlhood, and her life had been as exciting and varied as ours was monotonous.

Though she had grown up in our town, Parthia, in southern

Illinois, Myra Henshawe never, after her elopement, came back but once. It was in the year when I was finishing high school, and she must then have been a woman of forty-five. She came in the early autumn, with brief notice by telegraph. Her husband, who had a position in the New York offices of an Eastern railroad, was coming west on business, and they were going to stop over for two days in Parthia. He was to stay at the Parthian, as our new hotel was called, and Mrs. Henshawe would stay with Aunt Lydia.

I was a favorite with my Aunt Lydia. She had three big sons, but no daughter, and she thought my mother scarcely appreciated me. She was always, therefore, giving me what she called "advantages," on the side. My mother and sister were asked to dinner at Aunt Lydia's on the night of the Henshawes' arrival, but she had whispered to me: "I want you to come in early, an hour or so before the others, and get acquainted with Myra."

That evening I slipped quietly in at my aunt's front door, and while I was taking off my wraps in the hall I could see, at the far end of the parlor, a short, plump woman in a black velvet dress, seated upon the sofa and softly playing on Cousin Bert's guitar. She must have heard me, and, glancing up, she saw my reflection in a mirror; she put down the guitar, rose, and stood to await my approach. She stood markedly and pointedly still, with her shoulders back and her head lifted, as if to remind me that it was my business to get to her as quickly as possible and present myself as best I could. I was not accustomed to formality of any sort, but by her attitude she succeeded in conveying this idea to me.

I hastened across the room with so much bewilderment and concern in my face that she gave a short, commiserating laugh as she held out to me her plump, charming little hand.

"Certainly this must be Lydia's dear Nellie, of whom I have heard so much! And you must be fifteen now, by my mournful arithmetic — am I right?"

What a beautiful voice, bright and gay and carelessly kind — but she continued to hold her head up haughtily. She always did this on meeting people — partly, I think, because she was beginning to have a double chin and was sensitive about it. Her deep-set, flashing gray eyes seemed to be taking me in altogether — estimating me. For all that she was no taller than I, I felt quite overpowered by her

— and stupid, hopelessly clumsy and stupid. Her black hair was done high on her head, à la Pompadour, and there were curious, zigzag, curly streaks of glistening white in it, which made it look like the fleece of a Persian goat or some animal that bore silky fur. I could not meet the playful curiosity of her eyes at all, so I fastened my gaze upon a necklace of carved amethysts she wore inside the square-cut neck of her dress. I suppose I stared, for she said suddenly: "Does this necklace annoy you? I'll take it off if it does."

I was utterly speechless. I could feel my cheeks burning. Seeing that she had hurt me, she was sorry, threw her arm impulsively about me, drew me into the corner of the sofa, and sat down beside me.

"Oh, we'll get used to each other! You see, I prod you because I'm certain that Lydia and your mother have spoiled you a little. You've been overpraised to me. It's all very well to be clever, my dear, but you mustn't be solemn about it — nothing is more tiresome. Now, let us get acquainted. Tell me about the things you like best; that's the short cut to friendship. What do you like best in Parthia? The old Driscoll place? I knew it!"

By the time her husband came in I had begun to think she was going to like me. I wanted her to, but I felt I didn't have half a chance with her; her charming, fluent voice, her clear light enunciation bewildered me. And I was never sure whether she was making fun of me or of the thing we were talking about. Her sarcasm was so quick, so fine at the point — it was like being touched by a metal so cold that one doesn't know whether one is burned or chilled. I was fascinated, but very ill at ease, and I was glad when Oswald Henshawe arrived from the hotel.

He came into the room without taking off his overcoat and went directly up to his wife, who rose and kissed him. Again I was some time in catching up with the situation; I wondered for a moment whether they might have come down from Chicago on different trains; for she was clearly glad to see him — glad not merely that he was safe and had got round on time, but because his presence gave her lively personal pleasure. I was not accustomed to that kind of feeling in people long married.

Mr. Henshawe was less perplexing than his wife, and he looked more as I had expected him to look. The prominent bones of his

face gave him a rather military air; a broad, rugged forehead, high
cheek-bones, a high nose, slightly arched. His eyes, however, were
dark and soft, curious in shape — exactly like half-moons — and
he wore a limp, drooping mustache, like an Englishman. There was
something about him that suggested personal bravery, magnanim-
ity, and a fine, generous way of doing things.

"I am late," he explained, "because I had some difficulty in
dressing. I couldn't find my things."

His wife looked concerned for a moment, and then began to
laugh softly. "Poor Oswald! You were looking for your new dress
shirts that bulge in front. Well, you needn't! I gave them to the
janitor's son."

"The janitor's son?"

"Yes. To Willy Bunch, at home. He's probably wearing one to
an Iroquois ball tonight, and that's the right place for it."

Mr. Henshawe passed his hand quickly over his smooth, iron-
gray hair. "You gave away my six new shirts?"

"Be sure I did. You shan't wear shirts that give you a bosom, not
if we go to the poorhouse. You know I can't bear you in ill-fitting
things."

Oswald looked at her with amusement, incredulity, and bitterness. He turned away from us with a shrug and pulled up a chair.
"Well, all I can say is, what a windfall for Willy!"

"That's the way to look at it," said his wife teasingly. "And
now try to talk about something that might conceivably interest
Lydia's niece. I promised Liddy to make a salad dressing."

I was left alone with Mr. Henshawe. He had a pleasant way of
giving his whole attention to a young person. He "drew one out"
better than his wife had done, because he did not frighten one so
much. I liked to watch his face, with its outstanding bones and
languid, friendly eyes — that perplexing combination of something
hard and something soft. Soon my mother and uncle and my boy
cousins arrived. When the party was complete I could watch and
enjoy the visitors without having to think of what I was going to
say next. The dinner was much gayer than family parties usually
are. Mrs. Henshawe seemed to remember all the old stories and the
old jokes that had been asleep for twenty years.

"How good it is," my mother exclaimed, "to hear Myra laugh again!"

Yes, it was good. It was sometimes terrible, too, as I was to find out later. She had an angry laugh, for instance, that I still shiver to remember. Any stupidity made Myra laugh — I was destined to hear that one very often! Untoward circumstances, accidents, even disasters, provoked her mirth. And it was always mirth, not hysteria; there was a spark of zest and wild humor in it.

2

THE big stone house, set in its ten-acre park of trees and surrounded by a high, wrought-iron fence, in which Myra Driscoll grew up, was still, in my time, the finest property in Parthia. At John Driscoll's death it went to the Sisters of the Sacred Heart, and I could remember it only as a convent. Myra was an orphan, and had been taken into this house as a very little girl and brought up by her great-uncle.

John Driscoll made his fortune employing contract labor in the Missouri swamps. He retired from business early, returned to the town where he had been a poor boy, and built a fine house in which he took great pride. He lived in what was considered great splendor in those days. He kept fast horses, and bred a trotter that made a national record. He bought silver instruments for the town band, and paid the salary of the bandmaster. When the band went up to serenade him on his birthday and on holidays, he called the boys in and treated them to his best whisky. If Myra gave a ball or a garden-party, the band furnished the music. It was, indeed, John Driscoll's band.

Myra, as my aunt often said, had everything: dresses and jewels, a fine riding horse, a Steinway piano. Her uncle took her back to Ireland with him one summer and had her painted by a famous painter. When they were at home, in Parthia, his house was always open to the young people of the town. Myra's good looks and high spirits gratified the old man's pride. Her wit was of the kind that he could understand, native and racy, and none too squeamish. She was very fond of him, and he knew it. He was a coarse old codger, so unlettered that he made a poor showing with a pen. It was always told of him that when he became president of our national bank, he burned a lot of the treasury notes sent up to his house for him to sign, because he had " spoiled the sig-nay-ture." But he knew a great deal about men and their motives. In his own way he was picturesque, and Myra appreciated it — not many girls would have done so. Indeed, she was a good deal like him; the blood tie was very strong. There was never a serious disagreement between them until it came to young Henshawe.

Oswald Henshawe was the son of a German girl of good family, and an Ulster Protestant whom Driscoll detested; there was an old grudge of some kind between the two men. This Ulsterman was poor and impractical, a wandering schoolmaster, who had charge for a while of the high school in Parthia and afterwards taught in smaller towns about. Oswald put himself through Harvard with very little help from his parents. He was not taken account of in our town until he came home from college, a handsome and promising young man. He and Myra met as if for the first time and fell in love with each other. When old Driscoll found that Oswald was calling on his niece, he forbade him the house. They continued to meet at my grandfather's, however, under the protection of my Aunt Lydia. Driscoll so persecuted the boy that he felt there was no chance for him in Parthia. He roused himself and went to New York. He stayed there two years without coming home, sending his letters to Myra through my aunt.

All Myra's friends were drawn into the web of her romance; half a dozen young men understudied for Oswald so assiduously that her uncle might have thought she was going to marry any one of them. Oswald, meanwhile, was pegging away in New York, at a time when salaries were small and advancement was slow. But he managed to get on, and in two years he was in a position to marry. He wrote to John Driscoll, telling him his resources and prospects, and asked him for his niece's hand. It was then that Driscoll had it out with Myra. He did not come at her in a tantrum, as he had done before, but confronted her with a cold business proposition. If she married young Henshawe, he would cut her off without a penny. He could do so, because he had never adopted her. If she did not, she would inherit two-thirds of his property — the remaining third was to go to the Church. " And I advise ye to think well," he told her. " It's better to be a stray dog in this world than a man without money. I've tried both ways, and I know. A poor man stinks, and God hates him."

Some months after this conversation Myra went out with a sleighing party. They drove her to a neighboring town where Oswald's father had a school and where Oswald himself had quietly arrived the day before. There, in the the presence of his parents and of Myra's friends, they were married by the civil authority, and they went away on the Chicago express, which came through at two in the morning.

When I was a little girl my Aunt Lydia used to take me for a walk along the broad stone flagging that ran all the way around the old Driscoll grounds. Through the high iron fence we could see the Sisters, out for recreation, pacing two and two under the apple trees. My aunt would tell me again about that thrilling night (probably the most exciting in her life) when Myra Driscoll came down that path from the house, and out of those big iron gates, for the last time. She had wanted to leave without taking anything but the clothes she wore — and indeed she walked out of the house with nothing but her muff and her *porte-monnaie* in her hands. My prudent aunt, however, had put her toilet articles and some linen into a traveling-bag, and thrown it out of the back window to one of the boys stationed under an apple tree.

" I'll never forget the sight of her, coming down that walk and leaving a great fortune behind her," said Aunt Lydia. " I had gone out to join the others before she came — she preferred to leave the house alone. We girls were all in the sleighs, and the boys stood in the snow holding the horses. We had begun to think she had weakened, or maybe gone to the old man to try to move him. But we saw by the lights behind when the front door opened and shut, and here she came, with her head high, and that quick little bouncing step of hers. Your Uncle Rob lifted her into the sleigh, and off we went. And that hard old man was as good as his word. Her name wasn't mentioned in his will. He left it all to the Catholic Church and to institutions."

" But they've been happy, anyhow? " I sometimes asked her.

" Happy? Oh, yes! As happy as most people."

That answer was disheartening; the very point of their story was that they should be much happier than other people.

When I was older I used to walk around the Driscoll place alone very often, especially on spring days, after school, and watch the nuns pacing so mildly and measuredly among the blossoming trees where Myra used to give garden-parties and have the band to play for her. I thought of the place as being under a spell, like the Sleeping Beauty's palace; it had been in a trance, or lain in its flowers like a beautiful corpse, ever since that winter night when Love went out of the gates and gave the dare to Fate. Since then, chanting and devotions and discipline, and the tinkle of little bells that seemed forever calling the Sisters in to prayers.

I knew that this was not literally true; old John Driscoll had lived on there for many years after the flight of his niece. I myself could remember his funeral — remember it very vividly — though I was not more than six years old when it happened. I sat with my parents in the front of the gallery, at the back of the church that the old man had enlarged and enriched during the latter days of his life. The high altar blazed with hundreds of candles, the choir was entirely filled by the masses of flowers. The Bishop was there, and a flock of priests in gorgeous vestments. When the pall-bearers arrived, Driscoll did not come to the church; the church went to him. The Bishop and clergy went down the nave and met that great black coffin at the door, preceded by the cross and boys swinging cloudy censers, followed by the choir chanting to the organ. They surrounded, they received, they seemed to assimilate into the body of the church, the body of old John Driscoll. They bore it up to the high altar on a river of color and incense and organ-tone; they claimed it and enclosed it.

In after years, when I went to other funerals, stark and grim enough, I thought of John Driscoll as having escaped the end of all flesh; it was as if he had been translated, with no dark conclusion to the pageant, no " night of the grave " about which our Protestant preachers talked. From the freshness of roses and lilies, from the glory of the high altar, he had gone straight to the greater glory, through smoking censers and candles and stars.

After I went home from that first glimpse of the real Myra Henshawe, twenty-five years older than I had always imagined her, I could not help feeling a little disappointed. John Driscoll and his niece had suddenly changed places in my mind, and he had got, after all, the more romantic part. Was it not better to get out of the world with such pomp and dramatic splendor than to linger on in it, having to take account of shirts and railway trains, and getting a double chin into the bargain?

The Henshawes were in Parthia three days, and when they left, it was settled that I was to go on to New York with Aunt Lydia for the Christmas holidays. We were to stay at the old Fifth Avenue Hotel, which, as Myra said, was only a stone's throw from their apartment, "if at any time a body was to feel disposed to throw one, Liddy!"

3

My Aunt Lydia and I arrived at the Jersey City station on the day before Christmas — a soft, gray December morning, with a little snow falling. Myra Henshawe was there to meet us; very handsome, I thought, as she came walking rapidly up the platform, her plump figure swathed in furs — a fur hat on her head, with a single narrow garnet feather sticking out behind, like the pages' caps in old story-books. She was not alone. She was attended by a tall, elegant young man in a blue-gray ulster. He had one arm through hers, and in the other hand he carried a walking-stick.

"This is Ewan Gray," said Mrs. Henshawe, after she had embraced us. "Doubtless you have seen him play in Chicago. He is meeting an early train, too, so we planned to salute the morn together, and left Oswald to breakfast alone."

The young man took our hand-luggage and walked beside me to the ferryboat, asking polite questions about our trip. He was a Scotchman, of an old theatrical family, a handsome fellow, with a broad, fair-skinned face, sand-colored hair and mustache, and fine gray eyes, deep-set and melancholy, with black lashes. He took us up to the deck of the ferry, and then Mrs. Henshawe told him he had better leave us. "You must be there when Esther's train gets in — and remember, you are to bring her to dine with us tomorrow night. There will be no one else."

"Thank you, Myra." He stood looking down at her with a grateful, almost humble expression, holding his soft hat against his breast, while the snow-flakes fell about his head. "And may I call in for a few moments tonight, to show you something?"

She laughed as if his request pleased her. "Something for her, I expect? Can't you trust your own judgment?"

"You know I never do," he said, as if that were an old story.

She gave him a little push. "Do put your hat on, or you'll greet Esther with a sneeze. Run along."

She watched him anxiously as he walked away, and groaned: "Oh, the deliberation of him! If I could only make him hurry once. You'll hear all about him later, Nellie. You'll have to see a good deal of him, but you won't find it a hardship, I trust!"

The boat was pulling out, and I was straining my eyes to catch, through the fine, reluctant snow, my first glimpse of the city we were approaching. We passed the *Wilhelm der Grosse* coming up the river under tug, her sides covered with ice after a stormy crossing, a flock of sea-gulls in her wake. The snow blurred everything a little, and the buildings on the Battery all ran together — looked like an enormous fortress with a thousand windows. From the mass, the dull gold dome of the *World* building emerged like a ruddy autumn moon at twilight.

From the Twenty-third Street station we took the crosstown car — people were economical in those days — to the Fifth Avenue Hotel. After we had unpacked and settled our things, we went across the square to lunch at Purcell's, and there Mrs. Henshawe told us about Ewan Gray. He was in love with one of her dearest friends, Esther Sinclair, whose company was coming into New York for the holidays. Though he was so young, he had, she said, "a rather spotty past," and Miss Sinclair, who was the daughter of an old New England family and had been properly brought up, couldn't make up her mind whether he was stable enough to marry. "I don't dare advise her, though I'm so fond of him. You can see; he's just the sort of boy that women pick up and run off into the jungle with. But he's never wanted to marry before; it might be the making of him. He's distractedly in love — goes about like a sleep-walker. Still, I couldn't bear it if anything cruel happened to Esther."

Aunt Lydia and Myra were going to do some shopping. When we went out into Madison Square again, Mrs. Henshawe must have seen my wistful gaze, for she stopped short and said: " How would Nellie like it if we left her here, and picked her up as we come back? That's our house, over there, second floor — so you won't be far from home. To me this is the real heart of the city; that's why I love living here." She waved to me and hurried my aunt away.

Madison Square was then at the parting of the ways; had a double personality, half commercial, half social, with shops to the south and residences on the north. It seemed to me so neat, after the raggedness of our Western cities; so protected by good manners and courtesy — like an open-air drawing-room. I could well imagine a winter dancing party being given there, or a reception for some distinguished European visitor.

The snow fell lightly all the afternoon, and friendly old men with brooms kept sweeping the paths — very ready to talk to a girl from the country, and to brush off a bench so that she could sit down. The trees and shrubbery seemed well groomed and sociable, like pleasant people. The snow lay in clinging folds on the bushes and outlined every twig of every tree — a line of white upon a line of black. Madison Square Garden, new and spacious then, looked to me so light and fanciful, and Saint-Gaudens's Diana, of which Mrs. Henshawe had told me, stepped out freely and fearlessly into the gray air. I lingered long by the intermittent fountain. Its rhythmical splash was like the voice of the place. It rose and fell like something taking deep, happy breaths; and the sound was musical, seemed to come from the throat of spring. Not far away, on the corner, was an old man selling English violets, each bunch wrapped in oiled paper to protect them from the snow. Here, I felt, winter brought no desolation; it was tamed, like a polar bear led on a leash by a beautiful lady.

About the square the pale blue shadows grew denser and drew closer. The street lamps flashed out all along the avenue, and soft lights began to twinkle in the tall buildings while it was yet day — violet buildings, just a little denser in substance and color than the violet sky. While I was gazing up at them I heard a laugh close beside me, and Mrs. Henshawe's arm slipped through mine.

" Why, you're fair moonstruck, Nellie! I've seen the messenger

boys dodging all about you!" It was true, droves of people were going through the square now, and boys carrying potted plants and big wreaths. "Don't you like to watch them? But we can't stay. We're going home to Oswald. Oh, hear the penny whistle! They always find me out." She stopped a thin lad with a cap and yarn comforter but no overcoat, who was playing *The Irish Washerwoman* on a little pipe, and rummaged in her bag for a coin.

The Henshawes' apartment was the second floor of an old brownstone house on the north side of the square. I loved it from the moment I entered it; such solidly built, high-ceiled rooms, with snug fireplaces and wide doors and deep windows. The long, heavy velvet curtains and the velvet chairs were a wonderful plum-color, like ripe purple fruit. The curtains were lined with that rich creamcolor that lies under the blue skin of ripe figs.

Oswald was standing by the fire, drinking a whisky and soda while he waited for us. He put his glass down on the mantel as we opened the door, and forgot all about it. He pushed chairs up to the hearth for my aunt and me, and stood talking to us while his wife went to change her dress and to have a word with the Irish maid before dinner.

"By the way, Myra," he said, as she left us, "I've put a bottle of champagne on ice; it's Christmas Eve."

Everything in their little apartment seemed to me absolutely individual and unique, even the dinner service; the thick gray plates and the soup tureen painted with birds and big, bright flowers — I was sure there were no others like them in the world.

As we were finishing dinner the maid announced Mr. Gray. Henshawe went into the parlor to greet him, and we followed a moment later. The young man was in evening clothes, with a few sprays of white hyacinth in his coat. He stood by the fire, his arm on the mantel. His clean, fair skin and melancholy eyes, his very correct clothes, and something about the shape of his hands made one conscious of a cool, deliberate fastidiousness in him. In spite of his spotty past he looked, that night, as fresh and undamaged as the flowers he wore. Henshawe took on a slightly bantering tone with him and seemed to be trying to cheer him up. Mr. Gray would not sit down. After an interval of polite conversation he said to his

host: "Will you excuse me if I take Myra away for a few moments? She has promised to do something kind for me."

They went into Henshawe's little study, off the parlor, and shut the door. We could hear a low murmur of voices. When they came back to us Mrs. Henshawe stood beside Gray while he put on his caped cloak, talking encouragingly. "The opals are beautiful, but I'm afraid of them, Ewan. Oswald would laugh at me, but all the same they have a bad history. Love itself draws on a woman nearly all the bad luck in the world; why, for mercy's sake, add opals? He brought two bracelets for me to decide between them, Oswald, both lovely. How ever did they let you carry off two, Ewan?"

"They know me there. I always pay my bills, Myra. I don't know why, but I do. I suppose it's the Scotch in me."

He wished us all good-night.

"Give a kiss to Esther for me," said Mrs. Henshawe merrily at the door. He made no reply, but bent over her hand and vanished.

"What he really wanted was to show me some verses he's made for her," said Mrs. Henshawe as she came back to the fire. "And very pretty ones they are, for sweetheart poetry."

Mr. Henshawe smiled. "Maybe you obliged him with a rhyme or two, my dear? Lydia — " he sat down by my aunt and put his hand on hers — "I'd never feel sure that I did my own courting, if it weren't that I was a long way off at the time. Myra is so fond of helping young men along. We nearly always have a love-affair on hand."

She put her hand over his lips. "Hush! I hate old women who egg on courtships."

When Oswald had finished his cigar we were taken out for a walk. This was primarily for the good of her "figger," Myra said, and incidentally we were to look for a green bush to send to Madame Modjeska. "She's spending the holidays in town, and it will be dismal at her hotel."

At the florist's we found, among all the little trees and potted plants, a glistening holly tree, full of red berries and pointed like a spire, easily the queen of its companions. "That is naturally hers," said Mrs. Myra.

Her husband shrugged. " It's naturally the most extravagant."

Mrs. Myra threw up her head. " Don't be petty, Oswald. It's not a woollen petticoat or warm mittens that Madame is needing." She gave careful instructions to the florist's man, who was to take the tree to the Savoy; he was to carry with it a box of cakes, " of my baking," she said proudly. He was to ask for Mrs. Hewes, the house-keeper, and under her guidance he was to carry the tree up to Ma-dame Modjeska's rooms himself. The man showed a sympathetic interest and promised to follow instructions. Then Mrs. Henshawe gave him a silver dollar and wished him a Merry Christmas.

As we walked home she slipped her arm through mine, and we fell a little behind the other two. " See the moon coming out, Nellie — behind the tower. It wakens the guilt in me. No playing with love; and I'd sworn a great oath never to meddle again. You send a handsome fellow like Ewan Gray to a fine girl like Esther, and it's Christmas Eve, and they rise above us and the white world around us, and there isn't anybody, not a tramp on the park benches, that wouldn't wish them well — and very likely hell will come of it! "

4

THE next morning Oswald Henshawe, in a frock coat and top hat, called to take Aunt Lydia and me to church. The weather had cleared before we went to bed, and as we stepped out of our hotel that morning, the sun shone blindingly on the snow-covered park, the gold Diana flashed against a green-blue sky. We were going to Grace Church, and the morning was so beautiful that we decided to walk.

" Lydia," said Henshawe, as he took us each by an arm, " I want you to give me a Christmas present."

" Why, Oswald," she stammered.

" Oh, I have it ready! You've only to present it." He took a little flat package from his pocket and slipped it into her muff. He drew both of us closer to him. " Listen, it's nothing. It's some sleeve-buttons, given me by a young woman who means no harm, but doesn't know the ways of the world very well. She's from a breezy Western city, where a rich girl can give a present whenever she wants to and nobody questions it. She sent these to my office yesterday. If I send them back to her it will hurt her feelings; she would think I had misunderstood her. She'll get hard knocks here, of course, but I don't want to give her any. On the other hand — well, you know Myra; nobody better. She would punish herself and everybody else for this young woman's questionable taste. So I want you to give them to me, Lydia."

" Oh, Oswald," cried my aunt, " Myra is so keen! I'm not clever enough to fool Myra. Can't you just put them away in your office? "

" Not very well. Besides," he gave a slightly embarrassed laugh, " I'd like to wear them. They are very pretty."

" Now, Oswald . . ."

" Oh, it's all right, Lydia, I give you my word it is. But you know how a little thing of that sort can upset my wife. I thought you might give them to me when you come over to dine with us to-morrow night. She wouldn't be jealous of you. But if you don't like the idea . . . why, just take them home with you and give them to some nice boy who would appreciate them."

All through the Christmas service I could see that Aunt Lydia was distracted and perplexed. As soon as we got back to the hotel and were safe in our rooms she took the brown leather case from her muff and opened it. The sleeve-buttons were topazes, winy-yellow, lightly set in crinkly gold. I believe she was seduced by their beauty. " I really think he ought to have them, if he wants them. Everything is always for Myra. He never gets anything for himself. And all the admiration is for her; why shouldn't he have a little? He has been devoted to a fault. It isn't good for any woman to be humored and pampered as he has humored her. And she's often most unreasonable with him — most unreasonable! "

The next evening, as we were walking across the square to the Henshawes, we glanced up and saw them standing together in one of their deep front windows, framed by the plum-colored curtains. They were looking out, but did not see us. I noticed that she was really quite a head shorter than he, and she leaned a little towards him. When she was peaceful, she was like a dove with its wings folded. There was something about them, as they stood in the lighted window, that would have discouraged me from meddling, but it did not shake my aunt.

As soon as we were in the parlor, before we had taken off our coats, she said resolutely: "Myra, I want to give Oswald a Christmas present. Once an old friend left with me some cuff-links he couldn't keep — unpleasant associations, I suppose. I thought of giving them to one of my own boys, but I brought them for Oswald. I'd rather he would have them than anybody."

Aunt Lydia spoke with an ease and conviction which compelled my admiration. She took the buttons out of her muff, without the box, of course, and laid them in Mrs. Henshawe's hand.

Mrs. Henshawe was delighted. "How clever of you to think of it, Liddy, dear! Yes, they're exactly right for him. There's hardly any other stone I would like, but these are exactly right. Look, Oswald, they're the color of a fine Moselle." It was Oswald himself who seemed disturbed, and not overpleased. He grew red, was confused in his remarks, and was genuinely reluctant when his wife insisted upon taking the gold buttons out of his cuffs and putting in the new ones. "I can't get over your canniness, Liddy," she said as she fitted them.

"It's not like me, is it, Myra?" retorted my aunt; "not like me at all to choose the right sort of thing. But did it never occur to you that anyone besides yourself might know what is appropriate for Oswald? No, I'm sure it never did!"

Mrs. Myra took the laugh so heartily to herself that I felt it was a shame to deceive her. So, I am sure, did Oswald. During dinner he talked more than usual, but he was ill at ease. Afterwards, at the opera, when the lights were down, I noticed that he was not listening to the music, but was looking listlessly off into the gloom of the house, with something almost sorrowful in his strange, half-moon eyes. During an *entr'acte* a door at the back was opened, and a draft blew in. As he put his arm back to pull up the cloak which had slipped down from his wife's bare shoulders, she laughed and said: "Oh, Oswald, I love to see your jewels flash!"

He dropped his hand quickly and frowned so darkly that I thought he would have liked to put the topazes under his heel and grind them up. I thought him properly served then, but often since I have wondered at his gentle heart.

5

DURING the week between Christmas and New Year's Day I was
with Mrs. Henshawe a great deal, but we were seldom alone. It
was the season of calls and visits, and she said that meeting so many
people would certainly improve my manners and my English. She
hated my careless, slangy, Western speech. Her friends, I found,
were of two kinds: artistic people — actors, musicians, literary
men — with whom she was always at her best because she admired
them; and another group whom she called her " moneyed " friends
(she seemed to like the word), and these she cultivated, she told
me, on Oswald's account. " He is the sort of man who does well in
business only if he has the incentive of friendships. He doesn't
properly belong in business. We never speak of it, but I'm sure
he hates it. He went into an office only because we were young
and terribly in love and had to be married."

The business friends seemed to be nearly all Germans. On Sunday we called at half a dozen or more big houses. I remember very
large rooms, much upholstered and furnished, walls hung with
large paintings in massive frames, and many stiff, dumpy little sofas,
in which the women sat two-and-two, while the men stood about
the refreshment tables, drinking champagne and coffee and smoking fat black cigars. Among these people Mrs. Myra took on her
loftiest and most challenging manner. I could see that some of the
women were quite afraid of her. They were in great haste to rush
refreshments to her, and looked troubled when she refused anything. They addressed her in German and profusely complimented
her upon the way she spoke it. We had a carriage that afternoon,
and Myra was dressed in her best — making an especial effort on
Oswald's account; but the rich and powerful irritated her. Their
solemnity was too much for her sense of humor; there was a biting
edge to her sarcasm, a curl about the corners of her mouth that
was never there when she was with people whose personality
charmed her.

I had one long, delightful afternoon alone with Mrs. Henshawe
in Central Park. We walked for miles, stopped to watch the skating, and finally had tea at the Casino, where she told me about

some of the singers and actors I would meet at her apartment on New Year's Eve. Her account of her friends was often more interesting to me than the people themselves. After tea she hailed a hansom and asked the man to drive us about the park a little, as a fine sunset was coming on. We were jogging happily along under the elms, watching the light change on the crusted snow, when a carriage passed from which a handsome woman leaned out and waved to us. Mrs. Henshawe bowed stiffly, with a condescending smile. " There, Nellie," she exclaimed, " that's the last woman I'd care to have splashing past me, and me in a hansom cab! "

I glimpsed what seemed to me insane ambition. My aunt was always thanking God that the Henshawes got along as well as they did, and worrying because she felt sure Oswald wasn't saving anything. And here Mrs. Myra was wishing for a carriage — with stables and a house and servants, and all that went with a carriage! All the way home she kept her scornful expression, holding her head high and sniffing the purple air from side to side as we drove down Fifth Avenue. When we alighted before her door she paid the driver, and gave him such a large fee that he snatched off his hat and said twice: " Thank you, thank you, my lady! " She dismissed him with a smile and a nod. " All the same," she whispered to me as she fitted her latchkey, " it's very nasty, being poor! "

That week Mrs. Henshawe took me to see a dear friend of hers, Anne Aylward, the poet. She was a girl who had come to New York only a few years before, had won the admiration of men of letters, and was now dying of tuberculosis in her early twenties. Mrs. Henshawe had given me a book of her poems to read, saying: " I want you to see her so that you can remember her in after years, and I want her to see you so that we can talk you over."

Miss Aylward lived with her mother in a small flat overlooking the East River, and we found her in a bathchair, lying in the sun and watching the river boats go by. Her study was a delightful place that morning, full of flowers and plants and baskets of fruit that had been sent her for Christmas. But it was Myra Henshawe herself who made that visit so memorably gay. Never had I seen her so brilliant and strangely charming as she was in that sunlit study up under the roofs. Their talk quite took my breath away; they said such exciting, such fantastic things about people, books, music — anything; they seemed to speak together a kind of highly flavored special language.

As we were walking home she tried to tell me more about Miss Aylward, but tenderness for her friend and bitter rebellion at her fate choked her voice. She suffered physical anguish for that poor girl. My aunt often said that Myra was incorrigibly extravagant; but I saw that her chief extravagance was in caring for so many people, and in caring for them so much. When she but mentioned the name of someone whom she admired, one got an instant impression that the person must be wonderful, her voice invested the name with a sort of grace. When she liked people she always called them by name a great many times in talking to them, and she enunciated the name, no matter how commonplace, in a penetrating way, without hurrying over it or slurring it; and this, accompanied by her singularly direct glance, had a curious effect. When she addressed Aunt Lydia, for instance, she seemed to be speaking to a person deeper down than the blurred, taken-for-granted image of my aunt that I saw every day, and for a moment my aunt became more individual, less matter-of-fact to me. I had noticed this peculiar effect of Myra's look and vocative when I first met her, in Parthia, where her manner of addressing my relatives had made them all seem a little more attractive to me.

One afternoon when we were at a matinée I noticed in a loge a young man who looked very much like the photographs of a story-writer popular at that time. I asked Mrs. Henshawe whether it could be he. She looked in the direction I indicated, then looked quickly away again.

" Yes, it's he. He used to be a friend of mine. That's a sad phrase, isn't it? But there was a time when he could have stood by Oswald in a difficulty — and he didn't. He passed it up. Wasn't there. I've never forgiven him."

I regretted having noticed the man in the loge, for all the rest of the afternoon I could feel the bitterness working in her. I knew that she was suffering. The scene on the stage was obliterated for her; the drama was in her mind. She was going over it all again; arguing, accusing, denouncing.

As we left the theater she sighed: " Oh, Nellie, I wish you hadn't seen him! It's all very well to tell us to forgive our enemies; our enemies can never hurt us very much. But oh, what about forgiving our friends? " — she beat on her fur collar with her two gloved hands — " that's where the rub comes! "

The Henshawes always gave a party on New Year's Eve. That year most of the guests were stage people. Some of them, in order to get there before midnight, came with traces of make-up still on their faces. I remember old Jefferson de Angelis arrived in his last-act wig, carrying his plumed hat — during the supper his painted eyebrows spread and came down over his eyes like a veil. Most of them are dead now, but it was a fine group that stood about the table to drink the New Year in. By far the handsomest and most distinguished of that company was a woman no longer young, but beautiful in age, Helena Modjeska. She looked a woman of another race and another period, no less queenly than when I had seen her in Chicago as Marie Stuart, and as Katharine in *Henry VIII*. I remember how, when Oswald asked her to propose a toast, she put out her long arm, lifted her glass, and looking into the blur of the candlelight with a grave face, said: " To my coun-n-try! "

As she was not playing, she had come early, some time before the others, bringing with her a young Polish woman who was singing at the Opera that winter. I had an opportunity to watch Modjeska as she sat talking to Myra and Esther Sinclair — Miss Sinclair had once played in her company. When the other guests began to arrive and Myra was called away, she sat by the fire in a high-backed chair, her head resting lightly on her hand, her beautiful face half in shadow. How well I remember those long, beautifully modeled hands, with so much humanity in them! They were worldly, indeed, but fashioned for a nobler worldliness than ours; hands to hold a scepter, or a chalice — or, by courtesy, a sword.

The party did not last long, but it was a whirl of high spirits. Everybody was hungry and thirsty. There was a great deal of talk about Sarah Bernhardt's *Hamlet*, which had been running all week and had aroused hot controversy; and about Jean de Reszke's return to the Metropolitan that night, after a long illness in London.

By two o'clock everyone had gone but the two Polish ladies. Modjeska, after she put on her long cloak, went to the window, drew back the plum-colored curtains, and looked out. " See, Myra," she said with that Slav accent she never lost, though she read English verse so beautifully, " the square is quite white with moonlight. And how still all the ci-ty is, how still! " She turned to her friend; " Emelia, I think you must sing something. Something old . . . yes, from *Norma*." She hummed a familiar air under her breath and looked about for a chair. Oswald brought one. " Thank you. And we might have less light, might we not? " He turned off the lights.

She sat by the window, half draped in her cloak, the moonlight falling across her knees. Her friend went to the piano and commenced the *Casta Diva* aria, which begins so like the quivering of moonbeams on the water. It was the first air on our old music-box at home, but I had never heard it sung — and I have never heard it sung so beautifully since. I remember Oswald, standing like a statue behind Madame Modjeska's chair, and Myra, crouching low beside the singer, her head in both hands, while the song grew and blossomed like a great emotion.

When it stopped, nobody said anything beyond a low good-by. Modjeska again drew her cloak around her, and Oswald took them down to their carriage. Aunt Lydia and I followed, and as we crossed the square we saw their cab going up the avenue. For many years I associated Mrs. Henshawe with that music, thought of that aria as being mysteriously related to something in her nature that one rarely saw, but nearly always felt; a compelling, passionate, overmastering something for which I had no name, but which was audible, visible in the air that night, as she sat crouching in the shadow. When I wanted to recall powerfully that hidden richness in her, I had only to close my eyes and sing to myself: " *Casta diva, casta diva!* "

6

On Saturday I was to lunch at the Henshawes' and go alone with Oswald to hear Bernhardt and Coquelin. As I opened the door into the entry hall, the first thing that greeted me was Mrs. Henshawe's angry laugh, and a burst of rapid words that stung like cold water from a spray.

" I tell you, I will know the truth about this key, and I will go through any door your keys open. Is that clear? "

Oswald answered with a distinctly malicious chuckle: " My dear, you'd have a hard time getting through that door. The key happens to open a safety deposit box."

Her voice rose an octave in pitch. " How dare you lie to me, Oswald? How dare you? They told me at your bank that this wasn't a bank key, though it looks like one. I stopped and showed it to them — the day you forgot your keys and telephoned me to bring them down to your office."

" The hell you did! "

I coughed and rapped at the door . . . they took no notice of me. I heard Oswald push back a chair. " Then it was you who took my keys out of my pocket? I might have known it! I never forget to change them. And you went to the bank and made me and yourself ridiculous. I can imagine their amusement."

" Well, you needn't! I know how to get information without giving any. Here is Nellie Birdseye, rapping at the gates. Come in, Nellie. You and Oswald are going over to Martin's for lunch. He and I are quarreling about a key-ring. There will be no luncheon here today."

She went away, and I stood bewildered. This delightful room had seemed to me a place where light-heartedness and charming manners lived — housed there just as the purple curtains and the Kiva rugs and the gay water-colors were. And now everything was in ruins. The air was still and cold like the air in a refrigerating-room. What I felt was fear; I was afraid to look or speak or move. Everything about me seemed evil. When kindness has left people, even for a few moments, we become afraid of them, as if their reason had left them. When it has left a place where we have always found it, it is like shipwreck; we drop from security into something malevolent and bottomless.

" It's all right, Nellie." Oswald recovered himself and put a hand on my shoulder. " Myra isn't half so furious with me as she pretends. I'll get my hat and we'll be off." He was in his smoking-jacket and had been sitting at his desk, writing. His inkwell was uncovered, and on the blotter lay a half-written sheet of note-paper.

I was glad to get out into the sunlight with him. The city seemed safe and friendly and smiling. The air in that room had been like poison. Oswald tried to make it up to me. We walked round and round the square, and at Martin's he made me drink a glass of sherry, and pointed out the interesting people in the dining-room and told me stories about them. But without his hat, his head against the bright window, he looked tired and troubled. I wondered, as on the first time I saw him, in my own town, at the contradiction in his face: the strong bones, and the curiously shaped eyes without any fire in them. I felt that his life had not suited him; that he possessed some kind of courage and force which slept, which in another sort of world might have asserted themselves brilliantly. I thought he ought to have been a soldier or an explorer. I have since seen those half-moon eyes in other people, and they were always inscrutable, like his; fronted the world with courtesy and kindness, but one never got behind them.

We went to the theater, but I remember very little of the performance except a dull heartache, and a conviction that I should never like Mrs. Myra so well again. That was on Saturday. On Monday Aunt Lydia and I were to start for home. We positively did not see the Henshawes again. Sunday morning the maid came with some flowers and a note from Myra, saying that her friend Anne Aylward was having a bad day and had sent for her.

On Monday we took an early boat across the ferry, in order to breakfast in the Jersey station before our train started. We had got settled in our places in the Pullman, the moment of departure was near, when we heard an amused laugh, and there was Myra Henshawe, coming into the car in her fur hat, followed by a porter who carried her bags.

"I didn't plot anything so neat as this, Liddy," she laughed, a little out of breath, " though I knew we'd be on the same train. But we won't quarrel, will we? I'm only going as far as Pittsburgh. I've some old friends there. Oswald and I have had a disagreement, and I've left him to think it over. If he needs me, he can quite well come after me."

All day Mrs. Myra was jolly and agreeable, though she treated us with light formality, as if we were new acquaintances. We lunched together, and I noticed, sitting opposite her, that when she was in this mood of high scorn, her mouth, which could be so tender — which cherished the names of her friends and spoke them delicately — was entirely different. It seemed to curl and twist

about like a little snake. Letting herself think harm of anyone she
loved seemed to change her nature, even her features.

It was dark when we got into Pittsburgh. The Pullman porter
took Myra's luggage to the end of the çar. She bade us good-by,
started to leave us, then turned back with an icy little smile. " Oh,
Liddy dear, you needn't have perjured yourself for those yellow
cuff-buttons. I was sure to find out, I always do. I don't hold it
against you, but it's disgusting in a man to lie for personal decorations. A woman might do it, now . . . for pearls! " With a bright
nod she turned away and swept out of the car, her head high, the
long garnet feather drooping behind.

Aunt Lydia was very angry. " I'm sick of Myra's dramatics," she
declared. " I've done with them. A man never *is* justified, but if
ever a man was . . ."

PART II

1

TEN years after that visit to New York I happened to be in a sprawl-
ing overgrown West-coast city which was in the throes of rapid
development — it ran about the shore, stumbling all over itself, and
finally tumbled untidily into the sea. Every hotel and boarding-
house was overcrowded, and I was very poor. Things had gone
badly with my family and with me. I had come west in the middle
of the year to take a position in a college — a college that was as
experimental and unsubstantial as everything else in the place. I
found lodgings in an apartment-hotel, wretchedly built and already falling to pieces, although it was new. I moved in on a Sunday morning, and while I was unpacking my trunk, I heard, through
the thin walls, my neighbor stirring about; a man, and, from the
huskiness of his cough and something measured in his movements,
not a young man. The caution of his step, the guarded consideration of his activities, let me know that he did not wish to thrust
the details of his housekeeping upon other people any more than
he could help.

Presently I detected the ugly smell of gasoline in the air, heard a sound of silk being snapped and shaken, and then a voice humming very low an old German air — yes, Schubert's *Frühlingsglaube*; ta ta te-ta | ta-ta ta-ta ta-ta | ta. In a moment I saw the ends of dark neckties fluttering out of the window next mine.

All this made me melancholy — more than the dreariness of my own case. I was young, and it didn't matter so much about me; for youth there is always the hope, the certainty, of better things. But an old man, a gentleman, living in this shabby, comfortless place, cleaning his neckties of a Sunday morning and humming to himself . . . it depressed me unreasonably. I was glad when his outer door shut softly and I heard no more of him.

There was an indifferent restaurant on the ground floor of the hotel. As I was going down to my dinner that evening, I met, at the head of the stairs, a man coming up and carrying a large black tin tray. His head was bent, and his eyes were lowered. As he drew aside to let me pass, in spite of his thin white hair and stooped shoulders, I recognized Oswald Henshawe, whom I had not seen for so many years — not, indeed, since that afternoon when he took me to see Sarah Bernhardt play *Hamlet*.

When I called his name he started, looked at me, and rested the tray on the sill of the blindless window that lighted the naked stairway.

" Nellie! Nellie Birdseye! Can it be? "

His voice was quite uncertain. He seemed deeply shaken, and pulled out a handkerchief to wipe his forehead. " But, Nellie, you have grown up! I would not know you. What good fortune for Myra! She will hardly believe it when I tell her. She is ill, my poor Myra. Oh, very ill! But we must not speak of that, nor seem to know it. What it will mean to her to see you again! Her friends always were so much to her, you remember? Will you stop and see us as you come up? Her room is thirty-two; rap gently, and I'll be waiting for you. Now I must take her dinner. Oh, I hope for her sake you are staying some time. She has no one here."

He took up the tray and went softly along the uncarpeted hall. I felt little zest for the canned vegetables and hard meat the waitress put before me. I had known that the Henshawes had come on evil days and were wandering about among the cities of the Pacific coast. But Myra had stopped writing to Aunt Lydia, beyond a word of greeting at Christmas and on her birthday. She had ceased to give us any information about their way of life. We knew that several years after my memorable visit in New York, the railroad to whose president Oswald had long been private secretary was put into the hands of a receiver, and the retiring president went abroad to live. Henshawe had remained with the new management, but very soon the road was taken over by one of the great trunk lines, and the office staff was cut in two. In the reorganization Henshawe was offered a small position, which he indignantly refused — his wife wouldn't let him think of accepting it. He went to San Francisco as manager of a commission house; the business failed, and what had happened to them since I did not know.

I lingered long over my dismal dinner. I had not the courage to go upstairs. Henshawe was not more than sixty, but he looked much older. He had the tired, tired face of one who has utterly lost hope.

Oswald had got his wife up out of bed to receive me. When I entered she was sitting in a wheel-chair by an open window, wrapped in a Chinese dressing-gown, with a bright shawl over her feet. She threw out both arms to me, and as she hugged me, flashed into her old gay laugh.

" Now wasn't it clever of you to find us, Nellie? And we so safely hidden — in earth, like a pair of old foxes! But it was in the cards that we should meet again. Now I understand; a wise woman has been coming to read my fortune for me, and the queen of hearts has been coming up out of the pack when she had no business to; a beloved friend coming out of the past. Well, Nellie, dear, I couldn't think of any old friends that weren't better away, for one reason or another, while we are in temporary eclipse. I gain strength faster if I haven't people on my mind. But you, Nellie . . . that's different." She put my two hands to her cheeks, making a frame for her face. " That's different. Somebody young, and clear-eyed, chock-full of opinions, and without a past. But you may have a past already? The darkest ones come early."

I was delighted. She was . . . she was herself, Myra Henshawe! I hadn't expected anything so good. The electric bulbs in the room were shrouded and muffled with colored scarfs, and in that light she looked much less changed than Oswald. The corners of her mouth had relaxed a little, but they could still curl very scornfully upon occasion; her nose was the same sniffy little nose, with its restless, arched nostrils, and her double chin, though softer, was no fuller. A strong cable of gray-black hair was wound on the top of her head, which, as she once remarked, " was no head for a woman at all, but would have graced one of the wickedest of the Roman emperors."

Her bed was in the alcove behind her. In the shadowy dimness of the room I recognized some of the rugs from their New York apartment, some of the old pictures, with frames peeling and glass cracked. Here was Myra's little inlaid tea-table, and the desk at which Oswald had been writing that day when I dropped in upon their quarrel. At the windows were the dear, plum-colored curtains, their cream lining streaked and faded — but the sight of them rejoiced me more than I could tell the Henshawes.

" And where did you come from, Nellie? What are you doing here, in Heaven's name? "

While I explained myself she listened intently, holding my wrist with one of her beautiful little hands, which were so inexplicably mischievous in their outline, and which, I noticed, were still white and well cared for.

" Ah, but teaching, Nellie! I don't like that, not even for a temporary expedient. It's a cul-de-sac. Generous young people use themselves all up at it; they have no sense. Only the stupid and the phlegmatic should teach."

" But won't you allow me, too, a temporary eclipse? "

She laughed and squeezed my hand. " Ah, we wouldn't be hiding in the shadow if we were five-and-twenty! We were throwing off sparks like a pair of shooting stars, weren't we, Oswald? No, I can't bear teaching for you, Nellie. Why not journalism? You could always make your way easily there."

" Because I hate journalism. I know what I want to do, and I'll work my way out yet, if only you'll give me time."

" Very well, dear." She sighed. " But I'm ambitious for you. I've no patience with young people when they drift. I wish I could live their lives for them; I'd know how! But there it is; by the time you've learned the short cuts, your feet puff up so that you can't take the road at all. Now tell me about your mother and my Lydia."

I had hardly begun when she lifted one finger and sniffed the air. " Do you get it? That bitter smell of the sea? It's apt to come in on the night wind. I live on it. Sometimes I can still take a drive along the shore. Go on; you say that Lydia and your mother are at present in disputation about the possession of your late grandfather's portrait. Why don't you cut it in two for them, Nellie? I remember it perfectly, and half of it would be enough for anybody! "

While I told her any amusing gossip I could remember about my family, she sat crippled but powerful in her brilliant wrappings. She looked strong and broken, generous and tyrannical, a witty and rather wicked old woman, who hated life for its defeats, and loved it for its absurdities. I recalled her angry laugh, and how she had always greeted shock or sorrow with that dry, exultant chuckle which seemed to say: " Ah-ha, I have one more piece of evidence, one more, against the hideous injustice God permits in this world! "

While we were talking, the silence of the strangely balmy February evening was rudely disturbed by the sound of doors slamming and heavy tramping overhead. Mrs. Henshawe winced, a look of apprehension and helplessness, a tortured expression, came over her face. She turned sharply to her husband, who was resting peacefully in one of their old, deep chairs, over by the muffled light. " There they are, those animals! "

He sat up. " They have just come back from church," he said in a troubled voice.

" Why should I have to know when they come back from church? Why should I have the details of their stupid, messy existence thrust upon me all day long and half the night? " she broke out bitterly. Her features became tense, as from an attack of pain, and I realized how unable she was to bear things.

" We are unfortunate in the people who live over us," Oswald explained. " They annoy us a great deal. These new houses are poorly built, and every sound carries."

" Couldn't you ask them to walk more quietly? " I suggested.

He smiled and shook his head. " We have, but it seems to make them worse. They are that kind of people."

His wife broke in. " The palavery kind of Southerners; all that slushy gush on the surface, and no sensibilities whatever — a race without consonants and without delicacy. They tramp up there all day long like cattle. The stalled ox would have trod softer. Their energy isn't worth anything, so they use it up gabbling and running about, beating my brains into a jelly."

She had scarcely stopped for breath when I heard a telephone ring overhead, then shrieks of laughter, and two people ran across the floor as if they were running a foot-race.

" You hear? " Mrs. Henshawe looked at me triumphantly. " Those two silly old hens race each other to the telephone as if they had a sweetheart at the other end of it. While I could still climb stairs, I hobbled up to that woman and implored her, and she began gushing about ' mah sistah ' and ' mah son,' and what ' rahfined ' people they were. . . . Oh, that's the cruelty of being poor; it leaves you at the mercy of such pigs! Money is a protection, a cloak; it can buy one quiet, and some sort of dignity." She leaned back, exhausted, and shut her eyes.

" Come, Nellie," said Oswald, softly. He walked down the hall to my door with me. " I'm sorry the disturbance began while you were there. Sometimes they go to the movies and stay out later," he said mournfully. " I've talked to that woman and to her son, but they are very unfeeling people."

" But wouldn't the management interfere in a case of sickness? "

Again he shook his head. " No, they pay a higher rent than we do — occupy more rooms. And we are somewhat under obligation to the management."

2

I soon discovered the facts about the Henshawes' present existence. Oswald had a humble position, poorly paid, with the city traction company. He had to be at his desk at nine o'clock every day except Sunday. He rose at five in the morning, put on an old duck suit (it happened to be a very smart one, with frogs and a military collar, left over from prosperous times), went to his wife's room and gave her her bath, made her bed, arranged her things, and then got their breakfast. He made the coffee on a spirit lamp, the toast on an electric toaster. This was the only meal of the day they could have

together, and as they had it long before the ruthless Poindexters
overhead began to tramp, it was usually a cheerful occasion.

After breakfast Oswald washed the dishes. Their one luxury was
a private bath, with a large cupboard, which he called his kitchen.
Everything else done, he went back to his own room, put it in
order, and then dressed for the office. He still dressed very neatly,
though how he managed to do it with the few clothes he had I
could not see. He was the only man staying in that shabby hotel
who looked well groomed. As a special favor from his company
he was allowed to take two hours at noon, on account of his sick
wife. He came home, brought her her lunch from below, then
hurried back to his office.

Myra made her own tea every afternoon, getting about in her
wheel-chair or with the aid of a cane. I found that one of the
kindest things I could do for her was to bring her some little sandwiches or cakes from the Swedish bakery to vary her tinned biscuit. She took great pains to get her tea nicely; it made her feel
less shabby to use her own silver tea-things and the three glossy
English cups she had carried about with her in her trunk. I used
often to go in and join her, and we spent some of our pleasantest
hours at that time of the day, when the people overhead were
usually out. When they were in, and active, it was too painful to
witness Mrs. Henshawe's suffering. She was acutely sensitive to
sound and light, and the Poindexters did tramp like cattle — except that their brutal thumping hadn't the measured dignity which
the step of animals always has. Mrs. Henshawe got great pleasure
from flowers, too, and during the late winter months my chief
extravagance and my chief pleasure was in taking them to her.

One warm Saturday afternoon, early in April, we went for a drive
along the shore. I had hired a low carriage with a kindly Negro
driver. Supported on his arm and mine, Mrs. Henshawe managed
to get downstairs. She looked much older and more ill in her black
broadcloth coat and a black taffeta hat that had once been smart.
We took with us her furs and an old steamer blanket. It was a
beautiful, soft spring day. The road, unfortunately, kept winding
away from the sea. At last we came out on a bare headland, with
only one old twisted tree upon it, and the sea beneath.

"Why, Nellie!" she exclaimed, "it's like the cliff in *Lear*,

Gloucester's cliff, so it is! Can't we stay here? I believe this nice darky man would fix me up under the tree there and come back for us later."

We wrapped her in the rug, and she declared that the trunk of the old cedar, bending away from the sea, made a comfortable back for her. The Negro drove away, and I went for a walk up the shore because I knew she wanted to be alone. From a distance I could see her leaning against her tree and looking off to sea, as if she were waiting for something. A few steamers passed below her, and the gulls dipped and darted about the headland, the soft shine of the sun on their wings. The afternoon light, at first wide and watery pale, grew stronger and yellower, and when I went back to Myra it was beating from the west on her cliff as if thrown by a burning-glass.

She looked up at me with a soft smile — her face could still be very lovely in a tender moment. " I've had such a beautiful hour, dear; or has it been longer? Light and silence: they heal all one's wounds — all but one, and that is healed by dark and silence. I find I don't miss clever talk, the kind I always used to have about me, when I can have silence. It's like cold water poured over fever."

I sat down beside her, and we watched the sun dropping lower toward his final plunge into the Pacific. " I'd love to see this place at dawn," Myra said suddenly. "That is always such a forgiving time. When that first cold, bright streak comes over the water, it's as if all our sins were pardoned; as if the sky leaned over the earth and kissed it and gave it absolution. You know how the great sinners always came home to die in some religious house, and the abbot or the abbess went out and received them with a kiss? "

When we got home she was, of course, very tired. Oswald was waiting for us, and he and the driver carried her upstairs. While we were getting her into bed, the noise overhead broke out — tramp, tramp, bang! Myra began to cry.

" Oh, I've come back to it, to be tormented again! I've two fatal maladies, but it's those coarse creatures I shall die of. Why didn't you leave me out there, Nellie, in the wind and night? You ought to get me away from this, Oswald. If I were on my feet, and you laid low, I wouldn't let you be despised and trampled upon."

" I'll go up and see those people tomorrow, Mrs. Henshawe," I
promised. " I'm sure I can do something."

" Oh, don't, Nellie! " She looked up at me in affright. " She'd
turn a deaf ear to you. You know the Bible says the wicked are deaf
like the adder. And, Nellie, she has the wrinkled, white throat of
an adder, that woman, and the hard eyes of one. Don't go near
her! "

(I went to see Mrs. Poindexter the next day, and she had just
such a throat and just such eyes. She smiled, and said that the sick
woman underneath was an old story, and she ought to have been
sent to a sanatorium long ago.)

" Never mind, Myra. I'll get you away from it yet. I'll manage,"
Oswald promised as he settled the pillows under her.

She smoothed his hair. " No, my poor Oswald, you'll never stagger far under the bulk of me. Oh, if youth but knew! " She closed
her eyes and pressed her hands over them. " It's been the ruin of
us both. We've destroyed each other. I should have stayed with
my uncle. It was money I needed. We've thrown our lives away."

" Come, Myra, don't talk so before Nellie. You don't mean it.
Remember the long time we were happy. That was reality, just
as much as this."

" We were never really happy. I am a greedy, selfish, worldly
woman; I wanted success and a place in the world. Now I'm old
and ill and a fright, but among my own kind I'd still have my circle;
I'd have courtesy from people of gentle manners, and not have my
brains beaten out by hoodlums. Go away, please, both of you, and
leave me! " She turned her face to the wall and covered her head.

We stepped into the hall, and the moment we closed the door
we heard the bolt slip behind us. She must have sprung up very
quickly. Oswald walked with me to my room. " It's apt to be
like this, when she has enjoyed something and gone beyond her
strength. There are times when she can't have anyone near her.
It was worse before you came."

I persuaded him to come into my room and sit down and drink
a glass of cordial.

" Sometimes she has locked me out for days together," he said.
" It seems strange — a woman of such generous friendships. It's as
if she had used up that part of herself. It's a great strain on me

when she shuts herself up like that. I'm afraid she'll harm herself in some way."

" But people don't do things like that," I said hopelessly.

He smiled and straightened his shoulders. " Ah, but she isn't people! She's Molly Driscoll, and there was never anybody else like her. She can't endure, but she has enough desperate courage for a regiment."

3

THE next morning I saw Henshawe breakfasting in the restaurant, against his custom, so I judged that his wife was still in retreat. I was glad to see that he was not alone, but was talking, with evident pleasure, to a young girl who lived with her mother at this hotel. I had noticed her respectful admiration for Henshawe on other occasions. She worked on a newspaper, was intelligent and, Oswald thought, promising. We enjoyed talking with her at lunch or dinner. She was perhaps eighteen, overgrown and awkward, with short hair and a rather heavy face; but there was something unusual about her clear, honest eyes that made one wonder. She was always on the watch to catch a moment with Oswald, to get him to talk to her about music, or German poetry, or about the actors and writers he had known. He called her his little chum, and her admiration was undoubtedly a help to him. It was very pretty and naïve. Perhaps that was one of the things that kept him up to the mark in his dress and manner. Among people he never looked apologetic or crushed. He still wore his topaz sleeve-buttons.

On Monday, as I came home from school, I saw that the door of Mrs. Henshawe's room was slightly ajar. She knew my step and called to me: " Can you come in, Nellie? "

She was staying in bed that afternoon, but she had on her best dressing-gown, and she was manicuring her neat little hands — a good sign, I thought.

" Could you stop and have tea with me, and talk? I'll be good today, I promise you. I wakened up in the night crying, and it did me good. You see, I was crying about things I never feel now; I'd been dreaming I was young, and the sorrows of youth had set me crying! " She took my hand as I sat down beside her. " Do you

know that poem of Heine's, about how he found in his eye a tear
that was not of the present, an old one, left over from the kind
he used to weep? A tear that belonged to a long dead time of his
life and was an anachronism. He couldn't account for it, yet there
it was, and he addresses it so prettily: 'Thou old, lonesome tear!'
Would you read it for me? There's my little Heine, on the shelf
over the sofa. You can easily find the verse, *Du alte, einsame
Thräne!*"

I ran through the volume, reading a poem here and there where
a leaf had been turned down, or where I saw a line I knew well.
It was a fat old book, with yellow pages, bound in tooled leather,
and on the fly-leaf, in faint violet ink, was an inscription: "To
Myra Driscoll from Oswald," dated 1876.

My friend lay still, with her eyes closed, and occasionally one
of those anachronistic tears gathered on her lashes and fell on the
pillow, making a little gray spot. Often she took the verse out of my
mouth and finished it herself.

"Look for a little short one, about the flower that grows on the
suicide's grave, *die Armesünderblum'*, the poor-sinner's-flower. Oh,
that's the flower for me, Nellie; *die Arme — sünder — blum'!*" She
drew the word out until it was a poem in itself.

"Come, dear," she said presently, when I put down the book,
"you don't really like this new verse that's going round, ugly lines
about ugly people and common feelings — you don't really?"

When I reminded her that she liked Walt Whitman, she
chuckled slyly. "Does that save me? Can I get into your new
Parnassus on that dirty old man? I suppose I ought to be glad of
any sort of ticket at my age! I like naughty rhymes, when they
don't try to be pompous. I like the kind bad boys write on fences.
My uncle had a rare collection of such rhymes in his head that he'd
picked off fences and outbuildings. I wish I'd taken them down;
I might become a poet of note! My uncle was a very unusual man.
Did they ever tell you much about him at home? Yes, he had
violent prejudices; but that's rather good to remember in these
days when so few people have any real passions, either of love or
hate. He would help a friend, no matter what it cost him, and over
and over again he risked ruining himself to crush an enemy. But
he never did ruin himself. Men who hate like that usually have the

fist-power to back it up, you'll notice. He gave me fair warning, and then he kept his word. I knew he would; we were enough alike for that. He left his money wisely; part of it went to establish a home for aged and destitute women in Chicago, where it was needed."

While we were talking about this institution and some of the refugees it sheltered, Myra said suddenly: " I wonder if you know about a clause concerning me in that foundation? It states that at any time the founder's niece, Myra Driscoll Henshawe, is to be received into the institution, kept without charge, and paid an allowance of ten dollars a week for pocket money until the time of her death. How like the old Satan that was! Be sure when he dictated that provision to his lawyer, he thought to himself: ' She'd roll herself into the river first, the brach! ' And then he probably thought better of me, and maybe died with some decent feeling for me in his heart. We were very proud of each other, and if he'd lived till now, I'd go back to him and ask his pardon; because I know what it is to be old and lonely and disappointed. Yes, and because as we grow old we become more and more the stuff our forbears put into us. I can feel his savagery strengthen in me. We think we are so individual and so misunderstood when we are young; but the nature our strain of blood carries is inside there, waiting, like our skeleton."

It had grown quite dusk while we talked. When I rose and turned on one of the shrouded lights, Mrs. Henshawe looked up at me and smiled drolly. " We've had a fine afternoon, and Biddy forgetting her ails. How the great poets do shine on, Nellie! Into all the dark corners of the world. They have no night."

They shone for her, certainly. Miss Stirling, " a nice young person from the library," as Myra called her, ran in occasionally with new books, but Myra's eyes tired quickly, and she used to shut a new book and lie back and repeat the old ones she knew by heart, the long declamations from *Richard II* or *King John*. As I passed her door I would hear her murmuring at the very bottom of her rich Irish voice:

Old John of Gaunt, time-honoured Lan-cas-ter . . .

4

ONE afternoon when I got home from school I found a note from
Mrs. Henshawe under my door, and went to her at once. She
greeted me and kissed me with unusual gravity.

"Nellie, dear, will you do a very special favor for me tomorrow?
It is the 15th of April, the anniversary of Madame Modjeska's
death." She gave me a key and asked me to open an old trunk in
the corner. "Lift the tray, and in the bottom, at one end, you will
find an old pair of long kid gloves, tied up like sacks. Please give
them to me."

I burrowed down under old evening wraps and dinner dresses
and came upon the gloves, yellow with age and tied at both ends
with corset lacings; they contained something heavy that jingled.
Myra was watching my face and chuckled. "Is she thinking they
are my wedding gloves, piously preserved? No, my dear; I went
before a justice of the peace, and married without gloves, so to
speak!" Untying the string, she shook out a little rain of ten- and
twenty-dollar gold pieces.

"All old Irish women hide away a bit of money." She took up a
coin and gave it to me. "Will you go to St. Joseph's Church and
inquire for Father Fay; tell him you are from me, and ask him to
celebrate a mass tomorrow for the repose of the soul of Helena
Modjeska, Countess Bozenta-Chlapowska. He will remember; last
year I hobbled there myself. You are surprised, Nellie? Yes, I broke
with the Church when I broke with everything else and ran away
with a German free-thinker; but I believe in holy words and holy
rites all the same. It is a solace to me to know that tomorrow a mass
will be said here in heathendom for the spirit of that noble artist,
that beautiful and gracious woman."

When I put the gold back into the trunk and started making the
tea, she said: "Oswald, of course, doesn't know the extent of my
resources. We've often needed a hundred dollars or two so bitter
bad; he wouldn't understand. But that is money I keep for unearthly purposes; the needs of this world don't touch it."

As I was leaving she called me back: "Oh, Nellie, can't we go
to Gloucester's cliff on Saturday, if it's fine? I do long to!"

We went again, and again. Nothing else seemed to give her so much pleasure. But the third time I stopped for her, she declared she was not equal to it. I found her sitting in her chair, trying to write to an old friend, an Irish actress I had met at her apartment in New York, one of the guests at that New Year's Eve party. Her son, a young actor, had shot himself in Chicago because of some sordid love-affair. I had seen an account of it in the morning paper.

" It touches me very nearly," Mrs. Henshawe told me. " Why, I used to keep Billy with me for weeks together when his mother was off on tour. He was the most truthful, noble-hearted little fellow. I had so hoped he would be happy. You remember his mother? "

I remembered her very well — large and jovial and hearty she was. Myra began telling me about her, and the son, whom she had not seen since he was sixteen.

" To throw his youth away like that, and shoot himself at twenty-three! People are always talking about the joys of youth — but, oh, how youth can suffer! I've not forgotten; those hot southern Illinois nights, when Oswald was in New York, and I had no word from him except through Liddy, and I used to lie on the floor all night and listen to the express trains go by. I've not forgotten."

" Then I wonder why you are sometimes so hard on him now," I murmured.

Mrs. Henshawe did not reply to me at once. The corners of her mouth trembled, then drew tight, and she sat with her eyes closed as if she were gathering herself for something.

At last she sighed, and looked at me wistfully. " It's a great pity, isn't it, Nellie, to reach out a grudging hand and try to spoil the past for anyone? Yes, it's a great cruelty. But I can't help it. He's a sentimentalist, always was; he can look back on the best of those days when we were young and loved each other and make himself believe it was all like that. It wasn't. I was always a grasping, worldly woman; I was never satisfied. All the same, in age, when the flowers are so few, it's a great unkindness to destroy any that are left in a man's heart." The tears rolled down her cheeks, she leaned back, looking up at the ceiling. She had stopped speaking because her voice broke. Presently she began again resolutely. " But I'm made so. People can be lovers and enemies at the same time, you

know. We were. . . . A man and woman draw apart from that
long embrace, and see what they have done to each other. Perhaps
I can't forgive him for the harm I did him. Perhaps that's it. When
there are children, that feeling goes through natural changes. But
when it remains so personal . . . something gives way in one. In
age we lose everything; even the power to love."

" He hasn't," I suggested.

" He has asked you to speak for him, my dear? Then we have
destroyed each other indeed! "

" Certainly he hasn't, Mrs. Myra! But you are hard on him, you
know, and when there are so many hard things, it seems a pity."

" Yes, it's a great pity." She drew herself up in her chair. " And
I'd rather you didn't come any more for the time being, Nellie.
I've been thinking the tea made me nervous." She was smiling,
but her mouth curled like a little snake, as I had seen it do long
ago. " Will you be pleased to take your things and go, Mrs. Casey? "
She said it with a laugh, but a very meaning one.

As I rose I watched for some sign of relenting, and I said humbly
enough: " Forgive me, if I've said anything I shouldn't. You know
I love you very dearly."

She mockingly bowed her tyrant's head. " It's owing to me in-
firmities, dear Mrs. Casey, that I'll not be able to go as far as me
door wid ye."

5

For days after that episode I did not see Mrs. Henshawe at all. I
saw Oswald at dinner in the restaurant every night, and he reported
her condition to me as if nothing had happened. The short-haired
newspaper girl often came to our table, and the three of us talked
together. I could see that he got great refreshment from her. Her
questions woke pleasant trains of recollection, and her straightforward affection was dear to him. Once Myra, in telling me that it
was a pleasure to him to have me come into their lives again thus,
had remarked: " He was always a man to feel women, you know,
in every way." It was true. That crude little girl made all the difference in the world to him. He was generous enough to become
quite light-hearted in directing her inexperience and her groping

hunger for life. He even read her poor little " specials " and showed
her what was worst in them and what was good. She took correction well, he told me.

Early in June Mrs. Henshawe began to grow worse. Her doctors
told us a malignant growth in her body had taken hold of a vital
organ, and that she would hardly live through the month. She suffered intense pain from pressure on the nerves in her back, and
they gave her opiates freely. At first we had two nurses, but Myra
hated the night nurse so intensely that we dismissed her, and, as
my school was closed for the summer, I took turns with Oswald in
watching over her at night. She needed little attention except renewed doses of codeine. She slept deeply for a few hours, and the
rest of the night lay awake, murmuring to herself long passages
from her old poets.

Myra kept beside her now an ebony crucifix with an ivory Christ.
It used to hang on the wall, and I had supposed she carried it
about because some friend had given it to her. I felt now that she
had it by her for a different reason. Once when I picked it up from
her bed to straighten her sheet, she put out her hand quickly and
said: " Give it to me. It means nothing to people who haven't
suffered."

She talked very little after this last stage of her illness began;
she no longer complained or lamented, but toward Oswald her
manner became strange and dark. She had certain illusions; the
noise overhead she now attributed entirely to her husband. " Ah,
there he's beginning it again," she would say. " He'll wear me
down in the end. Oh, let me be buried in the king's highway! "

When Oswald lifted her or did anything for her now, she was
careful to thank him in a guarded, sometimes a cringing tone. " It's
bitter enough that I should have to take service from you — you
whom I have loved so well," I heard her say to him.

When she asked us to use candles for light during our watches,
and to have no more of the electric light she hated, she said accusingly, at him rather than to him: " At least let me die by candlelight; that is not too much to ask."

Father Fay came to see her almost daily now. His visits were
long, and she looked forward to them. I was, of course, not in her
room when he was there, but if he met me in the corridor he

stopped to speak to me, and once he walked down the street with
me talking of her. He was a young man, with a fresh face and pleasant eyes, and he was deeply interested in Myra. " She's a most
unusual woman, Mrs. Henshawe," he said when he was walking
down the street beside me. Then he added, smiling quite boyishly:
" I wonder whether some of the saints of the early Church weren't
a good deal like her. She's not at all modern in her make-up, is
she? "

During those days and nights when she talked so little, one felt
that Myra's mind was busy all the while — that it was even abnor-
mally active, and occasionally one got a clue to what occupied it.
One night when I was giving her her codeine she asked me a
question.

" Why is it, do you suppose, Nellie, that candles are in themselves religious? Not when they are covered by shades, of course —
I mean the flame of a candle. Is it because the Church began in the
catacombs, perhaps? "

At another time, when she had been lying like a marble figure
for a long while, she said in a gentle, reasonable voice:

" Ah, Father Fay, that isn't the reason! Religion is different from
everything else; because *in religion seeking is finding*."

She accented the word *seeking* very strongly, very deeply. She
seemed to say that in other searchings it might be the object of the
quest that brought satisfaction, or it might be something incidental
that one got on the way; but in religion, desire was fulfillment, it
was the seeking itself that rewarded.

One of those nights of watching stands out in my memory as
embracing them all, as being the burden and telling the tale of
them all. Myra had had a very bad day, so both Oswald and I were
sitting up with her. After midnight she was quiet. The candles were
burning as usual, one in her alcove. From my chair by the open
window I could see her bed. She had been motionless for more
than an hour, lying on her back, her eyes closed. I thought she was
asleep. The city outside was as still as the room in which we sat.
The sick woman began to talk to herself, scarcely above a whisper,
but with perfect distinctness; a voice that was hardly more than a
soft, passionate breath. I seemed to hear a soul talking.

" I could bear to suffer . . . so many have suffered. But why must it be like this? I have not deserved it. I have been true in friendship; I have faithfully nursed others in sickness. . . . Why must I die like this, alone with my mortal enemy? "

Oswald was sitting on the sofa, his face shaded by his hand. I looked at him in affright, but he did not move or shudder. I felt my hands grow cold and my forehead grow moist with dread. I had never heard a human voice utter such a terrible judgment upon all one hopes for. As I sat on through the night, after Oswald had gone to catch a few hours of sleep, I grew calmer; I began to understand a little what she meant, to sense how it was with her. Violent natures like hers sometimes turn against themselves . . . against themselves and all their idolatries.

6

On the following day Mrs. Henshawe asked to be given the Sacrament. After she had taken it she seemed easier in mind and body. In the afternoon she told Henshawe to go to his office and begged me to leave her and let her sleep. The nurse we had sent away that day at her urgent request. She wanted to be cared for by one of the nursing Sisters from the convent from now on, and Father Fay was to bring one tomorrow.

I went to my room, meaning to go back to her in an hour, but once on my bed I slept without waking. It was dark when I heard Henshawe knocking on my door and calling to me. As I opened it, he said in a despairing tone: " She's gone, Nellie, she's gone! "

I thought he meant she had died. I hurried after him down the corridor and into her room. It was empty. He pointed to her empty bed. " Don't you see? She has gone, God knows where! "

" But how could she? A woman so ill? She must be somewhere in the building."

" I've been all over the house. You don't know her, Nellie. She can do anything she wills. Look at this."

On the desk lay a sheet of note-paper scribbled in lead pencil: " *Dear Oswald: My hour has come. Don't follow me. I wish to be alone. Nellie knows where there is money for masses.*" That was all. There was no signature.

We hurried to the police station. The chief sent a messenger out

to the men on the beat to warn them to be on the watch for a distraught woman who had wandered out in delirium. Then we went
to Father Fay. " The Church has been on her mind for a long
while," said Henshawe. " It is one of her delusions that I separated
her from the Church. I never meant to."

The young priest knew nothing. He was distressed, and offered
to help us in our search, but we thought he had better stay at home
on the chance that she might come to him.

When we got back to the hotel it was after eleven o'clock. Oswald said he could not stay indoors; I must be there within call,
but he would go back to help the police.

After he left I began to search Mrs. Henshawe's room. She had
worn her heavy coat and her furs, though the night was warm.
When I found that the pair of Austrian blankets was missing, I
felt I knew where she had gone. Should I try to get Oswald at the
police station? I sat down to think it over. It seemed to me that
she ought to be allowed to meet the inevitable end in the way she
chose. A yearning strong enough to lift that ailing body and drag
it out into the world again should have its way.

At five o'clock in the morning Henshawe came back with an
officer and a Negro cabman. The driver had come to the station and
reported that at six last night a lady, with her arms full of wraps,
had signaled him at the side door of the hotel and told him to
drive her to the boat-landing. When they were nearing the landing, she said she did not mean to stop there, but wanted to go
farther up the shore, giving him clear directions. They reached
the cliff she had indicated. He helped her out of the cab, put her
rugs under the tree for her, and she gave him a ten-dollar gold
piece and dismissed him. He protested that the fare was too much,
and that he was afraid of getting into trouble if he left her there.
But she told him a friend was going to meet her, and that it would
be all right. The lady had, he said, a very kind, coaxing way with
her. When he went to the stable to put up his horse, he heard that
the police were looking for a woman who was out of her head, and
he was frightened. He went home and talked it over with his wife,
who sent him to report at headquarters.

The cabman drove us out to the headland, and the officer insisted upon going along. We found her wrapped in her blankets,

leaning against the cedar trunk, facing the sea. Her head had fallen forward; the ebony crucifix was in her hands. She must have died peacefully and painlessly. There was every reason to believe she had lived to see the dawn. While we watched beside her, waiting for the undertaker and Father Fay to come, I told Oswald what she had said to me about longing to behold the morning break over the sea, and it comforted him.

7

ALTHOUGH she had returned so ardently to the faith of her childhood, Myra Henshawe never changed the clause in her will which requested that her body should be cremated, and her ashes buried " in some lonely and unfrequented place in the mountains, or in the sea."

After it was all over, and her ashes sealed up in a little steel box, Henshawe called me into her room one morning, where he was packing her things, and told me he was going to Alaska.

" Oh, not to seek my fortune," he said, smiling. " That is for young men. But the steamship company have a place for me in their office there. I have always wanted to go, and now there is nothing to hold me. This poor little box goes with me; I shall scatter her ashes somewhere in those vast waters. And this I want you to keep for remembrance." He dropped into my hands the necklace of carved amethysts she had worn on the night I first saw her.

" And, Nellie — " He paused before me with his arms folded, standing exactly as he stood behind Modjeska's chair in the moonlight on that New Year's night; standing like a statue, or a sentinel, I had said then, not knowing what it was I felt in his attitude; but now I knew it meant indestructible constancy . . . almost indestructible youth. " Nellie," he said, " I don't want you to remember her as she was here. Remember her as she was when you were with us on Madison Square, when she was herself, and we were happy. Yes, happier than it falls to the lot of most mortals to be. After she was stricken, her recollection of those things darkened. Life was hard for her, but it was glorious, too; she had such beautiful friendships. Of course, she was absolutely unreasonable when she was jealous. Her suspicions were sometimes — almost fantastic." He smiled and brushed his forehead with the tips of his fingers, as if the memory of her jealousy was pleasant still, and perplexing still. "But that was just Molly Driscoll! I'd rather have been clawed by her, as she used to say, than petted by any other woman I've ever known. These last years it's seemed to me that I was nursing the mother of the girl who ran away with me. Nothing ever took that girl from me. She was a wild, lovely creature, Nellie. I wish you could have seen her then."

Several years after I said good-by to him, Oswald Henshawe died in Alaska. I have still the string of amethysts, but they are unlucky. If I take them out of their box and wear them, I feel all evening a chill over my heart. Sometimes, when I have watched the bright beginning of a love-story, when I have seen a common feeling exalted into beauty by imagination, generosity, and the flaming courage of youth, I have heard again that strange complaint breathed by a dying woman into the stillness of night, like a confession of the soul: "Why must I die like this, alone with my mortal enemy!"

~ *Thomas Mann* ~

DEATH IN VENICE

INTRODUCTION

DEATH IN VENICE, a sovereign masterpiece of modern prose, stands
both chronologically and spiritually at the center of its author's
life. It was published in 1911; it was the successor of *Royal Highness*; its author, who had already written *Buddenbrooks*, *Tonio
Kröger*, *Tristan*, and *Fiorenza*, was not to publish another major
imaginative work until *The Magic Mountain*, thirteen years later.
In order to grasp the high significance of these bare facts it will be
necessary to define both the sources of Thomas Mann's work and
the character of the unity of tone and intention which renders
that work so homogeneous.

In 1921 the University of Bonn conferred an honorary doctorate
upon Thomas Mann. In his letter of acknowledgment to the Dean

of the Philosophical Faculty, Mann emphasized the liberal spirit
of the university in selecting him for this honor. " For," he wrote,
" I am neither learned nor a teacher, rather a dreamer and a doubter
who is hard put to it to save and justify his own life." In using
these words Mann defined not only his own character but the character, as it seems to him, of the literary, the creative process itself.
" Only where the ' I ' is a problem is there any sense in writing."
But this impulse to save and justify the creative " I " is, in the
deepest of all senses, an other-regarding, even a " pedagogical " impulse. For man is a social being; he desires to justify himself first
to himself as a responsible and metaphysical creature, next to his
kind, to his contemporaries, and even to posterity. And in this
justification of the creative self there is inevitably inherent and implicit the justification both of other individuals and of the species
they represent. An austere but vital feeling for human brotherhood
is at the core of this conception of the creative process. " One loves
the human creature because he has a hard time — and because one
is human oneself." The artist, the articulate one, saves and justifies
not only himself but others; both his suffering and his work, though
so intimately his own, are vicarious. Thus all true art is at the same
time autobiographical and, however subtly and implicitly, propagandist — propagandist, if only through form, through beauty, be-
cause autobiographical, *because* all men are brothers and none can
save or justify himself without saving and justifying his fellows and
his race. In these facts and not in this or that conduct of fable or
choice of principles or intentions or maxims reside the moral quality and power of art as such — as such, in its own inevitable nature.
Under this aspect the æsthetic and moral categories are one. . . .
This bare and brief outline of Thomas Mann's theory of art and
of the life of the artist cannot pretend to touch upon its thousand
fruitful implications and applications. He has unfolded and eluci-
dated these in a number of essays; he will be seen, in the long run,
to be not only a great novelist but perhaps the profoundest critic
of his time.

In what special sense was the " I " of Thomas Mann a problem
and a conflict? Why did he have to save and justify himself? One

must assume, of course, the ultimate organization — the innate blending of sensitiveness and responsibility — which makes the artist. This being assumed, it may be said that Thomas Mann's problem and need for justification arose from the exact balance within him of sensitiveness and responsibility. The overwhelming impulse towards art, with its necessary accompaniments of superficial sloth, of dreamy inactivity, of worldly unpracticalness, gave him a bad conscience, produced in him what the psychoanalysts call a feeling of guilt. Sprung of a line of patrician merchants, he did not, as perhaps the very greatest artists do not, rebel against the normal life of man in its freer and nobler forms, but conceived it to be his duty, no less than another's, to guard, to conserve, or creatively to change and enlarge the fundamental values of man and of society. He has been magnificently able in the long run to achieve his ideal of artist and citizen. But this achievement lay far in the future in those early days when he retired to a little room in Rome to write *Buddenbrooks*. It was his task and his ideal then to save and justify his existence by a scrupulous account of its sources, its special character, and to lend this account its moral weight by the perfection, fullness, grandeur of its form. Thus he might be able to return to the conscientious North and, from within at least, feel that an equivalence had been established between himself and those comrades of his youth, the beloved of life and reality, who trod blithely and earnestly the honorable ways of their fathers and their kind. The lovely story of *Tonio Kröger* is the record, fresh, musical, youthful, more lyrical than his other works, of those days. Tonio is Mann, is the young author of *Buddenbrooks*, is the artist soul born into a settled and honorable society and seeking to justify itself and its being. . . .

With the publication of *Buddenbrooks*, probably the most massive and permanent prose work ever written by a man of twenty-five, that justification was outwardly achieved. But outwardly only! Mann himself continued to struggle with the demon — the demon of beauty which is sloth, withdrawal from life, vagabondage, romanticism, and therefore love of death and of war and so anti-civilizatory in drift and character. In this enchainment of ideas we see already of course the germ of *The Magic Mountain*. But what

Thomas Mann wrote in those early years was both more fragmentary and more one-sided. He wrote the short story *Gladius Dei*, which stated the theme and foreshadowed his dialoguized novel *Fiorenza*, the least perfect of his works, in which he settles his account with the Renaissance, with Lorenzo the Magnificent and his friends and city, with the menace of beauty that is mere beauty and therefore corrupts and cloys and creates the other extreme and its antithesis: Savonarola. But now — it was towards 1905 — Thomas Mann was ready to begin the structure of a human life that was still further to save and justify the life of art. In a house, patrician by both culture and inheritance, he found that admirable " companion," as he is fond of calling his wife, who has sustained and fortified him for a quarter of a century and who is the mother of his six children. It was a happy young husband who wrote the symbolic comedy *Royal Highness*, that story of one who, like the artist, stands outside of the normal necessities and duties of life and who is saved by a woman's energy and freshness and love. But neither wife nor child nor house nor gear can wholly save the artist. The menace of beauty remains. From some ambush the fatal arrow may fly. Neither fame nor years nor stringent labor nor civic virtue and its rewards can guard his feet from the edge of the abyss. For he treads the edge of an abyss — to do so is his nature and the nature of his task. He may grow dizzy when he seems most sure of himself. That dizziness is the theme of *Death in Venice*.

To project his idea Thomas Mann thought at first of retelling the story of the septuagenarian Goethe and that last tragic love of the aged poet for Ulrike von Levetzow. But that story was found to be too well documented to admit of the play of the creative imagination. A sojourn in Venice furnished Thomas Mann with incidents and visions that condensed about the remembered face and head of Gustav Mahler, and from these observations and visions arose the character of Gustave von Aschenbach and the story of his dizziness on the edge of the abyss of art. With all this there may have blended, though our author has barely admitted it, memories of the story and Venetian fate of the poet Platen, whose verses might well serve as a motto to *Death in Venice*.

> *Wer die Schönheit angeschaut mit Augen,*
> *Ist dem Tode schon anheimgegeben,*
> *Wird für keinen Dienst der Erde taugen. . . .*[1]

In the light of these observations *Death in Venice* may yield to the reader some of its brimming significance and beauty. In Aschenbach Thomas Mann projected, of course, a personal vision of his own later years. Aschenbach's methods and motives of work are his own — the strong sense of the artist's responsibility, the moral power that comes from the mastering of mighty tasks, and striving after " that noble purity, simplicity, and harmony of form " which, we are told, characterized Aschenbach's later works. And this personage grows dizzy on the edge of the abyss. Spirit succumbs to pure beauty without having first spiritualized it and must therefore suffer death. Were the Greeks able to look upon beauty bare and not perish? That question is woven into the story; it is suggested in the music of the very rhythms which here and there are unobtrusive echoes of the first hemistich of hexameters. Perhaps they were; perhaps the memories of them helped to lure Aschenbach to his undoing. We, at least, cannot. In us — to use the later phraseology of Thomas Mann — *Natur* and *Geist* are divided and we must, upon some plan, bring nature under the subjection of spirit before we can begin to live at all. Let it not be thought for a moment that Thomas Mann has anything in common with the conventional Christian denial of nature or the Christian identification of nature with sin. His ideas dwell on a wholly different plane, and Christianity, in this aspect, is to him part of that romantic love of death which fills him with dread. Nature and spirit must make peace upon other terms than the historic ones, and from that new blending a new humanism may arise.

Of the form of *Death in Venice* it is difficult to speak. What is said in the story of sensuous beauty applies here, that words can praise, but neither communicate nor reproduce it. Nor, by the same token, can even the ablest translation render either the savor of words nor the musicality of their combination nor, above all,

---

[1] " *He whose eyes have looked upon beauty is death's victim, useless he for any service of earth. . . .*"

the contributions of both structure and rhythm to the projection of the creative idea. I have read *Death in Venice* in the original text many times and it is but sober fact that each time I seem to grasp more fully its astonishing richness and perfection as a piece of prose — the complete embodiment of its intention in its form, the consummate union of precision with musicality, of philosophical scrupulousness with the flesh and blood of art. The miracle of art — the perfect union of *Natur* and *Geist* — is here achieved. The miracle of art, which life must imitate if our civilization is to be saved.

Ludwig Lewisohn

Gustave Aschenbach — or von Aschenbach, as he had been known officially since his fiftieth birthday — had set out alone from his house in Prince Regent Street, Munich, for an extended walk. It was a spring afternoon in the year of grace 19—, when Europe sat upon the anxious seat beneath a menace that hung over its head for months. Aschenbach had sought the open soon after tea. He was overwrought by a morning of hard, nerve-taxing work, work which had not ceased to exact his uttermost in the way of sustained concentration, conscientiousness, and tact; and after the noon meal found himself powerless to check the onward sweep of the productive mechanism within him, that *motus animi continuus* in which, according to Cicero, eloquence resides. He had sought but not found relaxation in sleep — though the wear and tear upon his system had come to make a daily nap more and more imperative — and now undertook a walk, in the hope that air and exercise might send him back refreshed to a good evening's work.

May had begun, and after weeks of cold wet a mock summer had set in. The English Gardens, though in tenderest leaf, felt as sultry as in August, and were full of vehicles and pedestrians near the city. But toward Aumeister the paths were solitary and still, and Aschenbach strolled thither, stopping awhile to watch the lively crowds in the restaurant garden with its fringe of carriages and cabs. Thence he took his homeward way outside the park and across the sunset fields. By the time he reached the North Cemetery, however, he felt tired, and a storm was brewing above Föhring; so he waited at the stopping-place for a tram to carry him back to the city.

He found the neighborhood quite empty. Not a wagon in sight, either on the paved Ungererstrasse, with its gleaming tram-lines stretching off toward Schwabing, nor on the Föhring highway. Nothing stirred behind the hedge in the stonemason's yard, where crosses, monuments, and commemorative tablets made a supernumerary and untenanted graveyard opposite the real one. The mortuary chapel, a structure in Byzantine style, stood facing it, silent in the gleam of the ebbing day. Its façade was adorned with Greek crosses and tinted hieratic designs, and displayed a symmetrically arranged selection of scriptural texts in gilded letters, all of them with a bearing upon the future life, such as: " They are entering into the House of the Lord " and " May the Light Everlasting shine upon them." Aschenbach beguiled some minutes of his waiting with reading these formulas and letting his mind's eye lose itself in their mystical meaning. He was brought back to reality by the sight of a man standing in the portico, above the two apocalyptic beasts that guarded the staircase, and something not quite usual in this man's appearance gave his thoughts a fresh turn.

Whether he had come out of the hall through the bronze doors or mounted unnoticed from outside, it was impossible to tell. Aschenbach casually inclined to the first idea. He was of medium height, thin, beardless, and strikingly snub-nosed; he belonged to the red-haired type and possessed its milky, freckled skin. He was obviously not Bavarian; and the broad, straight-brimmed straw hat he had on even made him look distinctly exotic. True, he had the indigenous rucksack buckled on his back, wore a belted suit of yellowish woollen stuff, apparently frieze, and carried a gray mackintosh cape across his left forearm, which was propped against his waist. In his right hand, slantwise to the ground, he held an iron-shod stick, and braced himself against its crook, with his legs crossed. His chin was up, so that the Adam's apple looked very bald in the lean neck rising from the loose shirt; and he stood there sharply peering up into space out of colorless, red-lashed eyes, while two pronounced perpendicular furrows showed on his forehead in curious contrast to his little turned-up nose. Perhaps his heightened and heightening position helped out the impression Aschenbach received. At any rate, standing there as though at survey, the man had a bold and domineering, even a ruthless, air, and his lips completed the picture by seeming to curl back, either by reason of some deformity or else because he grimaced, being blinded by the sun in his face; they laid bare the long, white, glistening teeth to the gums.

Aschenbach's gaze, though unawares, had very likely been inquisitive and tactless; for he became suddenly conscious that the stranger was returning it, and indeed so directly, with such hostility, such plain intent to force the withdrawal of the other's eyes, that Aschenbach felt an unpleasant twinge and, turning his back, began to walk away along the hedge, hastily resolving to give the man no further heed. He had forgotten him the next minute. Yet, whether the pilgrim air the stranger wore kindled his fantasy or whether some other physical or psychical influence came in play, he could not tell; but he felt the most surprising consciousness of a widening of inward barriers, a kind of vaulting unrest, a youthfully ardent thirst for distant scenes — a feeling so lively and so new, or at least so long ago outgrown and forgot, that he stood there rooted to the spot, his eyes on the ground and his hands clasped behind him, exploring these sentiments of his, their bearing and scope.

True, what he felt was no more than a longing to travel; yet coming upon him with such suddenness and passion as to resemble a seizure, almost a hallucination. Desire projected itself visually: his fancy, not quite lulled since morning, imaged the marvels and terrors of the manifold earth. He saw. He beheld a landscape, a tropical marshland, beneath a reeking sky, steaming, monstrous, rank — a kind of primeval wilderness-world of islands, morasses, and alluvial channels. Hairy palm-trunks rose near and far out of lush brakes of fern, out of bottoms of crass vegetation, fat, swollen, thick with incredible bloom. There were trees, mis-shapen as a dream, that dropped their naked roots straight through the air into the ground or into water that was stagnant and shadowy and glassy-green, where mammoth milk-white blossoms floated, and strange high-shouldered birds with curious bills stood gazing sidewise without sound or stir. Among the knotted joints of a bamboo thicket the eyes of a crouching tiger gleamed — and he felt his heart throb with terror, yet with a longing inexplicable. Then the vision vanished. Aschenbach, shaking his head, took up his march once more along the hedge of the stonemason's yard.

He had, at least ever since he commanded means to get about the world at will, regarded travel as a necessary evil, to be endured now and again willy-nilly for the sake of one's health. Too busy with the tasks imposed upon him by his own ego and the European soul, too laden with the care and duty to create, too preoccupied to be an amateur of the gay outer world, he had been content to know as much of the earth's surface as he could without stirring far outside his own sphere — had, indeed, never even been tempted to leave Europe. Now more than ever, since his life was on the wane, since he could no longer brush aside as fanciful his artist fear of not having done, of not being finished before the works ran down, he had confined himself to close range, had hardly stepped outside the charming city which he made his home and the rude country house he had built in the mountains, whither he went to spend the rainy summers.

And so the new impulse which thus late and suddenly swept over him was speedily made to conform to the pattern of self-discipline he had followed from his youth up. He had meant to bring his work, for which he lived, to a certain point before leaving for the country, and the thought of a leisurely ramble across the globe, which should take him away from his desk for months, was too fantastic and upsetting to be seriously entertained. Yet the source of the unexpected contagion was known to him only too well. This yearning for new and distant scenes, this craving for freedom, release, forgetfulness — they were, he admitted to himself, an impulse toward flight, flight from the spot which was the daily theater of a rigid, cold, and passionate service. That service he loved, had even almost come to love the enervating daily struggle between a proud, tenacious, well-tried will and this growing fatigue, which no one must suspect, nor the finished product betray by any faintest sign that his inspiration could ever flag or miss fire. On the other hand, it seemed the part of common sense not to span the bow too far, not to suppress summarily a

need that so unequivocally asserted itself. He thought of his work,
and the place where yesterday and again today he had been forced
to lay it down, since it would not yield either to patient effort or
a swift *coup de main*. Again and again he had tried to break or
untie the knot — only to retire at last from the attack with a shiver
of repugnance. Yet the difficulty was actually not a great one; what
sapped his strength was distaste for the task, betrayed by a fastidiousness he could no longer satisfy. In his youth, indeed, the nature
and inmost essence of the literary gift had been, to him, this very
scrupulosity; for it he had bridled and tempered his sensibilities,
knowing full well that feeling is prone to be content with easy
gains and blithe half-perfection. So now, perhaps, feeling, thus
tyrannized, avenged itself by leaving him, refusing from now on to
carry and wing his art and taking away with it all the ecstasy he had
known in form and expression. Not that he was doing bad work.
So much, at least, the years had brought him, that at any moment
he might feel tranquilly assured of mastery. But he got no joy of
it — not though a nation paid it homage. To him it seemed his
work had ceased to be marked by that fiery play of fancy which is
the product of joy, and more, and more potently, than any intrinsic content, forms in turn the joy of the receiving world. He
dreaded the summer in the country, alone with the maid who prepared his food and the man who served him; dreaded to see the
familiar mountain peaks and walls that would shut him up again
with his heavy discontent. What he needed was a break, an interim
existence, a means of passing time, other air and a new stock of
blood, to make the summer tolerable and productive. Good, then,
he would go a journey. Not far — not all the way to the tigers. A
night in a *wagon-lit*, three or four weeks of lotus-eating at some
one of the gay world's playgrounds in the lovely south. . . .

So ran his thoughts, while the clang of the electric tram drew
nearer down the Ungererstrasse; and as he mounted the platform
he decided to devote the evening to a study of maps and railway
guides. Once in, he bethought him to look back after the man in
the straw hat, the companion of this brief interval which had after
all been so fruitful. But he was not in his former place, nor in the
tram itself, nor yet at the next stop; in short, his whereabouts remained a mystery.

GUSTAVE ASCHENBACH was born at L—, a country town in the province of Silesia. He was the son of an upper official in the judicature, and his forbears had all been officers, judges, departmental functionaries — men who lived their strict, decent, sparing lives in the service of king and state. Only once before had a livelier mentality — in the quality of a clergyman — turned up among them; but swifter, more perceptive blood had in the generation before the writer's flowed into the stock from the mother's side, she being the daughter of a Bohemian musical conductor. It was from her he had the foreign traits that betrayed themselves in his appearance. The union of dry, conscientious officialdom and ardent, obscure impulse produced an artist — and this particular artist: author of the lucid and vigorous prose epic on the life of Frederick the Great; careful, tireless weaver of the richly patterned tapestry entitled *Maia*, a novel that gathers up the threads of many human fates in the warp of a single idea; creator of that powerful narrative *The Abject*, which taught a whole grateful generation that a man can still be capable of moral resolution even after he has plumbed the depths of knowledge; and lastly — to complete the tale of works of his mature period — the writer of that impassioned discourse on the theme of Mind and Art whose ordered force and antithetic eloquence led serious critics to rank it with Schiller's *Simple and Sentimental Poetry*.

Aschenbach's whole soul, from the very beginning, was bent on fame — and thus, while not precisely precocious, yet thanks to the unmistakable trenchancy of his personal accent, he was early ripe and ready for a career. Almost before he was out of high school he had a name. Ten years later he had learned to sit at his desk and sustain and live up to his growing reputation, to write gracious and pregnant phrases in letters that must needs be brief, for many claims press upon the solid and successful man. At forty, worn down by the strains and stresses of his actual task, he had to deal with a daily post heavy with tributes from his own and foreign countries.

Remote on one hand from the banal, on the other from the eccentric, his genius was calculated to win at once the adhesion of the general public and the admiration, both sympathetic and stimulating, of the connoisseur. From childhood up he was pushed

on every side to achievement, and achievement of no ordinary
kind; and so his young days never knew the sweet idleness and
blithe *laissez aller* that belong to youth. A nice observer once said
of him in company — it was at the time when he fell ill in Vienna
in his thirty-fifth year — " You see, Aschenbach has always lived
like this " — here the speaker closed the fingers of his left hand to
a fist — " never like this " — and he let his open hand hang relaxed from the back of his chair. It was apt. And this attitude was
the more morally valiant in that Aschenbach was not by nature
robust — he was only called to the constant tension of his career,
not actually born to it.

By medical advice he had been kept from school and educated
at home. He had grown up solitary, without comradeship; yet had
early been driven to see that he belonged to those whose talent is
not so much out of the common as is the physical basis on which
talent relies for its fulfillment. It is a seed that gives early of its
fruit, whose powers seldom reach a ripe old age. But his favorite
motto was " Hold fast "; indeed, in his novel on the life of Frederick the Great he envisaged nothing else than the apotheosis of
the old hero's word of command, " *Durchhalten*," which seemed
to him the epitome of fortitude under suffering. Besides, he deeply
desired to live to a good old age, for it was his conviction that only
the artist to whom it has been granted to be fruitful on all stages
of our human scene can be truly great, or universal, or worthy of
honor.

Bearing the burden of his genius, then, upon such slender shoulders and resolved to go so far, he had the more need of discipline
— and discipline, fortunately, was his native inheritance from the
father's side. At forty, at fifty, he was still living as he had commenced to live in the years when others are prone to waste and
revel, dream high thoughts and postpone fulfillment. He began his
day with a cold shower over chest and back; then, setting a pair of
tall wax candles in silver holders at the head of his manuscript,
he sacrificed to art, in two or three hours of almost religious fervor,
the powers he had assembled in sleep. Outsiders might be pardoned
for believing that his *Maia* world and the epic amplitude revealed
by the life of Frederick were a manifestation of great power working under high pressure, that they came forth, as it were, all in

one breath. It was the more triumph for his morale; for the truth was that they were heaped up to greatness in layer after layer, in long days of work, out of hundreds and hundreds of single inspirations; they owed their excellence, both of mass and detail, to one thing and one alone: that their creator could hold out for years under the strain of the same piece of work, with an endurance and a tenacity of purpose like that which had conquered his native province of Silesia, devoting to actual composition none but his best and freshest hours.

For an intellectual product of any value to exert an immediate influence which shall also be deep and lasting, it must rest on an inner harmony, yes, an affinity, between the personal destiny of its author and that of his contemporaries in general. Men do not know why they award fame to one work of art rather than another. Without being in the faintest connoisseurs, they think to justify the warmth of their commendations by discovering in it a hundred virtues, whereas the real ground of their applause is inexplicable — it is sympathy. Aschenbach had once given direct expression — though in an unobtrusive place — to the idea that almost everything conspicuously great is great in despite: has come into being in defiance of affliction and pain, poverty, destitution, bodily weakness, vice, passion, and a thousand other obstructions. And that was more than observation — it was the fruit of experience, it was precisely the formula of his life and fame, it was the key to his work. What wonder, then, if it was also the fixed character, the outward gesture, of his most individual figures?

The new type of hero favored by Aschenbach, and recurring many times in his works, had early been analyzed by a shrewd critic: " The conception of an intellectual and virginal manliness, which clenches its teeth and stands in modest defiance of the swords and spears that pierce its side." That was beautiful, it was *spirituel*, it was exact, despite the suggestion of too great passivity it held. Forbearance in the face of fate, beauty constant under torture, are not merely passive. They are a positive achievement, an explicit triumph; and the figure of Sebastian is the most beautiful symbol, if not of art as a whole, yet certainly of the art we speak of here. Within that world of Aschenbach's creation were exhibited many phases of this theme: there was the aristocratic self-command

that is eaten out within and for as long as it can conceals its bio-
logic decline from the eyes of the world; the sere and ugly outside,
hiding the embers of smoldering fire — and having power to fan
them to so pure a flame as to challenge supremacy in the domain
of beauty itself; the pallid languors of the flesh, contrasted with the
fiery ardors of the spirit within, which can fling a whole proud
people down at the foot of the Cross, at the feet of its own sheer
self-abnegation; the gracious bearing preserved in the stern, stark
service of form; the unreal, precarious existence of the born in-
trigant with its swiftly enervating alternation of schemes and desires — all these human fates and many more of their like one read
in Aschenbach's pages, and reading them might doubt the existence
of any other kind of heroism than the heroism born of weakness.
And, after all, what kind could be truer to the spirit of the times?
Gustave Aschenbach was the poet-spokesman of all those who labor at the edge of exhaustion; of the overburdened, of those who
are already worn out but still hold themselves upright; of all our
modern moralizers of accomplishment, with stunted growth and
scanty resources, who yet contrive by skillful husbanding and prodigious spasms of will to produce, at least for a while, the effect of
greatness. There are many such, they are the heroes of the age.
And in Aschenbach's pages they saw themselves: he justified, he
exalted them, he sang their praise — and they, they were grateful,
they heralded his name.

He had been young and crude with the times and by them badly
counseled. He had taken false steps, blundered, exposed himself,
offended in speech and writing against tact and good sense. But
he had attained to honor, and honor, he used to say, is the natural
goal toward which every considerable talent presses with whip and
spur. Yes, one might put it that his whole career had been one conscious and overweening ascent to honor, which left in the rear all
the misgivings or self-derogation which might have hampered him.

What pleases the public is lively and vivid delineation which
makes no demands on the intellect; but passionate and absolutist
youth can only be enthralled by a problem. And Aschenbach was
as absolute, as problematist, as any youth of them all. He had done
homage to intellect, had overworked the soil of knowledge and
ground up her seed-corn; had turned his back on the " mysteries,"

called genius itself in question, held up art to scorn — yes, even
while his faithful following reveled in the characters he created,
he, the young artist, was taking away the breath of the twenty-year-
olds with his cynic utterances on the nature of art and the artist
life.

But it seems that a noble and active mind blunts itself against
nothing so quickly as the sharp and bitter irritant of knowledge.
And certain it is that the youth's constancy of purpose, no matter
how painfully conscientious, was shallow beside the mature resolution of the master of his craft, who made a right-about-face,
turned his back on the realm of knowledge, and passed it by with
averted face, lest it lame his will or power of action, paralyze his
feelings or his passions, deprive any of these of their conviction or
utility. How else interpret the oft-cited story of *The Abject* than
as a rebuke to the excesses of a psychology-ridden age, embodied
in the delineation of the weak and silly fool who manages to lead
fate by the nose; driving his wife, out of sheer innate pusillanimity,
into the arms of a beardless youth, and making this disaster an
excuse for trifling away the rest of his life?

With rage the author here rejects the rejected, casts out the
outcast — and the measure of his fury is the measure of his con-
demnation of all moral shilly-shallying. Explicitly he renounces
sympathy with the abyss, explicitly he refutes the flabby humanita-
rianism of the phrase: "*Tout comprendre c'est tout pardonner.*"
What was here unfolding, or rather was already in full bloom, was
the "miracle of regained detachment," which a little later became
the theme of one of the author's dialogues, dwelt upon not without a certain oracular emphasis. Strange sequence of thought! Was
it perhaps an intellectual consequence of this rebirth, this new austerity, that from now on his style showed an almost exaggerated
sense of beauty, a lofty purity, symmetry, and simplicity, which
gave his productions a stamp of the classic, of conscious and deliberate mastery? And yet: this moral fiber, surviving the hamper-
ing and disintegrating effect of knowledge, does it not result in its
turn in a dangerous simplification, in a tendency to equate the
world and the human soul, and thus to strengthen the hold of the
evil, the forbidden, and the ethically impossible? And has not form
two aspects? Is it not moral and immoral at once: moral in so far

as it is the expression and result of discipline, immoral — yes, actually hostile to morality — in that of its very essence it is indifferent to good and evil, and deliberately concerned to make the moral world stoop beneath its proud and undivided scepter?

Be that as it may. Development is destiny; and why should a career attended by the applause and adulation of the masses necessarily take the same course as one which does not share the glamour and the obligations of fame? Only the incorrigible Bohemian smiles or scoffs when a man of transcendent gifts outgrows his carefree prentice stage, recognizes his own worth and forces the world to recognize it too and pay it homage, though he puts on a courtly bearing to hide his bitter struggles and his loneliness. Again, the play of a developing talent must give its possessor joy, if of a willful, defiant kind. With time, an official note, something almost expository, crept into Gustave Aschenbach's method. His later style gave up the old sheer audacities, the fresh and subtle nuances — it became fixed and exemplary, conservative, formal, even formulated. Like Louis XIV — or as tradition has it of him — Aschenbach, as he went on in years, banished from his style every common word. It was at this time that the school authorities adopted selections from his works into their textbooks. And he found it only fitting — and had no thought but to accept — when a German prince signalized his accession to the throne by conferring upon the poet-author of the life of Frederick the Great on his fiftieth birthday the letters-patent of nobility.

He had roved about for a few years, trying this place and that as a place of residence, before choosing, as he soon did, the city of Munich for his permanent home. And there he lived, enjoying among his fellow-citizens the honor which is in rare cases the reward of intellectual eminence. He married young, the daughter of a university family; but after a brief term of wedded happiness his wife had died. A daughter, already married, remained to him. A son he never had.

Gustave von Aschenbach was somewhat below middle height, dark and smooth-shaven, with a head that looked rather too large for his almost delicate figure. He wore his hair brushed back; it was thin at the parting, bushy and gray on the temples, framing a lofty, rugged, knotty brow — if one may so characterize it. The

nose-piece of his rimless gold spectacles cut into the base of his
thick, aristocratically hooked nose. The mouth was large, often
lax, often suddenly narrow and tense; the cheeks lean and furrowed,
the pronounced chin slightly cleft. The vicissitudes of fate, it
seemed, must have passed over this head, for he held it, plaintively,
rather on one side; yet it was art, not the stern discipline of an
active career, which had taken over the office of modeling these
features. Behind this brow were born the flashing thrust and parry
of the dialogue between Frederick and Voltaire on the theme of
war; these eyes, weary and sunken, gazing through their glasses, had
beheld the blood-stained inferno of the hospitals in the Seven
Years' War. Yes, personally speaking too, art heightens life. She
gives deeper joy, she consumes more swiftly. She engraves adventures of the spirit and the mind in the faces of her votaries; let
them lead outwardly a life of the most cloistered calm, she will in
the end produce in them a fastidiousness, an over-refinement, a
nervous fever and exhaustion, such as a career of extravagant passions and pleasures can hardly show.

EAGER though he was to be off, Aschenbach was kept in Munich
by affairs both literary and practical for some two weeks after that
walk of his. But at length he ordered his country home put ready
against his return within the next few weeks, and on a day between
the middle and the end of May took the evening train for Trieste,
where he stopped only twenty-four hours, embarking for Pola the
next morning but one.
   What he sought was a fresh scene, without associations, which
should yet be not too out-of-the-way; and accordingly he chose an
island in the Adriatic, not far off the Istrian coast. It had been well
known some years, for its splendidly rugged cliff formations on the
side next the open sea, and its population, clad in a bright flutter
of rags and speaking an outlandish tongue. But there was rain and
heavy air; the society at the hotel was provincial Austrian, and
limited; besides, it annoyed him not to be able to get at the sea —
he missed the close and soothing contact which only a gentle sandy
slope affords. He could not feel this was the place he sought; an
inner impulse made him wretched, urging him on he knew not
whither; he racked his brains, he looked up boats, then all at once

his goal stood plain before his eyes. But of course! When one
wanted to arrive overnight at the incomparable, the fabulous, the
like-nothing-else-in-the-world, where was it one went? Why, obviously; he had intended to go there, whatever was he doing here? A
blunder. He made all haste to correct it, announcing his departure
at once. Ten days after his arrival on the island a swift motor-boat
bore him and his luggage in the misty dawning back across the
water to the naval station, where he landed only to pass over the
landing-stage and on to the wet decks of a ship lying there with
steam up for the passage to Venice.

It was an ancient hulk belonging to an Italian line, obsolete,
dingy, grimed with soot. A dirty hunchbacked sailor, smirkingly
polite, conducted him at once belowships to a cavernous, lamplit
cabin. There behind a table sat a man with a beard like a goat's; he
had his hat on the back of his head, a cigar-stump in the corner
of his mouth; he reminded Aschenbach of an old-fashioned circus-
director. This person put the usual questions and wrote out a
ticket to Venice, which he issued to the traveler with many commercial flourishes.

"A ticket for Venice," repeated he, stretching out his arm to
dip the pen into the thick ink in a tilted ink-stand. "One first-
class to Venice! Here you are, *signore mio*." He made some scrawls
on the paper, strewed bluish sand on it out of a box, thereafter
letting the sand run off into an earthen vessel, folded the paper
with bony yellow fingers, and wrote on the outside. "An excellent
choice," he rattled on. "Ah, Venice! What a glorious city! Irresistibly attractive to the cultured man for her past history as well
as her present charm." His copious gesturings and empty phrases
gave the odd impression that he feared the traveler might alter his
mind. He changed Aschenbach's note, laying the money on the
spotted table-cover with the glibness of a croupier. "A pleasant
visit to you, signore," he said, with a melodramatic bow. "Delighted to serve you." Then he beckoned and called out "Next"
as though a stream of passengers stood waiting to be served, though
in point of fact there was not one. Aschenbach returned to the
upper deck.

He leaned an arm on the railing and looked at the idlers lounging along the quay to watch the boat go out. Then he turned his attention to his fellow-passengers. Those of the second class, both men and women, were squatted on their bundles of luggage on the forward deck. The first cabin consisted of a group of lively youths, clerks from Pola, evidently, who had made up a pleasure excursion to Italy and were not a little thrilled at the prospect, bustling about and laughing with satisfaction at the stir they made. They leaned over the railings and shouted, with a glib command of epithet, derisory remarks at such of their fellow-clerks as they saw going to business along the quay; and these in turn shook their sticks and shouted as good back again. One of the party, in a dandified buff suit, a rakish panama with a colored scarf, and a red cravat, was loudest of the loud: he outcrowed all the rest. Aschenbach's eye dwelt on him, and he was shocked to see that the apparent youth was no youth at all. He was an old man, beyond a doubt, with wrinkles and crow's-feet round eyes and mouth; the dull carmine of the cheeks was rouge, the brown hair a wig. His neck was shrunken and sinewy, his turned-up mustaches and small imperial were dyed, and the unbroken double row of yellow teeth he showed when he laughed were but too obviously a cheapish false set. He wore a seal ring on each forefinger, but the hands were those of an old man. Aschenbach was moved to shudder as he watched the creature and his association with the rest of the group. Could they not see he was old, that he had no right to wear the clothes they wore or pretend to be one of them? But they were used to him, it seemed; they suffered him among them, they paid back his jokes in kind and the playful pokes in the ribs he gave them. How could they? Aschenbach put his hand to his brow, he covered his eyes, for he had slept little, and they smarted. He felt not quite canny, as though the world were suffering a dreamlike distortion of perspective which he might arrest by shutting it all out for a few minutes and then looking at it afresh. But instead he felt a floating sensation, and opened his eyes with unreasoning alarm to find that the ship's dark sluggish bulk was slowly leaving the jetty. Inch by inch, with the to-and-fro motion of her machinery, the strip of iridescent dirty water widened, the boat maneuvered clumsily and turned her bow to the open sea. Aschenbach moved

over to the starboard side, where the hunchbacked sailor had set
up a deck-chair for him, and a steward in a greasy dress-coat asked
for orders.

The sky was gray, the wind humid. Harbor and island dropped
behind, all sight of land soon vanished in mist. Flakes of sodden,
clammy soot fell upon the still undried deck. Before the boat was
an hour out a canvas had to be spread as a shelter from the rain.

Wrapped in his cloak, a book in his lap, our traveler rested; the
hours slipped by unawares. It stopped raining, the canvas was taken
down. The horizon was visible right round: beneath the somber
dome of the sky stretched the vast plain of empty sea. But immeasurable unarticulated space weakens our power to measure
time as well: the time-sense falters and grows dim. Strange, shadowy figures passed and repassed — the elderly coxcomb, the goat-
bearded man from the bowels of the ship — with vague gesturings
and mutterings through the traveler's mind as he lay. He fell asleep.

At midday he was summoned to luncheon in a corridor-like
saloon with the sleeping-cabins giving off it. He ate at the head of
the long table; the party of clerks, including the old man, sat with
the jolly captain at the other end, where they had been carousing
since ten o'clock. The meal was wretched, and soon done. Aschenbach was driven to seek the open and look at the sky — perhaps it
would lighten presently above Venice.

He had not dreamed it could be otherwise, for the city had
ever given him a brilliant welcome. But sky and sea remained
leaden, with spurts of fine, mistlike rain; he reconciled himself to
the idea of seeing a different Venice from that he had always approached on the landward side. He stood by the foremast, his gaze
on the distance, alert for the first glimpse of the coast. And he
thought of the melancholy and susceptible poet who had once
seen the towers and turrets of his dreams rise out of these waves;
repeated the rhythms born of his awe, his mingled emotions of
joy and suffering — and easily susceptible to a prescience already
shaped within him, he asked his own sober, weary heart if a new
enthusiasm, a new preoccupation, some late adventure of the feelings could still be in store for the idle traveler.

The flat coast showed on the right, the sea was soon populous
with fishing-boats. The Lido appeared and was left behind as the

ship glided at half speed through the narrow harbor of the same
name, coming to a full stop on the lagoon in sight of garish, badly
built houses. Here it waited for the boat bringing the sanitary in-
spector.

An hour passed. One had arrived — and yet not. There was no
conceivable haste — yet one felt harried. The youths from Pola
were on deck, drawn hither by the martial sound of horns coming
across the water from the direction of the Public Gardens. They
had drunk a good deal of Asti and were moved to shout and hurrah
at the drilling *bersaglieri*. But the young-old man was a truly repulsive sight in the condition to which his company with youth had
brought him. He could not carry his wine like them: he was pitiably
drunk. He swayed as he stood — watery-eyed, a cigarette between
his shaking fingers, keeping upright with difficulty. He could not
have taken a step without falling, and knew better than to stir;
but his spirits were deplorably high. He buttonholed anyone who
came within reach, he stuttered, he giggled, he leered, he fatuously
shook his beringed old forefinger; his tongue kept seeking the
corner of his mouth in a suggestive motion ugly to behold. Aschenbach's brow darkened as he looked, and there came over him once
more a dazed sense, as though things about him were just slightly
losing their ordinary perspective, beginning to show a distortion
that might merge into the grotesque. He was prevented from dwelling on the feeling, for now the machinery began to thud again, and
the ship took up its passage through the Canale di San Marco which
had been interrupted so near the goal.

He saw it once more, that landing-place that takes the breath
away, that amazing group of incredible structures the Republic set
up to meet the awe-struck eye of the approaching seafarer: the
airy splendor of the palace and Bridge of Sighs, the columns of
lion and saint on the shore, the glory of the projecting flank of the
fairy temple, the vista of gateway and clock. Looking, he thought
that to come to Venice by the station is like entering a palace by
the back door. No one should approach save by the high seas, as
he was doing now, this most improbable of cities.

The engines stopped. Gondolas pressed alongside, the landing-
stairs were let down, customs officials came on board and did their
office, people began to go ashore. Aschenbach ordered a gondola.

He meant to take up his abode by the sea, and needed to be conveyed with his luggage to the landing-stage of the little steamers that ply between the city and the Lido. They called down his order to the surface of the water where the gondoliers were quarreling in dialect. Then came another delay while his trunk was worried down the ladder-like stairs. Thus he was forced to endure the importunities of the ghastly young-old man, whose drunken state obscurely urged him to pay the stranger the honor of a formal farewell. " We wish you a very pleasant sojourn," he babbled, bowing and scraping. " Pray keep us in mind. *Au revoir, excusez et bon jour, votre Excellence.*" He drooled, he blinked, he licked the corner of his mouth, the little imperial bristled on his elderly chin. He put the tips of two fingers to his mouth and said thickly: " Give her our love, will you, the p-pretty little dear " — here his upper plate came away and fell down on the lower one. . . . Aschenbach escaped. " Little sweety-sweety-sweetheart," he heard behind him, gurgled and stuttered, as he climbed down the rope stair into the boat.

Is there anyone but must repress a secret thrill, on arriving in Venice for the first time — or returning thither after long absence — and stepping into a Venetian gondola? That singular conveyance, come down unchanged from ballad times, black as nothing else on earth except a coffin — what pictures it calls up of lawless, silent adventures in the plashing night; or even more, what visions of death itself, the bier and solemn rites and last soundless voyage! And has anyone remarked that the seat in such a bark, the armchair lacquered in coffin-black and dully black-upholstered, is the softest, most luxurious, most relaxing seat in the world? Aschenbach realized it when he had let himself down at the gondolier's feet, opposite his luggage, which lay neatly composed on the vessel's beak. The rowers still gestured fiercely; he heard their harsh, incoherent tones. But the strange stillness of the water-city seemed to take up their voices gently, to disembody and scatter them over the sea. It was warm here in the harbor. The lukewarm air of the sirocco breathed upon him, he leaned back among his cushions and gave himself to the yielding element, closing his eyes for very pleasure in an indolence as unaccustomed as sweet. " The trip will be short," he thought, and wished it might last forever. They gently swayed away from the boat with its bustle and clamor of voices.

It grew still and stiller all about. No sound but the splash of the oars, the hollow slap of the wave against the steep, black, halbert-shaped beak of the vessel, and one sound more — a muttering by fits and starts, expressed as it were by the motion of his arms, from the lips of the gondolier. He was talking to himself, between his teeth. Aschenbach glanced up and saw with surprise that the lagoon was widening, his vessel was headed for the open sea. Evidently it would not do to give himself up to sweet *far niente*; he must see his wishes carried out.

" You are to take me to the steamboat landing, you know," he said, half turning round toward it. The muttering stopped. There was no reply.

" Take me to the steamboat landing," he repeated, and this time turned quite round and looked up into the face of the gondolier as he stood there on his little elevated deck, high against the pale gray sky. The man had an unpleasing, even brutish face, and wore blue clothes like a sailor's, with a yellow sash; a shapeless straw hat with the braid torn at the brim perched rakishly on his head. His facial structure, as well as the curling blond mustache under the short snub nose, showed him to be of non-Italian stock. Physically rather undersized, so that one would not have expected him to be very muscular, he pulled vigorously at the oar, putting all his body-weight behind each stroke. Now and then the effort he made curled back his lips and bared his white teeth to the gums. He spoke in a decided, almost curt voice, looking out to sea over his fare's head: " The signore is going to the Lido."

Aschenbach answered: " Yes, I am. But I only took the gondola to cross over to San Marco. I am using the *vaporetto* from there."

" But the signore cannot use the *vaporetto*."

" And why not? "

" Because the *vaporetto* does not take luggage."

It was true. Aschenbach remembered it. He made no answer. But the man's gruff, overbearing manner, so unlike the usual courtesy of his countrymen toward the stranger, was intolerable. Aschenbach spoke again: " That is my own affair. I may want to give my luggage in deposit. You will turn round."

No answer. The oar splashed, the wave struck dull against the prow. And the muttering began anew, the gondolier talked to himself, between his teeth.

What should the traveler do? Alone on the water with this tongue-tied, obstinate, uncanny man, he saw no way of enforcing his will. And if only he did not excite himself, how pleasantly he might rest! Had he not wished the voyage might last forever? The wisest thing — and how much the pleasantest! — was to let matters take their own course. A spell of indolence was upon him; it came from the chair he sat in — this low, black-upholstered armchair, so gently rocked at the hands of the despotic boatman in his rear. The thought passed dreamily through Aschenbach's brain that perhaps he had fallen into the clutches of a criminal; it had not power to rouse him to action. More annoying was the simpler explanation: that the man was only trying to extort money. A sense of duty, a recollection, as it were, that this ought to be prevented, made him collect himself to say:

" How much do you ask for the trip? "

And the gondolier, gazing out over his head, replied: " The signore will pay."

There was an established reply to this; Aschenbach made it, mechanically:

" I will pay nothing whatever if you do not take me where I want to go."

" The signore wants to go to the Lido."

" But not with you."

" I am a good rower, signore. I will row you well."

" So much is true," thought Aschenbach, and again he relaxed. " That is true, you row me well. Even if you mean to rob me, even if you hit me in the back with your oar and send me down to the kingdom of Hades, even then you will have rowed me well."

But nothing of the sort happened. Instead, they fell in with company: a boat came alongside and waylaid them, full of men and women singing to guitar and mandolin. They rowed persistently bow for bow with the gondola and filled the silence that had rested on the waters with their lyric love of gain. Aschenbach tossed money into the hat they held out. The music stopped at once, they rowed away. And once more the gondolier's mutter became audible as he talked to himself in fits and snatches.

Thus they rowed on, rocked by the wash of a steamer returning citywards. At the landing two municipal officials were walking up and down with their hands behind their backs and their faces turned toward the lagoon. Aschenbach was helped on shore by the old man with a boat-hook who is the permanent feature of every landing-stage in Venice; and having no small change to pay the boatman, crossed over into the hotel opposite. His wants were supplied in the lobby; but when he came back his possessions were already on a hand-car on the quay, and gondola and gondolier were gone.

"He ran away, signore," said the old boatman. "A bad lot, a man without a license. He is the only gondolier without one. The others telephoned over, and he knew we were on the look-out, so he made off."

Aschenbach shrugged.

"The signore has had a ride for nothing," said the old man, and held out his hat. Aschenbach dropped some coins. He directed that his luggage be taken to the Hôtel des Bains and followed the hand-car through the avenue, that white-blossoming avenue with taverns, booths, and pensions on either side it, which runs across the island diagonally to the beach.

He entered the hotel from the garden terrace at the back and passed through the vestibule and hall into the office. His arrival was expected, and he was served with courtesy and dispatch. The manager, a small, soft, dapper man with a black mustache and a caressing way, wearing a French frock coat, himself took him up in the lift and showed him his room. It was a pleasant chamber, furnished in cherry-wood, with lofty windows looking out to sea. It was decorated with strong-scented flowers. Aschenbach, as soon as he was alone, and while they brought in his trunk and bags and disposed them in the room, went up to one of the windows and stood looking out upon the beach in its afternoon emptiness, and at the sunless sea, now full and sending long, low waves with rhythmic beat upon the sand.

A solitary, unused to speaking of what he sees and feels, has mental experiences which are at once more intense and less articu-

late then those of a gregarious man. They are sluggish, yet more
wayward, and never without a melancholy tinge. Sights and impressions which others brush aside with a glance, a light comment,
a smile, occupy him more than their due; they sink silently in,
they take on meaning, they become experience, emotion, adventure. Solitude gives birth to the original in us, to beauty unfamiliar
and perilous — to poetry. But also, it gives birth to the opposite:
to the perverse, the illicit, the absurd. Thus the traveler's mind still
dwelt with disquiet on the episodes of his journey hither: on the
horrible old fop with his drivel about a mistress, on the outlaw
boatman and his lost tip. They did not offend his reason, they
hardly afforded food for thought; yet they seemed by their very
nature fundamentally strange, and thereby vaguely disquieting.
Yet here was the sea: even in the midst of such thoughts he saluted
it with his eyes, exulting that Venice was near and accessible. At
length he turned round, disposed his personal belongings and made
certain arrangements with the chambermaid for his comfort,
washed up, and was conveyed to the ground floor by the green-
uniformed Swiss who ran the lift.

He took tea on the terrace facing the sea and afterwards went
down and walked some distance along the shore promenade in the
direction of Hôtel Excelsior. When he came back it seemed to be
time to change for dinner. He did so, slowly and methodically
as his way was, for he was accustomed to work while he dressed;
but even so found himself a little early when he entered the hall,
where a large number of guests had collected — strangers to each
other and affecting mutual indifference, yet united in expectancy of
the meal. He picked up a paper, sat down in a leather armchair,
and took stock of the company, which compared most favorably
with that he had just left.

This was a broad and tolerant atmosphere, of wide horizons.
Subdued voices were speaking most of the principal European
tongues. That uniform of civilization, the conventional evening
dress, gave outward conformity to the varied types. There were
long, dry Americans, large-familied Russians, English ladies, German children with French *bonnes*. The Slavic element predomi-
nated, it seemed. In Aschenbach's neighborhood Polish was being
spoken.

About a wicker table next him was gathered a group of young folk in charge of a governess or companion — three young girls, perhaps fifteen to seventeen years old, and a long-haired boy of about fourteen. Aschenbach noticed with astonishment the lad's perfect beauty. His face recalled the noblest moment of Greek sculpture — pale, with a sweet reserve, with clustering honey-colored ringlets, the brow and nose descending in one line, the winning mouth, the expression of pure and godlike serenity. Yet with all this chaste perfection of form it was of such unique personal charm that the observer thought he had never seen, either in nature or art, anything so utterly happy and consummate. What struck him further was the strange contrast the group afforded, a difference in educational method, so to speak, shown in the way the brother and sisters were clothed and treated. The girls, the eldest of whom was practically grown up, were dressed with an almost disfiguring austerity. All three wore half-length slate-colored frocks of cloister-like plainness, arbitrarily unbecoming in cut, with white turnover collars as their only adornment. Every grace of outline was willfully suppressed; their hair lay smoothly plastered to their heads, giving them a vacant expression, like a nun's. All this could only be by the mother's orders; but there was no trace of the same pedagogic severity in the case of the boy. Tenderness and softness, it was plain, conditioned his existence. No scissors had been put to the lovely hair that (like the Spinnario's) curled about his brows, above his ears, longer still in the neck. He wore an English sailor suit, with quilted sleeves that narrowed round the delicate wrists of his long and slender though still childish hands. And this suit, with its breast-knot, lacings, and embroideries, lent the slight figure something " rich and strange," a spoilt and exquisite air. The observer saw him in half profile, with one foot in its black patent leather advanced, one elbow resting on the arm of his basket-chair, the cheek nestled into the closed hand in a pose of easy grace, quite unlike the stiff subservient mien which was evidently habitual to his sisters. Was he delicate? His facial tint was ivory-white against the golden darkness of his clustering locks. Or was he simply a pampered darling, the object of a self-willed and partial love? Aschenbach inclined to think the latter. For in almost every artist nature is inborn a wanton and treacherous proneness

to side with the beauty that breaks hearts, to single out aristocratic
pretensions and pay them homage.

A waiter announced, in English, that dinner was served. Gradually the company dispersed through the glass doors into the dining-
room. Late-comers entered from the vestibule or the lifts. Inside,
dinner was being served; but the young Poles still sat and waited
about their wicker table. Aschenbach felt comfortable in his deep
armchair, he enjoyed the beauty before his eyes, he waited with
them.

The governess, a short, stout, red-faced person, at length gave
the signal. With lifted brows she pushed back her chair and made
a bow to the tall woman, dressed in palest gray, who now entered
the hall. This lady's abundant jewels were pearls, her manner was
cool and measured; the fashion of her gown and the arrangement of
her lightly powdered hair had the simplicity prescribed in certain
circles whose piety and aristocracy are equally marked. She might
have been, in Germany, the wife of some high official. But there
was something faintly fabulous, after all, in her appearance, though
lent it solely by the pearls she wore: they were wellnigh priceless,
and consisted of ear-rings and a three-stranded necklace, very long,
with gems the size of cherries.

The brother and sisters had risen briskly. They bowed over their
mother's hand to kiss it, she turning away from them, with a slight
smile on her face, which was carefully preserved but rather sharp-
nosed and worn. She addressed a few words in French to the governess, then moved toward the glass door. The children followed,
the girls in order of age, then the governess, and last the boy. He
chanced to turn before he crossed the threshold, and as there was
no one else in the room, his strange, twilit gray eyes met Aschenbach's, as our traveler sat there with the paper on his knee, absorbed in looking after the group.

There was nothing singular, of course, in what he had seen. They
had not gone in to dinner before their mother, they had waited,
given her a respectful salute, and but observed the right and proper
forms on entering the room. Yet they had done all this so expressly,
with such self-respecting dignity, discipline, and sense of duty, that
Aschenbach was impressed. He lingered still a few minutes, then

he, too, went into the dining-room, where he was shown a table far off the Polish family, as he noted at once, with a stirring of regret.

Tired, yet mentally alert, he beguiled the long, tedious meal with abstract, even with transcendent matters: pondered the mysterious harmony that must come to subsist between the individual human being and the universal law, in order that human beauty may result; passed on to general problems of form and art, and came at length to the conclusion that what seemed to him fresh and happy thoughts were like the flattering inventions of a dream, which the waking sense proves worthless and insubstantial. He spent the evening in the park, that was sweet with the odors of evening — sitting, smoking, wandering about; went to bed betimes, and passed the night in deep, unbroken sleep, visited, however, by varied and lively dreams.

The weather next day was no more promising. A land breeze blew. Beneath a colorless, overcast sky the sea lay sluggish, and as it were shrunken, so far withdrawn as to leave bare several rows of long sand-banks. The horizon looked close and prosaic. When Aschenbach opened his window he thought he smelt the stagnant odor of the lagoons.

He felt suddenly out of sorts and already began to think of leaving. Once, years before, after weeks of bright spring weather, this wind had found him out; it had been so bad as to force him to flee from the city like a fugitive. And now it seemed beginning again — the same feverish distaste, the pressure on his temples, the heavy eyelids. It would be a nuisance to change again; but if the wind did not turn, this was no place for him. To be on the safe side he did not entirely unpack. At nine o'clock he went down to the buffet, which lay between the hall and the dining-room and served as breakfast-room.

A solemn stillness reigned here, such as it is the ambition of all large hotels to achieve. The waiters moved on noiseless feet. A rattling of tea-things, a whispered word — and no other sounds. In a corner diagonally to the door, two tables off his own, Aschenbach saw the Polish girls with their governess. They sat there very straight, in their stiff blue linen frocks with little turnover collars

and cuffs, their ash-blond hair newly brushed flat, their eyelids red
from sleep; and handed each other the marmalade. They had nearly
finished their meal. The boy was not there.

Aschenbach smiled. " Aha, little Phæax," he thought. " It seems
you are privileged to sleep yourself out." With sudden gayety he
quoted:

" *Oft veränderten Schmuck und warme Bäder und Ruhe.*"

He took a leisurely breakfast. The porter came up with his
braided cap in his hand, to deliver some letters that had been sent
on. Aschenbach lighted a cigarette and opened a few letters, and
thus was still seated to witness the arrival of the sluggard.

He entered through the glass doors and passed diagonally across
the room to his sisters at their table. He walked with extraordinary
grace — the carriage of the body, the action of the knee, the way he
set down his foot in its white shoe — it was all so light, it was at
once dainty and proud, it wore an added charm in the childish
shyness which made him twice turn his head as he crossed the
room, made him give a quick glance and then drop his eyes. He
took his seat, with a smile and a murmured word in his soft and
blurry tongue; and Aschenbach, sitting so that he could see him
in profile, was astonished anew, yes, startled, at the godlike beauty
of the human being. The lad had on a light sailor suit of blue and
white striped cotton, with a red silk breast-knot and a simple white
standing collar round the neck — a not very elegant effect — yet
above this collar the head was poised like a flower, in incomparable
loveliness. It was the head of Eros, with the yellowish bloom of
Parian marble, with fine serious brows, and dusky clustering ringlets standing out in soft plenteousness over temples and ears.

" Good, oh, very good indeed! " thought Aschenbach, assuming
the patronizing air of the connoisseur to hide, as artists will, their
ravishment over a masterpiece. " Yes," he went on to himself, " if
it were not that sea and beach were waiting for me, I should sit here
as long as you do." But he went out on that, passing through the
hall, beneath the watchful eye of the functionaries, down the steps
and directly across the board walk to the section of the beach reserved for the guests of the hotel. The bathing-master, a barefoot
old man in linen trousers and sailor blouse, with a straw hat,

showed him the cabin that had been rented for him, and Aschenbach had him set up table and chair on the sandy platform before
it. Then he dragged the reclining-chair through the pale yellow
sand, closer to the sea, sat down, and composed himself.

He delighted, as always, in the scene on the beach, the sight of
sophisticated society giving itself over to a simple life at the edge of
the element. The shallow gray sea was already gay with children
wading, with swimmers, with figures in bright colors lying on the
sand-banks with arms behind their heads. Some were rowing in
little keelless boats painted red and blue, and laughing when they
capsized. A long row of *capanne* ran down the beach, with little
platforms, where people sat as on verandas, and there was social
life, with bustle and with indolent repose; visits were paid, amid
much chatter, punctilious morning toilets hob-nobbed with comfortable and privileged dishabille. On the hard wet sand close to
the sea figures in white bath-robes or loose wrappings in garish
colors strolled up and down. A mammoth sand-hill had been built
up on Aschenbach's right, the work of children, who had stuck it
full of tiny flags. Vendors of sea-shells, fruit, and cakes knelt beside their wares spread out on the sand. A row of cabins on the left
stood obliquely to the others and to the sea, thus forming the
boundary of the enclosure on this side; and on the little veranda
in front of one of these a Russian family was encamped; bearded
men with strong white teeth, ripe, indolent women, a Fräulein
from the Baltic provinces, who sat at an easel painting the sea and
tearing her hair in despair; two ugly but good-natured children and
an old maidservant in a head-cloth, with the caressing, servile manner of the born dependent. There they sat together in grateful enjoyment of their blessings: constantly shouting at their romping
children, who paid not the slightest heed; making jokes in broken
Italian to the funny old man who sold them sweetmeats, kissing
each other on the cheeks — no jot concerned that their domesticity
was overlooked.

"I'll stop," thought Aschenbach. "Where could it be better
than here?" With his hands clasped in his lap he let his eyes swim
in the wideness of the sea, his gaze lose focus, blur, and grow vague
in the misty immensity of space. His love of the ocean had profound sources: the hard-worked artist's longing for rest, his yearn-

ing to seek refuge from the thronging manifold shapes of his fancy
in the bosom of the simple and vast; and another yearning, opposed to his art and perhaps for that very reason a lure, for the
unorganized, the immeasurable, the eternal — in short, for nothingness. He whose preoccupation is with excellence longs fervently to
find rest in perfection; and is not nothingness a form of perfection? As he sat there dreaming thus, deep, deep into the void, suddenly the margin line of the shore was cut by a human figure. He
gathered up his gaze and withdrew it from the illimitable, and lo,
it was the lovely boy who crossed his vision coming from the left
along the sand. He was barefoot, ready for wading, the slender legs
uncovered above the knee, and moved slowly, yet with such a
proud, light tread as to make it seem he had never worn shoes. He
looked toward the diagonal row of cabins; and the sight of the
Russian family, leading their lives there in joyous simplicity, distorted his features in a spasm of angry disgust. His brow darkened,
his lips curled, one corner of the mouth was drawn down in a
harsh line that marred the curve of the cheek, his frown was so
heavy that the eyes seemed to sink in as they uttered beneath the
black and vicious language of hate. He looked down, looked threateningly back once more; then giving it up with a violent and contemptuous shoulder-shrug, he left his enemies in the rear.

A feeling of delicacy, a qualm, almost like a sense of shame,
made Aschenbach turn away as though he had not seen; he felt
unwilling to take advantage of having been, by chance, privy to
this passionate reaction. But he was in truth both moved and ex-
hilarated — that is to say, he was delighted. This childish exhibition
of fanaticism, directed against the good-naturedest simplicity in the
world — it gave to the godlike and inexpressive the final human
touch. The figure of the half-grown lad, a masterpiece from nature's
own hand, had been significant enough when it gratified the eye
alone; and now it evoked sympathy as well — the little episode had
set it off, lent it a dignity in the onlooker's eyes that was beyond
its years.

Aschenbach listened with still averted head to the boy's voice
announcing his coming to his companions at the sand-heap. The
voice was clear, though a little weak, but they answered, shouting
his name — or his nickname — again and again. Aschenbach was

not without curiosity to learn it, but could make out nothing more exact than two musical syllables, something like Adgio — or, oftener still, Adjiu, with a long-drawn-out u at the end. He liked the melodious sound, and found it fitting; said it over to himself a few times and turned back with satisfaction to his papers.

Holding his traveling-pad on his knees, he took his fountain-pen and began to answer various items of his correspondence. But presently he felt it too great a pity to turn his back, and the eyes of his mind, for the sake of mere commonplace correspondence, to this scene which was, after all, the most rewarding one he knew. He put aside his papers and swung round to the sea; in no long time, beguiled by the voices of the children at play, he had turned his head and sat resting it against the chair-back, while he gave himself up to contemplating the activities of the exquisite Adgio.

His eye found him out at once, the red breast-knot was unmistakable. With some nine or ten companions, boys and girls of his own age and younger, he was busy putting in place an old plank to serve as a bridge across the ditches between the sand-piles. He directed the work by shouting and motioning with his head, and they were all chattering in many tongues — French, Polish, and even some of the Balkan languages. But his was the name oftenest on their lips, he was plainly sought after, wooed, admired. One lad in particular, a Pole like himself, with a name that sounded something like Jaschiu, a sturdy lad with brilliantined black hair, in a belted linen suit, was his particular liegeman and friend. Operations at the sand-pile being ended for the time, they two walked away along the beach, with their arms round each other's waists, and once the lad Jaschiu gave Adgio a kiss.

Aschenbach felt like shaking a finger at him. "But you, Critobulus," he thought with a smile, "you I advise to take a year's leave. That long, at least, you will need for complete recovery." A vendor came by with strawberries, and Aschenbach made his second breakfast of the great luscious, dead-ripe fruit. It had grown very warm, although the sun had not availed to pierce the heavy layer of mist. His mind felt relaxed, his senses reveled in this vast and soothing communion with the silence of the sea. The grave and serious man found sufficient occupation in speculating what name it could be that sounded like Adgio. And with the help of a

few Polish memories he at length fixed on Tadzio, a shortened
form of Thaddeus, which sounded, when called, like Tadziu or
Adziu.

Tadzio was bathing. Aschenbach had lost sight of him for a
moment, then descried him far out in the water, which was shallow
a very long way — saw his head, and his arm striking out like an
oar. But his watchful family were already on the alert; the mother
and governess called from the veranda in front of their bathing-
cabin, until the lad's name, with its softened consonants and long-
drawn u-sound, seemed to possess the beach like a rallying-cry; the
cadence had something sweet and wild: " Tadziu! Tadziu! " He
turned and ran back against the water, churning the waves to a
foam, his head flung high. The sight of this living figure, virginally
pure and austere, with dripping locks, beautiful as a tender young
god, emerging from the depths of sea and sky, outrunning the element — it conjured up mythologies, it was like a primeval legend,
handed down from the beginning of time, of the birth of form,
of the origin of the gods. With closed lids Aschenbach listened to
this poesy hymning itself silently within him, and anon he thought
it was good to be here and that he would stop awhile.

Afterwards Tadzio lay on the sand and rested from his bathe,
wrapped in his white sheet, which he wore drawn underneath the
right shoulder, so that his head was cradled on his bare right arm.
And even when Aschenbach read, without looking up, he was conscious that the lad was there; that it would cost him but the slightest turn of the head to have the rewarding vision once more in his
purview. Indeed, it was almost as though he sat there to guard the
youth's repose; occupied, of course, with his own affairs, yet alive to
the presence of that noble human creature close at hand. And his
heart was stirred, it felt a father's kindness: such an emotion as
the possessor of beauty can inspire in one who has offered himself
up in spirit to create beauty.

At midday he left the beach, returned to the hotel, and was carried up in the lift to his room. There he lingered a little time before the glass, and looked at his own gray hair, his keen and weary
face. And he thought of his fame, and how people gazed respectfully at him in the streets, on account of his unerring gift of words
and their power to charm. He called up all the worldly successes

his genius had reaped, all he could remember, even his patent of nobility. Then went to luncheon down in the dining-room, sat at his little table and ate. Afterwards he mounted again in the lift, and a group of young folk, Tadzio among them, pressed with him into the little compartment. It was the first time Aschenbach had seen him close at hand, not merely in perspective, and could see and take account of the details of his humanity. Someone spoke to the lad, and he, answering, with indescribably lovely smile, stepped out again, as they had come to the first floor, backwards, with his eyes cast down. " Beauty makes people self-conscious," Aschenbach thought, and considered within himself imperatively why this should be. He had noted, further, that Tadzio's teeth were imperfect, rather jagged and bluish, without a healthy glaze, and of that peculiar brittle transparency which the teeth of chlorotic people often show. " He is delicate, he is sickly," Aschenbach thought. " He will most likely not live to grow old." He did not try to account for the pleasure the idea gave him.

In the afternoon he spent two hours in his room, then took the *vaporetto* to Venice, across the foul-smelling lagoon. He got out at San Marco, had his tea in the Piazza, and then, as his custom was, took a walk through the streets. But this walk of his brought about nothing less than a revolution in his mood and an entire change in all his plans.

There was a hateful sultriness in the narrow streets. The air was so heavy that all the manifold smells wafted out of houses, shops, and cook-shops — smells of oil, perfumery, and so forth — hung low, like exhalations, not dissipating. Cigarette smoke seemed to stand in the air, it drifted so slowly away. Today the crowd in these narrow lanes oppressed the stroller instead of diverting him. The longer he walked, the more was he in tortures under that state which is the product of the sea air and the sirocco and which excites and enervates at once. He perspired painfully. His eyes rebelled, his chest was heavy, he felt feverish, the blood throbbed in his temples. He fled from the huddled, narrow streets of the commercial city, crossed many bridges, and came into the poor quarter of Venice. Beggars waylaid him, the canals sickened him with their evil exhalations. He reached a quiet square, one of those that exist at the city's heart, forsaken of God and man; there he rested awhile on the margin of a fountain, wiped his brow, and admitted to himself that he must be gone.

For the second time, and now quite definitely, the city proved that in certain weathers it could be directly inimical to his health. Nothing but sheer unreasoning obstinacy would linger on, hoping for an unprophesiable change in the wind. A quick decision was in place. He could not go home at this stage, neither summer nor winter quarters would be ready. But Venice had not a monopoly of sea and shore: there were other spots where these were to be had without the evil concomitants of lagoon and fever-breeding vapors. He remembered a little bathing-place not far from Trieste of which he had had a good report. Why not go thither? At once, of course, in order that this second change might be worth the making. He resolved, he rose to his feet and sought the nearest gondola-landing, where he took a boat and was conveyed to San Marco through the gloomy windings of many canals, beneath balconies of delicate marble traceries flanked by craven lions; round slippery corners of wall, past melancholy façades with ancient business shields re-flected in the rocking water. It was not too easy to arrive at his destination, for his gondolier, being in league with various lace-makers and glass-blowers, did his best to persuade his fare to pause, look, and be tempted to buy. Thus the charm of this bizarre passage through the heart of Venice, even while it played upon his spirit, yet was sensibly cooled by the predatory commercial spirit of the fallen queen of the seas.

Once back in his hotel he announced at the office, even before dinner, that circumstances unforeseen obliged him to leave early next morning. The management expressed its regret, it changed his money and receipted his bill. He dined, and spent the luke-warm evening in a rocking-chair on the rear terrace, reading the newspapers. Before he went to bed, he made his luggage ready against the morning.

His sleep was not of the best, for the prospect of another journey made him restless. When he opened his window next morning, the sky was still overcast, but the air seemed fresher — and there and then his rue began. Had he not given notice too soon? Had he not let himself be swayed by a slight and momentary indisposi-tion? If he had only been patient, not lost heart so quickly, tried to adapt himself to the climate, or even waited for a change in the weather before deciding! Then, instead of the hurry and flurry of departure, he would have before him now a morning like yesterday's on the beach. Too late! He must go on wanting what he had wanted yesterday. He dressed and at eight o'clock went down to breakfast.

When he entered the breakfast-room it was empty. Guests came in while he sat waiting for his order to be filled. As he sipped his tea he saw the Polish girls enter with their governess, chaste and morning-fresh, with sleep-reddened eyelids. They crossed the room and sat down at their table in the window. Behind them came the porter, cap in hand, to announce that it was time for him to go. The car was waiting to convey him and other travelers to the Hôtel Excelsior, whence they would go by motor-boat through the company's private canal to the station. Time pressed. But Aschenbach found it did nothing of the sort. There still lacked more than an hour of train-time. He felt irritated at the hotel habit of getting the guests out of the house earlier than necessary; and requested the porter to let him breakfast in peace. The man hesitated and withdrew, only to come back again five minutes later. The car could wait no longer. Good, then it might go, and take his trunk with it, Aschenbach answered with some heat. He would use the public conveyance, in his own time; he begged them to leave the choice of it to him. The functionary bowed. Aschenbach, pleased to be rid of him, made a leisurely meal, and even had a newspaper of the waiter. When at length he rose, the time was grown very short. And it so happened that at that moment Tadzio came through the glass doors into the room.

To reach his own table he crossed the traveler's path, and modestly cast down his eyes before the gray-haired man of the lofty brows — only to lift them again in that sweet way he had and direct his full soft gaze upon Aschenbach's face. Then he was past. "For the last time, Tadzio," thought the elder man. "It was all too brief!" Quite unusually for him, he shaped a farewell with his lips, he actually uttered it, and added: "May God bless you!" Then he went out, distributed tips, exchanged farewells with the mild little manager in the frock coat, and, followed by the porter with his hand-luggage, left the hotel. On foot as he had come, he passed through the white-blossoming avenue, diagonally across the

island to the boat-landing. He went on board at once — but the tale
of his journey across the lagoon was a tale of woe, a passage through
the very valley of regrets.

It was the well-known route: through the lagoon, past San
Marco, up the Grand Canal. Aschenbach sat on the circular bench
in the bows, with his elbow on the railing, one hand shading his
eyes. They passed the Public Gardens, once more the princely
charm of the Piazzetta rose up before him and then dropped behind, then came the great row of palaces, the canal curved, and
the splendid marble arches of the Rialto came in sight. The traveler
gazed — and his bosom was torn. The atmosphere of the city, the
faintly rotten scent of swamp and sea, which had driven him to
leave — in what deep, tender, almost painful drafts he breathed
it in! How was it he had not known, had not thought, how much
his heart was set upon it all! What this morning had been slight
regret, some little doubt of his own wisdom, turned now to grief,
to actual wretchedness, a mental agony so sharp that it repeatedly
brought tears to his eyes, while he questioned himself how he
could have foreseen it. The hardest part, the part that more than
once it seemed he could not bear, was the thought that he should
never more seen Venice again. Since now for the second time the
place had made him ill, since for the second time he had had to
flee for his life, he must henceforth regard it as a forbidden spot,
to be forever shunned; senseless to try weakness again, after he had
proved himself unfit. Yes, if he fled it now, he felt that wounded
pride must prevent his return to this spot where twice he had made
actual bodily surrender. And this conflict between inclination and
capacity all at once assumed, in this middle-aged man's mind, immense weight and importance; the physical defeat seemed a shameful thing, to be avoided at whatever cost; and he stood amazed at
the ease with which on the day before he had yielded to it.

Meanwhile the steamer neared the station landing; his anguish
of irresolution amounted almost to panic. To leave seemed to the
sufferer impossible, to remain not less so. Torn thus between two
alternatives, he entered the station. It was very late, he had not a
moment to lose. Time pressed, it scourged him onward. He hastened to buy his ticket, and looked round in the crowd to find the
hotel porter. The man appeared and said that the trunk had al-

ready gone off. " Gone already? " " Yes, it has gone to Como."
" To Como? " A hasty exchange of words — angry questions from
Aschenbach, and puzzled replies from the porter — at length made
it clear that the trunk had been put with the wrong luggage even
before leaving the hotel, and in company with other trunks was
now well on its way in precisely the wrong direction.

Aschenbach found it hard to wear the right expression as he
heard this news. A reckless joy, a deep incredible mirthfulness
shook him almost as with a spasm. The porter dashed off after
the lost trunk, returning very soon, of course, to announce that his
efforts were unavailing. Aschenbach said he would not travel without his luggage; that he would go back and wait at the Hôtel des
Bains until it turned up. Was the company's motor-boat still outside? The man said yes, it was at the door. With his native eloquence he prevailed upon the ticket-agent to take back the ticket
already purchased; he swore that he would wire, that no pains
should be spared, that the trunk would be restored in the twinkling
of an eye. And the unbelievable thing came to pass: the traveler,
twenty minutes after he had reached the station, found himself
once more on the Grand Canal on his way back to the Lido.

What a strange adventure indeed, this right-about-face of destiny — incredible, humiliating, whimsical as any dream! To be
passing again, within the hour, these scenes from which in profoundest grief he had but now taken leave forever! The little swift-
moving vessel, a furrow of foam at its prow, tacking with droll
agility between steamboats and gondolas, went like a shot to its
goal; and he, its sole passenger, sat hiding the panic and thrills of
a truant schoolboy beneath a mask of forced resignation. His breast
still heaved from time to time with a burst of laughter over the
contretemps. Things could not, he told himself, have fallen out
more luckily. There would be the necessary explanations, a few
astonished faces — then all would be well once more, a mischance
prevented, a grievous error set right; and all he had thought to have
left forever was his own once more, his for as long as he liked. . . .
And did the boat's swift motion deceive him, or was the wind
now coming from the sea?

The waves struck against the tiled sides of the narrow canal. At
Hôtel Excelsior the automobile omnibus awaited the returned

traveler and bore him along by the crisping waves back to the Hôtel des Bains. The little mustachioed manager in the frock coat came down the steps to greet him.

In dulcet tones he deplored the mistake, said how painful it was to the management and himself; applauded Aschenbach's resolve to stop on until the errant trunk came back; his former room, alas, was already taken, but another as good awaited his approval. " *Pas de chance, monsieur,*" said the Swiss lift-porter, with a smile, as he conveyed him upstairs. And the fugitive was soon quartered in another room which in situation and furnishings almost precisely resembled the first.

He laid out the contents of his handbag in their wonted places; then, tired out, dazed by the whirl of the extraordinary forenoon, subsided into the armchair by the open window. The sea wore a pale green cast, the air felt thinner and purer, the beach with its cabins and boats had more color, notwithstanding the sky was still gray. Aschenbach, his hands folded in his lap, looked out. He felt rejoiced to be back, yet displeased with his vacillating moods, his ignorance of his own real desires. Thus for nearly an hour he sat, dreaming, resting, barely thinking. At midday he saw Tadzio, in his striped sailor suit with red breast-knot, coming up from the sea, across the barrier and along the board walk to the hotel. Aschenbach recognized him, even at this height, knew it was he before he actually saw him, had it in mind to say to himself: " Well, Tadzio, so here you are again too! " But the casual greeting died away before it reached his lips, slain by the truth in his heart. He felt the rapture of his blood, the poignant pleasure, and realized that it was for Tadzio's sake the leave-taking had been so hard.

He sat quite still, unseen at his high post, and looked within himself. His features were lively, he lifted his brows; a smile, alert, inquiring, vivid, widened the mouth. Then he raised his head, and with both hands, hanging limp over the chair-arms, he described a slow motion, palms outward, a lifting and turning movement, as though to indicate a wide embrace. It was a gesture of welcome, a calm and deliberate acceptance of what might come.

Now daily the naked god with cheeks aflame drove his four fire-breathing steeds through heaven's spaces; and with him streamed the strong east wind that fluttered his yellow locks. A sheen, like white satin, lay over all the idly rolling sea's expanse. The sand was burning hot. Awnings of rust-colored canvas were spanned before the bathing-huts, under the ether's quivering silver-blue; one spent the morning hours within the small, sharp square of shadow they purveyed. But evening too was rarely lovely: balsamic with the breath of flowers and shrubs from the near-by park, while overhead the constellations circled in their spheres, and the murmuring of the night-girted sea swelled softly up and whispered to the soul. Such nights as these contained the joyful promise of a sunlit morrow, brim-full of sweetly ordered idleness, studded thick with countless precious possibilities.

The guest detained here by so happy a mischance was far from finding the return of his luggage a ground for setting out anew. For two days he had suffered slight inconvenience, and had to dine in the large salon in his traveling-clothes. Then the lost trunk was set down in his room, and he hastened to unpack, filling presses and drawers with his possessions. He meant to stay on — and on; he rejoiced in the prospect of wearing a silk suit for the hot morning hours on the beach and appearing in acceptable evening dress at dinner.

He was quick to fall in with the pleasing monotony of this manner of life, readily enchanted by its mild soft brilliance and ease. And what a spot it is, indeed! — uniting the charms of a luxurious bathing-resort by a southern sea with the immediate nearness of a unique and marvelous city. Aschenbach was not pleasure-loving. Always, wherever and whenever it was the order of the day to be merry, to refrain from labor and make glad the heart, he would soon be conscious of the imperative summons — and especially was this so in his youth — back to the high fatigues, the sacred and fasting service that consumed his days. This spot and this alone had power to beguile him, to relax his resolution, to make him glad. At times — of a forenoon perhaps, as he lay in the shadow of his awning, gazing out dreamily over the blue of the southern sea, or in the mildness of the night, beneath the wide starry sky, ensconced among the cushions of the gondola that bore him Lidowards after an evening on the Piazza, while the gay lights faded and the melting music of the serenades died away on his ear — he

would think of his mountain home, the theater of his summer
labors. There clouds hung low and trailed through the garden, violent storms extinguished the lights of the house at night, and the
ravens he fed swung in the tops of the fir trees. And he would feel
transported to Elysium, to the ends of the earth, to a spot most
carefree for the sons of men, where no snow is, and no winter, no
storms or downpours of rain; where Oceanus sends a mild and cooling breath, and days flow on in blissful idleness, without effort or
struggle, entirely dedicate to the sun and the feasts of the sun.

Aschenbach saw the boy Tadzio almost constantly. The narrow
confines of their world of hotel and beach, the daily round followed
by all alike, brought him in close, almost uninterrupted touch with
the beautiful lad. He encountered him everywhere — in the salons
of the hotel, on the cooling rides to the city and back, among the
splendors of the Piazza, and besides all this in many another going
and coming as chance vouchsafed. But it was the regular morning
hours on the beach which gave him his happiest opportunity to
study and admire the lovely apparition. Yes, this immediate happiness, this daily recurring boon at the hand of circumstance, this
it was that filled him with content, with joy in life, enriched his
stay, and lingered out the row of sunny days that fell into place so
pleasantly one behind the other.

He rose early — as early as though he had a panting press of
work — and was among the first on the beach, when the sun was
still benign and the sea lay dazzling white in its morning slumber.
He gave the watchman a friendly good-morning and chatted with
the barefoot, white-haired old man who prepared his place, spread
the awning, trundled out the chair and table onto the little platform. Then he settled down; he had three or four hours before
the sun reached its height and the fearful climax of its power; three
or four hours while the sea went deeper and deeper blue; three
or four hours in which to watch Tadzio.

He would see him come up, on the left, along the margin of the
sea; or from behind, between the cabins; or, with a start of joyful
surprise, would discover that he himself was late, and Tadzio already down, in the blue and white bathing-suit that was now his
only wear on the beach; there and engrossed in his usual activities
in the sand, beneath the sun. It was a sweetly idle, trifling, fitful

life, of play and rest, of strolling, wading, digging, fishing, swimming, lying on the sand. Often the women sitting on the platform would call out to him in their high voices: " Tadziu! Tadziu! " and he would come running and waving his arms, eager to tell them what he had done, show them what he had found, what caught — shells, seahorses, jelly-fish, and sidewards-running crabs. Aschenbach understood not a word he said; it might be the sheerest commonplace, in his ear it became mingled harmonies. Thus the lad's foreign birth raised his speech to music; a wanton sun showered splendor on him, and the noble distances of the sea formed the background which set off his figure.

Soon the observer knew every line and pose of this form that limned itself so freely against sea and sky; its every loveliness, though conned by heart, yet thrilled him each day afresh; his admiration knew no bounds, the delight of his eye was unending. Once the lad was summoned to speak to a guest who was waiting for his mother at their cabin. He ran up, ran dripping wet out of the sea, tossing his curls, and put out his hand, standing with his weight on one leg, resting the other foot on the toes; as he stood there in a posture of suspense the turn of his body was enchanting, while his features wore a look half shamefaced, half conscious of the duty breeding laid upon him to please. Or he would lie at full length, with his bath-robe around him, one slender young arm resting on the sand, his chin in the hollow of his hand; the lad they called Jaschiu squatting beside him, paying him court. There could be nothing lovelier on earth than the smile and look with which the playmate thus singled out rewarded his humble friend and vassal. Again, he might be at the water's edge, alone, removed from his family, quite close to Aschenbach; standing erect, his hands clasped at the back of his neck, rocking slowly on the balls of his feet, day-dreaming away into blue space, while little waves ran up and bathed his toes. The ringlets of honey-colored hair clung to his temples and neck, the fine down along the upper vertebræ was yellow in the sunlight; the scanty envelope of flesh covering the torso betrayed the delicate outlines of the ribs and the symmetry of the breast-structure. His armpits were still as smooth as a statue's, smooth the glistening hollows behind the knees, where the blue network of veins suggested that the body was formed of some stuff more transparent than mere flesh. What discipline, what precision of thought were expressed by the tense youthful perfection of this form! And yet the pure, strong will which had labored in darkness and succeeded in bringing this god-like work of art to the light of day — was it not known and familiar to him, the artist? Was not the same force at work in himself when he strove in cold fury to liberate from the marble mass of language the slender forms of his art which he saw with the eye of his mind and would body forth to men as the mirror and image of spiritual beauty?

Mirror and image! His eyes took in the proud bearing of that figure there at the blue water's edge; with an outburst of rapture he told himself that what he saw was beauty's very essence; form as divine thought, the single and pure perfection which resides in the mind, of which an image and likeness, rare and holy, was here raised up for adoration. This was very frenzy — and without a scruple, nay, eagerly, the aging artist bade it come. His mind was in travail, his whole mental background in a state of flux. Memory flung up in him the primitive thoughts which are youth's inherit-ance, but which with him had remained latent, never leaping up into a blaze. Has it not been written that the sun beguiles our at-tention from things of the intellect to fix it on things of the sense? The sun, they say, dazzles; so bewitching reason and memory that the soul for very pleasure forgets its actual state, to cling with doting on the loveliest of all the objects she shines on. Yes, and then it is only through the medium of some corporeal being that it can raise itself again to contemplation of higher things. Amor, in sooth, is like the mathematician who in order to give children a knowledge of pure form must do so in the language of pictures: so, too, the god, in order to make visible the spirit, avails himself of the forms and colors of human youth, gilding it with all imaginable beauty that it may serve memory as a tool, the very sight of which then sets us afire with pain and longing.

Such were the devotee's thoughts, such the power of his emo-tions. And the sea, so bright with glancing sunbeams, wove in his mind a spell and summoned up a lovely picture: there was the ancient plane tree outside the walls of Athens, a hallowed, shady spot, fragrant with willow blossom and adorned with images and

votive offerings in honor of the nymphs and Achelous. Clear ran
the smooth-pebbled stream at the foot of the spreading tree.
Crickets were fiddling. But on the gentle grassy slope, where one
could lie yet hold the head erect, and shelter from the scorching
heat, two men reclined, an elder with a younger, ugliness paired
with beauty, and wisdom with grace. Here Socrates held forth to
youthful Phædrus upon the nature of virtue and desire, wooing
him with insinuating wit and charming turns of phrase. He told
him of the shuddering and unwonted heat that come upon him
whose heart is open, when his eye beholds an image of the everlasting beauty; spoke of the impious and corrupt, who cannot conceive beauty though they see its image, and are incapable of awe;
and of the fear and reverence felt by the noble soul when he beholds a godlike face or a form which is a good image of beauty: how
as he gazes he worships the beautiful one and scarcely dares to look
upon him, but would offer sacrifice as to an idol or a god, did he
not fear to be thought stark mad. "For beauty, my Phædrus,
beauty alone, is lovely and visible at once. For, mark you, it is the
sole aspect of the spiritual which we can perceive through our
senses, or bear so to perceive. Else what should become of us, if
the divine, if reason and virtue and truth, were to speak to us
through the senses? Should we not perish and be consumed by love,
as Semele aforetime was by Zeus? So beauty, then, is the beauty-
lover's way to the spirit — but only the way, only the means, my
little Phædrus." . . . And then, sly arch-lover that he was, he said
the subtlest thing of all: that the lover was nearer the divine than
the beloved; for the god was in the one but not in the other — perhaps the tenderest, most mocking thought that ever was thought,
and source of all the guile and secret bliss the lover knows.

Thought that can merge wholly into feeling, feeling that can
merge wholly into thought — these are the artist's highest joy. And
our solitary felt in himself at this moment power to command and
wield a thought that thrilled with emotion, an emotion as precise
and concentrated as thought: namely, that nature herself shivers
with ecstasy when the mind bows down in homage before beauty.
He felt a sudden desire to write. Eros, indeed, we are told, loves
idleness, and for idle hours alone was he created. But in this crisis
the violence of our sufferer's seizure was directed almost wholly

toward production, its occasion almost a matter of indifference. News had reached him on his travels that a certain problem had been raised, the intellectual world challenged for its opinion on a great and burning question of art and taste. By nature and experience the theme was his own; and he could not resist the temptation to set it off in the glistering foil of his words. He would write, and moreover he would write in Tadzio's presence. This lad should be in a sense his model, his style should follow the lines of this figure that seemed to him divine; he would snatch up this beauty into the realms of the mind, as once the eagle bore the Trojan shepherd aloft. Never had the pride of the word been so sweet to him, never had he known so well that Eros is in the word, as in those perilous and precious hours when he sat at his rude table, within the shade of his awning, his idol full in his view and the music of his voice in his ears, and fashioned his little essay after the model Tadzio's beauty set: that page and a half of choicest prose, so chaste, so lofty, so poignant with feeling, which would shortly be the wonder and admiration of the multitude. Verily it is well for the world that it sees only the beauty of the completed work and not its origins nor the conditions whence it sprang; since knowledge of the artist's inspiration might often but confuse and alarm and so prevent the full effect of its excellence. Strange hours, indeed, these were, and strangely unnerving the labor that filled them! Strangely fruitful intercourse this, between one body and another mind! When Aschenbach put aside his work and left the beach he felt exhausted, he felt broken — conscience reproached him, as it were after a debauch.

Next morning on leaving the hotel he stood at the top of the stairs leading down from the terrace and saw Tadzio in front of him on his way to the beach. The lad had just reached the gate in the railings, and he was alone. Aschenbach felt, quite simply, a wish to overtake him, to address him and have the pleasure of his reply and answering look; to put upon a blithe and friendly footing his relation with this being who all unconsciously had so greatly heightened and quickened his emotions. The lovely youth moved at a loitering pace — he might easily be overtaken; and Aschenbach hastened his own step. He reached him on the board walk that ran behind the bathing-cabins, and all but put out his hand to lay it on shoulder or head, while his lips parted to utter a friendly salutation in French. But — perhaps from the swift pace of his last few steps — he found his heart throbbing unpleasantly fast, while his breath came in such quick pants that he could only have gasped had he tried to speak. He hesitated, sought after self-control, was suddenly panic-stricken lest the boy notice him hanging there behind him and look round. Then he gave up, abandoned his plan, and passed him with bent head and hurried step.

"Too late! too late!" he thought as he went by. But was it too late? This step he had delayed to take might so easily have put everything in a lighter key, have led to a sane recovery from his folly. But the truth may have been that the aging man did not want to be cured, that his illusion was far too dear to him. Who shall unriddle the puzzle of the artist nature? Who understands that mingling of discipline and license in which it stands so deeply rooted? For not to be able to want sobriety is licentious folly. Aschenbach was no longer disposed to self-analysis. He had no taste for it: his self-esteem, the attitude of mind proper to his years, his maturity and single-mindedness, disinclined him to look within himself and decide whether it was constraint or puerile sensuality that had prevented him from carrying out his project. He felt confused, he was afraid someone, if only the watchman, might have been observing his behavior and final surrender — very much he feared being ridiculous. And all the time he was laughing at himself for his serio-comic seizure. "Quite crestfallen," he thought. "I was like the gamecock that lets his wings droop in the battle. That must be the Love-God himself, that makes us hang our heads at sight of beauty and weighs our proud spirits low as the ground." Thus he played with the idea — he embroidered upon it, and was too arrogant to admit fear of an emotion.

The term he had set for his holiday passed by unheeded; he had no thought of going home. Ample funds had been sent him. His sole concern was that the Polish family might leave, and a chance question put to the hotel barber elicited the information that they had come only very shortly before himself. The sun browned his face and hands, the invigorating salt air heightened his emotional energies. Heretofore he had been wont to give out at once, in some new effort, the powers accumulated by sleep or food or outdoor air;

but now the strength that flowed in upon him with each day of sun
and sea and idleness he let go up in one extravagant gush of emotional intoxication.

His sleep was fitful; the priceless, equable days were divided one
from the next by brief nights filled with happy unrest. He went, indeed, early to bed, for at nine o'clock, with the departure of Tadzio
from the scene, the day was over for him. But in the faint grayness
of the morning a tender pang would go through him as his heart
was minded of its adventure; he could no longer bear his pillow
and, rising, would wrap himself against the early chill and sit down
by the window to await the sunrise. Awe of the miracle filled his
soul new-risen from its sleep. Heaven, earth, and its waters yet lay
enfolded in the ghostly, glassy pallor of dawn; one paling star still
swam in the shadowy vast. But there came a breath, a winged word
from far and inaccessible abodes, that Eos was rising from the side
of her spouse; and there was that first sweet reddening of the farthest strip of sea and sky that manifests creation to man's sense.
She neared, the goddess, ravisher of youth, who stole away Cleitos
and Cephalus and, defying all the envious Olympians, tasted beautiful Orion's love. At the world's edge began a strewing of roses, a
shining and a blooming ineffably pure; baby cloudlets hung illu-
mined, like attendant amoretti, in the blue and blushful haze;
purple effulgence fell upon the sea, that seemed to heave it forward
on its welling waves; from horizon to zenith went great quivering
thrusts like golden lances, the gleam became a glare; without a
sound, with godlike violence, glow and glare and rolling flames
streamed upwards, and with flying hoof-beats the steeds of the sun-
god mounted the sky. The lonely watcher sat, the splendor of the
god shone on him, he closed his eyes and let the glory kiss his lids.
Forgotten feelings, precious pangs of his youth, quenched long
since by the stern service that had been his life and now returned
so strangely metamorphosed — he recognized them with a puzzled,
wondering smile. He mused, he dreamed, his lips slowly shaped a
name; still smiling, his face turned seawards and his hands lying
folded in his lap, he fell asleep once more as he sat.

But that day, which began so fierily and festally, was not like
other days; it was transmuted and gilded with mythical significance. For whence could come the breath, so mild and meaning-

ful, like a whisper from higher spheres, that played about temple
and ear? Troops of small feathery white clouds ranged over the sky,
like grazing herds of the gods. A stronger wind arose, and Poseidon's
horses ran up, arching their manes, among them too the steers of
him with the purpled locks, who lowered their horns and bellowed
as they came on; while like prancing goats the waves on the farther
strand leaped among the craggy rocks. It was a world possessed,
peopled by Pan, that closed round the spellbound man, and his
doting heart conceived the most delicate fancies. When the sun
was going down behind Venice, he would sometimes sit on a bench
in the park and watch Tadzio, white-clad, with gay-colored sash,
at play there on the rolled gravel with his ball; and at such times
it was not Tadzio whom he saw, but Hyacinthus, doomed to die
because two gods were rivals for his love. Ah, yes, he tasted the envious pangs that Zephyr knew when his rival, bow and cithara,
oracle and all forgot, played with the beauteous youth; he watched
the discus, guided by torturing jealousy, strike the beloved head;
paled as he received the broken body in his arms, and saw the flower
spring up, watered by that sweet blood and signed forevermore with
his lament.

There can be no relation more strange, more critical, than that
between two beings who know each other only with their eyes, who
meet daily, yes, even hourly, eye each other with a fixed regard,
and yet by some whim or freak of convention feel constrained to
act like strangers. Uneasiness rules between them, unslaked curiosity, a hysterical desire to give rein to their suppressed impulse
to recognize and address each other; even, actually a sort of strained
but mutual regard. For one human being instinctively feels respect
and love for another human being so long as he does not know him
well enough to judge him; and that he does not, the craving he feels
is evidence.

Some sort of relation and acquaintanceship was perforce set up
between Aschenbach and the youthful Tadzio; it was with a thrill
of joy the older man perceived that the lad was not entirely unresponsive to all the tender notice lavished on him. For instance,
what should move the lovely youth, nowadays when he descended
to the beach, always to avoid the board walk behind the bathing-
huts and saunter along the sand, passing Aschenbach's tent in front,

sometimes so unnecessarily close as almost to graze his table or chair? Could the power of an emotion so beyond his own so draw, so fascinate its innocent object? Daily Aschenbach would wait for Tadzio. Then sometimes, on his approach, he would pretend to be preoccupied and let the charmer pass unregarded by. But sometimes he looked up, and their glances met; when that happened both were profoundly serious. The elder's dignified and cultured mien let nothing appear of his inward state; but in Tadzio's eyes a question lay — he faltered in his step, gazed on the ground, then up again with that ineffably sweet look he had; and when he was past, something in his bearing seemed to say that only good breeding hindered him from turning round.

But once, one evening, it fell out differently. The Polish brother and sisters, with their governess, had missed the evening meal, and Aschenbach had noted the fact with concern. He was restive over their absence, and after dinner walked up and down in front of the hotel, in evening dress and a straw hat; when suddenly he saw the nunlike sisters with their companion appear in the light of the arc-lamps, and four paces behind them Tadzio. Evidently they came from the steamer-landing, having dined for some reason in Venice. It had been chilly on the lagoon, for Tadzio wore a dark blue reefer-jacket with gilt buttons, and a cap to match. Sun and sea air could not burn his skin, it was the same creamy marble hue as at first — though he did look a little pale, either from the cold or in the bluish moonlight of the arc-lamps. The shapely brows were so delicately drawn, the eyes so deeply dark — lovelier he was than words could say, and as often the thought visited Aschenbach, and brought its own pang, that language could but extol, not reproduce, the beauties of the sense.

The sight of that dear form was unexpected, it had appeared unhoped for, without giving him time to compose his features. Joy, surprise, and admiration might have painted themselves quite openly upon his face — and just at this second it happened that Tadzio smiled. Smiled at Aschenbach, unabashed and friendly, a speaking, winning, captivating smile, with slowly parting lips. With such a smile it might be that Narcissus bent over the mirroring pool, a smile profound, infatuated, lingering, as he put out his arms to the reflection of his own beauty; the lips just slightly pursed, perhaps half-realizing his own folly in trying to kiss the cold lips of his shadow — with a mingling of coquetry and curiosity and a faint unease, enthralling and enthralled.

Aschenbach received that smile and turned away with it as though entrusted with a fatal gift. So shaken was he that he had to flee from the lighted terrace and front gardens and seek out with hurried steps the darkness of the park at the rear. Reproaches strangely mixed of tenderness and remonstrance burst from him: " How dare you smile like that! No one is allowed to smile like that! " He flung himself on a bench, his composure gone to the winds, and breathed in the nocturnal fragrance of the garden. He leaned back, with hanging arms, quivering from head to foot, and quite unmanned he whispered the hackneyed phrase of love and longing — impossible in these circumstances, absurd, abject, ridiculous enough, yet sacred too, and not unworthy of honor even here: " I love you! "

In the fourth week of his stay on the Lido, Gustave von Aschenbach made certain singular observations touching the world about him. He noticed, in the first place, that though the season was approaching its height, yet the number of guests declined and, in particular, that the German tongue had suffered a rout, being scarcely or never heard in the land. At table and on the beach he caught nothing but foreign words. One day at the barber's — where he was now a frequent visitor — he heard something rather startling. The barber mentioned a German family who had just left the Lido after a brief stay, and rattled on in his obsequious way: " The signore is not leaving — he has no fear of the sickness, has he? " Aschenbach looked at him. " The sickness? " he repeated. Whereat the prattler fell silent, became very busy all at once, affected not to hear. When Aschenbach persisted he said he really knew nothing at all about it, and tried in a fresh burst of eloquence to drown the embarrassing subject.

That was one forenoon. After luncheon Aschenbach had himself ferried across to Venice, in a dead calm, under a burning sun; driven by his mania, he was following the Polish young folk, whom he had seen with their companion, taking the way to the landing-stage. He did not find his idol on the Piazza. But as he sat there at

tea, at a little round table on the shady side, suddenly he scented
a peculiar odor, which, it seemed to him now, had been in the air
for days without his being aware: a sweetish, medicinal smell, associated with wounds and disease and suspect cleanliness. He sniffed
and pondered and at length recognized it; finished his tea and left
the square at the end facing the cathedral. In the narrow space the
stench grew stronger. At the street corners placards were stuck up,
in which the city authorities warned the population against the
danger of certain infections of the gastric system, prevalent during
the heated season; advising them not to eat oysters or other shell-
fish and not to use the canal waters. The ordinance showed every
sign of minimizing an existing situation. Little groups of people
stood about silently in the squares and on the bridges; the traveler
moved among them, watched and listened and thought.

He spoke to a shopkeeper lounging at his door among dangling
coral necklaces and trinkets of artificial amethyst, and asked him
about the disagreeable odor. The man looked at him, heavy-eyed,
and hastily pulled himself together. " Just a formal precaution, signore," he said, with a gesture. " A police regulation we have to put
up with. The air is sultry — the sirocco is not wholesome, as the
signore knows. Just a precautionary measure, you understand —
probably unnecessary. . . ." Aschenbach thanked him and passed
on. And on the boat that bore him back to the Lido he smelt the
germicide again.

On reaching his hotel he sought the table in the lobby and buried
himself in the newspapers. The foreign-language sheets had nothing. But in the German papers certain rumors were mentioned,
statistics given, then officially denied, then the good faith of the
denials called in question. The departure of the German and Austrian contingent was thus made plain. As for other nationals, they
knew or suspected nothing — they were still undisturbed. Aschenbach tossed the newspapers back on the table. " It ought to be
kept quiet," he thought, aroused. " It should not be talked about."
And he felt in his heart a curious elation at these events impending
in the world about him. Passion is like crime: it does not thrive on
the established order and the common round; it welcomes every
blow dealt the bourgeois structure, every weakening of the social
fabric, because therein it feels a sure hope of its own advantage.

These things that were going on in the dirty alleys of Venice, under cover of an official hushing-up policy — they gave Aschenbach a dark satisfaction. The city's evil secret mingled with the one in the depths of his heart — and he would have staked all he possessed to keep it, since in his infatuation he cared for nothing but to keep Tadzio here, and owned to himself, not without horror, that he could not exist were the lad to pass from his sight.

He was no longer satisfied to owe his communion with his charmer to chance and the routine of hotel life; he had begun to follow and waylay him. On Sundays, for example, the Polish family never appeared on the beach. Aschenbach guessed that they went to mass at San Marco and pursued them thither. He passed from the glare of the Piazza into the golden twilight of the holy place and found him he sought bowed in worship over a prie-Dieu. He kept in the background, standing on the fissured mosaic pavement among the devout populace, that knelt and muttered and made the sign of the cross; and the crowded splendor of the oriental temple weighed voluptuously on his sense. A heavily ornate priest intoned and gesticulated before the altar, where little candle-flames flickered helplessly in the reek of incense-breathing smoke; and with that cloying sacrificial smell another seemed to mingle — the odor of the sickened city. But through all the glamour and glitter Aschenbach saw the exquisite creature there in front turn his head, seek out and meet his lover's eye.

The crowd streamed out through the portals into the brilliant square thick with fluttering doves, and the fond fool stood aside in the vestibule on the watch. He saw the Polish family leave the church. The children took ceremonial leave of their mother, and she turned toward the Piazzetta on her way home, while his charmer and the cloistered sisters, with their governess, passed beneath the clock tower into the Merceria. When they were a few paces on, he followed — he stole behind them on their walk through the city. When they paused, he did so too; when they turned round, he fled into inns and courtyards to let them pass. Once he lost them from view, hunted feverishly over bridges and in filthy culs-de-sac, only to confront them suddenly in a narrow passage whence there was no escape, and experience a moment of panic fear. Yet it would be untrue to say he suffered. Mind and heart were drunk with passion, his footsteps guided by the dæmonic power whose pastime it is to trample on human reason and dignity.

Tadzio and his sisters at length took a gondola. Aschenbach hid behind a portico or fountain while they embarked, and directly they pushed off did the same. In a furtive whisper he told the boatman he would tip him well to follow at a little distance the other gondola, just rounding a corner, and fairly sickened at the man's quick, sly grasp and ready acceptance of the go-between's role.

Leaning among soft, black cushions he swayed gently in the wake of the other black-snouted bark, to which the strength of his passion chained him. Sometimes it passed from his view, and then he was assailed by an anguish of unrest. But his guide appeared to have long practice in affairs like these; always, by dint of short cuts or deft maneuvers, he contrived to overtake the coveted sight. The air was heavy and foul, the sun burnt down through a slate-colored haze. Water slapped gurgling against wood and stone. The gondolier's cry, half warning, half salute, was answered with singular accord from far within the silence of the labyrinth. They passed little gardens, high up the crumbling wall, hung with clustering white and purple flowers that sent down an odor of almonds. Moorish lattices showed shadowy in the gloom. The marble steps of a church descended into the canal, and on them a beggar squatted, displaying his misery to view, showing the whites of his eyes, holding out his hat for alms. Farther on a dealer in antiquities cringed before his lair, inviting the passer-by to enter and be duped. Yes, this was Venice, this the fair frailty that fawned and that betrayed, half fairy-tale, half snare; the city in whose stagnating air the art of painting once put forth so lusty a growth, and where musicians were moved to accords so weirdly lulling and lascivious. Our adventurer felt his senses wooed by this voluptuousness of sight and sound, tasted his secret knowledge that the city sickened and hid its sickness for love of gain, and bent an ever more unbridled leer on the gondola that glided on before him.

It came at last to this — that his frenzy left him capacity for nothing else but to pursue his flame; to dream of him absent, to lavish, loverlike, endearing terms on his mere shadow. He was alone, he was a foreigner, he was sunk deep in this belated bliss of his — all which enabled him to pass unblushing through ex-

periences wellnigh unbelievable. One night, returning late from
Venice, he paused by his beloved's chamber door in the second
storey, leaned his head against the panel, and remained there long,
in utter drunkenness, powerless to tear himself away, blind to the
danger of being caught in so mad an attitude.

And yet there were not wholly lacking moments when he paused
and reflected, when in consternation he asked himself what path
was this on which he had set his foot. Like most other men of
parts and attainments, he had an aristocratic interest in his forbears, and when he achieved a success he liked to think he had
gratified them, compelled their admiration and regard. He thought
of them now, involved as he was in this illicit adventure, seized of
these exotic excesses of feeling; thought of their stern self-command
and decent manliness, and gave a melancholy smile. What would
they have said? What, indeed, would they have said to his entire
life, that varied to the point of degeneracy from theirs? This life
in the bonds of art, had not he himself, in the days of his youth and
in the very spirit of those bourgeois forefathers, pronounced mocking judgment upon it? And yet, at bottom, it had been so like their
own! It had been a service, and he a soldier, like some of them; and
art was war — a grilling, exhausting struggle that nowadays wore
one out before one could grow old. It had been a life of self-
conquest, a life against odds, dour, steadfast, abstinent; he had
made it symbolical of the kind of overstrained heroism the time
admired, and he was entitled to call it manly, even courageous. He
wondered if such a life might not be somehow specially pleasing
in the eyes of the god who had him in his power. For Eros had received most countenance among the most valiant nations — yes,
were we not told that in their cities prowess made him flourish exceedingly? And many heroes of olden time had willingly borne his
yoke, not counting any humiliation such if it happened by the
god's decree; vows, prostrations, self-abasements, these were no
source of shame to the lover; rather they reaped him praise and
honor.

Thus did the fond man's folly condition his thoughts; thus did
he seek to hold his dignity upright in his own eyes. And all the
while he kept doggedly on the traces of the disreputable secret the
city kept hidden at its heart, just as he kept his own — and all that

he learned fed his passion with vague, lawless hopes. He turned over newspapers at cafés, bent on finding a report on the progress of the disease; and in the German sheets, which had ceased to appear on the hotel table, he found a series of contradictory statements. The deaths, it was variously asserted, ran to twenty, to forty, to a hundred or more; yet in the next day's issue the existence of the pestilence was, if not roundly denied, reported as a matter of a few sporadic cases such as might be brought into a seaport town. After that the warnings would break out again, and the protests against the unscrupulous game the authorities were playing. No definite information was to be had.

And yet our solitary felt he had a sort of first claim on a share in the unwholesome secret; he took a fantastic satisfaction in putting leading questions to such persons as were interested to conceal it, and forcing them to explicit untruths by way of denial. One day he attacked the manager, that small, soft-stepping man in the French frock coat, who was moving about among the guests at luncheon, supervising the service and making himself socially agreeable. He paused at Aschenbach's table to exchange a greeting, and the guest put a question, with a negligent, casual air: "Why in the world are they forever disinfecting the city of Venice?" "A police regulation," the adroit one replied; "a precautionary measure, intended to protect the health of the public during this unseasonably warm and sultry weather." "Very praiseworthy of the police," Aschenbach gravely responded. After a further exchange of meteorological commonplaces the manager passed on.

It happened that a band of street musicians came to perform in the hotel gardens that evening after dinner. They grouped themselves beneath an iron stanchion supporting an arc-light, two women and two men, and turned their faces, that shone white in the glare, up toward the guests who sat on the hotel terrace enjoying this popular entertainment along with their coffee and iced drinks. The hotel lift-boys, waiters, and office staff stood in the doorway and listened; the Russian family displayed the usual Russian absorption in their enjoyment — they had their chairs put down into the garden to be nearer the singers and sat there in a half-circle with gratitude painted on their features, the old serf in her turban erect behind their chairs.

These strolling players were adepts at mandolin, guitar, harmonica, even compassing a reedy violin. Vocal numbers alternated with instrumental, the younger woman, who had a high shrill voice, joining in a love-duet with the sweetly falsettoing tenor. The actual head of the company, however, and incontestably its most gifted member, was the other man, who played the guitar. He was a sort of baritone buffo; with no voice to speak of, but possessed of a pantomimic gift and remarkable burlesque *élan*. Often he stepped out of the group and advanced toward the terrace, guitar in hand, and his audience rewarded his sallies with bursts of laughter. The Russians in their parterre seats were beside themselves with delight over this display of southern vivacity; their shouts and screams of applause encouraged him to bolder and bolder flights.

Aschenbach sat near the balustrade, a glass of pomegranate-juice and soda-water sparkling ruby-red before him, with which he now and then moistened his lips. His nerves drank in thirstily the unlovely sounds, the vulgar and sentimental tunes, for passion paralyzes good taste and makes its victim accept with rapture what a man in his senses would either laugh at or turn from with disgust. Idly he sat and watched the antics of the buffoon with his face set in a fixed and painful smile, while inwardly his whole being was rigid with the intensity of the regard he bent on Tadzio, leaning over the railing six paces off.

The boy lounged there, in the white belted suit he sometimes wore at dinner, in all his innate, inevitable grace, with his left arm on the balustrade, his legs crossed, the right hand on the supporting hip; and looked down on the strolling singers with an expression that was hardly a smile, but rather a distant curiosity and polite toleration. Now and then he straightened himself, and with a charming movement of both arms drew down his white blouse through his leather belt, throwing out his chest. And sometimes — Aschenbach saw it with triumph, with horror, and a sense that his reason was tottering — the lad would cast a glance, that might be slow and cautious, or might be sudden and swift, as though to take him by surprise, to the place where his lover sat. Aschenbach did not meet the glance. An ignoble caution made him keep his eyes in leash. For in the rear of the terrace sat Tadzio's mother and governess; and matters had gone so far that he feared to make him·

self conspicuous. Several times, on the beach, in the hotel lobby, on the Piazza, he had seen, with a stealing numbness, that they called Tadzio away from his neighborhood. And his pride revolted at the affront, even while conscience told him it was deserved.

The performer below presently began a solo, with guitar accompaniment, a street song in several stanzas, just then the rage all over Italy. He delivered it in a striking and dramatic recitative, and his company joined in the refrain. He was a man of slight build, with a thin, undernourished face; his shabby felt hat rested on the back of his neck, a great mop of red hair sticking out in front; and he stood there on the gravel in advance of his troupe, in an impudent, swaggering posture, twanging the strings of his instrument and flinging a witty and rollicking recitative up to the terrace, while the veins on his forehead swelled with the violence of his effort. He was scarcely a Venetian type, belonging rather to the race of Neapolitan jesters, half bully, half comedian, brutal, blustering, an unpleasant customer, and entertaining to the last degree. The words of his song were trivial and silly, but on his lips, accompanied with gestures of head, hands, arms, and body, with leers and winks and the loose play of the tongue in the corner of his mouth, they took on meaning; an equivocal meaning, yet vaguely offensive. He wore a white sports shirt with a suit of ordinary clothes, and a strikingly large and naked-looking Adam's apple rose out of the open collar. From that pale, snub-nosed face it was hard to judge of his age; vice sat on it, it was furrowed with grimacing, and two deep wrinkles of defiance and self-will, almost of desperation, stood oddly between the red brows, above the grinning, mobile mouth. But what more than all drew upon him the profound scrutiny of our solitary watcher was that this suspicious figure seemed to carry with it its own suspicious odor. For whenever the refrain occurred and the singer, with waving arms and antic gestures, passed in his grotesque march immediately beneath Aschenbach's seat, a strong smell of carbolic was wafted up to the terrace.

After the song he began to take up money, beginning with the Russian family, who gave liberally, and then mounting the steps to the terrace. But here he became as cringing as he had before been forward. He glided between the tables, bowing and scraping, showing his strong white teeth in a servile smile, though the two deep furrows on the brow were still very marked. His audience looked at the weird creature as he went about collecting his livelihood, and their curiosity was not unmixed with disfavor. They tossed coins with their finger-tips into his hat and took care not to touch it. Let the enjoyment be never so great, a sort of embarrassment always comes when the comedian oversteps the physical distance between himself and respectable people. This man felt it and sought to make his peace by fawning. He came along the railing to Aschenbach, and with him came that smell no one else seemed to notice.

"Listen!" said the solitary, in a low voice, almost mechanically; "they are disinfecting Venice — why?" The mountebank answered hoarsely: "Because of the police. Orders, signore. On account of the heat and the sirocco. The sirocco is oppressive. Not good for the health." He spoke as though surprised that anyone could ask, and with the flat of his hand he demonstrated how oppressive the sirocco was. "So there is no plague in Venice?" Aschenbach asked the question between his teeth, very low. The man's expressive face fell, he put on a look of comical innocence. "A plague? What sort of plague? Is the sirocco a plague? Or perhaps our police are a plague! You are making fun of us, signore! A plague! Why should there be? The police make regulations, on account of the heat and the weather. . . ." He gestured. "Quite," said Aschenbach, once more, soft and low; and dropping an unduly large coin into the man's hat dismissed him with a sign. He bowed very low and left. But he had not reached the steps when two of the hotel servants flung themselves on him and began to whisper, their faces close to his. He shrugged, seemed to be giving assurances, to be swearing he had said nothing. It was not hard to guess the import of his words. They let him go at last and he went back into the garden, where he conferred briefly with his troupe and then stepped forward for a farewell song.

It was one Aschenbach had never to his knowledge heard before, a rowdy air, with words in impossible dialect. It had a laughing-refrain in which the other three artists joined at the top of their lungs. The refrain had neither words nor accompaniment, it was nothing but rhythmical, modulated, natural laughter, which the soloist in particular knew how to render with most deceptive real-

ism. Now that he was farther off his audience, his self-assurance had
come back, and this laughter of his rang with a mocking note. He
would be overtaken, before he reached the end of the last line of
each stanza; he would catch his breath, lay his hand over his mouth,
his voice would quaver and his shoulders shake, he would lose
power to contain himself longer. Just at the right moment each
time, it came whooping, bawling, crashing out of him, with a
verisimilitude that never failed to set his audience off in profuse
and unpremeditated mirth that seemed to add gusto to his own. He
bent his knees, he clapped his thigh, he held his sides, he looked
ripe for bursting. He no longer laughed, but yelled, pointing his
finger at the company there above as though there could be in all
the world nothing so comic as they; until at last they laughed in
hotel, terrace, and garden, down to the waiters, lift-boys, and servants — laughed as though possessed.

Aschenbach could no longer rest in his chair, he sat poised for
flight. But the combined effect of the laughing, the hospital odour
in his nostrils, and the nearness of the beloved was to hold him in
a spell; he felt unable to stir. Under cover of the general commotion
he looked across at Tadzio, and saw that the lovely boy returned
his gaze with a seriousness that seemed the copy of his own; the
general hilarity, it seemed to say, had no power over him, he kept
aloof. The gray-haired man was overpowered, disarmed by this
docile, childlike deference; with difficulty he refrained from hiding
his face in his hands. Tadzio's habit, too, of drawing himself up
and taking a deep sighing breath struck him as being due to an
oppression of the chest. "He is sickly, he will never live to grow
up," he thought once again, with that dispassionate vision to which
his madness of desire sometimes so strangely gave way. And compassion struggled with the reckless exultation of his heart.

The players, meanwhile, had finished and gone; their leader
bowing and scraping, kissing his hands and adorning his leave-
taking with antics that grew madder with the applause they evoked.
After all the others were outside, he pretended to run backwards
full tilt against a lamp-post and slunk to the gate apparently doubled
over with pain. But there he threw off his buffoon's mask, stood
erect, with an elastic straightening of his whole figure, ran out his
tongue impudently at the guests on the terrace, and vanished in the

night. The company dispersed. Tadzio had long since left the balustrade. But he, the lonely man, sat for long, to the waiters' great annoyance, before the dregs of pomegranate-juice in his glass. Time passed, the night went on. Long ago, in his parental home, he had watched the sand filter through an hour-glass — he could still see, as though it stood before him, the fragile, pregnant little toy. Soundless and fine the rust-red streamlet ran through the narrow neck, and made, as it declined in the upper cavity, an exquisite little vortex.

The very next afternoon the solitary took another step in pursuit of his fixed policy of baiting the outer world. This time he had all possible success. He went, that is, into the English travel bureau in the Piazza, changed some money at the desk, and posing as the suspicious foreigner, put his fateful question. The clerk was a tweed-clad young Britisher, with his eyes set close together, his hair parted in the middle, and radiating that steady reliability which makes his like so strange a phenomenon in the *gamin*, agile-witted South. He began: " No ground for alarm, sir. A mere formality. Quite regular in view of the unhealthy climatic conditions." But then, looking up, he chanced to meet with his own blue eyes the stranger's weary, melancholy gaze, fixed on his face. The Englishman colored. He continued in a lower voice, rather confused: " At least, that is the official explanation, which they see fit to stick to. I may tell you there's a bit more to it than that." And then, in his good, straightforward way, he told the truth.

For the past several years Asiatic cholera had shown a strong tendency to spread. Its source was the hot, moist swamps of the delta of the Ganges, where it bred in the mephitic air of that primeval island-jungle, among whose bamboo thickets the tiger crouches, where life of every sort flourishes in rankest abundance, and only man avoids the spot. Thence the pestilence had spread throughout Hindustan, raging with great violence; moved eastwards to China, westward to Afghanistan and Persia; following the great caravan routes, it brought terror to Astrakan, terror to Moscow. Even while Europe trembled lest the specter be seen striding westward across country, it was carried by sea from Syrian ports and appeared simultaneously at several points on the Mediterranean littoral; raised its head in Toulon and Malaga, Palermo and Naples, and

soon got a firm hold in Calabria and Apulia. Northern Italy had
been spared — so far. But in May the horrible vibrions were found
on the same day in two bodies: the emaciated, blackened corpses
of a bargee and a woman who kept a greengrocer's shop. Both cases
were hushed up. But in a week there were ten more — twenty,
thirty in different quarters of the town. An Austrian provincial,
having come to Venice on a few days' pleasure trip, went home
and died with all the symptoms of the pestilence. Thus was explained the fact that the German-language papers were the first
to print the news of the Venetian outbreak. The Venetian authorities published in reply a statement to the effect that the state
of the city's health had never been better; at the same time in-
stituting the most necessary precautions. But by that time the food
supplies — milk, meat, or vegetables — had probably been contaminated, for death unseen and unacknowledged was devouring and
laying waste in the narrow streets, while a brooding, unseasonable
heat warmed the waters of the canals and encouraged the spread of
the pestilence. Yes, the disease seemed to flourish and wax strong,
to redouble its generative powers. Recoveries were rare. Eighty out
of every hundred died, and horribly, for the onslaught was of the
extremest violence, and not infrequently of the " dry " type, the
most malignant form of the contagion. In this form the victim's
body loses power to expel the water secreted by the blood-vessels, it
shrivels up, he passes with hoarse cries from convulsion to convulsion, his blood grows thick like pitch, and he suffocates in a few
hours. He is fortunate indeed, if, as sometimes happens, the disease, after a slight *malaise*, takes the form of a profound unconsciousness, from which the sufferer seldom or never rouses. By the
beginning of June the quarantine buildings of the *ospedale civico*
had quietly filled up, the two orphan asylums were entirely occupied, and there was a hideously brisk traffic between the *Nuovo
Fundamento* and the island of San Michele, where the cemetery
was. But the city was not swayed by high-minded motives or regarded for international agreements. The authorities were more
actuated by fear of being out of pocket, by regard for the new exhibition of paintings just opened in the Public Gardens, or by apprehension of the large losses the hotels and the shops that catered
to foreigners would suffer in case of panic and blockade. And the

fears of the people supported the persistent official policy of silence and denial. The city's first medical officer, an honest and competent man, had indignantly resigned his office, and been privily replaced by a more compliant person. The fact was known; and this corruption in high places played its part, together with the suspense as to where the walking terror might strike next, to demoralize the baser elements in the city and encourage those antisocial forces which shun the light of day. There was intemperance, indecency, increase of crime. Evenings one saw many drunken people, which was unusual. Gangs of men in surly mood made the streets unsafe, theft and assault were said to be frequent, even murder; for in two cases persons supposedly victims of the plague were proved to have been poisoned by their own families. And professional vice was rampant, displaying excesses heretofore unknown and only at home much farther south and in the East.

Such was the substance of the Englishman's tale. " You would do well," he concluded, " to leave today instead of tomorrow. The blockade cannot be more than a few days off."

" Thank you," said Aschenbach, and left the office.

The Piazza lay in sweltering sunshine. Innocent foreigners sat before the cafés or stood in front of the cathedral, the center of clouds of doves that, with fluttering wings, tried to shoulder each other away and pick the kernels of maize from the extended hand. Aschenbach strode up and down the spacious flags, feverishly excited, triumphant in possession of the truth at last, but with a sickening taste in his mouth and a fantastic horror at his heart. One decent, expiatory course lay open to him; he considered it. Tonight, after dinner, he might approach the lady of the pearls and address her in words which he precisely formulated in his mind: " Madame, will you permit an entire stranger to serve you with a word of advice and warning which self-interest prevents others from uttering? Go away. Leave here at once, without delay, with Tadzio and your daughters. Venice is in the grip of pestilence." Then might he lay his hand in farewell upon the head of that instrument of a mocking deity; and thereafter himself flee the accursed morass. But he knew that he was far indeed from any serious desire to take such a step. It would restore him, would give him back himself once more; but he who is beside himself revolts at the idea of self-possession. There crossed his mind the vision of a white building with inscriptions on it, glittering in the sinking sun — he recalled how his mind had dreamed away into their transparent mysticism; recalled the strange pilgrim apparition that had wakened in the aging man a lust for strange countries and fresh sights. And these memories, again, brought in their train the thought of returning home, returning to reason, self-mastery, an ordered existence, to the old life of effort. Alas! the bare thought made him wince with a revulsion that was like physical nausea. " It must be kept quiet," he whispered fiercely. " I will not speak! " The knowledge that he shared the city's secret, the city's guilt — it put him beside himself, intoxicated him as a small quantity of wine will a man suffering from brain-fag. His thoughts dwelt upon the image of the desolate and calamitous city, and he was giddy with fugitive, mad, unreasoning hopes and visions of a monstrous sweetness. That tender sentiment he had a moment ago evoked, what was it compared with such images as these? His art, his moral sense, what were they in the balance beside the boons that chaos might confer? He kept silence, he stopped on.

That night he had a fearful dream — if dream be the right word for a mental and physical experience which did indeed befall him in deep sleep, as a thing quite apart and real to his senses, yet without his seeing himself as present in it. Rather its theater seemed to be his own soul, and the events burst in from outside, violently overcoming the profound resistance of his spirit; passed him through and left him, left the whole cultural structure of a lifetime trampled on, ravaged, and destroyed.

The beginning was fear; fear and desire, with a shuddering curiosity. Night reigned, and his senses were on the alert; he heard loud, confused noises from far away, clamor and hubbub. There was a rattling, a crashing, a low dull thunder; shrill halloos and a kind of howl with a long-drawn u-sound at the end. And with all these, dominating them all, flute-notes of the cruelest sweetness, deep and cooing, keeping shamelessly on until the listener felt his very entrails bewitched. He heard a voice, naming, though darkly, that which was to come: " The stranger god! " A glow lighted up the surrounding mist and by it he recognized a mountain scene like

that about his country home. From the wooded heights, from
among the tree-trunks and crumbling moss-covered rocks, a troop
came tumbling and raging down, a whirling rout of men and
animals, and overflowed the hillside with flames and human forms,
with clamor and the reeling dance. The females stumbled over the
long, hairy pelts that dangled from their girdles; with heads flung
back they uttered loud hoarse cries and shook their tambourines
high in air; brandished naked daggers or torches vomiting trails
of sparks. They shrieked, holding their breasts in both hands; coil-
ing snakes with quivering tongues they clutched about their waists.
Horned and hairy males, girt about the loins with hides, drooped
heads and lifted arms and thighs in unison, as they beat on brazen
vessels that gave out droning thunder, or thumped madly on drums.
There were troops of beardless youths armed with garlanded staves;
these ran after goats and thrust their staves against the creatures'
flanks, then clung to the plunging horns and let themselves be
borne off with triumphant shouts. And one and all the mad rout
yelled that cry, composed of soft consonants with a long-drawn
u-sound at the end, so sweet and wild it was together, and like
nothing ever heard before! It would ring through the air like the
bellow of a challenging stag, and be given back many-tongued; or
they would use it to goad each other on to dance with wild excess
of tossing limbs — they never let it die. But the deep, beguiling
notes of the flute wove in and out and over all. Beguiling too it was
to him who struggled in the grip of these sights and sounds, shamelessly awaiting the coming feast and the uttermost surrender. He
trembled, he shrank, his will was steadfast to preserve and uphold
his own god against this stranger who was sworn enemy to dignity
and self-control. But the mountain wall took up the noise and howling and gave it back manifold; it rose high, swelled to a madness
that carried him away. His senses reeled in the steam of panting
bodies, the acrid stench from the goats, the odor as of stagnant
waters — and another, too familiar smell — of wounds, uncleanness,
and disease. His heart throbbed to the drums, his brain reeled, a
blind rage seized him, a whirling lust, he craved with all his soul
to join the ring that formed about the obscene symbol of the god-
head, which they were unveiling and elevating, monstrous and

wooden, while from full throats they yelled their rallying cry. Foam dripped from their lips, they drove each other on with lewd gesturings and beckoning hands. They laughed, they howled, they thrust their pointed staves into each other's flesh and licked the blood as it ran down. But now the dreamer was in them and of them, the stranger god was his own. Yes, it was he who was flinging himself upon the animals, who bit and tore and swallowed smoking gobbets of flesh — while on the trampled moss there now began the rites in honor of the god, an orgy of promiscuous embraces — and in his very soul he tasted the bestial degradation of his fall.

The unhappy man woke from this dream shattered, unhinged, powerless in the demon's grip. He no longer avoided men's eyes nor cared whether he exposed himself to suspicion. And anyhow, people were leaving; many of the bathing-cabins stood empty, there were many vacant places in the dining-room, scarcely any foreigners were seen in the streets. The truth seemed to have leaked out; despite all efforts to the contrary, panic was in the air. But the lady of the pearls stopped on with her family; whether because the rumors had not reached her or because she was too proud and fearless to heed them. Tadzio remained; and it seemed at times to Aschenbach, in his obsessed state, that death and fear together might clear the island of all other souls and leave him there alone with him he coveted. In the long mornings on the beach his heavy gaze would rest, a fixed and reckless stare, upon the lad; toward nightfall, lost to shame, he would follow him through the city's narrow streets where horrid death stalked too, and at such time it seemed to him as though the moral law were fallen in ruins and only the monstrous and perverse held out a hope.

Like any lover, he desired to please; suffered agonies at the thought of failure, and brightened his dress with smart ties and handkerchiefs and other youthful touches. He added jewelry and perfumes and spent hours each day over his toilet, appearing at dinner elaborately arrayed and tensely excited. The presence of the youthful beauty that had bewitched him filled him with disgust of his own aging body; the sight of his own sharp features and gray hair plunged him in hopeless mortification; he made desperate efforts to recover the appearance and freshness of his youth and began paying frequent visits to the hotel barber. Enveloped in the white sheet, beneath the hands of that garrulous personage, he would lean back in the chair and look at himself in the glass with misgiving.

" Gray," he said, with a grimace.

" Slightly," answered the man. " Entirely due to neglect, to a lack of regard for appearances. Very natural, of course, in men of affairs, but, after all, not very sensible, for it is just such people who ought to be above vulgar prejudice in matters like these. Some folk have very strict ideas about the use of cosmetics; but they never extend them to the teeth, as they logically should. And very disgusted other people would be if they did. No, we are all as old as we feel, but no older, and gray hair can misrepresent a man worse than dyed. You, for instance, signore, have a right to your natural color. Surely you will permit me to restore what belongs to you? "

" How? " asked Aschenbach.

For answer the oily one washed his client's hair in two waters, one clear and one dark, and lo, it was as black as in the days of his youth. He waved it with the tongs in wide, flat undulations, and stepped back to admire the effect.

" Now if we were just to freshen up the skin a little," he said.

And with that he went on from one thing to another, his enthusiasm waxing with each new idea. Aschenbach sat there comfortably; he was incapable of objecting to the process — rather as it went forward it roused his hopes. He watched it in the mirror and saw his eyebrows grow more even and arching, the eyes gain in size and brilliance, by dint of a little application below the lids. A delicate carmine glowed on his cheeks where the skin had been so brown and leathery. The dry, anæmic lips grew full, they turned the color of ripe strawberries, the lines round eyes and mouth were treated with a facial cream and gave place to youthful bloom. It was a young man who looked back at him from the glass — Aschenbach's heart leaped at the sight. The artist in cosmetic at last professed himself satisfied; after the manner of such people, he thanked his client profusely for what he had done himself. " The merest trifle, the merest, signore," he said, as he added the final touches.

" Now the signore can fall in love as soon as he likes." Aschenbach
went off as in a dream, dazed between joy and fear, in his red
necktie and broad straw hat with its gay striped band.

A lukewarm storm-wind had come up. It rained a little now and
then, the air was heavy and turbid and smelt of decay. Aschenbach,
with fevered cheeks beneath the rouge, seemed to hear rushing and
flapping sounds in his ears, as though storm-spirits were abroad —
unhallowed ocean harpies who follow those devoted to destruction,
snatch away and defile their viands. For the heat took away his
appetite and thus he was haunted with the idea that his food was
infected.

One afternoon he pursued his charmer deep into the stricken
city's huddled heart. The labyrinthine little streets, squares, canals,
and bridges, each one so like the next, at length quite made him
lose his bearings. He did not even know the points of the compass; all his care was not to lose sight of the figure after which
his eyes thirsted. He slunk under walls, he lurked behind buildings
or people's backs; and the sustained tension of his senses and emotions exhausted him more and more, though for a long time he was
unconscious of fatigue. Tadzio walked behind the others, he let
them pass ahead in the narrow alleys, and as he sauntered slowly
after, he would turn his head and assure himself with a glance of
his strange, twilit gray eyes that his lover was still following. He
saw him — and he did not betray him. The knowledge enraptured
Aschenbach. Lured by those eyes, led on the leading-string of his
own passion and folly, utterly lovesick, he stole upon the footsteps
of his unseemly hope — and at the end found himself cheated.
The Polish family crossed a small vaulted bridge, the height of
whose archway hid them from his sight, and when he climbed it
himself they were nowhere to be seen. He hunted in three directions — straight ahead and on both sides the narrow, dirty quay —
in vain. Worn quite out and unnerved, he had to give over the
search.

His head burned, his body was wet with clammy sweat, he was
plagued by intolerable thirst. He looked about for refreshment, of
whatever sort, and found a little fruit-shop where he bought some
strawberries. They were overripe and soft; he ate them as he went.
The street he was on opened out into a little square, one of those

charmed, forsaken spots he liked; he recognized it as the very one where he had sat weeks ago and conceived his abortive plan of flight. He sank down on the steps of the well and leaned his head against its stone rim. It was quiet here. Grass grew between the stones, and rubbish lay about. Tall, weather-beaten houses bordered the square, one of them rather palatial, with vaulted windows, gaping now, and little lion balconies. In the ground floor of another was an apothecary's shop. A waft of carbolic acid was borne on a warm gust of wind.

There he sat, the master: this was he who had found a way to reconcile art and honors; who had written *The Abject*, and in a style of classic purity renounced Bohemianism and all its works, all sympathy with the abyss and the troubled depths of the outcast human soul. This was he who had put knowledge underfoot to climb so high; who had outgrown the ironic pose and adjusted himself to the burdens and obligations of fame; whose renown had been officially recognized and his name ennobled, whose style was set for a model in the schools. There he sat. His eyelids were closed, there was only a swift, sidelong glint of the eyeballs now and again, something between a question and a leer; while the rouged and flabby mouth uttered single words of the sentences shaped in his disordered brain by the fantastic logic that governs our dreams.

"For mark you, Phædrus, beauty alone is both divine and visible; and so it is the sense way, the artist's way, little Phædrus, to the spirit. But, now tell me, my dear boy, do you believe that such a man can ever attain wisdom and true manly worth, for whom the path to the spirit must lead through the senses? Or do you rather think — for I leave the point to you — that it is a path of perilous sweetness, a way of transgression, and must surely lead him who walks in it astray? For you know that we poets cannot walk the way of beauty without Eros as our companion and guide. We may be heroic after our fashion, disciplined warriors of our craft, yet are we all like women, for we exult in passion, and love is still our desire — our craving and our shame. And from this you will perceive that we poets can be neither wise nor worthy citizens. We must needs be wanton, must needs rove at large in the realm of feeling. Our magisterial style is all folly and pretense, our honorable repute a farce, the crowd's belief in us is merely laughable

And to teach youth, or the populace, by means of art is a dangerous practice and ought to be forbidden. For what good can an artist
be as a teacher, when from his birth up he is headed direct for the
pit? We may want to shun it, and attain to honor in the world;
but however we turn, it draws us still. So, then, since knowledge
might destroy us, we will have none of it. For knowledge, Phædrus,
does not make him who possesses it dignified or austere. Knowledge is all-knowing, understanding, forgiving; it takes up no position, sets no store by form. It has compassion with the abyss —
it is the abyss. So we reject it, firmly, and henceforward our concern shall be with beauty only. And by beauty we mean simplicity,
largeness, and renewed severity of discipline; we mean a return to
detachment and to form. But detachment, Phædrus, and preoccupation with form lead to intoxication and desire, they may lead
the noblest among us to frightful emotional excesses, which his
own stern cult of the beautiful would make him the first to condemn. So they too, they too, lead to the bottomless pit. Yes, they
lead us thither, I say, us who are poets — who by our natures are
prone not to excellence but to excess. And now, Phædrus, I will
go. Remain here; and only when you can no longer see me, then
do you depart also."

A few days later, Gustave Aschenbach left his hotel rather later
than usual in the morning. He was not feeling well, and had to
struggle against spells of giddiness only half physical in their nature,
accompanied by a swiftly mounting dread, a sense of futility and
hopelessness — but whether this referred to himself or to the outer
world he could not tell. In the lobby he saw a quantity of luggage
lying strapped and ready; asked the porter whose it was, and received in answer the name he already knew he should hear — that
of the Polish family. The expression of his ravaged features did
not change; he only gave that quick lift of the head with which we
sometimes receive the uninteresting answer to a casual query. But
he put another: " When? ' " After luncheon," the man replied.
He nodded, and went down to the beach.

It was an unfriendly scene. Little crisping shivers ran all across
the wide stretch of shallow water between the shore and the first
sand-bank. The whole beach, once so full of color and life, looked
now autumnal, out of season; it was nearly deserted and not even

very clean. A camera on a tripod stood at the edge of the water, apparently abandoned; its black cloth snapped in the freshening wind.

Tadzio was there, in front of his cabin, with the three or four playfellows still left him. Aschenbach set up his chair some half-way between the cabins and the water, spread a rug over his knees, and sat looking on. The game this time was unsupervised, the elders being probably busy with their packing, and it looked rather lawless and out-of-hand. Jaschiu, the sturdy lad in the belted suit, with the black, brilliantined hair, became angry at a handful of sand thrown in his eyes; he challenged Tadzio to a fight, which quickly ended in the downfall of the weaker. And perhaps the coarser nature saw here a chance to avenge himself at last, by one cruel act, for his long weeks of subserviency: the victor would not let the vanquished get up, but remained kneeling on Tadzio's back, press-ing Tadzio's face into the sand — for so long a time that it seemed the exhausted lad might even suffocate. He made spasmodic efforts to shake the other off, lay still, and then began a feeble twitching. Just as Aschenbach was about to spring indignantly to the rescue, Jaschiu let his victim go. Tadzio, very pale, half-sat up, and re-mained so, leaning on one arm, for several minutes, with darkening eyes and rumpled hair. Then he rose and walked slowly away. The others called him, at first gayly, then imploringly; he would not hear. Jaschiu was evidently overtaken by swift remorse; he fol-lowed his friend and tried to make his peace, but Tadzio motioned him back with a jerk of one shoulder and went down to the water's edge. He was barefoot, and wore his striped linen suit with the red breast-knot.

There he stayed a little, with bent head, tracing figures in the wet sand with one toe; then stepped into the shallow water, which at its deepest did not wet his knees; waded idly through it and reached the sand-bar. Now he paused again, with his face turned seaward; and next began to move slowly leftwards along the narrow strip of sand the sea left bare. He paced there, divided by an expanse of water from the shore, from his mates by his moody pride; a remote and isolated figure, with floating locks, out there in sea and wind, against the misty inane. Once more he paused to look: with a sud-den recollection, or by an impulse, he turned from the waist up, in an exquisite movement, one hand resting on his hip, and looked over his shoulder at the shore. The watcher sat just as he had sat that time in the lobby of the hotel when first the twilit gray eyes had met his own. He rested his head against the chair-back and followed the movements of the figure out there, then lifted it, as it were in answer to Tadzio's gaze. It sank on his breast, the eyes looked out beneath their lids, while his whole face took on the relaxed and brooding expression of deep slumber. It seemed to him the pale and lovely Summoner out there smiled at him and beckoned; as though, with the hand he lifted from his hip, he pointed outward as he hovered on before into an immensity of richest expectation.

Some minutes passed before anyone hastened to the aid of the elderly man sitting there collapsed in his chair. They bore him to his room. And before nightfall a shocked and respectful world received the news of his decease.

THE
VENETIAN GLASS
NEPHEW

PREFACE

In September 1924 Elinor Wylie wrote to me from the MacDowell Colony about *The Venetian Glass Nephew*. " It goes on fairly well, and I believe you'll like it. I shall have the first part completely finished for you to see when I come back, and the rest mapped out quite clearly. It's not another Jennifer — but perhaps that's as well." She had told me, before going to Peterborough, only that the new book was to be a kind of moral fairy-tale of the eighteenth century. I was prepared for the witty moral if not, entirely, for the glittering beauty which I found in the first third of the manuscript she brought with her to New York. Although contributor and editor, she and I were friends, and we conspired to let the *Nephew* appear as a serial in the *Century Magazine*.

The conspiracy had its little perils, dramatic now but disturbing then. She needed money. "Can the *Venetian Glass Nephew* help me at all, as yet?" she asked in a letter from New Canaan early in October. "I find I have unexpectedly to pay the interest, as well as the paying off, on the mortgage. There is a difference, though it takes an expert to understand. . . . Of course I hope you can manage this advance, but if you can't, don't picture me as suicidal in consequence. It is my reprehensible nature to welcome excitement and change, and the idea of being melodramatically foreclosed and forced to find another — and of course a better — place to live is in itself attractive to my mind. But one must do one's duty, hence this letter."

I arranged with the publishers of the magazine to let her have the whole amount she was being paid for the serial, without telling them that two-thirds of it were still to be written. As we both wanted it to appear as soon as possible, we ran another risk. The first part was in type before there was any second or third, and it was assigned to its month in the *Century* at a time when neither of us could be certain that the rest would follow at monthly intervals. What was most perilous, Elinor Wylie made only one copy of each part, which, exquisite and unique, came from New Canaan to New York and then went to the printers in New Hampshire. There were breathless weeks until the last proofs reached my office. Although I was troubled by the danger that the manuscript might be lost, I could not refuse to share a hazard which was so much more hers than mine. To her the risk was tonic. I think it kept her waywardly excited to realize that her sharp and shining prose had to take its chances in the mail and that the loss of it would be tragic to her plans.

Gay, erudite, precise, *The Venetian Glass Nephew* reads like a joyful holiday. It was written under stress. In her second novel Elinor Wylie felt she had to prove, to her exacting self even more than to others, that *Jennifer Lorn* had not been an accident. She must repeat the triumph to justify her turn from verse to prose. Hurt by the charge that she had deserted poetry, she must make it plain that she was novelist as well as poet. She had debts and bills to meet. Everything seemed crucial to her sensitive, proud nerves. At New Canaan, where she carried out what she had sketched at

Peterborough, she had a household with three small stepchildren to look after, and she could write only when they were at school. Yet the manuscript of the *Nephew* might almost be a fair copy, typed with sure fingers, hardly a single slight change or correction to a page.

No outer confusion could seriously disturb her inner will. When dejected, she was still gallant and humorous. " Did we not," she said in a letter the next year, " make a fine mistake in our youth — which was so very nearly contemporaneous — in becoming what . . . the Peterborough servants call *creators?* What a noble shoemaker — to choose a trade at random, or because shoemakers are always liberals — would not you have made, and I how excellent at contriving artificial flowers or the peep-show scenes inside Easter eggs! You will say that these also savor of creation, but our present trouble . . . springs from our stubborn attempt to utilize our wretched minds, to make unpleasant grayish convolutions work for us instead of trained and agile finger-tips and the beautiful rhythmic strength of habit. How lovely is benign stupidity! — as no one really ever wrote. Two years ago the *New Republic* would have had a poem from me on the subject. Now you must put up with a dull letter. It is hard on you, and I hope it is hard on the *New Republic*." Volatile as her temper was, she was actually as indestructible and resolute as water. She had a level of her own from which no circumstances could dam her long.

This strong native level of her mind cuts through the fantasy of *The Venetian Glass Nephew*. It is a fable of the marriage of Art and Nature, specifically Christian Art and Pagan Nature. Virginio has been made, not born. Even though Casanova himself (as Chastelneuf) has had a hand in the making, something less than natural blood runs in Virginio's mild veins. He may satisfy his uncle the Cardinal, according to whose pious desire he has been shaped, but he is not enough for his bride Rosalba, Nature's lively daughter. He can love, he cannot play. If this were a romantic plot, the ending might be happier and simpler, with the boy of Art adapting himself to the girl of Nature. Realism is sadder, if truer. In the conflict between Art and Nature it is Nature which must yield. Rosalba, despairing, takes the advice of Casanova, who knows there can be no compromise, only one conclusion. She enters a furnace at Sèvres and comes out porcelain. At last she is the right bride for a Virginio.

Elinor Wylie was too much a poet to let her moral stand like bare bones in a vacuum. She chose Venice for a setting and spun the story as if her language were ductile glass. Rosalba, her poet could make English say, " was a flame whose consummation may be bitter, but whose promissory blooming is tenderer than apple blossoms. To the five senses of an observer she was indeed imagined flowers to breathe, as she must have been velvet to touch, cream to taste, the crescent moon to gaze upon, and, to the listening ear, a melody repeated by a mocking-bird." Here are formal words fixed in a schematic pattern but glinting with the light which they catch and throw off. The whole book is built with the lovely, amused formality which this sentence has, and every paragraph flashes erudition.

Few novels so short and smiling can ever have been so learned. " The gondolas were black, but all their canopies were colored like the parterres of a prince's garden. The sunlight smelled of musk and peppermint; although the day was warm, a lady carried a muff of panther fur; she was followed by an Ethiopian in scarlet livery, bearing a letter sealed with Spanish wax. A naked child, an Eros cast in gilded bronze, drank from the sea-green shell of a melon, held high above his lips." Or again: " Peter Innocent breakfasted on a large bowl of chocolate and a very small piece of *marzipan*, of which he was inordinately fond. The other cardinals sprinkled spices in their cups, or drank coffee sweet with sugar and brandy; they ate a great many little birds, roasted with bacon and red pepper, and they had strawberries from Passeriano and peaches from Algiers, Everyone ate what he preferred; Braschi Onesti had candied chestnuts and champagne." Or again, within the drier field where erudition usually works: " The Chevalier, whatever his peccadillos, practiced only the higher forms of transcendental and divine magic, as opposed to nigromancy and goetia. . . . Here was no place for the Ahriman of the Persians, the Typhon of the Egyptians, the Python of the Greeks, the Croquemitaine, the obscene deity of the Sabbath. Let it be remembered that Isis was impeccable in her widowhood, that Diana Panthea was a virign; that Apollonius of Tyana never yielded to the seductions of pleasure; that

Plotinus of Alexandria was ascetic in the manner of his life; and that Raymond Lully was the victim of a hopeless passion which made him chaste forever. Vesper, not Lucifer, blazed now in the pentagram upon the marble pavement."

Such erudition may be decoration, but the decoration of *The Venetian Glass Nephew* seems intrinsic in it. If Elinor Wylie had been as curt as a fabulist or as abstract as a moralist she would have told her story to the intellect, not to the eye. Her story as she did tell it is all pictures. Everything in her Venice is brightly visible, from the blue balloon of the opening paragraph to the whipped cream and wafers of the ending. She had ransacked a decade of history for images that could be wittily drawn and beautifully colored. Curiosity will some day trace the historical facts she used to the books in which she found them. The list, headed by Vernon Lee's *Studies of the Eighteenth Century in Italy* and the *Memoirs* of Casanova and of Carlo Gozzi, will not be too long. Elinor Wylie was already full of her favorite century before she set herself to imagine Venice in its age of tinsel. Scrupulous as she might be about dates and streets and churches and costumes, her older memory was her major source. And her older memory served her less than her pictorial imagination. The *Nephew* was to be a poem as well as a moral tale. With a frolicking invention she enriched and confirmed the fairy-story, giving it such a look of life as Casanova and Alvise Luna gave Virginio, glass within, almost flesh and blood without.

In one of her letters Elinor Wylie quoted something she had read: " He liked the flavor of an imperfect world and the preposterousness of peccant humanity." "That's the principle," she added, " upon which I write my own immortal works! " It was the principle which made *The Venetian Glass Nephew* both laughing and tender. It gave the novel its charming justice by which, in the strife of Art with Nature, sympathy is on the side of Nature but skill is on the side of Art.

CARL VAN DOREN

BOOK I: *PETER INNOCENT*

"And then he wept a little, and fell to talking of
magic and macaroni."   PRINCE DE LIGNE

1. Blue Balloon

PETER INNOCENT BON was about to return to the Republic of Venice; although he had that very day entered upon the eighty-first
year of his age, his eyes, blue as veronica flowers, were even now
full of a child's tears. His heart was lighter than a flower; indeed,
it danced so high and airily, and teased the tenuous cord of his
mortality with such persistent malice, that he conceived of it as
a toy balloon, an azure plaything in a pantomime, caught by a
thread of gold to stable earth, and germane to the sky.

It will be unnecessary to explain to minds versed in such matters
that Peter Innocent Bon must by no means be confounded with
John Bona of Mondovi, a misapprehension imaginable in the ignorant, since both were cardinals and both distinguished scholars.
But wider far than the mere century of time separating the lives
of these holy men is the gulph that sunders their natures and their
activities. Consanguinity there may have been, in reason, but the
two were never spiritually akin. Peter Innocent undoubtedly possessed the Antwerp edition of his cousin's works, published in
1777, and the devotional treatise *De Sacrificio Missæ* was often in
his hands; a few marginal notes attest to application saddened by
bewilderment. To those desiring to achieve a better comprehension
of the character of Peter Innocent Bon, Cardinal priest and Cardinal prefect of the Congregation of the Propaganda, the historian
recommends a careful study of his poetical writings (Venice, 1790)
and his notes upon liturgical subjects (Parma, 1794). His memoirs,
surveying as they did almost the entire length of the eighteenth
century with a bland and illuminative eye, must have contained
matter of the highest interest; this valuable document was unfortunately destroyed by Madame de Staël in a passing fit of temper

during the composition of *Corinne*, merely because it contained a simple unadorned account of the coronation of Corilla Olimpica.

On this 8th of May 1782, Peter Innocent, clad in the gray-brown garb of the Franciscan Friars Minor, stood dreaming among delicate grotesques in the porch of his titulary church of St. Bonaventura. It was evening; the Roman sun had lost its imperial savagery, and tempered light lay tenderly upon the Cardinal's brow. His face, that had beheld the secular world for eighty years, was lifted to the more transparent heaven; forgetting Rome and even the Vatican, he regarded the Holy City above the horns of the new moon. He looked affectionately yet familiarly into the little loopholes of the stars, with none of the bitter hunger of the returning exile; to Peter Innocent the bread of earth was never salty, nor the stairs of heaven too steep. As a boy may see at evening the lighted windows of his mother's kitchen, he saw without surprise celestial preparation for his home-coming through a bright chink that may have been Aldebaran. Tugging at its gilded thread, his heart danced over him, a blue balloon in deeper aerial blue.

Above the chiseled silver of his head, his heart danced, expanded by happiness and an exquisite gratitude towards all humanity and the Son of God made man. In particular, his heart blessed the new Pope, Pius VI, for although Giovanni Angelo Braschi had ruled Christendom for some seven years, Peter Innocent never thought of him save as a handsome innovation, superseding with the suavest courtesy the Cardinal's dead patron and beloved friend, the Franciscan Clement XIV. Now this same Pius, whom Peter Innocent a little feared, the more that he was beautiful and brilliant and vain, proposed for reasons of his own to visit the green lagoons and golden palaces of Venice, having among his suite, again for reasons of his own, Peter Innocent Bon, Cardinal prefect of the Congregation of the Propaganda.

The Cardinal did not concern himself with reasons; he thought of Venice, and the bright thread pulled hard upon his heart. He had not seen that city for nearly thirty years; not since his brother Nicholas Bon was banished to the monastery of Venda by the Council of Ten and the Inquisitors of the Holy Office. In that same year Paul Dona was confined in the fortress of Palma, and

five years later the noble Angelo Querini was imprisoned in the
castle of St. Felice at Verona.

For a time the spirit of Peter Innocent suffered a faint infusion
of bitterness throughout its milk and honey; he began to believe
in spies and politics, and found himself disliking the Dominicans
without feeling any particular love for the Jesuits. But he managed
with admirable tact to hold himself aloof from all dissension, and
it is certain that his veined patrician hand was not among those
which upheld the fainting resolution of Lorenzo Ganganelli as the
pontiff traced the momentous syllables of the brief, *Dominus ac
redemptor*, and signed it Clement, servant of the servants of God.

But this was years, and happy years, ago, and today Peter Innocent could remember that all these brave and liberal senators
had been set free either by death or by the reforms of '63, and that
Querini had traveled in Switzerland and become a valued friend
of Voltaire's. The Cardinal had long ago forgiven Venice, and upon
this Ascension Eve his heart was a blue balloon because it was going
home.

He thought of himself as a child upon other Ascension eves and
morrows, in a past not dim at all, but radiant as a double dawn in
sky and water. He saw the *Bucintoro* setting forth from Santa
Lucia, a gilded barge arrayed in cloth of gold, with winged lions,
tritons, nereids, painted with gold and burnished by the sun, with
the great standard of the Republic crackling like lightning overhead. He thought of the ancient glory of Venice, and of the Lion
of the Evangelist. His gray habit of the Seraphic Order fell from
his shoulders, and he was a child again, in a coat of sapphire velvet,
with a silver feather in his cap.

Softly, very softly, the supple folds of dun color descended once
more over this remembered magnificence, and Peter Innocent felt
the worn, warm fabric about his fragile bones. Here, too, was cause
for gratitude, for the new Pope had permitted him to continue in
this ingenuous disguise, first granted him by the generosity of
Clement, so that he alone of the pontifical family went comfortably
impoverished, clad in the mystic tatters of Assisi. Within a remote
wing of the Vatican a wardrobe of ebony and figured brass guarded
vestments of white and red and green, of violet and black and the
more curious sheen of metal, with robes and rochets of a less sacral

character and rich liturgical gloves and stockings, intermixed with honorific decorations.

Peter Innocent loved best to drift, elusive as a skeleton leaf, along the streets of Rome, recognized by all, but accosted by none save an occasional German traveler or English milord; the legerity of the French mind made the Gallic visitor quick to comprehend his desire for solitude, and the very transparency of the masking rendered it invulnerable. Whether or not he believed himself effectively disguised remained a mystery to the last. He spoke but little; indeed it was a common saying at the time that Clement had forgotten to unseal his mouth; his smile, however, impressed even the most impious as a small flame burning perpetually within the silver shadow of his countenance.

At the conclusion of Vespers, he often knelt in a sculptured recess of the Church of St. Bonaventura, while the words *O salutaris hostia* were borne upon the wings of ancient music towards the benediction. As the priest, his shoulders wrapped in the humeral veil, lifted the monstrance from the lighted altar and with it described in that already consecrated air the sign of the cross, the tears of Peter Innocent aspersed like holy water whatever evil might survive within those walls, beneath that vaulted nave.

2. Consider the Lilies

NEAR St. George in Alga, upon an iridescent morning of mid-May, the Doge and Signory of Venice received the pontiff and his suite, conveying them thence to the Monastery of St. John and St. Paul, where they were sumptuously lodged. As the lacquered barge imposed its fan of ripples, like a peacock's tail, upon lagoon and narrowing canal, the visitors vied with one another in expressions of awe and contentment; they moved in the heart of a pearl whose orient skin was outer space. Peter Innocent alone was silent; his youth overwhelmed him as though every immemorial wave of the Adriatic were poured upon his pensive head. He bowed his face upon his folded hands; when he lifted his eyes again, they were dazzled by the great palaces of the Venetian patriciate, all arabesqued in marble and embossed by emblems. Here burned the silver torch of the Morosini; the silver ladder of the Gradenigo

scaled the heavens; the five-leaved roses of the house of Loredan endured in frosted stone so delicate that it appeared to spread a perfume on the air.

The gondolas were black, but all their canopies were colored
like the parterres of a prince's garden. The sunlight smelled of
musk and peppermint; although the day was warm, a lady carried a
muff of panther fur; she was followed by an Ethiopian in scarlet livery, bearing a letter sealed with Spanish wax. A naked child, an Eros
cast in gilded bronze, drank from the sea-green shell of a melon,
held high above his lips. Peter Innocent remembered that the
Italians of an elder day, while yet that day was young, made melancholy synonymous with wickedness, and gave to the verb to
" think " the sense of to " be sad." He took the meaning, but without a heavy mind; his heart's indulgence was poured like a libation
over Venice and absorbed in her waters.

He remembered his old friend, the priest called Testa, the
Diogenes of the spiders' webs, who shared his straw pallet with a
familiar rat, and lived on moldy bread and lentils. And he remembered, also, that other eccentric, the ancient with the iron bell, who
was used to stand upon the quays and bridges, crying out with his
own outlandish tongue and the bell's clapper, crying•upon all men
to be happy, in the name of God. And although this person was a
Moor and an infidel, he was nevertheless a philosopher and a lover
of humanity. Peter Innocent thought of him with kindness, pre-
ferring him, perhaps, for a reprehensible moment, to the Christian
priest, and wondering if he were not the wiser man. For Peter
Innocent, flying through sunlight followed by a peacock's tail of
foam, attired for once in all the splendor relative to his spiritual
and temporal state, had not forgotten that long before he had assumed this purple he had fared very happily as one of the jongleurs
of God. So, like the Moor, he rang continually a little bell whose
tongue was not of iron, but of gold, and bright and silent as a
flame.

The Cardinal Peter Innocent was at all times silent, since Pope
Clement had neglected to unseal his mouth; now he was hushed
into a profounder stillness by his private felicity, and by the high
and rapid speech of those about him. The Doge and the Procurator Manin were engaged in conversation with their illustrious

visitor Pius VI; although preserving every indication of reverence for His Holiness, the Venetian nobles did not hesitate to address him with fluency and animation. The Pope's nephew, the blond and arrogant Braschi Onesti, grandee of Spain and prince of the Holy Empire, stared somewhat haughtily upon these self-possessed patricians; he wore a coat of carnation velvet, and the little finger of his left hand was all but hidden by an emerald of fabulous value. At his knee the Abate Monti crouched like a beaten hound. " Consider the lilies — " and the Pope's device, cut on a hundred monuments in Rome, was an heraldic wind, blowing down lilies like waves of the sea! This, too, was inscribed on marbles by Canova and the recovered classical remains of Herculaneum; yet Solomon in all his glory had no finer coat than young Braschi Onesti, nor could his seal have utterly outshone that green intaglio graved with the head of Agrippina. So thought Peter Innocent, and as the thought was, for him, faintly malicious, his smile flickered for a moment like a flame that has had a pinch of salt sprinkled upon its clarity.

For here, and suddenly, a small regret, an obscure discomfort, touched the Cardinal with a pain no more important than may be inflicted by a kitten's ivory claw. So slight a blow it was that his mind scarcely recorded it; the glancing scratch cut the thin skin of his soul a little, as always, and if this same skin had been a visible thing, the closest scrutiny might have revealed a vast number of similar punctures, microscopically bleeding. This was the recurrent thorn in the clean flesh of Peter Innocent; this was his cross: he had no nephew.

So far as he knew, he was the only cardinal suffering under a like deprivation. He could not but consider the circumstance as a direct chastisement at the hand of God, yet he could not for the life of him decide wherefore the divine anger had so visited him; he examined his conscience, and found no really adequate sin. Nieces he had in plenty, the pretty flowering of Nicholas's romantic marriage; his sisters, having entered convents in early youth, might not, according to his code, be expected to serve him save by the efficacy of prayer. So far prayer had proved singularly inefficacious.

For his own part, he had prayed and fasted and made pilgrimages; there had been a period of hair shirts, but these had been

forbidden by Pope Clement and his physician as merely a pro-
tracted form of torture of dubious virtue under the peculiar
conditions.

Sometimes Peter Innocent wondered very vaguely and benig-
nantly at the number of nephews possessed by some of the more
powerful cardinals; it did not occur to his charity, however, to
regard these youths as a commodity procurable by other means
than the help of God and the wedded happiness of one's brothers
and sisters. Of late he had been pricked to a certain reverential
envy by the Pope's very evident satisfaction in the society of the
magnificent Braschi Onesti, haughty, negligently handsome, a
prince of nephews indeed, and, more lately, a prince of the Holy
Empire. Peter Innocent might himself have preferred a gentler
nephew, a creature malleable and engaging to the affections of a
mild old man, but at this moment he was immensely taken by
the carnation velvet coat and Cæsar's signet-ring.

It is conceivable that he may have permitted himself a passing
dream of parenthood — conceivable, but unlikely. The extreme
chastity of his body extended to his spirit, or perhaps it were juster
to say that the body and spirit of Peter Innocent were in this
eighty-first year of his age a single amalgam, made from two substances of equal purity. This much is probable; that returning at
a jocund season to a home of such miraculous loveliness as flowed
and floated in the waves and clouds of Venice, he felt within the
stiff and sanctified chrysalis of his flesh a lively movement as of
uncurling wings, such exquisite and painted films as a moth hangs
down to dry from the under side of a linden leaf. And he would
have provided with joyous gratitude an opportunity to any saint
to slit him down the back like a locust, if thereby might be freed a
younger, fairer, and, to his humility, more perfect being than Peter
Innocent Bon, perishing for this mystical offspring with all the
fervor of the elder phœnix.

So thinking, or, more precisely, feeling, Peter Innocent passed
into the Monastery of St. John and St. Paul, whose venerable porch
was a cavern dripping with refreshment after the full and golden
glare of noon.

3. Ritorno di Tobia

THE NEXT day dawned like a crocus, and all the lilies of the pontiff's suite arose in green and silver and vermilion.

Peter Innocent breakfasted on a large bowl of chocolate and a very small piece of marzipan, of which he was inordinately fond. The other cardinals sprinkled spices in their cups, or drank coffee sweet with sugar and brandy; they ate a great many little birds, roasted with bacon and red pepper, and they had strawberries from Passeriano and peaches from Algiers. Everyone ate what he preferred; Braschi Onesti had candied chestnuts and champagne.

Presently the Pope called Peter Innocent into his particular chamber. Pius was sitting up in bed; his beautiful ivory face looked grieved and weary under a canopy the color of pot-pourri, heavy with a like perfume. Across his knees lay Sanazzaro's *Arcadia*, stamped with the dolphin of the first Manutius. At his elbow stood an engraved goblet of clear water.

"Peter," he said in a soft voice, "after I have received the Doge and the assembled Signory and granted audience both public and private to various bishops of the Venetian territory, I shall be very tired. Yet, even so, I must assist, together with the Patriarch Giovanelli, at a *Te Deum* rendered by the voices of the ducal choir, accompanied by fivescore instruments under the baton of Pasquale Galuppi. I am ill; the journey has exhausted and the Republic's arrogance annoyed a mind already languid with affairs. May I count upon your friendship to support me in this hour of trial?"

Peter Innocent was overcome by pity and amaze at the Pope's condescension. He fell rustlingly to his knees, and picking up the pontifical slipper, which reposed upon a silken drugget by the bed, he kissed it with reverence. Pius smiled indulgently, extending his fine hand in a gesture of release to indicate a comfortable armchair plumped by pigeon-down. The Cardinal regained his feet rather shakily and sank among these cushions, breathless.

"Holiness," he whispered, "what singular good fortune makes me capable of serving you, and in what essential does such service lie?" Privately, he prayed the business might not be connected with the Inquisition or the liberal opinions of his brother Nicholas.

" Merely this and thus," replied the Pope, closing his eyes with an air of elegant fatigue. " This respectable choirmaster, Galuppi, has composed a cantata for five voices in my especial honor, and on the words of Gaspare Gozzi; it will be performed at the Incurabili this afternoon. Ludovico Manin pays for it, and it will be a very pretty compliment, but of course I cannot attend in person; the *Te Deum* will consume my extremest energies; my vitality can support no further burden. As the eldest prelate in my suite, you will make an acceptable substitute for the father of Christendom; as a Venetian, your presence will confer satisfaction, as, I trust, your sensibilities will receive pleasure; these men are your compatriots. May I rely upon you, my kind Peter? "

The Cardinal was deeply touched by these proofs of confidence; he was also overjoyed at the prospect of hearing the musical result of a collaboration between two beloved friends of his early manhood; he fancied he might meet them again and kiss their frosty cheeks. He had heard news of this cantata; its subject, the *Return of Tobias*, impressed him as being even more appropriate to his own obscure instance than to that of the sovereign pontiff. And he thought of the fresh virginal voices of the Incurabili, which had been taught to weave vocal harmonies as painstakingly as the fingers of less fortunate orphans are instructed in the intricacies of lace-making.

" Yes," he contrived to breathe, and " Gratitude," and " Holiness," and so was about to depart, when Pius stayed him with a gesture of white hands.

" Peter," he said affectionately, " if you are wearied by this ceremony, I will permit you to absent yourself from the festivities of the evening. Do as you please, my dear good fellow; you must have youthful affiliations to rebind, old memories to renew and cherish. I shall understand; this night is your own, unhampered by any duty to me. And, you know — " he smiled very sweetly, — " a higher power is vested in my unworthy person; you may do as you like, Peter, for tonight, without fear of the consequences." His smile grew more indulgent, and he laughed with a peculiar tenderness as Peter Innocent kissed his scented ring and left him.

4. Crystal Monsters

BLUE dusk, thicker than fog and tinted with expressed essence of
heaven along the falling color of the dew, enveloped Peter Innocent as he slipped from the lighted doorway of the Incurabili; the
music prolonged itself through other channels than his ears, and
seemed to influence the hue of the most distant star and the perfume of the nearest pomegranate flower. He was happy, but a little
loneliness, even a little fear, tinctured his mood. He had been
unable to identify either of his old friends, and had found himself
too shy to ask for them among the brocaded crowd of notables.
Unobserved, he had sought the consolation of the twilight; he
loved to be alone, but tonight his tranquillity had somehow failed
him. He felt cold and rather tremulous as a touch fell upon his
shoulder.

It was Alvise Luna, the glass-blower of Murano. He had grown
very old, and his pale eyes were sunken in a face blank and dusty
as a bag of yellow meal. Peter Innocent was shocked by the man's
appearance, and greeted him sympathetically.

" Eminence," said Luna in a voice threaded by a whine, " I had
not hoped to be recognized, nor, if recognized, acknowledged as
an acquaintance by your Eminence. I have fallen upon evil times.
I, whose ancestors worked in crystal for the great Duke of Buck-
ingham and visited Tuscany at the invitation of the munificent
Cosimo II, I have not, to be frank with you, one copper coin
wherewith to brighten another, I have drunk water for a fortnight,
and the things I have eaten are not fit to be mentioned in your
eminent presence. I am reduced to working for the infamous
Giorgio Barbaria, who wishes to manufacture black glass bottles
on the English lines; I have, as you may remember, considerable
knowledge of foreign factories, and he pays me a dog's wages to
instruct him. I am starving; my wife and children are starving; my
little grandchildren are already dead from malnutrition. May I
humbly beg your Eminence to aid me in my undeserved and dreadful trouble? "

This Luna was a liar and a sorcerer, and the Holy Office was
already upon his path, which led through some of the most un-

savory cellars of Venice, marked out by a slimy brilliance like the
track of a snail. But Peter Innocent did not know this, and had
he known, he would not have understood it. He saw that the man
was frightened, and he believed that he was hungry. As a matter
of fact, Luna had plenty of money and merely wanted more; at the
moment an enormous supper of polenta was distending his greasy
waistcoat. But he was a dyspeptic, and his wry neck and hollow
eyes looked wretched enough to move a more obdurate heart than
Peter Innocent's.

" Of course," said the gentle old man, " of course, my poor friend,
I will do what I can to help you."

An hour later Peter Innocent was picking his slow, uncertain
way down a damp and noisome corridor; Luna followed him, holding a candle as high as the dripping ceiling would permit. They
descended a worn flight of stone stairs and found themselves in a
low-vaulted chamber whose debased Byzantine arches were dimly
illuminated by a pair of ship's lanterns dependent therefrom.

This apartment was but too evidently a cellar, for a good three
inches of water, cold and ambiguous, polluted the embroidered
clocks upon the Cardinal's stockings. Nevertheless, certain portions
of the walls were covered by tapestries smoldering with the rich
fancies of the Renaissance, and a number of carved cabinets and
tables showed surfaces inlaid with brass or paneled in exotic lacquer. At one end of the chamber's secretive length, a small furnace
filled with wood ashes made a spot of expiring rose-amber in the
gloom.

Luna walked to the center of the room and, rapidly waving his
guttering tallow back and forth, ignited in a flash a score of white
wax candles cupped in colored glass. Peter Innocent saw that a
superb chandelier hung from the highest vaulting of the roof, a
fantastic thing of flowers and icicles and silver bells, tinkling in the
midst of squalor. And now, with a tinted radiance flooding every
corner of the cobwebbed cellar, a hundred graceful and preposterous shapes sprang into the enchanted view: winged and maned and
dolphin-finned, griffins and lions, stags and peacocks, and monsters
fabulously horned and taloned.

The Cardinal perceived in addition to these savage and exquisite creatures the accustomed implements of the glass-blower's

trade: pontils and blowpipes, pincers and wooden battledores. Upon a platform, raised above the pervasive dampness of the stone-flagged floor, stood the workman's chair, with its rigid parallel arms suggesting some rude instrument of torture. Seated within this strange machine was a mysterious stranger, wrapped in a black cloak, and wearing a small mask of black velvet.

Peter Innocent at once became aware of an element of masquerade in the appearance of this person. Having himself long ago assumed a disguise, albeit an holy one, he readily observed the same quality in the dress of others, and as readily ascribed it to the most innocuous desire for privacy. He took the gentleman to be a person of simple and retiring disposition, and acknowledged courteously and at once Luna's gesture of introduction. The stranger rose, displaying an impressive figure, tall and muscular. He wore a quantity of beautiful lace, and his rings were diamonds of the first brilliance; save for these elegant details, his clothes were of a uniform sable hue. His head was covered by a short chestnut peruke, and through the slits of his mask his eyes glinted very dark and bright. The skin of his face and hands was swarthy and faintly lined; the Cardinal judged him to be past his first youth.

"Your Eminence," said Luna in French, which he spoke fluently, having, for several disgraceful reasons, been much in Paris, "permit me to present Monsieur de Chastelneuf, Chevalier de Langeist." The latter title was pronounced in the German manner, and the Cardinal was at a loss to conjecture the stranger's nationality until he spoke. His manners were courtly, if a little antiquated and florid, but he conversed with a strong Venetian accent, and Peter Innocent had no doubt that he was a native of the Republic.

The Chevalier kissed the Cardinal's hand with immense politeness, and began at once to speak of the prelate's poetical works, displaying a quite remarkable knowledge and acumen. In this way, and through the use of copious quotation from the classics, the gentleman contrived to convey an impression of learning and respectability, and Peter Innocent felt sure he must be a person of consequence.

Such, in a measure, was indeed the case, for Monsieur de Chastelneuf, as this narrative must continue to call him, had at one time

or another attracted the attention of almost every court of Europe,
and on this very evening no less a notable than Messer Grand himself had given our gentleman much good advice not unconnected
with the miasmic quality of the Venetian air and the superior
salubrity of Munich or Vienna. And since it was the Chevalier's
invariable habit to travel in a superb English carriage, emblazoned
with the arms of a ruined lord, and as, moreover, he seldom traveled alone, he had been faced with the disagreeable necessity of
selling his diamonds and his point d'Alençon without delay. Save
for the fortunate intervention of Luna, who knew the Cardinal's
simplicity was good for at least a thousand sequins, Monsieur de
Chastelneuf might have been forced to part with his cross of the
Order of the Golden Spur. It is not surprising that his happiness
in greeting Peter Innocent was unfeigned and infectious.

Presently the Cardinal found himself ensconced within the glass-
blower's mis-shapen armchair, with dry slippers upon his feet, and
a couple of hot bricks under these. A glass of excellent Levantine
Muscat warmed his vitals; the long room appeared less cavernous,
and the crystal apparitions which filled it glowed like jewels in the
renewed stream of his own vivacity. His two companions were persons of wit and esoteric learning, and his admiration for Luna increased as he examined one by one the marvelous progeny of the
workman's art. As for the Chevalier, the delicacy of his mind was
equalled only by its ascetic and fastidious grace; Peter Innocent
was soothed and enraptured by this refined society.

The Chevalier removed his mask, and his face showed handsome and aquiline, almost Oriental in its dusky tints, yet all Venetian in the liveliness and valor which informed its every smile. He
had a nose like a falcon, and his deep-set eyes were black and gold.
He told Peter Innocent that he had, in his youth, been honored
by the friendship of Benedict XIV, who had once taken his advice
upon some little matters of no importance.

Suddenly Monsieur de Chastelneuf rose to his very considerable
height, at the same time making, for the benefit of Luna's eyes
alone, an enigmatical sign whose nature it is impossible to describe.
Luna also rose; the pair appeared to move in unison to some unheard and rhythmical injunction; salt and spices were destroyed
upon the fire, and their smoke permitted to dim the purer radiance

of the candle-flames. Then, at an unintelligible word pronounced by the altered voice of Chastelneuf, the incredible came to pass.

Peter Innocent beheld a golden griffin lift his wings to fan the air; a stag, of azure glass dappled with the same gold, stepped with a fairy pride across the expanse of Chinese lacquer which separated him from his mate, and the two, meeting, caressed each other with delicate gestures of affection. A humming-bird, with feathers blown in pearl-color and crimson, flew from his perch, alighting on the leafy chandelier; the spray that received him bent and swayed, and from its largest rose a petal drifted to the floor.

There is not the slightest use in pretending that Peter Innocent was shocked or even very greatly surprised. His mind moved happily in an atmosphere of miracles, and the charming nature of these phenomena precluded any suspicion of evil. He felt like a child who perceives at his first carnival a blue sky flowering with confetti, or who is presented at Christmas-time with one of those delightful German toys called Christbaum, bright with silver foil and tiny scarlet candles. So, without uncomfortable amazement, he stared enchanted at the delicious marvel of awakened life.

5. Piavola de Franza

It was Luna who finally crossed himself surreptitiously before addressing the Cardinal in hoarse and lowered tones.

" Eminence," he whispered, " you have seen what our combined skill can accomplish; this, however, is only the beginning. It is very pretty to watch these insects and atomies, but what would you say to a flying horse able to transport your Eminence to Ecbatana; or a Cameroonian gorilla, blown in the best *mille fiori* and capable of strangling, with thumb and finger, persons inimical to your Eminence's peace of mind? I have, too, an extremely practical Indian serpent, the poison fang ingeniously supplied with *aqua tofana*." And he laid his hand upon the lock of a great chest, bound with copper, which occupied one corner of the room.

Peter Innocent turned pale as milk; in another moment he would have been constrained to believe evil of Alvise Luna. But Chastelneuf observed the old man's uneasiness, and, stepping forward with an air of well-bred piety, he refilled the Cardinal's empty glass and reverently saluted his cold hand. Then he spoke very softly and persuasively.

"Monseigneur," he said, for despite his marked Italian accent he continued to employ the French language, "you must not be offended by the rough jests of my poor friend Luna; he is a stupid fellow, but good as bread, and of a simplicity truly pitiable in these wicked times. See how he has been persecuted by the Three, those sinister officials who deprived your noble brother of his liberty, and who have been the death of innumerable worthy citizens of Venice. Consider his industry, and talent, and then reflect upon his wretched circumstances and the sufferings of his devoted wife and children. I am sure you will consent to help him, Monseigneur; he asks no charity, but merely that you will patronize and encourage his beautiful craft by the purchase of one or two little articles of undoubted utilitarian and æsthetic value. This, for example — "

He made as if to open the iron-studded door of an inner chamber, but Luna stopped him with a clutch upon the arm and an imprecation. Chastelneuf smiled imperturbably and proceeded, flicking invisible dust grains from his satin sleeve:

"Your Eminence will graciously refrain from considering me presumptuous when I make clear the extent of our success in manipulating Murano glass; we are able to vitalize not only dumb animals, but even, with God's help, creatures formed in the divine image. It is a great responsibility, but I trust we acquit ourselves worthily as custodians of this sacred mystery. Monseigneur, you are ever in the company of the elect, but I, who am like your Eminence of a certain age, know all too well that the pangs of loneliness sometimes invade the most profoundly religious heart, and that our declining years, in their hallowed progression towards our Father's house, must needs require now and then the pitiful grace of human companionship, in salutation and farewell. If, then, the presence of a little being compact of modesty and sweetness, at once a daughter and a loving friend, blonde and ethereal as the ivory ladies of Carriera, could solace some spiritual hunger — "

He broke off and, silencing Luna by an imperious movement of the hand, walked firmly to the iron-studded door and opened it. Within, stiffly disposed upon a small gilt chair of French design, Peter Innocent could discern, though dimly, something like a large doll or a little girl; the creature appeared about sixteen years old, and wore a pale pink dress, trimmed with feather flowers in the best possible taste. A quantity of silvery-yellow hair fell to her shoulders, and her fair complexion was transparent and tinted like a shell. Her eyes were closed, her face tranquil and pretty. The Cardinal was forcibly reminded of the Poupée de France in the Merceria, and, less vividly, of his sisters attired for their first ball, which was that given by the Morosini for Count Oldenburg in 1708, when he himself was six years of age. Since that time he had not particularly observed female clothing, except now and then in shop-windows, and always rather to admire than to approve. He felt obscurely ill at ease, and although his heart was wrung by a certain air of pathos conveyed by the little figure propped on its gilded chair, he did not want to look at it any longer. He was distinctly relieved when Chastelneuf closed the closet door, which swung to with a ponderous clang of metal. Yet he was aware of a slight sense of cruelty towards the curious doll; it must be very lonely in the dark, behind the iron door.

"I should have no use, I am afraid, for this interesting example of your art," he said somewhat timidly to the two men, who regarded him with scarcely concealed disgust in their veiled and greedy gaze. "I should really find myself at a loss to care for so complicated a piece of mechanism. The — ah — the young lady looks so alarmingly fragile, and I fear I do not understand the requirements of such — ah — such rarities. But I trust you will be careful to find a purchaser in whose kindness you can confide this poor — ah, child; she seems a mere child." He paused, interrogating them with his anxious blue eyes; they nodded in gloomy affirmation.

It is said by adepts, who may or may not be fitted to pronounce upon the subject, that when a man relinquishes the love of women from his infancy he condemns his predestined virgin to eternal violence wrought upon her by the demons of debauch. It is hardly reasonable to suppose that this young person artificially formed from Venetian glass can have suffered a like fate, but it is an unfortunate fact that Alvise Luna sold her, within the next fortnight, to an elderly senator of atrocious morals and immense wealth. He did not find her fabric durable, and perhaps she had no soul.

The Chevalier was the first to break the uncomfortable silence; he was at once his suave and animated self. The Cardinal felt better immediately.

" I quite understand your scruples, Monseigneur," he cried with enthusiasm, " and oh, how rare it is, in this material age, to discover virtue so sensitive or sympathies so warm as yours are proved to be! But surely, surely, there is some elegant trifle, some elfin toy, which might serve to remind you of Venice and of your youth within her occult circle of lagoons. A little greyhound, perhaps, or a talking parakeet; we have been particularly successful with parakeets."

At this instant the stupendous plan struck Peter Innocent like a falling star. He was dizzied by the glittering impact, and swayed in his chair, but his gentle voice was perfectly clear and steady as he answered: " Monsieur de Chastelneuf," he said, " and you, my old friend Luna, there is indeed something which I have long wished to possess, and with which your truly admirable skill may be able to supply me. Do you think, by any fortunate chance, that you could make me a nephew? "

Luna, who knew Chastelneuf to a hair's breadth of precise disillusion, started in alarm as the other parted his smiling lips to reply; the glass-blower could have informed you to a semicolon of the exact witticism fluttering upon the Chevalier's tongue. To his overwhelming relief, the pungent butterfly was swallowed without the faintest grimace, and the words which actually emerged were models of chaste sobriety. A perfumed handkerchief passed across the mouth, the ghost of a sigh, and Chastelneuf's expression matched his speech. He was decorous, and only Luna knew the measure of his stoical abstention.

" Your Eminence," said the Chevalier, bowing, " does us too much honor thus to admit us into a consultation on family affairs. But, happily, we are most excellently fitted to advise and aid you in this respect; we have, I may say, made a specialty of nephews." And he reminded Luna, with the toe of his buckled shoe, that a cheerful demeanor was indicated for this occasion.

Alvise Luna was more than a little troubled; he had not bargained for so extensive an order and would have preferred to undertake a contract for a dragon or a Hyrcamean tiger any day. He

was a religious man at heart, and although he was strongly predisposed by nature and inheritance towards chicanery and murder, he
viewed with profound distrust the extra-natural and Hermetic
practices of his companion. To him there was something infinitely
alarming in the idea of pre-empting the power of Deity to shape
a being human at least in semblance, if not in soul, and he would
rather have made a dozen manticores than one small baby. Nevertheless, he fixed his mind upon the heavenly shimmer of a thousand sequins, and entered with tolerable good grace into the current discussion.

6. Aveeva Vadelilith

PETER INNOCENT had no difficulty whatever in obtaining from the
Pope full permission to absent himself for an indefinite number
of hours upon the third night after the strange adventure just related. This latter night was that of May 19th, the date of official
departure for the pontifical suite, but Pius bade the Cardinal do
as he pleased, and if he chanced to be too late to join the other
prelates upon their leaving Venice, he might easily overtake them,
said the Holy Father, during the journey of the following day,
which must be made by water, and slowly, as befitted so illustrious
a progress. He conferred his blessing upon the grateful old man
and, with the same indulgent smile, embraced him.

The season was Pentecost, and the water running in the veins
of Venice appeared like wine under the transmutation of the sun.
Pius VI, attired in the extreme of liturgical splendor, celebrated
mass at the Church of St. John and St. Paul. Passing out into the
Campo, he imparted his benediction to the multitude from a high
platform whose timbers were heavily overlaid with varnishes of
gold. No sooner was this ceremony accomplished than Peter Innocent, his heart no longer a blue balloon, but a swinging censer of
holy and aspiring prayer, hastened towards that equivocal quarter
of the town in whose bowels the mysterious cellar lay concealed.
He wore once more the indistinguished dress of a Franciscan friar,
and as he walked, his eyes were fixed upon the pages of a little
book whose covers bore the cruciform symbol of his faith.

Meanwhile Alvise and the Chevalier de Langeist awaited him

in the vaulted chamber of their secret activities; Luna was ob-
servably nervous, but Chastelneuf was calm and majestic, the very
picture of courtly self-possession in his coat of gold brocade and
black velvet breeches, with a jeweled order tangled in the rich
laces upon his breast.

" Rely upon my diplomacy," said this personage to his shivering
companion. " I have learned much since the days of Madame von
Wulfe and the grand operation. I alone of all the adepts of my
acquaintance have survived the wretched effects of Balsamo's petty
larcenies. Saint-Germain is dying in Hesse, under the unpleasant
pseudonym of Zaraski. Cagliostro has incurred the rigors of im-
prisonment and poverty; he has abundantly deserved a severer punishment. I saw him first at Aix, in Provence, a mere boy, sewing
cockleshells on his black oilcloth coat, while his young wife stood
at his elbow, holding a great crucifix of some base metal colored to
resemble gold. She was adorably pretty, but depraved. That was
twenty years ago, and I am wiser now; if my peculiar talents have
languished, my judgment has ripened and matured. I am entirely
satisfied with our preparations for tonight."

" That is all very well," sneered Luna, " but I have had all the
hard work. My lips are cracked, and my hands flayed by such un-
exampled labors; I have performed prodigies; my lungs are old
leather, and my windpipe scorched macaroni, yet you grudge me
a glass of your precious *monte pulciano,* and I suppose I am to
have a very dog's share of the money compared with your lion's
portion. So it always is. Poor honest fellow that I am, I never manage to look out for my own interests, and yet I am the best glass-
blower in the known world." And he began to weep in sincere
self-pity.

" Quite true," said Chastelneuf, with careless good nature, " and
a lovely bit of work you've done today; your masterpiece, I cordially assure you. We could get an enormous sum for this juvenile
Apollo from the director of the opera; he would make an ideal
soprano, and both sexes would go into indiscriminate ecstasies over
him if he appeared, shall we say, in the latest production of Cimarosa or Mozart? Of course I should have to alter my plans a little,
but he should have a golden voice, I promise you. Only, I think
our ingenuous prelate is, in the vernacular, the lucky draw in the

lottery; he will not talk, and as he is by nature close-mouthed, he will have to pay through the nose."

" Are you determined upon waiting until after midnight to perform the undertaking? " asked Luna, with an anxious scowl. " I should have thought Thursday the more suitable date, and Thursday has yet three hours to run. Surely the thing you are about to do may be described as a political and religious operation; I have been reading your copy of Paracelsus, with its interesting marginal notes, and Paracelsus says very plainly that Friday is a day exclusively reserved for amorous works. I cannot see the connection, although it is quite like you to try to turn the most serious occasion into a common love-affair."

" Common, do you say? " cried the Chevalier, indignantly. " _Cospetto! — Che bella cosa!_ Is it a common occurrence in my life, I ask you, to refrain for three entire days from all human enjoyments, to confine myself to a vegetarian diet, and to eschew intoxicating liquors? A pretty regimen for a gentleman of my faculties! Then, too, I have had the trouble of burning, upon rising and retiring, a costly perfume composed of the juice of laurels, salt, camphor, white resin, and sulphur, repeating at the same time the four sacred words. I beg to remind you that I am no longer an amateur, as in the past; _Paralis_ has advanced. As for the matter of the amorous operation, of course it is precisely that. Do you imagine I could send this poor innocent forth into the world improperly equipped to deal with his fellows? Friday it must be, or I'm a Turk! "

" As you please, as you please," grumbled Luna, resignedly. " I merely thought you might look very fine in a scarlet vestment, with a wreath of oak, poplar, fig, and pomegranate leaves; also I happen to have some ambergris, balm, grain of paradise, macis, and saffron lying idle about the place, which I understand are the correct perfumes for Thursday. But I was purely altruistic; for my own part I wish sincerely it were Tuesday, so that we might inaugurate an appalling work of vengeance. I fancy the blood-colored robe and the magical sword and dagger. There is a beautiful picture of them in Paracelsus."

His face was alight with eager satisfaction, but Chastelneuf silenced him with a haughty sign of disapproval.

"Nonsense!" he said impatiently. "You know nothing whatever about it, and I advise you to keep your long nose out of such
dangerous matters; these instruments of precision in the hands of
the ignorant are lethal to the soul. Now, if you have prepared the
inner chamber according to my directions, all is ready; but first let
us have a look at the boy."

Luna could not suppress a grin of pride as he led the way to
a heavily carved cupboard in the farthest corner of the room; the
thing was a veritable cathedral in miniature, Gothic and grotesque,
with a hundred saints and gargoyles leaning from among its wreaths
of fruit and flowers. He opened the door of this piece of furniture
to a cautious crack; Chastelneuf peered over his shoulder. The two
smiled joyously at each other as Luna closed the cupboard door
with care.

"Miraculous!" shouted the Chevalier, slapping Luna on the
back in a transport of enthusiasm. "Divine! And even now he
seems to live. Alvise, do you know you have given him a distinct
look of his reverend uncle; a sweet touch that; and oh, the delicacy
of the thing! The hair, the eyelashes, the very finger-nails! O mar-
vellous Luna!"

"It was a good thought that, to patronize your own tailor,
though it has cost us a pretty penny," began Luna, handsomely,
when a timid knock upon the outer door apprised the friends of
Peter Innocent's proximity.

While Luna engaged the Cardinal in more or less agreeable conversation, Chastelneuf disappeared into the inner apartment. The
time passed rapidly, and Peter Innocent had just finished his third
glass of wine and persuaded a pair of coral-colored crystal love-
birds to perch upon his forefinger when the all but inaudible strains
of a flute or violin recalled him from a waking dream. Guided by
Luna, he passed into the other chamber, whence these sounds proceeded, and there beheld a scene of ceremonial enchantment.

Let it be clearly understood at once that the Chevalier, whatever his peccadillos, practiced only the higher forms of transcendental and divine magic, as opposed to nigromancy and goetia;
otherwise he could have done nothing in the presence of such holiness as Peter Innocent's; the Cardinal moreover carried upon his
person a crucifix and a Book of Prayer, infallible talismans against

the evil one. Here was no place for the Ahriman of the Persians, the Typhon of the Egyptians, the Python of the Greeks, the Croquemitaine, the obscene deity of the Sabbath. Let it be remembered that Isis was impeccable in her widowhood, that Diana Panthea was a virgin; that Apollonius of Tyana never yielded to the seductions of pleasure; that Plotinus of Alexandria was ascetic in the manner of his life; and that Raymond Lully was the victim of a hopeless passion which made him chaste forever. Vesper, not Lucifer, blazed now in the pentagram upon the marble pavement, and Peter Innocent stepped forward without fear.

The chamber, which was both larger and higher than the anteroom, was hung with charming tapestries of rose and green, and the Chevalier was robed in vestments of sky-blue silk; a crown of violets encircled his chestnut peruke. His ring was enriched by a magnificent turquoise, and his clasps and tiara were of lapis-lazuli and beryl. The walls were covered with festoons of roses, myrtle, and olive, and the atmosphere quivered with the emanations of innumerable spices.

Upon the Parian floor there stood an altar of perfumes, and upon this altar there lay an unblemished lambskin, and upon this lambskin was traced in pure vermilion a pentagram with one point in the ascendant. It had been sprinkled with holy water, and dried by the smoke of myrrh and aloes, and over it Chastelneuf had uttered the names of the five genii, which are Gabriel, Raphael, Anael, Samael, and Oriphiel.

The adept towered above the tripod of evocation; he bore in the center of his breast a copper talisman with the character of Anael traced thereon, together with the words: " Aveeva Vadelilith."

Luna withdrew into the shadows, where he waved slowly an enormous fan of swan's feathers.

7. Conjuration of the Four

PETER INNOCENT came forward into the light, which fell with an effect of moonshine from the sacred lamp. He had no sense of fear and, what is more singular, no sense of sin; this appears to be indisputable proof of the beneficent quality of the ritual employed by Chastelneuf, upon this occasion at least. The Cardinal never told of that night's wonders, and had he done so he would certainly have been burnt by the Holy Office; but his conscience remained immaculate throughout. He had his private theories, however, concerning the Christian and supplementary ceremonies proper to the undertaking, and he held his book and his crucifix very firmly in his two hands as he confronted the Chevalier.

Chastelneuf lifted in the air the true and absolute magic wand, which must not be confounded with the simple divining-rod, or the trident of Paracelsus. This was composed of a single perfectly straight branch of the almond tree, cut with a golden pruning-knife at the exact moment of its flowering; one of the extremities was fitted with a triangular prism, and the other with a similar figure of black resin; this end of the wand was gilded, and that silvered. A long needle of magnetized iron pierced the entire length of this consecrated instrument, which was the verendum of the magus, too occult to be shown to uninitiate eyes; the Chevalier was probably unwise to employ it in the presence of the Cardinal and Luna, but he was a brave man, and very vain of his attainments.

" As this creature to whom we are about to impart the privilege of living is composed of natural elements, I purpose to invoke the spirits of these components, which are the Four: air, water, fire, and earth. He who is about to be born was formed from sand and holy water, fused in extremest heat and shaped by human breath. Through the agency of these powers, a spirit shall enter into this bodily image, but whether mortal or elemental I cannot tell, nor does it greatly matter."

Chastelneuf spoke thus with an authentic dignity, which deepened as he proceeded with the exorcisms. And now the Cardinal perceived behind the altar an object of funereal character, resembling a bier; it was covered by a white cloth whose folds conformed in some measure to the outlines of a corpse decently disposed for burial. The thing had been invisible a moment since; now the rays of the lamp were concentrated upon its ominous quiescence.

Tracing their symbol upon the air with an eagle's quill, the adept now intoned the prayer of the sylphs; he exorcized the water by the imposition of hands, and by mingling with it a little consecrated salt and the ash of incense. The aspergillum used was formed of twigs of vervain, periwinkle, sage, mint, and basil, tied by a thread expertly abstracted from a virgin's distaff and provided with a handle of hazelwood from a tree which had not yet fruited. The prayer of the undines was then recited with proper solemnity, and afterwards the prayer of the salamanders, so soon as the fire had been suitably exorcized by the sprinkling of salt, white resin, camphor, and sulphur, and by calling upon the kings of the sun and lightning, the volcanoes, and the great astral light. Lastly, the earth was exorcized by efficacious means, and the gnomic prayer pronounced. The Chevalier then lifted successively the sword, the rod, and the cup, and proclaimed, in a loud voice, the conjuration of the Four.

"Caput mortuum, the Lord command thee by the living and votive serpent! Cherub, the Lord command thee by Adam Jotchavah! Wandering Eagle, the Lord command thee by the wings of the Bull! Serpent, the Lord Tetragrammaton command thee by the angel and the lion! Michael, Gabriel, Raphael, and Anael! Flow, moisture, by the spirit of Eloim! Earth, be established by Adam Jotchavah! Spread, firmament, by Jahuvehu, Zebaoth! Fulfill, judgment, by fire in the virtue of Michael! Angel of the blind eyes, obey, or pass away with this holy water! Work, winged Bull, or revert to the earth, unless thou wouldst have me pierce thee with this sword! Chained Eagle, obey my sign, or fly before this breathing! This, by virtue of the Pentagram, which is the morning star, and by the name of the Tetragram, which is written in the center of the cross of light! Amen."

At this moment the white cloth covering the body seemed to move of its own volition, rising slowly until it floated free of the bier; its corners were drawn apart, and the fabric violently divided into four quarters. Upon a narrow trestle Peter Innocent saw the figure of a young man; he appeared very tall and slender in his complete immobility. He was dressed in the fantastic extreme of fashion, and his costume was the more singular in that it was entirely white. He wore a white velvet coat embroidered with silver spangles, a velvet waistcoat to match, white satin breeches, white silk stockings, and shoes with diamond buckles. His linen and lace were exquisite, and on one hand was placed a curious ring consisting of a large crystal set over white satin.

The Cardinal stared intently at the face of this elegant creature, but could distinguish little save the suggestion of a straight nose, arched eyebrows, and the glimmer of pale hair over a paler brow. The eyes were closed, the hands relaxed and quiet.

Meanwhile, above the tripod, the mystery thickened with the perfumed smoke; there came a loud command, a moon of radiance appeared, dissolved, and vanished, and with the most startling celerity the young man bounded from his couch and gracefully abased himself before the venerable prelate, in whom he seemed to recognize a father or a friend. At the same instant the Chevalier stepped forward and affected an introduction between the two, mingling simplicity with polished ease of manner.

All were visibly moved by this happy consummation of their ritual, and even Luna permitted a few tears of relief and cupidity to trickle down his dusty cheeks. Chastelneuf was laughing, shaking hands, and offering choice wines in slim Murano goblets to the Cardinal and his nephew. The boy smiled, bowed, and sipped with the most lifelike gestures of politeness; but Peter Innocent stood silent in a tranquillity like stone, bewitched and awed by his felicity, and gazing at his nephew with infinite love and wonder in his eyes.

8. Creature of Salt

UPON the most minute examination, Peter Innocent failed to discover anything in the appearance of his young kinsman — for as such we must henceforward consider him — which could suggest an abhuman origin or composition. True, the boy's skin was so fair as to seem almost translucent, and the luminous flax of his abundant hair had the fragility of spun glass; but these details merely served to give distinction to his undoubted beauty. It is possible that Luna had employed, in weaving with his breath these miraculous lovelocks, a secret method by which his ancestors had produced *vitro de trina*, or crystal lace, of such spider-web delicacy that it shattered at the vibrations of an angry voice or the too poignant wailing of a violin. The long gold eyelashes matched the hair; the eyes themselves were the color of sea water, the pure Venetian aquamarine.

As opposed to the very ornamental lightness of his physical

equipment, the young man's manner was composed and firm, and his perfect self-possession might have contained a hint of patronage had its affability been less pronounced. He ignored Luna with charming good humor, condescended to the Chevalier without offending him, and put Peter Innocent at his ease with equal facility and dispatch.

"My dearest uncle, my more than father," he cried with fastidiously restrained emotion, saluting the Cardinal on both cheeks with the utmost tenderness, while two bright glassy tears, volatile as quicksilver, fell shining through the air. "Chevalier, that's a sound wine, though heavy to my particular fancy. You don't happen to have such a thing as a *viola da gamba* about, do you? A little music would not be amiss — I am sure you sing — that sweet duet of Cimarosa's, let us say." And he began to hum, in an enchanting tenor, the words:

> "Prima che spunti
> In ciel l'aurora. . . ."

The Cardinal put out his hand and softly touched the white satin sleeve of his new nephew.

"Dear boy, it gives me the greatest satisfaction to witness your careless happiness," he said timidly, "but there is one thing, one slight precautionary measure, which I hesitate to omit, much as it grieves me to interrupt your singing. I wonder if I might trouble you for a little clear water?" he continued, turning to Luna with a courteous smile.

The Chevalier bounded forward, eager to serve, with the stoup of holy water from the evocative altar; but Peter Innocent shrank hastily away as he shook his silver head in refusal.

"Not that, I think, my kind friend. Believe me, I am very grateful, but if I might have only a cupful from the spring which I observed in the adjoining cellar, I should prefer — Ah, you are goodness itself; I thank you."

Peter Innocent took the water which Luna brought him in a cracked china cup; holding it very carefully, he blessed it according to the Roman ritual, thus establishing its potency against evil spirits. This was a different consecration, indeed, from that surrounding the furniture of the Chevalier's altar; this blessing, uttered in the old man's quiet voice, was spoken with another and a holier authority.

". . . that wherever thou art sprinkled every phantasy and wickedness and wile of diabolic deceit may flee and leave that place, and every unclean spirit. . . ." Thus was exorcized the creature of salt lurking invisible in the broken cup, and likewise the creature of water . . . " that thou mayst avail to uproot and expel this enemy with all his apostate angels, by the virtue of the same our Lord Jesus Christ."

Now was the water become a creature in the service of God's mysteries for the driving out of demons. In a whisper so low as to be wellnigh inaudible even to the boy, who at a sign had knelt upon the pavement with instinctive docility, Peter Innocent repeated certain formulæ of blessing especially efficacious against devils and invocative of divine protection. Clear drops of water fell upon the bowed and shining head.

Chastelneuf was secretly annoyed.

" That was quite unnecessary, I assure you," he said rather stiffly. " There is not an ounce of harm in the boy; the prescription calls for the purest ingredients, as Luna can tell you, and, for my own part, I have used the best magic known to the ancients. However, as you will. I suppose we all have our prejudices."

" I was sure you would understand an old man's anxiety," replied the Cardinal, pacifically. " And now I will not trespass longer upon your kindness, save to give you this little wallet with my profoundest gratitude, and to wish you both a very good morning."

It was morning, and between the cracks in the jalousies pale blades of light were driven like angelic swords.

" Where are you taking the boy, Eminence? " asked the Chevalier with renewed cheerfulness, playing a lively tune upon the jingling wallet, whose chorus was five thousand sequins. " Remember, he's scarcely used to a rough world as yet, and his finger-nails may be brittle for a day or two."

" We are going to the Church of St. John and St. Paul, my friend, where this poor child must receive the sacrament of baptism," Peter Innocent said slowly. He looked with pity and something perilously near adoration into the smooth, transparent countenance of the boy, who clasped his arm and smiled in meek response.

Mounting a short flight of steps, Monsieur de Chastelneuf flung open an iron-barred door, and suddenly dawn flooded the room like a river of golden water loosed upon it. Without, the canal still preserved a sleepy color, neither gray nor blue, but the housetops were painted in extravagant tints of rose and flame by a sun new-risen from the Adriatic.

"What name will you give the boy, Monseigneur?" inquired the Chevalier. "I feel a certain proprietary interest in his fortunes, which under your auspices must be uniformly happy, and I should like to know his name."

The Cardinal mused, considered, and replied.

"I believe I shall call him Virginio," he said, his eyes tracing the exquisite and ingenuous outlines of his nephew's half-averted face.

"A pretty name, but I trust it may not long be strictly appropriate; I have spared no pains to make your young friend a complete work of art, after the best natural patterns," answered the Chevalier de Langeist, with a not unpardonable pride, bowing deeply as Peter Innocent and his pale and luminous companion passed into the morning, and so were gone like a black pearl and a white, melting within a chalice of honeyed yellow wine.

BOOK II: *VIRGINIO*

" I had had an affair with the moon, in which there was neither sin nor shame." LAURENCE STERNE

9. Of Sappho Little, but All Roses

IN Angelo Querini's classical garden at Altichieri there stood a summer-house dedicated to the Goddess of Folly; this charming structure was, paradoxically enough, presided over by a bust of Marcus Aurelius and decorated with a motto from Montaigne. A more apposite taste had graced the dovecote with a Grecian Venus, and raised an altar to the spirit of tranquillity in the midst of abundances of sweet basil, lavender, and thyme.

Midway between an Egyptian sarcophagus and an Etruscan monument, both heavily overgrown with deep viridian moss, a marble bench disclosed its rosy veining to the September sun and seemed to invite a languorous repose in keeping with the season. From the door of the shadowed summer-house a young girl presently emerged; her lively glance surveyed the autumnal lawns and arbors, and instantly selected the carved and coral-colored seat as most benignant to her mood. She carried an armful of books; these she disposed within reach, herself reclining in the sunnier corner of the bench. She was soft and inscrutable as a Persian kitten.

A black kitten among the bright and gilded trees, with hazel eyes transfused with gold, and hair so dark that only at the temples a darkening golden tinge survived in smoky black. Her dress was black as soot; such a dress, decent and austere, as clothed Querini's admired and admirable young friend Fulvia Vivaldi in her Genevan retreat; too black, in spite of the clear muslin kerchief and the silver chain, for Rosalba Berni on her eighteenth birthday.

This was, then, the celebrated Rosalba, better known among the Arcadians of Italy as Sappho the Younger, or to the more affectionate few, the Infant Sappho. This child was an orphan by report, and by profoundly proven faith the ward and adoptive daughter of the noble and liberal Angelo Querini, ex-Senator of the Venetian patriciate and valued comrade of Voltaire. It was openly declared that she was a descendant of Francesco Berni the poet, to whose sparkling blood she owed her marvelous wit and the inventive lightness of her mind; other more insinuating murmurs attributed these qualities to an equally effervescent source: the whispered name of the Cardinal de Bernis was a veritable Arcadian diploma of mental grace, and Rosalba's eyebrows were distinctly French.

She had these brows, arched forever in a delicate amazement, drawn upon a smooth forehead; her dark hair grew in a point; and her eyes were large between black lashes; their expression was calm, but impertinent. Her mouth was curled like a scarlet petal in some early frost of irony; her skin was white as the rose of her baptismal name. Across her slightly tilted nose a score of golden freckles made her human; for the rest, in form and elegance of gesture, she was Artemis.

Yet not the Artemis of ivory or of quarried stone, however exquisite. Rosalba was more vital than opening roses or ripened fruit; she lived and moved and burned within the chilly greenery with a palpable warmth; she was a flame whose consummation may be bitter, but whose promissory blooming is tenderer than apple blossoms. To the five senses of an observer she was indeed imagined flowers to breathe, as she must have been velvet to touch, cream to taste, the crescent moon to gaze upon, and, to the listening ear, a melody repeated by a mocking-bird.

It was all to the credit of Monsieur de Chastelneuf that the five senses of this particular observer were so poetically acute; the young Virginio leaned upon a mossy column, while love for Rosalba Berni whirled over him like a fragrant wave and left him drowned in those same waters from which the mother of such love arose.

"'*O bianca Galatea!*'" said Virginio, politely, quoting Metastasio.

"My name is Sappho," Rosalba replied rather crossly. "I do not care for Italian verse; I prefer the classics, and, above all, Ossian. I am at present busy, very busy, with a translation of the latter, for the benefit of those unfortunate people who are unable to read it in the original Gaelic."

"Is it not written in English?" Virginio inquired timidly. "And have I not heard that Signor Cesarotti —"

"Be silent, if you cannot converse intelligently."

Rosalba pronounced these words with perfect calm; she was imperial rather than rude.

"Precisely," Virginio returned, with a gentle smile; she was suddenly aware that he was far more beautiful than any Adonis in Querini's garden. He reminded her of marble. Or was it marble of which he reminded her? Something more translucent; crystal, perhaps.

"I am reading, as you see," she said more kindly, "but I can spare you a few moments; I dare say you would like me to show you the books I have this very morning received from my kind friend and guardian. Approach, young sir; the gate is unlocked, and if you will wear white shoes, you must expect the dew to spoil them."

Virginio drew near her as one who visits, in simple reverence and awe, the shrine of an immortal; she laughed, and made a place for him beside her on the bench, among the richly bound volumes which surrounded her.

. " Here, my poor boy, are the *Confessions* of Rousseau; I suppose you have never read them. For my part, I have been familiar with their pages for years; this rose-colored levant is merely a new dress for an old and adored companion. Here is the *Cecilia* of Signorina Burney, published this same year in London; it will be so much Greek to you. Here is some real Greek; a manuscript copy of the Codex Palatinus, or Anthology of Cephalas; the original is unfortunately locked up in the Vatican library."

" Where could it be safer, or in the company of so many equally holy treasures? " asked Virginio in mild surprise, which turned to actual terror as Rosalba whirled upon him with the silken savagery of a little panther. It was now evident that, whoever her father, her mother must have been Italian.

" Are you a victim of superstition, and dare to enter these sacred shades? " she cried in honest indignation. Her eyes were burning amber, and the crisp tendrils of her hair appeared disturbed and shaken. Virginio trembled; a faint cracking sensation menaced his expanded heart.

" I am a Christian," he contrived to enunciate; he was very pale, and looked more than ever transparent. Rosalba was touched in spite of her convictions.

" Do not be distressed; I am myself a deist," she cried generously. Virginio put his cold hand over his sea-blue eyes; bright glassy tears fell into the air and lay like silver on the yellow linden tassels at Rosalba's feet. " My poor boy, we have all made mistakes," she told him, seriously; she found his emotion curiously disturbing. " Look, I am often very silly myself; I have wasted half my birthday morning in rereading a peculiarly childish novel by Carlo Gozzi. I am ashamed to admit that his fairy-stories have always had an attraction for my mind. Listen; it was this that I found so absorbing, this nonsense." And she proceeded to read the following passage from a shabby little book bound in colored paper, and furnished with a marker of green silk ribbon.

" ' A lady, adorned in the Venetian fashion, with a Florentine
petticoat, and a blue satin vest, apparently fresh from the mercer's,
trimmed with sleeves of the finest lace; she wore rings and bracelets
of the richest gold, and a necklace set with Indian diamonds.' "

10. Poesy Ring

ROSALBA's voice died into quivering silence; she hung her supercilious head, and the contemptuous petals of her lips parted to
sigh. " The *Cecilia* was given me as a special concession to feminine frivolity; it may also serve to improve my English," she murmured with apparent irrelevance. " It is a delightful book, I am
sure. And next year I am to have the *Encyclopédie*, if I am diligent.
Has not my dear Jean-Jacques a beautiful new dress, the exact
shade, would you say, of a pink geranium? "

Virginio's shining flaxen brows stirred faintly to a frown.

" Would you not prefer a beautiful new dress for the adornment
of your own divine beauty? " he inquired with respectful interest.
" I do not think a geranium-pink coat particularly suitable to the
charms of Monsieur Rousseau."

" Oh, but I would rather have yellow," cried Rosalba, in spite of
herself — " pale yellow like a frosted leaf, or rosier, like the sunny
side of peaches."

She stopped, sincerely sorry she had not been inventing pretty
images for a poem about philosophy or the ringlets of a child.
Shame tinted her cheek more delicately than imagination can contrive to color it. Virginio's veins were molten with love and pity.

As a matter of stern, immutable fact, Rosalba was hardly a fit
object for pity, although love enveloped her in a natural shower
like sunlight. In the Venice of her time, and indeed throughout
the whole of Arcadian Italy, she had from her precocious childhood
been petted as a tenth and darling Muse; flattery had been her
painted rattle, and early fame her skipping-rope. Yet since no visible
laurel had enwreathed her hair, and since her dress was somber with
decorum, Virginio saw not Sappho, but Cinderella.

A blush suffused Virginio's face; the blood showed clearly, like
wine that stains a pearly glass. From his hand he drew the curious

ring which the Chevalier de Langeist had given him. It was a large
crystal set over white satin; the band was gold, engraved with an
English motto.

"Will you accept this trifling gift upon the fortunate occasion
of your natal day?" he asked, with a graceful inclination of his
luminous head.

"Yes, and most gratefully," Rosalba replied, with a smile of simple pleasure. "This is precisely what I have longed to possess; this
must, I think, be an Indian diamond."

"Nearly, but not quite," Virginio admitted. "However, it is,
as you see, very singular and charming; that is magic written on
the gold. The words are possibly in cabalistic Hebrew; I know
at least that they are secret and in the highest degree potent for
conjuration."

"That is not Hebrew; that is English, I believe," said Rosalba,
pondering the inscription. "It says — but this is extraordinary — it
says: 'Fear God and love me.' The sentiment is elevated, and the
language extremely choice; the whole forms an appropriate motto
for a deist."

"The first words, yes; these are intended for the deist," explained Virginio, who did not have the slightest conception of the
meaning of this mysterious term. "The rest — that enchanting
phrase, if I may be permitted to repeat it, that legend: 'Love me,'
this is addressed to the woman, the goddess, the eternal, unattain-
able Diana. Accept the prayer; put on the ring, O loveliest." He
affixed the bauble, with a kiss, upon her middle finger, where it
hung a little loose; it had fitted his own slender ring finger to
perfection.

"I shall give you a guard," he said, "a guard of Indian diamonds." Rosalba laughed for joy.

"Touching the comparatively unimportant matter of my presence here today," Virginio continued suavely, retaining, with an air
of negligence, Rosalba's hand within his own, "I must explain that
I bear a letter to the noble Angelo Querini; it is upon the part of
my revered uncle and benefactor, Cardinal Bon. These two were
comrades in their season of tender youth; their hearts preserve the
innocence of that vanished aureate age. My uncle desires to intrust

me to the occasional kindness of his friend; he hopes I may be now and then allowed to visit Querini in his hallowed seclusion. I require, it seems, a certain amount of rustic air; my constitution is unfortunately fragile." Virginio did his charming best to appear pathetic, and succeeded admirably in the attempt; against the light his lifted hand moved in a crystalline transparency.

Rosalba frowned at the name of Cardinal, but Virginio had already learned to prefer a frown to a smile in such an instance; as a cardinal's nephew he was accustomed to many and repellent smiles upon inimical lips. He was rather grateful to the girl for her look of gravity; it was his profoundest wish to be taken seriously, and persons of both sexes were but too apt, in his brief experience, to credit him with a mental lightness commensurate with his physical mold.

"Why are you not in Rome?" Rosalba questioned somewhat accusingly. Her manner revealed fastidious distaste, and Virginio was deeply grieved by her intolerance.

"I am too ignorant as yet for Roman society," he said quietly. "My uncle has arranged for my education at the Academy of Nobles in Venice. The age of admission is only eleven, but I am very simple-minded, and, besides, nobody can be certain of my exact years. I have, for my own part, a strong conviction that I am not less than nineteen and not more than twenty."

"I should say you were tall for nineteen and remarkably silly for twenty," Rosalba answered cruelly. Then, as he stood silent and very pale, she put out her hand again and touched his fingers in impulsive pity. Her hand was warm and vibrating with life; Virginio's hand was cold and thin, and as she clasped it, an ominous cracking startled her with strangeness; she felt as if his fingers were so many brittle icicles.

"Be careful, signorina; you may injure yourself," said Virginio, sadly, examining his hands with the minutest care.

Rosalba looked at her own palm, where a tiny scratch showed scarlet; she could have sworn that a splinter of glass still clung there. Suddenly she was afraid; she stared at the boy in an enchantment of horror. The sun shrank up into a savage polar star, and the heavens were another color than blue. The trees had tongues, and when she shut her eyes, she could hear the shuffle of their heavy feet upon the protesting grass; its blades were presently to be reborn as serpents.

Then two bright glassy tears, volatile as quicksilver, fell shining through the disfigured day, and as they splashed upon Rosalba's little breast, she drew Virginio beyond her fear and comforted him in the security of innocence.

So, with the utmost simplicity, Rosalba Berni was constrained to fear God and love Virginio all in the space of five seconds, yet this thing, so quickly done, was not to be undone within the memory of that generation, and when the dark and the flaxen head were frost and silver, the event remained unchanged.

11. Calmon the Philosopher

"I TRUST that the noble Angelo Querini will approve our engagement," said Virginio in a tone of practical good sense, after a brief and iridescent cloud of unreality had enveloped them for a time in silence, whose mist dispersed too soon. "I think we should hasten to make known to him the history of the past fifteen minutes; he has been as a father to your girlhood, and he should be told of our betrothal without delay."

"H'm," and "M-yes," replied Rosalba, doubtfully; she was not certain that she wished to be betrothed; still less did she desire to acquaint her noble guardian with a fact so subject to the alterations of fancy. "Oh — shall we?" she inquired with a notable lack of enthusiasm.

"It is our duty." Such was Virginio's obdurate opinion; Rosalba accepted it, to her own surprise and considerable indignation. Dimly, as an inauspicious providence perceived through wizard crystal, she began to be aware that her lover was incapable of bending, however cruelly a clumsy world might break the refinement of his substance. In a prophetic flash she realized that she must henceforward and always, as the ancient Venetian proverb has it, handle him with white suède gauntlets steeped in rosewater.

Gentle and grave, and by her footfall half reluctant, she passed from the sumptuous autumnal sunlight of the garden into the chilly corridors of Querini's country house; the floors were paved in lozenges of gray and yellow marble, and upon the walls a long procession was frozen in magical decay, which had once issued like a rainbow from the fresh and glittering palette of Carpaccio.

At her side Virginio stepped delicately and very proudly, in shining contrast to her austere black silk and bloodless lawn; he wore his white satin coat with silver spangles, and the lace upon his shirt might almost have purchased Constantinople from the Ottoman princes.

To Angelo Querini, in his pillared library, frescoed in faintly gilded russet and religious blue, and presided over by a bronze bust of Lord Verulam, the boy was an apparition from the fabulous other side of the moon.

This impression was the more amazing in that Angelo Querini believed in neither apparitions nor fables save as the results of an imperfect digestion and an inferior intellect. His was a mind so purely rational that it had long since demanded and received absolute divorce from his naturally impetuous heart, which was thereby set at liberty to be as affectionate and foolish as it pleased without disturbing in the slightest degree Querini's mental conviction as to the profound selfishness of all human action. In this way his head was enabled to breathe the invigorating airs of philosophic disgust, while his heart enjoyed to the full a lifelong orgy of benevolence; Minerva might have sprung from his reasonable brow, but the daughter of his breast was Charity.

Therefore it was a foregone conclusion that the liberal cynic would overlook the irregularity of Virginio's birth, and the kind old man receive him as a son. Rosalba, until this moment free as a humming-bird nourished at the Muses' hands, felt the meshes of a sudden net envelop her in its invisible gossamer. Being herself a philosopher, she reflected sagely that the disquieting fact of her capture being now quietly accomplished, there was no further wisdom in revolt. Besides, in her innermost soul she no longer desired a freedom vacuous of Virginio, and as she took her guardian's congratulatory kiss, she succumbed for the first time in her life to the warm, delightful luxury of complete unreason.

In this delicious mental condition, she listened ravished to Virginio's account of his supernatural origin; neither the boy's simple confession nor Querini's kindly satirical smiles disturbed her in the slightest degree. Personally, and counter to every conviction which had so far upheld her brilliant intellect, she was inclined to credit her lover; but the whole question appeared to her of trifling importance compared with the exquisite grace wherewith Virginio expounded it, and she cared very little whether he had emerged from an Arabian orange or flown to earth upon the wings of the celebrated Green Bird, so long as he had come to her at last.

" This is a romance worthy of the invention of your friend the Count," said Querini, answering her thought. He was benignant, he was even tender, but Rosalba recognized the skeptical amusement in his eyes. She blushed, then blushed again more vividly, ashamed of blushing.

" The Count must be right, after all; this story, of whose accuracy I can entertain no doubt, must prove him right," she said firmly, opening her own eyes very wide in a glance of calm and arrogant assurance. No longer need she conceal her predilection for fairy-tales, nor fear to admit that her favorite author was, after all, not Monsieur Jean-Jacques Rousseau, but Count Carlo Gozzi. Magic was justified by experiment; it was become a verity, true, rational, and possible, like mathematics or the rights of man.

It is regrettable to be obliged to confess that the noble Angelo Querini did not share Rosalba's belief in Virginio's narrative; he felt quite certain that the handsome youth was the blue-eyed flower of Peter Innocent's wild oats. It is to the credit of his heart, however, that he viewed the supposed offspring of the Cardinal's folly with the most solicitous compassion and respect. His mind emitted a private spark of laughter, reflected in his eyes, perhaps, but admirably absent from his grave and courteous lips.

" Curious, curious indeed," he ruminated gently, while joining their hands with a logical deistic blessing. " These little ones are the children of superstition and vice, yet how powerless has been the error of their parents to infect their intrinsic loveliness! Oh, nature, virtue, reason, and Voltaire! Oh, excellent Helvétius! Philanthropically bestow upon these infants a ray of your own illumination! May their bodies remain pagan, their minds emancipated, and their moral qualities incorruptibly pure! " In his excitement he had

almost pronounced "Amen," but caught himself in time to substitute a sentiment from the *Republic* of Plato.

12. Uncles and Sons

AT this very moment, by one of those pleasing coincidences more
common in romantic fiction than among the ineptitudes of mortal
life, the Cardinal Peter Innocent Bon, Count Carlo Gozzi, and the
Chevalier de Langeist sat together within a turret chamber of the
haunted palace of Saint Canziano; upon the countenance of each
gentleman there brooded an expression of thoughtful melancholy.
The lofty room, open to the four great azure winds of heaven, was
festooned with cobwebs and dustily strewn with the Count's famous collection of Arabian and Neapolitan fairy-tales. These volumes, in many instances richly bound in ancient levantine leathers,
were fallen into a state of sad decay, repeated in the person of their
owner, who had worn the same wig for twenty years, and whose
silver shoe-buckles were broken. The door drooped upon its hinges,
the window-panes were starred and splintered, and from the carven
ceiling enormous spiders dangled mockingly above the absorbed
faces of the three friends.

It can occasion no undue surprise to learn that Peter Innocent
and Carlo Gozzi had been comrades since boyhood; the saintly and
fastidious prelate and the aristocratic dreamer were spiritual kinsmen from their hereditary cradles. It is not generally known to history, however, that the patrician Gozzi and the adventurer Chastelneuf had even the slightest acquaintance with each other, and indeed it was the invariable care of both to conceal the circumstance;
nevertheless, a sincere affection existed between them. It is possible
that this mutual esteem was the result of a certain pamphlet, lam-
pooning the Abbé Chiari, of which the Chevalier was the reputed
author. Such rumors had cost him dear in the opinion of the Council; they had, perhaps, rewarded him with the singular friendship of
Carlo Gozzi.

Chastelneuf was splendidly attired in ashen-gray velvet; a silver-
laced hat, a furred traveling-cloak, and a small white mask were
flung upon a lamed and tattered chair at his elbow. Peter Innocent
wore his severest habit; the slight disorder of its austerity suggested

another journey, less luxurious than the Chevalier's. Gozzi had
wrapped his emaciated form in a ragged dressing-gown, apparently
constructed from a bit of tapestry, in which the loves of Leda and
her swan had been decently terminated by the sempstress; a virtuous pair of shears had shortened the fable with the garment, and
left both the Count and Leda colder for their loss. Two senatorial
portraits by Titian and Tintoretto ignored the goblin chamber and
its occupants with respective airs of proud detachment and opulent
contempt.

" I had hardly expected to find my worthy — ahem — my interesting friend Monsieur de Chastelneuf a member of our little company, Carlo," said Peter Innocent, timidly. He disliked very much
the prospect of hurting anyone's feelings, but he had come all the
way from Rome on purpose to consult with the Count upon matters of secrecy and importance; the Chevalier's presence was a glittering blow to privacy, while his suave voice delicately divided
silence, as one cuts a precious fruit. The Cardinal, very kindly,
wished him in Vienna.

Chastelneuf glanced at the Count with smiling eyes beneath
lifted brows; the latter answered the unspoken question at once.

" My dear Peter," he cried rather impatiently, " do you suppose
the Chevalier has traveled post from the Austrian frontier, and that
at the gravest danger to his personal fortunes, for no better reason
than to interrupt our consultation? On the contrary, it is he who
shall resolve our difficulties; he has an excellent plan, and one
which cannot fail to meet with your approval. But first let me ask
you: did you furnish this vitreous young relative of yours with
letters of introduction to Angelo Querini? "

" I did, without doubt," the Cardinal assured him plaintively,
" and at the cost, moreover, of several severe pangs of conscience.
Querini is an estimable person in many respects, and my brother
Nicholas was devoted to him. I cannot forget, however, that the
man is an unbeliever and a Voltairian; he has insulted holy Church
upon various pretexts; he is a mocker and, I am afraid, a confirmed
philosopher."

" ' Mock on, mock on, Voltaire, Rousseau! ' " muttered Carlo,
who had seen the poem in manuscript among the papers of an
eccentric English scholar of his acquaintance. " ' And the wind

blows it back again! ' Where it listeth; true, very true. A detestable person, Querini; he cultivates plaster busts in his garden, which have devoured all the elves. But Chastelneuf says he has a pretty niece, a nymph by no means plaster."

The Chevalier permitted himself to smile slightly in replying.

" Not a niece, my dear Count; a ward is surely another matter."

" Why? " demanded Peter Innocent with unwonted asperity; as an uncle, he resented the implied sneer without understanding it.

" Ah, Eminence, spare my blushes upon such a question! " Chastelneuf cried gayly; an impudent and evasive laugh puzzled the Cardinal by its refined ribaldry.

" Do not quarrel, gentlemen," protested Gozzi, who was deriving a wicked satisfaction from this curious encounter between the powers of light and semi-darkness as represented by his friends. " We are all met today in order to discuss the future of two ingenuous young creatures in whom I, for my part, take the warmest and most fatherly interest."

" Two young creatures? " The Cardinal looked pale with alarm. " Did I understand you to say two, my dear Carlo? Virginio has never been, so far as I know, anything in the least like twins."

" There is no question of twins, save in so far as the sweet affinity of lovers may simulate the natal bond," began Carlo Gozzi, but the Chevalier interrupted him with something less than his customary politeness.

" Of course there can be no question of twins as yet," he said in a low, shocked voice, turning upon the Cardinal a face congealed into dignified horror. " We are barely arrived at the point of arranging a match between Virginio and the niece of Cardinal de Bernis, and already your Eminence is talking of twins. The thought is perhaps a little indelicate, although we may all indulge such hopes in the intimacy of our devotions. But as to the match, is it not exquisitely suitable, and can you possibly withhold your approval when I explain — "

" Marriage! Virginio married! " exclaimed Peter Innocent, wildly; and " Bernis! The niece of Cardinal de Bernis! " cried Carlo Gozzi with an almost comparable accession of surprise. " I thought he was going to study the Greek dramatists! " added the one, while the other ended: " And I, that she was the ward of Angelo Querini! "

13. Spiritual Fathers

"You were both quite correct in your conclusions," the Chevalier reassured them.

"The divining crystal upon my watch-chain informs me that Virginio has this moment opened a folio of Sophocles, while the noble Querini is giving the best possible proof of his benevolent guardianship by conferring a double blessing and a modest competence upon the betrothed pair; his notary has but just entered the room; I believe he is about to draw up a new will. It is all very charming and idyllic, and I congratulate your Eminence most heartily upon a felicitous solution of your problems." He bowed, nor could the Cardinal detect a look or gesture indicative of aught save urbanity and good humor.

"My problems were, after all, very simple, and you should not have come all the way from Vienna to solve them, Chevalier." Peter Innocent hoped he was not speaking too haughtily to this adventurous person; Carlo Gozzi healed whatever breach the gentle voice had made by laughing cynically and wiping his eyes upon a large bandanna handkerchief. It was impossible to say whether he was merry or sad.

"It was all my fault, Peter, my dear," said Carlo Gozzi. "I have been melancholy of late; I miss my poor Truffaldino and his company of masks. In parting, we embraced, weeping bitterly. I had not wept since that mischievous lunar moth, Teresa Ricci, flew away to the moon where she belonged, but now I cannot stay my tears. In vain have I attempted to be philosophical, which is merely to say heartless; my hopes have perished with the venerable comedy of Venice, which I must soon follow to undeserved oblivion. Meanwhile my one comfort has been the society of your delightful nephew; in him I have renewed my youth and experienced afresh the enchantment of fairy-tales and the ravishing pleasure of the impossible. I visited him in the somber Academy of Nobles. In his black uniform, enveloped in a bright blue cloak, he was precisely like one of the disinherited princes of my own fancy; I loved him, and I longed to see him happy."

"I know you have been goodness itself to the boy, my Carlo; he wrote me of lessons in Arabic and antique Spanish. He cannot have been lonely in your edifying society, and now with these new excitements and adventures in the classics into which Querini is about to introduce him, his days will be overflowing with aureate dreams indeed. What more can the lad desire? "

" Don't you understand, Eminence? " asked the Chevalier. He gazed sternly at the Cardinal, while true and generous indignation kindled within his smoldering golden eyes. His sinewy brown hand had sought and found his sword-hilt before it fell, still clenched, in recognition of Peter Innocent's silvered and benignant locks. " I beg your Eminence's pardon if I appear impetuous, but the boy, the poor boy, is, after all, very nearly human."

" Oh, I trust he is not merely human," interposed Gozzi. " There has been some talk of elementals, and I have always longed to meet an elemental. Virginio, with his translucent flesh, like flame made frost — Virginio is happily something better than human, or so I have believed."

" And is there something better on this inferior side of heaven? " Chastelneuf spoke with passion, and yet there was a perilous tenderness in his falcon look.

" We are all of us God's children, and fashioned in His image; we are moved by a breath of His divinity," said the Cardinal, softly and somewhat fearfully; but Carlo Gozzi was not satisfied.

" Did you or did you not, Monsieur de Chastelneuf, assure me, upon your honor as a gentleman, of this youth's supernatural origin? " he demanded hotly. " I have loved him like a son, because I conceived him to be magic incarnate; am I to learn now that he is a common mortal like myself, and perhaps of baser clay? " He stared significantly at the Chevalier, and his words were a challenge.

" Oh, no! Oh, no! " said Chastelneuf, wearily. " Calm yourself, my dear Count; your suspicions are unfortunately unfounded. The boy is all that you could wish him to be; he is an exquisite monster, a celestial prodigy, blown from the very air itself, and captured in an earthy net so fragile that its meshes could not withstand the violence of a mortal soul. I do not know to a certainty what spirit informs this mutable fabric; whether it be a creature of the elder world, nourished in the heart of a sapling or fallen from between the breasts of a cloud; only I think it lacks the roughness and the

pitifulness of humanity. Be content, both of you; the Cardinal
may have his angel, and the Count his elfin prince; Virginio will
never disappoint you. I have given him a ring; the same was given
me in my youth by a beloved friend, and its influence is infallibly
benign. If it should chance to light a little fire in that hollow heart
and set true tears burning in those glassy eyes, such marvels are not
harmful, but salutary and kind. I, too, have felt for Virginio an
affection fatherly and apprehensive; I have come from Vienna for
the express purpose of promoting his happiness, and it is my
prayer — yes, my profoundest supplication to my Maker — that
this happiness is about to be consummated."

He fell silent; to Gozzi, who knew him well, it was an amazement to perceive a veritable moisture dimming the vehement color
of his eyes.

Peter Innocent was moved; his countenance, placid and humane
as a sacred effigy, was turned toward the Chevalier in lenient concern, as Chastelneuf sat down and covered his face with his hand,
shaken by some curious fit of ardor or revolt.

"I will consent to any plan, within reason, which can promote
my nephew's ultimate happiness," said Peter Innocent, gravely.

Chastelneuf still bit his lip in tormented silence, but Gozzi burst
forth into voluble rejoicing as he wrung the Cardinal's hand with
warmth.

"Oh, good! Very good indeed! This is the best news I have heard
in a twelvemonth. Peter, I knew I could rely upon your merciful
heart when you were made to realize the boy's loneliness and isolation; Chevalier, my compliments to your invariable sagacity. Oh, it
will be an extremely charming little romance, a fairy-tale come true,
not desiccated and compressed within the pages of a book, but alive
and kicking its scarlet heels, as the ancient Bergamesque proverb
puts it. And the lad is actually a fantasy in Murano glass instead
of vulgar flesh and blood! I myself could not have invented a
prettier conceit, or one more gracefully in accordance with the best
magical traditions."

Peter Innocent observed this enthusiasm with indulgence, but
a natural anxiety led him to seek further enlightenment from his
friend.

"And who, pray, is the young lady whom I am about to embrace as the bride of Virginio and, consequently, my own child? If I am not mistaken, the Chevalier described her as a niece of Monseigneur de Bernis."

"Oh, niece if you like; that title does as well as another," said Chastelneuf, with recovered sprightliness. "And, indeed, I honor your scruples; nothing is more lamentable than lascivious gossip and scandalmongering. But in this case it can do no harm to admit what your Eminence, as a man of the world, must already have suspected, in view of a certain prelate's profane reputation; the fact, in fine, and to make a long story short, that this lovely girl is a daughter of Cardinal de Bernis and — "

"But must you make it short, Chevalier?" interrupted Gozzi. He made no effort to conceal his eagerness, and his wintry eyes were bright with anticipation. "Your stories are always so entertaining, and never too good to be true; I am sure that Peter will join me in urging you to continue at your leisure with the recital of this mysterious amour. Eh, Peter, my boy, are you with me?"

14. Nuns and Lovers

PETER INNOCENT, whose eyes were blue as veronica flowers, and whose inmost soul was as a silver reliquary of chaste design, felt somewhat at a loss to conjecture whether or no he was, precisely, with Carlo Gozzi at the immediate moment. A doubt, insidious and sinister, as to the exact nature of the company filtered between the argent filigree of his reflections; he smelled brimstone as the Count opened his tortoise-shell snuff-box, and observed with relief the normal outline of the Chevalier's elegantly buckled shoes. When he replied, his speech was tempered by unaccustomed caution.

"Carlo, I cannot quite say that I am with you, but I hope I shall never be very far from such an old and trusted friend; no difference can sever us that may not be bridged by a clasp of the hand. Only I wonder a little. Is it, was it, entirely suitable for Cardinal de Bernis to have a daughter?"

Gozzi appeared slightly embarrassed, but Chastelneuf assumed the responsibility of answering without a trace of hesitation.

"Monseigneur, I feel sure your fears will be set at rest when I explain this affair; its complete suitability is perhaps its chief charm to a refined mind. The Cardinal de Bernis was possibly, in his youth, faintly inclined towards profligacy; he was brilliant and well bred, but flippant and occasionally unwise. Some of the ladies upon whom he bestowed his butterfly favors shared his weakness; one alone of all that rainbow number remained modest and virginal even under the intoxication of love. I knew her; it might have been my privilege to preserve her delicate illusions from maculation at the hands of beasts. She was unwavering in her faith, which, most unhappily for her, was pinned not upon the bosom of her God, but starrily, like a bright religious order, over the shifting heart of François-Joachim de Bernis."

"Proceed," said Gozzi. "This begins to be amusing."

"The tale is not truly amusing," said Chastelneuf, meditatively. "It is sad, I am afraid, and its only happy ending is Rosalba, who is herself not an end, but a beginning. For the French Ambassador at Rome it is very sad; for a little Venetian widow it was, perhaps, sadder. I will tell it to you, if you like, but I cannot promise to make you laugh except at the ridiculous spectacle of my own tears."

"Go on, my friend," replied the inscrutable Gozzi. Peter Innocent was silent, but from an inner pocket he drew a fine cambric handkerchief, sweet with lavender.

"I am the villain of this piece, Eminence," the Chevalier continued with a sort of melancholy pride. "When I have finished, you will find it impossible to condemn Bernis; your feelings towards the innocuous partner of his unwisdom can be no harsher than regret softened by commiseration. Ah, Caterina, if I had never led you into that select conclave of libertines, you might even now be a happy wife and mother, and I, content and honored, the father of a lovelier creature than either Virginio or Rosalba! I may say without vanity," he added, "that in my youth I was not ill favored."

"Proceed! Proceed!" cried Gozzi, impatiently. "You were always as black as a Moor; Time has spilt no milk and roses from your leather cheek, over which you should waste your tears. Be good enough to stop crying, Jacques; tell your story."

"It is now nearly thirty years since I first saw Caterina," Chastelneuf went on. "She was but fourteen years old, and her little

face had all the blameless brilliance of a child's. I loved her, but
with a levity and cynicism incomprehensible to my maturer perceptions. I seduced her, but tenderly, for I had determined to make
her mine legally and for life. We spent hours in the gardens at
Saint-Blaise, where we ran races together; the prize, which I permitted her to win, was a pair of blue garters. I was captivated; her
candor, her ingenuousness, her vivacity, all contrived to make me
her slave, for the union of beauty, intelligence, and innocence has
ever swayed me.

"A parent, perhaps no crueler than her lover, but certainly for
the moment more severe, immured Caterina within a convent at
Murano; we were unable to meet, and had only the chilly comfort
of smuggled letters and the ambiguous tremors of hope as sus-
tenance for our reciprocal dreams. I gave her my portrait, commis-
sioning a young Piedmontese to render it in the smallest miniature;
he painted an exquisite St. Catherine of the same dimensions, and
a clever Venetian jeweler mounted them both in a ring. The
patron saint concealed my countenance, but the expert craftsman
had provided the fantastic setting with a hidden spring, and I fear
that my pictured eyes often disturbed the devout eyelids of poor
Caterina by hot and secular tears.

"This comedy continued for several months; I grew very thin
and mournful, and lived miracles of faithfulness in the mere denial of my natural instincts. At last I made bold to enter the convent chapel; one of the novices was about to take the veil, and I
knew I might pass unobserved among the crowd of visitors.

"After the investiture I walked into the convent parlor with
the other pious spectators, and standing within four paces of my
poor little love, I perceived her gazing at me in a species of ecstasy;
happiness made wide her hazel eyes and parted her lips to suspire
tenderness.

"Alas! I had no sooner conferred the fleeting joy of my smile
upon this unfortunate child than I robbed her again, and forever;
my heart, always elastic, rebounded from the small and shrinking
form of Caterina, to fall with terrific violence at the feet of a tall
nun beneath whose cool reserve a secret fire was visible, even as
her coif disclosed an unlicensed curl of red-gold hair above a face
fair to pallor and lovely to delirium. I was completely overcome;

my head swam among singing clouds, and I should assuredly have
fainted had not a kindly old lay sister led me into the sharp sea
winds of the conventual garden.

"If ever I write my memoirs, which I shall refuse to call confessions, since that infamous rascal Rousseau has profaned the title,
I may describe at leisured length the course of my infatuation
for the nun, Mary Magdalen, and its legendary end; I may aspire
to draw her portrait, more intimately even than my young Piedmontese drew it for me, naked upon a couch of black satin, demure
and shameless behind an ivory medallion of the Annunciation fitted
into the lid of a gold snuff-box.

"This refulgent lady was the friend of the Abbé de Bernis; she
had taken the veil out of pure caprice, and had the discretion to
conceal any unhappiness she may have felt. Her illustrious birth
and her extravagant liberality procured innumerable privileges denied to the other nuns; the tale of her amorous adventures must
not insult the laudable ears of your Eminence. Suffice it to say
that she and I between us plotted to debauch the peaceable simplicity of poor Caterina; I gave my darling to the power of the dog,
and in a room of mirrors, lighted by girandoles and candelabra of
rock crystal and gilded bronze, Bernis took the child in his arms
and drank her frightened tears with feverish avidity. I retired, laughing, to sup with Mary Magdalen in the adjoining chamber; the nun
was disguised as a handsome youth in rose-colored velvet and black
satin, and we devoured oysters and truffles from silver chafing-
dishes and fine Dresden china. The wines were burgundy and
champagne; I remember that I was excessively thirsty. I was mixing
a salad of anchovies and hard-boiled eggs when the door opened
and Bernis entered, followed by Caterina.

"Bernis was a man of forty; to my intolerant eye he was already
a little worn, a little thin; his good looks were faintly tainted by
effeminacy. He was invariably dressed in the extreme of elegance;
the beauty of his hands was proverbial.

"Now, with an air of the most polished courtesy, he offered
one of these miraculous hands to Caterina; he bowed, and I saw
nobility rise to his forehead, shaking back the perfumed flippancy
of his thoughts as a lion shakes back his mane. So I knew that
although I had abandoned my darling to the lion, the power of the

dog was dead. I am ashamed to admit that I was furiously jealous of Bernis.

"I cannot tell you the truth of this matter because I have never known it. What I conceive to be the truth seemed inconceivable at that confounding moment; the room, with its vain and equivocal elegance, its exquisite depravity, its engravings by Meunius and Toletana, the lovely epicene figure of the nun, the perverse integrity of the Ambassador's bearing, all conspired to render the scene incredible. Caterina, attired in a childish gown of green gauze, was composed and smiling; she looked up at Bernis, and her gaze was limpid with faith. I was very angry; knowing a portion of my loss, I raged inwardly, and longed to kill the two; the deeper significance of their mutual glances was hidden from my eyes by a curtain of blood."

15. Came Forth Sweetness

PETER INNOCENT had covered his face with the lavender-scented handkerchief, but Gozzi remained satirical and unmoved. The Chevalier brushed the back of his hand across his shining and dilated eyes, as if to dissipate the remembered darkness of crimson. He continued to speak in a measured and deliberate voice:

"I did not see Caterina again; she returned to the convent at Murano, and within the year her parents had married her to an honest Venetian lawyer, who adored and tormented her youth with an intolerable devotion. Bernis, as you know, was soon afterwards recalled to France; the nun Mary Magdalen and I were left to console each other with meditations upon infidelity. Our natures were but too similar; each libertine despised the other, and we parted without regret or charitable illusion, without prejudice, and without compassion for each other's spirits, subdued to such resemblance by the unloving flesh."

"Peter, if you can make, as the peasants say at Chioggia, either dragon's head or mermaid's tail of this unholy rigmarole, you are a cleverer man than I, and that I should be sorry to believe!" exclaimed Gozzi in exasperation, as the Chevalier's recital drew to an apparent close on a note of profound repentance.

Peter Innocent raised his seraphic and bewildered eyes, enlarged by tears too scorching to be cooled by a cambric handkerchief; he did not look at Gozzi or at Chastelneuf, but straight into the sky, a deep, blue pool reversed, suspended, spreading like a tree, like a shade, like the shadow of a sapphire rock.

" I can make neither head nor tail of this tragedy, Carlo," he answered, " yet, for my comfort, the Chevalier has made me believe it has a heart, and that not chimærical or devilish, but vulnerably human. I cannot understand, and yet, beneath the covert and obscure, I can feel the beating of a heart."

" You are a cleverer man than I, Peter," said Carlo Gozzi, who believed in elves. He said it in humility, for sometimes he believed in angels.

" You are right, Eminence; it is the heart of poor mortality which beats in my story, and echoes in your ears; the sound is the sum of human hearts which still vibrate in unison because, though broken, they have mended each other with love."

Chastelneuf spoke solemnly, but Gozzi questioned him with a quizzical scorn.

" Do you say love, O melancholy Jacques? "

" I say it," replied the Chevalier; the habitual visor of insolence masked his face upon the word. " To clarify the matter further for your Eminence's comprehension," he went on, in a light and cursive voice, " I must remind you that Bernis had no sooner become a power in France than he had the unfortunate honor of incurring the enmity of the royal favorite. He had the temerity to suggest that the Prince de Soubise was not a fit person to command the King's armies; the Pompadour was majestically offended, and when the Pope presented Bernis with a cardinal's hat, Louis bestowed it upon him with his own hands and forthwith exiled him to Soissons, where he remained for six years, a broken and embittered man."

" Lorenzo Ganganelli loved that man," said Peter Innocent.

" I know he did, and therefore his successor hates him, Eminence; when you return to Rome, you may do a kindness to a dying lion."

" Chevalier, I think you are wrong; I am very old, and I should only weary the Cardinal de Bernis," Peter Innocent replied modestly.

" Your nephew's sweetheart will not weary him," Chastelneuf

cried with a curiously happy laugh. "Wait; do not believe me a madman. I have more riddles to elucidate if you can spare me the patience."

"I have a fabulous appetite for old wives' tales," Gozzi admitted rudely, and Peter Innocent was quiet and kind in his silence.

"Good," said the Chevalier. "We were at Soissons, were we not? At Soissons in a cold December, with a northeast wind and seventy miles dividing it from the classic gayety of Versailles. Here, among Gothic churches and darker mediæval memories of Saint Crispin the Shoemaker and Louis the Pious, here where Becket prayed and Abélard despaired, Bernis came alone and sorrowful, having put his trust in princes, and served his country better than his King's mistress.

"Imagine, if you are something kindlier than stone, the desolation of that Christmas season, when in Soissons the Gothic roses of Notre Dame were carved in snow, and the Cardinal de Bernis sat alone in his vast apartment. He had caused no fire to be lighted, no supper to be laid, and when the chimes, like stars made audible, began to pierce the midnight with rejoicing, he stopped his ears against their voices and wept the burning tears of Lucifer fallen from heaven.

"At that moment, out of the darkness, upon the wings of the bells as it were, and feathered with snow like a little bird, Caterina came to him."

"Thank God!" said Carlo Gozzi, fervently. Peter Innocent said nothing.

"She folded him in her gray cloak, that was all feathered and furred with the snow, and she kissed his beautiful cold hands. It was the first kiss she had ever given him; she gave it to the lion who had delivered her from the power of the dog, at Venice, in the room of mirrors, on an evening of full carnival, when she was only fourteen years old."

"I am glad she came," said Carlo Gozzi, adding, after he had cleared his throat, "I suppose, then, that we are to understand that Rosalba Berni is the offspring of this interesting union!"

"Yes, you are to understand precisely that, my dear Count; I fear you are incapable of fully appreciating the poignancy of the

situation, but the bare facts you are at liberty to understand,"
answered the Chevalier with impudent urbanity. He finished the
tale, turning his blazing eyes towards Peter Innocent, who continued to say nothing.

"When Caterina came to Soissons on Christmas Eve, she was
seventeen years old and a widow. At the time Bernis was past
forty, and tired by the vanities of a Dead Sea dream, an ashy-
flavored world. Six years later, when Rosalba was born in the
South, her father could laugh very lightly as he sprinkled her
with almond blossoms and peach blossoms and cherry blossoms
or tickled her lips with a pigeon's feather. Perhaps he was happy
because he had been recalled to court, where he had magnificently
rejected the seals of office; perhaps he was happy because he was
Archbishop of Albi. Perhaps, on the other hand, he was happy
because of Rosalba, who had been born in happiness in the South,
in a farmhouse whose outer walls were covered with espaliered
peach trees, and whose windows were fringed with climbing roses.
Upon the day of her birth a golden peach knocked at the door
and a white rose flew into the window. Bernis ate the peach and
gave the rose to Caterina. To the child they gave the name Rosalba.

"At Albi, the Archbishop's palace is a fortified castle of the
Middle Ages, and perhaps it is not strange that Bernis loved better
the farmhouse with the espaliered fruit-trees. Here for five years
a golden age endured; a little world existed for a time, round and
smooth and perfect as a peach. A bitter stone was hidden in its
heart, but before Bernis set his teeth to that his felicity was absolute. Then, in the plenitude of summer, Caterina died.

"Bernis gave every rose in the garden to Caterina; she clasped
them with gentle indifference. In this same manner she accepted
his last kiss; he was glad enough to go to Rome, to assist at the
conclave which elected Lorenzo Ganganelli. He had a chill conviction of her forgetfulness.

"Rosalba was conveyed to Paris in the care of an impoverished
cousin of her father's; this gentlewoman was amiable, but frivolous and injudicious. Having acquired a little wealth through the
generosity of her kinsman Bernis, she repaired to Versailles, taking
the child with her. There, in the midst of that sumptuous, but
effete, civilization, Rosalba was remarked by Madame Necker for

her wit and beauty and selected as a playmate for that lady's precocious little daughter.

"Thus, while yet of tender years, the girl was made free of the best _philosophe_ society; by the time she was twelve she was among the shining ornaments of Madame Necker's Friday receptions; the Mondays of Madame Geoffrin, the Tuesdays of Madame Helvétius, were incomplete without Rosalba's elfin grace. Her cousin desired above all else a fashionable marriage for her protégée, but beneath brocaded petticoats the child's silk stockings, though gossamer and clocked with lace, were already obstinately blue. She refused, by impertinent implication, a round dozen of silver-gilded youths; Versailles was a blown Easter egg, excessively sugared, and she cared only for political reform and the awards of the Académie française."

16. Diversions at Ferney

"INTOLERABLE imp!" exclaimed Count Carlo Gozzi in disgust. "It is this same horror, this unfeminine baggage, this most ungentle lady, whom I have laughed to scorn in all my charming plays! She is the Princess Turandot, who utters riddles in the tone of an academician; she is Barberina, who has read Holbach while Carletti was dressing her hair. I had hardly realized the extent of her folly. However, if you, Chevalier, say she is pretty — and you do say so, do you not?"

"And good? You have assured me of her virtue?" faltered Peter Innocent.

The Chevalier regarded them with skillfully displayed contempt; he elevated his eyebrows the polite fraction of an inch.

"Eminence," he pronounced, "it is even possible, as the French pastry-cooks have it, to put too many perfect ingredients into a pound cake. Enough, they remind us, is better than dyspepsia. Yourself and the Count may live to regret the fact that Rosalba has never had a cold in the head or an illaudable impulse. Such things are, perhaps, disfiguring for the moment, but they humble the spirit of the young. Rosalba is not humble."

"Is she proud?" said Peter Innocent.

"Not in the least, Eminence," Chastelneuf replied. "She is

merely perfect. You may be completely at ease in her company;
she has the simplicity of the truly great."

Carlo Gozzi snorted indignantly, but Peter Innocent perceived
no cause for annoyance. His simplicity excelled Rosalba's.

"And her friendship with Voltaire?" he went on a little nervously in spite of the Chevalier's reassurances. "I have wondered,
do you know, whether that were quite desirable. Of course its results were most fortunate; there can be no doubt that Querini has
sheltered her from every tempered blast. But Voltaire as the intimate companion of a child of twelve — no, I confess the reflection
has troubled me."

"Monseigneur, as I said to Monsieur de Voltaire after reciting
thirty-six stanzas of that divine twenty-third canto of Ariosto, describing the madness of Roland with the most dreadful accuracy, —
when I had finished, I assure you, the philosopher fell upon my
neck, sobbing; tears were in all eyes — but, I repeat, as I said to
him at this affecting moment, you are too satirical, cher maître;
be human, as now, and like Ariosto you will be sublime! Oh, I
remember it very well! Your Eminence is right; there was a vein
of irony in the man which I must be the first to deprecate. And
yet he had intelligence; I think Rosalba was attracted by his intelligence. Then, too, you would not have her guilty of ingratitude,
and he was kind to her."

"He stole her from a convent, did he not?" inquired Gozzi,
who was beginning to be bored by the continued amiability of
his two friends. To his relief, Peter Innocent looked shocked; the
Chevalier remained incurably good-humored.

"Oh, quite!" the imperturbable Chevalier cried. "But such a
convent! Really, I cannot, in your Eminence's presence, attempt to
explain; there were, however, circumstances too distressing to recall. I should hardly go so far as to say he stole her; rescue is the
appropriate word, surely. The affair was shrouded in mystery;
some said she had been immured by her ambitious cousin for refusing to wed a one-eyed marquis; others that she had incurred
the enmity of the Neckers by embracing the free-trade principles
of Turgot. Still another version, and that which I am myself inclined to credit, ascribes her abduction to the machinations of a
rich Englishman, Milord Camphor or Camphile, who, returning

widowed from the East, beheld and desired, within the chilly inspiration of a single breath, Rosalba's loveliness and warm vivacity. It is but natural that the squire of Ferney, who had heard all of these stories in their most exaggerated forms, should have hastened to free this adorable creature from the chains of tyranny and vile superstition."

"And the name of this convent?" asked Peter Innocent, rather apologetically.

"That, Eminence, I am not at liberty to divulge; another time, perhaps. You see," the Chevalier added, "it was the same convent from which Monsieur de Voltaire had previously rescued Philiberte de Varicourt."

"Oho! Belle et Bonne!" exclaimed the Count, who evidently saw. Peter Innocent did not, but his modesty prevented him from demanding an explanation.

"Precisely. And here, very luckily for little Rosalba, our good friend Querini appeared upon the scene. He came to pay his last respects to Voltaire; the fatal journey to Paris had already been discussed; *Irène* was wellnigh completed, and the patriarch experienced, within his venerable breast, a lively and determined longing to visit once more the country of his birth. The noble Angelo Querini found the household at Ferney more or less at sevens, elevens, and thirteens, as the schoolchildren say; Rosalba was crying in the boot-closet under the stairs, and 'Belle et Bonne' was biting her nails in her boudoir. Monsieur de Voltaire and the Marquis de Villette were locked in the study drinking English punch and suffering from profound depression."

"What had occurred to disturb their philosophical serenity?" asked Gozzi, with an air of quiet satisfaction.

"Nothing; nothing at all, save that the Sage of Ferney had committed the trifling indiscretion of addressing Rosalba as 'Plus Belle et Plus Bonne' in the fascinating presence of Philiberte. Our little friend had just completed a very creditable Horatian ode, entitled 'To My Heroic Champion'; this she recited, wearing a neat new frock of dark blue merino, with her hair arranged in becoming ringlets. The result was curious, and, to a man of eighty-four, disturbing. I have sometimes suspected that his decease was hastened — but, no, these ladies' dainty and frangible shoulder-

blades must not be burdened by so deplorable an event as the
death of Voltaire! He perished of a surfeit of coffee and academic
honors."

" Unrepentant," said Carlo Gozzi with intense and pleasurable
conviction.

" Perhaps merely discourteous," said Chastelneuf, kindly.

Peter Innocent said nothing; he was absorbed in silent supplication for the immortal soul of François Arouet de Voltaire. The
Deity's replying silence appeared to him an unconditional consent to his request for leniency. The softened airs and mistier hues
of the Venetian afternoon surrounded this moment with a mild
halo of salvation, and Peter Innocent felt sure that the sage was
forgiven.

Far away, across the melancholy marshes of Altichieri, Virginio
and Rosalba, fantastically cloaked and masked, had seized the
same propitious moment to ascend the steps of the Chevalier's
elegant English carriage. They bore a large portmanteau and a
couple of bandboxes, and the noble Angelo Querini, as he slammed
the emblazoned door upon their smiles and blushes, wished them
Godspeed with all the prayerful emotion of his foolish heart,
while his sagacious brow condemned them for a pair of young
lunatics whirling in spangled frenzy towards a riddle and a doom.

BOOK III: ROSALBA

" But some, and these the elect among gardeners,
will always prefer China Roses."

CHRISTOPHER WARREN

17. Golden Bride

" AND now," murmured Chastelneuf with obvious regret, gazing
dreamily over the housetops, which the descending day had
diapered with a changed and more intricate design of shadow
— " and now, I repeat, my patient friends, there is little left to
tell. You have been indulgent; the hour grows older, and ma-

tures into a time more suited to adventure than to these vague
reminiscences. In a word, Querini adopted Rosalba upon the
spot; he conveyed her to Venice, and encouraged her in the study
of the arts and sciences. Poetry was her natural voice; the Arcadian
Academy received her with acclaim, and forthwith fell down and
kissed the abbreviated hem of her schoolgirl's gown. The Infant
Sappho was baptized in Castalia, and shaking the fountain drops
from her juvenile curls, she lifted up her throat to sing. The
rest you know; it cannot take me above five minutes to recount
the principal events of Rosalba's Venetian career. You must remember — "

"But is it quite necessary, Chevalier?" Gozzi inquired with
plaintive scorn. "We have all heard too much of the Infant
Sappho; some of us, impelled no doubt by morbid curiosity, have
even read her verses. We recall very vividly and with peculiar
pain the ridiculous festivities which marked her coronation at
Rome, and all the nauseating verbiage, which, with the bad
luxuriance of a weed, has kept her reputation virulently green.
If you desire to converse further about the past, I must beg you
to confine yourself to your own memories; why not favor us with
an account of your escape from the Leads?"

Chastelneuf smiled; he was well aware of the Count's savage
irony, but he turned to Peter Innocent with bland composure.

"If his Eminence wishes; I am always at his disposal."

"I should be charmed — " began the Cardinal; but Gozzi interposed in sincere alarm.

"For God's sake, Peter, do not encourage the rascal; the story
will be an affair of hours, and we have much to accomplish before nightfall. Did you succeed in procuring a suitable gown for
the girl, Jacques? You are accustomed to these matters; you have
seduced several milliners, and your taste is impeccable."

"I have arranged for everything; I have ordered the supper,
and bespoke the best string quartet in the four hospitals. The
casino is in readiness; I have not yet relinquished its key to the
new tenant, and my own servant has seen to it that there are
fresh fires on the hearths, fresh candles in the girandoles, and
fresh white roses in the crystal urns. I considered jasmine, I mused
on lilies of the valley, but I knew I was wrong; there must be

only white roses for this wedding night. Am I not wise, your Eminence? "

Peter Innocent was at a loss to reply; his blue eyes were clouded by fatigue and bewilderment.

" Wedding night? " he faltered, suddenly afraid. " Is it Virginio's wedding night? "

" That is for your Eminence to say," the Chevalier replied with courtly mendacity. " Also, it were only proper to await Virginio's own decision as to this momentous business; having seen Rosalba, I cannot question its affirmative nature. Carlo Gozzi and I have been planning a little surprise for the young people; a fête, *un petit dîner à deux*, quite simple, you comprehend, but complete in every detail. It is Rosalba's birthday; since the noble Angelo Querini adopted her, her garments have been fashioned with a severe disregard of the prevailing mode, and frivolity has been absent from her life. Even at her coronation she was permitted no greater magnificence than a Greek robe of virgin white; the material was velvet, I believe, but the cut was antiquated. The Arcadian Academy has adored her manner of dressing, so chaste, so austere, so truly classical; but Rosalba has been unhappy. ' This was well enough for Ferney,' she has said, ' but for Venice, no! I can be young only once; am I never to have a single little stitch *alla francese*, not even a plain lemon-colored Milordino with cloth-of-silver incisions, or a modest mantle of gold-green camelot lined with Canadian marten? I love my guardian with profound devotion, but I am, after all, a woman, and it is sad not to possess a robe of Holland *poussé*, trimmed with Spanish point! ' Oh, she has wept, your Eminence; she has grieved in secret; we must endeavor to console her. What do you think; are you for flame or peach or girlish primrose? I am convinced it must be yellow. Tell me, do you agree? "

Around the Cardinal's frosty and abstracted head a dozen rainbows seemed revolving in vertiginous arcs: colors of sun, of harvest moon, of comet's tail and hell-fire streamed out upon the increasing violet of dusk and lit all Venice with their fervency. He hesitated, and Gozzi answered for him.

" That is a problem for you and the milliner's apprentice to determine ecstatically between yourselves; it does not concern

Cardinal Bon. Peter, we have indeed hoped that our little festival in honor of these children might result in a wedding; for me there must ever be the happy conclusion to my fairy-tales, and I think tonight's performance will be the ultimate fantasy which I shall prepare for any stage. I do not care for the girl save as the inevitable partner for the prince; it is sufficient that she is pretty and not too intolerable a fool. But for Virginio I desire happiness, and over and above that good measure, a little pleasure running down, like shining bubbles, like golden grains. I had thought, myself, that what with music and dancing and a small quantity of very light wine to enliven them, the babes might frolic until dawn, and then we could all hire a gondola — for mine is at the pawnbroker's — and, proceeding to the Church of St. John and St. Paul, allow Peter to pronounce the blessing of holy Church upon their union. Then, perhaps, another gondola, and an alfresco breakfast upon the sands of the sea or in some rustic grove. What do you say, Peter? "

This time Peter Innocent was at the trembling point of reply, but the Chevalier sent him back into silence by an ejaculation of surprise.

"Good heavens! What an insanity is this, my dear Count! Surely the marriage must take place before supper; it is only right and *convenable* if the young people are to dance together all night. I could never countenance such indiscretion; I am sincerely shocked. ' Frolic until dawn ' indeed! But of course his Eminence will not permit it even for a moment."

"Confound you! " cried Carlo Gozzi. "You know perfectly well, Jacques, that I did not mean — "

"What? " said the Chevalier, demurely.

The Count looked at the Cardinal; then he sighed deeply and returned to its decaying sheath the jeweled Florentine dagger which his hand had for a moment caressed.

"Never mind; nothing. I meant nothing, since Peter Innocent is here; but beware how you annoy me, Chastelneuf."

"Oh, I intended no harm! " the Chevalier assured him gayly. "I am possibly a trifle over-scrupulous about the conventions, but you must contrive to forgive a finical old friend, Carlo. We must all be very kind tonight; as for the marriage, I leave its

hour to the choice of Cardinal Bon, and its subsequent good
fortune to the benevolence of Almighty God." Casting a triumphant glance at Carlo Gozzi, Chastelneuf bowed his head in
double humility to higher powers.

" If Virginio must really be married, I do not think it matters
very much whether I marry him before or after supper," said
Peter Innocent, gently. His delicately chiseled face was worn by
anxiety, but his voice was firm as he continued: " I had hoped,
as Carlo understands, that my dear nephew might find a conclusive felicity in the charitable embrace of the Church, as I have
done. My earthly joy has so nearly approached the heavenly, I
have so thirsted for the peace of God and have been so thank-
fully appeased, that I had prayed for him a like simplicity of
rapture. But if Carlo here, who has seen much of the lad's ex-
panding soul, concludes that the complications of the secular life
are indispensable to his content, so be it. Further, if the Chevalier's
account of young Rosalba Berni is but half so veracious as his
proven honor must guarantee, I am well satisfied of her worthi-
ness to be Virginio's wife. Therefore I will not withhold my consent from these nuptials; my heart awaits the lovers. Only, since
it is better to avoid a too precipitate deed, however valid, let us
follow Carlo's advice; the wedding shall take place tomorrow
morning at the Church of St. John and St. Paul, whose benisons
be upon these children."

The tower room was trembling in the violet dusk, like an
island pinnacle invaded by the tide; the tide was evening, which
rose rather than descended, flowing softly, smoothly, and invincibly
from the deep lagoons, without the lightest undulation of a wave,
without a sound, yet influential as the sea itself. Blue-violet and
gray, red-violet where the sun informed it, the evening drowned
the room in tinted darkness, until the faces of the three friends
floated like nebulous ocean monsters in the gloom: Peter Innocent's face was colored like a dead pearl, Carlo Gozzi's gleamed
phosphorescent yellow. The Chevalier's nervous hands wavered,
brown as water-weeds; his countenance was obscured.

The stairs which mounted to the tower chamber were crumbled
and hazardous, yet upon their peril someone climbed, a footfall
tinkled suddenly, incredibly tiny, a scampering as of winged mice,

a skimming as of swallows. The rumor neared; heels or hoofs clicked upon stone at a fawn's pace; feathers or gauzy fabrics rustled and flew. The rusty latch cried out, the leathern door creaked in a draft, and Rosalba was within the room.

By some perverse vagary of the evening clouds, the sun and moon crossed swords above her head; under this pointed arch of light she ran into the room. The sun's long final ray was rosy and dim; the moon's first ray was silvery green and poignant. But Rosalba was pure gold from head to foot; she was brighter than the swords of light. A chaplet of golden leaves confined the burnished shadow of her hair; her sandal thongs were gilded; her gown, an Arcadian travesty of Diana's, was cut from cloth of gold. Her face was clear and pale, and her little freckles powdered it tenderly, like grains of golden dust. Her eyes were gold made magically translucent.

Her quick glance swept the apartment in a single scintillation, then, uttering a wild and joyous cry, she rushed upon Peter Innocent with all the ardor and velocity of a shooting star.

He was afraid. She was throttling him with her slender arms, and yet her lips were soft upon his cheek, and somewhere, in the profoundest caverns of his heart, love moved and wondered, answering her from a dream.

"Darling, even if you are a Cardinal!" she said, "and lovely, even if you are an Eminence! Oh, you are beautiful, and like Virginio; I knew you at once! I shall adore you, and obey you always!" And she fell to kissing his hand. The fragility of those unresponsive and chilly finger-tips struck lightly yet insistently at her happiness, and she drew back in alarm, crying sadly:

"Oh, but you too, you too! You shiver and break when I touch you! Are you made of ice, that you cannot bear the little weight of my hand?"

Carlo Gozzi, to his own amazement, made a small sound of pity; the Chevalier stepped forward and took the girl's hand between his own. He kissed it gravely and essayed to speak. At that precise instant the door swung open, and Virginio, sheathed in a silver cloak, came softly into the room; he entered like the twilight, and Rosalba was quenched within his arms.

18. Too Many Pastry-cooks

"INEVITABLY ruin the meringue, as they say in Vienna!" the Chevalier concluded lightly, closing his tortoise-shell snuff-box with a sharp click.

"Ah, you are right; the whole affair is whipped cream, and we are endeavoring to turn it into good solid butter." Carlo Gozzi agreed; his face was thoughtful and surprisingly humane upon the reflection. "What is man? A fantastical puff-paste, as Webster truly remarks."

"I implore you not to be forever quoting the English tragedians, my dear Count; it is disconcerting, to say the least, in this enlightened eighteenth century of ours. If Shakspere and his barbaric kin could have been gently licked into shape by the suave cat-tongue of Addison, they might have been endurable. As it is, I beg you to consider my ear-ache, which is troublesome in November and cannot brook a Gothic brutality of syllables. Touching the puff-paste, the simile is just enough, if Virginio is a man. I thought, however, we had determined him an elemental."

"H'm," said Gozzi, dryly, "quite so, quite so. But, to my romantic fancy, an elemental moved among thunderstorms and whirlwinds; its least conceivable spirit was a snowfall. But Virginio is animated by the soul of an icicle or a small, pale skeleton leaf. I have no patience with him since he carries his arm in a sling."

"Come, come, my friend," cried Chastelneuf, "you are too hard on the boy. Rosalba is, after all, very impulsive; her dancing is hoydenish, and she is addicted to running races, like Atalanta gone mad. Look, there she is, at the end of the cypress alley; she seems to be indulging in a game of tag with his Eminence."

The scene, precisely etched in slender lines upon a clear green west of early winter, was the garden of a small casino near Venice; the hour was sunset. A delicate chill flavored the atmosphere with a perfume of frost and fallen leaves; the Chevalier wore his fur pelisse, and the Count was wrapped in a Bedouin cape of camel's hair; his head was covered by a scarlet nightcap.

Over the lawn, powdered with blown yellow petals, the noble Angelo Querini approached; his grave and judicial garments reproved the perished flowers. He seated himself upon a marble bench by the side of the two friends, first spreading a shawl of Scottish plaid against the frigidity of the stone. His eye sought the distant figure of Rosalba, which flitted unquietly along the vistas of the garden, exquisitely strange and savage in a cloak of tawny velvet lined with foxes' skins.

" She used never to be so wild a creature while she shared my roof," he said sadly. " She was always so studious, so docile, so domestic! God knows what possesses her poor little body; her tranquillity is turned to quicksilver. She runs like a rabbit, like a deer, to and fro within the confines of these walls, and at night she is very tired. I think she cries. She is afraid of Virginio."

" But Virginio is afraid of her! " cried Carlo Gozzi, rather angrily. " Rosalba is not afraid; she is a brave child. The boy is afraid; look at him now, leaning against the wall, as white as pumiced parchment, and as limp. He is a coward; how can he be afraid of a little woodland fawn like our Rosalba? "

It was true; the slim form of Virginio appeared crucified upon one of the stucco walls of the inclosure. His feet were crossed; his fair head drooped and fainted; one arm was outspread among the vines; the other hung in a black silk sling. There was an agony of weakness in the attitude; his transparent hand was clenched upon a broken tendril of vine.

" She is afraid of Virginio," Angelo Querini repeated obstinately.

" I believe you are both of you right; they are afraid of each other," said Chastelneuf. " Our experiment has not been wholly successful: two mild substances are, in the intimate fusion of marriage, beginning to effervesce; there are signs of an explosion. It is a pity, but the case is by no means hopeless."

Both Querini and Carlo Gozzi continued to stare indignantly at the pathetic spectacle of Virginio's despair. Querini felt a truly paternal solicitude for Rosalba, and Gozzi, upon learning that the girl was a confirmed admirer of his fairy drama, had quickly altered his opinion of her character and intellect. She appeared to him now the very embodiment of inner grace, and he reflected angrily that Virginio was a poor atomy to mate with this burning and spiritual child of love, who wore a wild beast's pelt above a heart more vulnerable than a little lamb's.

" The incident of the broken arm," drawled the Chevalier, himself regarding Virginio through half-shut eyelids, " was, you comprehend, somewhat alarming to our young friend here. He is timid and fears to repeat the experience; his wife is impetuous and inclined to be careless. It is true that she did not actually touch him; they were running along the laurel alley, and he stumbled and fell. I was able to repair the damage, but it has shaken him seriously. Apparently he blames Rosalba; she, for her part, is proud, and in the consciousness of innocence, wounded to the soul by his implicit reproach. Neither will speak; their silence is like a darkness over them, in which suspicion flourishes."

" What does Peter say? "

" Nothing, in words; evidently he grieves, however, and I think he holds us responsible for the failure of his nephew's happiness. He feels certain that a monastery, rather than marriage, is Virginio's natural haven. Rosalba he has forgiven, but he cannot look upon her without pain."

" Forgiven her! And for what fault, may I ask? Is it a crime on this unlucky infant's part that we have incontinently wedded her to a glass mannikin instead of decent blood and bone? God pardon us for our unholy meddling, for we have hurt the loveliest thing alive! "

Marvelous to relate, along the ancient leather of Carlo Gozzi's cheek a single glabrous tear moved slowly downward; the others observed it with awe, not attempting to answer until he had removed it with the sleeve of his burnous. Then the Chevalier cleared his throat and spoke briskly.

" I share your indignation, my dear Count, but the fact remains. Peter has forgiven Rosalba; you know we cannot prevent Peter from forgiving people even when they have done no harm. He is incapable of harboring resentment, but he must have the comfort of an occasional absolution to uphold him; he has remitted Rosalba's non-existent sins against Virginio. See how tenderly he addresses the elusive child. She shrinks, she starts like a doe transfixed by an arrow, yet Peter's shaft was feathered by compassion;

he let fly from the strings of his heart. He is a saint whose silver niche should never know these invasive anxieties; I have erred in giving him a nephew."

Virginio stirred and wavered against the wall; languidly he straightened his slight limbs to glide across the grass toward his wife. He was very pale, and his beautiful face appeared mute, and blinded by mysterious sorrow; its smooth, pure contours were immobile as a mask of gauze over the countenance of one lately dead.

19. Burning Leaf

" It is a pity Rosalba is late; she is always so fond of *perdrix au choux*, and François has surpassed himself this evening," Chastelneuf commented reflectively, emptying his champagne goblet for the twelfth time.

The salon of the little casino was brilliantly, yet softly, illuminated by innumerable candles, and the Murano mirrors which formed its walls steeped the repeated lights in cool sea-colored distances. The pyramid of grapes upon the table seemed molded from the same silvered glass, and the flowers themselves were a fountain of crystalline spray. Peter Innocent, Carlo Gozzi, and Angelo Querini stained the pale, bright chamber with their black and rusty-brown attire; the Chevalier's crimson startled it like a blow; only Virginio, resigned and pallid in pearly satin, fitted into the setting like a clear jewel clasped by a ring. His air of fragility was heightened by a cold and fearful lucency upon his brow; he looked ill, refused all food, and drank nothing save iced soda-water. He did not speak, but occupied his visibly shaking hands in the manufacture of little bread pellets. These were not grimy, as are the bread pellets of ordinary mortals; they appeared to acquire an added whiteness from the touch of his delicate and listless fingers.

" I overheard her tell Lucietta to repair the gray and lemon lutestring for tonight; one of the silver tassels was amiss, I think. Without doubt, she intended to dine with us; her absence begins to be alarming." Chastelneuf frowned into his replenished wine-glass.

" I will go search for her," cried Querini and Carlo Gozzi with simultaneous eagerness. Gozzi was already upon his feet; Querini was rising majestically from his carven chair. Peter Innocent said nothing; the silence of Virginio became appreciably more profound.

" Your pardon, gentlemen; I believe I am best fitted for this embassy." The Chevalier's voice was authoritative, and he was at the door in three great strides. " There is a bonfire in the garden," he threw back over his shoulder, like an irrelevant glove, as he passed from the room. The challenge, if challenge it were, seemed flung directly into Virginio's bloodless and impassive face. The boy was whiter than white glass, more quiet than fallen snow; his long, fair eyelashes were lowered over his chill cerulean eyes.

Chastelneuf ran hastily from the lighted house into the obscurity of the dusk; behind him the windows made tall parallelograms of radiance, tinted by curtains of rainbow silk; in front a stranger color tore the darkness into ribbons and flew upward in fringes of scarlet. " Merely the leaves which the gardener is burning," the Chevalier told himself in reassurance.

Nevertheless his buckled shoes leaped over the ground like the hoofs of a stallion, and he reached the end of the laurel alley three seconds in advance of Rosalba, who had danced into his vision on the instant, lighter, brighter, and more insensate than a burning leaf. Her cloak of fox-skins opened into wings, the air upheld her, and she floated into the heart of the fire.

In another second she was safe; Chastelneuf stood over her on the smoking grass and stamped out the sparks with his buckled shoes; he knelt and crushed between his sinewy hands the little ruffle of flame which scalloped the edges of her crumpled gown.

" Why were you so wicked, so cruelly wicked? " he cried. " Why did you not tell me that you wished to die? Do you understand that I am always here to give you whatever you want? Yes, even if it is death, I will give it to you; but sweetly flavored and in a golden box. I will give you the death of these others if you desire it; I will give you life such as you have not imagined save in heaven.

" My child, my child, you have observed that I love you, but have you comprehended the quality of my love? It is such as you

will never discover in the hollow veins of Virginio or among
the noble ganglions of Querini's intellect; it is love, lust, passion,
humility, and wonder; it is human, not divine, not animal, but
the love of mortal for mortal; it is at your service. I love you;
I have loved many times and in many fashions, but this love is
all your own. Use it as you will; I have no expectation that you
can return it in kind. I have done you an irreparable wrong; forgive
me; I entreat your forgiveness, my darling. I believed that I loved
Virginio, for he is the fair product of my ingenuity, but in attempting to provide him with those things needful to happiness
I have sacrificed you, who are worth a million pale Virginios. You
are the true child of my heart, and its ultimate affection; I will
even love you with a father's love, if I may not love you with a
lover's. I will subdue my spirit to your least command if you will
promise me to live! "

The Chevalier spoke with the most impassioned fervor, and
Rosalba smiled among her tawny furs to see him so perturbed.
In the midst of her own despair, she perceived nothing save cause
for mirth in the agitation of one whom she had always regarded
as a benevolent elderly gentleman, respectably conversant with the
Italian classics and the court circulars of Europe.

Chastelneuf experienced a pang of extreme humiliation; he felt
Rosalba's eyes, wild and acute as those of a trapped vixen, transfix
his chestnut peruke and pierce to the silver stubble beneath it.
The wrinkles upon his face were deepened as by acid, and his
falcon look grew weary with the recollection of unrestful years.
Rosalba, innocent alike of cruelty or compassion, shifted her gaze
without speaking, and then cried aloud in the voice of a prisoned
creature tardily released. Virginio, so veiled in twilight as to appear
no more than a moving part of the invisible, now glided from the
obscurity of the garden.

Rosalba shot upward like an impulsive flower nourished on
subterranean flame; she ran, a pointed blossom of the dragon
seed, straight to Virginio's heart. She might have been a dagger
in that heart; the boy drew himself erect, closed his eyes, and stood
swaying in an agony apparent as a wound. There was another and
a sharper cry, an echo and a confused murmuring; the two slim

figures clung together for an instant. Then they were again divided;
the blue translucent dusk flowed between them like a narrow river;
they stretched their hands to each other, and their tears fell into
the swift and narrow stream of time and were lost.

Chastelneuf forgot his own sorrowful anger in a sudden pity;
he was intolerably saddened by the spectacle of the lovers' frustration. He wanted nothing half so much as to see them happy and
at peace under the evening stars; their youth was darling to his
senses, like the smell of flowers or the flavor of wine, and he observed it without envy. He relinquished the luxury of self-com-
miseration, and reminding his vanity how easily he might have
been Rosalba's parent, he cleared his throat, straightened his chestnut peruke, and spoke.

"My children," he said in a tone admirably paternal and concerned, "I am inexpressibly grieved to witness your distress; I am
forced to conclude that all is not well between you. Trust me to
understand your reticences, but trust me yet again, and further, to
resolve your problems in my larger experience. If you will confide
in me, my dears, I can convince you of my ability to assist you in
any dilemma."

Even as he pronounced the words with such judicial calm, his
mind was troubled and his bowels wrung by a dreadful premonition; pity grew fierce as anger in his soul, and his heart gnawed
at his ribs.

Dimly as he now discerned the two figures confronting each
other across the profound spaces, colored more ambiguously than
twilight, of their mutual and mortal fear, he was yet aware of a
difference in air and attitude, which made Rosalba, to the peculiar
pattern of his own mind, the sadder by an infinity of pain.

Virginio stood silent and curiously withdrawn; his white satin
shoes were rooted to the ground, but he swayed in the windless
atmosphere, and the rustle of his garments and the glimmer of his
flaxen hair made a faint music and a fainter illumination, like the
stir of a sapling birch tree in the dark.

"Virginio?" said Rosalba, softly.

The rustle of silk and the glimmer of silvery gold appeared,
to the Chevalier's watchfulness, to assume a new quality; the one
had the tinkle, the other the sheen, of something cold and glassy.

The sapling birch tree wore no leaves; its slender branches were incased in crystal, and at the tip of every twig a smooth bright icicle hung tremulous.

"Virginio?" said Rosalba again, and again softly, but now she said it with despair.

The girl fluttered restlessly about; she was light as thistledown or dancing flame. Her little hands, emerging from the loose, voluminous wings of her mantle, were lifted continually towards Virginio in a gesture of supplication, mockery, and compassion. Although, in her brilliance, she was fire to Virginio's crackling ice, the Chevalier remembered suddenly that the essential substance of that element is delicate and tender and more malleable than the very air, whereas ice is denser even than water, and often hard as stone. And he reflected truly that it was Rosalba's spirit that must inevitably be wounded in this unnatural warfare, however brittle Virginio's bones might prove.

"Have you no word to say to me, my children?" he entreated, and at last Rosalba answered him. She turned from Virginio with recovered composure, and faced Chastelneuf with a look of great dignity and sedateness.

"I shall be most grateful for your support and guidance, Chevalier," she said politely. All tint or tremor of the fantastic had fallen from her aspect, and she was nothing stranger than a slight, elegant girl in a velvet cloak, who strove to appear haughty despite her evident fatigue, and whose pale and pretty countenance was wet with ingenuous human tears.

20. Spider-web Tangle

"I AM willing," cried Rosalba, "to do anything; anything, everything, or nothing; I am the servant of the Chevalier's advice."

"Anything within reason," amended Querini; his ward interrupted him with quite unfilial scorn.

"Oh, but anything, within or without, or far from reason as the moon from sirocco or I from Notre Dame de Paris! Reason is for old gentlemen, like you and Monsieur de Voltaire; the Chevalier understands my determination."

Chastelneuf, thus suddenly made free of the dedicated insanity of youth, smiled into the fire of cedar logs, pervaded by a sweeter, more scented warmth than theirs.

"Reason is not the goddess of emergencies." Carlo Gozzi spoke sententiously, ruffling his thin hair above a corrugated brow. Peter Innocent said nothing.

The little apartment was charming with its fawn-colored *boiseries* and rose-garlanded carpet; the books behind their gilded lattices enriched the walls by a soft and variegated pattern of their own. The room was called the *study*, after an English fashion; its air was warm and intimate. Everyone, with the exception of Virginio, preferred it to the pale and mirrored salon where he now sat alone, nibbling a long green strip of angelica and idly perusing the pages of Frederick Martens's *Natural History of Spitzbergen*. "There grows an Arctic flower," he read; but his tranquillity was now and again shattered by the heat and hurry of voices from the open door.

"It is the only solution," pronounced the Chevalier. His passing glow was fled, and melancholy possessed him, hollowing his eyes and parching the accustomed glibness of his speech. "I had forgotten my youth, I think," he continued, subdued to shame. "I remembered love, for that still lives in my breast, but I did not remember the races which I ran with Caterina in the gardens of Saint-Blaise; my rheumatisms obscured my mind. Virginio can embrace his wife in comfort; his body is attuned to marital bliss. I arranged for that; it was in my opinion of the first importance. But I totally neglected to provide for the lighter contingencies of courtship; he cannot support the rigors of hide-and-seek or the excitement of a bout of blindman's-buff. A handspring would be the end of him. He is a perfect husband, I assure you, but he can never be a playmate for this poor child. When you are older, my dear, it will not grieve you; the domestic pleasures of the *foyer* will suffice."

He ceased; Rosalba was weeping uncontrollably.

"No! No!" she murmured through her tears, "it is too difficult; I cannot bear it! Better a thousand times some violent change, some mad and excessive sacrifice! I lie in his arms at night; my breath is stilled because I love him, and his kisses close my lips over my laughter and my eyelids over my tears. But in the morning, when there is no more moonlight, and the sun is shining with the insistence of a golden trumpet made fire instead of sound, when all the red and yellow cockerels are crowing and the larks fly upward like particles of flame, then when I wake and look at him he is afraid. He trembles; when I spring up in the sunshine he trembles at my side; when I run to the window, he pulls the covers about his ears; when I fling the curtains apart to let the light rush in, he faints upon his pillow; the delicate vibration of the dawn afflicts him like a thunderstroke. I tell you, it is too difficult; I cannot bear it, and I would rather die than have it so."

"This is intolerably sad," said Peter Innocent. "The girl is not to blame, yet perhaps we shall have to put her into a convent."

But "Never! never! never!" cried his three companions with an equal rage, and Rosalba fell upon her knees before him and anointed his hands with her despair.

"There is nothing for it, after all, but the magic," the Chevalier repeated solemnly. With the utmost gentleness he raised Rosalba to her feet and conducted her to the shelter of a winged armchair near the hearth.

Reflected firelight rose and fell in rays upon her face, so that it shone unquietly between golden pallor and the color of blushes; so also her ringlets were transformed from bright to dark and back again to brighter. The gauzes of her dress were disarranged, and among their folds hung here a pink and here a scarlet leaf, and here a frosty flake of ashes. Always she seemed to move and waver in the leaping light, stirred partly by its changes and partly by the shaking of her own heart, and although she was slight and shaken, her look was brave and vibrant and alive.

"Yes, the magic by all means," she said eagerly, quickened to fervor by a radiance above and beyond the cedar flames. "I am not afraid; it will not hurt me if I am not afraid."

"*Non dolet!*" cried Angelo Querini in a terrible voice, shielding his countenance from view.

"But you can assure us that it will be purely beneficent, or white magic, my dear friend?" asked Peter Innocent, with anxious concern; he was shocked by the violence of the Chevalier's reply.

"I can assure you of nothing so absurd, your Eminence. The Deity may justly approve of the affair of Virginio; He cannot seriously object to the vivification of a few handfuls of harmless Murano sand and a pipkin of holy water. But it is another and a very different matter to deprive one of His creatures of the delights and powers bestowed upon her by Himself; we shall require the devil's aid in murdering Rosalba."

"Murder? Surely we are not talking of murder!" Peter Innocent made the sign of the cross, shivering visibly in the blast of horror invoked by the loud and bloody word.

"Ah, not officially, perhaps." The Chevalier's bitterness was profound and quiet; absently he lifted Rosalba's warm, sunburnt little hand to his twisted lips. "We shall, indeed, leave her the privilege of living; possibly, in her new and chastened state, she may be duly grateful. But of this Rosalba, this child who sits before us clothed in light and eloquent with the breath of God — of this Rosalba nothing will remain. Yet, if you prefer, we need not call it murder."

"Remember that it is my own wish; the Cardinal would have sent me to a convent."

The girl spoke gently and without irony, but Chastelneuf bowed his head as if a millstone hung upon his breast; what depth of water closed above that head, or whether tinged with salt or vinegar or gall, it were worse than useless to conjecture.

"It is your own wish; I will not dispute it," he said humbly. "I am, in point of fact, responsible for the plan; I myself proposed it, and, indeed, it appears to be the only unraveling, save the convent, of this deplorable tangle. Of course I could always rescue you from the convent," he added hopefully and under his breath to Rosalba. The girl did not heed him; her eyes were fixed upon Peter Innocent, and she addressed that venerable prelate with the desperate courage of a suppliant.

"I am no more afraid of black magic than of white, Eminence. In the whole world there is only one thing of which I am afraid, and that thing is Virginio's fear. Let me suffer this ordeal, whatever it may prove, and live thereafter in peace and contentment with my beloved husband; this is all I ask."

"A sacrifice proffered in such tenderness cannot come amiss to the mercy of God." Peter Innocent put forth his veined, trans-

parent hand in a gesture of reassurance, and Rosalba thanked him
with a pale, but valiant, smile.

" I shall have a word to interpose in this matter," said Angelo
Querini. " I do not believe in magic, either black or white; it is not
rational, logical, or decent. I do not wish Rosalba to be mixed up
in necromancy and kindred follies."

" I believe in magic, and that so religiously that I cannot countenance such practices as the Chevalier proposes; the danger to a
simple child like Rosalba is appalling. It is well enough, when I
write of it, for the Negress Smeraldina to be dipped into a caldron
of flame, emerging whiter than a clay pipe, but for this little fire-
bird to be caught and frozen into lifelessness, that is another story
altogether, too tragic for my perusal. Let us turn her into a fawn
or a vixen or a tawny panther, and set her free forever."

21. Method of the Brothers Dubois

" THERE is a villa at Strà, upon the banks of the Brenta, whose
aviaries contain eagles from the Apennines, and whose fenced in-
closures hold captive a hundred stags, wild roe, and mountain goats.
Do you believe, because the hornbeam is green and the myrtle
fragrant, that these creatures are happy? Rosalba, enchanted into
some savage form, would wound her bosom against thorny walls,
and find herself a prisoner among invisible labyrinths. She would
still be bound fast to Virginio, to run like a hound at his heel, or
flutter falcon-wise to his wrist. This were no freedom, but a strange
refinement of pain. Rather let her shrink into a china doll and have
done with feeling than that she should assume wings prematurely
broken or a hind's fleetness without liberty of heart! "

" You are an orator, Monsieur de Chastelneuf; allow me to congratulate you upon your eloquence." Thus spoke the noble Angelo
Querini, one time Senator of the Republic of Venice. " It might,
however, be employed in some worthier cause than the willful de-
ception of a young girl. We have none of us forgotten Madame
von Wulfe and the cruel farce of Quérilinth."

" I thank you for the compliment, my dear Querini; your ap-
probation is ever welcome. For the insult I forgive you, even as I

hope Madame von Wulfe has forgiven me. In the present matter
I can have no motive other than altruism, and I assure you of my
good faith. Nevertheless, it is for Rosalba to decide whether or no
I now embark upon what must prove for all concerned a solemn
and hazardous undertaking."

"I wish it; I demand it," Rosalba answered firmly. "Desperate
as the means must be, it is my only remedy for torment. I am prepared to incur the equivalent of death in order to achieve peace
for Virginio."

"The child is one of God's elected angels!" cried Peter Innocent in awe. "If she should unhappily perish in this dark adventure, she must in common fairness be canonized. Meanwhile I
wish I had her safe among the Poor Clares of Assisi; she is too
saintly for this secular arena of mortal life."

"Nonsense! She is nothing of the sort; she is merely a luckless
girl who loves a glass manikin instead of kind, consoling flesh and
blood!" the Chevalier retorted with sardonic insolence. It was
plain that his own flesh and blood were racked and poisoned by
revolt.

Monsieur de Chastelneuf was very pale. His eyes were sunken in
his head, and his face was ravaged like a starving man's. Yet, worn
and sharpened and intolerably wrung, he still maintained, despite
this betrayal of his body, a certain victory of spirit, a simple affair
of courage, perhaps, and accustomed coolness against heavy
odds. And again, it was plain that he did not suffer for himself
alone.

"Above all, we must be practical," he said, recovering perfectly
his manner of impudent composure. "There is a method — not
my own, I may say, but that of the celebrated Brothers Dubois,
late of Vincennes — whereby young ladies are rendered harmless
to the tranquillity of others and permanently deprived of their
surplus emotions. Quite frankly, it is magic of a vehement and
painful variety; the subject is ultimately transformed into fine
porcelain, but the process is not agreeable, and the result, although
miraculous, is somewhat inhuman. I have known fathers who sub-
mitted their daughters to the ordeal, husbands who forced it upon
their wives, but never, until this hour, have I known a woman to
desire the torture of her own free will. It is an agony more incisive

than birth or dissolution; I dare not veil the circumstance with pity."

"And may a woman undergo this terrible ordeal and live?" Carlo Gozzi alone found voice, and that the thinnest whisper, to inquire.

"Yes, she may live, and flourish, and be fair and decorous and delightful." Chastelneuf ground his strong white teeth upon the words. "She may, to all appearances and outward seeming, remain a mortal woman; for aught I know to the contrary a purified soul may burn peacefully within the pretty fabric of her body. But — she will be porcelain; fine porcelain, remember, and no longer clay. In a porcelain vessel filled with clear water a rose may live for a little while, but out of clay a rose may rise alive and blooming, set on the roots of elder roses. There is a difference, but it does not matter."

"Nothing matters except Virginio," said Rosalba, softly.

Even as the Chevalier drove sharp nails into his palms and bit his lip until he tasted blood, even as Peter Innocent bowed his lovely silver brow in sorrowful acquiescence, Virginio entered quietly and sadly, like the softer echo of Rosalba's voice.

None who looked upon him then wondered afterwards at the fabulous chivalry of the girl's devotion; the lovers looked into each other's eyes, and their eyes were tender, pitiful, and afraid. Virginio wore a quality of pure translucent beauty, unwarmed by earth, the beauty of an element like sea or air, or that refined and rarefied sunlight mirrored by the moon. He wore this beauty meekly, and with a slight and delicate timidity he approached his wife and folded her within his arms. Felicity hovered above their bending heads, flying nearer, yet never alighting; the wings of felicity were so nearly visible that to Carlo Gozzi they appeared feathered like those of the pigeons of Saint Mark, and to Peter Innocent like the Holy Ghost itself in the shape of a silver dove.

Furthermore, to Peter Innocent, whose mind was a missal book of sacred images, Virginio figured as the young John Baptist, wandering immaculate in the desert, and Rosalba as a small golden lioness, of equal virtue and simplicity, but pagan and untamable and shy.

So, like a pair of legendary children, they came to the Cardinal where he sat musing by the fire, and, moved by one impulse, sank upon their knees before him and inclined their bright locks to his blessing. The flaxen and the darkly burnished head bent side by side beneath his hand, and Peter Innocent's musings were made audible as prayer, and in the silence smoke rose like incense from the crumbling cedar logs, ascending through the chimney to the frosty night, and thence, perhaps, to heaven.

22. Pâte Tendre

" If you were hard paste, we should have to send you to Meissen," said the Chevalier, smiling and alert in an elegant new traveling-cloak of bottle-green broadcloth. The midday sun lay yellow along a vast map spread upon the writing-desk, and although it was November, the windows stood open to sweet and jocund breezes. An atmosphere of nervous gayety pervaded the study; a strapped portmanteau and a Florentine dressing-case occupied the settee, and seven large bandboxes were piled in a corner.

Upon the mantelpiece two crystal vases exhaled a mist of jasmine, and between these were set a number of china figurines of exquisite workmanship. A fantastic bellarmine grimaced at a Bow cupid, and a delicious Chelsea group of the Four Seasons, modeled by Roubiliac, and glowing with every floral tint, contrasted curiously with a fine white Derby biscuit statuette of Queen Charlotte and her children.

" Yes, Meissen for hard paste," repeated Chastelneuf, cheerfully, " and from that grim fortress you might come forth with a rosy Saxon complexion and no sensibilities whatever."

" And no freckles? " asked Rosalba, with a pardonable feminine eagerness.

" No, my love; you would be as pink as a sugar-plum and as smooth as whipped cream. However, Meissen is far too Germanic for your peculiar mentality, and you could never survive its furnaces. It must be either Sèvres or Marseilles, since Hannong of Strasbourg has been dead these two years, and you are averse to visiting England."

" I cannot forget that I am a Frenchwoman." Rosalba spoke with a faint trace of hauteur, gazing rather wistfully at the Chelsea figure of Spring, attired in a vernal dress of apple green and pearl-color.

"I should like to see you in white Marseilles faïence," said the Chevalier. "I once beheld a shepherdess in biscuit-porcelain, made in the factory of the Duc de Villeroy at Mennecy, which was almost worthy of you. Nevertheless, I believe we shall be wise in selecting Sèvres. It was the scene of the Brothers Dubois' amazing discovery; they were subsequently dismissed for drunkenness and the practice of venomous magic. They came to me with letters from the Prince of Courland, whom they had greatly assisted in the search for the philosophers' stone. I was able to resolve the slight difficulties they had encountered by means of my infallible compound of Hungarian crystal and native cinnabar. Overcome with gratitude, they presented me with the secret recipe associated with their name. Since then I have ever been in a position to turn ladies into porcelain, but I have not often availed myself of the opportunity; the process is opposed to my principles and natural proclivities."

"Dear Chevalier, I am quite familiar with your sentiments," murmured Rosalba, sympathetically and a little shyly. "But you will surely not refuse to aid me, upon this occasion, in my search for happiness. I have understood you to say, have I not, that you are capable of complete and single-handed success in the absence of the Brothers Dubois?"

"But yes, and fortunately, since the Brothers Dubois are at present inaccessibly situated in purgatory or some even less salubrious region," Chastelneuf assured her. "I need no help in the matter, save that of such skilled workmen as are to be found in any porcelain-factory, augmented by those supernatural agencies which I must not scruple to employ."

"I am glad it is to be Sèvres, when all is said and done." Rosalba gazed reflectively into a tortoise-shell mirror, comparing her image therein with the countenance of an enchanting china figure, sculptured by Clodion in the classic taste, which the Chevalier, bowing, presented to her view, poised daintily upon the palm of his hand.

"Oh, it is undoubtedly your *genre!*" cried Chastelneuf with enthusiasm, touching the girl's pale cheek with a respectfully tenta-

tive forefinger. " The true Sèvres, the soft paste of the old régime,
not this stony stuff they have derived from the Germans. You are
the finest *porcelaine de France;* I know the ingredients." And he
began to chant a medley of words, in which Rosalba was at some
pains to distinguish syllables analogous to " Fontainebleau sand
— pure sea salt — Aliante alum — and powdered alabaster." Certainly the Chevalier was a gentleman of various and esoteric learning, whose knowledge of humanity was both profound and nice.
Rosalba resigned her will to his, and faced the future with mingled
fortitude and acute curiosity.

" It is decided, then, that the Cardinal accompany us, while
Virginio remains with Querini and Carlo Gozzi, perfecting himself in the study of Greek, Latin, Arabic, and antique Spanish.
He will thus be enabled to compare philosophies with fairy-tales,
and to contemplate life with the stoicism of the one and the in-
souciance of the other. I have also suggested that he become proficient upon the flute and engage a really good fencing-master,"
said the Chevalier, divesting himself of his traveling-cloak and
taking a pinch of snuff.

" We depart in an hour's time," he continued lightly, consulting a sumptuous jeweled watch, " and you will doubtless prefer
to make your adieus to Virginio unattended by the most affectionate friend. I withdraw, therefore, but shall await you, with restrained impatience, in the adjoining apartment. I am sure we
shall have no cause to regret our decision in the matter of factories." His smile contrived a positive frivolity, and Rosalba experienced a thrill of gratitude.

" The Cardinal makes me feel that I am setting forth upon a
penitential pilgrimage," she said plaintively. " You are less alarming: allow it to remain a mere affair of millinery. I could almost
believe that we were going to Paris to select a costume for the
carnival."

" But that, in a way, is true enough, my child," cried Chastelneuf, retiring. As he went, he coughed thrice behind a fine lace
handkerchief, and wiped his eyes.

Presently Virginio knocked gently upon the door and entered
like a cloud of cooler air.

" Adieu, Virginio, my darling," whispered Rosalba.

"Adieu, adieu, my heart's beloved," the boy replied. Their voices were too low for audible trembling, but their hands, clinging together in the final instant, shook like thin white petals in a hurricane.

"Virginio, good-by."

"Good-by, Rosalba."

"I am going."

"I know; good-by, my love."

"Virginio — "

"My dear — "

"Good-by."

They embraced; bright glassy tears fell upon Rosalba's breast, and upon Virginio's cold hands Rosalba's tears fell quick and glittering as sunshower drops, and warm almost as the kisses wherewith they were mingled.

The great door closed at last between the lovers, leaving no sound; its painted panels confronted them severally with Pan's cruel nonchalance and Medusa's uncomfortable stare.

Virginio examined his finger-nails; they were quite uninjured, but the least finger of his left hand appeared to have suffered a slight sprain.

Rosalba, drawing on her white suède gloves, observed without surprise that both her wrists were faintly flecked with blood, as though a bracelet of thorns had lately clasped them.

23. Ordeal by Fire

THROUGH a landscape lightly strewn with snow, and rendered graciously austere by long, converging lines of leafless poplars, the three strange travelers approached the neighborhood of Paris.

The Chevalier's English carriage was commodious and softly cushioned, and the discomforts of the journey had been negligible; nevertheless a ponderable sadness was bound upon the shoulders of the adventurers, as if indeed they carried ambiguous packs too heavy for their spirits. Their chins were sunk against their breasts, and even Chastelneuf strove quite in vain to dissipate this burden by companionable chatter.

"Paris must wait," he observed to Rosalba. "Afterwards, when our affair is concluded, it will be time to think of the trousseau, which only Paris can fitly provide for a Frenchwoman. I consider you too fine for our Venetian barbarities of fashion, which tend ever to the extravagant and the capricious. You must see Bertin, of course; the Queen swears by her, although the little Polignac, always so demure and so chic, is of another opinion entirely. But you will choose for yourself; it is the prerogative of Venus."

Rosalba raised her satirically penciled brows the least reproving shade, and the Chevalier subsided into a conversation with Peter Innocent, who remained immersed in his breviary, vouchsafing now and again an absent-minded nod or a grieved monosyllable in response to the other's volubility.

" While I warmly second your decision as to the preservation of the strictest incognito, Eminence, I can assure you that no such peril attaches itself to our activities in this enlightened land of France as we should inevitably incur at home. In Venice we should have the Holy Office upon our tracks in a twinkling; here we need only fear the unfriendly attention of the Academy of Sciences.

" Instead of the Three and their spies, we must shun the associates of Bailly and Franklin. They are about to disturb the magnetic afflatus of Mesmer, but he, you know, is a charlatan."

" Yes? " said Peter Innocent, clutching his rosary.

They drove through the Forest of Meudon; beyond lay the park and the two châteaux. The sun was setting somewhere over their left shoulders.

" Have you heard that the Duc de Chartres is cutting down the magnificent chestnut alleys in the Palais Royal? " inquired the Chevalier.

His companions preserved a silence unbroken save by sighs.

Presently they reached the outskirts of the ancient town of Sèvres; at a little distance from the factory, whose dark bulk rose upon the river-bank, a curious tower was conspicuous above a clump of nameless trees.

" Private workroom of the Brothers Dubois," the Chevalier explained in hushed, oppressive accents.

" But they are dead, and the place is evidently deserted! " cried the Cardinal, his voice vibrating to the chill along his spine.

" True; only too true," said Chastelneuf.

Perhaps the vitreous tiles which roofed the structure possessed a coppery glaze, perhaps the doors and windows were bound with this red metal, or perhaps the setting sun performed a sinister miracle of transmutation and turned the tower into blood and flame. Its shape was very singular and menacing against the holy evening sky, where upon a field of violet a few small stars were visible. The carriage halted at a word from Chastelneuf and came to a standstill at the mouth of a clearing in the clump of trees; feathery grasses, tipped with snow, had overgrown the path. The horses stamped their feet in the stillness; steam floated in the thick clouds about their heads. The Chevalier's Spanish servant, shrouded to the eyes in a somber cloak, awaited his master's instructions with an air of taciturn complicity in some questionable design.

" Monseigneur, you will proceed to the inn at Versailles, where a fire, a feather bed, and a roasted fowl are in readiness," Chastelneuf declared, fixing the Cardinal with a hypnotic eye. " Rosalba and I must now go on alone."

" On foot? " Peter Innocent asked in a weak voice.

" On foot, but not far; Rosalba will have ample opportunity to dry her slippers before the night is out." The words were significant and sharp; the Cardinal shuddered.

" I am not afraid," said Rosalba, for the thousandth time, in a pitiful whisper. " They do not throw salt into the furnaces any more, nor use pulverized ox-bones, as they do in England."

" She need not suffer a second firing," said Chastelneuf. " I have concluded that no glaze is necessary, though, for that matter, the modern glaze is no longer by immersion, but by sprinkling, as in Christian baptism. But we shall leave Rosalba in the simple biscuit state. Console yourself, Eminence; your responsibility is heavy, but she shall be saved."

Peter Innocent found a slight support for his swooning spirit in the religious flavor of these final reassurances; he watched the pair depart through tears, and made his every breath a prayer as the trees met over the Chevalier's haughty head and took Rosalba into their equivocal embrace.

For one brief instant the tower was split by a streak of brightness, and all the vehemence of fire outraged the tranquillity of the twilit wood; then the door closed, the smoke dispersed, the fumes

faded in air, and with their going Peter Innocent was borne like
thistledown, by the swift agency of two black horses, along the
lonely road to Versailles.

24. Silver Cord

IN the ancient Satory quarter of Versailles, under the very shadow
of the new Cathedral of St. Louis, there lay a little tavern whose
sign bore the symbol of the Silver Bowman. In the only parlor the
narrow place afforded, a clear fire had been kindled, before whose
consolatory incandescence the Cardinal Peter Innocent Bon now
warmed his hands and meditated upon the wonders of the world.

The eighth of these, to his enchanted thinking, and which had
but this moment vanished in a visible smoke from between his
fingers, was not the greater nor the smaller Trianon, nor yet the
palace itself, nor the gardens nor the orangery. The thing had been
more marvelous than these, both magic and geometric; a flower
inclosed in a carven frame, a lovely formal pattern. A flake of snow,
fallen from the dove-colored skies of France, had melted in the
heat of the fire.

Although Peter Innocent had often found the Roman winter
of a severity too poignant for his anatomy to support without pain,
he had rarely encountered the mysteries of frost and snow, and now
his recollection wandered to the Christmas season of 1716, when
he had seen Venice no longer blue and gold, but muffled and
masked in whiteness. Oblivion like sleep had come at first upon
the town, and then a bitter wind, and finally, when the sun shone
again in the heavens, the palaces and church towers had flashed
and scintillated beneath a covering of quicksilver. All this was
memorable to Peter Innocent after many years, and he could picture the wine-shop, even, where his father had taken him for a
glass of malvasia from Epirus. He had been fourteen years old at
the time, the malvasia had tasted warm as imagined Acroceraunian
spring.

Since then, and so for uncounted Christmas seasons, Peter Innocent had forgotten the miracle of snow. Now he was enraptured,
and opening the casement against a stubborn blast of the north,
he filled his hands once more with the intricate crystals.

Yet all too soon the crystals dissolved again to icy moisture, and Peter Innocent considered beauty's evanescence as typified in those spilt drops of snow water.

A thin white wine of France stood in a green decanter by his elbow, but he foretasted it as cold astringent stuff; he wished Rosalba would return to brew him a glass of negus, with nutmeg in it, and the grated rind of a lemon.

A small volume bound in creamy vellum lay by the decanter, in a pool of green reflected light; he knew it for a copy of Rosalba's poems, printed at Pisa less than a year ago as a gift from Querini to his ward.

An absurd medley of quotation sprinkled the title-page with tags from Seneca and Catullus. Here cried the unchristian wastrel to his strumpet: " Remains to be slept the sleep of one unbroken night." Here the virtuous philosopher remarked, with equal gloom: " We are kindled and put out." Peter Innocent found the poems themselves hard to decipher in the failing light.

He picked up a fine Venetian edition of Theocritus, but the book fell open at an unknown line, and this is what he read: " The lamb is gone, the poor young thing is gone . . . a savage wolf has crunched her in his jaws, and the dogs bay; what profits it to weep, when of that lost creature not a bone nor a cinder is left? "

Peter Innocent poured out a measure of the thin white wine; the goblet was full to the brim, and a little wine was spilled upon the pages of the book, for the Cardinal's hand was trembling. He shivered, huddled in his worn habit of the Friars Minor; he wished very heartily that he had indeed borrowed the Chevalier's luxurious dressing-gown of quilted purple silk, as Rosalba had more than once suggested.

The streets of Versailles were veiled by falling snow, and the wheels of the few cabriolets and chariots which passed beneath the window of the inn were noiseless in their revolutions; only the occasional crack of a whip shattered the frosty silence. Peter Innocent was very lonely.

Almost, he believed, he would have welcomed the arrival of those visitors whom his shy secretiveness had so far avoided. His incognito had been studiously preserved; even the curious eye of Louis de Rohan Guéménée, Cardinal Grand Almoner and Archbishop of Strasbourg, had failed to mark the elusive wearer of the gray-brown garb of St. Francis.

With the benediction of Assisi's name, there came into Petei Innocent's mind a sudden longing to be comforted, and he turned, like a bewildered child, to the dear protection of his patron saint. His fingers sought and found the leaves of another book, wherein his own scholarly Italian hand had traced certain passages from the life of Francis. His sight, under the encroaching dusk, grew dim; then he saw plainly what was written in the book.

" O brother fire, most beautiful of all creatures, be courteous to me at this hour, knowing how well I have always loved thee and ever will for His love who created thee! "

Upon the instant, the fire upon the hearth appeared to lift its terrible head in anger and spring like a tiger at his throat; he put up his feeble arms in a defensive gesture, and dropped them again in despair. The portent was revenge from heaven.

For even now, at his advice, at his desire, Rosalba was giving her body to be burned. " Be courteous to me at this hour — " The hour was struck, and the jaws of the furnace had received the child.

He caught up the decanter of wine and flung it, a bubble of green glass, into the burning fangs of the fire, where it was destroyed in a moment. Then he fell upon his knees and would have beat out the flames with his hands; but his strength failed him, the monster leaped upward with a roar, and Peter Innocent felt its teeth fasten in his shoulder; then he fainted.

He was revived by the Chevalier's voice and Rosalba's touch upon his temples. The window stood open to the snow, which blew inward, golden particles emerging strangely from an infinity of blue dusk; a handful of snow was sprinkled over his eyes, which throbbed with fever. The fire still raged within its bars, but as Rosalba stooped to tend it, he could have sworn that she spoke in a low, caressing tone, and perhaps admonished it by a sign; presently the flames sank down and seemed to slumber.

The Chevalier's cloak was wet with snow, and his face confessed a weariness and lassitude most carefully excluded from his speech.

" All is well, Eminence," he said, flinging his laced hat upon the table with a long-drawn sigh of fatigue. " She has survived our ministrations; a diabolic ordeal has served its purpose, and she has returned to you alive. Of her courage I cannot speak; her present composure may speak for her, even in silence. Yet perhaps, of her charity, she has a word for those who have wronged her."

Rosalba leaned at ease against the window-frame, and the snow blew past her lifted head and powdered it with particles of gold. There was about her an air of perfect calm; she was poised, composed, and quiet, yet without stiffness; her attitude had the grace of a bird arrested in flight, a flower flexible, but unmoved by wind. Peter Innocent knew instinctively that her spirit was unstirred by any pang that may not be suffered by an exemplary child of seven.

Her face was exquisitely clear and fresh in every tilted line and smooth velvety surface; her hair was miraculously symmetrical, and its thick scallops had the quality of gilded bronze. Her mantle fell about her in delicate sculptured folds.

" God give you peace! " said Rosalba to Peter Innocent, with a gentle candor unaware of pity and its intolerable demands.

25. Interior by Longhi

How delicate a contrivance of language must lull the imagination to repose before it may sing or picture to itself, while half asleep, Rosalba's home-coming!

This must be spoken in a whisper, dreamed in a meditation, drawn in the palest colors of pearls, set to an accompaniment of reverential music, veiling silence with a silver veil.

In that hour when the shadows flow like clear blue water along the golden sands of day, in the mildness of afternoon, in a place profoundly quiet, Virginio and Rosalba met and kissed.

Their very garments were awed into submission, so that silk dared not rustle or flowers shed their fragrance; the heels of their shoes were dipped in magic, so that they made no sound, and a dimness like the smoke of incense obscured the shining of their hair.

Nothing else in the world was ever so soft as their lips and the clasp of their hands; these were softer than the wings of gray moths or the frosty feathers of dandelion seed.

A little brush, smoothing thin pigments on a polished cedar panel, may trace more lightly and precisely than any pen the figures of Virginio and Rosalba, the wedded lovers of a fairy-tale, who now live happy ever after, in Venice, in a world of porcelain and Murano mirrors.

It has been said, and that upon distinguished authority, that Pietro Longhi survived, in the amber peace of a mellowing century, until the age of eighty; the statement is difficult to refute.

For those who would believe it, there exists in support of this theory a small painting, bearing the artist's signature not only in the mere syllables of his name, but, more convincingly, in every curve and color of the scene itself.

The hand of a very old man is evident in the fine performance; the lines waver, the colors are subdued and etherealized. The hand is the hand of Longhi, and he was an old man when Rosalba returned to Venice in the amber twilight of a dying century.

This twilight fills the picture, and is reflected from the mirrors of the background; the faces of the lovers emerge like stars from this profundity of twilight. The figure of Peter Innocent is there, quiet as a carven saint in his niche; he wears the gray-brown habit of the Friars Minor, and his veined and fragile hands are folded upon a cross. That noble brow and faint ironic smile can only be Querini's, and Count Carlo Gozzi looks impish and melancholy in a new periwig and the rich mantle of a patrician. The Chevalier is absent; it is said he has retired to Bohemia.

The faces of the lovers are most beautiful and pure; the gentle and elegiac quality of their love appears unmarred by longing. Having forgotten fear and the requirements of pity, their tenderness becomes a placid looking-glass in which each beholds the other; the mercurial wildness which no longer moves them is fixed behind this transparent screen, lending brightness to the mirrored images.

At any moment they may awake; Virginio will put on his pearl-colored greatcoat and wrap an ermine tippet about Rosalba's throat, and the season being winter and very clear and cold, they will hurry to a fashionable pastry-cook's to eat whipped cream and wafers.

David Garnett

THE SAILOR'S RETURN

Perfection is in unity; prefer
One woman first, and then one thing in her.

DONNE

THE *Duke of Kent* came safe into Southampton Docks on the 10th of June 1858.

On board of her was a mariner named William Targett, returning to his own country as a passenger, having shipped at Lisbon. He was in no hurry to go ashore, and waited half an hour for the confusion to be straightened out on board, and the turmoil to subside on land, before he motioned to the young Negro who accompanied him to bear a hand with a large basket of woven grass. They carried it down the gangway between them and deposited it on the side of the dock.

"Stand there, Tulip, till I come back," said the sailor, who then went on board once more, to return carrying a small sea-chest on his shoulder and a wicker cage containing a parrot in his hand. Targett was a strongly made man, a trifle over six feet in height, with thick dun-colored hair bleached by the tropic sun, which had tanned his skin a darker color. He carried himself with an air of independence, or rather with that air of authority which comes with the habit of command. Beside this Hercules the African seemed a child, whose black and curly head scarcely reached to the seaman's shoulder. The most noticeable thing about Tulip was an ebony-black skin, without a touch of brown or of gray. In figure the Negro was fragile; he held himself straight as an arrow. His savage bones were small and delicate; one might have fancied them light as a bird's, and like a bird's bones filled with air. The features were regular; the nose short, but straight and thick, and as powerful as a tomcat's; the nostrils and lips spreading like those of a child pressed against the panes of a village sweet-shop; but the mouth itself was small, and the teeth were fine, regular, and white as sugar.

Both Targett and his companion were dressed in new but rough and coarsely made clothes, bought at a marine store in Lisbon, but the Negro, whose thick gold ear-rings betrayed his vanity, had wound a scarlet handkerchief round his throat, and his striking appearance soon attracted the attention of all the sailors and loafers at the docks. At another moment he would have been accosted by several, but the business of unloading the newly arrived vessel prevented anything more than passing salutes and jocular cries, to which the darky made no response beyond a proud toss of the head. Targett's return put an end to these attentions. Once clear of the docks, the sailor hailed a four-wheeler and drove to the Dolphin, one of the best houses in the center of the town. There he engaged a room and ordered hot dinner to be brought up for him and the young Negro.

In the evening he went out to a money-changer's and afterwards to a jeweler's. Ten minutes later he returned, whistling, to the Dolphin. Next morning saw him with his Negro, parrot, basket, and sea-chest at Southampton railway station. He took tickets for Poole and bundled his possessions into an empty carriage. As they were starting, a horsy-looking man got in with them. They traveled in silence until the stranger, who had been staring at Targett for half an hour, spoke:

" Reckon you've been abroad? "

Targett nodded. Then he glanced at Tulip, and at each of his possessions in turn, smiled, and said: " So you might guess, sir, from my having a parrot with me."

" Can he speak? " asked the horsy-looking man.

" Not extraordinary," answered the sailor, " but sometimes you could swear it was a baby crying."

" I've a family of seven of my own, thank you," said the horsy-looking man, " without parrots."

" I don't know where he learnt the trick," said Targett, " unless he was once in a large family like yours, but he has learnt it, and it's just like a young child, strike me if it ain't."

" Feathered bipeds they call those birds for being so human," said the stranger.

The line ran through Ringwood. There the horsy-looking man got out on his way to the stables at Stockbridge, and there, point-ing out of the window, the sailor spoke for the first time to his com-panion:

" This is my county. It begins here."

The blackamoor did not answer; he only looked at Targett with a worshipping face and then turned again to the landscape of Dorset and then back again to the sailor.

Next moment he was once more looking out of the window. His expression was alert and watchful. He started with every creak of the railway carriage; he listened to the grinding of the wheels and the puffing of the engine; and at every bump and jar of the slow train on the uneven track he glanced with apprehension at the basket, which lay beside him on the seat of the carriage and on which one of his lean hands rested.

Now that they were alone in the carriage, Targett watched the Negro silently for some moments, and a pitying smile came over his face.

" Now then, Tulip," he said, " take it easy. The train will do you no mischief."

The Negro looked at his master in a shamefaced way, at once humble and contrite, but the next minute he quivered like a grey-

hound as the train passed over a culvert, and again he clutched at
the basket.

" You can take Sambo out if you like," said the sailor.

Tulip at once undid the catch of the basket, which was a very
neatly made affair, pierced with a dozen small holes and orna-
mented with a pattern of dyed grasses, red and green, and with
handles at each end.

A little boy, between two and three years of age, in color the
duskiest shade of brown, was revealed lying upon his back, with
his eyes open, diligently sucking the first two fingers of his left
hand. For a moment or two the young stowaway lay motionless,
seeming to be dazzled by the light of day, but presently he sat up,
took his paw out of his mouth, and began to address Tulip in a
childish jargon, interrupting his odd words with peals of merry
laughter, shouts, and gurgles. Tulip picked him up out of his
basket, or covered cradle, and fondled him very lovingly, but presently set him down on the floor of the carriage, so that he could
trot about. Young Sambo was rather small for his age, but perfectly well made and very muscular, and he looked about him with
an air of calm inquiry and intelligence, noting the motion of the
train, the structure of the carriage, with its doors and windows;
and he ran across very soon to look out first on one side and then
on the other. In all this there was a total absence of fear, or of dismay, at finding himself in strange surroundings, very remarkable
in a young child. Targett watched the little boy with an approving
smile and took him onto his knee, and in that way they traveled
the rest of the way to Poole, with the sailor pointing out to Sambo
all the horses and cows in the fields which they could see from out
of the window.

. When they arrived at Poole, Sambo was not put back into his
basket, Targett telling the Negro to carry the little boy and leave
the luggage for a porter. The sailor then led the way to the Swan
Inn and asked for a bedroom.

The innkeeper's wife looked at him inquisitively.

" What ever's that? " she asked, peering past his elbow at Tulip
in the passage.

" My mate has a baby there; the rest of the things are being
brought along by a porter."

"A baby! You don't mean it!" exclaimed Mrs. Cherrett, the hostess of the Swan, and she pushed by Targett to see for herself.

"Why, it's black!" she exclaimed in a tone of horror. "Poor little chap — he's as black as his father. How dreadful! I didn't think they would have got so black at that age."

Sambo stared back at Mrs. Cherrett with perfect self-possession, while she fussed over him like a hen clucking over an egg. Her noise indeed had much the same effect, for all the women in the house came running into the passage until there were six or seven of them collected round Tulip. Soon they began to poke the little boy with their fingers and even to try to take him from the Negro's arms, while Sambo, with widely open eyes, glanced first questioningly and then appealingly at his protector.

"That's enough now," said Targett. "That child is in the proper hands; show me up now to my room."

"Don't let that nasty man keep him! Proper hands indeed! What can a man expect to know about children? We'll take the little boy down to the kitchen and look after him," cried one of the maids, and the cook actually laid her cheek against Sambo's sooty hide.

At this the barmaid gave a scream. "How can you, Mrs. Bascombe? Why, I wouldn't touch the creature for the world!"

"Come on, now," said Targett; "show us upstairs."

"Poor little shrimp!" said Mrs. Cherrett. "This way, sir. Maggie, you run and bring up some milk for the little boy."

"Or some potatoes and gravy, if you have got them," said Targett.

"I've never seen such a thing in my life," said the barmaid. "A sailorman coming back to England with a little blackamoor! I've known them bring parrots and monkeys often enough, but not children. Just like a black imp from hell too, but there's no knowing what won't take their fancy."

"So there's still hope for you, Annie. The sailorman might take you on his next voyage to Africa, and you would be as fine a curiosity there as the nigger boy is here," said the cook.

"You saucebox!" said Annie indignantly, and flounced into the bar. But she put her head back and said: "You had better take the blackamoor's father into the kitchen, Mrs. Bascombe. If you ask

him nicely, he'll make you a present of a black baby." Then recol-
lecting that she ought always to be quite ladylike, she mopped an
imaginary tear from her eye, tidied her hair, and took a sip of gin
and afterwards a second sip to calm her feelings and prepare herself for the next young farmer who stepped into the private bar.

The following day Targett and his Tulip went out shopping in
the morning (after carefully locking the little boy up in their room
so that the chambermaid could not get at him).

When they had walked up and down both sides of Market Street
and High Street, William Targett came at last to a decision and,
taking Tulip by the hand, entered the shop of Mrs. Frickes,
Modiste.

" I want you to rig this lady with the best dresses you have got;
for she is a lady. She is wearing these clothes because she has only
just come ashore, and now she wants the best of everything that
money can buy. Don't be afraid; I can pay for all." This was a
strange speech, but William uttered it slowly and deliberately, addressing himself to Mrs. Frickes in person.

That good woman stared very hard, but soon pulled out boxes
of dresses, for she never lost custom if she could help it.

Tulip remained unmoved until Targett said he would look back
in an hour's time. Then she took firm hold of his hand and said:

" Please stay to choose the dresses. I shall be afraid without
you."

Targett frowned, pulled his hand away, and swung his arms, but
he stayed in the shop after all, and Mrs. Frickes had to bring out
all the ready-made dress models of the latest fashions which she
had, and a dozen or two rolls of material.

One of the models was chosen for the good reason that it was
the only one which fitted. It was a cream silk, with red and golden
butterflies and flowers worked upon it, short sleeves, trimmed with
real Irish lace, and a ruffle of the same lace at the neck. Besides
this dress, two workaday gowns were ordered to be made. Having
bought the dresses, Targett remembered underclothes, and a crinoline, which had to be got at the draper's next door. Mrs. Frickes
very kindly came with the couple to Mr. Catt's. And there Targett
was at liberty to stand looking out of the window after he had said:

" A dozen pair of stockings, a dozen of handkerchiefs, and six of everything else."

Only once was he appealed to — on the subject of stays.

" We'll take a pair for luck," he decided, " but she need not wear them now."

Mr. Catt was sufficiently obliging to put a room at her disposal where Tulip could change her clothes. While she was dressing, Targett remembered shoes and sent round for a shoemaker to come to Mr. Catt's. At last Tulip was clothed, stockinged, and shod, the bills were paid, and they were ready to depart.

But the news that a Negro had turned out to be a woman in disguise had already begun to spread through the town, and as they came out of Mr. Catt's shop a dozen or more people were waiting to see her. A gasp of surprise, even of admiration, was heard on all sides, for Tulip was very finely dressed now and looked quite a grand lady in her new clothes, though, to be sure, her poor face was still black.

But she was so childishly happy, so innocently delighted, and gave the crowd such sweet smiles that any hostility they may have felt before was instantly dispelled. Nothing but wonder and pleasure at having seen such a sight remained in the minds of the onlookers.

Later in the day clothes were bought for the little boy Sambo, and when they took the train that evening he was no longer hidden in the basket, but made to sit on his mamma's knee and then on his papa's all the way to Dorchester. For that, of course, was the relationship of Targett, Tulip, and the black baby.

In his basket young Sambo had known how to lie quiet so that few people on the passage from Lisbon had suspected the child's existence. He had been brought up in the strict discipline of young Negroes, who are famous for an intelligence and self-control never seen at two years old in our white children. The little blacks acquire this precocity from the conditions of danger and hardship in which they live, for at any moment in Africa a leopard may slink into the village, an alligator crawl out of the nearest pond, a poisonous serpent rear itself up under the first tottering footsteps of a child. Such dangers are almost beyond our imagination; lions, leopards, rhinoceroses, and gigantic riverhorses, snakes, baboons, gorillas, and a thousand kinds of wild beasts infest the continent. The village may be stampeded by elephants drawn up in line like Nelson's fleet at the action of Trafalgar, each fifty yards from his towering tusky fellow, or it may be slowly sapped away by ants moving blindly over the earth in armies vaster than those which spread over Europe in the year 1812.

Indeed, it is not to be wondered at that the smallest children should be obedient, coming from such a land, where there is no need of parents calling up bogies, like the Great Agrippa, to terrify them. The chief difficulty that Targett and his Tulip found on ship-board was in keeping the child clean and in giving him exercise. He was of an age when he was able to eat any ordinary food, and indeed subsisted for the four days between Lisbon and Southampton on ship's biscuit soaked in gravy. Exercise was the difficulty, and after once or twice nearly having him discovered, his parents were forced to deny it him, for Targett had a particular reason for keeping the child hid. To be sure, his black skin rendered him nearly invisible in the dark, and sometimes his father would give him an airing at night. Otherwise he had to keep to his basket, to lie still and keep from making the slightest sound when strangers were by.

It was a great treat to Sambo and to his mother also now that this journey was over, for though it had not lasted more than six days it seemed to them as if it had been as many months.

In Dorchester their arrival made quite a stir; so much so, indeed, that wherever they went in the old town they found it wearing a holiday look, because so many people bustled out of the shops to see them, loitered along the same street, or stopped in the road and stared at them frankly and turned round to gape again until they were out of sight.

It was this that made Tulip tell Targett that Dorchester was a very much finer town than Poole. For the black girl liked the bustle as much as some English ladies would have disliked it, and that although she saw that it was largely because of herself and her child.

They had greeted Targett in her country with as much excitement as was now displayed on her arrival in England. They had made no bones about staring at him in Dahomey.

This remark of Tulip's set William at his ease, and without worrying about those who chose to stare, he made his way along the High Street till he came to Mrs. Gulliver's beer-house, where he asked for a room, and there they stayed the night. The next day Targett employed himself in visiting a tailor's, and in spying out the land, since he had business in Dorchester which demanded a certain amount of circumspection and inquiry.

This was no more nor less than the changing of the whole course of his life. Till that time he had been nothing but a mariner, having followed the sea for some fourteen years, ever since he was a boy of sixteen. Now he had decided to retire from his profession and become a publican. He had to inquire into the hundred details appertaining to the business he proposed to adopt, as well as the general state of the trade itself and the opportunities it afforded in that part of England.

The best thing he could do to find out this was to take his pipe and spend the day in the different bars and parlors of the Dorchester taverns. Thus Targett spent three days, drinking first with the landlord of one house and then with him of another. It was not hard after speaking of his life as a sailor and of the wonderful places that he had seen in the East to turn and say: "You fellows have the best of it ashore! Damme if I don't envy you your trade! Though I dare say you think that I should just broach a keg of rum and set to and you wouldn't hear any more of me for a week."

In the course of these conversations, and for the price of half a gallon of gin, Targett found out a great deal about the trade.

Tulip meanwhile spent most of her time indoors, in her room at Mrs. Gulliver's, looking after her little boy. Once a day she took him out for a walk, but the crowd of people that followed them sometimes became an embarrassment to her, particularly the children, who pressed about her legs and were not happy unless they could touch, pat, or pinch little Sambo.

Soon the word went round that the big stranger had left the sea in order to become a showman, and that Tulip and her baby and the parrot were the advance guard of his collection. Lions, hyenas, and other wild beasts were said to be on their way to Dorchester. This story, like many another of the same sort, never came to the ears of the man about whom it was told.

After a day's idleness, to let the fumes of rum punch and gin and water get out of his head, Targett put on his new suit of navy serge, took his stick of ivory, and called at the office of Wm. Estrich and Pardon, Brewers.

Old Mr. Estrich kept his visitor waiting twenty minutes and then came out of his office to inspect him. "What's your name and what's your business with me, sir?" he asked.

"My name is Targett, William Targett. I hold a master's certificate from Trinity House, but have no longer a command. Now I am leaving the sea and want to set up in the licensed trade, so I have come to you, thinking you can help me."

"Help you — what, with money? You are mistaken there!" said Mr. Estrich, looking hard at Targett.

"No, sir — I have plenty of that; help me to find a good house."

"Come into my office and sit down, Mr. Targett," said old Estrich.

When they were seated he continued: "If you must go into the licensed trade you must, and it is no business of mine to dissuade you. But the life of an innkeeper is not the life for everybody, and in particular it is not the life for a retired seaman. It is my experience of sailors that they drink hard, and while the bout is on they don't care if everything goes to the devil. Now, an innkeeper must always be sober enough to attend to his business, or if he isn't sober he must appear so. That's the reason why gentlemen's servants make good innkeepers — they are such damned hypocrites and toadies. No! If you're a seaman you had better go back to sea again. The land is no place for you."

Targett reached for his hat and stick and got up to go.

"Don't run off like that; good gracious me!" cried old Mr. Estrich, and then, banging a bell on his desk, he shouted: "Boy! Hi there, boy! Bring the tantalus and some clean glasses."

"If you bar seamen it is no good my wasting your time or mine any longer," said Targett, still standing.

"Sit down, Mr. Targett, sit down. If you must have a house you must. I was just warning you, but nobody likes good advice;

that's only natural. My father would have sent me into the navy when I was twelve years old, but I begged and prayed to stop at home, and my mother was on my side. I have never ceased to regret it. That is by the way; but what sort of house do you want? "

" It must be a good house, and the only house in the village. I don't want any bad blood with another man," said Targett.

" I haven't a house vacant anywhere. But how much money have you got? "

" I'm not sure yet," said Targett, " how much it amounts to, but there is plenty and to spare to rent such a house, or even to buy it if it were a small place."

" No, there are no licensed houses in the market; you can put that idea out of your head," said Mr. Estrich. " I'm sorry we have nothing. Wasn't young Stingo in here yesterday? " he shouted through the door. " Didn't he say something about wanting a tenant for the Sailor's Return at Maiden Newbarrow? "

A voice came from the room beyond, but Targett could not distinguish the words.

" Well, he told me he did," said Mr. Estrich. " Now then, Mr. Targett, I shall give you a letter for young Stingo, who wants a tenant, and you may suit each other. But mind you don't pay him more than thirty pounds a year in rent, and never get into his debt. Never get into debt at all, but least of all to your brewer."

After leaving Mr. Estrich, Targett went round to his acquaintances in the bars of Dorchester and stood them a number of drinks so as to find out the reputation that the Maiden Newbarrow public house had in the trade. That afternoon he went to Mr. Stingo's office and signed the lease for the Sailor's Return without even having visited the village.

Two days later Targett with Tulip and Sambo set off for Maiden Newbarrow, mounted upon a large wagon loaded with furniture which had been bought hastily in Dorchester.

They started early in the morning and had gone some miles when the sun rose. Their way lay along by-roads which led through rolling country towards the sea. The sun shone, the grass sparkled with dew, in the hedges there were bushes of faintly blushing dog-rose in full blossom. Tulip, perched high above the chestnut cart-horse in the shafts, began singing. Presently she fell silent and the seaman began a loud and rolling chanty. There was no one on the road that morning to hear them singing or to watch them pass by.

Goldfinches flew out of the hedges, yellow-hammers sped from bush to bush in front of them. A cuckoo late in changing his tune mocked as he flew from tree to tree. They passed through two villages and stopped in each of them long enough for the carter to get a can of beer and drink it.

At midday they entered a green valley which led through the downs to the sea. The road was enclosed by stone walls and bordered by occasional ash trees. A mile further on, the walls fell away and at the ends of the fields gates barred their progress.

Both Tulip and the sailor were silent as they drew round a corner into view of a small village.

There was an open green with high and mighty sycamores, and underneath them scattered groups of thatched cottages, with white walls.

Geese, grazing by the roadside, lifted their heads and walked away at their approach. A little boy who had been playing knuckle-bones stood up and stared while they passed.

They turned the corner and saw the Sailor's Return before them, standing alone a hundred yards or so from the village. It was a long, low house, heavily thatched, with a post standing at one side to take a sign, but the sign had decayed and the frame stood empty.

The shutters were up. On the left-hand side was another green, with a stream beyond. Some ducks embarked in it on seeing them. Across the front of the house was painted: " Stingo's Priory Ales." The painted letters were flaking off.

As they drew up from the village green to the inn several heads appeared over the garden walls, but these were soon withdrawn. One or two women came out of their cottages to look at the wagon, but went indoors again at once as if they had expected to see something else and were disappointed.

They came to rest in front of the inn. Targett climbed down and took little Sambo from Tulip, who jumped down after him and began to clap her hands with delight; then picking up Sambo, she danced up to the door. When William had unlocked it they saw before them a bare flagged passage; they smelt an odor of stale

beer. There were dead bees on the window-sill, and a spider scuttled
into the corner. Targett and Tulip saw these things, but they did
not think of them, for this was their home now — they had
traveled five thousand miles to find it.

The sailor flung up the shutters and unfastened a window. On
each side of the passage was a bar. Behind was a parlor and a
passage leading to the kitchen on one side and to the dining-room
on the other.

The kitchen was large and airy, with whitewashed beams. Beyond it there was a washhouse, a pantry, a scullery, and an out-
house leading to the stables.

Targett, however, did not look any further.

" Go, make a fire," said he to Tulip. " Undo our hamper. We
will bring in a table and chairs by and by, then set the meal, for
we shall be hungry when our work's done."

The carter had taken the ropes off the wagon, and the two men
began to unload the furniture. First came the glasses, which were
carried into a safe place. Then all the household goods — beds,
bedding, tables, wardrobes, chairs, chests of drawers, and wash-
stands; all were set down on the green in front of the house before
being carried indoors.

This was too interesting an event for the villagers of Maiden
Newbarrow to pass over altogether, though they were shy of the
newcomers and did not ordinarily permit themselves to display
curiosity. As usually is the case in England, they showed their
interest in their neighbors rather by surreptitious eavesdropping
than by direct observation or by open questions. However, on this
occasion Freddy Leake, the blacksmith, came up to Targett and
said:

" I suppose you are our new landlord. I'll lend you a hand moving in. Old Burden can spare me from the forge."

Targett gave him a keen look and shook hands with him, saying as he did so:

" That's right. My name is Targett and I am the landlord.
What's yours? "

" Fred Leake, smith's mate."

Other village people began to walk out to the public house in
twos and threes. When they reached it they lingered a moment,

almost stopped, and then walked on to the one cottage which lay
beyond the inn.

Old Mrs. Archer had never before had so many visitors in an
evening. Each leaned over her fence, pulled a sprig of sweet-
smelling marjoram, and said:

"New landlord's moving in, Mrs. Archer. There'll be some beer
for harvest."

"I don't know what the men want with all that beer. I am sorry
to see them come," said Mrs. Archer. "Better have no neighbors
than rowdy ones."

"They say there's a black woman he's brought along with him."

"There," said Mrs. Archer, "what did I tell you? Fine neighbors indeed. But it makes no difference to the men. They'll go
anywhere as long as they can get fuddled."

Soon the wagon was unloaded and the furniture was all carried
indoors, but not before there were further offers of assistance. First
came the postman, who had a letter for Mr. Targett from London,
which had to be signed for and which was sealed with red wax and
string. He seemed in no hurry and took off his coat and worked
away with a will. Then came Charley Nye, the rabbit-catcher, who
gave advice, although he did not do any work. At last they had
finished carrying in all the furniture and had arranged it in the
rooms somehow and had put up the beds. The carter harnessed his
horses, getting ready to go back to Dorchester. The smith and
Charley and one or two others who had joined them only waited
for his departure to go themselves, when a jingling was heard, and
the brewer's big dray came round the corner. The horses were fat
and shiny and moved with that slightly tipsy, dancing gait which
is the sign of all good brewery horses. Perhaps they give them
beer in the stables or feed them on the sprouted grains of barley.

The two men were as large and shiny as the horses, and the dray
itself was loaded high with barrels of beer, and here and there a
little keg of rum, a small firkin of port wine, a cask of sherry, and
a case of spirits.

Such a lot of barrels had not been seen for many years in Maiden
Newbarrow. The last tenant of the Sailor's Return had been heavily
in debt to Mr. Stingo, and at the end his credit had been so
utterly exhausted that when he had spent his ready money that

should have gone to pay the brewer, he could not buy the beer which was his stock-in-trade. On these occasions the public house was shut up, and then the women laughed and the men grumbled. So this great dray-load of barrels of all sorts and kinds of beer, twopenny, threepenny, and fourpenny, not to speak of foreign wines and spirits, was like the sight of a great treasure-ship to the farm laborers. The haymakers had seen it moving along the valley as they worked, from far off on each side of the road. Each one promised himself a happy evening at the Sailor's Return, for it was many weeks since they had tasted liquor other than the small beer some would brew for themselves. And the sight of those great barrels heaped upon the dray made their dry throats bearable to them; yes — even a pleasure. With each breath that they took of the dry hayseed dust, they promised themselves an extra pint of cool old ale that night.

"We shall have our work cut out to drink them dry," they said to each other as they pointed to the far-off dray, with the bulging barrels heaped upon it, and the fat brown horses flashing their polished brasses in the burning sun.

The great dray drew up, a ladder with crooked rungs of iron was put in position for the barrels to slide down, and then, attached to the thickest ropes, they were trundled behind the bar or let down into the cellar. Mallets were found to drive the bungs and spigots and to secure the wooden taps. Glasses were unpacked from the straw crate and rinsed. Soon the first pints of ale were frothing at the lips of the rabbit-catcher, the postman, and the smith's mate and the two draymen.

This sight on the evening of a hot June day overcame the shyness of the villagers. The men marched up in twos and threes and shouted a welcome to the sailor.

The next morning the potman came to the inn. This was a native of the Isle of Wight, whom Targett had engaged in Dorchester. He was a young man, by name Tom Madgwick, of about the middle size, fresh-complexioned, with curly hair and a merry disposition (if you would call a man so who was never known to laugh outright). But to make up for this peculiarity he was most of his time smiling and always seemed to have a joke of his own which it was his business to hide away, yet there was nothing supercilious in him; rather he was naturally innocent and civil in his manners and anxious to please. He was a hard worker too, and Targett could not have found a more honest servant had he searched through the whole kingdom.

Young Tom Madgwick's readiness to work was tested at the moment of his arrival, for there were a thousand jobs to be done that morning in the house. There were floors to be scrubbed, curtain rods to be fixed, carpets to be laid, beds to be pieced together, and all the furniture to be redisposed upon second thoughts about the house and moved from the rooms to which it had first been taken.

Then again some order was necessary in the arrangement of the bar, shelves had to be put up in new places to accommodate the bottles; in the cellars there were barrels to be lifted onto trestles, and many of these barrels had to be at once broached and tapped. In short there was enough hard work to last two men for nearly a week, and then in addition there was the bar to be minded whenever a carter dropped in for a quart of ale, or a child came over with a jug to carry beer for his father's dinner. Besides all this, Targett had to undertake the whole management of the house, both in keeping his accounts (which he neglected, logging them all, it is true, but rarely looking into the book afterwards or casting up his expenses or reckoning his profits) and also in provisioning the household. Thus at every moment he was called off to see the butcher, the baker, or the grocer or else he had to make out a list of things that must come out from Dorchester, and do this while the carrier's cart was waiting.

This part of his work was that which ordinarily is the business of the innkeeper's wife. Here was an opportunity for Targett to see his mistake in having brought with him a black Negro woman from Africa instead of choosing a plain honest stay-at-home woman of his own country. But this reflection never came into the sailor's head, and indeed it was one which all his life he never made. The reason must have been either that he liked this black woman of his so much that he never saw the inconvenience of her or else that it was his nature never to go back on any mistake once he had made it, or even to admit it to himself.

But it must not be imagined that Tulip was idle. No indeed, she took off the fine clothes that Targett had bought for her at Poole and, wearing nothing but her old sailor's jumper and a petticoat, worked all day, fetching and carrying, polishing the pewter mugs till they shone like silver, and cooking the dinner, though at first she made some laughable mistakes in that art. Then there was her little Sambo, whom she had always to be minding lest he should fall into any mischief or danger.

But however hard she might work, at the best it was but doing what she was bid, whereas if she had been an Englishwoman she would have managed a whole province of the household and taken it so completely off her husband's shoulders that he would never need to know that it existed and might all his life long believe that the beds made themselves each morning and changed their linen every Saturday of their own accord.

But Targett very soon found an occupation in which he could employ Tulip in all her spare time. That was in painting, for he had set to work to repaint all the woodwork of the house, room by room, within a week of moving in.

So poor Tulip was kept sandpapering away the paint and washing it down afterwards with hot water and soda in readiness for the first coat, then in mixing the paint and laying it on, then cleaning up all the spots of it that chanced to be spilt on the floor.

After a few more days she was given greater time for this job, for Targett found that the kitchen was beyond his management as much as it was beyond hers, and so he hired a woman to come in every morning to get the meals ready and afterwards to wash the dirty plates.

This woman was a body of about sixty, but very active, and strong enough to do a day's work at the wash-tub, so that during the week she was two whole days in the house, the first washing and the second ironing.

Her name was Eglantine Clall. She was a widow that had no sons or daughters, nor indeed any relatives living in that neighborhood. Only a young stonemason lived with her as her lodger. In the village she was rather passed over than spoken of, and had no cronies, so that when there was a wedding or any such junketing she could never take part in it. She made up for this by always attending funerals (which do not require particular invitation from the principal party).

Another man would have lightened his labor, but perhaps heightened the inconvenience, by calling in painters, paperhangers, and a carpenter; but Targett was trained to think that things were best done if he did them himself, and all the work of the renovation of the Sailor's Return (for it was nothing else) was done by him, Tulip, and their servant Tom.

This was like a true British sailor, who has come to be known all over the world as a "handy-man." There was no piece of work which Targett could not discover the knack of doing. His sea-chest held the proof of it, being three parts full of different tools, ranging from a bradawl to a sextant.

As this work proceeded, the Sailor's Return soon became the very picture of what a country inn should be. It had about it also something brisk and nautical, as much in the style of a crack China clipper as in that of a wayside hostelry.

The parrot's cage hung in the window, and the parrot greeted everyone who passed with a hearty: "Look alive! Look alive! Service! Service!" to which the sailor very soon trained it.

The front of the house had been whitewashed. Above the door was the figurehead from an old frigate, and this had now been repainted and regilded, so that it shone resplendent in the sun. The very curtains of the window were reefed back like the sails of a ship.

With all these improvements Targett and Tulip were kept so busy that they had very little time to go abroad or to make any acquaintance in the village. There too it was the busiest moment of the year. The spring had been a late one, and harvest followed quickly upon haymaking; all the laborers were kept working till after dark; the women went out into the fields, and even the children were set gleaning the last handfuls of corn.

When the first alterations had been completed, Targett began to think he would do well to buy himself a small stock of poultry and even a pig, and so lighten his butcher's bill. There were peelings and household scraps enough to go most of the way towards keeping a pig, while the grass in front of the inn, and the stream beside it, offered pasturage and recreation for three or four geese. Targett had no sooner decided on this addition than he asked who had goslings to sell in those parts, and hearing that Mr. Sturmey was the man, he took his hat and stick and went over to his farmhouse, which, surrounded by a little hamlet called Newbarrow Boys, was at a distance of some two miles, and half-way to the next village, Tarrant.

This was indeed almost the first time Targett had gone abroad from his public house, so busy had he been with his repairs.

As he walked he looked about him with pleasure. First came the village, then on higher ground the church, and when that was passed, the road took a sharp turn and all was out of sight except the high downs on either side of him, now golden with fields of ripe waving corn, or white with stubble, up to the top of the chalk, or very near it. In many of the fields the harvesters were working, and he wondered how they could build their wagon-load of sheaves to stand up on the sides of hills so perilously steep. Indeed, there were places there where the harvest was got in with extreme difficulty and where the sheaves had to be carried by hand to the wagons, across the whole breadth of the field.

Presently he was come to the farmhouse, where he looked about him but saw no one stirring. There was not even a yard dog left to salute him; the folk were away on the down harvesting, and the door of the farmhouse was opened to his knock by a tall woman dressed in the handsomest style, a silk gown, a lace cap, and a lace-trimmed apron — the farmer's wife for certain, though her attire was more suited to the grand lady of a manor house.

No sooner had Targett set eyes on her than a kind of wonder came into his face and he stood for a moment looking at her silently. And she also stood looking at him with amazement.

"Surely you are Lucy and my own sister," said Targett at length.

"And you William, come back from sea."

"I was seeking to buy some goslings, and now I have found you so near a neighbor. You are married, then, sister, I take it, to this farmer here."

" Yes, I am Mrs. Sturmey."

" Well, Lucy, kiss me. It is long since our last meeting, and the quarrel we had on that day seems unimportant now."

" That is true, William, but first I must ask you a question: It is you who are the innkeeper at Maiden Newbarrow? And is it true that you have brought home a black woman and her child? "

" Ay. I brought my Tulip with me, sister; what would you have me do? Indeed, I left the sea because of my Tulip."

" How can you keep her here, William? The scandal has already been talked about, and everywhere people say it is most shameful. They blame Mr. Stingo for letting the house to such a tenant. You must send her back, William; if she does not stay long I dare say it will be forgotten. Until then I cannot pretend to welcome you as our neighbor, though I bear you no ill feeling for the past."

Targett recoiled a step while his sister was speaking, and gazed at her with a peculiar expression. Then he shook his head and said: " You have not changed much, Lucy. You are the same as ever, but you should know me well enough to know that you cannot wheedle me."

Then he laughed. " Send away Tulip, Lucy, because you are such a fine lady! Why, my Tulip was a grander lady than you have ever seen, in Africa, and she brought me a great fortune. Why, the inn itself is Tulip's, and all that's in it; and as for you, Lucy, you can tell your husband to send elsewhere for his beer. He shall have none from me unless to please me he turn you away. For I cannot abide the disgrace of such a heartless woman being my sister."

When he had said this he walked away from the farm and began singing a chanty with bawdy words in it, and so got home without his geese, but with only a piece of knowledge which he would rather not have had. Indeed, meeting with that fine lady, his sister, seemed to him an evil omen, and from that moment on, Targett was ready to perceive any bad signs for the future which might have escaped his eyes before.

Nor were these altogether lacking, though many of them were so slight that the sailor would say all was imagination on his part and nothing more. Then he would utter an oath, pour himself out a glass of sherry, toss it off, and go about his work with a pleasant smile, all happiness again.

The things which would so move him were trivial enough — a couple of women standing in the road to watch Tulip with evil in their faces, an urchin calling out: " Black sheep, black sheep, have you any wool? " or a stray word spoken by the men when he was out of the bar, yet overheard.

But these things were soon dismissed from his mind, and even when he most strongly resented them, he always managed to argue himself out of his ill temper.

" After all," he said to himself, " my Tulip is a black and woolly-headed Negro, such as none of these bumpkins here could look at without wonder. 'Tis natural they should find her strange and should stare at her open-mouthed. No one likes what is out of the ordinary. Everyone's first thought is to do it a mischief, and I must not blame them for that. But when they get used to seeing her, all will be well; until then I must be careful, and she shall not walk through the village except when I am there with her."

Then it came into his mind that very soon he must do what he had been putting off day after day, ever since he had been in England, and that was visit London. His business there was to obtain a sum of money in cash by the sale of pearls and a little gold dust. This he had hoped to do without going to London, but he saw it was business outside the province of any country town. So thinking it over, Targett said to himself: " Ay, to London I must go, a city which I have never been in although I am an Englishman who has traveled over the whole world. And London is a port too; yet I have never chanced to sail from it."

Afterwards he spoke to Tulip, telling her why he must go to London and what a great city it was, and bid her live in the inn in a very retired way until his return.

Tulip listened to all he said very submissively, only saying to him at the end: " William, you do wrong to be jealous of me. You misjudge me if you think there is anyone among your white men here whom I should like to meet; no, I despise them all as much as I did all the black men in Africa. I love no one in the world but you, William."

This mistaking of his meaning touched Targett's heart, for he had been thinking of her safety and had cautioned her not to expose herself lest anyone should do her an ill turn, either by throw-

ing a stone or by insulting her. Of all men Targett was least inclined to be jealous, and as is so often the case with men who are
not jealous by nature, there was never any occasion for him to
be so.

For jealousy is the cause of half the infidelity in the world, and if
once a man find it has gained an entrance to his heart, he should
clap his hand instantly to his forehead and cry out: " What have I
here? " It is ten to one he will find a budding pair of horns.

" Well, Tulip," answered Targett, " think me jealous if you will,
but stay these three days indoors, lest some mischief be done you.
For I have an enemy not far off who might insult you, and the louts
here might pelt you with stones or filth."

And then he told her about his sister, and how even as boy and
girl they had hated each other, of their last quarrel before he went
to sea, and of their meeting again with one another at the door
of her husband's farmhouse.

Tulip listened to what he said and then shook her head and
slapped it as if she hoped to beat some understanding into it — but
still she could only wag her head, frown, and look puzzled. At last
she said:

" I cannot understand about your sister. It is too hard for me."

Then she looked up and saw William was smiling at her, and so
burst into a peal of happy laughter and hugged him, saying: " Your
sister has not hurt you, I see that by your smiling; so let's puzzle
no more about the naughty witch."

And letting go of William, Tulip danced about him, then suddenly stopped and asked him again about his journey, could he not
take her with him, and a thousand other questions. Would he see
the Queen there? Would he go and stay with her pretty husband,
Prince Albert? And she told William how the Queen had sent a
large picture of herself and the Prince Consort as a present to her
father, and how she had always loved to look at it.

Before Targett set out on his journey he called Tom Madgwick
aside and told him that he trusted him, and that he left Tulip
and little Sambo in his care, and that if any harm came to them he
would hold him responsible with his life. Then he cautioned Tom
against giving it out that his master was gone to London. No, he
should not think him further away than Poole and should ex-

pect him back at any moment. Also he should not serve any man too freely in the bar with spirits, but should put him off by saying there was none left in the bottle and his master had taken the key of the cellar with him.

Poor Tom Madgwick was greatly troubled by William's foresight against what seemed to him impossible calamities, and for some time after he had been given these confidential instructions he vexed his spirit by thinking them over. For the potman had an open ingenuous nature; he would never think ill of anyone, nor even suspect a strange dog of wishing to bite him, if it came up to him, and the hair bristling all down its back. Yet he did not think his master had been joking when he had warned him to be so much on his guard. No, he was certain that it was no jest when Targett told him that he would hold him responsible for Tulip's safety with his life. At last by thinking about the matter Tom hit upon a good explanation and then he went to Tulip and said to her: " Mrs. Tulip, I think Mr. Targett was a long time out of England."

" Yes, Tom, I have heard him say so."

" He has been a good while among savages and black people hasn't he? "

" Why, yes, Tom, he has lived among us in Africa."

" He has often been in danger, perhaps even in danger of his life, hasn't he? "

" No, Tom, what you would think great dangers are nothing to him. There is nothing in the world that is strong enough to hurt him. The sea cannot drown him; the fire cannot burn him; the lion cannot wound him with his paw; nor the elephant trample him with his feet. When he walks through the forest the snakes hide in holes and panthers look the other way."

" Yes, I should think that he gave as good as he got," said Tom.

" I tell you," said Tulip with her eyes sparkling, " I have seen him ride upon a crocodile as if it were a horse; he put a chain in its mouth as a bridle and so guided it and kept it from the river."

" I'll be blowed," said Tom; " then he isn't a man to be frightened of his own shadow, and yet there are no crocodiles here in Dorset, and he may have forgotten that in England we lead quiet lives and hardly have a riot in ten years."

After that Tom kept a sharp look-out for any mischief that might

be intended, and spent half an hour in locking up and barring the
house every night.

Nobody tried to break in, and his trouble was thrown away.
Targett was absent four days, and when he returned half an hour
after sunset, the house seemed to him to be looking wonderfully
sweet and peaceful, the very house he had wished for all along; so
he jumped off the new horse which he had bought in Dorchester,
and would have called out to Tom to come and take it, but at that
moment he heard the sound of someone playing his concertina.
Now, Tulip had never learnt to play the instrument, the reason
being that she had a little pipe or rustic flute of her own, on which
she would pick out her own savage tunes, and even make shift to
accompany Target when he sang sometimes, for she was musical.

" Can that be Tulip? " Targett asked himself, and then, throwing the bridle over a post of the fence, he walked to the end window,
for the sound came from the parlor.

There through the window he saw a stranger, all alone in the
room, with the concertina in his hands.

While Targett watched him the door opened and in came
Tulip, who, seeing her master's face against the window, ran
forward and threw it open. Meanwhile the man put down the
concertina, and Tulip said:

" Here is your brother come to see you William."

It was Targett's younger brother Harry, who had not seen him
since he was fifteen years old. William greeted him, and Harry
cried out:

" Well, William, I am glad to see you; you have a fine place
here and I am glad you have come back from sea. Tulip has entertained me well, and I must congratulate you on that young
rogue Sambo."

Harry Targett was a young man with a high ringing voice and
fair hair which grew so thick that no barber could keep it to a
parting. His complexion was pale; his eyes shining; there was a
marked Adam's apple in his throat.

" Where have you sprung from Harry? "

" Only think," cried Tulip, " he rode up to the house to have
a pint of ale; I looked out thinking it might be you, and then I

heard him ask Tom at the bar: ' Are you Mr. Targett? ' And then:
' Is he a seafaring man about thirty? ' "

" Tom was shy of answering me at first," said Harry, " but when
I said you were my brother he softened, and Tulip came running
in and made me wait here for the night in the hope that you
would come back."

Targett threw off his coat, and Tulip had to exclaim again and
again at the new clothes he had bought in London. Then while
he drew off his riding boots she spied a gold watch-chain and seals
hanging out from his fob. Targett drew it out and tossed it to her,
a gold hunter watch, set with diamonds. He pulled off his gloves,
and there was a fine belcher ring on his finger.

" I have some pretty trifles for you too, Tulip," he said, and
pulled out a cheap necklace and a bracelet of gold.

" And there are lots of fine things coming from town, for I
have done the greatest stroke of business you have ever heard of,
and I'm a rich man, Harry."

" I will say," he added, patting Tulip on the head, " that I owe
all my riches to Tulip here."

Tom came in then to call them to dinner, which was of a big
crab apiece, followed by ducklings with green peas. They drank
claret, which Tom was sent to fetch up from the cellar.

All through dinner Targett kept asking a thousand questions
of his brother Harry. How were John and Mrs. John and what
new nephews and nieces had he got? And how was Dolly? She
must be a fine girl now — and what of the baby Francis? How was
he? And how many of the old pastures had they broken up for
corn? All these questions and the answers to them are not to
the purpose of the story, only they filled up dinner. Then when
they went back to the parlor with some old brandy, and while
Tulip was fetching their pipes, Harry turned the tables.

" Nothing much happens on a farm, William," said he; " that
was the reason you gave our brother John for going to sea, and
that is why I often think myself of going away to America. There
is gold in California, and there are vast plains covered with wild
horses and buffaloes and Indians. But what have you been doing
these last ten years, William? For I am sure it is ten years since

you came back to visit us. It is your turn now, and you must tell
me your story."

"Drink up your brandy," said the sailor. "Go, Tom," he
shouted through the doorway; "go and burn us a pint of brandy.
I shall have to wet my throat if I am to spin you such a long yarn.

"It was in '48 that I left home for the third time. I shipped at
Bristol in the *Belsize*, bark, as second mate. We were carrying a
cargo of Birmingham goods for Guinea, to return laden with log-
wood and cocoa.

"I stayed in the *Belsize*, for she suited me, and the Guinea trade
was a change from southern seas and long cruises. In '51, when I
had been three years in the *Belsize* and was mate, we touched at
Whydah, and I was sent ashore with a boat's crew to see if the
merchants there could help us to make up a cargo. We had been
disappointed at Lagos; Whydah was out of our usual beat. My
men soon got into mischief in the town, and to stop further trouble
in a strange port I marched them back to the coast and sent them
on board, telling them to fetch me the next day, as the chacha,
Mr. de Souza, had offered me hospitality.

"In the night a regular hurricane blew up and the *Belsize* had
to slip her ground tackle and be off without me. That did not
worry me, for I expected her to come back in the next few days
and pick me up, when the sea had gone down a bit. However, the
weather continued wild for over a fortnight, and Captain Johnson,
having been driven getting on for a thousand miles of his way
home, thought it better to do without me then, meaning I suppose to come back for me on his next voyage, some two or three
months later.

"He never came, for the *Belsize* was cast away on Lundy Island
in a fog. I wrote of course to the owners by the next vessel out from
Whydah, and they treated me very handsomely, for they wrote back
sending me my wages and compensation money. Living at Whydah
I was two miles from the sea, and out of sight, they say, means
out of mind.

"Whydah, you know, is the chief town still left in the slave
trade, though that of course is nothing now to what it was once.
Being an Englishman, I was looked on with suspicion by all the
merchants except one, a Mr. Martinez, who treated me very

kindly and in whose house I stayed when I had no money. It so happened that a Brazilian ship put in after I had been living in the town about six months, and the captain was taken very ill with rheumatism. They were in want of an officer to take his place, as he was the only competent navigator on board of her. I had often asked Mr. Martinez how I could repay him for all his kindnesses. He had an interest in this Brazilian ship, which was nothing more nor less than a slaver, and now he came to me and said: 'Oh, Captain Targett, why were you born an Englishman? I would to Heaven you were a man of any other country; however, there is no help for it.' This was as good as asking me to run the boat over to Bahia for him, and seeing his distress, I offered myself. I did that to oblige him, but knowing it is a dangerous sort of trade, and that it is criminal for an Englishman to employ himself in it, I would not continue after that one voyage, although the handsomest offers were made to me to do so; neither would I take any money from Mr. Martinez for that trip. The Brazilian captain having recovered when I got back loaded with rum, I was the better able to decline all the propositions made to me. After that voyage I was once more at Whydah, but of course on a very different footing. On several occasions I went to the capital, Abomey, in the company of Mr. Martinez and by him was presented to His Sable Majesty King Gaze-oh. You know, Harry, I was afraid to be at Whydah after that voyage to the Brazils. Her Majesty's ship *Kingfisher* was often enough in the roads, and her captain had heard of what I had done, he might demand me from the Viceroy or even kidnap me away. I had no mind to be transported to Botany Bay as a slaver and a renegade. For that reason I decided to move to Abomey. While I was there I fell a good deal into the company of old King Gaze-oh. He was every inch a king and a very good friend to me, and it was he who gave me his daughter Gundemey, whom I call Tulip, in marriage, who otherwise would have been a captain in his army of Ama-johns, as they call them on the coast. After I had been living there two years, Gaze-oh was taken ill with the smallpox and died, leaving the kingdom to his son Geleley. When a king dies in that part of the world there is a very great slaughter made of the women in the palace so that he shall not go alone. On his death-bed Gaze-oh

made everyone swear to forgo this massacre; but yet I felt no
security, because Geleley and I were not suited to one another,
and he was the King. At such times it is hard to tell what that
people will not do, so the day before Gaze-oh died I left Abomey
and went back to Whydah, to Mr. Martinez, and through him got
safe passage to Portugal with Tulip and Sambo. Everyone on the
coast knew I had married old Gaze-oh's daughter, so I dressed
Tulip in man's clothes and kept Sambo hidden while I was on an
English ship. They were not likely to be on the look-out for me,
but I took no chances. Tulip had brought me eighty slaves as her
dowry, so that I was a rich man whilst at Abomey, though dependent on the favor of the King. But leaving so suddenly, I
could only carry with me that part of Tulip's fortune which was in
pearls and gold dust and ivory, yet that has fetched more than
five hundred pounds, enough to get me a hulk of my own."

"You'll not be off to sea again, surely," said Harry.

"No. I've got my Tulip and little Sambo and this public house
here, what I call my hulk, and now I shall live here happily to the
end of my days."

"What sort of a place is that town you spoke of?" asked Harry.

"Abomey lies less than a hundred miles from the sea, in country which has a wondrous soft and pleasant aspect, all fields of
corn dotted with palm orchards. The chief fault in its situation
is that there is very little drinking-water, and that is oftentimes
white with clay. In the town there are many great palaces; I
lodged in one of them. They are all thatched houses like here in
Dorset, with clay walls, but the thatch comes within a few feet
of the ground. The Komasi palace has two stories, the others only
one. Everything in Abomey is given up to the king and his
army. But you will never believe me now, Harry, when I tell you
that the army is half women, and they are more feared than are
the men. There are five or six thousand of these women in
Dahomey, and if Gaze-oh had not let me marry her, Tulip would
have been one of them, for she was in the band of archers, who
are young girls. The older women are all armed with muskets like
our own foot-soldiers in the Crimea.

"Once a year, in January, the king holds his own customs, and
then after that the bush-king holds his. By some Gaze-oh and

the bush-king are thought to be the same man. That is what I
say, but Tulip always says no. At the king's customs all evil-doers
are slain and the palace steps are planted with human heads. That
is a terrible time and the town runs red with blood. Yet even then
everything in the kingdom is only a kind of play-acting, for they
are an exceedingly happy people; drinking, dancing, singing, those
are the ways they pass the time; all is no more than dressing themselves up, one day as leopards, the next as bulls; and yet in the
middle of their fun they will be cruel and bloodthirsty. Tulip was
so much a favorite that I was privileged for her sake and saw only
the lighter side of life. They are the merriest people and care for
nothing so much as dancing and rum and women and masquerades.
The women are more the equals of the men than here in England.
You cannot imagine that, Harry. While I was there I drank
enough for six, though sometimes I would go forth with a party
to hunt elephants for the ivory or to capture slaves.

" It was my first hunt of that kind that brought me Tulip. The
King went out with a large party into the bush, taking me with
him, but he was seized with a colic and lay in his tent with no
taste for hunting. He sent for me then and told me I should not
miss seeing the sport, because he was a little indisposed, and that
seven of his Ama-johns were setting out, and that I should go
with them in charge of a eunuch. These huntresses were the elder
women, great fat things, but as strong as oxen, and all of them
noted shots. Each one carried an elephant-gun and had a young
girl with her to carry her bag of bullets and to wait on her. Tulip
was one of these. We were crossing a belt of open country, covered
with patches of tall, dry grass, and we went in a long line like
beaters to rouse any game there might be. I was at the end of
the line, and Tulip was next to me and beyond her the huntress
she served. I was just in the thick of some tall grass when they
roused an elephant at the other end of the line and fired at him.
But instead of there being one brute, there was a herd. When I
got out of the patch of long grass I was in, I saw twenty or thirty
of the great beasts charging up and down the line and throwing
headless bodies in the air, for the first thing your elephant does
is to pull off the head. I drew back into the tall grass at once
and lay there, while the brutes trampled up and down round the

bodies of the women; they stayed there trumpeting till long after sunset.

"At last the sound of their feet and of their cries died away in the distance. The moon was full, and the brightness of it extraordinary even for the tropics. When I put my head out of the grass and looked about me the first thing I saw was Tulip, not twenty yards off, doing the same thing. When she saw me she came out and took me by the hand, for she was glad to see anyone at that moment.

"I for my part was equally joyful and took her in my arms and kissed her, without thinking that it was an act that would have cost me my life had there been anyone there to see. Tulip was thirteen years old then, a pretty creature, not quite formed as a woman, for she was more backward than most of her race.

"Together we searched for the others, but found no one, only dark patches in the trampled grass, a broken gun, and the carcasses of three elephants. We dared not search long, for there were lions, leopards, and hyenas all about us, drawn to the spot by the smell of blood and the meat of the dead elephants. The roaring and screaming of these creatures was hideous, but we passed through them safely and slept unmolested in the open country. The air was cold, and Tulip lay very close to me, with her arms about my chest for warmth; she had lost her mantle and was bare above the waist. The next evening we got back to King Gaze-oh's camp, and by that time, Harry, I had conceived a very great affection for the child. We found that three of the other girls and one Amajohn were just got back. They were the only other survivors. I went directly to the King, where he lay on a couch in his tent. When he heard my story he showed very great concern, not for the loss of his huntresses, but for Tulip.

"'Captain William, Captain William,' he cried (for that was the name I used after my cruise to the Brazils), 'what shall I do now? The poor girl is undone; how can I save her? I know they will all whisper that you ravished her. I know that they will demand her head when I keep my customs.' Then he began to curse Dahomey and his ancestors and his people, saying that they were the most cruel, savage and bloodthirsty scoundrels in the world, and that there was no ruling them without perpetual slaughter.

I had heard him say a great deal to the same purpose on a former occasion, so that his words did not surprise me as much as they would otherwise have done. At last I told him that if he would give me Tulip I would convey her secretly out of his kingdom and that I would marry her.

" 'If you will take her,' said he, 'you will save the poor girl's life without flying the country either, but I would not wish you to have her, Captain William, for your own sake.' I asked him what he meant by that, and he answered that he could not give me his daughter except honorably, and then I should be his son and as much accountable to him as any of his family, and that if I used Tulip ill I should have to answer for it with my head, and that being a white man would not save me from the most horrible of deaths. I told him that I would run those risks willingly, only to have his daughter even if there were no question of her life, for I loved the child and had no doubt I should love the woman. All the while we were talking thus Tulip sat in one corner of the King's tent, cutting a thorn out of her foot and never looking my way or saying a word to her father. At last he turned to her and asked if she would trust herself with a white man, and said many things in my commendation. Tulip still sat puzzling over the thorn in her foot. When her father had said all he could think of (and that was a great deal more than was necessary), she said: 'I must first get this broken thorn out of my foot, Father.'

" Old Gaze-oh laughed at that, and we waited her pleasure. At last she put away her knife very carefully, got onto her feet, and looked me up and down for a few moments, and then she said: 'Yes, I will have him.' After that she took me by the hand and said: 'You are a very big man, Captain William, to be my husband; otherwise I like you well enough, as I think you must know already.'

" Well, well, it is a great change, Harry, to be here. Tulip feels it, to be sure, ten times more than I do; for her everything is as strange as it was for me in her father's kingdom. But our folk are not so merry as the Africans are, and that makes the greatest change for her, as she is used to laughter. Often she has asked me why the men here do not dance, why they never beat drums or clap their hands or shout songs in chorus. She thinks we are a very dull set of dogs here."

While William was speaking Tulip knelt in the corner, sitting back on her heels. It was strange to see her there in her English dress, with a full skirt, and her head bare, with its crop of short and curly wool.

"Do you remember, William, at the bush-king's customs, how they sang?"

And then Tulip began to sing a gay song of her own country.

"Take off those clothes, child," said William, "and dance for us." Tulip rose obediently and left the room. When she came back she was dressed strangely enough in what she thought came nearest to the costume of her own country; this was indeed nothing but a pair of white calico drawers held in place by a gayly colored silk scarf which William had given her. Round her head she had wound a band of broad white tape as a fillet. Her figure was very slender, her body very black. She was tattooed under the breasts on her belly. "Nay, Tulip," said William, "I fear you will scandalize Harry. He is not used as I am to seeing you black women without your clothes."

Tulip was offended by these words; her lip trembled, her eyes filled with tears. For she was naturally modest, and such a reflection upon her behavior wounded her. She caught up her little jacket and slipped it on at once, but William had no sooner spoken than he was sorry for his words. Harry, however, had taken them as a capital joke and laughed out aloud. In laughing he choked, spilt some brandy, and laughed again. "Silly girl, I was only joking with you," said William. "The less you wear, the better you look."

Tulip could never resist laughter; she was never sulky long, so that very soon she had forgiven William for what had angered her. Then she threw off her jacket, blew Harry a kiss, and called to William for music. What followed cannot be described, for a dance has to be seen with the eye; no words can imitate the dancer's gestures. Here it must suffice to say that William played his concertina, while at the same time he marked the tune by beating with his heel on a tin tea-tray, and that this tea-tray, put upside down on the floor, served very well for a drum. Whilst he did this he also sang, if one can call it singing, the chorus of a Negro song, which, sometimes high and sometimes low, came in again and again. Tulip began her entertainment by throwing a few cartwheels and by pulling a great many extravagant faces, which sent Harry into fits of laughter. After this opening she began the regular Dahomeyan dance to William's accompaniment. In this the whole body is incessantly agitated, the hands saw the air, the elbows are jerked back and forth so violently as to click together behind the back like the slow measure of castanets, the breasts tremble and shake, whilst the feet stamp, kick, and shuffle and the hips and buttocks move to and fro, round and round, backwards and forwards, all marking perfect time to the music, thus forming the most harmonious and edifying spectacle it is possible to imagine; that is, if the performer is young and pretty. Every now and then as she danced Tulip called out: " Faster, William, faster! " and the dance became more violent and more rapid. At last William gave a cry of exhaustion and threw himself back panting in his chair. Tulip brought the dance to an end by walking across the room on her hands, while William marked every step with a loud bang on the tea-tray. Tulip's body was glistening with sweat like a horse after a sharp gallop, but she was not winded as William was, and after throwing a shawl over her shoulders she began to sing herself.

So with Tulip sometimes singing and sometimes dancing while William played the concertina, they passed the hours of the night. Every little while Harry and William would take another glass of brandy grog. Now and then Tulip would take a sip, not too much, lest it should make her giddy.

Tulip's childhood had been passed, as William had told his brother, in a royal palace, and she had been taught the proper deportment for a king's daughter. No gracious feat of the body or trick of dancing had been omitted from her education.

After some time William wished to dance himself; he gave Harry the concertina, while he showed them a good hornpipe. After that he danced as Tulip had done, but he was not so perfect as she.

Harry stopped playing. His last glass of brandy had been too much for him, and when he stood up to stretch himself he staggered and would have fallen had not William caught him by the shoulder.

They led him to his bed; he tumbled into it and fell fast asleep.

But though William had come that day from London and had ridden out from Dorchester to Maiden Newbarrow, and although he had been drinking quite as heavily as his brother, Harry, his head was moderately clear and his appetite for pleasure was unquenched.

"Come along, Tulip," he cried. "See, it is a clear night; we will ride over the hill to the sea."

They went down then to the stable, fetched out William's new riding horse and the one on which Harry had been mounted, saddled them, and rode off.

The sky was already pale, and the horses, excited at being taken out at an hour strange to them, galloped down the road and straight through the village street.

William halloed as they passed the church, and Tulip answered with a loud cry, which you may be certain had never been heard before in Dorset.

When they had already passed some way into the open country, there was a scratching of lucifers, a snapping of flint on steel, then a rushlight or two, and a candle gleamed in the windows of the village as the old women looked out into the pale street.

William and Tulip soon passed Lucy's farm and breasted the down beyond.

Over the hill was the sea. There they went cautiously down a winding path that led them to the gap in the cliffs. Soon they dismounted, tied their horses to a tree, and ran down onto the beach.

It was high tide, and the sea was so calm that it might have been a great saucer of milk; gently moving but without a wave it brimmed up to the very lip of the shingle beach.

William threw off his coat, his shirt, and his trousers.

"Are there no sharks?" asked Tuilp.

"No, not in England."

Tulip had slipped on her seaman's trousers and an old coat of William's when she came riding. Now she flung them off and raced after him into the water. It was warmer to their bodies than the air of the August night.

They swam out in silence, Tulip's curly black head bobbing in the wake of William's fair one.

The coolness of the sea and the salt taste to it sobered William, and the exictement of his journey, of meeting with Harry, and the singing, the dancing, the music, and the ride, vanished. The fumes of brandy departed suddenly; he felt calm and at peace.

They swam back. As they got into their clothes William said:

" Glad we got away from Dahomey, Tulip? "

" I too am glad," answered Tulip.

" Your father was a good man all the same," said William as they untied the horses.

" Yes," said Tulip as they went up the cliff road. " His ghost cannot follow us here. Don't let's speak of him."

When they got back to Maiden Newbarrow the men had gone to work, the women were getting ready breakfast against their return; they stared at Tulip, who rode in front with her bare feet thrust into the leathers of Harry's stirrups, William's jacket hanging loosely in folds round her naked body, and her wet, woolly head shining.

Targett gave them each a cheerful " Good morning," but they did not answer until he turned towards them in his saddle.

Tom came running out and took their horses. Harry was still asleep and did not get up till past midday.

Then he embraced Tulip, wrung William's hand, and mounted his horse.

" I must get on to our sister Lucy's," said he; but in less than an hour he was back again.

" It seems I must choose between Lucy and Tulip, William. That's the greeting I got at the farm. She had heard of our jollification last night. So I told her straight out that I thought it was better to be black outside like Tulip than foul within like herself."

William laughed and asked Harry to come in, but Harry would not stay, he only bared his teeth in a grin which matched Tulip's own, waved his hand, set spurs to his horse, and was off to the home farm on the other side of the county.

Harry's words gave William a great deal of pleasure; he went about his business the next few days in high spirits, and began making a weathercock in the form of a full-rigged ship with all her canvas set.

But if he had not been so happy and high-spirited, whistling and singing as he cut out the sails, masts, and rigging in the sheet of copper, and afterwards polishing it, smoothing it, painting the sails white, the hull vermilion, and gilding the little figurehead, he must have observed a new surliness in the villagers. The men still came for their beer, as was natural, but the women did not speak to him when he went through the village.

By this time little Sambo was quite firm on his legs and was always running in and out of the house. His mother was very gentle with him and never scolded him in the harsh and strident way that the village women use to their children. But in a low voice she would reason with him when he was at fault, or so laughingly chide him that he was easily disposed to alter his ways for the better.

As a result of her tender treatment there was never a child of Sambo's years that cried so little or that had shed so few tears during its young life. He was indeed the most merry fellow imaginable, smiling at everyone he saw, though he had a certain shyness too, which made him keep his distance from strangers. Often he would stand in the doorway of the bar and smile winningly at any of the men who spoke to him, yet he would not trust himself to go to them when they called him, but only laugh and wag his head and hesitate.

Tulip made it her practice to go out with her child part of every morning. Then she would let him run where he would, and idly wander after the child, and often stand still for ten minutes at a stretch watching him play, and hold out her hand for her baby to come and take it. Sometimes they would wander into the village, but usually they went out on the other side from it, and then perhaps they would turn into a green meadow where she could sit down.

All the while Tulip was watching lest Sambo should run into some danger, and she kept her eyes open, though chiefly for dangers which are not to be met with in Dorset. Thus her glance always scanned the sky for eagles and vultures, the hedges for leopards and wildcats, and the ground itself for venomous serpents and noxious deadly insects. The only dangerous creatures which she and Sambo were ever likely to meet were the bulls, which in Dorsetshire are not shut up but go usually with the cows, and the rare vipers which were not often to be found so near to the village.

Sambo might, it is true, get stung by a nettle or a wasp, but there were no scorpions or poisonous spiders; he might prick his fingers on the spines of a straying hedgehog, but there were no angry porcupines to slap him full of quills with a smack of their tails. And as for lions, leopards, bears, baboons, and crocodiles, there was nothing of that kind. Tulip might surely have closed her eyes; her child was safe enough in England.

Yet even so the Negress found something to disquiet her, for one day she brought back Sambo early, walking faster than was usual with her and looking round to see if she were followed. Targett was outside the inn, varnishing his new weathercock before setting it up, and he noticed her unusual step and her agitation and hailed her:

"Tulip my girl, what is wrong this morning? Why do you look so?"

At first Tulip would not speak at all, but, knowing her well, Targett showed no impatience, only he set down his masterpiece, the full-rigged ship, and went to her and took her by the shoulder and kissed her poor black face and ran his fingers through her woolly hair.

So wheedling her, at length he got her to tell him her story; but even then she would only whisper it fearfully to him, as if afraid that someone would overhear her, though there was no one even in sight, and they stood together in an open space where no eavesdropper could come nigh them.

"William," said she, "I am very afraid for Sambo. The Black Doctor came up to me in the road just now, and I am afraid of him. He will do Sambo a mischief."

Targett was used to her speech, which came from her African ways of thinking, and so when she said "the Black Doctor," he understood her to mean nothing worse than the village parson, the Reverend Adrian Cronk.

"Why do you fancy that, Tulip?" he asked her. "What did the

parson do to you that you should be afraid of him on Sambo's account? "

" He came up to me as I was standing in the road," answered Tulip, whispering. " And he asked me what was the name of my little boy. I told him: ' Mr. Targett calls him Sambo.'

" Then he said you could not give him a name unless he was washed in the church, and after that was done he would be as white as snow. And unless we had him washed white, Sambo would be burnt in a fire with devils."

And then poor ignorant Tulip gave way completely and burst into loud sobs. For a long while nothing Targett could say or do would comfort her, and she only broke out afresh into pitiful moans and blubbering whenever he spoke. When he tried to take her into his arms she would have pushed him away, but that he held her fast.

And little Sambo, seeing his mother so distracted, ran up to her and hid himself in her skirts and began to wail and whimper himself to keep her company.

William then led her indoors and forced her to drink a can of beer, and argued with her soberly, and at last dried her tears.

But when he told her that what the parson said was true, and that children in England were always christened, her tears gushed forth again and she became quite distracted.

At last Targett got out of her what was at the bottom of her troubles, for she blubbered out:

" I want to keep my Sambo. I am black and I love my black baby. I shall never love him the same after he is washed white."

Targett then could scarcely forbear laughing at her for her heathen notion, and told her that Sambo would always be the same color; the parson could not change that, whatever he did. But for a long time Tulip would not believe him, and at last she said:

" If I am washed, can I be made white also? I would not mind so much then, but perhaps, William, you would not love me if I were not black."

At this Targett had to laugh outright. But although he laughed, he kissed her, and presently persuaded her that she had misunderstood the whole matter, though she still continued fearful of the effects of a baptism and convinced that the Black Doctor might be a danger to Sambo.

It was beyond the sailor's power to explain to Tulip the true nature of redemption. For not only was he by his habit of life naturally indifferent to religion, but he was somewhat hazy upon such matters as original sin, and even the communion itself. All he knew or could tell Tulip was that he was a Christian, that what was good enough for him should be good enough for her and for his children, and now they were in England and not in Africa and must live according to the English religion.

He told her, too, that here in Dorset there was only one God; and that he had written a book in which he had set down the early history of the world, which was called *The Holy Bible*. There was a second part of it, called *The New Testament*, which contained the life of Jesus Christ, who was the Son of God by a virgin, and that all our sins had been taken over by Christ, provided always that we believed in Him.

But while William told Tulip these things, it was apparent to her that he did not lay very much store by them and was not a bit afraid of the fire of which the Black Doctor had spoken. Indeed, William told her that it was time enough to go to church and worry oneself about such matters when one was old and past work, but one must always show a proper respect for the parson.

All this allayed Tulip's first terrors very much and gave rise to a singular notion in her head, and that was that the English God was nothing like so powerful or dangerous as the African gods to whom she was accustomed. For even her father, who was a King, trembled at the name of the Porro-men. No one in Dahomey could have said like her William that there was no need to worry about religion until one was old.

There the gods or devils (call them whichever you please) were so strong that their worshippers could have anything they desired, and in particular the Snake God and the Leopard God were powerful above the others. Almost every day a man was suddenly changed by one or other of these gods into a leopard or a snake, and would snatch up a child and carry him off in his jaws while the mother and father were powerless to resist.

And in the evening the man who had been changed into the

form of a beast would be back at his house in his own shape, and all his fellow-worshippers would be invited to partake of the sacred roast.

It was natural, therefore, that Tulip should have many questions to ask concerning the Holy Sacrament, and transubstantiation, but she soon found that it was nothing like what she had imagined it to be. This, you may be sure, was a very great consolation to her, yet the sight of the parson, Mr. Cronk, and the tolling of the church bells on a Sunday, always made poor heathen Tulip uneasy and secretly afraid that someone or other of the church-wardens in the form of a beast would pounce upon her or upon her Sambo.

This conversation was not to be left without fruit, though William dismissed it for the time being from his mind, for about a week or two later Mr. Molten, one of the farmers, was in the bar and asked him point blank had he had the child baptized yet.

" No," said William, " there's plenty of time for that."

" You have no call to name the child Sambo then," said the farmer. " I can call him young Sea-Coal or what I like and it's as much his name as Sambo is."

" But he answers to me when I call him Sambo," said William, and just then Sambo ran in so pertly that he made them all burst out laughing.

" Well," said the farmer, " I think young Sea-Coal is the better name for him, but whether it is Sea-Coal or Sambo, you'll have to have him christened if you are to live here and bring him up with our children at the school. We can't have him teaching them to worship heathen idols."

William laughed at this and said he would speak to the parson about the christening one of these days.

It was autumn, the harvest was all gathered in, the hedges were covered with the last blackberries, and William began to make provisions for the winter, when his public house would be the meeting-place every night for all the men of the village. Foreseeing this, he prepared to throw open another room, which led out of the public bar, so that they should not be too crowded. He had the whole of the room newly painted, and put in a hatchway to the bar, so that the men could be served without leaving the room.

Then thinking of the long winter evenings which were in store for all of them, he determined that there should be games in that room, so the men might play and keep amused.

First he painted a bull's head very like life, upon the wall in one corner, and drove a big hook into the wall between its nostrils. Then he found an old brass ring, just the ring that farmers use to put in the nose of a bull when he is young to hold him, and he fastened this ring to a line about five feet long and tied the other end to a staple in the ceiling so the ring hung freely. By swinging it with nice judgment, a man might get the ring to catch the hook, and so ring the bull. This game was one which Targett had heard say was the oldest parlor game in England, and it pleased him to have a sport of such antiquity in his bar. For the rest he had to go into Dorchester to buy a set of hooks and rings and parlor quoits, a target with darts, and a bagatelle table with two or three spare cues and balls, and a couple of sets of boxing gloves, for he thought every man ought to be able to use his fists. Besides these he planned to get a ruled slate with metal disks for shove-half-penny, a box or two of dominoes, a draughts-board with men, and a bag of marbles with a board for fox and geese or solitaire. Armed with all these he thought he could make the winter pass pleasantly enough for his patrons, the village yokels and the farmers and their sons. Then there was another toy which he added himself and which caused as much amusement as any of the others, particularly when there were any strangers in the company. This was nothing more than a quantity of pith balls, which he made by forcing the pith out of the young branches of an elder bush, and then dried them and rounded them carefully with his razor. Many a pint of beer was won and lost with these pith balls, for although they looked large and solid to the eye, and seemed as though a man might throw them like pebbles, they were such featherweight things that they could not be thrown at all. The strongest man might take one in his hand and hurl it with all his might, but when the pith ball left his hand it fell gently to the ground not a yard away. But there was a trick with these, and that was to set open the doors on each side of the room and let the draught catch them, and then they would blow right across the room and out into the passage.

In this way William prepared to amuse and entertain the men who came to drink a quart of ale at his house. For he loved all pastimes and sports himself, and on board ship had always found that they sweetened the voyage and prevented arguments and quarrels, and the hatching of any kind of mischief, most of which comes about, so he would say, from dullness and lack of something to do. Everything Targett did he did himself, so instead of ordering these things to come out by the carrier he rode one day into Dorchester to choose them himself, so they should be of the best quality made and just as he fancied.

I cannot say how it was but one or two women seeing him ride away, dressed very sprucely in his best with a new top hat on his head, inquired of each other:

"Where was Mr. Targett going?"

Someone then gave it out that he was away to London, and this piece of news, as they thought it, was spread by the means of an old woman selling buttons and combs and got carried to New-barrow Boys, where his sister Lucy lived in the farmhouse. From thence it got carried to the village beyond as a certain thing that Mr. Targett had gone away to London that morning.

When Targett got back to the village that night it was growing dark. Night falls before we expect it in the autumn; the traces of summer linger on into winter, and we resent the shorter hours of daylight all the more because there are still roses in the garden. But though it was dark it was not yet night; there was still a little color in the sky, held there by the storminess of the clouds, which, though they lay torn in savage ribbons, remained frozen and immobile, yet threatening. It was impossible to judge their distance; they might have been near or very far away. William let his horse drop into a walk. A sky like that always told him stories, calling up memories of other skies, and of all the scenes which those other skies had brought with them. The sky which he had in his mind's eye was just such a one as he had been watching for the last half-hour, but it was a Patagonian one. It had foretold his first passage round Cape Horn. How angry the sea had been, how cold! His heart had failed him as he had walked the deck, but it had proved only a threat; the tempest had not broken, and a fortnight later he had picked an orange in a garden in Valparaiso while a pretty girl lay in a hammock and laughed at him.

There was the shrill sound of women shouting. William looked down from the sky, and for the first few moments his eyes could distinguish nothing in the darkness which hung over the earth. Figures were moving in front of the inn. There were two or three flashes like a flint struck on steel, then a flame which died away quickly. William pulled up his horse and listened. At intervals a woman screamed out a few words.

"Smoke them out." "Fire the thatch." "Bring out the black sheep." Then she shrieked more rapidly: "Oh, the dirty nigger! Come and give her a singeing, boys! I'll make her dance, the ugly toad!" A man's voice said: "Best hand her out, Tom, or they will fire the house; there is no holding them; they will have her."

William did not wait longer, but pressing his horse with his knees, rode up at a gentle trot. As he approached he could see that there was a crowd gathered. Three or four figures were standing close in front of the inn, and all round at a little distance groups of silent figures were looking on. Targett rode straight up to the door of the Sailor's Return. There was a silence.

"What's this, neighbors?" he asked, with his hunting crop in his hand. It was some time before he got an answer, but at last one of the men on the outskirts of the crowd called out: "They have all come over from Newbarrow Boys; maybe your sister sent them."

"Yes, they all came from Newbarrow Boys and Tarrant about an hour ago," cried another man; "we were just watching them to see they didn't do any mischief."

"That Tom Madgwick is a bold fellow; when they went in the bar he drove them out with a gun in his hands and locked the door on them."

Targett found that the crowd seemed just as big as ever, but it was composed of his friends.

"Tom — how is this?" said he, for by this time Tom had opened the door. "Is it true that they came from the next village?"

"Yes," said Tom; "I think the others only came to look on. They took no part either way."

"Well, tell my sister, Mrs. Sturmey, and her husband," said William, "that if ever this happens again, or if my Tulip should meet with any harm, I hold them responsible, and shall spare no money to see them hanged." Then looking about him, he said: "Put away that gun, Tom, what would you do if some of these good neighbors of ours died of fright? It would mean transportation for you. Good night my friends; no more of this nonsense or I shall make an example that we shall all be sorry for."

He found Tulip much calmer and more self-possessed than any European woman would have been after such a riot. She was indeed contemptuous of them all and said that she could not be afraid of that rabble. He found that she had filled all the buckets she could find at the well behind the house, while the villagers were threatening to set it afire at the front.

The next day all the games, the darts and target, hooks and rings, and the bagatelle board and so forth came out by the carrier and were delivered at the inn. But William, who had been choosing them with so much care the day before, and looking forward for several days to fitting up the new parlor with them, had no pleasure in them now. Indeed, he would not even open the parcels until Tulip, knowing what was inside, beseeched him to do so that she might play with them. If she had not said this it is most likely that William would not have set them up at all. For when he considered that all his care in making his inn a pleasant place was but to give pleasure to that crowd of people whom he had found outside it the day before, he was filled with a kind of disgust and anger and knew not what to do. In this perplexity of his he would not even serve the men who came in that morning himself, but left it to Tom, until suddenly he said aloud: "What, Billy? Daren't you show your nose on the bridge, because the crew mutiny? Or because the bumboat women last night were saucy to you? Are you only a fair-weather commander?"

Saying that, he went straight to the bar and told Tom to leave it to him. "I'll serve these gentlemen here myself." This he roared out in a voice that made the glasses ring and the men in the taproom start up with surprise. And in the same voice of thundering geniality he held forth on the weather, on the price people were getting for Michaelmas geese, and the new stores of liquor which he was laying in for the coming winter. This voice of his drowned any desire the men there might have had to speak about the events of the night before; it overawed them, and almost dazed them with admiration for a man who could call such tones out of his chest. None of the village people presumed either then or afterwards to speak to Targett about the scene of that night directly, but only alluded to it sideways, saying that "busybodies were a nuisance, and old women who didn't mind their own affairs ought to be ducked in the stream." Or that "there are plenty of stuck-up women who would pine and die away if they weren't always making mischief."

In a week or so the first blustering gale of autumn broke upon them and kept them all indoors for three days, while outside the wind was howling and the rain streaming, and clouds hid the downs beyond the village. At the inn all was snug and warm, as well battened down as a ship in a gale. For those days they had a full house, and Tom had his work cut out to serve all the company. Targett made fires in both of the rooms, scattered sawdust, and sometimes opened a door to let a cloud of tobacco smoke out and a puff of air come in. This was a great change for Tulip and gave her a foretaste of what it would be like in the winter. The house smelt of wet leather and corduroy, of heavy shag, and of the beer drippings. Every now and then the door slammed, the house shook in a blast of wind, and then there would be a shout of greeting, a new buzz of talk, and the jingle of coppers as Tom flung them into the drawer. All day long the bar was full of men drinking and talking; all day long she could hear the click of the bagatelle balls or the tinkle of the ring striking against the hook on the bull's nose. The voices of the men subdued her; the smell from the bar sickened her.

During the day Tulip kept to the kitchen or the washhouse and sat still with Sambo at her knee, telling him stories. At night she felt better, her sickness left her, and as the quarter-hours struck on the grandfather clock her spirits rose. Soon the last maundering song would be ended, the last "Good night, all" would ring out, the last stumbling drunkard would grope his way out of the passage, and the door would be locked and bolted. Then William would come into the kitchen, wiping the sweat off his neck, inside the collar of his shirt. He reeked with sweat and beer and was moist all over with his work, his eyes were bloodshot with tobacco smoke; but happiness for Tulip began in the winter with closing time, after which she could gaze at William without restraint until he had staggered upstairs to their bedroom, had tumbled into bed and blown out the light.

After three days the rain was all spent, and though the wind continued for a while, the sun shone fitfully. The roads had been swept by water, leaving banks of clean sand and beds of polished gravel at the corners, while new channels at the side of the space in front of the inn revealed the force of the storm. The little stream was swollen to a brown and turbid river, which covered the stepping-stones. That morning, while Tom was having his dinner, and Targett was in the empty bar, there came a knock at the door, which stood open, and the parrot screamed out: " A pint of bitter, pint of bitter, sharp, Tom, sharp." William went out in some surprise and found a visitor waiting on the doorstep, but a visitor who dared not enter the house. It was the parson, Mr. Cronk.

" Are you Targett, the new landlord here? " he asked.

" Come in," said William. " If you wish to speak to me, step inside."

" No, no," said the clergyman; " I was merely passing, just passing, and I wanted to drop you a hint, Mr. Targett. I heard among my parishioners a rumor, it may be untrue, I hope you will be able to deny it — but a rumor that you had threatened Mrs. Sturmey."

William gazed at his visitor in astonishment.

The clergyman went on:

" You must withdraw that threat. I am responsible for the peace of the parish, and I cannot have you threatening my parishioners."

William looked at the clergyman and grinned. Then he nodded his head slowly and said:

" I did threaten them, sir. I threatened everyone at Newbarrow Boys, and my sister, Mrs. Sturmey, and her husband in particular, with the law. If they assault my wife and child, burgle or set fire to my house, I shall have them hanged or transported by the officers of the law. I repeat that threat Mr. Cronk."

The clergyman looked up at William indignantly, but the sailor was grinning. A moment later Mr. Cronk recovered himself and said: "By the way, Targett, I spoke to your, ahem, to your wife about the little Negro boy."

"That is right," said William. "I was coming to see you about it, but I've been busy ever since I came here, with painting the house and one thing and another."

"Then you give your permission to have him christened and brought up as a Christian?"

"I shall bring the child up to be a Christian like myself," said William, "and I shall send him to sea in a whaling vessel. He should make a good harpooneer."

"Good day Targett," said the clergyman. William grinned again, turned, and discovered Tulip, who had been eavesdropping, behind the door. There was in her face an expression of great alarm, mingled with relief, and coming on her suddenly like that, William burst out laughing, caught her by both hands, and whirled her out onto the doorstep of the inn. As he did so, the parson turned and looked back, and Tulip, catching sight of him, gave a scream and ran into the house. This incident tickled William's sense of humor and he burst into peal after peal of laughter that rang noisily through the air and even startled the old women gossiping in the village street. William laughed and laughed again; he found he could not stop and leaned up against the door-post weakly. While he laughed, the Reverend Adrian Cronk looked about him in terror lest he should have been seen leaving the inn. People would think Targett was laughing at him. The parson did not dare walk into the village, and on the spur of the moment jumped down into the ditch and crawled behind the carrier's cart-shed. There his coat was stuck all over with burdocks and cleavers, and his thumb scratched by a spray of bramble. His heart beat like a mill, everything whirled before his eyes, but he was happy for the moments he lay hidden; anything was preferable to walking through the village with that sailor laughing at him, and he was always happiest when only the eye of God was looking. He had never fancied God laughing at His creatures. When all was quiet, he peeped out, saw no one, and, thinking himself secure, slipped out into the road.

The reverend gentleman had of course been observed taking cover, but it did not surprise either of the old women who witnessed it. They put his retirement behind the cart-shed down to another reason — one which may apply to everyone, irrespective of the color of their cloth.

When William had recovered himself, he went indoors and found Tulip in the bar, her eyes goggling with excitement. Seeing him, she turned and ran for the staircase, but he caught her easily enough on the landing, and Tulip sank in a heap on the stairs. She could not run in her English skirts; without them she could outstrip the heavy seaman as easily as a deer.

"Why did you hide behind the door?" he asked her, teasing her. She panted like a wild creature in a trap as William held her, but she did not try to escape again.

"Why did you get upset by the old parson?" asked William again. ·

"I don't want him to see me. Why did you drag me out of the house?" said Tulip.

She was going to have a baby in April or May; that was the reason of her ailing lately. When William heard about it he picked her up, kissed her, and said: "Better two than one, my lass. They will be company for each other later on."

Sambo's christening was fixed for the end of October, but when the day came William found that Tulip would not go to the church. He had not thought of this, and for some time was puzzled to know what to do.

"You must take the child, Tulip," he said, "and give him to the clergyman. It won't take long."

But Tulip only moaned, shook her head, and refused again. William was not used to disobedience from her, and his face flushed with anger as he looked at the poor stubborn thing, sitting abjectly on her heels on the kitchen floor. Seeing him look so angry, with the veins swelling up on his neck, Tulip cowered away from him still more into the corner.

"Get up, Tulip, stand up, go to bed," said Targett. "If you aren't well enough to attend the christening you must go to bed and stay there for the rest of the day."

She obeyed him this time, though she moved slowly and went with a sullen look on her face, hanging her head and trailing her feet. William held back his anger while he watched her go and did not speak again. When the time came for the christening, he changed his clothes and took Sambo up in his arms and carried him to the church himself. On the way he found plenty to show him and to talk to him about; for first there was a goat which Sambo thought, after his father and mother, the most interesting person in the world; then when they were past the goat, there was a line of ducks walking to the stream. But going up the street William began to tell his son what kind of fish whales are, as big as ships, and in each whaler stands a harpooneer with a harpoon in his hand and lances by his side. Just at this point they met Mr. Cronk inside the church door, and William told Sambo then that if he was a good boy he would hear the end of the story in a minute or two. When he had been christened (with Thomas Madgwick and Eglantine Clall as his godfather and his godmother) he came running back asking him: "May I kill whales now?" William paid for the christening and laughed and said he would make him a harpooneer one day soon, and then he put five guineas in the poor-box. While his father brought the newly christened Samuel back, he told him more about the great whales off Australia, and the whaling ships, and of how, when the fish goes sounding to the bottom, the rope spins out of a wooden tub in which it is coiled, so that it smokes, and a man has to pour sea water on it out of the bailer lest it should catch fire.

When they got back home to the Sailor's Return, young Samuel would have stayed with his father in the bar to hear more of these wonders, but Targett bid him go upstairs to his mother. The child had his father too much in awe to disobey him, but went with leaden feet, lingering and looking back upon the stairs, while his mouth puckered, and when he came to his mother's room he began to weep. Tulip was lying on her bed, and was so changed by her fear that it was a wonder her own child knew her, for he had never seen her like that before, with her skin grey, her eyes rolling, her lips thrust out, and her whole face working and twitching as if she had lost her reason. On seeing her child come back to her, she seized hold of him very passionately, and then seeing that his color was still black, she began to cry with joy. Sambo struggled with his mother, and not liking to be laid hold of, he burst into tears and pushed her away and said to her:

" I want to go to Papa."

Tulip did not heed this, but picked him up violently and undressed him as fast as she could with her trembling fingers, and
then spent some little while looking him over to see if there were
any new marks upon his body. Finding nothing, she became somewhat comforted, took him into the bed with her, kissing him and
fondling him, so that at last Sambo stopped his crying and his struggling with her. To all her questions the child would only answer
at cross-purposes about big fish that swam in the sea called whales,
and how he was going to throw harpoons at them. Tulip kept asking him about the christening, but the child told her that the
clergyman had said he would go to sea like his father and would
catch whales. This puzzled his mother; she could not believe that
there was anything about whales in the church, but she got nothing else out of Sambo.

Next day she asked Mrs. Clall if there were any fishermen in the
church or in the Bible, and Mrs. Clall told her yes indeed, our
Lord and the Apostles were all fishermen. There was Jonah and
the whale, Tobit, the loaves and fishes, the miraculous draft of
fishes, and then the clergymen were all called " fishers of souls," not
to speak of the Flood and Noah's Ark.

Hearing all these mysteries explained gave Tulip the notion that
now she understood the Christian religion very well, and indeed it
seemed to her a reasonable and natural one for an island people,
who live by fishing and sailing about the world in great ships. Even
in her own country she had worshipped the sea. Later on, when she
saw the font itself she became still more persuaded of the truth of
her opinions concerning the Protestant religion of England as by
law established.

Targett now told her that she must bestir herself, and under his
direction she made a great quantity of sloe gin. This meant gathering several bushels of sloes, which were then ripe and thick in
all the hedgerows. When this was done and she had sorted them
out, keeping the best ones, she had to prick each one in a dozen
places with a needle and then slip them into the bottles which
William had washed out and made ready. When the bottles were
filled with sloes, Tulip poured in the gin, which she drew from
the cask of gin in the cellar, and William drove in the corks and

dipped them in a pan of melted sealing-wax and stamped them with a seal which he had carved out beforehand in a block of lead. The device on it was a target with an arrow piercing it, with the words " Sailor's Return." This waxing and sealing the bottles was unnecessary, indeed unheard of, at this stage in the making of sloe gin. The bottles had all to be uncorked and the liquor decanted in six months' time, but the truth is that William had only just fashioned the seal and had to use it on something.

There were few incidents until Christmas came to break the monotony of the winter. William was busy serving the people who flocked to his public house, often coming from five or six miles off, because his place was so much spoken of. The Sailor's Return at Maiden Newbarrow had indeed something of a name, both on account of a black woman being there and because the new landlord had made the place so handsome, and entirely different from the miserable little pot-house which it had been for twenty years before his coming. The bleak years of the " hungry 'forties," when bad harvest had followed after bad harvest, were forgotten, and the Dorchester riots and transportations had quite gone out of men's minds. Since the end of the war the people found themselves better off than they had been since the eighteenth century, or in other words within the memory of man. Once again a laborer could eat butcher's meat at least one day a week, could drink beer, and sometimes, if he liked, taste a dram of spirits. But the Sailor's Return would have fared badly if it had depended on laborers. Though their weak heads are the ones which get soonest fuddled, and they are the ones who stagger away from the public house, they have only drunk a wretched three pints of small beer. Underfed laborers who work for long hours bring small profits to the publican, who depends on a robuster breed of men — the farmers and the higglers of all sorts.

Whenever money passes from hand to hand in the country the innkeeper gets his fair share of it. Not a sow can be splayed, a load of straw sold for thatching, or an order for seeds placed, without going to the inn about it. This money which goes into the publican's pocket with every bargain made is money well spent, for vendor and purchaser alike are given in exchange what they most want, courage, confidence, and contentment, and if the latter is

lacking, the unfortunate party can always come again and buy a
golden draft of philosophy to sweeten his bad bargain. The money
that goes to the inn is well spent; both sides know it, and the prosperity of our brewers and licensed houses is a fair index of the number of bargains struck in the country parts of England.

Had Maiden Newbarrow been a market town, had it even had
a couple of horse-fairs in the year, or a race meeting held on High
Newbarrow Down, then the Sailor's Return would have flourished,
and Targett would have had the inn his heart desired. But Maiden
Newbarrow is no more than a village, and though a certain trade
is done there in sheep, wool, and mutton, most of the bargains
were struck in the large Dorchester bars. Still there were a certain
number of glasses drunk in the parlor of the Sailor's Return to
cement the buying and selling of sheep-dip, pigs, butter, or fleeces.
In particular it was the local butchers, drovers, higglers, and gyp-
sies with ponies to sell who resorted there. Now and then came a
straying sailor, taking a short cut from Poole to Weymouth or
Portland, and then Targett would be sure of a long talk and a long
drink himself. Sometimes he would even ask the fellow to stop the
night there, and they would sit up till all hours shouting and drinking burnt brandy, all of course at William's expense. Their stories
were of sailing vessels, ports, harbors, harbor-masters, newfangled
methods, Yankee clippers, and the emigrant trade to Australia. It
was not every stray seaman, of course, who would find such a welcome waiting him. Sometimes Targett would only nod at the fellow and leave him in Tom's hands. But all the sailors who came,
whatever their reception might be, would spend some little while
looking over the house thoroughly, fingering the fittings Targett
had put in, and admiring them silently. They were slow to take
their departure, and would look round once or twice at the sign
before they went away down the road, as if they were saying to
themselves:

"The Sailor's Return, please God that I also may return and
find such a house as this waiting for me."

But though he had chosen to be an innkeeper, the most sociable
business which a man can undertake, where his trade must depend
very much on communicating his own high spirits to his customers,
thereby exciting their appetites to enjoy his other spirits, Targett

was not naturally fond of company. Neither was he a man who spoke of his plans or his feelings. Thus his conversation was always about outside things, such as weather, crops, markets, news from town, maritime intelligence, and the like. This reserve or closeness of his in speech made him all the more respected in Maiden New-barrow by those who resorted to his inn.

It was now springtime. The rains had stopped in the middle of March, the storms were over and the sun shone. Millions of flow-ers burst into blossom and birds into song on the same day. Tulip regained something of her natural gayety and went out for walks, though she was near her time. Targett, who had been drinking heavily for nearly a month, came out of the house and gazed with bloodshot eyes at the green pastures dotted with ewes and lambs. He shook himself like a spaniel coming out of the water and called out to Tom to set open the window; then he went himself to dig the garden. The trouble that often comes between man and wife before the birth of a child had been all the worse because of the weather. Now that was changed, Targett and Tulip found them-selves changed also.

And as the endless rain and slush, the falls of snow, and the thaws in February had made Targett drink, beginning in the morn-ing and sitting all through the day in front of the fire, with a glass of whisky by his side, so the sun now made him put the bottle by. In winter the inn had been full of men, shaking off the rain from the brims of their sou'westers, or brushing the melting snow from the shoulders of their top-coats, blowing their red noses between thumb and finger, and swigging spirits till their bleary eyes watered again. Only in that way could they face the bitter east wind, the driving sleet, and the long tramp home when the day's work was done, splashing through the strings of puddles and slipping at every step in two inches of mud.

The sun shone out, the boys sang as they went to work in the morning, and everyone had a friendly greeting for his neighbor. In a week's time the road was thick with dust, and they were rolling the young wheat in the fields. Winter was forgotten, everyone was working hard with a new courage. Nobody came into the bar in the fine weather or drank spirits, only at midday the men would stop and call to Tom to bring them out a pint of ale, and gulp it down quickly to quench their thirst whilst they kept their eyes fixed on the fields towards which they were bound. Hedging and ditching, carting dung and spreading muck were forgotten, the cows were turned out of the stalls except at milking-time. Indoor work was over, and everyone was busy rolling, harrowing, and getting a fine tilth on the arable land to sow seeds.

In the evenings the laborers searched for pewits' eggs as they crossed the meadows on the way home; on Sunday the boys went bird's-nesting. The farmyards were full of hens with strings of chickens or ducklings just chipped out of the eggs; puppies, calves, foals, and droves of newly farrowed porkers staggered, sprawled, or trotted in every direction.

Tulip gave birth to an infant daughter in the middle of April.

Mrs. Clall attended her, and William spent the day making a prawn net, not that he wanted the net, but because it occupied his attention, and he could sit downstairs in the room below listening while he was making it. For several hours there was nothing to hear except Mrs. Clall moving to and fro across the bedroom; Tulip did not cry out or moan. But at last there was a faint cry, a whining noise, and then William ran upstairs three steps at a time and found Mrs. Clall with a baby girl in her arms.

"Give it back to her," said he, seeing that Tulip was gazing at the child, in agony lest it should be taken away. When Tulip was given it, she smiled peacefully and soon afterwards fell asleep. The baby was a lighter color than Sambo, a silvery gray, with staring eyes, and a thin crop of dark red curly hair, like a Rothschild lamb. Targett was not disappointed with the child and went downstairs full of joy, and when he saw his half-finished prawn net lying on the floor laughed at himself and said aloud: "I have no use for a prawn net, God bless my heart; if ever I should have a fancy to go prawning, Miller would have lent me one." Then taking it up he looked at it critically, and still laughing put it away with his gear, saying to himself:

"Well, it will come in useful next time; that is, if Tulip should breed again."

When a child has been born, the whole house is usually upset, and there is a great deal of extra work. But there was less trouble with Tulip than there would have been had she been an Englishwoman. Tom Madgwick had to light a good many fires and boil a great many kettles, and William had to look after Sambo for most of the day, but beyond this there was no change in their lives, except that Mrs. Clall found another woman to come in one day a week to work at the wash-tub. Tulip would have got up on the second day, but Targett ordered her to stay in bed, and made her lie there a week, though it was against her wish. As soon as Tulip was up and about, she took charge of Sambo again, as well as her new baby. About a fortnight after this a parcel came addressed to Mrs. Tulip Targett. Inside there was a letter (which she would have thrown away had not William been with her) with a silver and coral rattle from Harry, and a christening mug from the rest of the family. Targett took the letter and read it aloud:

TARGETT'S FARM

MY DEAR TULIP,

We heard the good news of your having a little daughter, although William did not write, as he should have done, getting the good news from Lucy, who is I should say very jealous; you are a good enough Christian I know to forgive her. She has no children of her own, and that is what makes her angry. However, she has been the means of my sending this coral for the baby.

What will you call her I wonder.

The rest of the family send a silver christening mug, and you must have her christened or they will think you didn't like it. I cannot get away in this fine weather, but have hopes of seeing you in about ten days' time when we shall be less busy.

With best wishes and love to Sambo.

Hoping you and the infant are doing well,

Yours obediently,

HARRY TARGETT

This letter and the presents gave William more pleasure than he had ever expected to feel upon a like occasion. Harry he knew was friendly to him and fond of Tulip, but he would not have expected him to take the trouble to buy a present or write a letter. Besides that, he could guess well enough what sort of letter Lucy must have written upon the occasion of the baby being born, and he knew that it was all owing to Harry that the others had sent a christening mug. This was as good an answer to Lucy as he could wish them to make, and he laughed when he thought how angry she would be when she heard of it, as she surely would do, even if they themselves did not tell her they had given it. And Targett took the mug into the bar and showed it to the men there and told them that his family had sent it, although he would have sworn that he did not care what any of his family thought of him and was quite content to be a law unto himself.

Harry rode up to the inn one lovely morning in May and arrived just as they were sitting down to the midday meal. He was singing at the top of his voice, and he went on with his song while William came to the open door. Tom ran out to take his horse, Sambo thrust his head out, peeping between his father's legs, and Tulip waved her arms wildly from the window and put her finger to her lips.

Harry finished the last bar of his song, vaulted off his horse, and shook William by the hand. " You'll have woken the baby, Harry," said William, laughing. " What a voice you have got! Have you fallen in love? "

Tulip came out then and Harry picked her up off the ground for a moment and said: " I saw you, Tulip. But what does it matter? You see your baby isn't crying."

Tulip wriggled out of his grasp like a wild thing, half turned to run from him, but then came back, caught him by the sleeve of his coat, and drew him after her through the house into the garden, where her baby was. The little creature was awake, lying on its back with wide-open gray eyes, staring at the silver rattle hanging above it.

The midday meal was just ready; Harry and Tulip came back into the kitchen. But while Tulip was beaming with the natural pride of a mother, Harry looked grave. He was thinking that he would not like his own children to be born that nasty gray color, and that though Tulip was a good creature, William had done wrong in bringing her back with him to England and in begetting these children that were neither one thing nor the other. But these reflections only showed themselves by a moment of thoughtfulness, and when he next spoke to Tulip it was with great tenderness and gentleness, perhaps all the more so because she looked changed to him. Her figure was no longer slim and like an arrow. Her body was heavier; he had noticed that when he lifted her. Her native grace was not yet gone; soon it would vanish, and then no one would believe that William had called her Tulip because she had seemed to him like that brilliant flower, swaying upon its slender, green, cylindrical, and sappy stalk.

Tulip was far from guessing Harry's thoughts, and they sat down gayly at the table, laughing when Harry said the baby looked as if it had been left out in the rain, and that perhaps if Sambo had been born in England he would have been paler in color.

It did not occur to William to wonder what his brother might be thinking about him, for he never bothered himself with what other people did, or worried about questions of right and wrong. He did what he wanted to do, and never went back into the past to find anything in his life to regret, nor forward into the future to find cause for fear.

Now Harry was come they were a merry party. William called Tom to bring them a second quart of ale to take with their cheese, and while they drank it Harry told him all the news from the farm. This was principally of their sister Dolly and of her chances of getting married.

She had had a valentine from Stevie Barnes and had shown it to everyone. Now she was sorry she had shown it, for Stevie meant business, and Dolly could not hide her love for him any longer. It was a good match; Stevie's father was getting an old man, and Stevie would have Gibraltar Farm.

But Dolly was eaten up with vexation, just because she had begun by laughing at him. Two or three Sundays ago, while the others were at church, she had asked Stevie into the house. Somehow the couple lost reckoning of the time, and when the family got back, there they were sitting by the fire like man and wife. Since then Dolly had refused to see Stevie, but Harry had seen him and had told him to let her sulk. Harry then told them about Dolly's other young men, and made Tulip laugh with a story of how she had gone skating in the dark with Jem Budd. The ice had broken; since then she would never even hear of Jem without impatience.

While he was still talking about Dolly, there was a knock on the door and the postman handed in a letter for William. He took his knife and slit the seal, and cast his eye over the page. Then he stopped laughing and stared at it again. All of a sudden he jumped up from the table cursing, and started as if he would go out of the door, but stood still before he got to it as if he were dazed; then he began swearing again, so wildly and with such filthy language that Harry thought he had gone out of his senses. Tulip also had sprung to her feet and stood watching William, ready to execute the first command which he might give her. For some moments nothing came from William's mouth but great oaths and threats, all mixed up with such a torrent of obscene words that anyone might have thought he was a mad pirate at sea.

At last, however, he noticed the silent figure of Tulip standing beside him, with her eyes fixed on him questioningly, and then he turned on her and caught hold of her, though still with the knife in his hand. But Tulip did not flinch from him as William clasped her and said: " No, my girl, never fear, I shall never turn you adrift! Damn their black hearts! " and with that fell once more to cursing and swearing. A moment later he said to Harry, who was questioning him what he meant by this frenzy: " Read that! Tell me, do you not smell the hand of that bitch, our own sister at Newbarrow Boys? "

Harry took the letter from him and read it over. It ran as follows:

JACOB STINGO & SONS, BREWERS & MALTSTERS
STINGO'S PRIORY ALES

DORCHESTER

Confidential

DEAR MR. TARGETT:

I am under the unpleasant necessity of writing to you on a private matter connected with yourself. It has been brought to my knowledge that you are living with a woman to whom you are not married — a colored woman. Very strong representations have been made to me by respectable residents in Newbarrow and district against my continuing to let premises to a man of loose character. I may say I fully concur with this view, and should never allow any of my tenants to set a bad example in matters of Christian duty and morality to the villagers amongst whom they live. At the same time I do not wish to lose such a good tenant as you have otherwise shown yourself, and conceive that you may be able to see your error and repent of your laxity. I consider, however, that it is my

duty to give you notice, as from next Lady Day, unless you termi-
nate your unfortunate association with this female and give me a
positive undertaking that you will give no cause for similar scandals
in the future. I am sure you will understand my position in this
matter, and trust you will be able to see clearly what is not only
your duty, but also so much to your interest.

Yours faithfully,

JACOB STINGO, JR.

Harry turned pale as he read the letter, and his tight lips and
flashing eyes showed his indignation. But when William started
again for the door, he cried out to him: " Softly, William, softly;
you must think over this affair before you act. Did you never plan
a battle before you started fighting in Dahomey? "

" What is that? " asked William, turning round in the doorway.
" Leave him to me, I will teach him to send me insolent letters."

" Wait a minute," said Harry. " If you go I will come with you,
but first answer my questions, William."

" Fire away then, Harry; what is it you want to know? "

" Well, you are not married to Tulip, are you? "

" I don't know," said William; " perhaps not in England."

" Are you married to any other woman? "

" What a question, Harry! "

" Well, William, you are a sailor, but you are not married to
anyone else are you? "

" God help me if I am."

" You won't send Tulip away? " asked Harry.

William swore by way of reply.

" Not on any account? "

" Lose Tulip for a stinking pot-house, Harry? By God, do you
take me for a weevil? Did you not hear me say that this inn and
everything in it was bought with Tulip's pearls? Lose my Tulip,
who has borne me two children and who left her father's palace to
wash dirty pots of beer because she loved me? Send away my Tulip?
It is clear, Harry, that you have never loved a woman." Harry
flushed.

" Yet you would not marry her? " he asked.

William gazed at his brother as thunderstruck. " Marry her?
That was not what he said. Marry her? " Then William dropped

into a chair and broke into a roar of laughter that frightened Tulip
more than any of his oaths. " Will that do the trick, think you,
Harry? Well, by God, we will be married today." And then William began laughing again till he sobbed. At last he was able to
ask Tulip to fetch him a drink. When she had brought him a
glass of beer he gulped down a mouthful, mopped his brow, and
dried the tears in his eyes.

" We were married," said he, " in Dahomey, but the only one
I can call a parson was a frightful fellow compared with the chap
we have here. He was dressed in a royal leopard-skin hung all over
with the teeth of alligators, and he was a priest of the sacred
python. But Tulip was given me by three women, who put her
hands in mine and told me to treat her well, to feed her and give
her clothes, and to beat her when she was bad. It may not be a
proper wedding here, but it took from sunrise until after midnight,
and it was on a Sunday too." Then his thoughts coming back to
the business in hand, William struck the table with his fist and
cried out: " We will be married tomorrow. I shall go now and see
the parson about it." But poor Tulip had not followed all William's
talk. She had understood the oaths and the threats and what he
said about their marriage in Dahomey, all but the letter itself. And
that seemed to her to have but one explanation: namely, that there
was an evil spirit in it, and that some wizard or enchanter had
William in his power, for in her country she had seen men and
women bewitched often enough. Everything she heard him say
since then made her think that she was right in her fears, and when
William bellowed out that they were to be married the next day,
they having been married so long already, she could not keep from
bursting into sobs.

" Oh, my poor William, my dear William," said she, " some
enemy has charmed you surely. Have you forgotten that we were
married when I was fourteen years old, and how you had to send
for me three times, at dawn, at noon, and at sunset, and then how
three women of my fetish brought me to you at midnight after
the feast? You spoke of the panther man; he was sacrificed at the
So-sin customs for his many crimes; have you forgotten that? "
Tulip uttered these words in the most desperate tones, laying hold
of William as she spoke, by the knees as he sat in his chair, and

gazing into his eyes, while the tears streamed down her own smudge cheeks. And she shook him with all her might as if she would thereby bring him to his senses. All this caused Harry a good deal of surprise, but to William it appeared natural enough, for he understood her African superstition and understood that she had taken the letter for an enchantment.

" No, Tulip, Harry here will tell you that there is no witchcraft in this. It is only a plot to turn us out of the inn, and to defeat it you and I must be married as soon as possible — this time by a white man. Remember he did no harm to Sambo and he will do no harm either to you or me." Tulip turned to Harry, who confirmed this very solemnly and presently succeeded in persuading her that her William was still himself, and that he had not fallen into the power of a magician.

Targett was all on fire for wedlock now, and wanted to set about it at once. He soon found, however, that matters of this sort cannot be settled out of hand. For when he got back from the vicarage he said sorrowfully: " Tulip and I cannot be married under the month, plague take the parson. There are a thousand things to fuss about before I can make an honest woman of her as they call it. Our banns must be read three times and that takes three Sundays."

Harry thought the sad voice in which William spoke was very comical and laughed outright. " You were always like that, William," he said, " always in a hurry. You could never bear to wait for anyone. Did you never have to wait for the next tide when you were a sailor? "

" You think a deep-water sailor is the same thing as a bargeman, or a Poole harbor pilot Harry. Wait for the tide indeed! But that is waiting for God; this is waiting for a poxy parson."

The news of the marriage was soon all over the village, and the marriage became the staple of conversation until it took place. While many of the more strait-laced sort were reconciled to Targett by the news, others who were ready to tolerate sin did not rejoice to see a heathen woman married in their church, just as they had been themselves. The strongest disapproval was excited among the sinners, now that their hero Targett had had to knuckle under to parson. For look at it as they might, they could find nothing to

admire in his having a black wife. Mr. Cronk, the clergyman, was
delighted; for weeks he went about with a happy face, planning
how by degrees he would bring Tulip into the fold, and thus imagined himself a missionary, though one who had not to endure
the hardships of a tropical climate. Young Mr. Stingo was as much
surprised as he was pleased when Mr. Cronk wrote and told him
of the approaching marriage, for though glad to keep his tenant,
he had never known that vice could get such a hold on a man as
to make him marry a colored woman rather than part from her.
But the clergyman and the brewer were the only ones to be genuinely pleased by the marriage. Lucy could not believe the news,
and when she arrived at the vicarage, rather red in the face from
walking, and rather out of breath, and heard it confirmed, she
could not hide her indignation.

"You must refuse to marry them," she said. "It is a scandal; it
is an insult to me and to every respectable married woman in the
parish. They are taking advantage of you, Mr. Cronk. I know my
brother. You must forbid the banns."

"I do not know what you mean Mrs. Sturmey," answered the
clergyman. "Your brother shows a sincere desire to repair his
faults in the only way possible, and I rejoice at the wedding. Remember the parable of the prodigal son, and do not show a suspicion of your brother that is beneath you."

"My brother marrying a nigger, here in this village under my
eyes!" exclaimed Lucy. "I tell you he is making fun of you, of all
of us; he is doing it to insult respectable people. He thinks he is
doing something very clever, but it has got to be stopped."

"I fear that you misjudge your brother," said Mr. Cronk; "he
is by no means a wholly bad man, only a man of bad habits. You
should labor to reclaim him Mrs. Sturmey. As a Christian you must
see that the only way for him to repair his error is by marrying the
woman, whatever she may be on the surface."

"Fiddlesticks," said Lucy, marching to the door with her skirts
rustling. "William has probably got half a dozen wives already.
Marriage is the only thing that he can think of to prevent his being
turned out of the inn, as he ought to be." Lucy slammed the door
behind her and walked back to Newbarrow Boys.

The morning of the wedding was bright and clear, with hot sunshine. A swarm of bees came out of Mrs. Everitt's skep about eleven o'clock in the morning, and Mrs. Everitt roused the village by beating on her coal-shovel with a pair of tongs. As she was fetching them the bees settled on a gooseberry bush, and drooped to the ground, but she went on beating the fire-irons for half an hour, until everyone came out to look from a safe distance. She was still beating them as William with Tulip on his arm walked down the village street, and she did not stop till they had gone into the church. The sound pleased Tulip; it reminded her of the drums at her father's court. She was glad also to see that so many people had come to watch her being married, and she smiled at everyone they passed in the road. William had ordered the wedding dress from Poole, and the crinoline was so large that Tulip had only just managed to squeeze out of the door of the inn; it was an ivory silk brocade cut short three inches above Tulip's ankles, showing her white silk stockings; her head was covered with a veil of real lace, her white kid gloves reached to the elbow, and, it being tulip-time, she carried a large bunch of scarlet tulips in her hand.

William wore a blue frock coat with a velvet collar and large brass buttons; his legs were encased in a pair of tartan trousers strapped under his boots, and his white bow tie was three times the size of any which had been seen in the neighborhood. He carried a pair of dogskin gloves, and the ivory walking-stick of a Dahomeyan Cabosheer, which dignity had been conferred on him by His Majesty King Gaze-oh. On his head was a large white beaver with straight sides and a very curly brim. A few yards behind the couple walked Tom Madgwick leading Sambo by one hand, while in the other he carried a large nosegay. Behind him came Mrs. Clall with the baby in her arms. The little creature was silent, but Sambo never stopped asking questions, and Tom was hard put to think of suitable replies. Everyone was waiting in the street or near the church to see them go by, and among the villagers were several people from Tarrant. But though there were a great many onlookers, and many among them nodded to Targett or touched their hats, hardly anyone came into the church to see the service. When William would have led her up the aisle, Tulip withdrew her hand from his arm and hurried to the font, where she knelt for a moment or two in prayer, bowing her head to the ground. Then she rose up and scattered something into the font. Just then William came to her and after whispering a word in her ear, led her forward up the aisle.

Mr. Cronk was standing by the altar rails as this took place, and he saw nothing of what had passed, and the other persons were not yet got properly into the church, so that little notice was taken of what Tulip had done. After the marriage was over and William had signed the book in the vestry, Mrs. Clall came forward with the baby and it was christened. William gave it the name of Sheba, which he thought suitable. But it was then at the christening that Mr. Cronk saw a handful of rice in the water, some few of the grains floating, and more lying at the bottom, together with one or two shells which he believed to be water snails. On perceiving these objects he was much shocked, though not at all puzzled by how they came to be there, since he assumed the rice had been thrown at the wedding, and as for the snails, he was convinced that the sexton had saved himself trouble by filling the font from the pond outside, and he determined to speak to him about it. That evening he went back to the font to take out the snails and show them to the old man, but he found that they were really bright little cowrie shells, so he put them into his waistcoat pocket and thought no more of the matter. He would never have believed it, had anyone told him that a heathen sacrifice to Neptune, or Nate, the God of the Sea, had taken place in his church that morning. When the christening was over, William and Tulip returned to the inn, flaunting themselves openly in their fine clothes quite as if they were the quality.

" That sailorman thinks he can do anything because of his money," said one woman to another as they passed. " He has more money than he knows what to do with, and he throws it about shamefully. Look at what he has spent in painting that public house. Every door and every window has had three good coats of paint since he has been in the place; and then goodness knows how much he has spent on gilding with real gold leaf on the signboard, and then that blessed weathercock of his. You would think he could find some work to do without making that there weathercock."

"Who knows how he came by all that money either? Not by honest work, I'll be bound," answered another.

"And no more sense with it," replied her neighbor, "but to marry a black woman. Our English girls aren't good enough for him."

"Yes, poor fellow," said Mrs. Everitt, who had just taken her swarm of bees, "I am afraid he must have picked up the habit abroad, and when once a habit gets hold of a man, there is never any breaking him of it."

"If I had the breaking of him, I would soon cure him of going after a black woman," passed through the minds of the two first speakers as they gazed at Targett's handsome figure going up the street, but neither of them spoke. They were both vigorous women in the prime of life.

Tulip and William had expected Harry for the wedding. He was, indeed, to have been the best man. When they got back to the inn they found out what had occurred. For just as they reached the door, a dogcart drove up covered with mud, and there was Harry with Mrs. John Targett, the wife of William's elder brother, and his sister Dolly, and Francis, a boy of fourteen, who barely remembered his seafaring brother.

The party had met with an accident on the way; a train had startled the horse soon after they had crossed the railway with Dolly driving. Before Harry could take the reins they were off the road and onto the heath, and in a moment the dogcart had overturned, throwing them all into a bog-hole. No one had been hurt except Harry, who had put his thumb out of joint and was silent from pain, but the ladies' dresses were ruined; Mrs. John's temper had suffered even more than her dress, and all of the party were gloomy except the boy Francis. Dolly succeeded in appearing cheerful, for she remembered that they had come to celebrate her brother William's wedding. Poor Tulip was puzzled when Dolly threw a bag of rice, all stuck together with muddy water, into her face, but she joined in her laughter, and then Dolly gave her a squeeze (which was easier to manage than a kiss) and asked to see the baby. Mrs. John Targett did not greet Tulip at all nor William either. As soon as she had been helped out of the dogcart she

walked into the house and made her way to the scullery, where she
spent half an hour trying to wash out the stains of mud. The over-
turning of the dogcart had been the greatest joke that Francis had
ever known in his life; he was still beside himself with joy when
he thought of Mrs. John and Dolly rolling out into a mud-hole in
their best dresses. For some minutes after their arrival he was
doubled up with laughter. At last, however, he was able to speak
and, addressing Dolly, said, pointing to Tulip: " If you only had
her complexion no one would notice the mud." A moment later
he asked William why he had not brought home a monkey, like
the uncle of a friend of his, instead of . . . But at that moment
Harry gave him a very hard box on the ear. The young rascal burst
into tears and went indoors to hide. Meanwhile Mrs. Clall arrived
carrying little Sheba, and Tom leading Sambo. Dolly at once seized
the baby, which began to cry, but her aunt was equal to her and
shouted the infant down with its praises. After a few moments Mrs.
Clall took it again and went into the house. Dolly then turned her
attention to Sambo. The blackness of his skin took her aback even
more than the blackness of his mother, but good nature triumphed.
She kissed him, and the little boy grinned at her so roguishly that
she could not but like him.

Harry had now unloaded the wedding presents. Chief in magnificence was a wedding cake, but unfortunately the accident had
proved fatal to its beauty. The icing, which should have been a field
of virgin snow, was shattered into fragments, one side was flattened,
and the corner was sodden with marsh water. William, however,
declared that it would taste all the better, and carried it indoors,
where the others followed him, bearing other offerings. Of these
the most remarkable was a present from Dolly to the bride — of a
pair of black kid gloves, which might have been made from Tulip's
own skin after the glow of health had left it. Harry's present was
a gaudy crimson shawl, which only a gypsy woman would have
worn; but he had guessed right and Tulip was delighted with it.
William was so astonished at the arrival of his relations that he
did not remember their wants, but Tulip, who from the beginning
was accustomed to social occasions such as this, ran at once into
the bar, returning with a bottle of port, glasses, and a corkscrew.
Dolly swallowed the wine which Tulip gave her with relish, for she

was tired. Tulip filled her glass again and cut her a large chunk of the wedding cake, and after filling other glasses went in search of Francis, whom she found in the bar-parlor, still whimpering from the box on his ear. She gave the boy first a glass of port and then a kiss; the wine he liked, but the kiss he wasn't sure about, for he noticed a strange smell that faintly disgusted him, but increased his curiosity about her. In another minute they were good friends engaged in playing a game of bagatelle, and before they parted Tulip made him promise to pay her a visit in the summer. Left to themselves William and Dolly were soon at their ease.

"You have made this a fine place William," she said, looking round her. " Did you put up that picture in wool? I made sure you did," she went on as William nodded; " you always used to have pictures of ships even before you went off to sea."

"That is the *James Baines*, and it is a good likeness of her too. She came up with us once off Cape Verde; my word, she was a picture with all her canvas. No steam vessel will ever lower the record of the *James Baines*: from Liverpool to Melbourne in sixty-three days."

"I should think not," said Dolly. " Did you put those white ropes reefing back the curtains? That is like a sailor."

"Those are bo'sun's lanyards," said William. " We old fellows all get like that, you may notice; we cannot help playing that we are still afloat. There's an old boy of eighty whom I know at Swanage, and his place is a museum all over. You could swear that you were in Noah's quarters in the Ark."

"But you are glad to be settled now, William; you are happy, aren't you? " Dolly asked, and blushed.

"Yes, to be sure," said William, " I am glad to have this place for my sweet Tulip. But you would never guess what a lot of work there is to do here. And now when are you getting married, Dolly? " he asked.

" I never! I suppose that devil Harry has been saying things about me." But Dolly went on at once to talk to William about her young man, a thing which she would not have done with any of the other members of her family. Between them they had finished the bottle of port when Mrs. John came in, declaring that they must start for home at once. She was tolerably free of mud now, but not in the best of tempers, and she set at once upon Dolly.

"What a sight you look, dear! Gracious me! Plastered with mud like a mangold. I should think you must have had quite enough wine too," for Dolly was waving her glass in reply.

William took another bottle out of the cupboard and uncorked it, but Mrs. John firmly refused to drink.

"Now, William, where is Harry? And where is Francis? Get them to put the horse in at once. We shall not be back before dark; we have had enough accidents without being benighted." Dolly was then sent off to the scullery to wash herself, and William was sent to the stables. Then Mrs. John eyed the bottle of port, eyed the wedding cake, and once more eyed the port. At the moment she looked very like a duck gecking first one way and then the other before it dare approach the morsel which has been thrown to it. Her hand was on the bottle when she heard a step, and Harry came into the room with a silly smile and his hand in bandages. He had drunk a lot of brandy to deaden the pain while Tom had been pulling at his thumb. Five minutes later Mrs. John had got the party into the dogcart and they were driving off. They had only been at the Sailor's Return for little over the half-hour, but not one of them was quite sober except herself. At parting they kissed Tulip with great warmth; Mrs. John was already in the dog-cart. She was consoled by finding that the great cheese which her husband had sent for William had not been unpacked. She pushed it under her feet and spread her skirts over it. Targett's farm was celebrated for its cheeses. They drove away; henceforward Mrs. John was in alliance with Lucy.

The day after the wedding little Sheba looked poorly; she shivered and Tulip found she would not take the breast. The child fretted all through the night, and William grumbled at the noise. "Sambo was never like that," he said. Next morning the baby was feverish, and Tulip came to William and asked him to bleed her, but this he refused to do. When he spoke, however, of fetching the doctor, Tulip became upset and persuaded him that the child would be well soon, saying that all her family had been subject to agues in infancy. In the end William decided not to call the doctor, for he guessed that Tulip would be afraid of him, and he thought himself that the excitements of the wedding day might

have changed Tulip's milk, and that this was the whole trouble
with Sheba. It would make the matter worse, he thought, if Tulip
were now to be frightened. Besides that, William had not a much
greater opinion of the country doctors in England than of those
in Africa. Two days afterwards Sheba died of pneumonia. Tulip
did not cry, she walked about slowly all the next day and did nothing. William said to her several times: " I ought to have fetched
the doctor," and so Tulip came to think that the doctor had made
Sheba die because they had insulted him. The second day after
Sheba's death she was buried in Maiden Newbarrow churchyard.
It was a clear morning. In the elms half a dozen birds were singing;
their music filled the pauses in the service. The child's parents were
the only mourners, and Tulip wore the black gloves that Dolly had
given her for a wedding present. When they came back from the
funeral, William went to dig the garden. Sambo ran out to him
and began to dig also. The sun was hot and the borders were full
of flowers. When William looked up he saw a sparrow carrying
a straw in its mouth being blown away by the wind. High up
in the sky there were swifts wheeling. Two or three cuckoos were
chasing each other in the tops of the elms. When William had
dug for an hour, he sent Sambo into the house to fetch him
a pot of beer, and watched him bring it. The little boy's face
was set in a frown; he carried the pot in both hands and staggered as he walked with his excess of care. Indoors Tulip was making the beds; she stopped for a moment and looked out of the
window and saw William take the can of beer and slowly drink it
nearly dry and then bend down and give Sambo a sip. As she drew
up the bedclothes she sprinkled them with tears, which made circles
of moisture on the sheets, but hung in drops on the blankets.
Tulip looked at them sparkling in the sun, and soon afterwards she
stopped crying. When she had finished making the beds, she folded
up the little blankets and quilt of the baby's cot and put them
away in a drawer; then she carried the cot itself upstairs into the
loft.

   That evening William missed her when he came back from
serving in the bar. She was nowhere in the house; he called but
she did not answer. About midnight he heard the latch of the door
click, and going to look, found Tulip. Seeing him, she started, but

as he did not seem angry she came towards him and reached up and put her arms on his shoulders. " Come along, my girl, you must turn in now," said William, but he asked her no questions as to where she had been or what she had been doing. Next morning everyone was talking of what Tulip had done that night, for it was desecration and a great scandal to the village, and saying that the vicar must punish her. She had been at the baby's grave and had thrown away the flowers which Mrs. Clall had laid on it in the afternoon. In their place she had dug a little pit and had set in it a crock of milk, and at the foot of the grave she had put the child's rattle and one or two toys, with a little wooden horse of Sambo's, and these she had set so firmly in the earth that they were almost buried. Early in the morning the gravedigger had found them; he had broken the crock with his foot so that the milk was spilt on the earth, and had kicked the toys out of the ground so that they were broken. Later on, a cat found a little of the milk left in the corner of the crock, and the village children saw the rattle and the broken toys. They carried them away and fought over them.

Mrs. Clall told Tom Madgwick, Tom told his master, and Targett walked down to the churchyard, where there was nothing to be seen but a smear of milk on the clay. He had expected to find more and did not think it worth while speaking about it to Tulip or to the clergyman.

The weather was now fine so that there was little business at the inn. William was free all day long to do what he liked, and spent most of his time working in the garden with Tulip lying near him in a chair, with her feet on the garden bench. Sambo ran between them or dug his own little patch of garden which William had given him in one corner. The whole morning would pass away like this, and then the afternoon, without William or Tulip talking to each other; every now and then Sambo must be answered and the silence would be broken by the child's prattle and the parents' voices. Tulip watched her husband for hours as he worked. His broad back was cut by red braces, his shirt was made of that large blue and white checked material which had not yet been discarded in the navy. It was always a surprise for her to see a man so busy as William. He was a free man, yet he worked harder than an African slave. Cuckoos called, goldfinches sang in the elms, the weeks of perfect summer weather followed one another, marked only by the flowers in the garden and the dishes on the table. The first gooseberries were followed by the first peas, and they in their turn by broad beans, cherries, and red currants. Only one incident occurred in six weeks, and that was no more than a fleeting glimpse of the red face and the broad back, covered in black silk, of Mrs. John Targett driving past in a dogcart.

William and Tulip looked after her as they came from feeding the goslings which William had just bought.

" Paying my sister Lucy a visit! " he said.

" Will she come here afterwards? " asked Tulip.

" Not much chance of that."

" I hope she keeps on that tack always," said Tulip smiling. " But who was driving? It was not Harry."

" That must be her nephew, Charlie Tizard."

Two or three days after this William received a letter from Harry. It ran as follows:

TARGETT'S FARM

DEAR WILLIAM,

I am writing to say you may expect me on Tuesday next week, as I wish to pay you and Tulip a farewell visit before I leave England. If I know your mind, we think alike about farming and it being no life for a young man. I, a younger son, cannot ever expect a farm of my own. Never to marry, and to live on a laborer's wages all my life, is my inheritance and prospects. I therefore sail Saturday following for New Orleans, and fancy that in a few months I shall be fighting Indians and killing buffaloes with the best of them.

Your affectionate brother,

HARRY TARGETT

William read it aloud to Tulip, who was so dismayed at the thought of losing Harry that her eyes filled with tears, but William told her that there was no cause to weep, that Harry was doing the right thing in going, and that she must make young Francis take his place.

" I shall give him a hundred pounds to start with," he declared. " Harry cannot have a penny of his own except what John gives him. I wonder that he has saved his passage money. He is quite right; a farmer never sees anything of the world beyond the nearest market town. Harry is too much of a man to live by scraping dung out of a yard. He aspires to fortune, as I have done myself in my time. I shouldn't have found you if I had not run off to sea."

When Harry came he did not show much of this fire and dash. He was paler than usual and confessed that he was distressed at his departure. However, there was no talk of turning back now that he had said good-by to all his friends round Targett's Farm. It was late when he arrived, and after a scanty supper he retired to bed. Next morning Tulip found herself alone with him, and after breakfast asked him had he no girl he was sorry to leave behind.

That made him laugh, and he answered her: " No one as much as you, dear Tulip." He was going to kiss her then, but seeing her still serious and gazing into his eyes with a look of grave inquiry, he became rather shamefaced and said: " It is because of the girls I am going, Tulip. There have been half a dozen or so; I cannot marry and now the country is too hot to hold me." He sighed, then smiled, and added: " I shall be forgotten in three months," and sighed again. " Never mind," said Tulip, " you are not going to be a sailor, you will find plenty of girls in America." Harry laughed at this and told her she was the best creature in the world. Her simple words comforted him.

In the afternoon William drove Tulip and Harry to the sea and took them out sailing. Directly they were on board he began talking about America and the Americans and of what Harry would find when he had crossed the ocean. But Harry did not enjoy the motion of the boat and could not pay very much attention to what William was saying. Very soon he felt that he hated America, and that perhaps it would be better to enlist in the army. But then he reflected that he had already paid his passage money, and that there was no escaping doing what he had planned for so long and looked forward to so much and which now seemed to him to be the worst thing he could have chosen. Meanwhile William was telling him that he ought to settle somewhere near York River and grow tobacco. Very soon he went on to talk about shipbuilding, and how the Yankees had captured the Australian emigrant trade with their clippers, until we had got it back by buying American-built ships like the *James Baines* and the *Lightening*, and that soon we should be building fast clippers ourselves.

As they were driving home, Tulip asked suddenly: "What color are the girls in America, William?" Both the brothers laughed at this question, and William told her that they were of all colors, and that the Negroes were slaves from Dahomey and all along the coast, who had been sold to the plantations. "Oh, that riff-raff," said Tulip. "My family has sold thousands of them every year. They are all wretches who ought to have been killed at the annual customs, but my ancestors the kings of Dahomey have always been very kind men and have always spared as many lives as they could, and sold the wretches off to the white men at Whydah. You will not find the kind of girl you want among people like that." She was so earnest on this subject that Harry at last promised her that he would never marry a black girl, though she could not understand why the two men laughed at her. That evening William mixed a big bowl of cold punch; Tulip alternately played on her little pipe and danced, and both the brothers sang. By midnight Harry had got thoroughly drunk. As he was trying to dance he slipped on the floor. Then, sitting up, he said to William: "I love your little black girl, I swear I do. She is a dear creature, but you know, William, you should not have brought her to England. You should not, William, because, you see, she is black. You should not forget that, because you ought not to mix the two breeds." William laughed at this. "Wait till you have married the King of Spain's daughter, Harry; then you can talk. Now it is time for you to come along to bed." But Harry would not go to bed until Tulip had kissed him, had told him that she loved him, and promised that she bore no malice for what he had said, which she did very readily because she had not overheard his words. Next day Tom harnessed the dogcart, and William and Harry drove off. William was going with his brother all the way to Southampton. It would do him good, he said, to go aboard a ship once more. In his pocket he put the bag in which he kept all his money. He had not yet spoken to Harry of what he was going to give him, and indeed had not decided in his own mind how much he could spare him.

The day after the departure of Harry and William, Tulip dressed herself in her best clothes: namely, those she had worn at her wedding, except that on this occasion she wore a poke bonnet of cream-colored straw, with a scarlet riband instead of a veil. There

was no kind of occasion for this fine raiment, which she put on
only because there was no one whose opinion she valued to see
her, and because she wanted to wear her wedding dress twice. In
the matter of the love of fine clothes there was very little difference between Tulip and any grand lady in London. While she
dressed herself thus, she thought of how her sisters would crowd
about her if they could see her in these English clothes. What
questions they would ask her! What fun they would all have together if she were at home, even if it were only for an hour!

Her life here, so she said to herself, was only William and Sambo,
and the memory of little Sheba, and nothing outside. She did not
regret it, yet she missed the crowds, the constant stream of people,
and the continual excitement of the palace. And more than all she
missed the ceremonies, the color, the military reviews, and the
dances far into the night. Thinking of this, Tulip saw again in her
mind's eye the great open square in front of the Komasi palace, a
space of beaten red clay, the ocherous dust lying thick on the
ground, the sun blazing, a crowd gathered to watch, the little boys
darting naked here and there, and then the shuffle of the soldiers
in their blue uniforms with white sashes and white fillets, and the
banging of the drums. In front marched the terrible razor women
with skulls hanging at their girdles. All that was over. Never again
would she hear the cymbals and the drums. How they had rolled
and throbbed and filled the whole town so that even the earth
had trembled! How she had danced to that music on the hot
sulphurous nights!

Tulip called Sambo and giving him a toy to carry, a present for
his little dead sister, she set off with him, and together they sauntered through the village street to the churchyard. As Tulip looked
about her at the green landscape of the English country her mind
was busy with memories, and she could not help comparing the
place where she had been brought up and the place where she was
now living. It seemed to her that the white people here, although
they could do so much, did not know how to live; that their lives
were like the lives of animals and not like those of human beings.
They went out all day into the fields like the cows going out to
graze; when they came back at night they chewed the cud like
cows, and if they talked at all talked slowly and awkwardly. They

seemed always to be asleep, and even in their moments of ill temper they did not wake up. Then Tulip began to imagine a mixed
world, half Africa and half England. If a dozen drums with pipes,
cymbals, and rattles were set on the village green, would that bring
the people out to dance? Tulip laughed aloud at the incongruity
of such people dancing to proper music; then she thought of the
laborers' soiled corduroy trousers and their huge hobnailed boots,
and she was silent with disgust. She entered the churchyard and
told Sambo to thrust the doll he was carrying into the little mound
of Sheba's grave. They did not linger in a place where so many
ghosts of strange people were likely to be met with. Near to the
church there was a farm with its yard shut from the road by a high
stone wall.

While she was loitering beneath this wall, Tulip heard a sudden
sound in the road and saw a forkful of cow-dung, together with
something bloody and very filthy, lying in front of her in the road
at her feet. She looked up at once and caught sight of the tip of a
boy's nose, and then had just time to take a step backwards and
so dodge another forkful of filth. There were whispers on the other
side of the wall, and she heard the words: "Come on quick, turn
old Jemmy loose on her," and then there was the sound of boys
running away across the yard. One or two specks of filth had fallen
on Tulip's sleeve. She stopped and cleaned them off as best she
could with a handful of leaves. The entrance of the farmyard was
some little way down the road. Just before Tulip got abreast of it,
she heard boys shouting, and banging of a stick on the wooden
doors of the shed, and the sound of a beast rushing to and fro.
The next moment a red bull ran out into the road and, pulling up
short, slipped down. When the brute got up he looked about him,
glowered at Tulip and Sambo, shook his head, and bellowed.
Tulip noticed how dusty the bull's coat was; straws were clinging
to him, and on his withers there was a dark patch stained with
damp. She bent down and picked Sambo up in her arms. While
she was stooping, two boys and a young man rushed out after the
bull and threw stones. One of these stones struck Tulip on the
temple. Still gripping Sambo in her left hand, she stooped to pick
up the stone. Her head swam, for a moment she fumbled; the blood
was running down the side of her cheek. Then she grasped the

stone — it was a large yellow flint — and she looked up. The bull
was moving towards her; Tulip yelled, and still holding Sambo
under her arm, ran straight at him, screaming at the top of her
voice. Just before she reached him, the bull turned broadside on
to her, and looking at her out of one eye, broke into a gallop and,
nearly knocking down one of the boys, disappeared into the yard.
Tulip stopped, and at once Sambo began howling at the top of his
voice. Facing her she saw a young man holding a prong. Tulip
raised her arm with the stone in her hand, but she did not throw it.

" Tamuley, Tamuley," screamed Tulip. The young man looked
at her uneasily.

" I ain't afraid of you," he said, shifting his feet. " I ain't done
nothing to you. I didn't know you were there."

Tulip screamed at him again in the Ffon gibberish of her own
country; her face was covered with blood, and it was this blood that
set Sambo screaming. Tulip still waved the stone round her head,
and the young man slowly walked back to the yard gate. Tulip
now turned her attention to Sambo and tried to still his cries.
When she had got a little way down the road, there were loud
guffaws of laughter behind her. At home Tulip washed away the
blood and found a deep cut on the top of her temple in the wool,
but it did not hurt her very much or for very long. The bloodstains
and spatters of dung on her wedding dress seemed to her much
more serious, but they were all got rid of with long soaking in cold
water.

After this Tulip kept close about the inn, but she did not escape
persecution. Once, Tom being absent for a minute, she went into
the bar to serve a carter. Seeing her, he swore and made as if to go
for her. This time Tulip was able to turn the tables, for she first
dashed a pint of beer into his face and then, taking sure aim,
threw the tankard after it, cutting him on the bridge of the nose.
The carter beat a retreat into the open air, and Tulip ran out the
opposite way into the garden. This incident roused up a greater
hostility against her than there had ever been before; boys haunted
the garden hedges in order to throw stones at her and Sambo, and
friends of the carter shouted out abuse of her whenever they came
near to the inn. Poor Tom Madgwick found this very alarming,
he was never easy unless he were close at hand, and he begged

Tulip every day to keep within doors, if only for his peace of mind, and in his anxiety he carried buckets of water upstairs in case of fire. What is more, he kept the shot-gun loaded under the counter of the bar, in case the worst should happen. Mrs. Clall was even more upset than Tom, which came from her living in the village. But her feeling was not terror, she did not look for any mischief to be done, but was full of shame to be seen going to work at the inn. It is true that she loved Sambo and respected Tulip, and felt pity for her, but she got so much abuse from the old women her neighbors that she declared that she was ill, and took to her bed so as to stop away. This weakness of hers had one excellent result; it kept Tulip busy in the house, so that she was not always fretting to go outdoors.

William, though expected every day, did not return.

Tulip was not one soon to become uneasy. She was inured to a life full of dangers and of accidents, and a few days' delay on a journey was nothing strange to her. Moreover she had the greatest confidence in William and knew he could take care of himself very well. Yet, as he had been absent now for a week, she began to wonder and unconsciously to look out for him.

When William had been gone ten days and Tulip and Tom had been left more and more alone, and cut off from the village, Tulip heard a knock at the door and went to open it. A visitor was a rare thing now at the inn, for only one or two laborers and the blacksmith and his mate still frequented the bar in the evening. In the middle of the day a farmer or a higgler would sometimes come and drink a glass. Such men of course were above the opinion of the village people; the others, who were hardened drinkers, were indifferent to it or below it.

On the doorstep was a lady whom Tulip at once guessed was William's sister, for she had the same open-hearted face and splendid figure, and when she spoke Tulip was sure of the relationship, for she had the soft burring voice of all the Targetts, only her eyes were different, small eyes with a greedy look in them.

Though she was standing below Tulip on the step, she rose a head above her, and her rich dress with its full crinoline filled the narrow doorway of the inn.

" May I come in? " she asked.

"I think that you must be Mrs. Sturmey," said Tulip.

"Yes, I am William's sister. I have long wanted to have a look at you; not that I ever expected to pay you a visit, since I do not approve of William's bringing you here or of his marrying you."

"Will you come in all the same, please?" said Tulip.

Mrs. Sturmey entered, and her small eyes flitted over the things that she saw, sorting them immediately into two classes: those she would like for herself and those she would not.

"I see you have a parrot," she said. "Did you bring that with you?" At her look the bird began its slow, uneasy dance.

"William had it before I knew him," said Tulip. "He brought it back from Brazil." And at these words Lucy said to herself that the least William could have done was to bring her a parrot, but then of course William had no family feeling. A moment afterwards Sambo came into the room, but his aunt at once placed him in the second class, among the undesirables. She asked his age, while the little boy gazed at her with perfect composure.

"He is three years old," said Tulip. "He will be four next October."

"I suppose you both find the climate very trying after Africa," said Mrs. Sturmey. "They say the change of air makes children very delicate."

Tulip silently cut a piece of cake and poured out a glass of sherry, but her sister-in-law refused any refreshment.

"How long is it, then, that you have known William?" she asked. "Not long before you left Africa, I suppose?"

Tulip counted on her fingers. "We have been married five years now," she answered. "But I saw William six months before I married him, on his first visit to Abomey."

Mrs. Sturmey seemed greatly surprised at this information, and without saying anything she silently looked several times first at Sambo and then at his mother.

"You know the village people do not like William having a black wife with a black child," she said at last. "They think it very wrong, just as I do."

At these words Tulip's whole face shone with delight and her teeth flashed as she smiled broadly.

" Well, there is very strong feeling against William," Lucy went
on. " The men will not come to the public house, and they threaten
to do all sorts of things, though only behind his back of course."

" William can lick all that trash," said Tulip.

" Perhaps he might," answered Lucy. " Of course one need not
pay attention to what the laborers say, but William has gone away,
and it is not very safe for you. Mr. Sturmey and I both think that
you and the little boy ought to go back to wherever you came
from."

" My country is far away, and here even the name of our King
is unknown," said Tulip.

" If anything happens to you, I know that William will lay it
at our door, which would be most unjust," said Lucy. " It is all his
fault for bringing you here. But he will say that it is because we
did not accept you as part of the family. But where is William? "

Tulip's face showed plainly that she could not answer this question, only after a minute she said: " William is all right. I do not
worry about him."

" Suppose he has deserted you," said Lucy. " What will happen
then? I think that he sees that he made a mistake, and that it would
be better for you to go away for your own sake and for the sake
of the little boy. William is quite untrustworthy. He did not tell
anybody the first time that he went off to sea, and left everything
to my brother John in the most heartless way. I don't think that
you will see William again, and the best thing for you is to go and
live at Dorchester for a time; then if William does not come back
you should go on to Southampton or Bristol."

" I shall wait here," said Tulip. " You cannot frighten a black
girl like me; I have seen a lot of worse people than any of you are
here."

Lucy looked at her sister-in-law gently, for, much as she disliked
her existence, she approved her spirit.

" You know that I do not like you," she said, " for you can
never be one of us, but I came here today to see if my husband
and I can do anything to help you. William has never done anything for us, but that does not affect what is my duty. I have
spoken about you to Mr. Cronk, and he agrees that you will never

be happy here, and that the little boy ought not to live here. They say native children never do well in England. When you come to me for help, you shall have it, for no doubt William has taken all the money with him."

Tulip, who had been watching her visitor with a puzzled expression, rose at these words and left the room, returning directly afterwards with a purse.

" Will you pray for me? " she asked, and giving a meaning smile put the purse into her sister-in-law's hand: " Please pray for me."

" Of course I shall. I always do pray for you," said Lucy.

" Different prayers now," said Tulip.

" What are you giving me this money for? Do you want me to take care of it for you? " asked Lucy.

" Yes."

" Very well. You ought to leave the village at once," said Lucy.

" Not till you have prayed, with good prayers for me and Sambo."

Tulip regained her composure as Mrs. Sturmey stowed away the purse in her pocket. She had been frightened, but now as she accompanied her sister-in-law to the front door she smiled cynically.

" People are much the same the whole world over," she thought. Often and again she had seen her father paying money to a witch or a wizard. Once they had taken money, they were powerless for two or three months to do any harm. Lucy, she thought, was well worth any money. After she had shut the door, Tulip danced down the passage in triumph.

All her African experience had taught her that witches do not visit one when they mean mischief. Now that Lucy was paid, no doubt the village people would behave better to her and would not frighten Sambo any more.

Tulip was surprised when the next day two or three men shouted threateningly at the inn as they were passing on their way back home from work.

Targett came back after an absence of three weeks.

It was close on midnight when Tulip was woken up by hearing a man moving in the house. She got out of bed and, taking William's cutlass in her hand, went downstairs, moving very softly, for she thought it was some man come from the village that had broken in to rob or maybe to murder her. There was a light in the dining-room, so she threw open the door, lifting up the point of the cutlass as she did so. William was sitting taking off his boots.

" Why, Tulip, how you did startle me! " he said, and getting up from his seat, took her in his arms. " Who were you expecting, lass, with that cutlass? You should have woken Tom."

" Are you alone? " asked Tulip.

" Yes, who should I have with me? I am glad to be back."

By the light of the candle Tulip saw that William had a black eye and a cut lip. His fine coat was gone; in its place was a seaman's jersey. He was dirty and unshaven. He looked thinner and more vigorous than when he had left.

" Is there any food in the house? " he asked. Tulip brought a ham, a loaf of bread, cheese, and a bottle of sherry.

As William carved the ham, Tulip saw his hands were trembling with hunger. He took a few mouthfuls at once. Tulip drew the cork from the bottle and poured him out a glass of wine. At the taste of it, William sighed and lay back in his chair. He ate silently, only interrupting himself to say: " Cut some more of the ham. I shall be ready for it as fast as you cut it."

At last he stopped her and began eating cheese. Tulip waited silently. When he had finished she brought the decanter of brandy and William's slippers and filled his pipe.

" No, thanks, Tulip. I'll turn in now."

Before he went to sleep he asked: " How's Sambo? " Then he added " I went to Goodwood — to the races. And there I was robbed."

Next morning William went into the bar before breakfast to speak with Tom and ask him how trade had been going in his absence. While he was talking with him Tulip went out in front of the house to let out the geese. As she and Sambo were watching the birds, she saw a wagon that was passing along the road draw up and the men with it stop and look at her. But now that William was back she felt secure, and so she did not retreat indoors as she might otherwise have done.

Just then Tom was saying that he had been anxious ever since they had set on Mrs. Tulip in the village, and that since people had turned so very disobliging he had kept the gun loaded behind the bar.

William had not heard a word of this from Tulip, so he questioned Tom very particularly and got the whole story from him. Now that he heard it William understood better what had led Tulip to bring down his cutlass with her the night before, unsheathed and naked in her hand, but this was only another example of what he was familiar with already from numberless incidents in Africa — that is, Tulip's courage. Such boldness was nothing like so surprising as it would have been in a white woman. While William was talking with Tom he heard a shouting outside, with several great oaths, and the words: "Drown the little bastard in the stream, Jemmy. We won't have them here breeding black babies in England." Then came the crack of a whip and a howl from Sambo.

William ran to the door and saw that a carter was standing near Tulip flourishing his whip, while his boy was dragging Sambo along by the hair towards the brook. But directly William came out, the fellow dropped the whip and ran, while his boy let go of Sambo and, trying to jump the brook, missed his footing and fell in on his knees, though he picked himself up and scrambled out the other side, and so made good his escape with only a wetting. Seeing the carter run so earnestly, William did not chase the man, but went up to Tulip, who was drying Sambo's tears, and put his arm round her and told her that her tormentors would soon learn that he was back, and that he would not leave her again on any account, and bid her have no fear. But Tulip was not hurt, nor much distressed, for the carter, who was the man whose nose she had broken with the pint pot, had not used his whip on her, and she had stood still, knowing that William was at hand. Finding no mischief had been done, William picked up the carter's great whip, all bound round with two or three score brass rings. He cracked it once or twice; then he noticed the team of horses and loaded wagon standing in the roadway near by.

The carter and his boy were out of sight now, so William smiled to himself and turned the leaders' head towards the inn, and drew the wagon out of the road, just outside his own doorway. Then he told Tom to give each horse its nosebag and to chain the wheels, and went himself in to breakfast, laughing at the fix in which the carter had got himself. After breakfast William spent some time washing himself and shaving, and then got Tulip to cut his hair, and every now and then gave a glance out of the window at the wagon, but there was still no sign of the carter. It was just before midday, and the horses were still standing patiently, when William saw a rough-looking customer coming to the inn. He was a stout fellow with a body round as a barrel, with a very red face, a cauliflower ear, and a colored handkerchief knotted round his throat.

William went out to the doorstep and asked him: " Have you come to fetch away the team? "

" Not that I know of," answered the man. " I came for a quart of ale, but if you want them taken anywhere, I'll do the job."

" No, someone will come along presently, and it is no business of mine," answered Targett, and he went indoors and drew the customer his beer.

When he had taken a swig at it the fellow asked William if any of the neighboring farmers were short of hands, for he was in need of a job. Then he added: " I'm a pug by rights and one who has earned good money in the ring."

The word *earned* seemed to take his fancy, for he repeated it several times with various oaths. " I believe you," said William with an amused glance at the man's ear. " You look as if you had earned it."

" When I was a youngster," the prizefighter went on, " the purses were smaller and the men bigger. Why, you can see men today fighting for fifty pounds a side that would never have been allowed in the ring fifteen years ago. Look at Sayers! Tom Sayers champion of the world! At ten stone! For why, I ask you. Because there isn't a heavyweight in England that can box! "

The prize-ring and everything relating to it was a topic in which William took great interest, so that now he drew himself a glass of beer and prepared to listen, while the stranger continued after lowering his voice to a whisper:

" Someone has put it round that I'm too old. I want to find that fellow. I'll twist his liver. Too old! There's a very big surprise coming for some of them this winter when I get in the ring again."

"That's right," said William. "That's the spirit that wins many a fight. No man is beaten till he thinks he is."

"That's God's truth," said the boxer. "But Harry Broome there at the Albion in Portsmouth, he was champion himself for a bit, like his brother Johnny, he wouldn't put up ten quid for me, the dirty Brum! 'It's no use, Jack,' he said to me, 'you'll never see the inside of a ring again. Any good sailor boy of twenty is worth more to me than you are.' I'll teach his young cocks to fight! Why, I've lived all my life in Portsmouth and I've never met the sailor yet who could stand up to me for twenty rounds."

Targett laughed at this. "I am a sailor myself," he said. "I might take you at your word, you know."

The pugilist drank off his beer and looked Targett up and down with a crafty eye, but a fight there and then offered him no attractions.

"I'm not saying anything against sailors, mister, but things aren't what they were, nor yet what they ought to be, in England."

"That's right," said William, and drawing the man another pint he told him to have a drink at his expense, for he loved the noble science which he had often heard had made England what she was and which distinguished Britons from every kind of foreigner.

The boxer swore that William was a gentleman and at once continued his story.

"Seeing Harry Broome would not have me, the damned flashy Brum, I walked to London and went into Alec Keane's house, the Three Tuns in Moor Street. Now, Alec used to be the finest sportsman in England; anyone will tell you that he has done more for the ring than any licensed gentleman living; but Alec just said to me: 'Jack, old friend, I've got my hands full with a nigger boy, and I've no money to spare for you, though you look fine.' A British sportsman backing a bloody black man and letting Jack Sait starve! It isn't right."

William would have interrupted his visitor, but the fellow went on: "And then there are the Sheenies. They are taking up the game now they see that there is money in it; but they can't box, they only bite and butt and use the spikes on their boots."

"You must expect to fight all comers," said William. "And I

have known niggers who could stand up to any man, and who would fight as fair as you could wish."

Just then Mr. Molten, a farmer from Tarrant, entered the bar and said: " I've come for my team and my wagon Mr. Targett, and I don't advise you to try any of your nonsense with me."

" I am glad that you have stepped round, sir," answered William. " I was saying to my man Tom just now that there ought to be a pound in the village where we could put your horses. Your man ran off like a hare; I don't know where he will have got to by now unless he has enlisted himself in the army, but he has so little stomach for fighting that I should not think that they would keep him long."

" There was a whip too," said the farmer.

" I am keeping the whip," said William. " If you ever do see that carter of yours again, tell him that I am keeping it on purpose for him." Then William picked up the whip, and going out to where the team was standing, he amused himself for some moments by cracking it, so that the horses fidgeted.

" Come on, now, both of you," cried the prizefighter. " Put up your mauleys and the best man shall have the whip. I love a fight and I will see fair play."

But the farmer was already turning his horses round and affected not to hear when William laughed and said:

" I think I can keep the whip without fighting any of our dung-yard bumpkins." Then as the farmer was getting into his wagon he called out to him: " This bloodthirsty chap here wants a job. You might take him on as your new carter. He is an old prizefighter, he tells me."

" I don't want any new carter," grumbled the farmer, who resented Targett's way of chaffing him. " And I don't need any of your advice, Mr. Targett."

Then he turned round on the edge of the wagon, scratched his head, and added: " A prizefighter, is he? Well, maybe I can find a job for him then, if he'll come along of me, and if he's willing."

Jack Sait did not need telling twice and scrambled over the tail-board of the wagon; the farmer struck the horses a blow with the doubled reins and they moved off.

That evening the bar was full. Many of the old customers were

back in their places. William did not serve, but leaned over the
bar in his fine clothes, smoking a pipe. He scarcely spoke; if addressed, he nodded his head, or took the pipe from his mouth and
blew out a puff of smoke or spat. There was nothing new in all this
for William. It had been just the same thing before, often enough,
when he had dealt with an unruly crew; in every latitude men are
the same. William did not despise them for fawning on him now
that he had come back to the village. He did not think it strange
that they should flock good-temperedly to drink, underneath the
very whip with which he had threatened one of their mates. Indeed, had the carter come in to ask him for a glass of beer in the
evening, though he had run from him that morning, the only thing
that would have surprised William would have been that he should
have got over his fear and be ready to stand the chaff of the others.
William expected to be stood a drink by that carter before many
weeks were out.

Now and then the beaming face of black Tulip was thrust
through a hatchway at the back of the bar. She never looked in
without a reasonable excuse.

" Tom, here is the corkscrew," she would say on one occasion,
on the next reprove him for using a dirty cloth on the glasses and
hand him a clean one. At last she could restrain herself no longer
and she walked into the bar crowded with men, the very men who
had been threatening or shouting at her for the three weeks past
whenever they had caught sight of her.

" Are you going to sit up for the gentleman who left his whip
behind him? " she asked in a ringing, insolent voice.

Then she tossed her head, and without glancing to right or left,
without looking at any of the men in the bar, swaggered to the
door. " Don't chase any more of them, William," she said, " or we
shall lose all our trade." She slammed the door after her as the
men roared at this sally.

William knocked out his pipe. " I'll say good-night, then, for fear
I should get into more mischief. Tom will look after you gentlemen."

But although William had achieved a triumph that day, his difficulties were not yet over. His horse and trap had disappeared on
his excursion to Goodwood, together with his rings, his watch and

chain, and his best suit of clothes. Next day he asked Tom Madg-wick for the sum of money he had left in his hands while he was away.

" Mrs. Tulip has had it, sir," said Tom.

William asked Tulip what she had done with the money. For the first minute she did not understand. Then she put her finger on her lips and whispered: " I gave it all to the witch, to buy prayers from her."

" To the parson? " asked William scornfully.

" No, to your sister. She was full of mischief when she came here, but I gave her that money, and now she won't do us any harm."

At first William could make nothing of what poor deluded Tulip told him, but he showed very plainly his relief that the money had gone to one of his own family. " Well, I must get the money back. I will send Tom round to the farm with a note."

" No, William, please do not do that. It will mean that she will do great harm to us. She came to threaten me. Tell me, did you not have bad luck while you were away? That was Lucy's doing. If I had not paid that money you might never have come back. She threatened Sambo also."

The idea of his sister having strange powers amused William, and he could not help grinning as Tulip spoke. Perhaps if Lucy had not been his sister, but an African, and if all this had taken place in Dahomey and not in Dorset, he would have been less skeptical. However, his curiosity was awakened, for he felt sure that Lucy must have come with some purpose, and that the last thing she could have intended was to work on Tulip's fears in order to extract money from her. " What did Lucy say when she came? " he asked. Tulip pouted. " She said that I must go away to Africa and that I must take Sambo away from here, and that I had done you a great deal of harm. She said you would never come back while I was still here. . . ." Tulip burst into tears. She could not tell William that Lucy had said he had deserted her and gone to America with Harry. William picked her up in his arms and sat down in the high-backed chair with her on his knee. " What else did she say? "

" She said that Sambo would die as she had made our little Sheba die."

" Did she say why she had come? "

" She came to get the money," said Tulip. " I am not stupid about those witch people, William. You know yourself how they used to come to my father and tell him all sorts of dreadful things — that it would not rain for a year; that it would not stop raining for a year; that the cattle would all die; that leopards would kill all the women who were with child. My father used to listen to them, just as I listened to Lucy, and then get up without saying anything and go to his treasury and come back with a rich present. Then the witch would go away, and nothing like he had described would come to pass. But if my father had been a mean man, if he had loved his treasure better than his people, they would have all died of hunger or thirst and there would have been no children born that year, except in the royal houses."

" What did Lucy say when you gave her the money? "

" She said she would take care of me now."

William wrote a note and sent it to Lucy's husband by Tom Madgwick, telling him to wait for an answer. It ran as follows:

THE SAILOR'S RETURN

Sir:

I beg to inform you that while I was away your wife, and my sister, called here without my permission and took away the sum of seventeen pounds.

Please hand it to bearer, who has my authority to receive it, and who will give you a written receipt for it. I shall take no further proceedings in the matter after you have refunded the amount.

Yours obediently,

WILLIAM TARGETT

Tom was a long time gone. When he was back, he handed William a small canvas bag with money, and told him that the letter which he had delivered had thrown them into a very great disturbance at Newbarrow Boys. Mr. Sturmey had read it before Tom, his face had flushed, and he had gone off, calling for his wife and saying: " What's this, what's this, money and kept secret? " High words had followed between husband and wife, who were wrangling for an hour before Mr. Sturmey came out again with the bag of money and asked Tom for a receipt. The return of this money was fortunate, for now William could pay what was owing to the brewer and see his way clear for another month more. To get some more in hand, William decided to sell Tulip's trinkets and rings, and in that way he thought he could tide over until the winter. Then he had another chance of bringing his ship into port, or so he thought. That was that he knew the name of a horse which he believed would win the St. Leger, for William had always had great belief in his own luck.

Tulip could now go out again in safety, but she did not venture far, for she feared Lucy, and though she did not dare argue with William any more, she was full of terror now that he had got back the money which she thought she had spent so well. When William asked her for the necklace of brilliants he had given her and for her gold bangles and her rings, she ran to fetch them with a merry face and gave him all, not keeping one thing back. Then putting her arms round his neck, she begged him to give them all to Lucy, or to some powerful wizard who could protect them against her.

Next morning Francis Targett, who had ridden over on his pony, arrived on his promised visit, in a high state of excitement and delight as he was to stay two or three days and he had never slept away from home before.

Early in the afternoon Tulip, Francis, and Sambo, taking baskets with them, went out into the fields to gather mushrooms. The sun was hot, and when they had got as many of the buttons as would make a jar of catchup they sat down, and Francis, asking first one question and then another about Africa, led Tulip on to tell him something of the history of her country, while Sambo ran up and down over the turf chasing the little blue butterflies and the meadow browns.

" The first of our kings in the written history," she began, " was Agarjah the Great. There is not much to tell about him except that he defeated everyone, and he was the first to raise an army of women and so make Dahomey into the greatest kingdom in Africa. The names of many of the peoples whom he conquered are now unknown, for he left no living creature behind him where his armies had passed. But among the peoples whom he conquered and who still exist are the Jackins, the Tuffos, the Mackies, and until recently the Oyos. He captured Save, the chief town of the Whydahs; then he raided the coast towns, defeated the Dutch, looted the white men's factories, and took many of them prisoners, but pardoned them. When the English Governor took part against him, he had him killed. The second King was Boss Hardy, a wicked man and a bad King. When his father died he drowned his elder brother, Zinga, in the sea, because he knew that it was not lawful to shed the royal blood. Very soon trouble came on him to punish him for this, for it does not do to obey the laws only by words and to disobey what the words mean. The Mew with half the army — "

" What is the Mew? " asked Francis, interrupting her.

" The Mew is the second general who commands the left wing of the army," answered Tulip. " Over him there is the Gaw, who is the chief general. The Mew revolted, but the Gaw defeated him. But perhaps this does not interest you? It is a lesson which I used to learn when I was a little girl. Would you rather that I talked to you about elephants? "

" No, go on, tell me about the Mew," said Francis.

" I have told you — the Gaw defeated the Mew. Then the Oyos attacked the King, who ran away and hid in the English fort at Whydah with Mr. Gregory while they burnt Abomey and Kana, shouting with joy. After that Boss Hardy had to pay tribute to the Oyos every year, which continued as a drain and a dishonor to our country until my father defeated and utterly subdued them and enlisted the surviving Oyos in his army. Boss Hardy then became afraid of the Whydahs and persuaded a prince of that country to follow his own evil example, for in that way he hoped that the Whydahs would be punished as he had been himself. This young man killed his elder brother, the King, and ate his heart, and not long afterwards became white with leprosy and died miserably. After his death, while the old Gaw was away fighting, the Why-dahs attacked Whydah, which had always been an object of their desire. They captured the town and slew the viceroy, but when the Gaw returned they were easily driven out again with great slaughter. Boss Hardy then made one named Tanga Viceroy of Whydah. He was not an entire man, but a gelded creature taken from the women's quarters in the royal palace. In spite of that,

when he was made Viceroy he would not be contented with less
than two hundred wives, buying all the most beautiful girls up
and down the coast. He was not jealous, though, for he amused
himself by watching their pleasures with his guests whom he invited to his palace for that purpose, and if there was ever any dispute among the women, Tanga judged between them. After a time
this strange creature, having risen so high as to be Viceroy, fancied
that he would make himself king, not that he could hope to found
a dynasty. The first thing that he did was to attack the Englishman, Gregory, in his fort, but in this he was unsuccessful, and
while he wasted his time there, messengers ran to warn Boss Hardy
of Tanga's treachery. The King at once sent an army to Whydah,
and Tanga shut himself up in his palace with his wives and all his
friends. Then, before his eyes, all that crew of men and women cut
each other's throats until only Tanga was left alive; he ran out of
his palace, and a woman shot him as he came down the steps.
When they looked inside the doors, they saw a lake of blood. I
have always felt sorry for poor Tanga, and I fancy that he must
have been very fat and always laughing in his high voice, and that,
having been brought up among women, he missed that kind of
life and had to start something of the same sort where he would
be still a servant helping women to lovers even when he had been
made master.

"Towards the end of his life Boss Hardy became jealous of
everyone, as if he were mad. First he tried to kill his brother-in-law
Shampoo, who, warned by his sister, ran off to the Whydahs, who
made him their general. Then the King became jealous of the old
Gaw who had served him faithfully all his life and who had saved
him a hundred times from the consequences of his own cowardice
and folly. Boss Hardy had his general tied up and, taking a cutlass,
began to cut his head off in front of the palace in the great square
of Abomey. But when he had finished his speech to the troops, his
heart failed him, for he was afraid. He struck the Gaw one blow
with a shaking hand, then he threw down the cutlass and began
screaming, while the old man, with his head half cut off, lay looking at his master without making a sound, and it is said smiling,
though his face was all over blood. At last Boss Hardy gave the
order for the Gaw to be strangled."

" That's beastly," said Francis. " What happened to the brute in the end? I hope he was murdered."

" Oh no indeed," said Tulip. " After that he sent an army against the Whydahs, but Shampoo retreated before it and drew it on into the lagoons, and there set on it, killing all but twenty-four men, whom he sent back to the King with insulting messages. Their fate was worse than those that died in battle, for Boss Hardy put them all to death with his own hand as an example to his sol-diers, so that they should learn never to be defeated. Ten years after that the Whydahs again attacked Whydah, but there hap-pening to be a very brave Englishman called Ajangan in the town, they could not capture it. Boss Hardy died when he was seventy years old, and there was great rejoicing. He was my great-great-grandfather. I hope you do not think that I am like him. I have told you that story," Tulip went on, " so that you should under-stand what sort of people we are; cruel, savage, and liking the sight of blood. Here in England you never do cruel things like those I have been telling you about. There are no people like my great-great-grandfather here; only good people. All the same I think we laugh more and have more fun than you do." And saying this, Tulip laughed herself, pinched Francis in the arm, and then, pick-ing up their baskets of mushrooms, they set out for home. On the way Sambo suddenly looked at Francis with a sly smile very dif-ferent from his usual grin, pointed to his clenched fist, and nodded. When his uncle bent down to him he opened his fingers; stuck to his moist brown palm were the speckled wings of a little blue butterfly.

When Francis and Tulip came in sight of the inn they saw that the door was wide open, with a hurdle lying across the threshold, and William's coat beside it on the ground; then, as they drew nearer, the loud rumor of many voices came to their ears. There was no one in either of the bars, but looking further they found the kitchen and the scullery full of men, whilst in the orchard be-yond, groups of laborers were standing under the apple trees. A silence fell when Tulip entered the kitchen, and in that moment she could hear the sound of heavy boots in the bedroom. She stood still then, threw up her hands, and, without waiting to be told, fled upstairs, and Sambo ran after her.

"The governor's been fighting and has got hurt," said one of the men to Francis. "They have taken him upstairs," and suddenly Francis saw that in the scullery two men were holding a limp figure in a chair, from which he would have slid, and that this figure was spitting blood. The boy went forward to see better; there was a basin of blood, a bucket of water, and several bloodstained cloths. "That is the fellow who did it. He'll swing for it if the governor dies." "Coo, how his ear does bleed!" said the onlookers, grinning foolishly. It was Jack Sait of Portsmouth; occasionally he made noises, asking for something, but no words could be distinguished. Francis turned back and found Tom Madgwick coming down the stairs. "How did this happen?" he asked.

"I was in the cellar," answered Tom. "I don't know how it started. I was bottling sherry. When I came up I saw Freddy Leake come in at the door. He asked me for a bucket of water and said the captain was out in the orchard giving a fearful hiding to a fellow that had come along with Mr. Molten and his carter from Tarrant, and that they had fought two rounds already.

"We filled the bucket, and then went out into the orchard, and for the first minute we couldn't see anyone there because of the little dip in the ground. When we had got close up to him we saw Captain Targett lying as if he were dead, and that chap there sitting under a tree all over blood. There has been foul play somewhere." Then Tom turned to the men in the kitchen and shouted angrily: "Now then, you get out of here," and pointed to the door. "A lot of dirty cowards," he cried as they moved out of the room, leaving only the old blacksmith Burden and his mate Freddy Leake, who were holding up the drooping figure of the boxer. "There's been foul play, and not one of them will own to seeing anything, but I saw them poking their heads over the hedge. There will be some questions for them to answer." Then Tom turned to the smith. "That chap must be taken in to the police," he said.

"That's all right, mate," answered Fred; "we won't let him go."

Just at that moment there was the sound of a woman's skirts rustling, and Tulip appeared in the doorway. Her eyeballs rolled; the flashing whites were the only movement in her black and stolid face; her hands were folded in front of her.

"Have you sent for the doctor?" she asked, and almost as soon

as she had spoken, without waiting for an answer, she went out of •
the room.

At her words all the men started guiltily; no one had thought
of the doctor.

"I'll ride over and fetch him," said Francis, who wanted to do
something. "Where does he live?" And while the blacksmith
began to give directions Tom ran to saddle the pony.

As Francis went out he met Tulip coming down the stairs again.
"Tell the doctor that William's skull is broken," she said. "I can
feel the edges of the bone."

"How is he?" asked Francis.

"I think that they have killed him," she answered simply, and
at these words the boy ran out, jumped on his pony before Tom
had fixed the girths, and a moment afterwards was galloping out
of the village. When he had seen the doctor, who promised to
come at once, Francis returned to the inn, where he found Freddy
Leake, who had dropped in to talk over the fight with Tom and
have a pint of beer. It was already dark, and the bar was lit by
candles instead of the usual lamp.

"Well, the first thing I saw," said Freddy, "was a lot of the
chaps going up the lane, but I thought nothing of that at the time.
Then I stepped up here to the bar to have a glass of beer, for the
forge makes me thirsty in this weather; not that I'm a drinking
man."

At these words Tom gave Francis a wink and the blacksmith took
another pull at his tankard and went on:

"Mr. Targett was here and drew me my glass, and then I said I
must be getting along, for there was a horse waiting for his shoes.
Mr. Targett stepped out into the road with me, and just then Mr.
Molten came up with his carter and that fellow there, and Mr. Molten said something about a whip. You know what an easy way Mr.
Targett has of chaffing. Well, he began like that with the carter;
he told him he must be careful about running or he would strain
his heart. I can tell you it made me laugh to hear him. Carter did
not like that and said: 'That black girl of yours is too saucy for our
liking, Mr. Targett, and you set her up in it by dressing her as if
she were a lady. What she wants is a touch of a whip like mine.
You can have it if you will promise to use it, but if you don't I

shall use it on her myself the first time that ever I see her. It's my whip and we have come to take it, if we have to use force.' Mr. Targett hit him then and swore he would give a thrashing he would remember, but this other fellow they call Jack — "

" Sait his name is," said Tom. " He's an old prizefighter, that has been known a long time at Portsmouth."

" Well, he pushed in between them and told Mr. Targett to take him on if he wanted a fight, and then Mr. Molten said: ' We have brought him along on purpose; you won't ride over him in a hurry.' I could see that something was coming then, you understand, so I let them wait for me down at the forge. Mr. Targett pulled his coat off, but the Portsmouth fellow suggested going somewhere quieter, and we all went round the end of the house into the orchard."

" Sait his name is," said Tom for the second time. " I have seen him several times at Portsmouth and Gosport hanging round the public houses in company with sailors; he's a known man there, but getting too old for his business."

" Well, then they started," said the smith. " Mr. Targett is the taller, and a bit longer in the reach, but the other fellow is a strong enough chap too. Mr. Targett held him off all the time and kept slipping and ducking and jumping back out of his reach, and for the first minute Sait was chasing him round and round in a circle. But he never hit Mr. Targett; that is, there was no blow to speak of. Presently Mr. Targett seemed to think that he had gone far enough, for he stood his ground toe to toe with him, and then didn't he leather him! That was when the blood began to fly, for every second or two Mr. Targett would catch him on that swollen ear of his. Mr. Molten and his carter hadn't anything to say then, for they had been calling out to Sait when he looked like winning. The fight was all one way after that, and I think myself that the reason was that Mr. Targett was too quick for him. He always seemed to get away from Sait's blows; he kept stopping them with his elbows, and dodging them." And the smith got up, stuck out his elbows, bobbed his head, and gave a tremendous blow in the empty air.

" Several times the other fellow got hold of him, but Mr. Targett shook him off and then started hammering him again, and never let his ear alone. At last Sait got both his arms round him and hugged him, and I could see Mr. Targett laughing in his face, and he caught him a right-handed round-arm blow on his ear as they went down together with the Portsmouth chap on top."

" Well, that was round number one," said Tom. " What happened after that? "

" Well, as soon as they got up, Mr. Molten started swearing at Sait. ' Jack,' he said, ' you damned liar, you have made a fool of me in front of all the fellows here, and taken a sovereign of mine too. If I ever see you round my farm again I'll let daylight into you! ' and with that he climbed over the hedge and we could hear him cursing the fellows in the lane and telling them to get back to their work. I thought Mr. Targett would have hurt himself then with laughing. He said to the fellow: ' I reckon you have *earned* your sovereign; *earned* it, old man; now shall we go and have a drink, mate, to the big surprise that's coming in the ring? ' but Sait would not agree to that. ' I'll fight to a finish,' he said, ' the same as I always do. Maybe in another hour's time I shall stop you of laughing.'

" In the second round it was the same thing over again, only it lasted longer, and Mr. Targett knocked Sait off his feet once, but he got up again and they went on. The end of that round was just the same as the first one, Mr. Targett laughing at the fellow, and fibbing him on the ear while Sait hugged him and threw him. It was only then that you could see the other fellow's strength. Well, that was all I saw. When Mr. Targett got up, there wasn't a mark on him beyond a cut lip, and Sait lay there streaming with blood. The carter was bending over him, and then Mr. Targett said to me: ' Freddy,' he said, ' run and get some water for him, there's a good fellow. Fetch a bucketful.' Those were the last words I heard Mr. Targett say."

" There must have been foul play while your back was turned," said Tom.

" They were two to one! " cried Francis.

" And there was no sign of that carter when we came out with the bucket," said Tom.

" Well, we know what Sait said down at the smithy, before they drove him in to Dorchester," said Freddy Leake, emptying his tankard.

" What is his story? " asked Francis.

" Just half a pint more, Tom," said the smith. " Why, his story is this: he says that after I went they started fighting again, and that Mr. Targett hit him a blow between the eyes that half stunned him, and then took hold of him and threw him and fell with him, and that is all he knows about it."

" You won't get me to believe that," said Tom scornfully.

" Why not? " asked Francis; " that may be the truth, for if William was on the ground the carter might have kicked him."

" Ay, that he might," said Freddy. " Another half a pint, Tom."

" Yes, but if carter kicked him," said Tom drawing the beer, " Jack Sait saw him do it, and if he won't tell on him it is because it was as much his doing as carter's."

The door opened and the doctor entered.

" This way, sir," said Tom, and taking a candle he showed him down the passage and up the stairs. He did not come back.

Francis could hear the doctor's footsteps in the room overhead, and then the sound of some question addressed to Tulip. There was no answer, only the sound of footsteps on the plank floor and the splash of water being poured into a basin.

" Coo — you ought to have seen your brother jabbing him on his great ear," said Freddy. Francis did not reply; he shivered, listening to what was going on in the room above, where the doctor's voice sounded like the rapid snipping of scissors. When this sound stopped, there were a few words from Tulip, spoken clearly and sufficiently loud for the boy to hear: " I understand. . . . I have seen this before. . . . I understand. . . ."

The doctor came downstairs and without saying a word went out of the house. There was the noise of the wheels of his gig as he turned his horse round, and then the trot of his horse going away.

" Coo — your brother is a heavy man to handle," said the blacksmith. " Tom and I had a job with him on the stairs."

The boy sat silent for another five minutes till the door opened softly and Mrs. Clall put her head into the bar. " Doctor says he cannot last through the night," she said. The parrot scraped in its cage. " Time, gentlemen, please. Time," it said feebly.

" I thought he would be taken," said Freddy. Then he added: " Tell Tom I shall want another half-pint before he shuts up."

Francis picked up the candle and went out to the stable. The air was warm and still and the flame did not flicker out of doors. While he saddled his pony Francis began to cry, and in his pain first kissed the shaggy face of the little cob and then struck the animal several times with his clenched fist. As he rode away he saw Tulip's shadow black against the curtain. When he had been riding half an hour he dismounted to cut a stick from a hedge, and after that he thrashed the pony unmercifully as he rode. Before midday William's elder brother, John Targett, drove up to the inn with Francis beside him. They were met by Tom, who told them that William had died in the night, and showed them up to the bed-room where Tulip was still sitting. When they entered she was talking rapidly in a low voice in English, but neither of them could distinguish the words, and so they could not know that she was addressing William's spirit, which she believed was there in the room with her, unaltered by death and having the same desires as before it left the body.

John Targett gazed for a few moments at the face of his younger brother, while Francis tried to conceal his emotion by speaking to Sambo. But when Tulip said to them that Tom would give them each a glass of wine, he burst into tears and left the room.

John Targett was very like William in the face, only a trifle more burly and not so tall, so that Tulip knew at once who he was and felt at home with him.

" A terrible end," he said. " All of our family seem to come by death violently. This is a shocking affair, and for no one more than you. I cannot forgive myself for not coming to see William; there are so many things to attend to every day, and suddenly death separates us. I meant to come at the wedding. I sent a cheese, but they never gave it to William; he would have liked to have tasted our cheese again. Well, now I suppose there is a great deal of business to be done, and I had better undertake to deal with it."

John went downstairs and without beating about the bush told

Tom to hand over the keys and any money in his charge, and to put up the shutters and lock the door, which had not been done. The same evening John visited the undertaker and the clergyman, and the next morning drove in to Dorchester to see the coroner. It appeared after a rough valuation of the effects at the inn that all the debts left by the dead man could be discharged, and that after this had been done there would be a sum of twenty or thirty pounds for the widow.

After William's death Tulip sat motionless in the room with the corpse. The blinds were drawn and the windows shut. Sometimes she spoke in a low voice, and, what was strange, always in English, but often she was silent for hours at a time, and motionless also, but at last she was driven out by the coroner's man and the under-taker.

On the morning of the funeral several parties arrived at the Sailor's Return. In one dogcart came Mrs. John Targett and her nephew, Charlie Tizard, who went out into the orchard to smoke a pipe. In the next came Dolly and her husband (for she had been married now a few weeks). Then in a third dogcart came Lucy and Mr. Sturmey. Tulip had dressed herself that day in a black dress; over her head she wore a black lace shawl which concealed almost all her face, and she wore also the black gloves Dolly had given her.

When she went downstairs she found the company assembled, waiting to start for the churchyard. There was a sound of the men moving to and fro in the next room with the coffin, and carrying it out to the hearse, which had been hired from Wareham. Dolly kissed Sambo, and took Tulip in her arms; then she introduced her husband who shook hands. Stevie Barnes was a thin young man with a nutcracker nose and jaw, and was ill at ease, being the only person not attired in full mourning. Mr. Sturmey also came up to Tulip and said it was very extraordinary they had not met before. Then he smiled at her and nodded encouragement, though Tulip did not notice this. Her face was calm. She was entirely occupied in the effort of following correctly a foreign ritual and behaving as she knew William would have wished her to behave. She was stiff and silent, for she knew that any breach of decorum would be a bad omen. The whole village of Maiden Newbarrow attended the funeral, and many others who had known William had come in from the neighboring parishes. This was not only due to the fact that he had been generally respected, but also that he had become notable by the manner of his death. Those who most regretted that they had not seen him get his injuries now thought they would make up in some degree by coming to see him buried.

All the Targett family had brought wreaths, and in addition there was one sent by Mr. Stingo, and another from old Mr. Estrich.

After the service Dolly walked back with Tulip, and the whole company sat down to dinner.

John carved and said grace. In the conversation which followed, William and the existence of Tulip and Sambo were ignored, for Dolly was now separated from Tulip, who sat at the bottom of the table with Sambo between Francis and Charlie Tizard and they were silent throughout the meal.

When dinner was over they went into the adjoining room, where John addressed the assembled family. William, he said, was his brother, and he, as the head of the family, had to perform the duty of looking into his affairs. In the last year William had run through a small fortune, and now there was nothing to show for it. Fortunately there was enough to cover the debts, and after disposing of the inn there would be a small balance for his widow, which would enable her to look about her. Mr. Stingo had met him in a generous spirit and had relieved them of the tenancy of the inn. He himself was going to put up a headstone to William and would pay for it out of his own pocket, as he felt that he ought not to be forgotten.

" What will happen to the child? " asked Dolly, when her brother had finished speaking; " we must remember that he is our nephew."

" I don't think we have much reason to call that little black boy a relative of ours," said Lucy.

There was a moment's silence, then John said: " I have spoken to Mr. Cronk about the child. Lucy, you can also keep an eye on them for the present; and now I am going to give Mrs. William a sum of money to go on with."

" How long can she stay here? " asked Dolly.

" The sale is next week, and she had better move out at once."

" There is no reason she should stay here that I can see," said

Dolly. " Couldn't she come home with us? " And she turned to her husband.

" Do what you think right about it, Dolly," said Stevie.

But when the question was put to her, Tulip shook her head.

" I'm all right," she said, " I have Sambo."

" I do not know that she is a fit person to have the child," said Lucy. " We can't foster a heathen."

" I have asked Mr. Cronk to decide what should be done about the child, and he is writing to some friends of his. We can safely leave the question in his hands," said John. " For the present the child is to stay with her."

" She is a most unsuitable person to be given money. I think it ought to be given to someone who can be relied on," said Lucy.

" William would not like you to have his money," said Tulip.

There was a silence, then Francis laughed.

" Give it to Tulip," said Dolly, " it belongs to her."

" What Dolly says is quite right," answered John. " I have no legal right to give the money to anyone but Mrs. William, and I shall do best to stick to the law."

He rose, looked at his watch, and said: " It is blowing up for rain; we had better be moving."

They all got up, scraping their chairs.

" Well, Mrs. William, here is the money. I have no doubt William would have given it to you himself," and he took out a small canvas bag as he spoke.

" Here are fifteen pounds, which is the money from the sale of everything except the furniture. I have sold the linen and plate and most of the bedroom furniture, privately. Things never fetch much at a sale. I reckon there should be another ten pounds coming to you later on, but I shall see to it that a proper provision is made for you."

The members of the Targett family dispersed. Outside, their traps were waiting; Tom had been harnessing the horses.

At parting Dolly kissed Tulip, and Francis gave her sixpence to buy sweets for Sambo.

Lucy and her husband drove away silently, for Lucy considered that she had been insulted, and that John had shown himself weak and hesitating as ever.

That night Tulip was left alone, and she sat up late packing her things. First she took down all her dresses and her clothes and spread them on the bed and on the table and the chest of drawers. She stayed for a long while fingering the silks and satins, and then began to fold them up, and burst into a flood of tears. She carried them in her arms downstairs, opened the kitchen door, and went out into the orchard; afterwards she brought paper, several armfuls of straw, and a faggot from the woodpile.

She set light to her bonfire, and when it was ablaze she threw all the finery William had given her upon the flames. One by one she threw the garments, first a silk shawl, then a pair of silk stockings, and then an embroidered gown. While she was employed in this fashion Tom, who had been woken by the light shining in his window, looked out.

" What ever are you doing there Mrs. Tulip? " he asked her.

But Tulip did not answer, and by the light of the flaming faggots he could see what she was about. He was ashamed then to say any more to her, though his good sense was shocked by the destruction of so many fine things, several of which she had worn but once, when William had first brought them home to her.

When she had finished burning her fine clothes, not sparing one thing, and leaving herself nothing but the clothes she wore ordinarily in the kitchen, she smeared her head in the ashes, singeing her woolly crop of hair. She went indoors after that and left the last flames to die away by themselves. Just then the first heavy drops of the storm of rain, which John had foretold, fell like a shower of stones.

Next day Tom was up early, for he was going that morning back to his home at Cowes. When he had had his breakfast he knocked at the door of her room and Tulip opened it; she had not undressed that night, nor for that matter had she slept. " I am just come to say good-by, Mrs. Tulip, to you and to Sambo," said Tom.

" Where are you going, then, Tom? " asked she.

" Well, I must be going to my home, and then looking out for a new place, you know," said Tom. " I must say good-by now or I shall not get to Southampton tonight."

" Why, take me with you," said Tulip. " I am going to Southampton myself. I shall not stay here, or they will make me give up

Sambo. The parson is to steal Sambo. William never wanted his
son to be a parson; he was to be a harpooneer."

" Yes, I have heard him say so often," answered Tom. " Come
along, then, with me, Mrs. Tulip, if you want to go to Southampton. I shall be near home there and will soon find you lodgings; you
know, my home is at Cowes, and we are always going to and fro
to Southampton, and I have great acquaintance in that town."

Tulip had only a little bundle with her and was soon ready. The
carrier was waiting outside for Tom to take him to the station, for
he had a chest with him, and Tulip and Sambo drove off without
anyone taking any notice of them. But even when she got to
Southampton, where Tom found her very respectable lodgings,
Tulip did not fancy she was clear of the clergyman. She had learnt
that distance meant very little to the superior white people who
had money. She made then all haste to get a ship to take herself
and Sambo out of England, one that was bound for the coast of
Guinea and that would set her down within five or six hundred
miles of her father's kingdom. She was a long time inquiring at
the docks, but fruitlessly. Either there was no ship in the port
bound that way, or else the sailors would not listen to her, but
only answered her very lewdly. Thus Tulip spent two months in
the town without finding the ship she wanted. Every week she had
to pay the woman a pound for the room and for the food which she
and Sambo ate.

One day after she had been seeking thus for a ship for over two
months, she came in with Sambo to her lodging, and the woman
who boarded them said to her:

" Why, Mrs. Targett, only this minute there was a clergyman
here asking after you. He is but this moment gone; if you run up
the street towards the Bar-gate, you will be sure to catch him."

Tulip did not wait longer but to secure her purse, and picking
up Sambo, ran into the street, but then she did not run towards
the Bar-gate, but the other way to the docks.

So she went running and hurrying down towards the harbor almost ready to get aboard the first ship she came to and travel to
any part of the world, for she was quite out of breath with fear.
Just as she got to the docks she was hailed by a seaman.

" Hullo, my lass," cried he, " you are the purchase I have been looking for. I'm tired of the gear in this country, and wish I were back at Whydah. Come on, my girl, and give me some proper fun. I'll do your business for you."

Now, what struck Tulip's ear was not his offering at her, for she had been plentifully pestered in this way all the time that she had been in Southampton, but that word Whydah, which was just the place of all others which she aimed at reaching.

She stopped dead in her tracks and went up to him and asked him gently: " Do you know Whydah, then? "

" Why, my lass, I have just come from Whydah, and we sail again tomorrow for the coast."

" Oh, take me to your captain, then," said Tulip, " for Whydah is near to my home, and I want to find a ship to carry me there."

" Take you to the captain! " cried the sailor laughing. " Nay, he's too old for such business, but I'll do your turn and give you half a crown for it."

" No, sailor," said Tulip, but smiling, for she would not offend the man if she could help it, since he was her one hope. " I know you sailors, you'll find another girl easily. But please take me to your captain, for my husband was the captain of a trading vessel on the coast and was most likely a friend of his."

The fellow was then overcome by her beseeching and imploring him to take her to his captain, and though he would not do that, he led her along to the house where the captain of his ship lodged, and then left her on the doorstep to try her luck. As it fell out, the captain was just drinking a cup of tea and warming his feet at the fire, and he heard Tulip's voice when she asked for him. The woman who opened the door would have shut it in Tulip's face, for she hated a Negro like the plague, but Tulip stuck her foot in the jamb and kept her parleying.

" Tell the captain I am Mrs. Targett, and I am the widow of a friend of his." Now, as it chanced, what Tulip said thus in mere bravado was truth, and the captain had indeed known Targett, or at any rate heard speak of him often enough, and since he had got back to England had heard him spoken of again, with particulars of his death. He came then to the door, with the teapot in his hand, and said that Tulip might come in, which she did instantly, holding Sambo by the hand. The captain eyed her up and down and, seeing that she was respectably dressed, though very plainly, asked her what service he could do her.

"Only give me a passage, with my little boy, to Whydah," said she. "I am the daughter of a great man in Dahomey, and now my husband, Captain Targett, is dead, and I want to go back to Africa. If I stay here, who knows what will become of my little Sambo? He will be treated as if he were a slave, he will be only a dirty nigger, but in Dahomey he will be a great man, and cousin of the heir to the throne."

"Well," said the captain, "I have never carried any passengers and I won't carry a woman on board my ship. It is a bad place enough as it is, but it would be hell if I had a woman aboard. But I will take your little boy if you like, for the sake of Captain Targett, whom I have often heard of; indeed, I believe I met him."

Tulip began then to beg and beseech him to take her as well, and would have fawned on him and licked his boots, to see if that would move him. But the captain remained firm, and indeed told her not to say another word or he would not take the boy either. So that at last Tulip was forced to be silent and stood turning the thing over in her mind.

But considering that the clergyman was waiting for her now at her lodgings, come to take Sambo from her and send him God knows where into what orphanage or asylum, and that then he would stay a dirty nigger all his life, and that she would lose him anyhow; thinking, as I say, of this, she nodded her head, and taking Sambo's hand put it silently into the captain's. For she could not speak for fear that she should start a-blubbering or a-moaning, and so offend.

"Well, I'll take him on board right away," said the captain. "We sail tomorrow on the tide, and he shall sleep aboard the ship. The steward will look after him."

Then Tulip took out her purse and said: "This is all the money I have got, but I have more coming, ten or twelve pounds more, and I will pay it to you when you come back if this is not enough for a child's passage. And if there be any balance to spare, pay it to my cousin the Prince Choodaton and commend Sambo to him."

The captain laughed at this and said he would not take her money, but afterwards he took it, saying:

" I will not charge you any passage money, but this will serve
for me to hire bearers on Whydah beach to take your boy up-
country. I shall see him safe into the hands of Choodaton. He is
a man I have heard spoken of. Come along, my lad, you shall come
and see my ship and the sailors dancing on the deck."

So Tulip took farewell of her child, and not so tenderly, either,
as she might have done if the captain had not been there with his
boots just laced up, waiting to take Sambo on board. And all little
Sambo thought of was to see the sailors dancing on the deck, for
he did not know that he was to lose his mother.

When she had left them, Tulip wandered about for some time
like a demented thing. But at last some drunken sailors clutching
at her set her off running, and she got a fair way out of the town
on the west side and lay down in a ditch and rested there that
night. Next morning she would not go back to Southampton, lest
the ship had not sailed and the clergyman should find her, so she
wandered out into the country.

For some days she traveled about aimlessly, begging her food
at cottages, and then she directed her steps to Dorsèt, since there
was money waiting for her there.

When she got to Maiden Newbarrow it was late, past eleven
o'clock at night, and she was very weary with walking. She went
to the inn, and finding the doors locked, pushed in the catch of the
kitchen window and so got inside the house. She lay down then
in an empty room and was soon asleep, lying on the bare boards.
When she awoke she heard someone moving, and the voices of a
man and of a woman and before she could get onto her feet the
door opened. In the doorway was the wife of the new tenant, for
they were moving in that day and were expecting their furniture
to come that morning.

" Why, Fred, what ever's here? " she cried; then looking at
Tulip's black face, she exclaimed: " I'll be bound it's the poor
creature that ran away, Mr. Targett's wife."

Her husband then came into the room, and they questioned
Tulip about what she had done, and where she had been, and told
her that Jack Sait had been found guilty of murder two days since,
and that he would be hanged in six weeks' time.

" A villain like that deserves no mercy," said the new landlord;

" murdering a licensed man. You have a pleasure left to look forward to; for I warrant you will be glad to see the brute hanged."

" Why should I? " answered Tulip. " I have seen so many deaths, I do not care about them any more."

While they were still talking, the wagon loaded with their furniture drove up, and the wagoners began to unload it. At first Tulip only watched the men moving to and fro, but presently she reflected that the new glasses must be rinsed, and the beds made, and that there was a great deal of work to be done on such a day, so she set to work with the others. Then she saw a new kettle and drew water from the well, and filled it, and after lighting the fire she brewed a pot of tea and took it in to the new mistress. As Tulip's grace or beauty, if one can use such a word about a black Negro woman, was now a good deal faded by her recent misfortunes, the innkeeper's wife never thought of Tulip as likely to attract the men. And seeing the Negress would make herself useful, she spoke to her husband about letting her stay on.

He was a good-natured enough man and was fond of a joke, so he said: " Yes, Minnie, she can do all the dirty work, and she won't show it, that's one thing. Yes, let her stay on and welcome; she can rinse out the glasses behind the bar, and she will cost us nothing for wages, or next to nothing. Yes, no one shall say I turned the poor creature out of doors now she has nowhere to go."

Thus Tulip went on living at the inn, working all day long as the drudge of everyone about the place. In the village they were used to her, and now that she was always dressed in the poorest cast-off clothes her mistress had given her, nobody shouted at her or jeered as she went by. But by degrees her name changed from Mrs. Tulip to Mrs. Two Lips, because as Tulip grew older and uglier her lips grew broader and more blubbery.

Three months after she had come back, Tulip sent the rest of her money to the captain at Southampton, but she never got an answer or an acknowledgment from him, and not knowing how to get news of Sambo, had to live on without any.

Some ten years later John Targett was killed by a bull, and Harry came back on a visit to his native country, his business being to make over the farm to Francis, his younger brother. While he was in England he heard all the circumstances of William's death and that Tulip was living and still at the Sailor's Return.

He did not visit her, although business took him to Maiden Newbarrow to see Lucy. Ten years in America had changed him. He had fought in the Southern army in the Civil War, he had learned to know the Negro better than he did when he first met Tulip, and he would have said, better than his brother William ever could have done. Certainly he had made more money out of Negroes than William had by selling poor Tulip's pearls, though not so pleasantly. Tulip heard of his visit to Lucy. She was not surprised, she was not even disappointed that he did not come to see her, for she had learned to know her station in life, and she did her duty in it very well.

Joseph Hergesheimer

TUBAL CAIN

I

ALEXANDER HULINGS sat at the dingy, green-baize-covered table, with one slight knee hung loosely over the other, and his tenuous fingers lightly gripping the time-polished wooden arms of a hickory chair. He was staring somberly, with an immobile, thin, dark countenance, at the white plaster wall before him. Close by his right shoulder a window opened on a tranquil street, where the vermilion maple buds were splitting; and beyond the window a door was ajar on a plank sidewalk. Some shelves held crumbling yellow calf-bound volumes, a few new, with glazed black labels; at the back was a small cannon stove, with an elbow of pipe let into the plaster; a large steel engraving of Chief Justice Marshall hung on the wall; and in a farther corner a careless pile of paper, folded in dockets or tied with casual string, was collecting a gray film of neglect. A small banjo clock, with a brass-railed pediment and an elongated picture in color of the Exchange at Manchester, traced the regular, monotonous passage of minutes into hour.

The hour extended, doubled; but Alexander Hulings barely shifted a knee, a hand. At times a slight convulsive shudder passed through his shoulders, but without affecting his position or the concentrated gloom. Occasionally he swallowed dryly; his grip momentarily tightened on the chair, but his gaze was level. The afternoon waned; a sweet breath of flowering magnolia drifted in at the door; the light grew tender; and footfalls without sounded far away. Suddenly Hulings moved; his chair scraped harshly over the bare floor and he strode abruptly outside, where he stood facing a small tin sign nailed near the door. It read:

ALEXANDER HULINGS
COUNSELOR AT LAW

With a violent gesture, unpremeditated even by himself, he forced his hand under an edge of the sign and ripped it from its place. Then he went back and flung it bitterly, with a crumpling impact, away from him, and resumed his place at the table.

It was the end of that! He had practiced law seven, nine, years, detesting its circuitous trivialities, uniformly failing to establish a professional success, without realizing his utter legal unfitness. Before him on a scrap of paper were the figures of his past year's activities. He had made something over nine hundred dollars. And he was thirty-four years old! Those facts, seen together, dinned failure in his brain. There were absolutely no indications of a brighter future. Two other actualities added to the gloom of his thoughts — one was Hallie Flower, that would have to be encountered at once, this evening; and the other was — his health.

He was reluctant to admit any question of the latter; he had the feeling, almost a superstition, that such an admission increased whatever, if anything, was the matter with him. It was vague, but increasingly disturbing; he had described it with difficulty to Doctor Veneada, his only intimate among the Eastlake men, as a sensation like that a fiddlestring might experience when tightened remorselessly by a blundering hand.

"At any minute," he had said, "the damned thing must go!"

Veneada had frowned out of his whiskers.

"What you need," the doctor had decided, "is a complete change. You are strung up. Go away; forget the law for two or three months. The Mineral is the place for you."

Alexander Hulings couldn't afford a month or more at the Mineral Spring; and he had said so with the sharpness that was one of the disturbing symptoms of his condition. He had had several letters, though, throughout a number of years, from James Claypole, a cousin of his mother, asking him out to Tubal Cain, the iron forge which barely kept Claypole alive; and he might manage that — if it were not for Hallie Flower. There the conversation had come to an inevitable conclusion.

Now, in a flurry of violence that was, nevertheless, the expression of complete purpose, he had ended his practice, his only livelihood; and that would — must — end Hallie.

He had been engaged to her from the day when, together, they had, with a pretense of formality, opened his office in Eastlake. He had determined not to marry until he made a thousand dollars in a year; and, as year after year slipped by without his achieving that amount, their engagement had come to resemble the unemotional contact of a union without sex. Lately Hallie had seemed almost content with duties in her parental home and the three evenings weekly that Alexander spent with her in the formal propriety of a front room.

His own feelings defied analysis; but it seemed to him that, frankly surveyed, even his love for Hallie Flower had been swallowed up in the tide of irritability rising about him. He felt no active sorrow at the knowledge that he was about to relinquish all claim upon her; his pride stirred resentfully; the evening promised to be uncomfortable — but that was all.

The room swam about him in a manner that had grown hatefully familiar; he swayed in his chair; and his hands were first numb with cold and then wet by perspiration. A sinking fear fastened on him, an inchoate dread that he fought bitterly. It wasn't death from which Alexander Hulings shuddered, but a crawling sensation that turned his knees to dust. He was a slight man, with narrow shoulders and close-swinging arms, but as rigidly erect as an iron bar; his

mentality was like that too, and he particularly detested the variety
of nerves that had settled on him.

A form blocked the doorway, accentuating the dusk that had
swiftly gathered in the office, and Veneada entered. His neckcloth
was, as always, carelessly folded, and his collar hid in rolls of fat;
a cloak was thrown back from a wide girth and he wore an incongruous pair of buff linen trousers.

" What's this — mooning in the dark? " he demanded. " Thought
you hadn't locked the office door. Come out; fill your lungs with
the spring and your stomach with supper."

Without reply, Alexander Hulings followed the other into the
street.

" I am going to Hallie's," he said in response to Veneada's unspoken query.

Suddenly he felt that he must conclude everything at once and
get away; where and from what he didn't know. It was not his
evening to see Hallie and she would be surprised when he came up
on the step. The Flowers had supper at five; it would be over now,
and Hallie finished with the dishes and free. Alexander briefly told
Veneada his double decision.

" In a way," the other said, " I'm glad. You must get away for
a little anyway; and you are accomplishing nothing here in Eastlake. You are a rotten lawyer, Alexander; any other man would have
quit long ago, but your infernal stubbornness held you to it. You
are not a small-town man. You see life in a different, a wider way.
And if you could only come on something where your pig-headed-
ness counted there's no saying where you'd reach. I'm sorry for
Hallie; she's a nice woman, and you could get along well enough
on nine hundred — "

" I said I'd never marry until I made a thousand in a year,"
Hulings broke in, exasperated.

" Good heavens! Don't I know that? " Veneada replied. " And
you won't, you — you mule! I guess I've suffered enough from your
confounded character to know what it means when you say a thing.
I think you're right about this. Go up to that fellow Claypole and
show him what brittle stuff iron is compared to yourself. Seriously,
Alex, get out and work like the devil at a heavy job; go to bed with

your back ruined and your hands raw. You know I'll miss you — means a lot to me, best friend."

A deep embarrassment was visible on Veneada; it was communicated to Alexander Hulings, and he was relieved when they drew opposite the Flowers' dwelling.

It was a narrow, high, brick structure, with a portico cap, supported by cast-iron grilling, and shallow iron-railed balconies on the second story. A gravel path divided a small lawn beyond a gate guarded by two stone greyhounds. Hallie emerged from the house with an expression of mild inquiry at his unexpected appearance. She was a year older than himself, an erect, thin woman, with a pale coloring and unstirred blue eyes.

" Why, Alex," she remarked, " what ever brought you here on a Saturday? " They sat, without further immediate speech, from long habit, in familiar chairs.

He wondered how he was going to tell her. And the question, the difficulty, roused in him an astonishing amount of exasperation. He regarded her almost vindictively, with covertly shut hands. He must get hold of himself. Hallie, to whom he was about to do irreparable harm, the kindest woman in existence! But he realized that whatever feeling he had had for her was gone forever; she had become merged indistinguishably into the thought of Eastlake; and every nerve in him demanded a total separation from the slumberous town that had witnessed his legal failure.

He wasn't, he knew, normal; his intention here was reprehensible, but he was without will to defeat it. Alexander Hulings felt the clumsy hand drawing tighter the string he had pictured himself as being; an overwhelming impulse overtook him to rush away — anywhere, immediately. He said in a rapid blurred voice:

" Hallie, this — our plans are a failure — that is, I am. The law's been no good; I mean, I haven't. Can't get the hang of the — the damned — "

" Alex! " she interrupted, astonished at the expletive.

" I'm going away," he gabbled on, only half conscious of his words in waves of giddy insecurity. " Yes; for good. . . . I'm no use here! Shot to pieces, somehow. Forgive me. Never get a thousand."

Hallie Flower said in a tone of unpremeditated surprise:
" Then I'll never be married! "

She sat with her hands open in her lap, a wistfulness on her countenance that he found only silly. He cursed himself, his impotence,
bitterly. Now he wanted to get away; but there remained an almost
more impossible consummation — Hallie's parents. They were old;
she was an only child.

" Your father — " he muttered.

On his feet he swayed like a pendulum. Viselike fingers gripped
at the back of his neck. The hand of death? Incredibly he lived
through a stammering, racking period, in the midst of which a
cuckoo ejaculated seven idiotic notes from the fretted face of a
clock.

He was on the street again; the cruel pressure was relaxed; he
drew a deep breath. In his room, a select chamber with a " private "
family, he packed and strapped his small leather trunk. There was
nowhere among his belongings a suggestion of any souvenir of the
past, anything sentimental or charged with memory. A daguerreo-
type of Hallie Flower, in an embossed black case lined with red
plush, he ground into a shapeless fragment. Afterwards he was
shocked by what he had done and was forced to seek the support
of a chair. He clenched his jaw, gazed with stony eyes against the
formless dread about him.

He had forgotten that the next day was Sunday, with a corresponding dislocation of the train and packet service which was to
take him West. A further wait until Monday was necessary. Alexander Hulings got through that too; and was finally seated with
Veneada in his light wagon, behind a clattering pair of young
Hambletonians, with the trunk secured in the rear. Veneada was
taking him to a station on the Columbus Railroad. Though the
morning had hardly advanced, and Hulings had wrapped himself
in a heavy cape, the doctor had only a duster, unbuttoned, on his
casual clothing.

" You know, Alex," the latter said — " and let me finish before
you start to object — that I have more money than I can use. And,
though I know you wouldn't just borrow any for cigars, if there
ever comes a time when you need a few thousands, if you happen
on something that looks good for both of us, don't fail to let me

know. You'll pull out of this depression; I think you're a great man, Alex — because you are so unpleasant, if for nothing else."

The doctor's weighty hand fell affectionately on Hulings's shoulder.

Hulings involuntarily moved from the other's contact; he wanted to leave all — all of Eastlake. Once away, he was certain, his being would clarify, grow more secure. He even neglected to issue a characteristic abrupt refusal of Veneada's implied offer of assistance; though all that he possessed, now strapped in his wallet, was a meager provision for a debilitated man who had cast safety behind him.

The doctor pulled his horses in beside a small, box-like station, on flat tracks, dominated by a stout pole, to which was nailed a ladder-like succession of cross-blocks.

Alexander Hulings was infinitely relieved when the other, after some last professional injunctions, drove away. Already, he thought, he felt better; and he watched, with a faint stirring of normal curiosity, the station master climb the pole and survey the mid-distance for the approaching train.

The engine finally rolled fussily into view, with a lurid, black column of smoke pouring from a thin belled stack, and dragging a rocking, precarious brigade of chariot coaches scrolled in bright yellow and staring blue. It stopped, with a fretful ringing and a grinding impact of coach on coach. Alexander Hulings's trunk was shouldered to a roof; and after an inspection of the close interiors he followed his baggage to an open seat above. The engine gathered momentum; he was jerked rudely forward and blinded by a cloud of smoke streaked with flaring cinders.

There was a faint cry at his back, and he saw a woman clutching a charring hole in her crinoline. The railroad journey was an insuperable torment; the diminishing crash at the stops, either at a station or where cut wood was stacked to fire the engine, the choking hot waves of smoke, the shouted confabulations between the captain and the engineer, forward on his precarious ledge — all added to an excruciating torture of Hulings's racked and shuddering nerves. His rigid body was thrown from side to side; his spine seemed at the point of splintering from the pounding of the wooden rails.

An utter mental dejection weighed down his shattered being; it was not the past but the future that oppressed him. Perhaps he was going only to die miserably in an obscure hole; Veneada probably wouldn't tell him the truth about his condition. What he most resented, with a tenuous spark of his customary obstinate spirit, was the thought of never justifying a belief he possessed in his ultimate power to conquer circumstance, to be greatly successful.

Veneada, a man without flattery, had himself used that word great in connection with him.

Alexander Hulings felt dimly, even now, a sense of cold power; a hunger for struggle different from a petty law practice in Eastlake. He thought of the iron that James Claypole unsuccessfully wrought; and something in the word, the implied obdurate material, fired his disintegrating mind. " Iron! " Unconsciously he spoke the word aloud. He was entirely ignorant of what, exactly, it meant; what were the processes of its fluxing and refinement; forge and furnace were hardly separated in his thoughts. But out of the confusion emerged the one concrete stubborn fact — iron!

He was drawn, at last, over a level grassy plain, at the far edge of which evening and clustered houses merged on a silver expanse of river. It was Columbus, where he found the canal packets lying in the terminal-station basin.

II

THE WESTBOUND packet, the *Hit or Miss*, started with a long horn-blast and the straining of the mules at the tow-rope. The canal-boat slipped into its placid banked waterway. Supper was being laid in the gentlemen's cabin, and Alexander Hulings was unable to secure a berth. The passengers crowded at a single long table; and the low interior, steaming with food, echoing with clattering china and a ceaseless gabble of voices, confused him intolerably. He made his way to the open space at the rear. The soundless, placid movement at once soothed him and was exasperating in its slowness. He thought of his journey as an escape, an emergence from a suffocating cloud; and he raged at its deliberation.

The echoing note of a *cornet-à-piston* sounded from the deck above; it was joined by the rattle of a drum; and an energetic band swept into the strains of *Zip Coon*. The passengers emerged from supper and gathered on the main deck; the gayly lighted windows streamed in moving yellow bars over dark banks and fields; and they were raised or lowered on the pouring black tide of masoned locks. If it had not been for the infernal persistence of the band Alexander Hulings would have been almost comfortable; but the music, at midnight, showed no signs of abating. Money was collected, whisky distributed; a quadrille formed forward. Hulings could see the women's crinolines, the great sleeves and skirts, dipping and floating in a radiance of oil torches. He had a place in a solid bank of chairs about the outer rail and sat huddled in his cape. His misery, as usual, increased with the night; the darkness was streaked with immaterial flashes, disjointed visions. He was infinitely weary, and faint from a hunger that he yet could not satisfy. A consequential male at his side, past middle age, with close whiskers and a mob of seals, addressed a commonplace to him; but he made no reply. The other regarded Hulings with an arrogant surprise, then turned a negligent back. From beyond came a clear, derisive peal of girlish laughter. He heard a name — Gisela — pronounced.

Alexander Hulings's erratic thoughts returned to iron. He wondered vaguely why James Claypole had never succeeded with Tubal Cain. Probably, like so many others, he was a drunkard. The man who had addressed him moved away — he was accompanied by a small party; and another took his vacant place.

" See who that was? " he asked Hulings. The latter shook his head morosely. " Well, that," the first continued impressively, " is John Wooddrop."

Alexander Hulings had an uncertain memory of the name, connected with —

" Yes, sir — John Wooddrop, the ironmaster. I reckon that man is the biggest — not only the richest but the biggest — man in the state. Thousands of acres, mile after mile; iron banks and furnaces and forges and mills; hundreds of men and women — all his. Like a European monarch! Yes, sir; resembles that. Word's law — says: ' Come here! ' or ' Go there! ' His daughter is with him too; it's clear she's got the old boy's spirit — and his lady. They get off at Harmony; own the valley; own everything about."

Harmony was the place where Hulings was to leave the canal;
from there he must drive to Tubal Cain. The vicarious boastfulness
of his neighbor stirred within him an inchoate antagonism.

"There is one place near by he doesn't own," he stated sharply.

"Then it's no good," the other promptly replied. "If it was,
Wooddrop would have it. It would be his or nothing — he'd see
to that. His name is Me, or nobody."

Alexander Hulings's antagonism increased and illogically fastened
on the ironmaster. The other's character, as it had been stated, was
precisely the quality that called to the surface his own stubborn
will of self-assertion. It precipitated a condition in which he expanded, grew determined, ruthless, cold.

He imagined himself, sick and almost moneyless, and bound for
Claypole's failure, opposed to John Wooddrop, and got a faint
thrill from the fantastic vision. He had a recurrence of the conviction that he, too, was a strong man; and it tormented him with
the bitter contrast between such an image and his actual present
self. He laughed aloud, a thin, shaken giggle, at his belief persisting
in the face of such irrefutable proof of his failure. Nevertheless, it
was firmly lodged in him, like a thorn pricking at his dissolution,
gathering his scattered faculties into efforts of angry contempt at
the laudation of others.

Veneada and Hallie Flower, he realized, were the only intimates
he had gathered in a solitary and largely embittered existence. He
had no instinctive humanity of feeling, and his observations,
colored by his spleen, had not added to a small opinion of man
at large. Always feeling himself to be a figure of supreme importance, he had never ceased to chafe at the small aspect he was
obliged to exhibit. This had grown, through an uncomfortable
sense of shame, to a perpetual disparagement of all other triumph
and success.

Finally the band ceased its efforts, the oil lights burned dim, and
a movement to the cabins proceeded, leaving him on a deserted
deck. At last, utterly exhausted, he went below in search of a berth.
They hung four deep about the walls, partly curtained, while the
floor of the cabin was filled with clothes-racks, burdened with a
miscellany of outer garments. One place only was empty — under
the ceiling; and he made a difficult ascent to the narrow space. Sleep

was an impossibility — a storm of hoarse breathing, muttering, and sleepy oaths dinned on his ears. The cabin, closed against the outer air, grew indescribably polluted. Any former torment of mind and body was minor compared to the dragging wakeful hours that followed; a dread of actual insanity seized him.

Almost at the first trace of dawn the cabin was awakened and filled with fragmentary dressing. The deck and bar were occupied by men waiting for the appearance of the feminine passengers from their cabin forward, and breakfast. The day was warm and fine. The packet crossed a turgid river, at the mouths of other canal routes, and entered a wide pastoral valley.

Alexander Hulings sat facing a smaller, various river; at his back was a barrier of mountains, glossy with early laurel and rhododendron. His face was yellow and sunken, and his lips dry. John Wooddrop passed and repassed him, a girl, his daughter Gisela, on his arm. She wore an India muslin dress, wide with crinoline, embroidered in flowers of blue and green worsted, and a flapping rice-straw hat draped in blonde lace. Her face was pointed and alert.

Once Hulings caught her glance, and he saw that her eyes seemed black and — and — impertinent.

An air of palpable satisfaction emanated from the ironmaster. His eyes were dark too; and, more than impertinent, they held for Hulings an intolerable patronage. John Wooddrop's foot trod the deck with a solid authority that increased the sick man's smoldering scorn. At dinner he had an actual encounter with the other. The table was filling rapidly; Alexander Hulings had taken a place when Wooddrop entered with his group and surveyed the seats that remained.

" I am going to ask you," he addressed Hulings in a deep voice, " to move over yonder. That will allow my family to surround me."

A sudden unreasonable determination not to move seized Hulings. He said nothing; he didn't turn his head nor disturb his position. John Wooddrop repeated his request in still more vibrant tones. Hulings did nothing. He was held in a silent rigidity of position.

" You, sir," Wooddrop pronounced loudly, " are deficient in the ordinary courtesies of travel! And note this, Mrs. Wooddrop " — he turned to his wife — " I shall never again, in spite of Gisela's importunities, move by public conveyance. The presence of individuals like this — "

Alexander Hulings rose and faced the older, infinitely more important man. His sunken eyes blazed with such a feverish passion that the other raised an involuntary palm.

" Individuals," he added, " painfully afflicted."

Suddenly Hulings's weakness betrayed him; he collapsed in his chair with a pounding heart and blurred vision. The incident receded, became merged in the resumption of the commonplace clatter of dinner.

Once more on deck, Alexander Hulings was aware that he had appeared both inconsequential and ridiculous, two qualities supremely detestable to his pride; and this added to his bitterness toward the ironmaster. He determined to extract satisfaction from the other for his humiliation. It was characteristic of Hulings that he saw himself essentially as John Wooddrop's equal; worldly circumstance had no power to impress him; he was superior to the slightest trace of the complacent inferiority exhibited by last night's casual informer.

The day waned monotonously; half dazed with weariness, he heard bursts of music; far, meaningless voices; the blowing of the packet horn. He didn't go down again into the cabin to sleep, but stayed wrapped in his cloak in a chair. He slept through the dawn and woke only at the full activity of breakfast. Past noon the boat tied up at Harmony. The Wooddrops departed with all the circumstance of worldly importance and in the stir of cracking whip and restive, spirited horses. Alexander Hulings moved unobserved, with his trunk, to the bank.

Tubal Cain, he discovered, was still fifteen miles distant, and — he had not told James Claypole of his intended arrival — no conveyance was near by. A wagon drawn by six mules with gay bells and colored streamers and heavily loaded with limestone finally appeared, going north, on which Hulings secured passage.

The precarious road followed a wooded ridge, with a vigorous stream on the right and a wall of hills beyond. The valley was largely uninhabited. Once they passed a solid, foursquare structure of stone, built against a hill, with clustered wooden sheds and a great wheel revolving under a smooth arc of water. A delicate white vapor trailed from the top of the masonry, accompanied by rapid, clear flames.

"Blue Lump Furnace," the wagon-driver briefly volunteered. "Belongs to Wooddrop. But that doesn't signify anything about here. Pretty near everything's his."

Alexander Hulings looked back, with an involuntary deep interest in the furnace. The word *iron* again vibrated, almost clanged, through his mind. It temporarily obliterated the fact that here was another evidence of the magnitude, the possessions, of John Wooddrop. He was consumed by a sudden anxiety to see James Claypole's forge. Why hadn't the fool persisted, succeeded?

"Tubal Cain's in there." The mules were stopped. "What there is of it! Four bits will be enough."

He was left beside his trunk on the roadside, clouded by the dust of the wagon's departure. Behind him, in the direction indicated, the ground, covered with underbrush, fell away to a glint of water and some obscure structures. Dragging his baggage, he made his way down to a long, wooden shed, the length facing him open on two covered hearths, some dilapidated troughs, a suspended ponderous hammer resting on an anvil, and a miscellaneous heap of rusting iron implements — long-jawed tongs, hooked rods, sledges, and broken castings. The hearths were cold; there was not a stir of life, of activity, anywhere.

Hulings left his trunk in a clearing and explored farther. Beyond a black heap of charcoal, standing among trees, were two or three small stone dwellings. The first was apparently empty, with some whitened sacks on a bare floor; but within a second he saw through the open doorway the lank figure of a man kneeling in prayer. His foot was on the sill; but the bowed figure, turned away, remained motionless.

Alexander Hulings hesitated, waiting for the prayer to reach a speedy termination. But the other, with upraised, quivering hands, remained so long on his knees that Hulings swung the door back impatiently. Even then an appreciable time elapsed before the man inside rose to his feet. He turned and moved forward, with an abstracted gaze in pale-blue eyes set in a face seamed and scored by time and disease. His expression was benevolent; his voice warm and cordial.

" I am Alexander Hulings," that individual briefly stated; " and I suppose you're Claypole."

The latter's condition, he thought instantaneously, was entirely described by his appearance. James Claypole's person was as neglected as the forge. His stained breeches were engulfed in scarred leather boots, and a coarse black shirt was open on a gaunt chest.

His welcome left nothing to be desired. The dwelling into which he conducted Hulings consisted of a single room, with a small shed kitchen at the rear and two narrow chambers above. There was a pleasant absence of apology for the meager accommodations. James Claypole was an entirely unaffected and simple host.

The late April evening was warm; and after a supper, prepared by Claypole, of thick bacon, potatoes, and saleratus biscuit, the two men sat against the outer wall of the house. On the left Hulings could see the end of the forge shed, with the inevitable water-wheel hung in a channel cut from the clear stream. The stream wrinkled and whispered along spongy banks, and a flicker hammered on a resonant limb. Hulings stated negligently that he had arrived on the same packet with John Wooddrop, and Claypole retorted:

" A man lost in the world! I tried to wrestle with his spirit, but it was harder than the walls of Jericho."

His eyes glowed with fervor. Hulings regarded him curiously. A religious fanatic! He asked:

" What's been the trouble with Tubal Cain? Other forges appear to flourish about here. This Wooddrop seems to have built a big thing with iron."

" Mammon! " Claypole stated. " Slag; dross! Not this, but the Eternal World." The other failed to comprehend, and he said so irritably. " All that," Claypole specified, waving toward the forge, " takes the thoughts from the Supreme Being. Eager for the Word, and a poor speller-out of the Book, you can't spend priceless hours shingling blooms. And then the men left, one after another, because I stopped pandering to their carnal appetites. No one can indulge in rum here, in a place of mine sealed to God."

" Do you mean that whisky was a part of their pay and that you held it back? " Alexander Hulings demanded curtly. He was without the faintest sympathy for what he termed such arrant folly.

" Yes, just that; a brawling, froward crew. Wooddrop wanted to buy, but I wouldn't extend his wicked dominion, satisfy fleshly lust."

" It's a good forge, then? "

" None better! I built her mostly myself, when I was laying up the treasure that rusted; stone on stone, log on log. Heavy, slow work. The sluice is like a city wall; the anvil bedded on seven feet of oak. It's right! But if I'd known then, I should have put up a temple to Jehovah."

Hulings could scarcely contain his impatience.

" Why," he ejaculated, " you might have made a fine thing out of it! Opportunity, opportunity, and you let it go by. For sheer — "

He broke off at a steady gaze from Claypole's calm blue eyes. It was evident that he would have to restrain any injudicious characterizations of the other's belief. He spoke suddenly:

" I came up here because I was sick and had to get out of Eastlake. I left everything but what little money I had. You see — I was a failure. I'd like to stay with you awhile; when perhaps I might get on my feet again. I feel easier than I have for weeks." He realized, surprised, that this was so. He had a conviction that he could sleep here, by the stream, in the still, flowering woods. " I haven't any interest in temples," he continued, " but I guess — two men — we won't argue about that. Some allowance on both sides. But I am interested in iron; I'd like to know this forge of yours backward. I've discovered a sort of hankering after the idea; just that — iron. It's a tremendous fact, and you can keep it from rusting."

III

THE FOLLOWING morning Claypole showed Alexander Hulings the mechanics of Tubal Cain. A faint reminiscent pride shone through the later unworldly preoccupation. He lifted the sluice gate, and the water poured through the masoned channel of the forebay and set in motion the wheel, hung with its lower paddles in the course. In the forge shed Claypole bound a connection, and the short haft of the trip-hammer, caught in revolving cogs, raised the ponderous head and dropped it, with a jarring clang, on the anvil. The blast

of the hearths was driven by water wind, propelled by a piston in a
wood cylinder, with an air chamber for even pressure. It was all so
elemental that the neglect of the last years had but spread over the
forge an appearance of ill repair. Actually it was as sound as the
clear oak largely used in its construction.

James Claypole's interest soon faded; he returned to his chair
by the door of the dwelling, where he laboriously spelled out the
periods of a battered copy of Addison's *Evidences of the Christian
Religion*. He broke the perusal with frequent, ecstatic ejaculations;
and when Hulings reluctantly returned from his study of the forge
the other was again on his knees, lost in passionate prayer. Hulings
grew hungry — Claypole was utterly lost in visions — cooked some
bacon and found cold biscuit in the shedlike kitchen.

The afternoon passed into a tenderly perfumed twilight. The
forge retreated, apparently through the trees, into the evening.
Alexander Hulings sat regarding it with an increasing impatience;
first, it annoyed him to see such a potentiality of power lying fallow,
and then his annoyance ripened into an impatience with Claypole
that he could scarcely contain. The impracticable ass! It was a crime
to keep the wheel stationary, the hearths cold.

He had a sudden burning desire to see Tubal Cain stirring with
life; to hear the beat of the hammer forging iron; to see the dark,
still interior lurid with fire. He thought again of John Wooddrop,
and his instinctive disparagement of the accomplishments of others
mocked both them and himself. If he, Alexander Hulings, had had
Claypole's chance, his beginning, he would be more powerful than
Wooddrop now.

The law was a trivial foolery compared to the fashioning, out of
the earth itself, of iron. Iron, the indispensable! Railroads, in spite
of the popular, vulgar disbelief, were a coming great factor; a thousand new uses, refinements, improved processes of manufacture
were bound to develop. His thoughts took fire and swept over him
in a conflagration of enthusiasm. By heaven, if Claypole had failed,
he would succeed! He, too, would be an Ironmaster!

A brutal chill overtook him with the night; he shook pitiably;
dark fears crept like noxious beetles among his thoughts. James
Claypole sat, with his hands on his gaunt knees, gazing, it might
be, at a miraculous golden city beyond the black curtain of the

world. Later Hulings lay on a couch of boards, folded in coarse blankets and his cape, fighting the familiar evil sinking of his oppressed spirit. He was cold and yet drenched with sweat. . . . If he were defeated now, he thought, if he collapsed, he was done, shattered! And in his swirling mental anguish he clung to one stable, cool fact; he saw, like Claypole, a vision; but not gold — great shadowy masses of iron. Before dawn the dread receded; he fell asleep.

He questioned his companion at breakfast about the details of forging.

" The secret," the latter stated, " is — timber; wood, charcoal. It's bound to turn up; fuel famine will come, unless it is provided against. That's where John Wooddrop's light. He counts on getting it as he goes. A furnace'll burn five or six thousand cords of wood every little while, and that means two hundred or more acres. Back of Harmony, here, are miles of timber the old man won't loose up right for. He calculates no one else can profit with them and takes his own time."

" What does Wooddrop own in the valleys? "

" Well — there's Sally Furnace; the Poole Sawmill tract; the Medlar Forge and Blue Lump; the coal holes on Allen Mountain; Marta Furnace and Reeba Furnace — they ain't right hereabouts; the Lode Orebank; the Blossom Furnace and Charming Forges; Middle and Low Green Forges; the Auspacher Farm — "

" That will do," Hulings interrupted him moodily; " I'm not an assessor."

Envy lashed his determination to surprising heights. Claypole grew uncommunicative, except for vague references to the Kingdom at hand and the dross of carnal desire. Finally, without a preparatory word, he strode away and disappeared over the rise toward the road. At supper he had not returned; there was no trace of him when, inundated with sleep, Hulings shut the dwelling for the night. All the following day Alexander Hulings expected his host; he spent the hours avidly studying the implements of forging; but the other did not appear. Neither did he the next day, nor the next.

Hulings was surprisingly happy; entirely alone, but for the hidden passage of wagons on the road and the multitudinous birds that inhabited the stream's edge, in the peaceful, increasing warmth

of the days and nights his condition slowly improved. He bought
supplies at the packet station on the canal and shortly became as
proficient at the stove as James Claypole. Through the day he sat
in the mild sunlight or speculated among the implements of the
forge. He visualized the process of iron-making; the rough pigs —
there were sows, too, he had gathered — lying outside the shed had
come from the furnace. These were put into the hearths and
melted — stirred perhaps; then — what were the wooden troughs
for? — hammered, wrought on the anvil. Outside were other ir-
regularly round pieces of iron, palpably closer in texture than the
pig. The forging of them, he was certain, had been completed.
There were, also, heavy bars, three feet in length, squared at each
end.

Everything had been dropped apparently at the moment of James
Claypole's absorbing view of another, transcending existence. Late
in an afternoon — it was May — he heard footfalls descending from
the road; with a sharp, unreasoning regret, he thought the other
had returned. But it was a short, ungainly man with a purplish face
and impressive shoulders. " Where's Jim? " he asked with a marked
German accent.

Alexander Hulings told him who he was and all he knew about
Claypole.

" I'm Conrad Wishon," the newcomer stated, sinking heavily
into a chair. " Did Jim speak of me — his head forgeman? No! But
I guess he told you how he stopped the schnapps. Ha! James got
religion. And he went away two weeks ago? Maybe he'll never be
back. This " — he waved toward the forge — " means nothing to
him.

" I live twenty miles up the road, and I saw a Glory wagon coming on — an old Conestoga, with the Bible painted on the canvas,
a traveling Shouter slapping the reins, and a congregation of his
family staring out the back. James would take up with a thing like
that in a shot. Yes, sir; maybe now you will never see him again.
And your mother's cousin! There's no other kin I've heard of; and
I was with him longer than the rest."

Hulings listened with growing interest to the equable flow of
Conrad Wishon's statements and mild surprise.

" Things have been bad with me," the smith continued. " My wife, she died Thursday before breakfast, and one thing and another. A son has charge of a coaling gang on Allen Mountain, but I'm too heavy for that; and I was going down to Green Forge when I thought I'd stop and see Jim. But, hell! — Jim's gone; like as not on the Glory wagon. I can get a place at any hearth," he declared pridefully. " I'm a good forger; none better in Hamilton County. When it's shingling a loop I can show 'em all! "

" Have some supper," Alexander Hulings offered.

They sat late into the fragrant night, with the moonlight patterned like a gray carpet at their feet, talking about the smithing of iron. Conrad Wishon revealed the practical grasp of a life capably spent at a single task, and Hulings questioned him with an increasing comprehension.

" If you had money," Wishon explained, " we could do something right here. I'd like to work old Tubal Cain. I understand her."

The other asked: " How much would it take? "

Conrad Wishon spread out his hands hopelessly. " A lot; and then a creekful back of that! Soon as Wooddrop heard the triphammer he'd be after you to close you down. Do it in a hundred ways — no teaming principally."

Hulings's antagonism to John Wooddrop increased perceptibly; he became obsessed by the fantastic thought of founding himself — Tubal Cain — triumphantly in the face of the established opposition. But he had nothing — no money, knowledge, or even a robust person. Yet his will to succeed in the valleys hardened into a concrete aim . . . Conrad Wishon would be invaluable.

The latter stayed through the night and even lingered, after breakfast, into the morning. He was reluctant to leave the familiar scene of long toil. They were sitting lost in discussion when the beat of horses' hoofs was arrested on the road, and a snapping of underbrush announced the appearance of a young man with a keen, authoritative countenance.

" Mr. James Claypole? " he asked, addressing them collectively.

Alexander Hulings explained what he could of Claypole's absence.

" It probably doesn't matter," the other returned. " I was told the forge wasn't run, for some foolishness or other." He turned to go.

"What did you want with him — with Tubal Cain?" Conrad Wishon asked.

"Twenty-five tons of blooms."

"Now, if this was ten years back — "

The young man interrupted the smith, with a gesture of impatience, and turned to go. Hulings asked Conrad Wishon swiftly:

"Could it be done here? Could the men be got? And what would it cost?"

"It could," said Wishon; "they might, and a thousand dollars would perhaps see it through."

Hulings sharply called the retreating figure back. "Something more about this twenty-five tons," he demanded.

"For the Penn Rolling Mills," the other crisply replied. "We're asking for delivery in five weeks, but that might be extended a little — at, of course, a loss on the ton. The quality must be first grade."

Wishon grunted.

"Young man," he said, "blooms I made would hardly need blistering to be called steel."

"I'm Philip Grere," the newcomer stated, "of Grere Brothers, and they're the Penn Rolling Mills. We want good blooms soon as possible and it seems there's almost none loose. If you can talk iron, immediate iron, let's get it on paper; if not, I have a long way to drive."

When he had gone Conrad Wishon sat staring, with mingled astonishment and admiration, at Hulings.

"But," he protested, "you don't know nothing about it!"

"You do!" Alexander Hulings told him; he saw himself as a mind, of which Wishon formed the trained and powerful body.

"Perhaps Jim will come back," the elder man continued.

"That is a possibility," Alexander admitted. "But I am going to put every dollar I own into the chance of finishing those twenty-five tons."

The smith persisted: "But you don't know me; perhaps I'm a rascal and can't tell a puddling furnace from a chafery."

Hulings regarded him shrewdly.

"Conrad," he demanded, "can Tubal Cain do it?"

"By *Gott*," Wishon exclaimed, "she can!"

After an hour of close calculation Conrad Wishon rose with surprising agility.

" I've got enough to do besides sitting here. Tubal Cain ought to have twenty men, anyhow; perhaps I can get eight. There's Mathias Slough, a good hammer-man. He broke an elbow at Charming, and Wooddrop won't have him back; but he can work still. Hance, a good nigger, is at my place, and there is another — Surrie. Haines Zerbey, too, worked at refining, but you'll need to watch his rum. Perhaps Old Man Boeshore will lend a hand, and he's got a strapping grandson — Emanuel. Jeremiah Stell doesn't know much, but he'd let you cut a finger off for a dollar." He shook his head gravely. " That is a middling poor collection."

Alexander Hulings felt capable of operating Tubal Cain successfully with a shift of blind paralytics. A conviction of power, of vast capability, possessed him. Suddenly he seemed to have become a part of the world that moved, of its creative energy; he was like a piece of machinery newly connected with the forceful driving whole. Conrad Wishon had promised to return the next day with the men he had enumerated, and Alexander opened the small scattered buildings about the forge. There were, he found, sufficient living-provisions for eight or ten men out of a moldering quantity of primitive bed furnishings, rusted tin, and cracked glass. But it was fortunate that the days were steadily growing warmer.

Wishon had directed him to clean out the channel of the forebay, and throughout the latter half of the day he was tearing heavy weeds from the interstices of the stones, laboring in a chill slime that soon completely covered him. He removed heavy rocks, matted dead bushes, banked mud; and after an hour he was cruelly, impossibly weary. He slipped and bruised a shoulder, cut open his cheek; but he impatiently spat out the blood trailing into his mouth, and continued working. His weariness became a hell of acute pain; without manual practice his movements were clumsy; he wasted what strength he had. Yet as his suffering increased he grew only more relentlessly methodical in the execution of his task. He picked out insignificant obstructions, scraped away grass that offered no resistance to the water-power. When he had finished, the forebay, striking in at an angle from the stream to the wheel, was meticulously clean.

He stumbled into his dwelling and fell on the bed, almost instantly asleep, without removing a garment, caked with filth; and never stirred until the sun again flooded the room. He cooked and ravenously ate a tremendous breakfast and then forced himself to walk the dusty miles that lay between Tubal Cain and the canal. His legs seemed to be totally without joints, and his spine felt like a white-hot bar. At the store about which the insignificant village of Harmony clustered he ordered and paid for a great box of supplies, later carried by an obliging teamster and himself to the forge.

Once more there, he addressed himself to digging out the slag that had hardened in the hearths. The lightest bar soon became insuperably ponderous; it wabbled in his grasp, evaded its purpose. Vicious tears streamed over his blackened countenance and he maintained a constant audible flow of bitter invective. But even that arduous task was nearly accomplished when dark overtook him.

He stripped off his garments, dropping them where he stood, by the forge shed, and literally fell forward into the stream. The cold shock largely revived him and he supped on huge tins of coffee and hard flitch. Immediately after, he dropped asleep as if he had been knocked unconscious by a club.

At mid-morning he heard a rattle of conveyance from the road and his name called. Above he found a wagon, without a top, filled with the sorriest collection of humanity he had ever viewed, and drawn by a dejected bony horse and a small wicked mule.

" Here they are," Conrad Wishon announced; " and Hance brought along his girl to cook."

Mathias Slough, the hammer-man, was thin and gray, as if his face were covered with cobwebs; Hance, Conrad's " nigger," black as an iron bloom, was carrying upside down a squawking hen; Surrie, lighter, had a dropped jaw and hands that hung below his knees; Haines Zerbey had pale, swimming eyes, and executed a salute with a battered flat beaver hat; Old Man Boeshore resembled a basin, bowed in at the stomach; his mouth had sunk on toothless gums, but there was agility in his step; while Emanuel, his grandson, a towering hulk of youth, presented a facial expanse of mingled pimples and down. Jeremiah Stell was a small, shriveled man, with dead-white hair on a smooth, pinkish countenance.

Standing aside from the nondescript assemblage of men and transient garments, Alexander Hulings surveyed them with cold determination; two emotions possessed him — one of an almost humorous dismay at the slack figures on whom so much depended; and a second, stronger conviction that he could force his purpose even from them. They were, in a manner, his first command; his first material from which to build the consequence, the success, that he felt was his true expression.

He addressed a few brief periods to them; and there was no warmth, no effort to conciliate, in his tones, his dry statement of a heavy task for a merely adequate gain. He adopted this attitude instinctively, without forethought; he was dimly conscious, as a principle, that underpaid men were more easily driven than those overfully rewarded. And he intended to drive the men before him to the limit of their capability. They had no individual existence for Alexander Hulings, no humanity; they were merely the implements of a projection of his own; their names — Haines Zerbey, Slough — had no more significance than the terms *bellows* or *tongs*.

They scattered to the few habitations by the stream, structures mostly of logs and plaster; and in a little while there rose the odorous smoke and sputtering fat of Hance's girl's cooking. Conrad Wishon soon started the labor of preparing the forge. Jeremiah Stell, who had some slight knowledge of carpentry, was directed to repair the plunger of the water-wind apparatus. Slough was testing the beat and control of the trip-hammer. Hance and Surrie carried outside the neglected heaps of iron hooks and tongs.

Conrad explained to Alexander Hulings:

" I sent word to my son about the charcoal; he'll leave it at my place, but we shall have to haul it from there. Need another mule — maybe two. There's enough pig here to start, and my idea is to buy all we will need now at Blue Lump; they'll lend us a sled, so's we will have it in case old Wooddrop tries to clamp down on us. I'll go along this afternoon and see the head furnace-man. It will take money."

Without hesitation Hulings put a considerable part of his entire small capital into the other's hand. At supper-time Conrad Wishon returned with the first load of metal for the Penn Rolling Mills contract.

Later Hance produced a wheezing accordion and, rocking on his
feet, drew out long, wailing notes. He sang:

> " *Brothers, let us leave*
> *Bukra Land for Hayti;*
> *There we be receive'*
> *Grand as Lafayette.*"

"With changes of men," Conrad continued to Alexander Hulings, " the forges could run night and day, like customary. But
with only one lot we'll have to sleep. Someone will stay up to tend
the fires."

In the morning the labor of making the wrought blooms actually
commenced. Conrad Wishon and Hance at one hearth, and Haines
Zerbey with Surrie at the other, stood ceaselessly stirring, with long
iron rods, the fluxing metal at the incandescent cores of the fires.
Alexander then saw that the troughs of water were to cool the
rapidly heating rods. Conrad Wishon was relentless in his insistence on long working of the iron. There were, already, muttered
protests. "The damn stuff was cooked an hour back!" But he
drowned the objections in a surprising torrent of German-American
cursing.

Hulings was outside the shed when he heard the first dull fall
of the hammer; and it seemed to him that the sound had come
from a sudden pounding of his expanded heart. He, Alexander Hulings, was making iron; his determination, his capability and will,
were hammering out of the stubborn raw material of earth a foot-
hold for himself and a justification! The smoke, pouring blackly,
streaked with crimson sparks, from the forge shed, sifted a fine soot
on the green-white flowers of a dogwood tree. A metallic clamor
rose; and Emanuel, the youth, stripped to the waist and already
smeared with sweat and grime, came out for a gulping breath of
unsullied air.

The characteristics of the small force soon became apparent.
Conrad Wishon labored ceaselessly, with an unimpaired power at
fifty apparent even to Alexander's intense self-absorption. Of the
others, Hance, the Negro, was easily the superior; his strength was
Herculean, his willingness inexhaustible. Surrie was sullen. Mathias
Slough constantly grumbled at the meager provisions for his com-

fort and efforts; yet he was a skillful workman. When Alexander
had correctly gauged Zerbey's daily dram the latter, too, was useful;
but the others were negligible. They made the motions of labor,
but force was absent.

Alexander Hulings watched with narrowed eyes. When he was
present the work in the shed notably improved; all the men except
Conrad avoided his implacable gaze. He rarely addressed a remark
to them; he seemed withdrawn from the operation that held so
much for him. Conrad Wishon easily established his dexterity at
" shingling a loop."

Working off a part of a melting sow, he secured it with wide-
jawed shingling tongs; and, steadying the pulsating mass on an iron
plate, he sledged it into a bloom. For ten hours daily the work
continued, the hearths burned, the trip-hammer fell and fell. The
interior of the shed was a grimy shadow lighted with lurid flares
and rose and gentian flowers of iron. Ruddy reflections slid over
glistening shoulders and intent, bitter faces; harsh directions, voices,
sounded like the grating of castings.

The oddly assorted team was dispatched for charcoal and then
sent with a load of blooms to the canal. Hance had to be spared,
with Surrie, for that; the forge was short of labor, and Alexander
Hulings joined Conrad in the working of the metal. It was, he
found, exhausting toil. He was light and unskilled, and the mass on
the hearth slipped continually from his stirring; or else it fastened,
with a seeming spite, on his rod, and he was powerless to move it.
Often he swung from his feet, straining in supreme, wrenching
effort. His body burned with fatigue, his eyes were scorched by
the heat of the fires; he lost count of days and nights. They merged
imperceptibly one into another; he must have dreamed of his racking exertions, for apparently they never ceased.

Alexander became indistinguishable from the others, all clean-
ness was forgotten; he ate in a stupefaction of weariness, securing
with his fingers whatever was put before him. He was engaged in a
struggle the end of which was hidden in the black smoke perpetually hanging over him; in the torment of the present, an inhuman
suffering to which he was bound by a tyrannical power outside his
control, he lost all consciousness of the future.

The hammer-man's injured arm prevented his working for two

days, and Alexander Hulings cursed him in a stammering rage, before which the other was shocked and dumb. He drove Old Man Boeshore and his grandson with consideration for neither age nor youth. The elder complained endlessly; tears even slid over his corrugated face; the youth was brutally burned, but Hulings never relaxed his demands.

It was as if they had all been caught in a whirlpool, in which they fought vainly for release — the whirlpool of Alexander Hulings's domination. They whispered together, he heard fragments of intended revolt; but under his cold gaze, his thin, tight lips, they subsided uneasily. It was patent that they were abjectly afraid of him. . . . The blooms moved in a small but unbroken stream over the road to the canal.

He had neglected to secure other horses or mules; and, while waiting for a load of iron on the rough track broken from the road to the forge, the horse slid to his knees, fell over, dead — the last ounce of effort wrung from his angular frame. The mule seemed impervious to fatigue; with his ears perpetually laid back and a raised lip, his spirit, his wickedness, persisted in the face of appalling toil. The animal's name, Hulings knew, was Alexander; he overheard Hance explaining this to Old Man Boeshore:

" That mule's bound to be Alexander; ain't nobody but an Alexander work like that mule! He's bad too; he'd lay you cold and go right on about his business."

Old Man Boeshore muttered something excessively bitter about the name Alexander.

" If you sh'd ask me," he stated, " I'd tell you that he ain't human. He's got a red light in his eye, like — "

Hulings gathered that this was not still directed at the mule.

More than half of the order for the Penn Rolling Mills had been executed and lay piled by the canal. He calculated the probable time still required, the amount he would unavoidably lose through the delay of faulty equipment and insufficient labor. If James Claypole came back now, he thought, and attempted interference, he would commit murder. It was evening, and he was seated listlessly, with his chair tipped back against the dwelling he shared with Conrad Wishon. The latter, close by, was bowed forward, his head, with a silvery gleam of faded hair, sunk on his breast. A catbird was whistling an elaborate and poignant song, and the invisible stream passed with a faint, choked whisper.

"We're going to have trouble with that girl of Hance's," Wishon pronounced suddenly; "she has taken to meeting Surrie in the woods. If Hance comes on them, there will be wet knives!"

Such mishaps, Alexander Hulings knew, offered real menace to his success. The crippling or loss of Hance might easily prove fatal to his hopes; the Negro, immensely powerful, equable, and willing, was of paramount importance.

"I'll stop that!" he declared. But the trouble developed before he had time to intervene.

He came on the two Negroes the following morning facing each other with, as Conrad had predicted, drawn knives. Hance stood still; but Surrie, with bent knees and the point of his steel almost brushing the grass, moved about the larger man. Hulings at once threw himself between them.

"What damned nonsense's this?" he demanded. "Get back to the team, Hance, and you, Surrie, drop your knife!"

The former was on the point of obeying, when Surrie ran in with a sweeping hand. Alexander Hulings jumped forward in a cold fury and felt a sudden numbing slice across his cheek. He had a dim consciousness of blood smearing his shoulder; but all his energy was directed on the stooped figure falling away from his glittering rage.

"Get out!" he directed in a thin, evil voice. "If you are round here in ten minutes, I'll blow a hole through your skull!"

Surrie was immediately absorbed by the underbrush.

Hulings had a long diagonal cut from his brow across and under his ear. It bled profusely, and as his temper receded, faintness dimmed his vision. Conrad Wishon blotted the wound with cobwebs; a cloth, soon stained, was bound about Alexander's head, and after dinner he was again in the forge, whipping the flagging efforts of his men with a voice like a thin leather thong. If the labor was delayed he recognized that the contract would not be filled. The workmen were wearing out, like the horse. He moved young Emanuel to the hauling with Hance, the wagon now drawn by three mules. The hammer-man's injured arm had grown inflamed and he was practically one-handed in his management of the trip-hammer.

While carrying a lump of iron to the anvil the staggering, ill-assorted group with the tongs dropped their burden and stood gaz-ing stupidly at the fallen, glowing mass. They were hardly revived by Hulings's lashing scorn. He had increased Haines Zerbey's daily dram, but the drunkard was now practically useless. Jeremiah Stell contracted an intermittent fever; and though he still toiled in the pursuit of his coveted wage, he was of doubtful value.

Alexander Hulings's body had become as hard as Conrad's knotted forearm. He ate huge amounts of half-cooked pork, washed hastily down by tin cups of black coffee, and fell into instant slum-ber when the slightest opportunity offered. His face was matted by an unkempt beard; his hands, the pale hands of an Eastlake lawyer, were black, like Hance's, with palms of leather. He sur-veyed himself with curious amusement in a broken fragment of looking-glass nailed to the wall; the old Hulings, pursued by incho-ate dread, had vanished. . . . In his place was Alexander Hulings, a practical iron man! He repeated the descriptive phrase aloud, with an accent of arrogant pride. Later, with an envelope from the Penn Rolling Mills, he said it again, with even more confidence; he held the pay for the blooms which he had — it seemed in another exist-ence — promised to deliver.

He stood leaning on a tree before the forge; within Conrad Wishon and Hance were piling the metal hooks with sharp, ring-ing echoes. All the others had vanished magically, at once, as if from an exhausted spell. Old Man Boeshore had departed with a piping implication, supported by Emanuel, his grandson.

Alexander Hulings was reviewing his material situation. It was three hundred and thirty dollars better than it had been on his arrival at Tubal Cain. In addition to that he had a new store of confidence, of indomitable pride, vanity, a more actual support. He gazed with interest toward the near future, and with no little doubt. It was patent that he could not proceed as he had begun; such combinations could not be forced a second time. He intended to remain at James Claypole's forge, conducting it as though it were his own — for the present, anyhow — but he should have to

get an efficient working body; and many additions were necessary
— among them a blacksmith shop. He had, with Conrad Wishon,
the conviction that Claypole would not return.

More capital would be necessary. He was revolving this undeniable fact when, through the lush June foliage, he saw an open carriage turn from the road and descend to the forge clearing. It held
an erect, trimly whiskered form and a Negro driver. The former
was John Wooddrop. He gazed with surprise, that increased to a
recognition, a memory, of Alexander Hulings.

" Jim Claypole? " he queried.

" Not here," Hulings replied, even more laconic.

" Nonsense! I'm told he's been running Tubal Cain again. Say
to him — and I've no time to dawdle — that John Wooddrop's
here."

" Well, Claypole's not," the other repeated. " He's away. I'm
running this forge — Alexander Hulings."

Wooddrop's mouth drew into a straight hard line from precise
whisker to whisker. " I have been absent," he said finally. It was
palpably an explanation, almost an excuse. Conrad Wishon appeared from within the forge shed. " Ah, Conrad! " John Wooddrop ejaculated pleasantly. " Glad to find you at the hearth again.
Come and see me in the morning."

" I think I'll stay here," the forgeman replied, " now Tubal
Cain's working."

" Then, in a week or so," the ironmaster answered imperturbably.

All Alexander Hulings's immaterial dislike of Wooddrop solidified into a concrete, vindictive enmity. He saw the beginning of a
long, bitter, stirring struggle.

IV

" THAT's about it! " Conrad Wishon affirmed. They were seated
by the doorway of the dwelling at Tubal Cain. It was night, and
hot; and the heavy air was constantly fretted by distant, vague thunder. Alexander Hulings listened with pinched lips.

" I saw Derek, the founder at Blue Lump, and ordered the metal;
then he told me that Wooddrop had sent word not to sell a pig
outside his own forges. That comes near closing us up. I misdoubt

that we could get men, anyhow — not without we went to Pittsburgh; and that would need big orders, big money. The old man's got us kind of shut in here, with only three mules and one wagon — we couldn't make out to haul any distance; and John Wooddrop picks up all the loose teams. It looks bad, that's what it does. No credit too; I stopped at Harmony for some forge hooks, and they wouldn't let me take them away until you had paid. A word's been dropped there likewise."

Hulings could see, without obvious statement, that he occupied a difficult position; it was impossible seemingly, with his limited funds and equipment, to go forward, and — no backward course existed; nothing but a void, ruin, the way across which had been destroyed. He turned with an involuntary dread from the fleeting contemplation of the past, mingled with monotony and suffering, and set all his cold, passionate mind on the problem of his future. He would, he told himself, succeed with iron here. He would succeed in spite of John Wooddrop — no, because of the ironmaster; the latter increasingly served as a concrete object of comparison, an incentive, a deeply involved spectator.

He lost himself in a gratifying vision, when Conrad's voice, shattering the facile heights he had mounted, again fastened his attention on the exigencies of the present.

"A lot of money!" the other repeated. "I guess we'll have to shut down; but I'd almost rather drive mules on the canal than go to John Wooddrop."

Hulings declared: "You'll do neither, and Tubal Cain won't shut down!" He rose, turned into the house.

"What's up?" Wishon demanded at the sudden movement.

"I'm going after money," Hulings responded from within — "enough. A packet is due east before dawn."

If the canal boat had seemed to go slowly on his way to Harmony, it appeared scarcely to stir on his return. There was no immediate train connection at Columbus, and he footed the uneven shaded streetways in an endless pattern, unconscious of houses, trees, or passing people, lost in the rehearsal of what he had to say, until the horn of an immediate departure summoned him to a seat in a coach.

The candles at each end sent a shifting, pale illumination over the cramped interior, voluminous skirts and prodigiously whiskered countenances. Each delay increased his impatience to a muttering fury; it irked him that he was unable to declare himself, Alexander Hulings, to the train captain, and by the sheer bulk of that name force a more rapid progress.

Finally in Eastlake, Veneada gazed at him out of a silent astonishment.

" You say you're Alex Hulings! " the doctor exclaimed. " Some of you seems to be; but the rest is — by heaven, iron! I'll admit now I was low about you when you left, in April; I knew you had gimp, and counted on it; however — " The period expired in a wondering exhalation. Veneada pounded on his friend's chest, dug into his arm. " A horse! " he declared.

Alexander Hulings impatiently withdrew from the other's touch.

" Veneada," he said, " once you asked me to come to you if I wanted money, if I happened on a good thing. I said nothing at the time, because I couldn't picture an occasion when I'd do such a thing. Well — it's come. I need money, and I'm asking you for it. And, I warn you, it will be a big sum. If you can't manage it I must go somewhere else; I'd go to China, if necessary; I'd stop people, strangers, on the street.

" A big sum," Hulings reiterated somberly; " perhaps ten, perhaps twenty, thousand. Not a loan," he added immediately, " but an investment — an investment in me. You must come out to Harmony. I can't explain, it wouldn't sound convincing in Eastlake. In the valleys, at Tubal Cain, the thing will be self-evident. I have made a beginning with practically nothing; and I can go on. But it will require capital, miles of forest, furnaces built, Pittsburgh swept bare of good men. No " — he held up a hardened, arresting palm — " don't attempt to discuss it now. Come out to Tubal Cain and see; learn about John Wooddrop and how to turn iron into specie."

At the end of the week there were three chairs canted against the stone wall of the little house by the stream that drove Tubal Cain Forge. Conrad Wishon, with a scarlet undershirt open on a broad, hairy chest, listened with wonderment to the sharp periods of Alexander Hulings and Veneada; he heard incredulously mammoth sums of money estimated, projected, dismissed as commonplace. Veneada said:

" I've always believed in your ability, Alex; all that I questioned was the opportunity. Now that has gone; the chance is here. You've got those steel-wire fingers of yours about something rich, and you will never let go. It sounds absurd to go up against this Wooddrop, a despot and a firmly established power; anyone might well laugh at me, but I feel a little sorry for the older man. He doesn't know you.

" You haven't got insides, sympathies, weaknesses, like the others of us; the thing is missing in you that ordinarily betrays human men into slips; yes — compassion. You are not pretty to think about, Alex; but I suppose power never really is. You know I've got money and you know, too, that you can have it. As safe with you as in a bank vault! "

" We'll go back to Eastlake tomorrow," Hulings decided, " lay out our plans and draw up papers. We'll buy the loose timber quietly through agents; I'll never appear in any of it. After that we can let out the contracts for two furnaces. I don't know anything about them now; but I shall in a week. Wishon had better live on here, pottering about the forge, until he can be sent to Pittsburgh after workmen. His pay will start tomorrow."

" What about Tubal Cain, and that fellow — what's his name? "

" Claypole, James. I'll keep a record of what his forge makes, along with mine, and bank it. Common safety. Then I must get over to New York, see the market there, men. I have had letters from an anchor-foundry in Philadelphia. There are nail-factories, locomotive shops, stove plate, to furnish. A hundred industries. I'll have them here in time — rolling-mills you will hear back in the mountains. People on the packets will see the smoke of my furnaces — Alexander Hulings's iron! "

" You might furnish me with a pass, so that I could occasionally walk through and admire," Veneada said dryly.

Hulings never heard him.

" I'll have a mansion," he added abstractedly, " better than Wooddrop's, with more rooms — "

" All full, I suppose, of little glorious Hulings! " the doctor interrupted.

Alexander regarded him unmoved. His thoughts suddenly returned to Hallie Flower. He saw her pale, strained face, her clasped hands; he heard the thin echo of her mingled patience and dismay: "Then I'll never be married!" There was no answering stir of regret, remorse; she slipped forever out of his consciousness, as if she had been a shadow vanishing before a flood of hard, white light.

V

GREATLY to Alexander Hulings's relief, Doctor Veneada never considered the possibility of a partnership; it was as far from one man's wish, for totally different reasons, as from the other's.

"No, no, Alex," he declared; "I couldn't manage it. Some day, when you were out of the office, the widow or orphan would come in with the foreclosure, and I would tear up the papers. Seriously, I won't do — I'm fat and easy and lazy. My money would be safer with me carefully removed from the scene."

In the end Alexander protected Veneada with mortgages on the timber and land he secured about Harmony through various agents and under different names. Some of the properties he bought outright, but in the majority he merely purchased options on the timber. His holdings in the latter finally extended in a broad, irregular belt about the extended local industries of John Wooddrop. It would be impossible for the latter, when, in perhaps fifteen years, he had exhausted his present forests, to cut an acre of wood within practicable hauling distance. This accomplished, a momentary grim satisfaction was visible on Hulings's somber countenance.

He had, however, spent all the money furnished by Dr. Veneada, without setting the foundations of the furnaces and forges he had projected, and he decided not to go to his friend for more. There were two other possible sources of supply: allied iron industries — the obvious recourse — and the railroads. The latter seemed precarious; everywhere people, and even print, were ridiculing the final usefulness of steam traffic; it was judged unfit for heavy and continuous hauling — a toy of inventors and fantastic dreaming; canals were the obviously solid means of transportation. But Alexander Hulings became fanatical overnight in his belief in the coming empire of steam.

With a small carpetbag, holding his various deeds and options, and mentally formulating a vigorous expression of his opinions and projections, he sought the doubtful capital behind the Columbus Transportation Line. When, a month later, he returned to Tubal Cain, it was in the company of an expert industrial engineer, and with credit sufficient for the completion of his present plans. He had been gone a month, but he appeared older by several years. Alexander Hulings had forced from reluctant sources, from men more wily, if less adamantine, than himself, what he desired; but in return he had been obliged to grant almost impossibly favorable contracts and preferences. A tremendous pressure of responsibility had gathered about him; but under it he was still erect, coldly confident, and carried himself with the special pugnacity of small, vain men.

On a day in early June, a year from the delivery of his first contract at Tubal Cain, he stood in a fine rain at the side of a light road-wagon, drawn, like John Wooddrop's, by two sweeping young horses, held by a Negro, and watched the final courses of his new furnace. The furnace itself, a solid structure of unmasoned stone, rose above thirty feet, narrowed at the top to almost half the width of its base. Directly against its face and hearth was built the single high interior of the cast-house, into which the metal would be run on a sand pig-bed and harden into commercial iron.

On the hill rising abruptly at the back was the long wall of the coal-house, with an entrance and runway leading to the opening at the top of the furnace stack. Lower down, the curving, artificial channel of the forebay swept to where the water would fall on a ponderous overshot wheel and drive the great tilted bellows that blasted the furnace.

The latter, Alexander knew, must have a name. Most furnaces were called after favorite women; but there were no such sentimental objects in his existence. He recalled the name of the canal packet that had first drawn him out to Harmony — the *Hit or Miss*. No casual title such as that would fit an enterprise of his. He thought of Tubal Cain, and then of Jim Claypole. He owed the latter something; and yet he wouldn't have another man's name. . . . Conrad Wishon had surmised that the owner of Tubal Cain had vanished — like Elijah — on a Glory wagon. That was it — Glory Furnace! He turned and saw John Wooddrop leaning forward out of his equipage, keenly studying the new buildings.

"That's a good job," the ironmaster allowed; "but it should be — built by Henry Bayard, the first man in the country. It ought to do very well for five or six years."

"Fifty," Hulings corrected him.

John Wooddrop's eyes were smiling.

"It's all a question of charcoal," he explained, as Wishon had, long before. "To be frank, I expect a little difficulty myself, later. It is surprising how generally properties have been newly bought in the county. I know, because lately I, too, have been reaching out. Practically all the available stuff has been secured. Thousands of acres above you, here, have been taken by a company, hotel — or something of the sort."

"The Venealic Company," Hulings said; and then, in swelling pride, he added: "That's me!" Wooddrop's gaze hardened. Alexander Hulings thought the other's face grew paler. His importance, his sense of accomplishment, of vindication, completely overwhelmed him. "And beyond, it is me!" he cried. "And back of that, again!" He made a wide, sweeping gesture with his arm. "Over there; the Hezekiah Mills tract — that's me too; and the East purchase, and on and round. Fifty — this Glory Furnace, and ten others, could run on for a century.

"You've been the big thing here — even in the state. You are known on canal boats, people point you out; yes, and patronize me. You did that yourself — you and your women. But it is over; I'm coming now, and John Wooddrop's going. You are going with those same canal boats, and Alexander Hulings is rising with the railroads."

He pounded himself on the chest, and then suddenly stopped. It was the only impassioned speech, even in the disastrous pursuit of the law, that he had ever made; and it had an impotent, foolish ring in his ear, his deliberate brain. He instantly disowned all that part of him which had betrayed his ordinary silent caution into such windy boasting. Hulings was momentarily abashed before the steady scrutiny of John Wooddrop.

"When I first saw you," the latter pronounced, "I concluded that you were unbalanced. Now I think that you are a maniac!"

He spoke curtly to his driver, and was sharply whirled away through the gray-green veil of rain and foliage. Hulings was left with an aggravated discontent and bitterness toward the older man, who seemed to have the ability always to place him in an unfavorable light.

VI

Dr. Veneada returned for the first run of metal from Glory Furnace; there were two representatives of the other capital invested, and, with Alexander Hulings, Conrad Wishon, and some local spectators, they stood in the gloom of the cast-house waiting for the founder to tap the clay sealing of the hearth. Suddenly there was a rush of crackling white light, pouring sparks, and the boiling liquid flooded out, rapidly filling the molds radiating from the channels stamped in the sand bed. The incandescent iron flushed from silver to darker, warmer tones.

A corresponding warmth ran through Alexander Hulings's body; Glory Furnace was his; it had been conceived by him, and his determination had brought it to an actuality. He would show Wooddrop a new type of " maniac." This was the second successful step in his move against the ironmaster, in the latter's own field. Then he realized that he, too, might now be called Ironmaster. He directed extensive works operated under his name; he, Hulings, was the head! Already there were more than a hundred men to do what he directed, go where he wished. The feeling of power, of consequence, quickened through him. Alexander held himself, if possible, more rigidly than before; he followed every minute turn of the casting, tersely admonished a laborer.

He was dressed with the utmost care; a marked niceness of apparel now distinguished him. His whiskers were closely trimmed, his hair brushed high under a glossy tile hat; he wore checked trousers, strapped-on glazed Wellington boots, and a broadcloth coat, fitted closely to his waist, with a deep rolling collar; severe neckcloth, and a number of seals on a stiff twill waistcoat. Veneada, as always, was carelessly garbed in wrinkled silk and a broad planter's hat. It seemed to Alexander that the other looked conspicuously older than he had only a few months back; the doctor's face was pendulous, the pouches beneath his eyes livid.

Alexander Hulings quickly forgot this in the immediate pressure of manufacture. The younger Wishon, who had followed his father into Alexander's service, now came down from the charcoal stacks in a great sectional wagon drawn by six mules, collared in bells and red streamers. The pigs were sledged in endless procession from Glory, and then from a second furnace, to the forges that reached along the creek in each direction from Tubal Cain. The latter was worked as vigorously as possible, but Alexander conducted its finances in a separate, private column; all the profit he banked to the credit of James Claypole. He did this not from a sense of equity, but because of a deeper, more obscure feeling, almost a superstition, that such acknowledgment of the absent man's unwitting assistance was a safeguard of further good fortune.

The months fled with amazing rapidity; it seemed to him that one day the ground was shrouded in snow, and on the next dogwood was blooming. No man in all his properties worked harder or during longer hours than Alexander; the night shift at a forge would often see him standing grimly in the lurid reflections of the hearths; charcoal-burners, eating their flitch and potatoes on an outlying mountain, not infrequently heard the beat of his horse's hoofs on the soft moss, his domineering voice bullying them for some slight oversight. He inspired everywhere a dread mingled with grudging admiration; it was known that he forced every possible ounce of effort from workman and beast.

Nevertheless, toward the end of the third summer of his success he contracted a lingering fever, and he was positively commanded to leave his labors for a rest and change. He sat on the porch of the house he had commenced building, on a rise overlooking the eddying smoke of his industries, wrapped in a shawl, and considered the various places that offered relaxation; he could go to the sea, at Long Branch, or to Saratoga, the gayety and prodigality of which were famous. . . . But his thought returned to his collapse four years before; he heard Veneada counseling him to take the water of the Mineral Springs. He had been too poor then for the Mineral; had he gone there, he would have arrived unnoticed. By heaven, he would go there now! It was, he knew, less fashionable than the other places; its day had been twenty, thirty years before. But it represented once more his progress, his success; and, in the company of his personal servant, his leather boxes strapped at the back of his lightest road-wagon, he set out the following morning.

Almost sixty miles of indifferent roads lay before him; and, though he covered, in his weakened condition, far more than half the distance by evening, he was forced to stay overnight at a roadside tavern. The way was wild and led through narrow, dark valleys, under the shadow of uninhabited ridges, and through swift fords. Occasionally he passed great, slow Conestoga wagons, entrained for the West, leather-hooded, ancient vehicles, and men on horses.

The wagon broke suddenly into the smooth, green valley that held the Mineral Springs. Against a western mountain were grouped hotels; a bridge, crossing a limpid stream; pointed kiosks in the Chinese taste; and red gravel walks. The hotel before which Alexander stopped, a prodigiously long, high structure painted white, had a deep porch across its face, with slender columns towering up unbroken to the roof and festooned with trumpet flowers. A bell rang loudly for dinner, and there was a colorful flow of crinoline over the porch, a perfumed, flowery stir, through which he impatiently made his way, followed by Negro boys with his luggage.

Within, the office was high and bare, with a sweeping staircase, and wide doors opened on a lofty thronged dining-room. Above, he was led through interminable narrow corridors, past multitudinous closed doors, to a closetlike room completely filled by a narrow bed, a chair and a corner wash-stand; this, with some pegs in the calcined wall and a bell-rope, completed the provisions for his comfort. His toilet was hurried, for he had been warned that extreme promptness at meals was more than desirable; and, again below, he was led by a pompous Negro between long, crowded tables to a place at the farther end. The din of conversation and clatter of dishes were deafening. In the ceiling great connected fans were languidly pulled by black boys, making a doubtful circulation.

His dinner was cold and absurdly inadequate, but the table claret was palatable. And, after the isolation of Tubal Cain, the droves of festive people absorbed him. Later, at the bar, he came across an acquaintance, a railroad director, who pointed out to Alexander what notables were present. There was an Englishman, a lord; there was Bartram Ainscough, a famous gambler; there — Alexander's arm was grasped by his companion.

"See that man — no, farther — dark, in a linen suit? Well, that's Partridge Sinnox, of New Orleans." He grew slightly impatient at

Hulings's look of inquiry. " Never heard of him! Best-known pistol-shot in the States. A man of the highest honor. Will go out on the slightest provocation." His voice lowered. " He's said to have killed twelve — no less. His companion there — from Louisiana too — never leaves him. Prodigiously rich — canefields."

Alexander Hulings looked with small interest at the dueler and his associate. The former had a lean, tanned face, small black eyes that held each a single point of light, and long, precise hands. Here, Alexander thought, was another form of publicity, different from his own. As always, his lips tightened in a faint contempt at pretensions other than his, or that threatened his pre-eminence. Sinnox inspired none of the dread or curiosity evident in his companion; and he turned from him to the inspection of a Pennsylvania coal-magnate.

The colonnade of the hotel faced another cultivated ridge, on which terraced walks mounted to a pavilion at the crest; and there, through the late afternoon, he rested and gazed down at the Springs or over to the village beyond. Alexander was wearier than he had supposed; the iron seemed suddenly insupportably burdensome, a longing for lighter, gayer contacts possessed him. He wanted to enter the relaxations of the Springs.

Dancing, he knew, was customary after supper; and he lingered over a careful toilet — bright blue coat, tight black trousers, and flat, glistening slippers, with a soft cambric ruffle. Alexander Hulings surveyed his countenance in a scrap of mirror and saw, with mingled surprise and discontent, that he — like Veneada — bore unmistakable signs of age, marks of strife and suffering; his whiskers had a plain silvery sheen. Life, receding unnoticed, had set him at the verge of middle age. But at least, he thought, his was not an impotent medial period; if, without material success, he had unexpectedly seen the slightly drawn countenance meeting him in the mirror, he would have killed himself. He realized that coldly. He could never have survived an established nonentity. As it was, descending the stairs to supper, immaculate and disdainful, he was upheld by the memory of his accomplishments, his widening importance, weight. He actually heard a whispered comment: " Hulings, iron."

VII

After supper the furnishings of the dining-room were swept aside by a troop of waiters, while a number of the latter, with fiddles and cornets, were grouped on a table, over which a green cloth had been spread. With the inevitable scraping of strings and preliminary unattended dance, a quadrille was formed. Alexander, lounging with other exactly garbed males in the doorway, watched with secret envy the participants in the figures gliding from one to another. As if from another life he recalled their names; they were dancing Le Pantalon now; La Poulee would follow; then the Pastorale and L'Eté.

Above the spreading gauze, the tulle and glacé silks of the women, immense candelabra of glass pendants and candles shone and glittered; the rustle of crinoline, of light, passing feet, sounded below the violins and blown cornets, the rich husky voices calling the changes of the quadrille.

He was troubled by an obscure desire to be a center of interest, of importance, for the graceful feminine world about him. Sinnox, the man from New Orleans, was bowing profoundly to his partner; a figure broke up into a general boisterous gallopading — girls, with flushed cheeks, swinging curls, spun from masculine shoulder to shoulder. The dance ended, and the floating, perfumed skirts passed him in a soft flood toward the porch.

Without, the colonnade towered against a sky bright with stars; the night was warm and still. Alexander Hulings was lonely; he attempted to detain the acquaintance met in the bar, but the other, bearing a great bouquet of rosebuds in a lace-paper cone, hurried importantly away. A subdued barytone was singing: _Our Way across the Mountain, Ho!_ The strains of a waltz, the Carlotta Grisi, drifted out, and a number of couples answered its invitation.

A group at the iron railing across the foot of the colonnade attracted his attention by its excessive gayety. The center, he saw, was a young woman, with smooth bandeaux and loops of black hair, and a goya lily caught below her ear. She was not handsome, but her features were animated, and her shoulders as finely white and sloping as an alabaster vase.

It was not this that held his attention, but a sense of familiarity, a feeling that he had seen her before. He walked past the group, without plan, and, meeting her gaze, bowed awkwardly in response to a hesitating but unmistakable smile of recognition. Alexander stopped, and she imperiously waved him to join the number about her. He was in a cold dread of the necessity of admitting, before so many, that he could not recall her name; but obviously all that she desired was to swell the circle of her admirers, for, beyond a second nod, she ignored him.

The Southerner was at her shoulder, maintaining a steady flow of repartee, and Alexander envied him his assured presence, his dark, distinguished appearance. The man who had been indicated as Sinnox's companion stood by Hulings, and the latter conceived a violent prejudice for the other's meager yellow face and spiderlike hand, employed with a cheroot.

Alexander hoped that somebody would repeat the name of the girl who had spoken to him. A woman did, but only in the contracted, familiar form of Gisela. . . . Gisela — he had heard that too. Suddenly she affected to be annoyed; she arched her fine brows and glanced about, her gaze falling upon Alexander Hulings. Before he was aware of her movement a smooth white arm was thrust through his; he saw the curve of a powdered cheek, an elevated chin.

"Do take me out of this!" she demanded. "New Orleans molasses is — well, too thick."

Obeying the gentle pressure of her arm, he led her down the steps to the graveled expanse below. She stopped by a figure of the Goddess of Health, in filigree on mossy rocks, pouring water from an urn. Her gown was glazed green muslin, with a mist of white tulle, shining with particles of silver. The goya lily exhaled a poignant scent.

"I didn't really leave because of Mr. Sinnox," she admitted; "a pin was scratching, and I was devoured with curiosity to know who you were, where I had met — "

Suddenly, in a flash of remembered misery, of bitter resentment, he recognized her — Gisela, John Wooddrop's daughter. The knowledge pinched at his heart like malicious fingers; the starry night, the music and gala attire, his loneliness had betrayed him

into an unusual plasticity of being. He delayed for a long breath, and
then said dryly: " I'm Alexander Hulings."

" Not — " she half cried, startled. She drew away from him, and
her face grew cold. In the silence that followed he was conscious of
the flower's perfume and the insistent drip of the water falling from
the urn. " But I haven't met you at all," she said, " I don't in the
least know you." Her attitude was insolent, and yet she unconsciously betrayed a faint curiosity. " I think you lacked delicacy to
join my friends — to bring me out here! "

" I didn't," he reminded her; " you brought me."

Instantly he cursed such clumsy stupidity. Her lower lip pro-
truded disdainfully.

" Forgive me," she said, dropping a curtsy, " but I needn't keep
you."

She swept away across the gravel and up the stairs to the veranda.
It was evident that the group had not separated; for almost immediately there rose a concerted laughter, a palpable mockery, drifting
out to Alexander.

His face was hot, his hands clenched in angry resentment. More
than anything else, he shrunk from being an object of amusement,
of gibes. It was necessary to his self-esteem to be met with grave
appreciation.

This was his first experience of the keen assaults of social weap-
ons, and it inflicted on him an extravagant suffering. His instinct
was to retire farther into the night, only to return to his room when
the hotel was dark, deserted. But a second, stronger impulse sent
him deliberately after Gisela Wooddrop, up the veranda stairs, and
rigidly past the group gazing at him with curious mirth.

An oil flare fixed above them shone down on the lean, saturnine
countenance of Partridge Sinnox. The latter, as he caught Alexander Hulings's gaze, smiled slightly.

That expression followed Alexander to his cramped room; it
mocked him as he viciously pulled at the bell-rope, desiring his servant; it was borne up to him on the faint strains of the violins. And
in the morning it clouded his entire outlook. Sinnox's smile expressed a contempt that Alexander Hulings's soul could not endure.
From the first he had been resentful of the Southerner's cheap
prestige. He added the qualifying word as he descended to breakfast.

Sinnox, as a dueler, roused Hulings's impatience; he had more than once faced impromptu death — iron bars in the hands of infuriated employees — and he had overborne them with a cold phrase. This theatrical playing with pistols — cheap! Later, in the crowded bar, he was pressed elbow to elbow with Sinnox and his companion; and he automatically and ruthlessly cleared sufficient space for his comfort. Sinnox's associate said, in remonstrance:

" Sir, there are others — perhaps more considerable."

" Perhaps! " Alexander Hulings carelessly agreed.

Sinnox gazed down on him with narrowed eyes.

" I see none about us," he remarked, " who would have to admit the qualification."

Alexander's bitterness increased, became aggressive. He met Sinnox's gaze with a stiff, dangerous scorn:

" In your case, at least, it needn't stand."

" Gentlemen," the third cried, " no more, I beg of you." He grasped Alexander Hulings's arm. " Withdraw! " he advised. " Mr. Sinnox's temper is fatal. Beyond a certain point it cannot be leashed. It has caused great grief. Gentlemen, I beg — "

" Do you mean — " Sinnox demanded, and his face was covered by an even, dark flush to the sweep of his hair.

" Cheap! " Alexander repeated aloud, sudden and unpremeditated.

The other's temper rose in a black passion; he became so enraged that his words were mere unintelligible gasps. His hand shook so that he dropped a glass of rock and rye splintering on the floor. " At once! " he finally articulated. " Scurvy — "

" This couldn't be helped," his companion proclaimed, agitated. " I warned the other gentleman. Mr. Sinnox is not himself in a rage, his record is well known. He was elbowed aside by — "

" Alexander Hulings! " that individual pronounced.

He was aware of the gaze of the crowding men about him; already he was conscious of an admiration roused by the mere fact of his facing a notorious bully. Cheap! The director joined him.

" By heavens, Hulings, you're in dangerous water. I understand you have no family."

" None! " Alexander stated curtly.

Illogically he was conscious of the scent of a goya lily. Sinnox was propelled from the bar, and his friend reappeared and conferred with the director.

"At once!" Hulings heard the former announce. "Mr. Sinnox . . . unbearable!"

"Have you a case of pistols?" the director asked. "Mr. Sinnox offers his. I believe there is a quiet open back of the bathhouse. But my earnest advice to you is to withdraw; you will be very little blamed; this man is notorious, a professional fighter. You have only to say — "

"Cheap!" Alexander thought, fretful at having been involved in such a ridiculous affair. He was even more deliberate than usual; but, though he was certain of his entire normality, the faces about him resembled small, bobbing balloons.

Alexander finished his drink — surprised to find himself still standing by the bar — and silently followed the director through the great hall of the hotel out onto the veranda and across the grass to a spot hidden from the valley by the long, low bulk of the bathing-house.

Sinnox and his companion, with a polished mahogany box, were already there, while a small, curious group congregated in the distance. Sinnox's friend produced long pistols with silken-brown barrels and elegantly carved ivory stocks, into which he formally rammed powder and balls. Alexander Hulings was composed; but his fingers were cold, slightly numb, and he rubbed them together angrily. Not for an instant did he think that he might be killed; other curious, faint emotions assailed him — long-forgotten memories of distant years; Veneada's kindly hand on his shoulder; the mule called Alexander because of its aptitude for hard labor; John Wooddrop's daughter.

He saw that the pistols had been loaded; their manipulator stood with them, butts extended, in his grasp. He began a preamble of customary explanation, which he ended by demanding, for his principal, an apology from Alexander Hulings. The latter, making no reply, was attracted by Sinnox's expression of deepening passion; the man's face, he thought, positively was black. Partridge Sinnox's entire body was twitching with rage. . . . Curious, for a seasoned, famous dueler!

Suddenly Sinnox, with a broken exclamation, swung on his heel, grasped one of the pistols in his second's hands, and discharged it point-blank at Alexander Hulings.

An instant confused outcry rose. Alexander heard the term " Insane! " pronounced, as if in extenuation, by Sinnox's friend. The latter held the remaining undischarged pistol out of reach; the other lay on the ground before Partridge Sinnox. Alexander's face was as gray as granite.

" That was the way he did it," he unconsciously pronounced aloud.

He wondered slowly at the fact that he had been unhit. Then, with his hand in a pocket, he walked stiffly up to within a few feet of Sinnox and produced a small, ugly derringer, with one blunt barrel on top of the other.

At the stunning report that followed, the vicious, stinging cloud of smoke, he seemed to wake. He felt himself propelled away from the vicinity of the bathhouse; low, excited exclamations beat upon his ears: " Absolutely justified! " " Horrible attempt to murder! " " Get his nigger and things. Best for the present." He impatiently shook himself free from his small following.

" Did I kill him? " he demanded.

There was an affirmative silence.

In his wagon, driving rapidly toward Tubal Cain, a sudden sense of horror, weakness, overtook him; the roadside rocked beneath his vision.

" Mordecai," he said to his coachman, " I — I shot a man, derringered him."

The Negro was unmoved.

" Man 'at fool round you, he's bound to be killed! " he asserted. " Yes, sir; he just throwed himself right away! "

Alexander Hulings wondered how John Wooddrop's daughter would be affected. At least, he thought grimly, once more self-possessed, he had put a stop to her laughter at his expense.

VIII

IN the weeks that followed he devoted himself energetically to the finishing of the mansion in course of erection above Tubal Cain. It was an uncompromising, square edifice of brick, with a railed bel-

vedere on the roof, and a front lawn enclosed by a cast-iron fence.
On each side of the path dividing the sod were wooden Chinese
pagodas like those he had seen at the Mineral Springs; and masoned
rings for flower-beds, and ferneries, artificially heaped stones, with
a fine spray from concealed pipes. Rearing its solid bulk against the
living greenery of the forest, it was, he told himself pridefully, a
considerable dwelling. Within were high walls and flowery ceilings,
Italian marble mantels and tall mirrors, black carved and gilded
furniture, and brilliant hassocks on thick-piled carpet.

The greater part of the labor was performed by the many skilled
workmen now employed in his furnaces and forges. He was utterly
regardless of cost, obligations, of money itself. Alexander had always
been impatient at the mere material fact of wealth, of the possession and the accumulation of sheer gold. To him it was nothing
more than a lever by which he moved men and things; it was a ladder that carried him above the unnoticed and unnotable. He could
always get money, at need, from men or iron; to debts he never gave
a thought — when they fell due they were discharged or carried on.

His reason for finishing his dwelling with such elaboration was
obscure. Veneada had laughed at him, speaking of small Hulings,
but he harbored no concrete purpose of marriage; there was even no
dominant feminine figure in his thoughts. Perhaps faintly at times
he caught the odor of a goya lily; but that was probably due to the
fact that lilies were already blooming in the circular conservatory of
highly colored glass attached to his veranda.

The greater part of the house was darkened, shrouded in linen.
He would see, when walking through the hall, mysterious and shadowy vistas, lengthened endlessly in the long mirrors, of dusky carpet, and alabaster and ormolu, the faint glitter of the prisms hung
on the mantel lamps. Clocks would strike sonorously in the depths
of halls, with the ripple of cathedral chimes. He had a housekeeper,
a stout person in oiled curls, and a number of excessively humble
Negro servants. Alexander Hulings got from all this an acute pleasure. It, too, was a mark of his success.

He had, below, on the public road, a small edifice of one room,
which formed his office, and there he saw the vast number of men
always consulting with him; he never took them above to his house.
And when they dined with him it was at the hotel, newly built by

the packet station on the canal — functions flooded with the prodigal amounts of champagne Hulings thought necessary to his importance.

Most of his days were spent in his road-wagon, in which he traveled to Pittsburgh, West Virginia, Philadelphia, where he had properties or interests. In the cities of his associates he also avoided their homes, and met them in hotels; discussed the terms of business in bars or public parlors. With women of position he was at once indifferent and ill at ease, constantly certain that he was not appearing to good advantage, and suspecting their asides and enigmatic smiles. He was laboriously, stiffly polite, speaking in complimentary flourishes that sometimes ended in abrupt constraint. At this, afterwards, he would chafe, and damn the superior airs of women.

He had returned from such an expedition to Wheeling, and was sitting in his office, when a vehicle pulled up before his door. Deliberate feet approached and John Wooddrop entered. The latter, Alexander realized enviously, was an excessively handsome old man; he had a commanding height and a square, highly colored countenance, with close white sideburns and vigorous silver hair. His manner, too, was assured and easy. He greeted Alexander Hulings with a keen, open smile.

" Everything is splendid here! " he proclaimed. " I looked in that chafery down stream, and the metal was worked like satin. Fine weather for the furnaces — rain's ugly; a furnace is like a young girl."

Hulings wondered — contained and suspicious — what the other wanted. Wooddrop, though they passed each other frequently on the road, had not saluted him since the completion of Glory Furnace. He thought for a moment that already the older man was feeling the pinch of fuel scarcity and that he had come to beg for timber. In such a case Alexander Hulings decided coldly that he would not sell Wooddrop an ell of forest. In addition to the fact that the complete success of one or the other depended ultimately on his rival's failure, he maintained a personal dislike of John Wooddrop; he had never forgotten the humiliation forced on him long before, in the dining-room of the packet, the *Hit or Miss*; he could not forgive Wooddrop's pre-eminence in the iron field. The latter was a legend of the manufacture of iron.

However, any idea of the other's begging privilege was immediately banished by John Wooddrop's equable bearing. He said:

"I want to speak to you, Hulings, about a rather delicate matter. In a way it is connected with my daughter, Gisela. You saw her, I believe, at the Springs."

Alexander Hulings somberly inclined his head.

"Of course," Wooddrop continued, "I heard about the difficulty you had with that Louisiana bravo. I understand you acted like a man of spirit and were completely exonerated; in fact, I had some small part in quashing legal complications. This was done not on your account, but because of Gisela, who confided to me that she held herself in blame. Mr. Hulings," he said gravely, "my feeling for my daughter is not the usual affection of parent for child. My wife is dead. Gisela — But I won't open a personal subject with you. I spoke as I did merely, in a way, to prepare you for what follows. My daughter felt that she did you a painful wrong; and I have come, in consequence, to offer you my goodwill. I propose that we end our competition and proceed together, for the good of both. Consolidated, we should inevitably control the iron situation in our state; you are younger, more vigorous than myself, and I have a certain prestige. Sir, I offer you the hand of friendly co-operation."

Alexander Hulings's gaze narrowed as he studied the man before him. At first he had searched for an ulterior motive, need, in Wooddrop's proposal; but he quickly saw that the proposal had been completely stated. Illogically he thought of black ringleted hair and glazed muslin; he heard the echo of water dripping from a stone urn. Lost in memories, he was silent, for so long that John Wooddrop grew impatient. He cleared his throat sharply; but Hulings didn't shift a muscle. Alexander was thinking now of the order he had filled the first summer at Tubal Cain, of his brutal labor and bitter, deferred aspirations. His rise, alone, had been at the price of ceaseless struggle; it was not yet consummated; but it would be — it must, and still alone. Nothing should rob him of the credit of his achievement; no person coupled with him might reduce or share his triumph. What he said sounded inexcusably harsh after the other's open manner.

" Only," he said — " only if the amalgamated industries bear my name — the Alexander Hulings Ironworks."

John Wooddrop's face darkened as he comprehended the implied insult to his dignity and position. He rose, so violently thrusting back the chair in which he had been sitting that it fell with a clatter.

" You brass trumpet! " he ejaculated. " You intolerable little bag of vanity! Will you never see yourself except in a glass of flattery or intolerable self-satisfaction? It would be impossible to say which you inspire most, contempt or pity."

Strangely enough, Hulings didn't resent the language applied to him. He gazed at Wooddrop without anger. The other's noise, he thought, was but a symptom of his coming downfall. He was slowly but surely drawing the rope about the throat of Wooddrop's industries.

" Absolutely the last time," the other stuttered. " Now you can go to hell on your own high horse! Blinded by your own fatuousness — don't see where the country is running. You may impose on others, but I know your business, sir; and it's as hollow as a tin plate stove. The times will soon kick it in."

John Wooddrop stamped away from Hulings in a rage.

IX

THAT evening Alexander Hulings wondered what Gisela had told her father; he wondered more vaguely what she had thought of him — what, if at all, she still thought. He had had a formal room illuminated for his cigar after dinner; and he sat, a small, precise figure, with dust-colored hair and a somber, intent countenance, clasping a heavy roll of expensive tobacco, in a crimson plush chair. The silence, the emptiness about him, was filled with rich color, ponderous maroon draperies, marble slabs, and fretted tulipwood.

It suddenly struck him that, by himself, he was slightly ridiculous in such opulence. His house needed a mistress, a creature of elegance to preside at his table, to exhibit in her silks and jewels another sign of his importance. Again, as if from the conservatory, he caught a faint poignant perfume.

Gisela Wooddrop was a person of distinction, self-possessed and charming. There was a subtle flavor in thus considering her father's daughter — old Wooddrop's girl — and himself. He rose and walked to a mirror, critically surveying his countenance — yes, it was well marked by age, yet it was sharp in outline; his step was springy; he felt none of the lassitude of increasing years.

He was in his prime. Many young women would prefer him, his house and name, to the windy pretensions of youthful scapegoats. A diamond necklace was a convincing form of courtship. There was no absolute plan in his thoughts that night; but, in the dry romantic absorption of the days that followed, a fantastic purpose formed and increased — he determined to marry Gisela Wooddrop.

He had for this, he assured himself, some slight encouragement; it was patent that her father had entirely misread the girl's intent in suggesting an end to the hostilities which had made impossible any social intercourse. She was interested in him; the duel with Sinnox had captured her imagination. Women responded surprisingly to such things. Then she had held that it had been partly her fault! Now it seemed to him that he understood why he had built so elaborately since his return from the Mineral Springs; unconsciously — all the while — it has been for his wife — for Gisela.

There were great practical difficulties in the realization of his desire, even in his opportunity to present his question; to see Gisela Wooddrop long enough and sufficiently privately to explain all he hoped. He was, too, far past the age of romantic assignations, episodes; he could no more decorate a moonlit scene beneath a window. Alexander could not count on adventitious assistance from emotional setting: his offer could carry only its grave material solidity. Often he laughed curtly at what momentarily seemed an absurd fantasy, a madness approaching senility; then his pride would flood back, reassert the strength of his determination, the desirability of Alexander Hulings.

X

THE OCCASION evaded him; the simplicity of his wish, of the bald relationship between the Wooddrops and Tubal Cain, preventing it more surely than a multiplication of barriers. He never consid-

ered the possibility of a compromise with John Wooddrop, a retreat from his position. Alexander thought of Gisela as a possible
addition to his dignity and standing — of the few women he had
seen she possessed the greatest attractions — and he gave no
thought of a sacrifice to gain her. She was to be a piece with the
rest of his success — a wife to honor his mansion, to greet a selected few of his friends and wear the gold and jewels purchased
by the Hulings iron.

He made no overt attempt to see her, but waited for opportunity. Meantime he had commenced to think of her in terms of
passionless intimacy. Alexander Hulings was a solitary man — except for his industrial activity his mind was empty, and Gisela
Wooddrop quickly usurped the hours after dinner, the long drives
through massed and unscarred forests. He recalled her minutely —
every expression that he had seen, every variation of dress. Wooddrop's daughter was handsomely provided for; but Alexander Hulings's wife would be a revelation in luxury. In New York he bought
a pair of India cashmere shawls, paying a thousand dollars for them,
and placed them on a chair, ready —

The weeks multiplied; and he got such pleasure from the mere
thought of Gisela sweeping through his rooms, accompanying him
to Philadelphia, shining beside him at the opera, that he became
almost reluctant to force the issue of her choice. He was more than
customarily careful with his clothes; his silk hats were immaculate;
his trousers ranged in color from the most delicate sulphur to
astounding London checks; he had his yellow boots polished with
champagne, his handkerchiefs scented with essence of nolette and
almond. For all this, his countenance was none the less severe, his
aptitude for labor untouched; he followed every detail of iron
manufacture, every improved process, every shift in the market.

The valley about Tubal Cain now resembled a small, widely
scattered town; the dwellings of Hulings's workmen extended to
the property line of the Blue Lump Furnace; roads were cut,
bridges thrown across the stream. The flutter of wings, the pouring birdsong and vale of green, that Alexander had found had
given place to a continuous, shattering uproar day and night — the
charging of furnaces; the dull thunder of the heavy wagons of
blooms; the jangle of shingling-sledges and monotonous fall of trip-

hammers — mingled and rose in a stridulous volume to the sky, accompanied by chemical vapors, uprushing cinders, and the sooty smoke of the forges. A company store had been built and stocked, and grimy troops of laborers were perpetually gathered, off shift, by its face.

Harmony itself, the station on the canal, had expanded; the new hotel, an edifice of brick with a steep slate roof and iron grilling, faced a rival saloon and various emporia of merchandise. An additional basin had been cut in the bank for the loading of Alexander Hulings's iron onto the canal boats.

He had driven to the canal — it was early summer — to see about a congestion of movement; and, hot, he stopped in the hotel for a pint of wine in a high glass with cracked ice. The lower floor was cut in half by a hall and stairs; on the right the bar opened onto the narrow porch, while at the left a ladies' entrance gave way to the inevitable dark, already musty parlor. The bar was crowded, and, intolerant of the least curtailment of his dignity or comfort, he secured his glass and moved across the hall to the stillness of the parlor.

A woman was standing, blurred in outline, at one of the narrow windows. She turned as he entered; he bowed, prepared to withdraw, when he saw that it was Gisela Wooddrop. She wore white muslin, sprigged in orange chenille, with green ribbons, and carried a green parasol. Alexander stood motionless in the doorway, his champagne in one hand and a glossy stovepipe hat in the other. He was aware of a slight inward confusion, but outwardly he was unmoved, exact. Gisela, too, maintained the turn of her flexible body, her hands on the top of the parasol. Under her bonnet her face was pale, her eyes noticeably bright. Alexander Hulings said:

"Good afternoon!"

He moved into the room. Gisela said nothing; she was like a graceful painted figure on a shadowy background. A complete ease possessed Alexander.

"Miss Wooddrop," he continued, in the vein of a simple statement. She nodded automatically. "This is a happy meeting — for me. I can now express my gratitude for your concern about a certain unfortunate occurrence at the Mineral Springs. At the same time, I regret that you were caused the slightest uneasiness."

She shuddered delicately.

"Nothing more need be said about that," she told him. "I explained to my father; but I was sorry afterwards that I did it and — and put him to fresh humiliation."

"There," he gravely replied, "little enough can be discussed. It has to do with things that you would have limited patience with, strictly an affair of business. I was referring to your susceptibility of heart, a charming female quality."

He bowed stiffly. Gisela came nearer to him, a sudden emotion trembling on her features.

"Why don't you end it?" she cried, low and distressed. "It has gone on a long while now — the bitterness between you; I am certain in his heart Father is weary of it, and you are younger — " She broke off before the tightening of his lips.

"Not a topic to be developed here," he insisted.

He had no intention, Alexander Hulings thought, of being bent about even so charming a finger. And it was well to establish at once the manner in which any future they might share should be conducted. He wanted a wife, not an intrigante or Amazon. Her feeling, color, rapidly evaporated, and left her pallid, confused, before his calm demeanor. She turned her head away, her face lost in the bonnet, but slowly her gaze returned to meet his keen inquiry. His impulse was to ask her, then, at once, to marry him; but he restrained that headlong course, feeling that it would startle her into flight. As it was, she moved slowly toward the door.

"I am to meet a friend on the western packet," she explained; "I thought I heard the horn."

"It was only freight," he replied. "I should be sorry to lose this short opportunity to pay you my respects; to tell you that you have been a lot in my thoughts lately. I envy the men who see you casually, whenever they choose."

She gazed at him with palpable surprise gathering in her widely opened eyes. "But," she said breathlessly, "everybody knows that you never address a polite syllable to a woman. It is more speculated on than any of your other traits."

He expanded at this indication of a widespread discussion of his qualities.

"I have had no time for merely polite speeches," he responded. "And I assure you that I am not only complimentary now; I mean that I am not saluting you with vapid elegance. I am awaiting only a more fitting occasion to say further."

She circled him slowly, with a minute whispering of crinoline, her gaze never leaving his face. Her muslin, below her white, bare throat, circled by a black velvet band, was heaving. The parasol fell with a clatter. He stooped immediately; but she was before him and snatched it up, with crimson cheeks.

"They say that you are the most hateful man alive!" she half breathed.

"Who are 'they'?" he demanded contemptuously. "Men I have beaten and women I failed to see. That hatred grows with success, with power; it is never wasted on the weak. My competitors would like to see me fall into a furnace stack — the men I have climbed over, and my debtors. They are combining every month to push me to the wall, a dozen of them together, yelping like a pack of dogs. But they haven't succeeded; they never will!" His words were like the chips from an iron bloom. "They never will," he repeated harshly, "and I have only begun. I want you to see my house some time. I planned a great part of it with you in mind. No money was spared. . . . I should be happy to have you like it. I think of it as yours."

All the time he was speaking she was stealing by imperceptible degrees toward the door; but at his last, surprising sentence she stood transfixed with mingled wonder and fear. She felt behind her for the open doorway and rested one hand against the woodwork. A ribald clatter sounded from the bar, and without rose the faint, clear note of an approaching packet. Her lips formed for speech, but only a slight gasp was audible; then her spreading skirts billowed through the opening and she was gone.

Alexander Hulings found that he was still holding his silk hat; he placed it carefully on the table and took a deep drink from the iced glass. He was conscious of a greater feeling of triumph than he had ever known before. He realized that he had hardly needed to add the spoken word to the impression his being had made on

Gisela Wooddrop. He had already invaded her imagination; the legend of his struggle and growth had taken possession of her. There remained now only a formal declaration, the outcome of which he felt almost certain would be in his favor.

Again in his house, he inspected the silk hangings of the particularly feminine chambers. He trod the thick carpets with a keen anticipation of her exclamations of pleasure, her surprise at convenient trifle after trifle. In the stable he surveyed a blooded mare she might take a fancy to; he must buy a light carriage, with a fringed canopy — yes, and put a driver into livery. Women liked such things.

At dinner he speculated on the feminine palate; he liked lean mountain venison, and a sherry that left almost a sensation of dust on the tongue; but women preferred sparkling hock and pastry, fruit preserved in white brandy, and pagodas of barley sugar.

Through the open windows came the subdued clatter of his forges; the hooded candles on the table flickered slightly in a warm eddy, while corresponding shadows stirred on the heavy napery, the Sheffield, and delicate creamy Belleek of his dinner service — the emblem of his certitude and pride.

XI

IN October Alexander Hulings took Gisela Wooddrop to the home that had been so largely planned for her enjoyment. They had been married in a private parlor of the United States Hotel, in Philadelphia, and after a small supper had gone to the Opera House to see *Love in a Village*, followed by a musical *pasticcio*. Gisela's mother had died the winter before, and she was attended by an elderly distant cousin; no one else was present at the wedding ceremony except a friend of Gisela's — a girl who wept copiously — and Dr. Veneada. The latter's skin hung in loose folds, like a sack partially emptied of its contents; his customary spirit had evaporated too; and he sat through the wedding supper neither eating nor speaking, save for the forced proposal of the bride's health.

Gisela Wooddrop and Alexander Hulings, meeting on a number of carefully planned, apparently accidental occasions, had decided to be married while John Wooddrop was confined to his room by severe gout. In this manner they avoided the unpleasant certainty of his refusal to attend his daughter's, and only child's, wedding. Gisela had not told Alexander Hulings what the aging ironmaster had said when necessarily informed of her purpose. No message had come to Alexander from John Wooddrop; since the ceremony the Hulings had had no sign of the other's existence.

Alexander surveyed his wife with huge satisfaction as they sat for the first time at supper in their house. She wore white, with the diamonds he had given her about her firm young throat, black enamel bracelets on her wrists, and her hair in a gilt net. She sighed with deep pleasure.

" It's wonderful! " she proclaimed, and then corroborated all he had surmised about the growth of her interest in him; it had reached forward and back from the killing of Partridge Sinnox. " That was the first time," she told him, " that I realized you were so — so big. You looked so miserable on the canal boat, coming out here those years ago, that it hardly seemed possible for you merely to live; and when you started the hearths at Tubal Cain everyone who knew anything about iron just laughed at you — we used to go down sometimes and look at those killing workmen you had, and that single mule and old horse.

" I wasn't interested then, and I don't know when it happened; but now I can see that a time soon came when men stopped laughing at you. I can just remember when Father first became seriously annoyed, when he declared that he was going to force you out of the valleys at once. But it seemed you didn't go. And then in a few months he came home in a dreadful temper, when he found that you controlled all the timber on the mountains. He said of course you would break before he was really short of charcoal. But it seems you haven't broken. And now I'm married to you; I'm Gisela Hulings! "

" This is hardly more than the beginning," he added; " the foundation — just as iron is the base for so much. I — we — are going on," he corrected the period lamely, but was rewarded by a charming smile. " Power! " he said, shutting up one hand, his straight, fine features as hard as the cameo in his neckcloth.

She instantly fired at his tensity of will.

" How splendid you are, Alexander! " she cried. " How tremen-
dously satisfactory for a woman to share! You can have no idea
what it means to be with a man like a stone wall!

" I wish," she said, " that you would always tell me about your
work. I'd like more than anything else to see you going on, step
by step up. I suppose it is extraordinary in a woman. I felt that
way about Father's iron, and he only laughed at me; and yet once
I kept a forge daybook almost a week, when a clerk was ill. I think
I could be of real assistance to you, Alexander."

He regarded with the profoundest distaste any mingling of his,
Alexander Hulings's, wife and a commercial industry. He had married in order to give his life a final touch of elegance and proper
symmetry. No, no; he wanted Gisela to receive him at the door
of his mansion, in fleckless white, as she was now, and jewels, at
the end of his day in the clamor and soot of business and put it
temporarily from his thoughts.

He was distinctly annoyed that her father had permitted her to
post the forge book; it was an exceedingly unladylike proceeding.
He told her something of this in carefully chosen, deliberate words;
and she listened quietly, but with a faint air of disappointment.

" I want you to buy yourself whatever you fancy," he continued;
" nothing is too good for you — for my wife. I am very proud of
you and insist on your making the best appearance, wherever we
are. Next year, if the political weather clears at all, we'll go to Paris,
and you can explore the mantua-makers there. You got the shawls
in your dressing-room? "

She hesitated, cutting uncertainly with a heavy silver knife at a
crystallized citron.

Then, with an expression of determination, she addressed him
again:

" But don't you see that it is your power, your success over men,
that fascinates me; that first made me think of you? In a way this
is not — not an ordinary affair of ours; I had other chances more
commonplace, which my father encouraged, but they seemed so
stupid that I couldn't entertain them. I love pretty clothes, Alexander; I adore the things you've given me; but will you mind my
saying that that isn't what I married you for? I am sure you don't
care for such details, for money itself, in the least. You are too

strong. And that is why I married you, why I love to think about you, and what I want to follow, to admire and understand."

He was conscious of only a slight irritation at this masculine-sounding speech; he must have no hesitation in uprooting such ideas from his wife's thoughts; they detracted from her feminine charm, struck at the bottom of her duties, her privileges and place.

" At the next furnace in blast," he told her with admirable control, " the workmen will insist on your throwing in, as my bride, a slipper; and in that way you can help the charge."

Then, by planning an immediate trip with her to West Virginia, he abruptly brought the discussion to a close.

Alexander was pleased, during the weeks which followed, at the fact that she made no further reference to iron. She went about the house gravely busy with its maintenance, as direct and efficient as he was in the larger realm. Almost her first act was to discharge the housekeeper. The woman came to Alexander, her fat face smeared with crying, and protested bitterly against the loss of a place she had filled since the house was roofed.

He was, of course, curt with her and ratified Gisela's decision; but privately he was annoyed. He had not even intended his wife to discharge the practical duties of living — thinking of her as a suave figure languidly moving from parlor to dining-room or boudoir; however, meeting her in a hall, energetically directing the dusting of a cornice, in a rare flash of perception he said nothing.

XII

HE would not admit, even to himself, that his material affairs were less satisfactory than they had been the year before, but such he vaguely knew was a fact. Speculation in Western government lands, large investments in transportation systems for the present fallow, had brought about a general condition of commercial unrest. Alexander Hulings felt this, not only by the delayed payment for shipments of metal but in the allied interests he had accumulated. Merchandise was often preceded by demands for payment; the business of a nail-manufactory he owned in Wheeling had been cut in half.

He could detect concern in the shrewd countenance and tones

of Samuel Cryble, a hard-headed Yankee from a Scotch Protestant valley in New Hampshire, who had risen to a position of his chief assistant and, in a small way, copartner. They sat together in the dingy office on the public road and silently, grimly, went over invoices and payments, debts and debtors. It was on such an occasion that Alexander had word of the death of Dr. Veneada.

Hulings's involuntary concern, the stirred memories of the dead man's liberal spirit and mind — he had been the only person Alexander Hulings could call friend — speedily gave place to a growing anxiety as to how Veneada might have left his affairs. He had been largely a careless man in practical matters.

Alexander had never satisfied the mortgage he had granted Veneada on the timber properties purchased with the other man's money. He had tried to settle the indebtedness when it had first fallen due, but the doctor had begged him to let the money remain as it was.

" I'll only throw it away on some confounded soft-witted scheme, Alex," he had insisted. " With you, I know where it is; it's a good investment."

Now Hulings recalled that the second extension had expired only a few weeks before Veneada's death, incurring an obligation the settlement of which he had been impatiently deferring until he saw the other.

He had had a feeling that Veneada, with no near or highly regarded relatives, would will him the timber about the valleys; yet he was anxious to have the thing settled. The Alexander Hulings Company was short of available funds. He returned to Eastlake for Veneada's funeral; and there, for the first time, he saw the cousins to whom the doctor had occasionally and lightly alluded. They were, he decided, a lean and rapacious crew.

He remained in Eastlake for another twenty-four hours, but was forced to leave with nothing discovered; and it was not until a week later that, again in his office, he learned that Veneada had made no will. This, it seemed, had been shown beyond any doubt. He rose, walked to a dusty window, and gazed out unseeingly at an eddy of dead leaves and dry metallic snow in a bleak November wind.

After a vague, disconcerted moment he shrewdly divined exactly

what would occur. He said nothing to Cryble, seated with his back
toward him; and even Gisela looked with silent inquiry at his absorption throughout supper. She never questioned him now about
any abstraction that might be concerned with affairs outside their
pleasant life together.

The inevitable letter at last arrived, announcing the fact that,
in a partition settlement of Veneada's estate by his heirs, it was
necessary to settle the expired mortgage. It could not have come,
he realized, at a more inconvenient time.

He was forced to discuss the position with Cryble; and the latter heard him to the end with a narrowed, searching vision.

"That money out of the business now might leave us on the
bank," he asserted. "As I see it, there's but one thing to do — go
over all the timber, judge what we actually will need for coaling,
buy that — or, if we must, put another mortgage on it — and let
the rest, a good two-thirds, go."

This, Alexander acknowledged to himself, was the logical if not
the only course. And then John Wooddrop would purchase the
remainder; he would have enough charcoal to keep up his local
industries beyond his own life and another. All his — Alexander's
— planning, aspirations, sacrifice, would have been for nothing.
He would never, like John Wooddrop, be a great industrial despot,
or command, as he had so often pictured, the iron situation of the
state. To do that he would have to control all the iron the fumes
of whose manufacture stained the sky for miles about Harmony.
If Wooddrop recovered an adequate fuel supply Alexander Hulings would never occupy more than a position of secondary importance.

There was a bare possibility of his retaining all the tracts again
by a second mortgage; but as he examined that, it sank from a
potentiality to a thing without substance. It would invite an investigation, a public gleaning of facts, that he must now avoid. His
pride could not contemplate the publication of the undeniable
truth — that what he had so laboriously built up stood on an in-
secure foundation.

"It is necessary," he said stiffly, "in order to realize on my calculations, that I continue to hold all the timber at present in my
name."

"And that's where you make a misjudgment," Cryble declared, equally blunt. "I can see clear enough that you are letting your personal feeling affect your business sense. There is room enough in Pennsylvania for both you and old Wooddrop. Anyhow, there's got to be somebody second in the parade, and that is a whole lot better than tail end."

Alexander Hulings nodded absently; Cryble's philosophy was correct for a clerk, an assistant, but Alexander Hulings felt the tyranny of a wider necessity. He wondered where he could get the money to satisfy the claim of the doctor's heirs. His manufacturing interests in West Virginia, depreciated as they were at present, would about cover the debt. Ordinarily they were worth a third more; and in ten years they would double in value. He relentlessly crushed all regret at parting with what was now his best property and promptly made arrangements to secure permanently the timberland.

Soon, he felt, John Wooddrop must feel the pinch of fuel shortage; and Alexander awaited such development with keen attention. As he had anticipated, when driving from the canal, he saw that the Blue Lump Furnace had gone out of blast, its workmen dispersed. Gisela, the day before, had been to see her father; and he was curious to hear what she might report. A feeling of coming triumph, of inevitable, worldly expansion, settled comfortably over him, and he regarded his wife pleasantly through a curtain of cigar smoke.

They were seated in a parlor, already shadowy in an early February dusk; coals were burning brightly in a polished open stove, by which Gisela was embroidering in brightly colored wool on a frame. She had the intent, placid expression of a woman absorbed in a small, familiar duty. As he watched her, Alexander Hulings's satisfaction deepened — young and fine and vigorous, she was preeminently a wife for his importance and position. She gazed at him vacantly, her eyes crinkled at the corners, her lips soundlessly counting stitches, and a faint smile rose to his lips.

He was anxious to hear what she might say about John Wooddrop, and yet a feeling of propriety restrained him from a direct question. He had not had a line, a word or message, from Wooddrop since he had married the other's daughter. The aging man, he knew, idolized Gisela; and her desertion — for so John Wood-drop would hold it — must have torn the ironmaster. She had, however, been justified in her choice, he contentedly continued his train of thought. Gisela had everything a woman could wish for. He had been a thoughtful husband. Her clothes, of the most beautiful texture and design, were pinned with jewels; her deftly moving fingers flashed with rings; the symbol of his success, his —

"My father looks badly, Alexander," she said suddenly. "I wish you would see him, and that he would talk to you. But you won't and he won't. He is very nearly as stubborn as yourself. I wish you could make a move; after all, you are younger. . . . But then, you would make each other furious in a second." She sighed deeply.

"Has he shown any desire to see me?"

"No," she admitted. "You must know he thinks you married me only to get his furnaces; he is ridiculous about it — just as if you needed any more! He has been fuming and planning a hundred things since his charcoal has been getting low."

She stopped and scrutinized her embroidery, a naïve pattern of rose and urn and motto. He drew a long breath; that was the first tangible indication he had had of the working-out of his planning, the justification of his sacrifice.

"I admire Father," she went on once more, conversationally; "my love for you hasn't blinded me to his qualities. He has a surprising courage and vigor for an — Why, he must be nearly seventy! And now he has the most extraordinary plan for what he calls 'getting the better of you.' He was as nice with me as possible, but I could see that he thinks you're lost this time. . . . No, the darker green. Alexander, don't you think the words would be sweet in magenta?"

"Well," he demanded harshly, leaning forward, "what is this plan?"

She looked up, surprised at his hard impatience.

"How queer you are! And that's your iron expression; you know it's expressly forbidden in the house, after hours. His plan? I'm certain there's no disloyalty in telling you. Isn't it mad, at his age? And it will cost him an outrageous amount of money. He is going to change the entire system of all his forges and furnaces. It seems stone coal has been found on his slopes; and he is going to blow in with that, and use a hot blast in his smelting."

Alexander Hulings sat rigid, motionless; the cigar in his hand cast up an unbroken blue ribbon of smoke. Twice he started to speak, to exclaim incredulously; but he uttered no sound. It seemed that all his planning had been utterly overthrown, ruined; in a manner which he — anyone — could not have foreseen. The blowing in of furnaces with hard coal had developed since his entrance into the iron field. It had not been generally declared successful; the pig produced had been so impure that, with working in an ordinary or even puddling forge, it had often to be subjected to a third, finery fire. But he had been conscious of a slow improvement in the newer working; he had vaguely acknowledged that some time anthracite would displace charcoal for manufacturing-purposes; in future years he might adopt it himself.

But John Wooddrop had done it before him; all the square miles of timber that he had acquired with such difficulty, that he had retained at the sacrifice of his best property, would be worthless. The greater part of it could not be teamed across Wooddrop's private roads or hauled advantageously over a hundred intervening streams and miles. It was all wasted, lapsed — his money, dreams!

"It will take over a year," she went on. "I don't understand it at all; but it seems that sending a hot blast into a furnace, instead of the cold, keeps the metal at a more even temperature. Father's so interested you'd think he was just starting out in life — though, really, he is an old man." She laughed. "Competition has been good for him."

All thrown away; in vain! Alexander Hulings wondered what acidulous comment Cryble would make. There were no coal deposits on his land, its nature forbade that; besides, he had no money to change the principal of his drafts. He gazed about at the luxury that surrounded Gisela and himself; there was no lien on the house, but there still remained some thousands of dollars to pay on the carpets and fixtures. His credit, at least, was unimpeachable; decorators, tradespeople of all sorts, had been glad to have him in their debt. But if any whisper of financial stringency escaped, a horde would be howling about his gate, demanding the settlement of their picayune accounts.

The twilight had deepened; the fire made a ruddy area in the gloom, into the heart of which he flung his cigar. His wife embroidered serenely. As he watched her, noting her firm, well-modeled features, realizing her utter unconsciousness of all that he essentially at that moment was, he felt a strange sensation of loneliness, of isolation.

Alexander Hulings had a sudden impulse to take her into his confidence, to explain everything to her — the disaster that had overtaken his project of ultimate power, the loss of the West Virginia interest, the tightness of money. He had a feeling that she would not be a negligible adviser — he had been a witness of her efficient management of his house — and he felt a craving for the sympathy she would instantly extend.

Alexander parted his lips to inform her of all that had occurred; but the habit of years, the innate fiber of his being, prevented. A wife, he reminded himself, a woman, had no part in the bitter struggle for existence; it was not becoming for her to mingle with the affairs of men. She should be purely a creature of elegance, of solace, and, dressed in India muslin or vaporous silk, ornament a divan, sing French or Italian songs at a piano. The other was manifestly improper.

This, illogically, made him irritable with Gisela; she appeared, contentedly sewing, a peculiarly useless appendage in his present stress of mind. He was glum again at supper, and afterwards retired into an office he had had arranged on the ground floor of the mansion. There he got out a number of papers, accounts, and passbooks; but he spent little actual time on them. He sat back in his chair, with his head sunk low, and mind thronged with memories of the past, of his long, uphill struggle against oblivion and ill health.

Veneada was gone; yes, and Conrad Wishon too — the supporters and confidants of his beginning. He himself was fifty years old. At that age a man should be firmly established, successful, and not deviled by a thousand unexpected mishaps. By fifty a man's mind should be reasonably at rest, his accomplishment and future secure; while there was nothing of security, but only combat, before him.

Wooddrop had been a rich man from the start, when he, Alexander Hulings, at the humiliating failure of the law, had had to face life with a few paltry hundreds. No wonder he had been obliged to contract debts, to enter into impossibly onerous agreements! Nothing but struggle ahead, a relentless continuation of the past years; and he had reached, passed, his prime!

There, for a day, he had thought himself safe, moving smoothly toward the highest pinnacles; when, without warning, at a few words casually pronounced over an embroidery frame, the entire fabric of his existence had been rent! It was not alone the fact of John Wooddrop's progressive spirit that he faced, but now a rapidly accumulating mass of difficulties. He was dully amazed at the treacherous shifting of life, at the unheralded change of apparently solid ground for quicksand.

XIII

THOUGH the industries centered about Tubal Cain were operated and apparently owned by the Alexander Hulings Iron Company, and Hulings was publicly regarded as their proprietor, in reality his hold on them was hardly more than nominal. At the erection of the furnaces and supplementary forges he had been obliged to grant such rebates to the Columbus Transportation interest in return for capital, he had contracted to supply them at a minimum price such a large proportion of his possible output, that, with continuous shifts, he was barely able to dispose advantageously of a sixth of the year's manufacture.

He had made such agreement confident that he would ultimately control the Wooddrop furnaces; when, doubling his resources, he would soon free himself from conditions imposed on him by an early lack of funds. Now it was at least problematic whether he would ever extend his power to include the older man's domain. His marriage with Gisela had only further separated them, hardening John Wooddrop's resolve that Hulings should never fire a hearth of his, a determination strengthened by the rebuilding of Wooddrop's furnaces for a stone-coal heat.

The widespread land speculation, together with the variability of currency, now began seriously to depress the country, and, more especially, Alexander Hulings. He went to Philadelphia, to Washington, for conferences; but returned to his mansion, to Gisela, in an increasing somberness of mood. All the expedients suggested,

the legalizing of foreign gold and silver, the gradual elimination
of the smaller state-bank notes, an extra coinage, one after another
failed in their purpose of stabilization; acute panic threatened.

Alexander was almost as spare of political comments to his wife
as he was of business discussion. That, too, he thought, did not
become the female poise. At times, bitter and brief, he condemned
the Administration; during dinner he all but startled a servant into
dropping a platter by the unexpected violence of a period hurled at
the successful attempts to destroy the national bank. And when,
as — he declared — a result of that, the state institutions refused
specie payment, and a flood of rapidly depreciating paper struck at
the base of commerce, Alexander gloomily informed Gisela that
the country was being sold for a barrel of hard cider.

He had, with difficulty, awhile before secured what had appeared
to be an advantageous order from Virginia; and, after extraordinary
effort, he had delivered the iron. But during the lapsing weeks,
when the state banks refused to circulate gold, the rate of exchange
for paper money fell so far that he lost all his calculated profit,
and a quarter of the labor as well. The money of other states depreciated in Pennsylvania a third. In addition to these things
Alexander commenced to have trouble with his workmen — wages,
too, had diminished, but their hours increased. Hulings, like other
commercial operators, issued printed money of his own, good at
the company store, useful in the immediate vicinity of Tubal Cain,
but valueless at any distance. Cryble, as he had anticipated, re-
counted the triumph of John Wooddrop.

"The old man can't be beat!" he asserted. "We've got a nice
little business here. Tailed on to Wooddrop's, we should do good;
but you are running it into an iron wall. You ain't content with
enough."

Cryble was apparently unconscious of the dangerous glitter that
had come into Hulings's gaze. Alexander listened quietly until the
other had finished, and then curtly released him from all connection or obligation with himself. James Cryble was undisturbed.

"I was thinking myself about a move," he declared. "This concern is pointed bull-headed onto destruction! You're a sort of
peacock," he further told Hulings; "you can't do much besides
spread and admire your own feathers. But you'll get learned."

Alexander made no reply, and the other shortly after disappeared from his horizon. Cryble, he thought contemptuously, a man of routine, had no more salience than one of the thousands of identical iron pigs run from Glory Furnace. There commenced now a period of toil more bitter, more relentless, than his first experience in the valleys; by constant effort he was able to keep just ahead of the unprofitable labor for the Columbus Railroad. The number of workmen grew constantly smaller, vaguely contaminated by the unsettled period, while his necessity increased. Again and again he longed to strip off his coat and superfluous linen and join the men working the metal in the hearths; he would have felt better if he could have had actual part in rolling and stamping the pig-beds, or even in dumping materials into the furnace stack.

As it was, consumed by a fever of impatience and concern, the manufacture of his iron seemed to require months between the crude ore and the finished bars and blooms. He detected a growing impotence among laborers, and told them of it with an unsparing, lashing tongue. A general hatred of him again flashed into being; but it was still accompanied by a respect amounting to fear.

He was approached, at a climax of misfortune, by representatives of the railroad. They sat, their solid faces rimmed in whiskers, and smooth fingers playing with portentous seals, in his office, while one of their number expounded their presence.

"It's only reasonable, Hulings," he stated suavely, "that one man can't stand up against present conditions. Big concerns all along the coast have gone to wreck. You are an exceptional man, one we would be glad to have in our company; and that, briefly, is what we have come to persuade you to do — to merge your activities here into the railroad; to get on the locomotive with us.

"Long ago you were shrewd enough to see that steam transportation was the coming power; and now — though for the moment we seem overextended — your judgment has been approved. It only remains for you to ratify your perspicacity and definitely join us. We can, I think, offer you something in full keeping with your ability — a vice-presidency of the reorganized company and a substantial personal interest."

Alexander attended the speaker half absently, though he realized that probably he had arrived at the crisis of his life, his career; his attention was rapt away by dreams, memories. He saw himself again, saturated with sweat and grime, sitting with Conrad Wishon against the little house where they slept, and planning his empire of iron; he thought again, even further back, of the slough of anguish from which he had won free; and persistently, woven through the entire texture, was his vision of iron and of pride. He had sworn to himself that he would build success from the metal for which he had such a personal affinity; that he would be known as the great ironmaster of Pennsylvania; and that unsubstantial ideal, tottering now on the edge of calamity, was still more potent, more persuasive, than the concrete and definite promises of safety, prosperity, the implied threat, of the established power before him.

He had an objective comprehension of the peril of his position, his negligible funds and decreasing credit, the men with accounts clamoring for settlement; he thought absurdly of a tessellated floor he had lately laid in his vestibule, the mingled aggression and uncertainty on every hand; but his subjective self rose up and dominated him. Louder than any warning was the cry, the necessity, for the vindication of the triumphant Alexander Hulings, perpetually rising higher. To surrender his iron now, to enter, a mere individual, however elevated, into a corporation, was to confess himself defeated, to tear down all the radiant images from which he had derived his reason for being.

Hulings thought momentarily of Gisela; he had, it might be, no right to involve her blindly in a downfall of the extent that now confronted him. However, he relentlessly repressed this consideration, together with a vague idea of discussing with her their — his — position. His was the judgment, the responsibility, that sustained them; she was only an ornament, the singer of little airs in the evening; the decoration, in embroidery and gilt flowers, of his table.

He thanked the speaker adequately and firmly voiced his refusal of the offer.

"I am an iron man," he stated in partial explanation; "as that I must sink or swim."

"Iron," another commented dryly, "is not noted for its floating-properties."

" I am disappointed, Hulings," the first speaker acknowledged; " yes, and surprised. Of course, we are not ignorant of the condition here; and you must also know that the company would like to control your furnaces. We have offered you the palm, and you must be willing to meet the consequences of your refusal. As I said, we'd like to have you too — energetic and capable; for, as the Bible reads, ' He that is not for me — ' "

When they had gone, driving in a local surrey back to the canal, Alexander Hulings secured his hat and, dismissing his carriage, walked slowly down to Tubal Cain Forge. An increasing roar and uprush of sooty smoke and sparks marked the activity within; the water poured dripping over the water-wheel, through the channel he had cleared, those long years back, with bleeding hands; strange men stood at the shed opening; but the stream and its banks were exactly as he had first seen them.

His life seemed to have swung in a circle from that former day to now — from dilemma to dilemma. What, after all, did he have, except an increasing weariness of years, that he had lacked then? He thought, with a grim smile, that he might find in his safe nine hundred dollars. All his other possessions suddenly took on an unsubstantial aspect; they were his; they existed; yet they eluded his realization, brought him none of the satisfaction of an object, a fact, solidly grasped.

His name, as he had planned, had grown considerable in men's ears, its murmur rose like an incense to his pride; yet, underneath, it gave him no satisfaction. It gave him no satisfaction because it carried no conviction of security, no personal corroboration of the mere sound.

What, he now saw, he had struggled to establish was a good opinion in his own eyes, that actually he was a strong man; the outer response, upon which he had been intent was unimportant compared with the other. And in the latter he had not moved forward a step; if he had widened his sphere, he had tacitly accepted heavier responsibilities — undischarged. A flicker hammered on a resonant limb, just as it had long ago. How vast, eternal, life was! Conrad Wishon, with his great arched chest and knotted arms, had gone into the obliterating earth.

Death was preferable to ruin, to the concerted gibes of little men, the forgetfulness of big; once, looking at his graying countenance in a mirror, he had realized that it would be easier for him to die than fail. Then, with a sudden twisting of his thoughts, his mind rested on Gisela, his wife. He told himself, with justifiable pride, that she had been content with him; Gisela was not an ordinary woman, she had not married him for a cheap and material reason, and whatever admiration she had had in the beginning he had been able to preserve. Alexander Hulings was certain of that; he saw it in a hundred little acts of her daily living. She thought he was a big man, a successful man; he had not permitted a whisper of his difficulties to fret her serenity, and, by heaven, he thought with a sharp return of his native vigor, she never should hear of them; he would stifle them quietly, alone, one by one.

The idea of death, self-inflicted, a flaccid surrender, receded before the flood of his returning pride, confidence. Age, he exulted, had not impaired him; if his importance was now but a shell, he would fill it with the iron of actuality; he would place himself and Gisela forever beyond the threats of accident and circumstance.

XIV

GISELA had been to Philadelphia, and she was unusually gay, communicative; she was dressed in lavender and rose net, with black velvet, and about her throat she wore a sparkling pendant that he had never before noticed.

" I hope you'll like it," she said, fingering the diamonds; " the shape was so graceful that I couldn't resist. And you are so generous, Alexander! "

He was always glad, he told her briefly, to see her in new and fine adornments. He repressed an involuntary grimace at the thought of the probable cost of the ornament. She could hardly have chosen a worse time in which to buy jewels. Not only his own situation but the whole time was one for retrenchment. The impulse to tell her this was speedily lost in his pride of her really splendid appearance. He himself had commanded her to purchase whatever she fancied; he had explained that that — the domain of beauty — was exclusively hers; and it was impossible to complain at her first considerable essay.

Here his feeling was rooted in the deepest part of his being —
he was, after all, twenty-five years older than Gisela; and, as if in
a species of reparation for the discrepancy, he owed her all the
luxury possible. This he had promised her — and himself; and an
inability to provide gowns and necklaces and gewgaws was a most
humiliating confession of failure, a failure unendurable to him on
every plane. Alexander, too, had told her finally that she had no
place in his affairs of business; and after that he could not very
well burden her with the details of a stupid — and momentary —
need for economy.

"I got a bouquet-holder," she continued — "sweet, in chased
gold, with garnets. And a new prayer-book; you must see that —
bound in carved ivory, from Paris." He listened with a stolid face
to her recital, vaguely wondering how much she had spent; how
long the jeweler would wait for settlement. "And there was a wonderful Swiss watch I thought of for you; it rang the hours and — "

"That," he said hastily, "I don't need. I have two excellent
watches."

"But you are always complaining!" she returned, mildly surprised. "I didn't get it, but told the man to put it aside. I'll write
if you don't want it."

"Do!"

Suddenly he felt weary, a twinge of sciatica shot through his
hip; he must keep out of the damp cast-houses, with their expanses
of wet sand. But actually he was as good as he had ever been; better,
for he now saw clearly what he must accomplish, satisfy. The present national crisis would lift; there was already a talk of the resumption of gold payment by the state banks; and the collapse of a firm
associated with him in a rolling mill had thrown its control into
his hands. Steam power had already been connected, and he could
supply the railroad corporation with a certain number of finished
rails direct, adding slightly to his profit.

The smallest gain was important, a scrap of wood to keep him
temporarily afloat on disturbed waters; he saw before him, close
by, solid land. But meantime more than one metaphorical wave
swept over his head, leaving him shaken. The Columbus people
returned a shipment of iron, with the complaint that it was below
the grade useful for their purpose. He inspected the rejected bars

with his head forgeman, and they were unable to discover the deficiency.

"That's good puddled iron," the forgeman asserted. "I saw the pig myself, and it could have been wrought on a cold anvil. Do they expect blister steel?"

Alexander Hulings kept to himself the knowledge that this was the beginning of an assault upon his integrity, his name and possessions. At court he could have established the quality of his iron, forced the railroad to accept it within their contract. But he had no money to expend on tedious legal processes; and they knew that in the city.

"We can get a better price for it than theirs," he commented.

The difficulty lay in supplying a stated amount. The forgeman profanely explained something of his troubles with labor:

"I get my own anvils busy, and perhaps the furnaces running out the metal, when the damn charcoal-burners lay down. That's the hardest crowd of niggers and drunken Dutch that ever cut wood! It's never a week but one is shot or has his throat cut; and some of the coal they send down looks like pine ash."

At their home he found Gisela with the draperies of the dining-room in a silken pile on the carpet.

"I'm tired of this room," she announced; "it's too — too heavy. Those plum-colored curtains almost made me weep. Now what do you think of this? A white marble mantel in place of that black, and a mirror with wreaths of colored gilt. An apple-green carpet, with pink satin at the windows, draped with India muslin, and gold cords, and Spanish mahogany furniture — that's so much lighter than this." She studied the interior seriously. "Less ormolu and more crystal," Gisela decided.

He said nothing; he had given her the house — it was her world, to do with as she pleased. The decorating of the dining-room had cost over three thousand dollars. "And a big Chinese cage, full of finches and rollers." He got a certain grim entertainment from the accumulating details of her planning. Certainly it would be impossible to find anywhere a wife more unconscious of the sordid details of commerce. Gisela was his ideal of elegance and propriety.

Nevertheless, he felt an odd, illogical loneliness fastening on him here, where he had thought to be most completely at ease. His mind, filled with the practical difficulties of tomorrow, rebelled against the restriction placed on it; he wanted to unburden himself of his troubles, to lighten them with discussion, give them the support of another's belief in his ability, his destiny; but, with Cryble gone, and his wife dedicated to purely æsthetic considerations, there was no one to whom he dared confess his growing predicament.

Marriage, he even thought, was something of a failure — burdensome. Gisela, in the exclusive role of a finch in an elaborate cage, annoyed him now by her continual chirping song. He thought disparagingly of all women; light creatures fashioned of silks and perfume, extravagant. After supper he went directly into his office room.

There, conversely, he was irritated with the accounts spread perpetually before him, the announcements of fresh failures, depreciated money and bonds. He tramped back and across the limited space, longing to share Gisela's tranquillity. In a manner he had been unjust to her; he had seen, noted, other women, his own was vastly superior. Particularly she was truthful, there was no subterfuge, pretense, about her; and she had courage, but — John Wooddrop's daughter — she would have. Alexander Hulings thought of the old man with reluctant admiration; he was strong; though he, Hulings, was stronger. He would, he calculated brutally, last longer; and in the end he would, must win.

XV

YET adverse circumstances closed about him like the stone walls of a cell. The slightest error or miscalculation would bring ruin crashing about his pretensions. It was now principally his commanding interest in the rolling-mill that kept him going; his forges and furnaces, short of workmen, were steadily losing ground. And, though summer was at an end, Gisela chose this time to divert the labor of a considerable shift to the setting of new masoned flower-beds. He watched the operation somberly from the entrance of the conservatory attached, like a particolored fantastic glass bubble, to his house.

"It won't take them over four or five days," Gisela said at his shoulder.

He positively struggled to condemn her foolish waste, but not a word escaped the barrier of his pride. Once started, he would have to explain the entire precarious situation to her — the labor shortage, the dangerous tension of his credit, the inimical powers anxious to absorb his industry, the fact that he was a potential failure. He wished, at any sacrifice, to keep the last from his wife, convinced as she was of his success.

Surely in a few months the sky would clear and he would triumph — this time solidly, beyond all assault. He rehearsed this without his usual conviction; the letters from the Columbus System were growing more dictatorial; he had received a covertly insolent communication from an insignificant tool-works.

The Columbus Railroad had written that they were now able to secure a rail, satisfactory for their purpose and tests, at a considerably lower figure than he demanded. This puzzled him; knowing intimately the whole iron situation, he realized that it was impossible for any firm to make a legitimate profit at a smaller price than his. When he learned that the new contracts were being met by John Wooddrop his face was ugly — the older man, at a sacrifice, was deliberately, coldly hastening his downfall. But he abandoned this unpleasant thought when, later, in a circuitous manner, he learned that the Wooddrop rolling-mills, situated ten miles south of the valleys, were running on a new, secret, and vastly economical system.

He looked up, his brow scored, from his desk. Conrad Wishon's son, a huge bulk, was looking out through a window, completely blocking off the light. Alexander Hulings said:

"I'd give a thousand dollars to know something of that process!"

The second Wishon turned on his heel.

"What's that?" he demanded.

Alexander told him. The other was thoughtful.

"I wouldn't have a chance hereabouts," he pronounced; "but I'm not so well known at the South Mills. Perhaps —"

Hulings repeated moodily:

"A thousand dollars!"

He was skeptical of Wishon's ability to learn anything of the

new milling. It had to do obscurely with the return of the bars
through the rollers without having to be constantly re-fed. Such
a scheme would cut forty men from the pay-books.

A black depression settled over him, as tangible as soot; he felt
physically weary, sick. Alexander fingered an accumulation of bills;
one, he saw, was from the Philadelphia jeweler — a fresh extravagance of Gisela's. But glancing hastily at its items, he was puzzled
— "Resetting diamond necklace in pendant, fifty-five dollars." It
was addressed to Gisela; its presence here, on his desk, was an error.
After a momentary, fretful conjecturing he dismissed it from his
thoughts; women were beyond comprehension.

He had now, from the sciatica, a permanent limp; a cane had
ceased to be merely ornamental. A hundred small details, falling
wrongly, rubbed on the raw of his dejection. The feeling of loneliness deepened about him. As the sun sank, throwing up over the
world a last dripping bath of red-gold light, he returned slowly to
his house. Each window facing him flashed in a broad sheet of
blinding radiance, a callous illumination. A peacock, another of
Gisela's late extravagances, spread a burnished metallic plumage,
with a grating cry.

But the hall was pleasantly still, dim. He stood for a long minute,
resting, drawing deep breaths of quietude. Every light was lit in
the reception-room, where he found his wife, seated, in burnt-
orange satin and bare powdered shoulders, amid a glitter of glass
prisms, gilt, and marble. Her very brilliance, her gay, careless smile,
added to his fatigue. Suddenly he thought: " I am an old man with
a young wife!" His dejection changed to bitterness. Gisela said:

" I hope you like my dress; it came from Vienna, and was wick-
edly expensive. Really I ought to wear sapphires with it; I rather
think I'll get them. Diamonds look like glass with orange."

Her words were lost in a confused blurring of his mind. He
swayed slightly. Suddenly the whole circumstance of his living, of
Gisela's babbling, became unendurable. His pride, his conception
of a wife set in luxury above the facts of existence, a mere symbol
of his importance and wealth, crumbled, stripping him of all pretense. He raised a thin, darkly veined and trembling hand.

" Sapphires! " he cried shrilly. " Why, next week we'll be lucky
if we can buy bread! I am practically smashed — smashed at fifty

and more. This house that you fix up and fix up, that dress and the diamonds and clocks, and — and — They are not real; in no time they'll go, fade away like smoke, leave me — us — bare. For five years I have been fighting for my life; and now I'm losing; everything is slipping out of my hands. While you talk of sapphires; you build bedamned gardens with the men I need to keep us alive; and peacocks and — "

He stopped as abruptly as he had commenced, flooded with shame at the fact that he stood before her self-condemned; that she, Gisela, saw in him a sham. He miserably avoided her gaze and was surprised when she spoke, in an unperturbed warm voice:

"Sit down, Alexander; you are tired and excited." She rose and, with a steady hand, forced him into a chair. "I am glad that, at last, you told me this," she continued evenly; "for now we can face it, arrange, together. It can't be so bad as you suppose. Naturally you are worn, but you are a very strong man; I have great faith in you."

He gazed at her in growing wonderment; here was an entirely different woman from the Gisela who had chattered about Viennese gowns. He noted, with a renewed sense of security, the firmness of her lips, her level, unfaltering gaze. He had had an unformulated conviction that in crises women wrung their hands, fainted. She gesticulated toward the elaborate furnishings, including her satin array:

"However it may have seemed, I don't care a bawbee about these things! I never did; and it always annoyed Father as it annoyed you. I am sorry, if you like. But at last we understand each other. We can live, fight, intelligently."

Gisela knew; regret, pretense, were useless now, and, curiously, in that knowledge she seemed to come closer to him; he had a new sense of her actuality. Yet that evening she not only refused to listen to any serious statements, but played and sang the most frothy Italian songs.

XVI

ON the day following he felt generally upheld. His old sense of power, of domination, his contempt for petty men and competitions, returned. He determined to go to Pittsburgh himself and study the labor conditions; perhaps secure a fresh, advantageous connection. He was planning the details of this when a man he knew only slightly, by sight, as connected with the coaling, swung unceremoniously into his office.

" Mr. Hulings, sir," he stammered, " Wishon has been shot — killed."

" Impossible! " he ejaculated.

But instantly Alexander Hulings was convinced that it was true. His momentary confidence, vigor, receded before the piling adversities, bent apparently upon his destruction.

" Yes, his body is coming up now. All we know is a watchman saw him standing at a window of the Wooddrop mills after hours and shot him for trespassing — spying on their process."

Alexander's first thought was not of the man just killed, but of old Conrad, longer dead. He had been a faithful, an invaluable assistant; without him Hulings would never have risen. And now he had been the cause of his son's death! A sharp regret seized him, but he grew rapidly calm before the excitement of the inferior before him.

" Keep this quiet for the moment," he commanded.

" Quiet! " the other cried. " It's already known all over the mountains. Wishon's workmen have quit coaling. They swear they will get Wooddrop's superintendent and hang him."

" Where are they? " Hulings demanded.

The other became sullen, uncommunicative. " We want to pay them for this," he muttered. " No better man lived than Wishon."

Alexander at once told his wife of the accident. She was still surprisingly contained, though pale. " Our men must be controlled," she asserted. " No further horrors! "

Her attitude, he thought, was exactly right; it was neither callous nor hysterical. He was willing to assume the burden of his responsibilities. It was an ugly, a regrettable occurrence; but men had been killed in his employ before — not a week passed without an accident, and if he lost his head in a welter of sentimentality he might as well shut down at once. Some men lived, struggled upward. It was a primary part of the business of success to keep alive.

Gisela had correctly found the real danger of their position — the thing must go no further. The sky had clouded and a cold rain commenced to fall. He could, however, pay no attention to the weather; he rose from a partial dinner and departed on a score of complicated and difficult errands. But his main concern, to locate and dominate the mobbing charcoal-burners, evaded his straining efforts. He caught rumors, echoed threats; once he almost overtook them, yet, with scouts placed, they avoided him.

He sent an urgent message to John Wooddrop, and, uncertain of its delivery, himself drove in search of him; but Wooddrop was out somewhere in his wide holdings; the superintendent could not be located. A sense of an implacable fatality hung over him; every chance turned against him, mocked the insecurity of his boasted position, deepened the abyss waiting for his inevitable fall.

He returned finally, baffled and weary, to his house, yet still tense with the spirit of angry combat. A species of fatalism now enveloped him in the conviction that he had reached the zenith of his misfortunes; if he could survive the present day . . . A stableman met him at the veranda.

" Mrs. Hulings has gone," the servant told him. " A man came looking for you. It seems they had Wooddrop's manager back in the mills tract and were going to string him up. But you couldn't be found. Mrs. Hulings, she went to stop it."

An inky cloud floated nauseously before his eyes — not himself alone, but Gisela dragged into the dark whirlpool gathered about his destiny! He was momentarily stunned, with twitching hands and a riven, haggard face, remembering the sodden brutality of the men he had seen in the smoke of charring, isolated stacks; and then a sharp energy seized him.

" How long back? " Hulings demanded.

" An hour or more, perhaps a couple."

Alexander raged at the mischance that had sent Gisela on such an errand. Nothing, he felt, with Wooddrop's manager secured, would halt the charcoal-burners' revenge of Wishon's death. The rain now beat down in a heavy diagonal pour, and twilight was gathering.

" We must go at once for Mrs. Hulings," he said. Then he saw Gisela approaching, accompanied by a small knot of men. She walked directly up to him, her crinoline soggy with rain, her hair plastered on her brow; but her deathly pallor drove all else from

his observation. She shuddered slowly, her skirt dripping ceaselessly about her on the sod.

" I was too late! " she said in a dull voice. " They had done it! "
She covered her eyes, moved back from the men beside her, from
him. " Swinging a little . . . all alone! So sudden — there, before
me! " A violent shivering seized her.

" Come," Alexander Hulings said hoarsely; " you must get out
of the wet. Warm things. Immediately! "

He called imperatively for Gisela's maid, and together they assisted her up to her room. There Gisela had a long, violent chill;
and he sent a wagon for the doctor at Harmony.

The doctor arrived, disappeared above; but, half an hour later,
he would say little. Alexander Hulings commanded him to remain
in the house. The lines deepened momentarily on Hulings's countenance; he saw himself unexpectedly in a shadowy pier-glass and
stood for a long while subconsciously surveying the lean, grizzled
countenance that followed his gaze out of the immaterial depths.
" Alexander Hulings," he said aloud, in a tormented mockery; " the
master of — of life! "

He was busy with the local marshal when the doctor summoned
him from the office.

" Your wife," the other curtly informed him, " has developed
pneumonia."

Hulings steadied himself with a hand against a wall.

" Pneumonia! " he repeated, to no one in particular. " Send again
for John Wooddrop."

He was seated, a narrow, rigid figure, waiting for the older man,
in the midst of gorgeous upholstery. Two facts hammered with
equal persistence on his numbed brain: one that all his projects,
his dream of power, of iron, now approached ruin, and the other
that Gisela had pneumonia. It was a dreadful thing that she had
come on in the mills tract! The Columbus System must triumphantly absorb all that he had, that he was to be. Gisela had been
chilled to the bone; pneumonia! It became difficult and then impossible to distinguish one from the other — Gisela and the iron
were inexplicably welded in the poised catastrophe of his ambition.

Alexander Hulings rose, his thin lips pinched, his eyes mere
sparks, his body tense, as if he were confronting the embodied force

that had checked him. He stood upright, so still that he might have been cast in the metal that had formed his vision of power, holding an unquailing mien. His inextinguishable pride cloaked him in a final contempt for all that life, that fate, might do. Then his rigidity was assaulted by John Wooddrop's heavy and hurried entrance into the room.

Hulings briefly repeated the doctor's pronouncement. Wooddrop's face was darkly pouched, his unremoved hat a mere wet film, and he left muddy exact footprints wherever he stepped on the velvet carpet.

" By heaven! " he quavered, his arms upraised. " If between us we have killed her — " His voice abruptly expired.

As Alexander Hulings watched him the old man's countenance grew livid, his jaw dropped; he was at the point of falling. He gasped, his hands beating the air; then the unnatural color receded, words became distinguishable: " Gisela! . . . I'd never forgive! Hellish! " It was as if Death had touched John Wooddrop on the shoulder, dragging a scarifying hand across his face, and then briefly, capriciously withdrawn.

" Hulings! Hulings," he articulated, sinking weakly on a chair, " we must save her. And, anyhow, God knows we were blind! " He peered out of suffused rheumy eyes at Alexander, appalling in his sudden disintegration under shock and the weight of his years. " I'm done! " he said tremulously. " And there's a good bit to see to — patent lawyer tomorrow, and English shipments. Swore I'd keep you from it "; he held out a hand; " but there's Gisela, brought down between us now, and — and iron's colder than a daughter, a wife. We'd best cover up the past quick as we can! "

At the instant of grasping John Wooddrop's hand Alexander Hulings's inchoate emotion shifted to a vast realization, blotting out all else from his mind. In the control of the immense Wooddrop resources he was beyond, above, all competition, all danger. What he had fought for, persistently dreamed, had at last come about — he was the greatest ironmaster of the state!

⊷§ *George S. Kaufman* §⊷
⊷§ *Morrie Ryskind* §⊷
⊷§ *Ira Gershwin* §⊷

OF THEE I SING

FOREWORD

IN *Of Thee I Sing* I believe that we discover the happiest and most
successful native music-stage lampoon that has thus far come the
way of the American theater. With it, further, I believe that American musical comedy enters at length upon a new, original, and
independent lease of life. That its genealogical tree betrays traces
of the plum juices of the late W. S. Gilbert and certain minor
blood strains of the later Charles H. Hoyt is more or less evident,
but, once the fact is allowed, it may quickly be dismissed, for the
exhibit is fully able to stand on its own feet and to offer itself in
its own authentic light.

The reading of a music-show script imposes upon the library
armchair a somewhat different attitude from the reading of a dramatic play. That difference is the same difference that attaches to
the mood of theater-going in the instance of a music-show on the

one hand and a dramatic play on the other. In the case of the music-show, a volitional predisposition to light pleasure and even gayety, a humor for intellect on the loose, a leaning to confetti criticism, are essential. The music-show is not for pundits in their punditical moments but for pundits, if at all, in such rare moments as they think and argue with laughter. I accordingly invite the more sober species of reader to engage this script with his top hat cocked saucily over his mind, with his ear filled with the hint of gay tunes, and with his eye made merry by the imagined picture of all the relevant and appropriate clowns in the persons of actors, of madly painted canvas, and of appetizing femininity. Only by so approaching it will he get from it what its authors would wish him to.

A glance backward over the modern American musical stage will disclose it to have followed, with little deviation, routine and rusty tracks. In endless succession that stage has given us the so-called romantic musical comedies with their proud princesses in love with humble naval lieutenants and their humble slaveys cinderellaed by proud princes, the revues with their vaudeville comedians and peafowl ladies, the shows laboriously manufactured out of dull comedies previously displayed on the legitimate stage, and the German and Austrian importations adapted to what has been believed to be the American taste by the insertion into their books of a sufficient number of facetious allusions to Congress, Yonkers, and Mrs. Aimée Semple McPherson. Here and there, there has, occasionally, been a mild effort to break away from the established patterns, but the effort has been so mild that it has come to naught, and what has resulted has been, at bottom, much the same old thing. It remained for the authors of *Of Thee I Sing* two years ago to introduce into this swamp, in the show called *Strike Up the Band*, the novel bloom that paved the way for the fuller and more highly perfumed sardonic hothouse that the present show is.

In *Strike Up the Band* a sound brand of broad satire was applied to the American music-show stage of our time. That broad satire, smeared generously upon a slapstick, is now applied again, and very much more thwackingly and amusingly, in *Of Thee I Sing*. Pour a couple of cocktails into your sobriety and turn the page.

GEORGE JEAN NATHAN

Of Thee I Sing was produced by Sam H. Harris at the Music Box, New York, on Saturday night, December 26, 1931, with the following cast:

LOUIS LIPPMAN	SAM MANN
FRANCIS X. GILHOOLEY	HAROLD MOFFET
MAID	VIVIAN BARRY
MATTHEW ARNOLD FULTON	DUDLEY CLEMENTS
SENATOR ROBERT E. LYONS	GEORGE E. MACK
SENATOR CARVER JONES	EDWARD H. ROBINS
ALEXANDER THROTTLEBOTTOM	VICTOR MOORE
JOHN P. WINTERGREEN	WILLIAM GAXTON
SAM JENKINS	GEORGE MURPHY
DIANA DEVEREAUX	GRACE BRINKLEY
MARY TURNER	LOIS MORAN
MISS BENSON	JUNE O'DEA
VLADIMIR VIDOVITCH	TOM DRAAK
YUSSEF YUSSEVITCH	SULO HEVONPAA
THE CHIEF JUSTICE	RALPH RIGGS
SCRUBWOMAN	LESLIE BINGHAM
THE FRENCH AMBASSADOR	FLORENZ AMES
SENATE CLERK	MARTIN LEROY
GUIDE	RALPH RIGGS

Photographers, Policemen, Supreme Court Justices, Secretaries, Sightseers, Newspapermen, Senators, Flunkies, Guests, etc.:

The Misses Ruth Adams, Olgene Foster, Peggy Greene, Yvonne Gray, Billie Seward, Grenna Sloan, Adele Smith, Jessica Worth, Kathleen Ayres, Bobbie Brodsley, Martha Carroll, Mary Carroll, Ann Ecklund, Virginia Franck, Dorothy Graves, Georgette Lampsi, Terry Lawlor, Lillian Lorray, Martha Maggard, Mary Mascher, Anita Pam, Barbara Smith, Baun Sturtz, Peggy Thomas, Patricia Whitney.

The Messrs. Robert Burton, Ray Clark, Charles Conklin, Frank Erickson, Jack Fago, Frank Gagen, Hazzard Newberry, Jack Ray, Bruce Barclay, Tom Curley, Leon Dunar, Michael Forbes, David Lawrence, Charles McClelland, Richard Neely, John McCahill.

The Jack Linton Band: Jack Linton, Dave Allman, Charles Bennett, Walter Hinger, Milton Hollander, Frank Miller, Pete Shance, Jake Vander Meulen.

THE SCENES

ACT I
{
MAIN STREET
A HOTEL ROOM
ATLANTIC CITY
MADISON SQUARE GARDEN
ELECTION NIGHT
WASHINGTON
}

ACT II
{
THE WHITE HOUSE
THE CAPITOL
THE SENATE
AGAIN THE WHITE HOUSE
THE YELLOW ROOM
}

ACT I

SCENE 1: *Any city in America — with a political parade in progress. The marchers, with their torchlights and banners, move against a shadowy background of skyscrapers, churches, and — almost certainly — speakeasies. Across this background is flung a huge election banner, on which are gargantuan reproductions of the faces of the party's candidates. High-lit and prominent is the party battle-cry:*

FOR PRESIDENT:
JOHN P. WINTERGREEN

The name of the Vice-presidential candidate, however, is lost in shadow. As for the countenances of the candidates, it is a little hard to pick them out in the general blur, and the chances are that that's a break for the party.

The procession shambles across the scene, singing as it goes. The song is a combination of all the campaign tunes of the past, into most of which the recurrent phrase: "Wintergreen for President," seems mysteriously to fit. This brilliant slogan is repeated on many of the banners, with "Win With Wintergreen" another favorite. On other banners are such sentiments as:

"Vote for Prosperity and See What You Get."
"A Vote for Wintergreen Is a Vote for Wintergreen."
"Hawaii Wants Wintergreen."
"Turn the Reformers Out."
"Wintergreen — a Man's Man's Man."
"Wintergreen — the Flavor Lasts."
"He Kept Us Out of Jail."
"Even Your Dog Loves John P. Wintergreen."
"The Full Dinner Jacket."

As the procession wends its way a line or two of lyric emerges from the general singing:

"He's the man the people choose —
Loves the Irish and the Jews."

It passes on into darkness, band playing, banners flying, torches flaring.

Scene 2: *A room in a hotel, and a pretty shabby room it is. It is, however, the temporary headquarters of those mysterious politicians who make up the National Campaign Committee. It's not that they couldn't afford a better hotel, for the party is notoriously rich, but somehow this room seems thoroughly in keeping with the men who occupy it.*

Two of the committeemen are present when the curtain goes up. Their names are Francis X. Gilhooley and Louis Lippman, and they are, of course, representatives of those two races which the candidate so loves. Mr. Gilhooley sits in his shirtsleeves at a small table, and between drinks of White Rock — well, maybe not White Rock — he is trying to work out a game of solitaire. Mr. Lippman, also coatless, sprawls on the bed with a newspaper.

The room is thick with cigar smoke.

Mr. Lippman yawns, stretches, and puts down his newspaper. There comes a knock on the door.

LIPPMAN. Come in.
[*A Chambermaid enters, carrying towels.*]
CHAMBERMAID. I brought you some towels. [*To Gilhooley, as she passes him.*] I'm just going to the bathroom.

GILHOOLEY. First door to the left.

[*The Maid disappears into the bathroom as the telephone rings.*]

LIPPMAN [*at the phone*]. So what? . . . Who? . . . What's his name? . . . Throttle *what?* . . . Must have the wrong room. This is the National Committee . . . I say this is the National Campaign Committee. [*Hangs up.*] Some fellow downstairs.

[*The Chambermaid re-enters.*]

GILHOOLEY. Did you find it?

CHAMBERMAID. Shall I turn the bed down now?

LIPPMAN. Sure. Go ahead.

CHAMBERMAID. I can't turn it down unless you get off it.

LIPPMAN. Oh, then the hell with it!

CHAMBERMAID. Yes, sir. Shall I come back later?

LIPPMAN. Why not?

CHAMBERMAID. Yes, sir.

[*She goes.*]

LIPPMAN. Nice girl.

GILHOOLEY [*rising and stretching*]. Ho-hum! Certainly is great to take it easy for a while.

LIPPMAN. Yep. It was a tough convention, all right.

GILHOOLEY. I'll say it was tough. Sixty-three ballots.

LIPPMAN. But we put the ticket over. That's the big thing.

GILHOOLEY. Well, there's still the election. I don't mind telling you I'm a little bit worried.

LIPPMAN. Say, we never lost an election yet, and we've had a lot worse candidates.

GILHOOLEY. It ain't just the candidates — it's the whole party.

LIPPMAN. What do you mean, the whole party?

GILHOOLEY. Mm. I think maybe they're kind of getting wise to us.

LIPPMAN. Say! If they haven't got wise to us in forty years, they'll never get wise.

GILHOOLEY. Yah, but I don't like the way they've been acting lately. You know, we never should have sold Rhode Island.

LIPPMAN. We've got a great ticket, haven't we? For President: John P. Wintergreen. He even *sounds* like a President.

GILHOOLEY. That's why we picked him.

LIPPMAN. And for Vice-president — [*Hesitates.*] — what's the name of that fellow we nominated for Vice-president?

GILHOOLEY. Ah — Pitts, wasn't it?

LIPPMAN. No, no — it was a longer name.

GILHOOLEY. Barbinelli?

LIPPMAN. No.

GILHOOLEY. Well, that's longer.

LIPPMAN. You're a hell of a National Committeeman. Don't even know the name of the Vice-president we nominated.

> [*Matthew Arnold Fulton enters. Mr. Fulton owns a string of newspapers, and he is not without power in this land of ours. There are the customary greetings.*]

LIPPMAN. Hey, Fulton! To decide a bet: what's the name of that fellow we nominated for Vice-president?

FULTON. What? Oh — Schaeffer, wasn't it?

GILHOOLEY. That's right!

LIPPMAN. No, no! Schaeffer turned it down.

FULTON. Oh, yes.

GILHOOLEY. Wait a minute! Wait a minute! Are you sure we nominated a Vice-president?

FULTON. Of course. Didn't I make the nominating speech?

GILHOOLEY. Oh, yeah.

FULTON [*thoughtful*]. What was his name again?

GILHOOLEY. Well, think a minute. How did you come to nominate him?

LIPPMAN. Who introduced him to you?

FULTON. Nobody introduced him. I picked his name out of a hat. We put a lot of names in a hat, and this fellow lost.

> [*The telephone again.*]

LIPPMAN. Hello . . . No, no, you've got the wrong room. . . . What's his name again? . . . Gotabottle? . . . Oh, Throttlebottom. Wait a minute. [*To the others.*] Guy named Bottlethrottle says he has an appointment with somebody here.

FULTON. Never heard of him.

GILHOOLEY. Not me.

LIPPMAN [*into phone*]. Must have the wrong room. Tell him

this is the National Committee. . . . Well, then tell him it *isn't*
the National Committee. . . . Hello. And give me room service,
will you?

GILHOOLEY [*lighting a cigar*]. What do you know, Matty?

FULTON. I know I'm thirsty.

GILHOOLEY [*producing a bottle*]. Got just the ticket.

FULTON. Had it analyzed?

GILHOOLEY. Had it psychoanalyzed.

LIPPMAN. Room service? This is 413. Listen — send up a half
a dozen bottles of White Rock, a couple of ginger ales — [*To the
others.*] Who's paying for this?

GILHOOLEY. General party expense.

LIPPMAN [*into phone*]. Make that a dozen White Rock. And
some dill pickles. [*Hangs up.*] Well, Matty, how's the newspaper
king?

FULTON. Well, if you want to know, a little bit worried.

LIPPMAN. What's the matter?

FULTON. Well, I've just been over to the office doing some
long-distance phoning. Called up about twenty of my editors all
over the country, and it's not going to be the cinch we figured on.

GILHOOLEY [*to Lippman*]. What did I tell you?

LIPPMAN. What did you find out?

FULTON. Just that. It isn't going to be cinch we —

[*Enter Senators Carver Jones and Robert E. Lyons.
Senator Jones is from the West, and Senator Lyons
is from the South. And maybe you don't think they
know it.*]

JONES. Ah, gentlemen, good evening!

LYONS. Gentlemen!

GILHOOLEY. Hello, Senator!

LIPPMAN. Senator!

FULTON. How about Wintergreen? Is he coming over?

JONES [*right up on the rostrum*]. My friends, I am informed
on excellent authority that John P. Wintergreen will shortly honor
us with his presence.

FULTON. Fine! Gentlemen, you probably wonder why I asked
you over here.

LYONS [*sighting the liquor and pouring himself a good one*]. Something about a drink, wasn't it?

FULTON. Senator Jones —

JONES [*bounding to his feet*]. My friends —

FULTON. Senator Jones —

JONES. My good friends —

FULTON. You're a man that keeps his ear close to the ground. What do they think about the ticket in the West?

JONES. My very good friends. [*He clears his throat.*] John P. Wintergreen is a great man — one of the greatest that the party has nominated since Alexander Franklin. . . .

LYONS. And Robert E. Lee.

JONES. Unfortunately, however, while the people of the West admire our party, and love our party, and respect our party, they do not trust our party. And so, gentlemen, in the name of those gallant boys who fought overseas, and the brave mothers who sent them, we must not, we cannot, we dare not allow Russian Bolshevism to dump cheap Chinese labor on these free American shores! Gentlemen, I thank you. [*He finishes his drink and sits.*]

FULTON. Thank you, sir. And now, Senator Lyons, tell us about the South.

LYONS [*who doesn't need to be asked twice*]. Gentlemen, you ask me about the South. It is the land of romance, of roses and honeysuckle, of Southern chivalry and hospitality, fried chicken and waffles, salad and coffee.

LIPPMAN. No dessert?

FULTON. Thank you, gentlemen. That just about confirms what my editors have been telling me. The people of this country demand John P. Wintergreen for President, and they're going to get him whether they like it or not. And between you and me, gentlemen, I don't think they like it. [*There is a knock on the door.*] Come in.

> [*The door is slowly opened. Enter a timid little man — hopefully smiling. His name, believe it or not, is Alexander Throttlebottom.*]

THROTTLEBOTTOM. Hi, gentlemen!

FULTON. Yes, sir. What can we do for you?

THROTTLEBOTTOM [*all smiles*]. Hello, Mr. Fulton.

FULTON. I'm afraid I don't quite place you. Your face is familiar, but —

THROTTLEBOTTOM. I'm Throttlebottom.

FULTON. What?

THROTTLEBOTTOM. Alexander Throttlebottom.

JONES [*pushing him right out*]. We're very busy, my good man. If you'll just —

THROTTLEBOTTOM. But I'm Throttlebottom.

FULTON. I understand, Mr. Teitelbaum, but just at present —

GILHOOLEY. You come back later on.

LIPPMAN. After we're gone.

THROTTLEBOTTOM [*insistent about it*]. But I'm Throttlebottom. I'm the candidate for Vice-president.

FULTON. That's the fellow!

GILHOOLEY. Of course!

LIPPMAN. Sure!

FULTON. What's your name again?

THROTTLEBOTTOM. Alexander —

FULTON. Of course! I nominated you! Alexander! Boys, this is — What's your first name, Mr. Alexander?

THROTTLEBOTTOM. That's my first name. Alexander.

FULTON. Well, well, Alexander Alexander.

GILHOOLEY. Well, that certainly is a coincidence.

> [*A Waiter has arrived with the accessories. Check in hand, he looks uncertainly around for the victim.*]

THROTTLEBOTTOM. But that isn't my last name. It's Throttlebottom.

LIPPMAN. Throttle what?

THROTTLEBOTTOM. Bottom.

LIPPMAN. How do you spell it?

THROTTLEBOTTOM. [*As he starts to spell, Lippman takes the check from the Waiter and writes.*] "T-h-r-o-t-t-l-e-b-o-t-t-o-m."

LIPPMAN. Right! And thank you very much.

> [*The Waiter goes, and with him the signed check.*]

FULTON. Well, sir, we're very glad indeed to see you, and very proud to have you on our ticket. Sit down.

[*They all sit, leaving no place for Throttlebottom.*]

THROTTLEBOTTOM. Thanks. I won't sit. I'm only going to stay a minute. There's something I came up to see you about.

FULTON. What's that?

THROTTLEBOTTOM. Being Vice-president. I want to know if you won't let me off.

FULTON. What!

GILHOOLEY. What do you mean?

THROTTLEBOTTOM. I don't want to be Vice-president. I want to resign.

FULTON. Why, you can't do that!

JONES. That's treason!

LYONS. Absurd, suh!

LIPPMAN. Why don't you want to be Vice-president? That's a good job.

THROTTLEBOTTOM. It's — it's on account of my mother. Suppose she found out?

FULTON. You've got a mother?

GILHOOLEY. He's got a mother.

LIPPMAN. This is a fine time to tell us!

FULTON. Yes, why didn't you tell us? You can't back out now. Everything's printed.

GILHOOLEY. Listen — she'll never hear about it.

JONES. Of course not.

THROTTLEBOTTOM. But maybe she will. Somebody may tell her.

LIPPMAN. Who'll tell her?

FULTON. Nobody'll know!

GILHOOLEY. You'll forget it yourself in three months.

FULTON. Of course!

LIPPMAN [*ever the salesman*]. Besides, suppose something should happen to the President?

THROTTLEBOTTOM. What?

LIPPMAN. Suppose something should happen to the President? Then you become President.

THROTTLEBOTTOM. Me?

LIPPMAN. Sure.

THROTTLEBOTTOM. President! Say!

LIPPMAN. Let's drink to that! To our next President!

> [*There is a great passing of glasses, and Throttle-
> bottom comes out of it without one. He dashes
> into the bathroom and emerges with one of those
> green tumblers.*]

GILHOOLEY. Our next President!

JONES. Our next President!

> [*And he enters. John P. Wintergreen himself.*]

WINTERGREEN. I'll drink to that! [*Takes the glass from the
extended arm of Jones and drinks.*]

JONES [*as the others greet him*]. You dirty crook!

WINTERGREEN. I'll drink to that too!

LIPPMAN. Well, how's the candidate?

WINTERGREEN. Thirsty. Say, doesn't a fellow get a drink?
[*He sees the drink Throttlebottom has just poured for himself, and
takes it from his hand.*] Ah! Thank you, waiter. And get me one of
those dill pickles, will you?

THROTTLEBOTTOM. But I'm not —

WINTERGREEN. There they are — right over there. [*Throttlebottom obediently goes for the pickle.*] Well, gentlemen, it certainly was a great convention. I never expected to get the nomination. Didn't want the nomination. Never was so surprised as when
my name came up. [*Takes pickle from Throttlebottom and gives
him the empty glass.*]

GILHOOLEY. Who brought it up, anyhow?

FULTON. Yah. Who was that in the back calling: "Wintergreen!"

WINTERGREEN. That was me. Most spontaneous thing you
ever saw. So here I am, gentlemen — nominated by the people, absolutely my own master, and ready to do any dirty work the committee suggests. [*In one quick movement he takes the full glass
Throttlebottom has finally succeeded in getting for himself, and
replaces it with the pickle.*]

LYONS. Mr. President —

WINTERGREEN. I'll drink to that too! Anything else, gentle-

men? Anything at all! [*Fulton, meanwhile, is nervously pacing.*]
What's the matter, Fulton? Something wrong? You're not sober,
are you?

FULTON [*his tone belying the words*]. No, no! I'm all right.

WINTERGREEN. Must be something up. [*A look at the others.*]
What's the matter?

LIPPMAN [*deprecatingly*]. A lot of schmoos.

FULTON. Well, it's this way. Begins to look as though there
may be a little trouble ahead.

WINTERGREEN. Trouble?

FULTON. I don't think the people are quite satisfied with the
party record.

WINTERGREEN. Who said they were?

FULTON. Well, you know what Lincoln said.

WINTERGREEN. Who?

FULTON. Lincoln.

GILHOOLEY. What did he say?

WINTERGREEN. Was it funny?

FULTON. " You can fool some of the people all the time, and
you can fool all of the people some of the time, but you can't fool
all of the people all of the time."

WINTERGREEN. Was that Lincoln?

THROTTLEBOTTOM. Abraham J. Lincoln.

WINTERGREEN. It's different nowadays. People are bigger
suckers.

GILHOOLEY. We made one bad mistake. Never should have
sold Rhode Island.

WINTERGREEN. Rhode Island! Nobody missed it! [*A gesture
indicating its size.*] Where is Rhode Island now? Anybody know?

FULTON. New York some place. Never get it back.

WINTERGREEN [*a slap of the hands*]. I'll tell you what! We'll
leave it out of the campaign — not mention it! [*There is a chorus
of approval.*] Yes, sir, that's the idea — we won't mention it!

THROTTLEBOTTOM. But suppose somebody else brings it up?

WINTERGREEN. Don't answer 'em! It takes two to make an
argument. [*Gazes curiously at Throttlebottom.*] I thought this was
a closed meeting.

FULTON. Sure it is. Why?

WINTERGREEN [*whispering*]. Who's that?

FULTON [*also whispering*]. Vice-president.

WINTERGREEN [*whispers*]. What?

FULTON. This is Mr. Wintergreen. Mr. — ah — ah —

THROTTLEBOTTOM [*who has also forgotten it*]. Ah — ah — Throttlebottom.

[*They shake hands.*]

WINTERGREEN. Haven't I seen you before some place?

THROTTLEBOTTOM. I gave you that dill pickle.

WINTERGREEN. Of course!

FULTON. But look here, Mr. President — it's not only Rhode Island. There've been a whole lot of things the last four years.

GILHOOLEY. How about the four years before that?

WINTERGREEN. I'll tell you what — let's stick to the party record of 1776. That was a good year.

LIPPMAN. What's the matter with 1492?

WINTERGREEN. We can use that year too. We won't mention anything before 1492 or after 1776. That gives us pretty nearly three hundred years.

FULTON. Say, that's great!

LYONS. Just a minute, suh! Down South the people want to hear about the Civil War.

WINTERGREEN. What year was that?

LYONS [*exploring his pockets*]. I haven't got the exact figures with me, but it was around 1812.

WINTERGREEN. 1812 — let's see. . . .

THROTTLEBOTTOM. What year was 1812?

WINTERGREEN. Well, how about putting the Civil War back in 1776?

LYONS. Perfectly satisfactory, suh. Perfectly satisfactory.

JONES. Eminently fair.

FULTON. Yah, but it isn't enough.

GILHOOLEY. No! What we need is a good live issue!

FULTON. Yes! That's what we need — an issue. Something that everybody is interested in and that doesn't matter a damn. Something the party can stand on.

THROTTLEBOTTOM [*who has to know everything*]. Excuse me, gentlemen, but what party are we?

WINTERGREEN. We've got plenty of time for that. The important thing is to get elected.

JONES. You see, we're Republicans in most states.

LYONS. But the South is Democratic.

JONES. Oh, sure! We're Democrats down there.

THROTTLEBOTTOM [*to Wintergreen*]. I had a dog that was bitten by a Democrat.

WINTERGREEN [*whispers to Jones*]. Who the hell is that?

JONES [*whispers*]. Vice-president.

[*The Chambermaid returns.*]

CHAMBERMAID. Excuse me. [*She goes through the bathroom door.*]

FULTON. Boys, I tell you this is serious. We've got to get something that'll take hold of the popular imagination — sweep the country.

LIPPMAN. The country could stand a good sweeping.

JONES. Mr. Fulton is quite correct.

CHAMBERMAID [*emerging from the bathroom*]. Can I turn the bed down now?

FULTON. What?

CHAMBERMAID. Can I turn the bed down now?

FULTON. Say — come here a minute. [*The Maid and Throttlebottom both start toward Fulton.*] [*To Throttlebottom*] No, not you! [*To the Maid*] You're an American citizen?

CHAMBERMAID. Yes, sir.

FULTON. Ever vote?

CHAMBERMAID [*What an idea!*]. Oh, no, sir.

FULTON. What do you care more about than anything else in the world?

CHAMBERMAID. I don't know. Money, I guess.

GILHOOLEY. That's no good.

WINTERGREEN. Brings up Rhode Island.

FULTON. Of course, money. We all want money. But there must be something else, isn't there?

CHAMBERMAID [*thinks*]. No — I like money.

FULTON [*exasperated*]. But after money what?

CHAMBERMAID. Well, maybe love.

FULTON. Love?

CHAMBERMAID. Yeh. You know, to meet a nice young fellow that's crazy about you, and you're crazy about him, and you get engaged, and then you get married, and — you know — love.

THROTTLEBOTTOM [*a trifle fussed*]. Sure.

FULTON [*rather thoughtful*]. Oh, yes. Thank you. Thank you very much.

CHAMBERMAID. Shall I turn the bed down now, sir!

FULTON. Not now. Come back later on.

CHAMBERMAID. Yes, sir. [*Starts to go.*]

FULTON. Ah — here you are. [*Starts to give her a coin. Throttlebottom reaches for it.*] No, not you.

CHAMBERMAID. Thank you, sir. [*Goes.*]

LIPPMAN. Well, you got a lot out of that.

WINTERGREEN. Put women into politics and that's what you get. Love.

GILHOOLEY. Love!

FULTON [*slowly*]. What's the matter with love?

THROTTLEBOTTOM. I like love!

FULTON. People *do* care more about love than anything else. Why, they steal for it, they even kill for it.

WINTERGREEN. But will they vote for it?

FULTON. You bet they will! If we could find some way to put it over — why, we could get every vote. Everybody loves a lover; the whole world loves a — [*Stops as he gets an idea; looks fixedly at Wintergreen.*]

WINTERGREEN. What's the matter?

FULTON. I've got it!

THROTTLEBOTTOM. He's got it!

FULTON. You've got to fall in love!

WINTERGREEN. You're crazy!

FULTON. You've got to fall in love with a typical American girl!

WINTERGREEN. Huh?

LIPPMAN. What good's that?

GILHOOLEY. What are you talking about?

JONES. What for?

FULTON. Wait a minute! You make love to her from now till Election Day as no girl was ever made love to before!

WINTERGREEN. What's the gag?

GILHOOLEY. Yeah!

LIPPMAN. So what?

FULTON. My God, are you blind? You do this right and you'll get elected by the greatest majority that the American people ever gave a candidate! You'll get every vote!

WINTERGREEN. But wait a minute —

GILHOOLEY. I think there's something in it.

JONES. It sounds good!

LYONS. Certainly does!

LIPPMAN. Say!

FULTON. I tell you it's great!

WINTERGREEN. But look here —

FULTON. You'll go down in history as the greatest lover this country has ever known! You'll be the romantic ideal of every man, woman, and child in America!

WINTERGREEN. Oh, no! I don't want anything like that!

FULTON. But, man, it's the biggest thing in the world! A hundred million hearts will beat as one; they'll follow your courtship in every state in the Union! You meet the girl, you fall in love with her, you propose, you're accepted, and you're swept into the White House on a tidal wave of love!

WINTERGREEN. But there's nobody I'm in love with! I'm not in love with anybody!

FULTON. We'll get the girl! That'll be easy!

LIPPMAN. My wife's sister!

FULTON. I've got the idea! We'll have a contest — a nationwide contest to select Miss White House — choose the most beautiful girl from every state — get them all together at Atlantic City, pick the winner, and you fall in love with her!

[Chorus: "Yah!" "Great!" "That's it!"]

WINTERGREEN. But suppose I *don't* fall in love with her!

THROTTLEBOTTOM. Then *I* get her!

FULTON. You can't *help* falling in love with her! The most beautiful girl in America! I tell you this is wonderful! [*Into the telephone.*] Give me Beekman 5000.

WINTERGREEN. Give me another drink!

LIPPMAN. Let's all have another drink! Scotch or rye, Jack?

WINTERGREEN. Both!

FULTON. Give me Jenkins! Hello!

LIPPMAN. Say when!

FULTON. That's what I said — Jenkins!

WINTERGREEN. That's enough! [*Takes the bottle instead of the glass.*]

FULTON. Jenkins? Fulton! Stop the presses! John P. Wintergreen will run for President on a one-word platform: Love! National beauty contest in Atlantic City to select Miss White House! Now listen! I want a love cartoon on the front page of every one of my papers from now till Election Day! Right! And call up Coolidge and tell him I want a thousand words on love tomorrow morning!

CURTAIN

SCENE 3: *Atlantic City — with the beauty contest in full swing. The scene is a section of the boardwalk, and the various candidates for First Lady are in about three-quarter-piece bathing-suits. For it is notorious, of course, that the prime requisite for a First Lady is that she should look well in a bathing-suit.*

To music and lyric the candidates introduce themselves:

> Who is the lucky girl to be?
> Ruler of Washington, D. C.?
> Who is to be the blushing bride?
> Who will sleep at the President's side?
> Strike up the cymbals, drum and fife!
> One of us is the President's future wife!

> We're in Atlantic City
> To meet with the committee,
> And when they've made their mind up
> The winner will be signed up.
> The prize is consequential —
>   Presidential!
> Our bodies will bear witness
>   To our fitness.

If a girl is sexy
She may be Mrs. Prexy!
One of us is the President's future wife!

[*Enter the Gentlemen of the Press, cameras in hand.*]

PHOTOGRAPHERS

More important than a photograph of Parliament,
Or a shipwreck on the sea —
What'll raise the circulation
Of our paper through the nation
Is the dimple on your knee.

More important than a photograph of Parliament,
Or a Western spelling bee,
Or the latest thing in science,
For our pleasure-loving clients,
Is the dimple on your knee.

GIRLS

More important than a photograph of Parliament
Is the dimple on my knee:
But supposing I am losing
When the judges are a-choosing —
What will my poor future be?

Do I have to go back to the cafeteria
With my lovely dimpled knee?
Does a girl who's so ambitious
Have to work at washing dishes?
I'm afraid that worries me.

PHOTOGRAPHERS

Don't worry, little girl,
For even if you lose the prize —
Don't worry, little girl,
Myself, I can't resist your eyes.

GIRLS

I'll worry, if you please,
Until you tell what's on your mind.

PHOTOGRAPHERS

Don't worry, little girl —
I've asked my heart and this is what I find –
Don't worry, little girl,
Don't worry, little girl.

GIRLS

Why shouldn't we worry?

PHOTOGRAPHERS

Because, because, because, because,
Because you're in the money,
With a smile that's sweet and sunny,
    I could fall for you myself.

Because, because, because, because
Your looks are so appealing
They have given me a feeling
    I could fall for you myself.

The thrills you're sending through me
Are doing something to me
The opposite of gloomy —
If they don't want you, *I* want you!

Because, because, because, because,
Because your ways are simple,
And your knee can show a dimple,
    I could fall for you myself.

[Next: *The Committee headquarters in one of the grander Boardwalk hostelries. A few banners on the walls proclaim the fact that this is no longer just a hotel parlor, but the center of national interest. A few dozen girls, still in bathing-suits, are scattered around the room.*

Enter Mr. Fulton, followed by the faithful Gilhooley and a handful of newspapermen and newsreelers.]

GILHOOLEY [*to the Movie men*]. Come on, boys! Set 'em up right here — that'll give you a good angle! Hello, ladies!

FULTON. Well, well! What a crowd! How are you, ladies? This certainly is a big day, all right! Must be ten thousand people outside this hotel! Never saw so much excitement in all my life!

ONE OF THE GIRLS. Say! What does a President's wife have to do, anyhow?

GILHOOLEY. That depends on the President.

[*A young woman comes forward to greet Mr. Fulton. She is chiefly distinguished from the other girls by the fact that she is dressed. Her name is Mary Turner.*]

MARY. Good morning, Mr. Fulton.

FULTON. Well, Miss Turner! Having quite a day, huh?

MARY. Quite a day, Mr. Fulton.

FULTON. Heard some very nice things about the way you've been handling this. Afraid I'll have to give you a raise.

MARY. Well, I'm afraid I'll have to take it.

[*Enter those two pillars of the government — Senators Jones and Lyons.*]

LYONS. Afternoon, gentlemen! Ladies!

FULTON. Ah, here's some of the committee now! Good afternoon, gentlemen!

JONES. Mr. Fulton! Good afternoon, ladies! Good afternoon. [*Beams on the Photographers.*] Well! Quite a battery you have here — quite a battery!

LYONS. Gentlemen of the press!

JONES. Very glad to see you, gentlemen! Always glad to meet the newspaper boys!

[*Enter a lad named Jenkins, who is one of Fulton's various assistants.*]

JENKINS. Good morning, chief!

FULTON. Oh, hello, Jenkins!

JONES. Hello, there! I've met you before! Never forget a face! Just tell me — we've met before? Am I right?

JENKINS. Right you are, Senator!

JONES [*SO pleased with himself*]. Right! Where was it?

JENKINS. San Francisco. That opium joint on 4th Street.

JONES [*not so pleased*]. Well, I guess I got the wrong man. Remarkable resemblance, though, remarkable resemblance.

[*Throttlebottom enters. Still hoping.*]

THROTTLEBOTTOM. Hello, everybody! Hello, Mr. Fulton!

GILHOOLEY. Hello, there!

JONES. How are you?

LYONS. Good morning, suh!

FULTON. Who is that guy?

GILHOOLEY. Vice-president.

FULTON. Oh, yes. Hello! How are you?

THROTTLEBOTTOM. Are these the girls? I'm Mr. Throttlebottom. [*Sights a promising girl.*] Hello! How are you?

THE GIRL. Fine!

THROTTLEBOTTOM. Is your mother down here with you?

THE GIRL [*she's no fool*]. Yes, sir.

THROTTLEBOTTOM. Oh! Well! Never mind!

FULTON [*goes to Throttlebottom*]. Say, look here a minute. You know, Vice-presidents don't usually go around in public. They're not supposed to be seen.

THROTTLEBOTTOM. But I'm not Vice-president yet. Couldn't I go around a little longer?

GILHOOLEY. That isn't the point. If you're going to be Vice-president you've got to practice up for it. You've got to go in hiding.

THROTTLEBOTTOM. But I came up the back way.

FULTON. You shouldn't have come at all. Suppose somebody sees you?

GILHOOLEY. We'd lose the election.

THROTTLEBOTTOM. You mean you want me to hide from everybody?

JONES. That's it!

FULTON. Right!

THROTTLEBOTTOM [*gets an idea*]. I could go back to my old business.

FULTON. What's that?

THROTTLEBOTTOM. I used to be a hermit.

FULTON. Great!

GILHOOLEY. That's the idea!

THROTTLEBOTTOM. The only thing is, I thought you might want me to make some speeches.

FULTON. No, no!

GILHOOLEY. You just go and sit in your cave.

THROTTLEBOTTOM [*thinks it over*]. I know. I could go back to the cave and write my speeches there.

FULTON. That's the idea!

JONES. Perfect!

GILHOOLEY. And make 'em there, too!

JONES. Don't let anybody find you — don't let anybody see you.

THROTTLEBOTTOM. I won't. I won't even come out in February to cast my shadow. [*He goes.*]

> [*Enter, then, a particularly beauteous girl named Diana Devereaux. She is from the South, as one speedily discovers when she speaks.*]

DIANA. Mo'nin', Senator Lyons.

LYONS. Well, Miss Devereaux! And how is the fairest flower of the South?

DIANA. Senator Lyons, that's the prettiest thing been said to me since I left Louisiana. I sure been gettin' pow'ful homesick.

ONE OF THE GIRLS [*who seems to be a little embittered*]. She sure is getting pow'ful Southern.

LYONS. You're just a breath of the old Southland.

DIANA. Senator, you keep on sayin' sweet things like that and I'm just going to throw my arms right around your neck.

FULTON. You never made me an offer like that, Miss Devereaux.

DIANA. Why, Mr. Fulton!

FULTON. Yes, sir, when I look around I'm sorry I didn't run for President myself.

DIANA. You'd make a mighty nice consolation prize. Wouldn't he, girls?

FULTON. Now, now! Matter of fact, we're getting up some consolation prizes. Got that list, Jenkins?

JENKINS. Here you are, sir.

FULTON. Of course the first prize, as you all know, is Mr.

Wintergreen himself. The second prize is a season pass to Coney
Island. And the third prize is an autographed photograph of
Clara Bow, or ten cents in gold. [*There is a burst of cheering in the
distance. Enter Wintergreen, followed by Lippman and practically all the reporters in the world.*] Well, well! The candidate himself! Hello, Jack!

WINTERGREEN. Hello, there!

FULTON. Ladies, permit me to introduce your future husband, John P. Wintergreen! Here they are, Jack. How do you like
'em?

WINTERGREEN [*a trifle nervously*]. Why, they're wonderful.
Hello! How are you?

FULTON. Say something to them.

WINTERGREEN. Well, ladies, this certainly is a pleasure. All
I can say is I love you, and you're the only girls I have ever loved.
[*With growing nervousness.*] And after we're married, I hope you'll
all be happy, and — listen, Fulton, I can't go through with this.

FULTON. You've got to go through with it.

WINTERGREEN. But I don't know any of these girls! How
can I marry them? If it was only somebody I knew, like — Lippman, what ever became of your wife's sister?

LIPPMAN [*with a shake of the head*]. Not in a bathing-suit.

FULTON. By the way, Jack, I want you to meet Miss Diana
Devereaux.

LYONS. Miss Devereaux, may I have the honor —

DIANA. Mr. President, I'm mighty happy to meet you! I
hope we're going to see a lot of each other.

WINTERGREEN. Any hope of yours, Miss Devereaux, is a hope
of mine, I hope.

DIANA. You keep on saying sweet things like that and I'm
just going to throw my arms right around your neck.

> [*The Girls chime in when she is half-way through
> the sentence and finish it right with her, Southern
> accent and all.*]

WINTERGREEN. Seems to be quite an echo here.

DIANA [*playing with his lapel*]. Have you-all got a fraternity
pin?

WINTERGREEN. Well, would a safety pin do?

DIANA. Mr. Wintergreen, you've got the grandest sense of humor.

MARY. All right, Mr. Fulton.

FULTON. And now, ladies — attention, please! The time has come for the final test. [*The Girls start a general primping and there is an excited buzz.*] It has been a grueling contest — you have been under a great strain. And we of the committee want to thank you — and through you the three million others who took part in this contest, only ninety-eight per cent of whom had to be sent home for misbehavior. And now, ladies, the judges await you. And may the best girl win.

GIRLS [*to music*]
> Who is the lucky girl to be —
> Ruler of Washington, D. C.?

DIANA
> Bye-bye, Mr. President — I'm a-prayin'
> I'm the little lady they're okayin'.

GIRLS
> Strike up the cymbals, drum, and fife:
> One of us is the President's future wife!

> [*They go. Wintergreen, his nervousness mounting, is left alone in the room. But not quite alone, for at her desk in the corner Mary Turner is quietly working.*]

WINTERGREEN [*as he sees her*]. Oh! [*Takes a moment.*] Say! [*She turns.*] You haven't got a drink on you, have you?

MARY. Why, no. I'm sorry.

WINTERGREEN. That's all right. Didn't want it anyhow. [*Pacing.*]

MARY. Little bit nervous?

WINTERGREEN [*whirling*]. Who? Me? What have I got to be nervous about?

MARY. That's what I was wondering. Twenty-four of the most beautiful girls in the country — and you get the winner. Lot of men would like to be in your shoes.

WINTERGREEN. Yeah, but it's my bedroom slippers I'm worrying about. . . . Say, you've been watching them — who do you think it's going to be?

MARY. I couldn't say. Likely to be any one of them.

WINTERGREEN. That's what I was afraid of. But which one? What's your guess?

MARY. Well, don't hold me to it, but I shouldn't be surprised if it were Miss Devereaux.

WINTERGREEN. Devereaux! I thought so! That's the one with the Southern exposure?

MARY. That's Miss Devereaux. She's a good-looking girl, don't you think?

WINTERGREEN [in heavy Southern accent]. Yes, she's a good-looking gal, all right.

MARY [falling right into line]. Don't you-all like good-looking gals?

WINTERGREEN. Down Carolina way we're all a-crazy about good-looking gals, but we-all don't like 'em talking that-a-way.

MARY. How do you-all like 'em to talk, sure enough?

WINTERGREEN [abandons the dialect]. Say, that's terrible, isn't it? If she wins would I have to listen to that all the time?

MARY. But she does it charmingly. And she's very beautiful.

WINTERGREEN. Beautiful, yeah — I like a beautiful girl — they're all right, but — [He stumbles.] when a fellow gets married he wants a home, a mother for his children.

MARY. You've got children?

WINTERGREEN. No, no, I mean if I was married. You see, when you're married — well, you know.

MARY. Well, I think Miss Devereaux might listen to reason. And she'd make a very beautiful mother for your children.

WINTERGREEN. Will you stop saying beautiful? I don't know anything about these girls, any of them. What kind of wives they'd make — whether they could sew, or make a bed, or cook. They don't look as though they'd ever had a skillet in their hands. Say, what *is* a skillet?

MARY. You wouldn't have to worry about that in the White House. They have plenty of servants there.

WINTERGREEN. The White House — yeah, but some day

we'll have to move out of the White House. Then what? The Old Presidents' Home? There'll be no servants there. She'll have to cook.

MARY. Then she'll cook. And like it.

WINTERGREEN. But will *I* like it? Why, the average girl to-day can't cook — she can't even broil an egg.

MARY. Nonsense! Every girl can cook.

WINTERGREEN [*scornfully*]. Every girl can cook — can you?

MARY. I certainly can!

WINTERGREEN. Then what are you doing here?

MARY [*right back at him*]. I'm holding down a job! And I can cook, and sew, and make lace curtains, and bake the best darned corn muffins you ever ate! And what do you know about that?

WINTERGREEN. Did you say corn muffins?

MARY. Yes, corn muffins!

WINTERGREEN. Corn muffins! You haven't got one on you, have you?

MARY. I haven't far to go. [*Opens a drawer in her desk.*] It's lunch, but you can have it.

WINTERGREEN. Oh, I couldn't do that!

MARY. Please! [*As he reaches.*] The second from the left is a corn muffin. That's an apple.

WINTERGREEN [*taking muffin*]. Well! You must let me take you to lunch some day. [*Samples it.*] Why — it melts in the mouth! It's — it's marvelous.

MARY. And I'm the only person in the world who can make them without corn.

WINTERGREEN. What a muffin! Say, I don't even know your name.

MARY. That's right — you don't.

WINTERGREEN. Mine's Wintergreen.

MARY. I know. Mine's Turner.

WINTERGREEN. Just Turner?

MARY. Mary Turner.

WINTERGREEN [*suddenly*]. Say, why in God's name didn't you get into this contest?

MARY. One of the three million?

WINTERGREEN. Well, you know what the first prize is?

MARY. Yeah, can you imagine?

WINTERGREEN. And you get your picture in the paper.

MARY. Having tea on the lawn with the Filipino delegation. And you throwing the medicine-ball at the Cabinet.

WINTERGREEN. Oh, do we have to have a Cabinet?

MARY. What would you throw the medicine-ball at? Me?

WINTERGREEN [*suddenly sobered*]. Gosh, it'd be fun with you. We could have a grand time.

MARY [*the Southern accent*]. Why, Mr. Wintergreen —

WINTERGREEN. No, I mean it! Listen — I've only got a minute — maybe less than that! I love you! I know it's awful sudden, but in a minute it'll be too late! Let's elope — let's get out of here!

MARY. But — but wait a minute! You don't know me!

WINTERGREEN. I know you better than those girls! [*A gesture.*] You can make corn muffins, and — you're darned cute-looking, and — I love you!

MARY. But I don't know you!

WINTERGREEN. What's there to know? I'm young, I'm a swell conversationalist, and I've got a chance to be President! And besides that you love me!

MARY. But it's absurd! Why, you can't —

WINTERGREEN. The hell I can't! [*He seizes her and starts kissing her.*] It's fate, Mary, that's what it is — fate! [*Kisses her again.*] Why, we were meant for each other — you and me!

MARY. You and *I!*

WINTERGREEN. All right, you and I!

> [*A burst of music. The sound of many voices as the doors are thrown open. Enter Fulton and the Committee, full of importance.*]

FULTON [*sings*]

> As the chairman of the committee,
> I announce we've made our choice;
> Ev'ry lover from Dubuque to Jersey City
> Should rejoice!

COMMITTEE

> We rejoice!
> When the angels up there designed her,

They designed a thoroughbred;
And on March the Fourth the President will find her
Worthy of his board and bed.

FULTON. And now it thrills me to introduce the rarest of American beauties, the future First Lady of the land — a fit consort for the ruler of our country. Gentlemen — Miss Diana Devereaux!

[Diana appears, a golden crown on her head, followed by all the other Girls.]

ALL

How beautiful, beautiful, beautiful!
How utterly, utterly so!
The charming, the gracious, the dutiful
Diana Devereaux.

FULTON. The committee will now tell why she was chosen — with music!

ALL

Never was there a girl so fair;
Never was there a form so rare;

DIANA. I could throw my arms right around your neck!

ALL

A voice so lyrical
Is given few;
Her eyes a miracle
Of Prussian blue;
Ruby lips and a foot so small;
As for hips — she has none at all!

What a charming epiglottis!
What a lovely coat of tan!
Oh, the man who isn't hot is
Not a man!

She's a bargain to whom she's wed;
More than worthy his board and bed!

FULTON

Says the chairman of the committee,
Let the newsmen now come in.

[*To Diana.*]

For the sound reels you must look your best, my pretty.
Have the interviews begin!

COMMITTEE

  We shall go and bring them in!

WINTERGREEN

  Stop! No!
  Though this may be a blow,
  I simply cannot marry
   Diana Devereaux!

ALL

  What's this? What's this?
  He says he cannot marry
   Diana Devereaux!

COMMITTEE

  You mean you will not marry
   Diana Devereaux!

WINTERGREEN

Please understand — it isn't that I would jilt or spurn 'er:
It's just that I love someone else.

ALL

Who?

WINTERGREEN [*reprovingly*]

Whom! . . . Mary Turner.

ALL

   The man is mad!
   Or else a cad!
  He'll have to take her —
  He can't forsake her!

DIANA

   This jilting me,
   It cannot be!
  This lousy action
  Calls for retraction!

COMMITTEE

  We must know why
  You should prefer
  Instead of Di
  A girl like her.

GIRLS
> Yes, tell us why
> You should prefer
> Instead of Di
> A girl like her.

WINTERGREEN
> All that I can say of Mary Turner
> Is that I love Mary Turner.

COMMITTEE
> What's to be done?
> Though she has won,
> Though she is signed up,
> He's made his mind up!
> His love he'd ruther
> Give to the other.
> What shall we do now?
> What is our cue now?

DIANA
> He will do nothing of the sort;
> First we'll settle this thing in court.
> [*To Wintergreen.*]
> You seem to think Miss Turner hits the spot;
> But what has she got that I haven't got?

ALL
> Yes, what has *she* got that *she* hasn't got!

WINTERGREEN
> My Mary makes corn muffins!
> [*To Diana.*]
> Can you make corn muffins?

DIANA
> I can't make corn muffins!

ALL
> She can't make corn muffins!

WINTERGREEN
> Some girls can bake a pie,
> Made up of prunes and quinces;
> Some make an oyster fry —
> Others are good at blintzes.

> Some lovely girls have done
> Wonders with turkey stuffin's,
> But I have found the one
> Who can really make corn muffins.

[*He passes muffins to the Committee.*]

DIANA

Who cares about corn muffins? All I demand is justice!

COMMITTEE

> Corn muffins —
> Though other girls are good at turkey stuffin's,
> She takes the cake, for she can bake corn muffins —
> Corn muffins —
> He's not to blame for falling if she's able
> To serve them at his table.

[*The Committee samples the muffins and is overwhelmed.*]

> Great, great!
> It really must be fate!
> We must declare these muffins
> The best we ever ate!

ALL

> There's none but Mary Turner
> Could ever be his mate!

> There's none but Mary Turner
> Could ever be his mate!

> Let's all rejoice!

[*One and all, with the exception of Diana, they burst into a joyous dance, expressing the ecstasy that is theirs at the very existence of so remarkable a young woman. On this pæan of joy the curtain falls.*]

SCENE 4: *Madison Square Garden — the height of the campaign. One sees first the outside of the Garden, and across it a great banner bearing the pictures of Wintergreen and Mary Turner. " WOO WITH WINTERGREEN," the slogan now runs, and beneath it: " LOVERS! VOTE FOR JOHN AND MARY!" Of Mr. Throttlebottom, or whatever his name is, there is just no mention at all.*

A band plays. Drawn by the ballyhoo, a crowd gathers and goes gayly into the Garden, singing and cheering.

Inside the Garden, then, with the proceedings in full swing. A Garden that is packed to the rafters with cheering humanity, alive with cold-drink venders, and hot-dog salesmen, and everything that goes with so great an occasion. Over the rostrum there hangs the inevitable loud speaker, set in a cluster of lights that send a concentrated glow down on the platform. The various committeemen occupy the platform seats, and the two center chairs are conspicuously empty, obviously waiting for the stellar pair. When the scene starts, Fulton is in the midst of an impassioned address.

FULTON. . . . seventeen hundred and seventy-six, eighteen hundred and twelve, eighteen hundred and sixty-one, eighteen hundred and ninety-eight, and nineteen hundred and seventeen! [*There is loud applause as he stops for a sip of water.*] And so, my friends, on Tuesday next yours is a great privilege. You will cast your ballots for the greatest cause and the greatest emotion known to the heart of mankind! Love! [*Applause.*] Yes, my good friends, for love! For love and for the greatest of all lovers! John P. Wintergreen! [*He sits down to great applause.*]

LOUD SPEAKER [*through the cluster of megaphones that hangs overhead*]. Attention, please! Next Wednesday night: Jack Sharkey, American champion of the world, versus Max Schmeling, German champion of the world, for the championship of the world! [*Applause.*]

FULTON [*again to his feet*]. And, my friends, as a good American, I believe that Jack Sharkey will win! [*Applause; he sits.*]

LOUD SPEAKER. Attention, please! Message for Dr. Hugo Kristmacher! Dr. Kristmacher! Your wife just telephoned the box-office and says not to come home tonight. [*Applause.*]

FULTON. And now, my good people, it is my great pleasure and privilege to introduce a man who has served his country long and gloriously, a man who has for many years waged a great and single-handed fight for what he considered his own interests. The silver-tongued orator of the golden West, Senator Carver Crockett Jones! [*Applause.*]

[*Senator Jones rises.*]

LOUD SPEAKER. Attention, please! While Senator Jones is speaking you will be entertained by the world's greatest wrestlers, Vladimir Vidovitch, the Harlem Heaver, and Yussef Yussevitch, the Terrible Turk, in a match for the world's championship.

> [*Two Attendants dash out and quickly unroll a mat. Then enter, from opposite sides, Vidovitch and Yussevitch. As they reach the arena they drop their bathrobes and stand revealed as great three-hundred-pounders, with arms like tree-trunks. There is the sound of a gong. Simultaneously the Wrestlers go into action, and Senator Jones starts his speech.*]

JONES. My friends! We have arrived at a great moment in our history. Magnificent though our past has been, it dwindles into utter insignificance beside the brilliance of our future destiny. Gaze into that future, my friends, and what do you see? What do you see? [*At this moment what one chiefly sees is the rear eleva-tion of Vidovitch, which is being stared at with something akin to admiration by Yussevitch.*] There it is, my friends, for all the world to envy. [*The Wrestlers reverse, and it is now Yussevitch that is starred. They break, and resume wrestling as Jones resumes talking.*] Not for us the entangling alliances of Europe, not for us the ally-ing entanglances of Asia. [*A burst of applause. The Wrestlers, at the moment, have a complicated double scissors hold on each other, but their arms are free. Pausing in their labors, they join in the applause.*] Here, then, we stand, alone in our strength, solitary in our splendor, the greatest and most glorious country that God Almighty put upon earth — the United States of AMERICA!!! [*The Wrestlers, relinquishing a complicated hold, jump to their feet and salute. The Crowd bursts into applause.*] And so, my friends — [*One of the Wrestlers makes a sensational dive for the other's legs, throwing him to the mat with a crash. The Crowd sets up a cheering and yelling, egging on the Wrestlers. The Committeemen sitting behind Jones crowd to the edge of the rail to look on; the whole Crowd is on its feet. Jones tries bravely to talk against this for a moment, but his own interest in the Wrestlers finally gets the better of him. He joins the cheerers. It all comes to a climax as one of the men finally gets the other down. Cheers. Applause. Bows. The Wrestlers exit; the Attendants roll up the mat; the Crowd settles back.*]

FULTON. And now, my friends, while we are waiting for our beloved candidate — [*There is a hullabaloo at the entrance — the sound of a scuffle, voices, etc. The Crowd gets to its feet as the noise mounts. Enter Throttlebottom, trying to fight off four Policemen and a couple of Garden Attendants. As he comes into view it is seen that he is practically in tatters, his coat off, his collar askew. He struggles to the foot of the platform stairs.*] Here, here, here! What's all this? Who is this man? Stop that noise! What is this? [*The noise quiets down. The Policemen stand holding tightly onto Throttlebottom, two to each arm. Behind him stand the Garden Attendants, one of whom has picked up a huge iron bar somewhere.*] What is all this? What do you want here?

THROTTLEBOTTOM [*tears himself loose and gets half-way up the steps*]. But wait, wait! I'm Throttlebottom! I'm the Vice-president. Here — look! I'm Throttlebottom! [*Takes a banner from his pocket and unrolls it. Sure enough, it reads: "For Vice-President: Alexander Throttlebottom."*]

FULTON. Oh, yes! Yes! It's all right, officers. This man is all right!

[*Throttlebottom gets up on the platform. The other Committeemen come forward to greet him, but not too cordially. Throttlebottom, meanwhile, is trying to get his clothes together, stuffing his shirt into his trousers, getting his collar back on.*]

FULTON. What are you doing here? Why didn't you stay in your cave?

THROTTLEBOTTOM. The other hermits objected.

FULTON [*at the rostrum, reluctantly*]. My friends, we have an unexpected surprise for you. It is your great and rare privilege to hear a few words from — [*Throttlebottom prompts him.*] Alexander Throttlebottom [*He pronounces the name with great care.*] — candidate for [*Throttlebottom prompts him again, first looking at the banner himself.*] — Vice-president. [*Then, as an afterthought.*] Of the United States of America. [*The Crowd is silent.*]

> [*Throttlebottom advances to the rostrum; takes his speech from his pocket. It unrolls all the way to the ground, turning out to be about ten feet long. A pleased expression spreads over his face; recognition is his at last.*]

LOUD SPEAKER [*just as Throttlebottom opens his mouth to speak*]. Attention, please! At the end of the first period in Montreal: Boston Bruins, 3; Chicago White Sox, 1. [*The machine clanks off; Throttlebottom again gets ready to speak. Once more a slow smile comes over his face.*] Attention, please! There will now be an intermission of fifteen minutes.

> [*There is a great pushing back of chairs; everybody gets up and starts to leave.*]

THROTTLEBOTTOM. No, no, no! No!

> [*The various noises merge into a greater and growing noise. Cries of " Wintergreen! " " Here comes Wintergreen! " Flashlights. Cheering. Music. Enter Wintergreen and Mary Turner, preceded by Policemen. To the accompaniment of cheers and handshaking, they advance to the platform and go up the stairs. There is a great shaking of hands with the Committeemen. Throttlebottom, as the presidential procession gets up onto the platform, is simply pushed right out of the way by the Policemen and practically falls down the stairs on the other side. Here he is met by other Policemen and is ignominiously dragged out of the place, kicking and protesting. Meanwhile, as the noise subsides, Wintergreen and Mary take their seats, and Fulton advances to the rostrum to introduce them.*]

FULTON [*stilling the tumult with upraised hand*]. No need to tell you who the next speakers will be. They are the most beloved couple in America today, the most beloved couple that have ever run for the highest office in the gift of the American people. There have been many great lovers in history. But Romeo never loved Juliet, Dante never loved Beatrice, Damon never loved Pythias, as John P. Wintergreen loves Mary Turner. [*Applause.*] My friends, the issue of this campaign is a simple one. We do not talk to you about war debts or wheat or immigration — we appeal to your hearts, not your intelligence. It is the old, old story, yet ever new — the sweetest story ever told. John P. Wintergreen, candidate for President of the United States of America, loves Mary Turner. Mary Turner, the most beautiful, the loveliest example of typical American womanhood — and I defy our opponents to say otherwise — loves John P. Wintergreen. He has proposed to her in forty-seven states of the Union, and in forty-seven states she has accepted him. Tonight she will give him her answer in the great Empire State of New York! John and Mary, stand up! [*They do so.*] Can you look at them and not be thrilled by their youth, their charm, their passion? Ladies and gentlemen, I give you John P. Wintergreen and Mary Turner!

> [*Fulton sits down as pandemonium breaks loose. Wintergreen and Mary come forward; the tumult slowly dies.*]

WINTERGREEN. My friends, I come before you in this final rally of the campaign not as John P. Wintergreen the candidate, not as John P. Wintergreen the statesman, but as a simple man in love. So I beg you to bear with me for a moment while I ask the girl of my dreams if she will be my heart's delight. [*There is applause as he turns to Mary.*] Miss Turner, there has been something on my mind for a long, long time.

MARY. Yes, Mr. Wintergreen?

WINTERGREEN [*the hesitant lover*]. May I not call you — Mary?

MARY. I wish you would — John.

WINTERGREEN. Do you remember that night we first walked together, on the boardwalk in Atlantic City?

MARY. With the moon shining overhead?

WINTERGREEN. And the lights rippling on the water. Do you

remember what I said to you, Mary, as I took your dear hand in mine?

MARY. You said — [*She drops her eyes.*] that I reminded you of your mother, who had been dead these many years.

WINTERGREEN. And in the cornfields of Kansas, on the plains of Arizona, in the mountains of Nebraska, I whispered to you how much you were beginning to mean to me.

MARY. Our friendship has been a wonderful thing to me.

WINTERGREEN. And in the cave in Kentucky — [*Two Photographers dash on. Wintergreen stops until picture is taken.*] — when you were frightened of the darkness, I put my arm around your trembling shoulder and drew you to me.

MARY. You were so brave, so strong.

WINTERGREEN. Mary, I can conceal it from you no longer. Look at me, darling. [*He tilts her face up.*] I love you. [*The Crowd breaks into great cheers and applause. Wintergreen stops them with a gesture.*] Yes, Mary, I love you. [*A gesture to halt applause that has not come.*]

MARY. Why, John! I hardly know what to say.

WINTERGREEN. Say that you love me, Mary, and that you will be mine.

MARY. I do love you, John. [*Applause. The Crowd on its feet. Wintergreen again checks them.*]

WINTERGREEN. And if I am elected President, you will marry me?

MARY [*with simple determination*]. I will.

WINTERGREEN [*turns quickly to the crowd, his arm still around Mary*]. Citizens, it is up to you! Can you let this glorious romance end unhappily!

MARY. Can you tear asunder two loving hearts whom God hath joined together!

WINTERGREEN. I put my faith and trust in the American people! Go then to the polls on Tuesday and show the whole world that the United States of America stands first, last, and always for Love! Are you with me?

ALL [*on their feet*]. YES!

FULTON. Sing 'em the campaign song, Jack! Sing the campaign love-song!

WINTERGREEN

> Of thee I sing, baby,
> Summer, autumn, winter, spring, baby,
> You're my silver lining,
> You're my sky of blue,
> There's a love-light shining,
> All because of you.
> Of thee I sing, baby,
> You have got that certain thing, baby,
> Shining star and inspiration,
> Worthy of a mighty nation,
> Of thee I sing!

[*The Crowd yells itself blue in the face. When they are good and blue, the curtain falls.*]

SCENE 5: *Election Night. The roar of the Crowd, the blowing of horns, the tooting of sirens. A band that plays furiously. The voice of a nation is speaking, and the results are being thrown upon a motion-picture screen. Faster and faster they come — bulletins from here, there, and everywhere; photographs of the candidate, photographs of Mary Turner, photographs of people that have nothing to do with anything. And returns, returns, returns:*

WHITESIDE, VERMONT
Indications are that Wintergreen has swept the
town by a plurality of 154

WATERVILLE, MASS.
Early returns show Wintergreen well ahead.
First election district gives:
> Wintergreen　　　　　12
> Scattering　　　　　　1

A Picture of John P. Wintergreen

A Picture of Mary Turner

ATLANTA, GA.
16 election districts out of 184 give:

Wintergreen	12,736
Jefferson Davis	1,653

NEW YORK, N. Y.
126 election districts report:

Wintergreen	72,639
Bryan	128
Absent	4
Late	2

A Picture of Mary Turner

A Picture of Wintergreen

A Picture of George Washington, of all people

LANDSLIDE, NEB.

John P. Wintergreen	12,538
A Man Named Wilkins	1

A Picture of Patrick Henry

HOLLYWOOD, CAL.

Wintergreen	160,000
Mickey Mouse	159,000
Gloria Swanson's First Husband	84,638

John P. Wintergreen Casting Ballot No. 8 at Public School 63 at 6.05 o'clock this morning.
[*And a picture of him doing so.*]

John P. Wintergreen Casting Ballot No. 168 at Public School 145 at 8.10 o'clock this morning and 2.25 this afternoon.

NEW YORK, N. Y.

Alexander Throttlebottom, Vice-presidential candidate, gets his shoes shined preparatory to entering election booth.
[*But one sees only the feet.*]

A Picture of the White House

Wintergreen again

NEW YORK, N. Y.
8 Rubbers Out of 150 Give:

Culbertson	300
Lenz	200
Grand Slam	1,000
Vulnerable	1,500

More pictures:
Benjamin Franklin
Babe Ruth [*just for good measure*].

NEW YORK, N. Y.
41 Election Districts give:

Wintergreen	46,572
Walter Hampden	136
Mae West	82

LEXINGTON, KENTUCKY

Wintergreen	27,637
Light Wines and Beer	14
Straight Whisky	1,850,827

Pictures again:
John P. Wintergreen
Patrick Henry
Primo Carnera
Man o' War

MANCHESTER, ENGLAND

Wintergreen	14,653
King George	3
Queen Mary	1

ROME, ITALY

127 Election Districts give:

Wintergreen	0
Mussolini	828,638

NEW YORK, N. Y.

Empire State gives Wintergreen plurality of 1,627,535, with only three counties missing

LATER

Three missing New York counties located by Pinkerton men in northeast Nebraska

More pictures:
George Washington
The Marx Brothers

NEW YORK, N. Y.
First Returns from Wall St. Give:

Wintergreen   192,000

Radio   5¾

Goldman, Sachs   2⅛

And still more pictures:
The White House
The Capitol
The Roxy
Roxy Himself
A Friend of Roxy's
An Unidentified Man
[*Who looks suspiciously like the Vice-presidential
candidate.*]

MACY'S BASEMENT

Wintergreen   ~~$1.50~~   97¢

(Only one to a customer)

RICHMOND, VA.

Wintergreen   98,728

Mason   499

Dixon   1

Mason & Dixon   500

ST. LOUIS, MO.

				R	H	E
Cardinals	000	010	000	1	4	1
Giants	000	000	002	2	5	0

All returns indicate that
Wintergreen is sweeping
Country!

Wintergreen lacks
only four votes
to win!

WINTERGREEN
CASTS LAST
FOUR VOTES!

WINTERGREEN
ELECTED!

Our Next President!
[A *beaming picture of* Wintergreen.]

Our Next First Lady!
[*Miss Turner at her gayest.*]

BULLETIN
At a late hour tonight the defeated candidate sent the
following telegram to John P. Wintergreen, the winner:
" Heartily congratulate you on your splendid victory and
charge fraud in Indiana, Illinois, Nebraska, Montana,
Washington, Ohio, and Massachusetts."

BULLETIN
At midnight tonight Alexander Throttlebottom refused
to concede his election as Vice-President.

NEXT WEEK:
NORMA SHEARER
in
" THE LOVE GIRL "

And, to finish off, the Metro-Goldwyn lion. It opens its mouth. It crows.

CURTAIN

SCENE 6: *On the steps of the Capitol, Washington, D. C. It is Inauguration Day, and the scene is one of flashing uniforms and surging crowds. Except for a cleared space in which the all-important ceremony is to take place — two ceremonies, as a matter of fact — the steps are packed with diplomats, Army and Navy attachés, Cabinet members, Senators, Congressmen, and anyone else who could get a ticket. As background for all this there looms the Capitol itself, with the great dome polishing it all off.*

A hush falls on the crowd. The proceedings are about to begin.

Enter, to music, the nine judges of the Supreme Court of the United States — wrapped in their black robes, and all looking astonishingly like a certain Chief Justice who shall be nameless.

The Judges sing.

JUDGES
 We're the one —
    two —
     three —
      four —
       five —
        six —
         seven —
          eight —
           nine Supreme Court judges;
 As the super-Solomons of this great nation,

We will supervise today's inauguration,
And we'll superintend the wedding celebration,
    In a manner official
    And judicial.

ALL

One, two, three, four, five, six, seven, eight, nine
    Supreme Court judges!

JUDGES

We have powers that are positively regal —
Only we can take a law and make it legal.

ALL

They're the A. K.s who give the O. K.s —
One, two, three, four, five, six, seven, eight, nine
    Supreme Court judges!

[*There is a great fanfare of trumpets in the distance
— a swelling cheer.*]

ALL

Hail, hail, the ruler of our gov'ment!
Hail, hail, the man who taught what love meant!
    Clear, clear the way
On his inaugural and wedding day!
Hail, hail, the mighty ruler of love!
Hail, hail, the man who made us love love!
    Hip, hip, hooray!
For his inaugural and wedding day!
    Hurray!

[*Enter, to terrific cheering, Wintergreen and the
Committee. High-hatted, frock-coated.*]

CHIEF JUSTICE. And now, Mr. President, if you don't mind,
we'd like your inaugural address.

WINTERGREEN [*to music*]

I have definite ideas about the Philippines,
    And the herring situation up in Bismarck;

I have notions on the salaries of movie queens,
  And the men who sign their signatures with *this* mark!

[*He makes a cross.*]

But on this glorious day I find
I'm sentimentally inclined,
And so —
I sing this to the girls I used to know:

Here's a kiss for Cinderella,
  And a parting kiss for May;
Toodle-oo, good-by! This is my wedding day!
Here's a final smile for Della,
  And the lady known as Lou;
Toodle-oo, good-by! With bach'lor days I'm through!

[*And the girls in question, believe it or not, parade
tantalizingly by him.*]

Though I really never knew them,
  It's a rule I must obey;
I am singing good-by to them
  In the customary way.
My regards to Arabella,
  And to Emmaline and Kay;
Toodle-oo, dear girls, good-by! This is my wedding day!

ALL

He is toodle-ooing all his lady loves,
  All the girls he didn't know so well;
All the innocent and all the shady loves —
  Oh, dinga donga dell!

Bride and groom! Their future should be glorious;
  What a happy story they will tell!
Let the welkin now become uproarious —
  Oh, dinga donga, dinga donga dell!

[*On a platform at the head of the stairs, as if by
magic, there appears Mary Turner, gorgeous in
bridal attire.*]

Clear the way!
Hail the bride!
Sweet and gay —
Here comes the bride!

MARY

Is it true or am I dreaming?
Do I go to heav'n to stay?
Never was a girl so happy on her wedding day!

CHIEF JUSTICE. Do you, John P. Wintergreen, solemnly swear to uphold the Constitution of the United States of America and to love, honor, and cherish this woman so long as you two shall live?

WINTERGREEN. I do.

CHIEF JUSTICE. Do you, Mary Turner, promise to love, honor, and cherish this man so long as you two shall live?

MARY. I do.

CHIEF JUSTICE. Therefore, by virtue of the power that is vested in me as Chief Justice, I hereby pronounce you President of the United States, man and wife.

WINTERGREEN. Mary!

MARY. John!

[*They embrace; the Crowd yells its head off.*]

WINTERGREEN and MARY

Is it true or am I dreaming?
Do I go to heav'n to stay?
Never was a girl so happy on her wedding —

[*Enter, of all people, Diana Devereaux. And is she annoyed?*]

DIANA. Stop! Halt! Pause! Wait!

ALL

Who is this intruder?
There's no one could be ruder!
What's your silly notion
In causing this commotion?

DIANA [*recitative, and with highly operatic interludes*]. I was

the most beautiful blossom in all the Southland. I was sent up
north to enter the contest, with the understanding that the winner
was to be the President's wife. The committee examined me. My
lily-white body fascinated them. I was chosen. It was the happiest
moment of my life.

ALL. Yes, yes, go on! Yes, yes, go on!

DIANA. Suddenly the sky fell — suddenly for no reason at all,
no reason at all, this man rejected me. All my castles came tumbling down. And so I am serving him with a summons — for breach
of promise!

ALL

> What! What!
> The water's getting hot!
> She says he made a promise —
> A promise he forgot!

DIANA

> It's true! It's true!

CHIEF JUSTICE

> The day he's getting married,
> You put him on the spot!

ALL

> It's dirty work of Russia —
> A communistic plot!

WINTERGREEN

Please understand! It wasn't that I would jilt or spurn 'er;
It's just that there was someone else!

ALL. Whom?

WINTERGREEN [*correcting them*]. Who! Mary Turner!

CHIEF JUSTICE

> We're having fits!
> The man admits
> This little sinner
> Was really winner!

DIANA

> I couldn't see
> His jilting me,
> And so I'm doing
> A bit of suing.

ALL

And if it's true she has a claim,
You should be called a dirty name!
Yes, if it's true she has a claim,
Then you're a dirty, dirty name!

MARY

John, no matter what they do to hurt you,
The one you love won't desert you.

DIANA

I'm a queen who has lost her king:
Why should she wear the wedding ring?

WINTERGREEN

Some girls can bake a pie,
   Made up of prunes and quinces,
Some make an oyster fry —
   Others are good at blintzes.
Some lovely girls have done
   Wonders with turkey stuffin's,
But I have found the one
   Who can really make corn muffins!

ALL

Yes, he has found the one
Who can really make corn muffins.

DIANA. Who cares about corn muffins? All I demand is justice!

WINTERGREEN and MARY. Which is more important — corn muffins or justice?

ALL. Which is more important — corn muffins or justice?

CHIEF JUSTICE. If you will wait a moment — you'll have our decision. Forty — seven — eleven —

[*The Justices leap into a football huddle. After a moment they resume their positions.*]

CHIEF JUSTICE. The decision of the Supreme Court is — corn muffins!

ALL

Great! Great!
It's written on the slate!

There's none but Mary Turner
Could ever be his mate!

DIANA

It's I, not Mary Turner,
Who should have been his mate;
I'm off to tell my story
In ev'ry single state!

CHIEF JUSTICE

Be off with you, young woman,
He's married to his mate!
Be off with you, young woman,
He's married to his mate!

[Diana goes, but she'll be heard from again.]

ALL

There's none but Mary Turner
Could ever be his mate!
There's none but Mary Turner
Could ever be his mate!

WINTERGREEN

Of thee I sing, baby,
Summer, autumn, winter, spring, baby —
Shining star and inspiration,
Worthy of a mighty nation,
Of thee I sing!

CURTAIN

ACT II

SCENE 1: *The President's office, in the White House. And not only the President's office, but the President's wife's office, too. There are several indications of this joint occupancy. The Presidential desk, for example, is divided into two sections — one piled high with various state papers, and the other lined with perfumes, powders, and the other perquisites of femininity. Great portraits of George* and Martha Washington look down from on high; the governmental eagle adorns the curtains.

The same Jenkins who used to work for Mr. Fulton is now secretary to the President, and with Mrs. Wintergreen's secretary, Miss Benson, he is hard at work when the curtain rises. Enter, to music, about two dozen more secretaries. They all get together in a little song and dance — an old White House custom:

> Oh, it's great to be a secret'ry
>   In the White House, D. C.
> You get inside information on Algeria;
> You know ev'ry move they're making in Liberia.
> You learn what's what and what is not
>   In the land of the free.
> Ev'ry corner that you turn you meet a notable
> With a statement that is eminently quotable —
>   Oh, it's great to be a secret'ry
>   In the White House, D. C.

> [A White House Guide enters, followed by a crowd
> of Sightseers. They are plainly from the country —
> men with loosely wrapped umbrellas, women with
> waistlines not in the right place, and a terrible
> child or two.]

GUIDE. And this, ladies and gentlemen, is the executive office. This is the room in which the President discharges his official duties, and has been occupied by every President since Hoover. On your right stands the famous double desk used by the President and Mrs. Wintergreen in administering the affairs of the country. During the 1912 coal shortage this room was used as a garage. Right this way, please. We are now entering the room from which, on a historic occasion, the Spanish Ambassador jumped out of the window, in the very nick of time. Here the diplomatic corps gathers once a month to pay its formal respects to the chief executive, and here too the Cabinet assembles when —

> [The last Sightseer is through the door.]
> [The telephone on the desk rings.]

JENKINS. Hello. . . . Who? . . . No, the Coolidges don't live here any more!

MISS BENSON [*holding a perfume bottle up to the light*]. Mrs. Wintergreen is running low on Chanel No. 5.

JENKINS [*consulting a schedule*]. Looks like a pretty full day. [*Reads.*] Delegation from South America —

MISS BENSON. What's eating them?

JENKINS. Usual thing. Want Hollywood cleaned up. [*Looking at list.*] Delegation of Camisole Indians — they want scalping restored. Committee of cotton-manufacturers — that's for Mrs. Wintergreen. They want her to bring back cotton stockings.

MISS BENSON. Oh, they do, eh?

JENKINS. Mayors of fourteen American cities — [*Another Secretary enters with newspaper clippings.*] Well?

SECRETARY. Morning editorials.

[*He goes, Jenkins looks the clippings over; shakes his head.*]

MISS BENSON. What's the matter?

JENKINS. Same thing. They're still harping on it.

MISS BENSON. You mean Devereaux?

JENKINS [*as he reads*]. Mm.

MISS BENSON. What's it say?

JENKINS. Nothing new. They just think she got a raw deal.

MISS BENSON. A lot of people think that.

JENKINS [*crumpling a clipping*]. Just as well if he doesn't see this one. You know, it wouldn't surprise me a bit —

[*Another Secretary enters.*]

SECRETARY. Mr. Jenkins —

JENKINS. Yes?

SECRETARY. Those people are here now. Can you see them?

JENKINS. Show them into the Blue Room.

SECRETARY. Yes, sir. [*Goes.*]

JENKINS. Want to come along? Delegation from the Virgin Islands.

MISS BENSON. Well, well! And what are they after?

JENKINS. They want their name changed. They claim it's hurting business.

[*They go, as another Guide enters with a sightseeing party. A Sailor or two. A Swede. A Dutchman.*]

GUIDE. Right this way, please — follow me. This, ladies and

gentlemen, is the executive office. It is in this room that the President signs the many laws that govern your everyday life, and from which he controls the various departmental activities. [*One of the Sightseers emerges a bit from the crowd, eagerly taking in the scene. He turns out to be, of all people, Alexander Throttlebottom.*] Here come the various heads of government for daily consultation with the executive, and to receive from him the benefit of his wide experience. It is in this room — [*To Throttlebottom, who has strayed a little too far from the group.*] I beg your pardon, sir, but would you please stay over there with the others? You see, we're personally responsible in case anything is stolen.

THROTTLEBOTTOM [*meekly rejoining the group*]. Yes, sir.

GUIDE [*opens door*] Thank you. [*Resuming his formal tone.*] Now, are there any questions?

A SIGHTSEER. Does the President live here all year round?

GUIDE. All year round. Except when Congress is in session.

SIGHTSEER. Where does the Vice-president live?

GUIDE. Who?

SIGHTSEER. The Vice-president. Where does he live?

GUIDE [*taking a little red book out of his pocket*]. Just one moment, please. Vice-regent, viceroy, vice societies — I'm sorry, but he doesn't seem to be in here.

THROTTLEBOTTOM [*so mildly*]. I can tell you about that.

GUIDE. What?

THROTTLEBOTTOM. I know where the Vice-president lives.

GUIDE. Where?

THROTTLEBOTTOM. He lives at 1448 Z Street.

GUIDE. Well, that's very interesting. He has a house there, has he?

THROTTLEBOTTOM. Well, he lives there.

GUIDE. All by himself?

THROTTLEBOTTOM. No, with the other boarders. It's an awfully good place. Mrs. Spiegelbaum's. It's a great place, if you like Kosher cooking.

GUIDE. Think of your knowing all that! Are you a Washingtonian?

THROTTLEBOTTOM. Well, I've been here since March 4. I came down for the inauguration, but I lost my ticket.

GUIDE. You don't say! Well! First time you've been to the White House?

THROTTLEBOTTOM [*nods*]. I didn't know people were allowed in.

GUIDE. You seem to know the Vice-president pretty well. What kind of fellow is he?

THROTTLEBOTTOM. He's all right. He's a nice fellow when you get to know him, but nobody wants to know him.

GUIDE. What's the matter with him?

THROTTLEBOTTOM. There's nothing the matter with him. Just Vice-president.

GUIDE. Well, what does he do all the time?

THROTTLEBOTTOM. He sits around in the parks, and feeds the pigeons, and takes walks, and goes to the movies. The other day he was going to join the library, but he had to have two references, so he couldn't get in.

GUIDE. But when does he do all his work?

THROTTLEBOTTOM. What work?

SIGHTSEER. Doesn't he preside over the Senate?

THROTTLEBOTTOM. What?

GUIDE. Sure he does! That's the Vice-president's job.

THROTTLEBOTTOM. What is?

GUIDE. To preside over the Senate.

THROTTLEBOTTOM. Over what?

GUIDE. The Senate. You know what Senators are, don't you?

THROTTLEBOTTOM. Sure — I saw them play yesterday.

GUIDE. No, no! The Vice-president presides over the Senate. It meets in the Capitol.

THROTTLEBOTTOM. When does it?

GUIDE. Right now! It's going on now!

THROTTLEBOTTOM [*frenzied*]. How do you get there?

GUIDE. The Capitol?

THROTTLEBOTTOM. Yeah!

GUIDE. Street car at the door — right up Pennsylvania Avenue.

THROTTLEBOTTOM [*hurrying out*]. Street car at the door — right up Pennsyl — [*Turns back.*] — what's the name of that place?

GUIDE. The Senate!

THROTTLEBOTTOM. The Senate! [*He dashes out.*]

GUIDE. Right this way, please. [*Opens door.*] Here the diplo-matic corps gathers monthly to pay its formal respects to the chief executive, and here too the Cabinet assembles upon the occasion of its weekly meetings —

> [*They go. In the distance there is a fanfare of trumpets; Jenkins and Miss Benson enter and take their places at the Presidential chairs. Enter, then, the President and Mary.*]

WINTERGREEN and MARY: Good morning!

JENKINS and MISS BENSON: Good morning!

> [*Wintergreen looks out the window, through which is visible the panorama of Washington, with the Washington Monument prominent in the foreground.*]

WINTERGREEN. What a country — what a country! Jenkins, what monument is that?

JENKINS [*promptly*]. Grant's Tomb.

WINTERGREEN. Oh, yes. Well, what's on the schedule this morning? Ah, here we are! [*Takes up some letters.*] Tell the Secre-tary of the Navy to scrap two battleships.

JENKINS. What?

WINTERGREEN. Scrap two and build four. Disarmament.

JENKINS. Yes, sir.

WINTERGREEN. Cablegram to the President of San Domingo: "Congratulations on beginning your second day in office. That's five I owe you, and will bet you double or nothing on tomorrow."

JENKINS. Yes, sir.

WINTERGREEN. Tell the Secretary of War to stand ready to collect that bet.

JENKINS. Yes, sir.

WINTERGREEN. Letter to the Friars' Club, 48th Street, New York City. "Dear Brother Friars: Regret very much I cannot take part in this year's minstrel show. Owing to conditions in the South, I do not think it would be wise for me to black up." [*Looks through the pile of letters.*] I get the lousiest mail for a President!

MARY. Emily! Take a cablegram to the Queen of Roumania.

MISS BENSON. Yes, ma'am.

MARY. Queen of Roumania. " Dear Marie: I have been trying out that new soap you are selling, and I predict an even greater success for it than you had with the shaving-cream. Jack joins me in sending love. Do write and tell us all about Carol."

WINTERGREEN. And that French girl. . . . Jenkins!

JENKINS. Yes, sir.

WINTERGREEN. Take a memo to the Secretary of State: " Referring to last Tuesday night's poker game, please note that the Liberian Minister's check for twelve dollars and forty-five cents has been returned for lack of funds. Kindly get a new minister for next Tuesday night's game, and add twelve dollars and forty-five cents to the Liberian national debt."

JENKINS. Yes, sir.

WINTERGREEN. Get the Governor of Maryland on the phone and ask him what horse he likes in the fourth at Pimlico.

JENKINS. Yes, sir.

WINTERGREEN [*brandishing a telephone bill*]. And tell the telephone company that this is not my bill. [*Hands it to secretary.*] That long-distance call was March 3rd.

JENKINS. Yes, sir.

WINTERGREEN. Anybody in the anteroom?

JENKINS. Yes, sir. Secretary of the Navy, Secretary of Agriculture, and four zebras.

WINTERGREEN. Zebras?

JENKINS. There's a man who wants to give them to you.

WINTERGREEN [*thinking it over*]. Well, I could use two.

[*A Secretary enters with a wooden board, covered with electric buttons. A long wire is attached to it.*]

JENKINS. All ready, Mr. President. Time to press a button.

WINTERGREEN. So early in the morning?

JENKINS. Opening of the International Corn-Growing Exposition. Button No. 1. . . . Ready. . . . Press.

WINTERGREEN [*presses button, then laughs*]. Say, Jenkins, I never will forget the time I reopened the Bank of the United States by mistake. [*Jenkins beats a hasty retreat.*] [*The telephone rings.*] Hello! [*Annoyed, hands the instrument to Mary.*] For you!

MARY. Who is it?

WINTERGREEN. The butcher!

MARY. Hello! . . . Oh, good morning, Mr. Schneidermann.
. . . Fine, thank you. . . . Now, let me see. What have you got
that's good? . . . Well, we had lamb chops yesterday. . . . They
are? Well, wait a minute. [*To Wintergreen.*] John, who's coming
to dinner tonight?

WINTERGREEN. What? Let me see — the Chief Justice, the
Attorney General, Jackie Cooper, and those three judges that got
paroled. That's six.

MARY [*as she returns to phone*]. That's eight with us. . . .
Hello, Mr. Schneidermann. Make it sixteen lamb chops —

WINTERGREEN. Wait a minute! What about that dirigible?

MARY. What?

WINTERGREEN. That dirigible from Germany. If that gets in
we've got to have *them.*

MARY. Oh, dear! How many are there?

WINTERGREEN. Ah — sixty-four passengers, and of course two
stowaways — that's sixty-six.

MARY. That's seventy-four in all.

WINTERGREEN. But they may not get here.

MARY. But when'll we know? . . . Just a minute, Mr.
Schneidermann. [*Back to Wintergreen, pretty testily.*] I've got to
know whether they're going to get here.

WINTERGREEN. How do I know? Take a chance! You can
always use lamb chops.

MARY [*back to phone, wearily*]. Listen, Mr. Schneidermann.
A hundred and forty-eight lamb chops. . . . That's right. . . .
Now, how is your asparagus? . . . Well, make it a carload of asparagus, and about seventy-five loaves of rye bread. That's all,
thank you.

JENKINS [*entering*]. Beg pardon, sir. Another button.

WINTERGREEN. What's this? [*Reads.*] Opening of a new
speakeasy on 52d Street, New York. Didn't I open that yesterday?

JENKINS. Yes, sir. This is the reopening. They closed it last
night. [*He goes.*]

MARY [*coming to Wintergreen with a stack of bills in her
hand*]. John, look at these grocery bills!

WINTERGREEN. Well, what about it?

MARY. I've simply got to have a bigger allowance.

WINTERGREEN. Again! For God's sake, Mary!

MARY. Well, I can't help it. Fifty people to dinner every night. And Senators to breakfast every morning. It mounts up.

WINTERGREEN. I've got to have them! It's business!

MARY. Then you've got to give me enough to feed them.

WINTERGREEN. Where am I going to get it from?

MARY. Get it from! If you had any gumption you'd ask Congress for a raise.

WINTERGREEN. Ask Congress for a raise! I'm lucky they don't lay me off!

[*Jenkins enters.*]

JENKINS. I beg your pardon.

WINTERGREEN. It's all right. What is it?

JENKINS. The Secretary of Agriculture and the Secretary of the Navy are still waiting.

WINTERGREEN. I forgot. Have them come in.

SECRETARY. The Secretary of Agriculture!

[*He enters. It turns out to be our old friend Lippman.*]

LIPPMAN. Hello, Jack! Hello, Mary!

WINTERGREEN. Hello, Secretary!

SECRETARY. The Secretary of the Navy!

[*Enter Gilhooley. It seems that Wintergreen took care of the boys.*]

WINTERGREEN. Sit down, boys. Sorry I kept you waiting.

LIPPMAN. That's all right.

GILHOOLEY. O.K., chief.

WINTERGREEN. Well, what's on your mind, Louis? How's agriculture?

LIPPMAN. That's what I came to talk to you about. Listen, Jack! I don't know anything about agriculture. I told you I wanted the Treasury.

WINTERGREEN. What's the matter with agriculture?

LIPPMAN. Agriculture's all right — it's those farmers. Wheat, wheat! All they know is raise wheat! And then they raise hell with me because nobody wants it.

WINTERGREEN. Why do you let them raise so much?

LIPPMAN. How can you stop 'em? I did all I could. I invited

the seven-year locusts, but they didn't come. Even the locusts don't want their lousy wheat. And they're always complaining about being in one place all the time — they want to travel.

GILHOOLEY. You call that trouble. How'd you like to have a lot of sailors on your neck?

WINTERGREEN. What do *they* want — two wives in every port?

GILHOOLEY. Yeah. And any port in a storm. And no storms. And they won't stand for those bells any more. They want to know what time it is the same as anybody else. But that's not the big thing.

WINTERGREEN. Well?

GILHOOLEY. It's the ocean. They don't like the ocean.

WINTERGREEN. Which ocean don't they like?

GILHOOLEY. All of them. They say it's a nice place to visit, but they don't want to live there. It's no place to bring up a family.

WINTERGREEN [*thinking it over*]. The farmers want to travel and the sailors want to settle down. . . . I've got it! Have them change places!

LIPPMAN. What?

WINTERGREEN. It'll solve the whole problem! Sailors don't know anything about farming — in two years there won't *be* any wheat! You'll have a wheat shortage!

LIPPMAN. And I'll get hell again!

WINTERGREEN. And look what it does for business! You get the farmers on the boats; the traveling salesmen will come back to the farmhouses — you know, to stay overnight! Why, I haven't heard a good story in years!

[*A Secretary enters.*]

SECRETARY. The Secretary of State!

[*He comes in. It is Fulton.*]

FULTON. Hello, boys. Everybody.

WINTERGREEN. How are you, Matty?

FULTON [*all business*]. What are you doing, Jack? Important?

WINTERGREEN. Just chinning.

FULTON [*a look toward the doors*]. Can you keep the room clear for a little while?

WINTERGREEN. Sure. What's up?

FULTON [*starts toward door*]. Shall I tell 'em?

WINTERGREEN. No, here we are. [*Presses a buzzer.*]

LIPPMAN [*starting off*]. See you later.

FULTON. No, no. Want you fellows to stay.

[*Jenkins enters.*]

WINTERGREEN. I don't want to be disturbed for a little while.

JENKINS. Yes, sir.

FULTON. Just a minute. When Senators Jones and Lyons get here, bring 'em in.

JENKINS. Yes, sir.

FULTON. And nobody else.

JENKINS. Yes, sir. What shall I do about the press conference?

FULTON. Have 'em wait! [*Jenkins goes. Fulton waits for the doors to close.*] There's hell to pay!

WINTERGREEN. What's the matter?

FULTON. Devereaux!

MARY. John!

[*He puts an arm around her.*]

WINTERGREEN. What about her?

FULTON. The thing has been growing for weeks — you know that, boys — [*This to Lippman and Gilhooley.*]

WINTERGREEN. What has?

FULTON. Well, you know there's always been a certain bunch that said Devereaux didn't get a square deal.

WINTERGREEN. A handful of Southerners!

FULTON. At the beginning, yes. But now it's spreading all over the country!

WINTERGREEN. What do you mean?

MARY. What's happened?

FULTON. I'll tell you what I mean. Yesterday the Federation of New Jersey Women's Clubs came out solid for Devereaux.

MARY. John! [*A sob from Mary.*]

FULTON. And this morning I got a petition from the Kansas

City Elks — demanding Devereaux! And the same thing'll happen
with the Moose and the Shriners!

> [*Enter Senators Jones and Lyons.*]
> [*A nod or two from the others.*]

FULTON. Good! I've just been telling the President how
things stand!

JONES. Mr. President, I cannot overstate the case. The West
is up in arms.

LYONS. The South, suh, is on fire!

JONES. Nebraska has just declared martial law! A posse has
been formed!

LYONS. In Louisiana you have been hanged in effigy!

WINTERGREEN [*defiant*]. How do the Philippines feel about
it?

MARY. It's all my fault!

WINTERGREEN. No! I'd rather have you than Nebraska!

FULTON. It doesn't matter whose fault it is. We've got to do
something! We've got to do something to counteract this Devereaux propaganda!

WINTERGREEN. I'll tell you what we'll do! [*Presses a buzzer.*]
We carried forty-eight States in the campaign, didn't we? Mary
and I?

FULTON. Yeah!

WINTERGREEN. And there was Devereaux propaganda then!
But we licked it before and we can do it again! [*As Jenkins enters.*]
Those newspapermen still out there?

JENKINS. Yes, sir.

WINTERGREEN. Bring 'em in when I ring!

JENKINS. Yes, sir. [*Goes.*]

WINTERGREEN. The trouble with you boys is you're yellow!

FULTON. Now, look here!

WINTERGREEN. One sock and you're ready to quit! We've got
to fight, that's all! I'm as good as I ever was! And so's Mary! And
we still love each other! [*Turning to her.*] Don't we?

MARY [*with spirit*]. You bet we do!

WINTERGREEN [*swinging back onto the men*]. There you are!
We're not through! We haven't begun to fight! By God, we can
tour again if we have to! I can still sing! Once a trouper, always a

trouper! [*Mary is freshening the lipstick and powdering the face.*]
What do you say, boys? Are you with me?

ALL. Yes!

[*Wintergreen presses the buzzer.*]

FULTON. You got to put it over, Jack!

WINTERGREEN. I'll put it over! I'll give them the best performance since Richard Mansfield! Are you ready, Mary?

MARY [*finishing the make-up job*]. Ready!

WINTERGREEN [*as a Secretary enters*]. Bring in those newspapermen!

[*Music strikes up. Enter the Newspapermen.*]

WINTERGREEN. Well, gentlemen, what's on your mind?

REPORTERS [*singing it, of course*]
We don't want to know about the moratorium,
    Or how near we are to beer,
        Or about the League of Nations,
        Or the seventeen vacations
    You have had since you've been here.

Here's the one thing that the people of America
    Are beside themselves to know:
        They would like to know what's doing
        On the lady who is suing
    You — Diana Devereaux?

        Ev'rybody wants to know:
        What about Miss Devereaux?
        From the highest to the low:
        What about Miss Devereaux?

WINTERGREEN
        It's a pleasant day —
        That's all I can say!

MARY
    Here's the one thing we'll announce:
    Love's the only thing that counts!

REPORTERS
            People want to know:
            What of Devereaux?

WINTERGREEN

> When the one you love is near,
> Nothing else can interfere.

ALL

> When the one you love is near,
> Nothing else can interfere.

WINTERGREEN

> Here's some information
> I will gladly give the nation:
> I am for the true love,
> Here's the only girl I do love.

MARY

> I love him and he loves me
> And that's how it will always be,
> So what care we about Miss Devereaux?
>
> Who cares what the public chatters?
> Love's the only thing that matters.

WINTERGREEN

> Who cares
> If the sky cares to fall in the sea?
> Who cares what banks fail in Yonkers,
> Long as you've got a kiss that conquers?
> Why should I sigh?
> Life is one long jubilee,
> So long as I care for you
> And you care for me.

> [*This argument being unanswerable, the Reporters
> go, completely convinced. The Committee, highly
> pleased, surrounds Wintergreen and congratulates
> him.*]

WINTERGREEN. Nothing at all, boys! I owe it all to the little
woman!

MARY. You were grand, John!

FULTON. I never heard you in better voice!

WINTERGREEN. Did you hear that F sharp I gave them?

GILHOOLEY. Great!

WINTERGREEN [*letting his voice loose for a second in a snatch of operatic aria*]. Do you know what I'll do? I'll go on the radio every night! Mary and I!

FULTON. National Biscuit Co.! They've been after you!

JONES. National Biscuit! That's a very popular hour in the West!

WINTERGREEN. A new song every night! I'll even get a megaphone!

MARY. And we can make records!

WINTERGREEN [*ever practical*]. No, dear. They don't sell any more!

FULTON. Well, every little helps!

MARY. And I can still bake!

WINTERGREEN. What!

MARY. Corn muffins! Corn muffins for the unemployed!

WINTERGREEN. That's my girl! You feed 'em and I'll sing to them! We'll get the country back! Give us a week and they'll forget that Devereaux ever lived! [*A chorus of approval from the Committee.*] And you fellows wanted to quit! Why, we haven't begun to fight! This is a cinch! What would you do if a real fight came along! [*Enter a dozen Secretaries.*] What's this?

SECRETARIES. The French Ambassador!

WINTERGREEN. I can't see him! [*Enter another dozen Secretaries.*] And what's this?

SECRETARIES. The French Ambassador!

WINTERGREEN. I can't see him!

> [*Enter half a dozen French Soldiers, in full uniforms and oh! what beards! They line up and sing, it being an old rule that French Soldiers always sing when they line up.*]

> Garçon, s'il vous plaît,
> Encore Chevrolet Coupé;
> Papah, pooh, pooh, pooh!
> A vous toot dir veh, à vous?
> Garçon, q'est-ce que c'est?
> Tra la, Maurice Chevalier!

> J'adore crêpes Suzette
> Et aussi Lafayette!

And now we give the meaning of our song:
We're six of the fifty million and we can't be wrong!

> [*Enter the French Ambassador. You never saw so
> many medals.*]

FRENCH SOLDIERS. Ze French Ambassador!

WINTERGREEN. I still can't see him!

FRENCH AMBASSADOR [*sings*]. I am the Ambassador of France!

WINTERGREEN. Europe?

FRENCH AMBASSADOR [*recitative*]. And I have come here to see a grievous wrong righted. My country is deeply hurt. Not since the days of Louis the Seventh, the Eighth, the Ninth, the Tenth, and possibly the Eleventh have such a thing happen!

WINTERGREEN. What's troubling you?

FRENCH AMBASSADOR. You have done a great injustice to a French descendant — a lovely girl whose rights have been trampled in the dust!

ALL. Who is she? What's her name?

FRENCH AMBASSADOR. Her name is Diana Devereaux.

ALL. Diana Devereaux! Diana Devereaux! Since when is she of French descent?

FRENCH AMBASSADOR

> I've been looking up her family tree,
> And I have found a most important pedigree!
>
> She's the illegitimate daughter
> Of an illegitimate son
> Of an illegitimate nephew
> Of Napoleon!

ALL [*awed*]. Napoleon!

FRENCH AMBASSADOR

> She offers aristocracy
> To this bizarre democracy,
> Where naught is sacred but the old simoleon!
> I must know why
> You crucify

My native country
With this effront'ry,
To the illegitimate daughter of an illegitimate son
Of an illegitimate nephew of Napoleon!

ALL

To the illegitimate daughter of an illegitimate son
Of an illegitimate nephew of Napoleon!

COMMITTEE

You so-and-so!
We didn't know
She had a tie-up
So very high up.
She's the illegitimate daughter of an illegitimate son
Of an illegitimate nephew of Napoleon!

[*The voice of Diana is heard in the distance. A snatch of aria. She enters, singing.*]

DIANA

I was the most beautiful blossom in all the Southland.

WINTERGREEN and MARY. We know all that.

FRENCH AMBASSADOR. You know all that — but you *don't* know the misery of this poor little girl who has suffered. Because —

COMMITTEE. Because —

WINTERGREEN and MARY. Because?

FRENCH AMBASSADOR. Because?

DIANA [*It seems to be a reprise*]

Because, because, because, because —
I won the competition,
But I got no recognition,
And because he broke my heart!
Because, because, because, because —
The man who ought to love me
Tried to make a monkey of me;
Double-crossing from the start!
I might have been First Lady,
But now my past is shady;
Oh, pity this poor maidie!

FRENCH AMBASSADOR. And there's the man who ought to pay!

ALL

> Because, because, because, because —
> She won the prize for beauty
> And he didn't do his duty,
> He has broken her poor heart!

FRENCH AMBASSADOR. You see how this poor child has suffered. And so, on behalf of France, I demand that your marriage be annulled and that you marry Diana!

WINTERGREEN. Never! Never!

FRENCH AMBASSADOR. Then you will arouse the anger of France and you must be prepared to face the consequences!

> [*The French contingent, with Diana, marches off,
> singing: " Garçon, s'il vous plaît." There is a mo-
> mentous pause.*]

FULTON. Jack, you've got to do something about this!

WINTERGREEN. Leave my Mary? Never!

FULTON

> We are all in this together;
> We are birdies of a feather;
> And if you don't change your thesis,
> Then our party goes to pieces!

LYONS

> All our jobs you'll be destroying
> With your attitude annoying.

GILHOOLEY

> You will get us all in trouble!
> And in spades, sir, which is double!

WINTERGREEN

> I will never leave my Mary!

LYONS

> Since he's acting so contrary,
> Send him off on a vacation!

GILHOOLEY

> I suggest his resignation!

WINTERGREEN

> Resignation?

ALL

> Resignation!

FULTON

> You've got to face it — this is a crisis!
> To leave your Mary, you may decline,
> But to save us, my good advice is —
>   You resign!

ALL

> Yes, resign!

WINTERGREEN

> I assure you, though it's a crisis,
> To leave my Mary I must decline
> And I don't care what your advice is,
>   I decline to resign!

MARY

>   We decline to resign!

ALL

> He is stubborn — we must teach him;
> I'm afraid we must impeach him!
>
> He is stubborn — we must teach him;
> He has forced us to impeach him!
>   You decline to resign,
>   So we'll teach you!
>   We'll impeach you!
>   You decline to resign —
> We don't envy you at all!
>   You decline to resign,
>   So we'll teach you,
>   We'll impeach you!
>   You decline to resign —
> Humpty Dumpty has to fall!

> [*They go — leaving Wintergreen and Mary alone.
> In the circumstances there is only one thing to
> do — and they do it. They sing a reprise.*]

Who cares
If the sky cares to fall in the sea?
We two together can win out;
Just remember to stick your chin out.

> Why should we sigh?
> Life is one long jubilee —
> So long as I care for you
> And you care for me.

[*The lights dim; the curtains come together.*]

SCENE 2: *A Capitol corridor, just outside the United States Senate.*
A smartly dressed page comes out of the Senate door; another
goes in.

Enter, then, the Committee — those same five boys. As they
come in Fulton is doing the talking.

FULTON. Say, I'm just as sorry as anybody. I like Jack as
much as you do, and I'd give my shirt not to have to do this.

JONES. We can't be sentimental at a time like this.

GILHOOLEY. Say! Wait a minute! If he's put out of office,
who becomes the President?

JONES. Why, the Vice-president, of course.

LIPPMAN. Who's that?

FULTON [*as it dawns on him*]. We haven't got a Vice-president.

GILHOOLEY. Sure we have! He came up to the room!
> [*Enter Alexander Throttlebottom. He is panting,*
> *having run all the way from the White House. The*
> *Committee continues its argument.*]

FULTON [*suddenly remembering*]. Pitts! I nominated him!
> [*A chorus of dissent. Lippman: "No, that wasn't*
> *his name!" Jones: "It was Schaeffer!" Lyons:*
> *"No, Pitts!" Gilhooley: "No, it was a longer*
> *name, Barbinelli!"*]
> [*Throttlebottom, who has been listening to all this*
> *in full expectation of imminent discovery, now*
> *comes over to them.*]

THROTTLEBOTTOM. Hello, gentlemen!

FULTON. It was Alexander something.

GILHOOLEY. Yah, that's it!

THROTTLEBOTTOM. Throttlebottom.

GILHOOLEY. That's right!

[*A chorus from the others.* "*Yes, that's right!*"]

FULTON [*realizing that it is a stranger who has spoken*]. Oh! Thank you. [*Hands him a cigar.*]

THROTTLEBOTTOM. Oh, thank you, Mr. Fulton.

FULTON [*looking at him*]. Haven't I seen you before some place?

THROTTLEBOTTOM. I'm Throttlebottom.

FULTON. Huh?

THROTTLEBOTTOM. Throttlebottom. The Vice-president. That's how I knew the name.

[*A chorus of greetings.* "*Well, hello!*" "*Where have you been?*" "*Well, for God's sake!*" "*Here! Have a light!*"]

FULTON. Well, for heaven's sake! Just the fellow we were looking for!

GILHOOLEY. Yes, sir!

FULTON. We want to talk to you!

THROTTLEBOTTOM. Me?

LYONS. That's what!

FULTON. We've got a surprise for you!

THROTTLEBOTTOM [*covering his eyes*]. A surprise?

LIPPMAN. Sure! Remember I told you you had a chance to be President?

THROTTLEBOTTOM. Yeah!

FULTON. Well, we've been thinking it over and we're going to make you President!

GILHOOLEY. That's what we are!

THROTTLEBOTTOM. President! Say! You mean of the United States?

JONES. That's what we do!

THROTTLEBOTTOM. But what was the matter with the other fellow?

FULTON. We're going to impeach him!

GILHOOLEY. He wouldn't play ball with us!

THROTTLEBOTTOM. Well, I don't play very well — you see this finger —

FULTON. Come on! Let's get started!

GILHOOLEY. Yeah, we've got work to do!

THROTTLEBOTTOM. You really mean it? I'm not Vice-president any more?

JONES. Not if we impeach the President!

THROTTLEBOTTOM. Well, when do we do that?

JONES. Right now! Come on!

FULTON. You've got to preside over the Senate!

THROTTLEBOTTOM. And after that I'll be President?

LYONS. That's what you will!

> [*The Committee enters the Senate. Throttlebottom is about to follow when a Scrubwoman comes along the corridor.*]

THROTTLEBOTTOM. President! Say! [*To the Scrubwoman.*] How will that sound? President Alexander Bottlethrottom. [*Corrects himself.*] Throttlebottom.

SCRUBWOMAN. Huh?

THROTTLEBOTTOM [*He has to tell someone*]. I'm going to be President!

SCRUBWOMAN. I'd rather have this job. It's steady. [*She goes, just as Wintergreen and Jenkins arrive from the other side.*]

JENKINS. Well, it's a dirty trick, chief. That's all I've got to say.

WINTERGREEN. It's politics. They've got to eat, too.

JENKINS. Want me to go in with you?

WINTERGREEN. No. I want to handle this alone.

JENKINS. More power to you, chief. [*Takes his hand; holds it during the following speech.*] And I want you to know that if the worst comes to the worst, and they fire you out —

WINTERGREEN. I know — if they fire me out you want a job with the next President.

JENKINS. Right! [*He goes.*]

> [*Wintergreen starts for the door into the Senate.*]

THROTTLEBOTTOM. Hello, Mr. President. Hey!

WINTERGREEN. Hey?

THROTTLEBOTTOM. I'll bet you don't remember me, do you?

WINTERGREEN [*after a searching gaze*]. You're the fellow that gave me that dill pickle.

THROTTLEBOTTOM. That's right.

WINTERGREEN. What are you doing now?

THROTTLEBOTTOM. I'm Vice-president.

WINTERGREEN. You don't say! Lost your other job, huh?

THROTTLEBOTTOM. Well, I'm going to have a good job now, because I'm going to be President.

WINTERGREEN [*realizing it*]. Say, that's right! If they kick me out, that makes you President.

THROTTLEBOTTOM. Say, I wonder if you'd mind doing me a favor?

WINTERGREEN. Sure!

THROTTLEBOTTOM. You see, I don't know anything about being President. I just found out today how to be Vice-president.

WINTERGREEN. Well, that's something.

THROTTLEBOTTOM. Isn't there some book I could read?

WINTERGREEN. Yes. I'm writing one. *What Every Young President Ought to Know.*

THROTTLEBOTTOM. Has it got pictures?

WINTERGREEN. It's got everything! Tells you just what to do! Of course the first four years are easy. You don't do anything except try to get re-elected.

THROTTLEBOTTOM. That's pretty hard these days.

WINTERGREEN. It looks that way. The next four years you wonder why the hell you wanted to be re-elected. And after that you go into the insurance business and you're all set.

THROTTLEBOTTOM. Well, couldn't I save a lot of time and go right into the insurance business?

WINTERGREEN. No, you've got to work yourself up.

THROTTLEBOTTOM. Yeah, but it's a pretty hard job, being President. You've got to keep on writing those Thanksgiving proclamations, no matter what — and then there's that other bunch, Congress. I guess there isn't anything you can really do about Congress, is there?

WINTERGREEN. Take my advice and keep them out of Washington.

THROTTLEBOTTOM. Can you do that?

WINTERGREEN. St. Patrick did it. Keep them out if you have to quarantine the place. Get the measles.

THROTTLEBOTTOM. I had measles once.

WINTERGREEN. Yeah, but you never had Congress. That's worse.

THROTTLEBOTTOM. Oh! What about those messages that the President is always sending to Congress — who reads those, anyway?

WINTERGREEN. The fellow who prints 'em.

THROTTLEBOTTOM. Well, wouldn't everybody read them if you made 'em funnier?

WINTERGREEN. No, we've had some pretty funny ones.

THROTTLEBOTTOM. Couldn't you make a speech instead? Then they'd *have* to listen.

WINTERGREEN. No, no! You've got to be careful about speeches. You only make a speech when you want the stock market to go down.

THROTTLEBOTTOM. What do you do when you want the stock market to go up?

WINTERGREEN [*fairly falling on his neck*]. Oh! wouldn't I like to know!

CURTAIN

SCENE 3: *Inside the Senate Chamber. The great desk of the presiding officer, mounted on a dais; in circles around him the desks of the Senators. Senators with Dundrearies, Senators with long white beards, Senators of all kinds and descriptions.*

When the curtain rises they are all in their places, and Throttlebottom is on high. The roll is being called, to music of course, and the Senators sway rhythmically back and forth in time to the music, humming as they do so.

THROTTLEBOTTOM. The Senator from North Dakota!

SENATOR. Present!

THROTTLEBOTTOM. Check! . . . The Senator from Minnesota!

SENATOR. Present!

THROTTLEBOTTOM. Check! . . . The Senator from Lou'siana!

SENATOR. Present!

THROTTLEBOTTOM. Check! . . . The Senator who's from Montana!

SENATOR. Present!

THROTTLEBOTTOM. Check! . . . The Senator who's from Alaska! [*A new state, by the way.*]

SENATOR. Present!

THROTTLEBOTTOM. Check! . . . The Senator who's from Nebraska!

SENATOR. Present!

THROTTLEBOTTOM. Check! . . .

> The Senators from other States
> Will have to bide their time,
> For I simply can't be bothered
> When the names don't rhyme!

[*The Senators continue to hum and to sway; led by Throttlebottom, they now go into song.*]

> The country thinks it's got depression;
> Ha! Ha! Ha!
> Just wait until we get in session!
> Ha! Ha! Ha!
> The people want a lot of action;
> Ho! Ho! Ho!
> We're here to give them satisfaction!
> Ho! Ho! Ho!
> Today is really full of laughter,
> Ha! Ha! Ha!
> Compared to what will follow after!
> Ha! Ha! Ha!
> There's action ev'ry minute when this happy group
> convenes;
> To get business into tangles
> We can guarantee more angles
> Than the town of Boston guarantees in beans!
> If you think you've got depression
> Wait until we get in session

And you'll find out what depression really means!

CLERK. It is now twelve o'clock noon and the Senate of the United States is hereby declared in session.

THROTTLEBOTTOM. Thanks. Gentlemen, when you hear the musical note it will be exactly twelve o'clock noon. [*And he brings the gavel down — right on his watch.*] Well, gentlemen, I'm glad to meet you all. You'll have to excuse me for not knowing much about this job. I see I made one mistake already — I went and got shaved. Now let's get at things — I'm only going to be with you one day, so let's make it a pip.

CLERK. The first thing before the Senate is unfinished business!

THROTTLEBOTTOM. But aren't we going to impeach the President?

CLERK. Unfinished business!

SENATOR FROM MASSACHUSETTS. Mr. Chairman! Mr. Chairman!

CLERK [*to Throttlebottom*]. That's you.

THROTTLEBOTTOM. Oh, I thought I was just Vice-president.

CLERK. You must recognize the Senator from Massachusetts.

THROTTLEBOTTOM. Oh, hello! How's everything in Massachusetts?

SENATOR FROM MASSACHUSETTS. Mr. Chairman! I rise to protest against a great injustice! In 1775 Paul Revere made the famous ride that saved this country from the greedy clutch of England.

THROTTLEBOTTOM. That's right — I read about that. [*Informally, to the Clerk.*] He went from one house to another, and he knocked on the door, and by the time they came out he was at the next house.

SENATOR FROM MASSACHUSETTS. Paul Revere's name has been given the affectionate tribute of a grateful people. But what of that gallant figure who is even more responsible? Gentlemen, what about Jenny, Paul Revere's horse? [*Applause.*] Surely, gentlemen, Jenny is entitled to the protection of a governmental pension. A bill providing such a pension was introduced into this body in the year 1804 and came up for its first reading in 1852.

THROTTLEBOTTOM. I wasn't here then.

SENATOR FROM MASSACHUSETTS. Gentlemen, in these hundred and fifty-five years Jenny has not been getting any younger. I ask you, gentlemen, what are we going to do about Jenny?

THROTTLEBOTTOM. Well, that's unfinished business if I ever heard it.

SENATOR JONES. May I point out to the Senator from Massachusetts that Jenny is dead?

THROTTLEBOTTOM. She is? What do you think of that? Good old Jenny! When did she die?

SENATOR JONES. She died in 1805.

THROTTLEBOTTOM. The Senate will rise for one minute in silent tribute to the departed horse from Massachusetts. [*They rise; he bangs the gavel.*] Well, that finishes Jenny. Is there any other unfinished business?

SENATOR LYONS. Mr. Chairman! Gentlemen! I crave the indulgence of this august body while I say a few words in honor of my wife's birthday. [*Applause.*] And I move you, Mr. Chairman, that the Senate appropriate five thousand dollars for flowers to be sent her on this historic occasion.

A SENATOR. Second the motion!

THROTTLEBOTTOM. All in favor say " Aye "! [*A full-throated " Aye " from the assemblage.*] Motion carried! [*To the Clerk.*] Put in my card. . . . Now, what comes next? How about impeaching the President?

CLERK [*handing him a sheet of paper*]. Mr. Vice-president —

THROTTLEBOTTOM. What's this?

CLERK. The following committees are ready to report.

THROTTLEBOTTOM [*consulting the paper*]. Committee on Aviation. . . . Airedales. . . . Bloomingdale's. . . . [*Closes his eyes, one finger suspended over the paper.*] Eenie, meenie, minie, mo. Catch a committee by the toe. If they holler give 'em dough, eenie, meenie, minie, mo. [*Places his finger on the paper, looks to see which committee he has selected.*] Committee on Unemployment.

SENATOR JONES. The Committee on Unemployment is gratified to report that due to its unremitting efforts there is now more unemployment in the United States than ever before.

THROTTLEBOTTOM. Now we're getting some place! Now let's impeach the President.

SENATOR FROM MASSACHUSETTS. Mr. Chairman! I would like to call the attention of the Senate to a matter that has been puzzling me for some time. It has to do with a very interesting bridge hand, in which the cards were distributed as follows: East held the four aces, West the four kings, North the four queens, and South — ah — nothing of any importance.

LYONS [*rising indignantly*]. Mr. Chairman! The South will never be satisfied with a hand like that!

[*A fanfare of trumpets.*]

PAGES [*announcing*]. The President of the United States!

THROTTLEBOTTOM. Who?

CLERK. The President of the United States!

[*He enters.*]

CLERK. The next business before the Senate is the resolution on the impeachment of the President!

THROTTLEBOTTOM [*to Wintergreen*]. Won't you sit down while we kick you out?

[*Enter, to music, Fulton and the Committee.*]

COMMITTEE [*in harmony*]. Whereas —

LYONS. At a meeting of the Senate at which a quorum was present a motion was made and it was proposed that —

COMMITTEE. Whereas —

LYONS. John P. Wintergreen had undertaken to marry the winner of a contest held at Atlantic City —

COMMITTEE. Whereas —

LYONS. His subsequent refusal to marry the winner, Miss Diana Devereaux, will lead to dire international complications —

COMMITTEE. Whereas —

LYONS. Now therefore be it resolved that President John P. Wintergreen be, and he hereby is, impeached from the said office of President of these United States.

JONES. I second the resolution.

FULTON. Our first witness — the French Ambassador.

[*Enter the six French Soldiers.*]

SOLDIERS

> Garçon, s'il vous plaît,
> Encore, Chevrolet Coupé;

Papah, pooh, pooh pooh!
A vous toot dir vay à vous?

SENATORS

We say how d'you do,
Which means that we welcome you;
We're glad of the chance
To say hello to France.

[*The French Ambassador enters.*]

FRENCH AMBASSADOR

You've dealt a lovely maid
A blow that is injurious;
A very dirty trick was played
And France is simply furious!

SENATORS

He says a lovely maid
Was dealt a blow injurious;
He says a dirty trick was played
And France is simply furious.

FULTON. Ambassador, please explain why France should be concerned about the plaintiff.

FRENCH AMBASSADOR

She's the illegitimate daughter of an illegitimate son
Of an illegitimate nephew of Napoleon!

ALL

Napoleon!

FRENCH AMBASSADOR

She's contemplating suicide
Because that man he threw aside
A lady with the blue blood of Napoleon.
What sort of man
Is this who can
Insult my country
With this effront'ry?

ALL

To the illegitimate daughter of an illegitimate son
Of an illegitimate nephew of Napoleon!

FRENCH AMBASSADOR. The Atlantic City witnesses! [*Enter the girls in bathing-suits.*] And Miss Diana Devereaux!

DIANA. I have come all ze way from France to bring ze greetings.

FRENCH AMBASSADOR. Tell your story, little one. Commencez, s'il vous plaît.

DIANA [*sings*].

> Jilted, jilted,
> I'm a flow'r that's wilted;
> Blighted, blighted,
> Till the wrong is righted;
> Broken, broken,
> By a man soft-spoken;
> Faded, faded,
> Heaven knows why.
> When men are deceivers, I'm afraid,
> 'Tis sad to be a trusting maid.
> Jilted, jilted, jilted am I,
> Oh, what is there left but to die?

ALL

> Just as in the Frankie and Johnnie song —

THROTTLEBOTTOM

> He done her wrong, he done her wrong —

ALL

> Jilted, jilted, jilted is she!
> Oh, what is there left but — to dee?

[*The Senate is visibly affected.*]

THROTTLEBOTTOM. And now, Mr. President, what have you to say for yourself?

WINTERGREEN

> Impeach me! Fine me! Jail me! Sue me!
> My Mary's love means much more to me!

THROTTLEBOTTOM

> Enough, enough! We want no preachment!
> It's time to vote on his impeachment!

ALL

> It's time to vote on his impeachment!

THROTTLEBOTTOM. The Senator from Minnesota?

SENATOR. Guilty!

THROTTLEBOTTOM. Check! . . . The Senator from North Dakota?

SENATOR. Guilty!

THROTTLEBOTTOM. Check! . . . The Senator from Lou'siana?

SENATOR. Guilty!

THROTTLEBOTTOM. Check! . . . The Senator who's from Montana?

> [*And at this dramatic moment, in breaks Mary Turner Wintergreen.*]

MARY. Stop! Stop! Stop!

WINTERGREEN. Mary!

MARY [*to music*]

Before you go any further, with your permission,
I must tell you of my husband's delicate condition.

ALL. Delicate condition! What do you mean?

MARY [*such a gay song*]

> I'm about to be a mother;
> He's about to be a father;
>> We're about to have a baby:
>>> I must tell it,
>>> These doings compel it!
> Oh, I'm about to be a mother;
> He's about to be a father;
> We're about to have a baby —

ALL

> A baby!

MARY

> A baby to love and adore —
> Who could ask for anything more?

ALL [*dancing happily*]

> She's about to be a mother;
> He's about to be a father;
>> They're about to have a baby:
>>> We can't bother
>>> A budding young father!

WINTERGREEN. Mary, is it true? Am I to have a baby?

MARY. It's true, John, it's true!

WINTERGREEN. It's wonderful, it's wonderful — water! Water! [*He faints.*]

DIANA. It eez a fine countree — I am compromised and she has ze babee!

THROTTLEBOTTOM. Gentlemen, gentlemen — this country has never yet impeached an expectant father. What do you say?

SENATORS. Not guilty!

THROTTLEBOTTOM [*to the Clerk*]. Check that!

FRENCH AMBASSADOR

Sacre! I go to the telegraph office to cable my report:
This is American trickery of the most reprehensible sort!

DIANA. I was the most beautiful blossom — [*The Ambassador takes her by the hand; leads her away.*] — in all the Southland.

SENATOR FROM MASSACHUSETTS. Great work, Jack! You'll be reinstated in the hearts of the American people.

SENATOR JONES. You're doing your duty by posterity.

WINTERGREEN. Posterity? Why, posterity is just around the corner.

ALL

Posterity is just around the corner!

[*Senators bring out tambourines.*]

Posterity is just around the corner!
It really doesn't pay to be a mourner.
Posterity is just around the corner!
Posterity is here — I don't mean maybe!
There's nothing guarantees it like a baby!
Posterity is here and will continue!
We really didn't know you had it in you!
Posterity!
Is in its infancy!

WINTERGREEN

I sing to ev'ry citizen and for'gner:
Posterity is just around the corner!

[*Throttlebottom, with a bass drum, is leading a march around the room.*]

We'll soon be pulling plums, like Jackie Horner!
Posterity is just around the —
ALL
Oomposterity, oomp-osterity, oompah, oompah, oomp-posterity.
Oomp-posterity, oomp-posterity, oompah, oompah, oom-
Posterity is just around the corner!
Around the corner!

CURTAIN

SCENE 4: *A corridor in the White House.*
[*Enter Jenkins and Miss Benson.*]

JENKINS. It'll certainly be great to have a baby in the White House. I wonder when it'll be born.

MISS BENSON. Let's see — they were married March 4, weren't they?

JENKINS. That's right.

MISS BENSON [*counting on her fingers*]. April, May, June, July, August, September, October, November, DECEMBER! It'll be born in December.

JENKINS. How do you know?

MISS BENSON. Well, it won't be born *before* December.

JENKINS. How do you know?

MISS BENSON. Oh, the President wouldn't do a thing like that. He'd never be re-elected.

JENKINS. You can't tell. Might be the very thing that would re-elect him.

MISS BENSON. It's certainly wonderful the way this has lined people up behind the President.

JENKINS. Yeah, but we don't know what France is going to do. She's still liable to make trouble.

MISS BENSON. My, you'd think a woman could have a baby without France butting in.

JENKINS. Well, fifty million Frenchmen — they've got to do something.

MISS BENSON. Let 'em do it in Paris. Why should they come over here and —

WINTERGREEN [*singing as he enters*]. "Somebody's coming to our house; somebody's coming to stay —" Oh, hello.

JENKINS. Hi, chief!

MISS BENSON. Good morning, Mr. President. And how is Mrs. Wintergreen this morning?

WINTERGREEN [*vaguely*]. Who? Mrs. Wintergreen? [*Realizes that there is such a person.*] Oh, she's fine! Fine! Yes, sir! [*Tapping his own chest.*] Should have seen the breakfast I ate!

MISS BENSON. Tell me, Mr. President. Ah — [*Hesitantly.*] — when is the baby expected?

WINTERGREEN. Well, of course you can't tell about such things, but we think some time in Novem — December. [*Another quick correction.*] December.

MISS BENSON [*with a look at Jenkins*]. Oh, December.

WINTERGREEN. Yes, we sort of thought December would be a nice month. End the old year right and all that sort of thing. Have a cigar? Oh, pardon me, the baby isn't born yet.

[*Enter Fulton.*]

FULTON. Hello, Jack!

WINTERGREEN. Hello, there! Should have seen the breakfast I ate. [*To the Secretaries.*] See you later.

MISS BENSON [*to Jenkins*]. I told you December.

JENKINS. Well, I'd still like to make a bet on it.

[*The Secretaries go.*]

FULTON. Well, Jack, how are you? And how's the wife?

WINTERGREEN. Fine, fine! Never felt better.

FULTON. Mighty smart girl, Mary. She certainly saved the day for us.

WINTERGREEN. *She* saved the day? I suppose I was just an innocent bystander?

FULTON. I don't mean that, but I thought it sort of came as a surprise to you.

WINTERGREEN. Surprise? Why, I planned the whole thing. I foresaw the situation months ago.

FULTON. Anyway, it settled France. They're still yelling, but

there's nothing they can do about it. The American people are behind you to a man. How'd you ever get the idea, Jack?

WINTERGREEN. Why, it wasn't anything. Nothing at all. Anybody in my place would have done the same.

FULTON. Yes, sir, it'll be a wonderful thing to have a baby
in the White House.

WINTERGREEN. You mean instead of a President?

FULTON. No, no, Jack — I mean it. I tell you, there's something about the patter of baby feet, trickling down the stairs. . . .

[Enter the French Ambassador.]

FRENCH AMBASSADOR. Gentlemen!

FULTON [with a bow]. Monsieur!

FRENCH AMBASSADOR [with an elaborate bow]. Monsieur
President.

WINTERGREEN. You all alone?

FRENCH AMBASSADOR. But yes.

WINTERGREEN. Where are those six guys who used to march
in ahead of you — [His gesture carries out the idea of crossed bayo-
nets, and even goes a bit further by bringing thumb and nose into
close juxtaposition.] — you know.

FRENCH AMBASSADOR. They could not come today. They have
dancing lesson.

WINTERGREEN. You look kind of naked without them.

FRENCH AMBASSADOR [acknowledges this with a bow]. You
will pardon this intrusion, Monsieur, but I have received another
note from my country.

WINTERGREEN. That's all right. We've got a lot of notes
from your country, and some of them were due ten years ago.

FRENCH AMBASSADOR. But this is not a promise to pay — this
is serious.

WINTERGREEN. Shoot!

FRENCH AMBASSADOR [bows]. Monsieur, I have good news for
you. France consents to your having the child.

FULTON. Ah!

WINTERGREEN. France consents?

FRENCH AMBASSADOR. Freely.

WINTERGREEN. Why, that's wonderful of her. Good old

France! Do you mind if I tell my wife, so she can go ahead? [*Ambassador bows.*] You've no idea how this will please her. Won't take me a minute — I'll be right back.

FRENCH AMBASSADOR. But one moment, monsieur. [*Wintergreen pauses.*] France consents, but on one condition.

WINTERGREEN. Yeah?

FRENCH AMBASSADOR. France must have the baby!

FULTON and WINTERGREEN: WHAT?

FRENCH AMBASSADOR. Do not be hasty, monsieur. You must understand the desperate situation of my country. For fifty years the birth-rate of France has been declining, declining, declining.

WINTERGREEN. What's that got to do with me?

FRENCH AMBASSADOR. You must see, monsieur. If you had married Mademoiselle Devereaux, as you have promise, the baby she is French. But now you have taken away from France one baby, and she demand replacement.

WINTERGREEN. Never!

FULTON. I should say not!

FRENCH AMBASSADOR. It is the old law, monsieur; an eye for an eye, a tooth for a tooth, and a baby for a baby.

WINTERGREEN. You'll get no tooth from my baby!

FRENCH AMBASSADOR. The tooth, the whole tooth, and nothing but the tooth!

WINTERGREEN. Not one tooth!

FRENCH AMBASSADOR. That is your final word?

WINTERGREEN. It is! Good day, monsieur!

FRENCH AMBASSADOR. Good day! [*Clicks his heels; salutes; turns and starts out.*] Lafayette, we are coming! [*Goes.*]

FULTON. What do you think France'll do?

WINTERGREEN. What's the worst she can do? Sue us for what she owes us?

FULTON. But that other thing! France is awful touchy about her birth-rate!

WINTERGREEN. What are you worrying about? I fixed *this* up, didn't I?

FULTON. What?

WINTERGREEN. Well, Mary's going to have a baby, isn't she?

FULTON. Yes!

WINTERGREEN. Well! Next year I make a tour of France! Lafayette!

[He salutes.]

CURTAIN

SCENE 5: *The Yellow Room of the White House. And is it yellow? But it is also very beautiful — and endless. It extends as far as the eye can reach — a vista of hallway, and polished floor, and chandeliers, and ladies in evening clothes, and men in magnificent uniforms. White-wigged flunkies move in and out of the assemblage.*

At the rise of the curtain an endless line of diplomats is presenting the Wintergreens with an endless line of baby carriages. The flunkies bellow the names as they accept the carriages — " Compliments of Ecuador," " Compliments of Bolivia," " Compliments of Spain," " Compliments of Lithuania." And then, for finale, an exceedingly small baby carriage. You've guessed it — " Compliments of Scotland."

[*There is a burst of music.*]

ALL

Oh, trumpeter, trumpeter, blow your golden horn!
Oh, trumpeter, trumpeter, blow your golden horn!
A White House baby will very soon be born,
A White House baby will very soon be born!
    Blow your horn!

With a hey, nonny nonny, and a ha cha cha!
With a hey, nonny nonny, and a ha cha cha!

There's something glorious happening today
For all the citizens of the U. S. A.
A White House baby will very soon be born!
Oh, trumpeter, blow your horn,

Oh, trumpeter, blow your horn,
Oh, trumpeter, blow your horn,
Your golden horn, your golden horn!

[*The Doctor enters.*]

Oh, doctor, doctor, what's the news, we pray?
We've waited for your bulletin all day.

DOCTOR

The baby of the President and frau
Will be here almost any minute now.

ALL

With a hey, nonny nonny, and a ha cha cha!
With a hey, nonny nonny, and a ha cha cha!

Oh, doctor, here is the one thing we must know,
We're all of us anxious and we've got to know:
The baby, is it to be a girl or boy?
        A baby girl or boy?
        A nation's pride and joy!
We must know whether it's a girl or boy —
        A girl or boy?

DOCTOR

        On that matter no one budges,
            For all cases of the sort
        Are decided by the judges
            Of the Supreme Court.

FLUNKIES. The Supreme Court!
[*Enter the Supreme Court.*]

JUDGES. We're the one, two, three, four, five, six, seven,
eight, nine Supreme Court Judges.

ALL

With a hey, nonny nonny, and a ha cha cha!
With a hey, nonny nonny, and a ha cha cha!

About the baby — will it be
A boy or girl — a he or she?

JUDGES

> On that matter no one budges
> For all cases of the sort
> Are decided by the judges
> Of the Supreme Court.

FLUNKIES. The Secretary of Agriculture!

[*Enter Lippman.*]

LIPPMAN

> The farmers in the dell,
> The farmers in the dell,
> They all keep a-asking me:
> A boy or a gel?

FLUNKIES. The Secretary of the Navy!

[*Enter Gilhooley.*]

GILHOOLEY

> All the sailors in the Navy
> Of these great United States,
> Do not eat their bowls of gravy,
> Nor the captains nor the mates.
> They refuse to jib an anchor,
> Strike a boom, or heave a sail
> Till you've satisfied their hanker:
> Is it female or a male?

FLUNKIES. Senator Carver Jones!

[*Enter Jones.*]

JONES

> Out on the prairie,
> The cowboys all keep asking of me:
> He or a she —
> She or a he?
> Out on the prairie,
> For baby boy or girl they are keen,
> But they want nothing in between.

FLUNKIES. Senator Robert E. Lyons!

[*Enter Lyons.*]

LYONS

> 'Way down upon the Swanee River
> Folks are filled with joy,

But they want to know what will the stork deliver?
    Will it be a girl or boy?

ALL
      There's something glorious happening today;
        A baby will be born,
        A baby will be born.
      Oh, trumpeter, trumpeter, blow your golden horn!
      [*Enter Wintergreen, followed by Fulton and Jenkins.*]

FULTON. Take it easy, Jack! Nothing can happen to her.

WINTERGREEN. I know, but at a time like this — Mary in there alone — [*A chorus of greeting from all.*] Oh! Hello! God, I'm nervous! Anybody got a drink? [*Every man brings out a flask.*] Thanks. When I think of Mary in there alone — [*Takes a drink.*] Well, I guess it's not going to be so hard for her.

GILHOOLEY. How is Mary?

WINTERGREEN. Finest little woman in the world! When I think of what she's got to — anybody got a drink? [*The flasks come out again. He takes Gilhooley's, although he still has Fulton's in his hand.*] Well, I guess I'd better not mix them.

MISS BENSON. Oh, Mr. Wintergreen!

WINTERGREEN [*wheeling*]. Any news?

MISS BENSON. The baby will be here any moment.

      [*An excited buzz from the crowd.*]

WINTERGREEN. Tell 'em I'm ready. [*Miss Benson goes.*] My God! You hear that? What do I do now? Anybody got a drink?

CHIEF JUSTICE. Gentlemen, duty calls. The baby is now being born. We must decide the sex.

WINTERGREEN. You decide?

CHIEF JUSTICE. We do, sir.

JUDGES
        On that matter no one budges,
          For all cases of the sort
        Are decided by the judges
          Of the Supreme Court!
      [*They retire.*]

WINTERGREEN. I shouldn't be drinking at a time like this. [*To Jenkins and the Committee.*] Here! Take it away! [*Jenkins*

reaches for the flask. *Wintergreen pulls away.*] Oh, no, you don't.
My wife's the finest little woman in the world! And I can lick anybody that says she ain't!

FLUNKIES [*announcing*]. The French Ambassador!

WINTERGREEN. Bring him in!

FRENCH AMBASSADOR. Your Excellency! I have another message from France!

WINTERGREEN. Not a nickel!

FRENCH AMBASSADOR. Will you surrender the baby?

WINTERGREEN. Never! Give my baby to France and have it
eat snails and get ptomaine poisoning! Never!

FRENCH AMBASSADOR. Then, sir, I am instructed to say that
with the birth of the child France severs diplomatic relations!

WINTERGREEN. Hurray!

FRENCH AMBASSADOR. And that is not all, sir. I wish furthermore to report —

> [*Two Flunkies enter and blow a fanfare on their
> trumpets. The Supreme Court re-enters.*]

JUDGES. Whereas —

CHIEF JUSTICE. A child has been born to the President of the
United States and his consort —

JUDGES. Whereas —

CHIEF JUSTICE. The Supreme Court of the United States has
been called upon to determine the sex of the aforesaid infant —

JUDGES. Whereas —

CHIEF JUSTICE. By a strict party vote it has been decided
that —

JUDGES. It's a boy!

> [*The committee and guests press around Winter-
> green to congratulate him.*]

WINTERGREEN. A boy! That makes me a father! Thank you!
Thank you very much! I certainly am a lucky man! Boy, the cigars!
Smoke up, everybody! Here you are, ladies and gentlemen! Have a
cigar, Frenchy!

FRENCH AMBASSADOR. My thanks, monsieur. On behalf of
France permit me to offer my felicitations.

WINTERGREEN. Attaboy! Let bygones be bygones! Have another cigar!

FRENCH AMBASSADOR. And permit me also to inform you that France hereby severs diplomatic relations! [*He reaches for the cigar.*]

WINTERGREEN [*closes the humidor with a bang*]. Then the hell with you!

FRENCH AMBASSADOR. You understand what this means, monsieur?

WINTERGREEN. I do! [*Takes back the first cigar.*] It means no smoke!

FRENCH AMBASSADOR. Precisely. And where there is no smoke there is fire. I am instructed to say, monsieur, that this means that the French government will —

[*The Flunkies re-enter. Another fanfare. The Justices re-enter.*]

JUDGES. Whereas —

CHIEF JUSTICE. A child has been born to the President of the United States and his consort —

WINTERGREEN. Hey! We had that.

CHIEF JUSTICE. But you are having it again, sir. This one is a girl!

[*All crowd around Wintergreen to congratulate him again.*]

WINTERGREEN. A girl! That makes me a father and a mother. Twins! That's a little more than I counted on!

JENKINS. Cigars, sir?

WINTERGREEN. No. Cigarettes this time! A boy and a girl! Well!

FRENCH AMBASSADOR [*sings*]

> Oh, I can stand no more,
> My temper's getting gingery;
> This certainly will lead to war!
> This insult added to injury!

You realize what you have done, sir? You have taken away from France not one baby, but two!

WINTERGREEN. That's it! Blame me for everything!

FRENCH AMBASSADOR. What you have done to Mademoiselle Devereaux! That poor little girl! Where is she? What is she doing?

[*In the distance Diana is heard singing " I was the most beautiful blossom."*]

WINTERGREEN. She's still singing. [*Diana enters.*] You like that song, don't you?

FRENCH AMBASSADOR. My poor motherless one! My sweet blossom of the Southland!

FLUNKIES [*announcing*]. The Vice-president of the United States!

THROTTLEBOTTOM [*knitting a baby's sweater*]. Is the baby born yet? I just got this finished!

WINTERGREEN. Only one? Where's the other one?

THROTTLEBOTTOM [*pulls out second sweater*]. I thought something like that might happen!

FRENCH AMBASSADOR. Once and for all, monsieur, what are you going to do? What are you going to do about Mademoiselle Devereaux and her babies?

WINTERGREEN. Well, she can have her own babies.

DIANA. But I am not married, monsieur.

WINTERGREEN. What's that got to do with it?

FRENCH AMBASSADOR. Everything. The family has been illegitimate long enough.

WINTERGREEN. Then let her get married!

FRENCH AMBASSADOR. Exactly! But it was agreed, monsieur, that she was to marry the President of the United States.

WINTERGREEN. But she can't have me! I'm married!

FRENCH AMBASSADOR. Then it is war, sir! When the President of the United States fails to fulfill his duty ——

WINTERGREEN. That's it! I've got it!

ALL. Got what?

WINTERGREEN. It's in the Constitution! When the President of the United States is unable to fulfill his duties, his obligations are assumed by —

THROTTLEBOTTOM. The Vice-president! I get her!

CHIEF JUSTICE. Article Twelve!

FRENCH AMBASSADOR. Monsieur, you are a genius!

THROTTLEBOTTOM [*to Wintergreen*]. I could throw my arms right around your neck!

WINTERGREEN. Oh, no, you don't! Hers!
  [*The Trumpeters re-enter. Another fanfare.*]
WINTERGREEN. Oh, my God!
CHIEF JUSTICE. It's all right. The boys are merely practicing.
  [*There is a great burst of music, and from the more
  intimate quarters of the White House there comes
  into the room a great canopied bed, hung with
  gold, and silver, and bald-headed eagles. In it is
  Mary Turner Wintergreen, a twin on each arm.
  Wintergreen advances to greet her; the crowd
  bursts into song. And of all the songs in the world,
  you'd never guess what they pick out. It's " Of
  Thee I Sing, Baby."*]

THE CURTAIN FALLS

Essays

THE HISTORY of literature is full of accidents. In 1923 the New Pearson's announced a series of prizes for contributions, and asked me to act as one of the judges for the essays. After I had agreed to do it, the editor asked me further if I would write out for the magazine a statement of what I thought an essay ought to be. I was just then very busy, and I remember thinking that I would not have promised to be a judge if I had known I was expected to be a contributor too. But I had promised, and it seemed easier to do the extra work than to explain why I could not. So, angry with myself for the painstaking habits which have never allowed me to dash things off as other writers say they are able to do, I wrote A Note on the Essay, which I suppose has been more widely read than anything I have ever written.

"The sonnet has a standard form very much as a man has. Leave off the sestet of your sonnet and you do about what a god does when he leaves the legs off a man. The drama has a standard form very much as a rendezvous has. Write a drama in which no spark is exchanged between the audience and the action and you have done what fate does when it keeps lovers from their meeting. The novel has a standard form very much as a road has. You may set out anywhere you like and go wherever you please, at any gait, but you must go somewhere, or you have made what is no more a novel than some engineer's road would be a road if it had neither beginning, end, nor direction. But the essay! It may be of any length, breadth, depth, weight, density, color, savor, odor, appearance, importance, value, or uselessness which you can or will give it. The epigram bounds it on one side and the treatise on the other, but it has in its time encroached upon the territory of both of them, and it doubtless will do so again. Or, to look at the essay from another angle, it is bounded on one side by the hellfire sermon and on the other by the geometrical demonstration; and yet it ranges easily between these extremes of heat and cold and occasionally steals from both of them. It differs from a letter by being written to more — happily a great many more — than one person. It differs from talk chiefly by being written at all.

" Having to obey no regulations as to form, the essay is very free to choose its matter. The sonnet, by reason of its form, tends to deal with solemn and not with gay themes. The drama, for the same reason, tends to look for intense and not for casual incidents. The novel tends to feel that it must carry a considerable amount of human life on its back. The essay may be as fastidious as a collector of carved emeralds or as open-minded as a garbage-gatherer. Nothing human, as the platitude says, is alien to it. The essay, however, goes beyond the platitude and dares to choose matter from numerous non-human sources. Think of the naturalists and their essays. Think, further, of the range of topics for essayists at large. Theodore Roosevelt in an essay urges the strenuous life; Max Beerbohm in an essay defends cosmetics. De Quincey expounds the fine art of murder, Thoreau the pleasures of economy, William Law the blisses of prayer, Hudson the sense of smell in men and in animals, Schopenhauer the ugliness of women, Bacon the advantages of a garden, Plutarch the traits of curiosity, and A. C. Benson the felicity of having nothing much in the mind. All, in fact, an essayist needs to start with is something, anything, to say. He gets up each morning and finds the world spread out before him, as the world was spread out before Adam and Eve the day they left Paradise. With the cosmos, past, present, and future, to pick from, the essayist goes to work. If he finds a topic good enough he may write a good essay, no matter how he writes it.

" He may. There is still, however, the question of his manner. Thousands of dull men have written millions of true things which no one but their proof-readers, wives, or pupils ever read. If each essayist could take out a patent on each subject into which he dips his pen, and could prevent any other pen from ever dipping into it after him, he might have better luck. But there are no monopolists in this department. Would research find in all the hoards of books or all the morgues of manuscripts a single observation which has never been made twice? Competition in such affairs is free and endless. The only law which gives an essayist a right to his material is the law which rules that the best man wins. The law does not say in what fashion he must be best. Any fashion will do. Let him be more sententious than others, like Bacon; or more harmonious, like Sir Thomas Browne; or more elegant, like Addison; or more direct, like Swift; or more hearty, like Fielding; or more whimsical, like Lamb; or more impassioned, like Hazlitt; or more encouraging, like Emerson; or more Olympian, like Arnold; or more funny, like Mark Twain; or more musical, like Pater; or more impish, like Max Beerbohm; or more devastating, like Mencken. Let the essayist be any of these things and he may have a copyright till someone takes it away from him. What matters is the manner. If he has good matter, he may write a good essay; if he has a good manner he probably *will* write a good essay.

" An essay is a communication. If the subject of the discourse were the whole affair, it would be enough for the essayist to be an adequate conduit. If the manner were the whole affair, any versatile fellow might try all the manners and have a universal triumph. But back of matter and manner both lies the item which is really significant. The person who communicates, anything in any way, must be a person. His truth must have a tone, his speech must have a rhythm which are his and solely his. His knowledge or opinions must have lain long enough inside him to have taken root there;

and when they come away they must bring some of the soil clinging to them. They must, too, have been shaped by that soil — as
plants are which grow in cellars, on housetops, on hillsides, in the
wide fields, under shade in forests. Many kinds of men, many kinds
of essays! Important essays come from important men."

The New Pearson's died soon after this note was published, and
I forgot it. Four or five years later an anthologist dug it out and re-
printed it in a volume of essays for students. Since then it has appeared almost every year in some new anthology or textbook. Students in high schools inquire of me, in formal letters, if I have
written anything else. The anthologists use it, I suppose, because
it is a kind of introduction to any collection of essays. It saves an
editor trouble. The students read it because they are required to.
Though I wrote it almost by accident, it must have helped form a
good many opinions as to what an essay is. If I had foreseen any
such fortune for it I might have written it with more calculation,
and possibly with less effect.

If I were writing such a note now, after thirteen years, I should
not even think of using the overworked and outworn adjectives
" whimsical " and " devastating " or of looking at the essay " from
another angle." It is all I can do to make myself remember that
these expressions were once fresh. Nor should I, now, think it particularly humorous to write about the essay's easy form in an essay
shaped as rigorously as this. That was a private joke which so far as
I know nobody but me has ever noticed. But in what I had to say
about the essay, defining and describing it, I find I have nothing to
add or to change.

" The epigram bounds it on one side and the treatise on the
other." Consider This Simian World, which I myself would rather
have written than any other essay I have ever read. If there were an
epigram like " Men are but monkeys of a larger growth " and if
there were a treatise on anthropology in the light of all zoology,
Clarence Day's essay would lie neatly between them, as pointed as
the epigram, as far-ranging as the treatise. Other writers have compared men with monkeys or seen the world as a zoo. Only Clarence
Day ever enlarged these comparisons with so much sight and insight, so much wit and imagination. What if the dominant race on
the earth were descended from the ants, or from the cats, or from

the elephants? What would its civilization be like? Clarence Day imagines it. But the rulers of the earth did descend " (broadly speaking) from ape-like or monkeyish beings." Human life is simian. Clarence Day studies its traits with its origins always in mind. Here was a chance to make all the significant observations on the race of man, and it is hard to think of one which Clarence Day does not make. He is no less thoroughgoing because he is amusing. Humor is not the enemy of his thought. *This Simian World* is the quintessence of anthropology, a lively abstract of the ways of the human world.

" Think of the naturalists and their essays." I have included two. The one by Julian Huxley goes to the ants for an example of biological relativity and applies it to mankind. W. H. Hudson talks about geese, which he, like any person of judgment, admires and respects above all domestic birds. " Think, further, of the range of topics for essayists at large." H. M. Tomlinson tells how, on a liner " too lofty even to notice the Atlantic," he saw a derelict schooner and remembered the might and terror of the ocean. George Jean Nathan brings together his intimate recollections of three famous men, and Carl Van Vechten, in the company of Peter Whiffle, meets an anonymous French entertainer in a New York café. Maurice Baring discusses high-brows and low-brows, and Ernest Newman the elastic language of harmony: " Of all the wonders of all the arts, surely harmony in music is the most wonderful." H. L. Mencken sketches the character of his publisher, describes a camp-meeting in the hills of Tennessee, and expounds the nature of slang. " Many kinds of men, many kinds of essays."

C.V.D.

Clarence Day

THIS SIMIAN WORLD

How I hate the man who talks about the " brute creation," with an ugly emphasis on BRUTE! . . . As for me, I am proud of my close kinship with other animals. I take a jealous pride in my Simian ancestry. I like to think that I was once a magnificent hairy fellow living in the trees, and that my frame has come down through geological time via sea jelly and worms and Amphioxus, Fish, Dinosaurs, and Apes. Who would exchange these for the pallid couple in the Garden of Eden?

W. N. P. BARBELLION

I

LAST Sunday, Potter took me out driving along upper Broadway, where those long rows of tall new apartment houses were built a few years ago. It was a mild afternoon and great crowds of people were out. Sunday afternoon crowds. They were not going any-where — they were just strolling up and down, staring at each other, and talking. There were thousands and thousands of them.

" Awful, aren't they! " said Potter.

I didn't know what he meant. When he added: " Why, these crowds," I turned and asked: " Why, what about them? " I wasn't sure whether he had an idea or a headache.

" Other creatures don't do it," he replied, with a discouraged expression. " Are any other beings ever found in such masses, but vermin? Aimless, staring, vacant-minded — look at them! I can get no sense whatever of individual worth, or of value in men as a race, when I see them like this. It makes one almost despair of civiliza-tion."

I thought this over for a while, to get in touch with his attitude. I myself feel differently at different times about us human beings: sometimes I get pretty indignant when we are attacked (for there is altogether too much abuse of us by spectator philosophers) and yet at other times I too feel like a spectator, an alien; but even then I had never felt so alien or despairing as Potter. I cast about for the probable cause of our difference. " Let's remember," I said, " it's a simian civilization."

Potter was staring disgustedly at some vaudeville sign-boards.

" Yes," I said, " those for example are distinctively simian. Why should you feel disappointment at something inevitable? " And I went on to argue that it wasn't as though we were descended from eagles, for instance, instead of (broadly speaking) from ape-like or monkeyish beings. Being of simian stock, we had simian traits. Our development naturally bore the marks of our origin. If we had inherited our dispositions from eagles we should have loathed vaudeville. But as cousins of the Bandarlog, we loved it. What could you expect?

Descended from eagles

II

I<small>F</small> we had been made directly from clay, the way it says in the Bible, and had therefore inherited no intermediate characteristics — if a god, or some principle of growth, had gone that way to work with us, he or it might have molded us into much more splendid forms.

But considering our simian descent, it has done very well. The only people who are disappointed in us are those who still believe that clay story. Or who — unconsciously — still let it color their thinking.

There certainly seems to be a power at work in the world, by virtue of which every living thing grows and develops. And it tends toward splendor. Seeds become trees, and weak little nations grow great. But the push or the force that is doing this, the yeast as it were, has to work in and on certain definite kinds of material. Because this yeast is in us, there may be great and undreamed-of possibilities awaiting mankind; but because of our line of descent there are also queer limitations.

Strange forgotten dynasties

III

In those distant invisible epochs before men existed, before even the proud missing link strutted around through the woods (little realizing how we his great-grandsons would smile wryly at him, much as our own descendants may shudder at us, ages hence), the various animals were desperately competing for power. They couldn't or didn't live as equals. Certain groups sought the headship.

Many strange forgotten dynasties rose, met defiance, and fell. In the end it was our ancestors who won, and became simian kings, and bequeathed a whole planet to us — and have never been thanked for it. No monument has been raised to the memory of those first hairy conquerors; yet had they not fought well and wisely in those far-off times, some other race would have been masters, and kept us in cages, or shot us for sport in the forests while they ruled the world.

So Potter and I, developing this train of thought, began to imagine we had lived many ages ago and somehow or other had alighted here from some older planet. Familiar with the ways of evolution elsewhere in the universe, we naturally should have wondered what course it would take on this earth. " Even in this out-of-the-way corner of the Cosmos," we might have reflected, " and on this tiny star, it may be of interest to consider the trend of events." We should have tried to appraise the different species as they wandered around, each with its own set of good and bad

characteristics. Which group, we'd have wondered, would ever contrive to rule all the rest?

And how great a development could they attain to thereafter?

IV

If we had landed here after the great saurians had been swept from
the scene, we might first have considered the lemurs or apes. They
had hands. Æsthetically viewed, the poor simians were simply grotesque; but travelers who knew other planets might have known
what beauty may spring from an uncouth beginning in this magic
universe.

Still — those frowzy, unlovely hordes of apes and monkeys were
so completely lacking in signs of kingship; they were so flighty,
too, in their ways, and had so little purpose, and so much love for
absurd and idle chatter, that they would have struck us, we thought,
as unlikely material. Such traits, we should have reminded ourselves, persist. They are not easily left behind, even after long
stages; and they form a terrible obstacle to all high advancement.

V

The bees or the ants might have seemed to us more promising.
Their smallness of size was not necessarily too much of a handi-
cap. They could have made poison their weapon for the subjuga-
tion of rivals. And in these orderly insects there was obviously a
capacity for labor, and co-operative labor at that, which could
carry them far. We all know that they have a marked genius: great
gifts of their own. In a civilization of super-ants or bees, there
would have been no problem of the hungry unemployed, no
poverty, no unstable government, no riots, no strikes for short
hours, no derision of eugenics, no thieves, perhaps no crime at all.

Ants are good citizens: they place group interests first.

But they carry it so far, they have few or no political rights. An
ant doesn't have the vote, apparently; he just has his duties.

This quality may have something to do with their having group
wars. The egotism of their individual spirits is allowed scant expression, so the egotism of the group is extremely ferocious and

active. Is this one of the reasons why ants fight so much? They go
in for State Socialism, yes, but they are not internationalists. And
ants commit atrocities in and after their battles that are — I wish
I could truly say — inhuman.

But, conversely, ants are absolutely unselfish within the community. They are skillful. Ingenious. Their nests and buildings are
relatively larger than man's. The scientists speak of their paved
streets, vaulted halls, their hundreds of different domesticated animals, their pluck and intelligence, their individual initiative, their
chaste and industrious lives. Darwin said the ant's brain was " one
of the most marvelous atoms in the world, perhaps more so than
the brain of man " — yes, of present-day man, who for thousands
and thousands of years has had so much more chance to develop his
brain. . . . A thoughtful observer would have weighed all these
excellent qualities.

When we think of these creatures as little men (which is all
wrong of course) we see they have their faults. To our eyes they
seem too orderly, for instance. Repressively so. Their ways are more
fixed than those of the old Egyptians, and their industry is painful
to think of, it's hyper-Chinese. But we must remember this is a
simian comment. The instincts of the species that you and I belong to are of an opposite kind; and that makes it hard for us to
judge ants fairly.

But we and the ants are alike in one matter: the strong love of
property. And instead of merely struggling with Nature for it, they
also fight other ants. The custom of plunder seems to be a part of
most of their wars. This has gone on for ages among them, and continues today. Raids, ferocious combats, and loot are part of an ant's
regular life. Ant reformers, if there were any, might lay this to their
property sense, and talk of abolishing property as a cure for the evil.
But that would not help for long unless they could abolish the love
of it.

Ants seem to care even more for property than we do ourselves.
We men are inclined to ease up a little when we have all we need.
But it is not so with ants: they can't bear to stop; they keep right
on working. This means that ants do not contemplate; they heed
nothing outside of their own little rounds. It is almost as though
their fondness for labor had closed fast their minds.

Conceivably they might have developed inquiring minds. But this would have run against their strongest instincts. The ant is knowing and wise; but he doesn't know enough to take a vacation. The worshipper of energy is too physically energetic to see that he cannot explore certain higher fields until he is still.

Even if such a race had somehow achieved self-consciousness and reason, would they have been able therewith to rule their instincts, or to stop work long enough to examine themselves, or the universe, or to dream of any noble development? Probably not. Reason is seldom or never the ruler: it is the servant of instinct. It would therefore have told the ants that incessant toil was useful and good.

"Toil has brought you up from the ruck of things," Reason would have plausibly said. "It's by virtue of feverish toil that you have become what you are. Being endlessly industrious is the best road — for you — to the heights." And, self-reassured, they would then have had orgies of work; and thus, by devoted exertion, have blocked their advancement. Work and order and gain would have withered their souls.

VI

LET us take the great cats. They are free from this talent for slavehood. Stately beasts like the lion have more independence of mind than the ants — and a self-respect, we may note, unknown to primates. Or consider the leopards, with hearts that no tyrant could master. What fearless and resolute leopard-men they could have fathered! How magnificently such a civilization would have made its force tell!

A race of civilized beings descended from these great cats would have been rich in hermits and solitary thinkers. The recluse would not have been stigmatized as peculiar, as he is by us simians. They would not have been a credulous people, or easily religious. False prophets and swindlers would have found few dupes. And what generals they would have made! What consummate politicians!

Don't imagine them as a collection of tigers walking around on their hind legs. They would have only been like tigers in the sense that we men are like monkeys. Their development in appearance and character would have been quite transforming.

Instead of the small flat head of the tiger, they would have had clear smooth brows; and those who were not bald would have had neatly parted hair — perhaps striped.

Their mouths would have been smaller and more sensitive; their faces most dignified. Where now they express chiefly savageness, they would have expressed fire and grace.

They would have been courteous and suave. No vulgar crowding would have occurred on the streets of their cities. No mobs. No ignominious subway-jams.

Imagine a cultivated coterie of such men and women, at a ball, dancing. How few of us humans are graceful! They would have all been Pavlovas.

Like ants and bees, the cat race is nervous. Their temperaments are high-strung. They would never have become as poised or as placid as — say — super-cows. Yet they would have had less insanity, probably, than we. Monkeys' (and elephants') minds seem precariously balanced, unstable. The great cats are saner. They are intense, they would have needed sanitariums; but fewer asylums. And their asylums would have been not for weak-minded souls, but for furies.

They would have been strong at slander. They would have been far more violent than we, in their hates, and they would have had fewer friendships. Yet they might not have been any poorer in real friendships than we. The real friendships among men are so rare that when they occur they are famous. Friends as loyal as Damon and Pythias were are exceptions. Good fellowship is common, but unchanging affection is not. We like those who like us, as a rule, and dislike those who don't. Most of our ties have no better footing than that; and those who have many such ties are called warm-hearted.

The super-cat-men would have rated cleanliness higher. Some of us primates have learned to keep ourselves clean, but it's no large proportion; and even the cleanest of us see no grandeur in soap-manufacturing, and we don't look to manicures and plumbers for

social prestige. A feline race would have honored such occupations. J. de Courcy Tiger would have felt that nothing *but* making soap, or being a plumber, was compatible with a high social position; and the rich Vera Pantherbilt would have deigned to dine only with manicures.

None but the lowest dregs of such a race would have been lawyers spending their span of life on this mysterious earth studying the long dusty records of dead and gone quarrels. We simians naturally admire a profession full of wrangle and chatter. But that is a monkeyish way of deciding disputes, not a feline.

We fight best in armies, gregariously, where the risk is reduced; but we disapprove usually of murderers, and of almost all private combat. With the great cats it would have been just the other way round. (Lions and leopards fight each other singly, not in bands, as do monkeys.)

As a matter of fact, few of us delight in really serious fighting. We do love to bicker; and we box and knock each other around, to exhibit our strength; but few normal simians are keen about bloodshed and killing; we do it in war only because of patriotism, revenge, duty, glory. A feline civilization would have cared nothing for duty or glory, but they would have taken a far higher pleasure in gore. If a planet of super-cat-men could look down upon ours, they would not know which to think was the most amazing: the way we tamely live, five million or so in a city, with only a few police to keep us quiet, while we commit only one or two murders a day, and hardly have a respectable number of brawls; or the way

great armies of us are trained to fight — not liking it much, and
yet doing more killing in war-time and shedding more blood than
even the fiercest lion on his cruelest days. Which would perplex
a gentlemanly super-cat spectator the more, our habits of wholesale
slaughter in the field, or our spiritless making a fetish of " order "
at home?

It is fair to judge peoples by the rights they will sacrifice most
for. Super-cat-men would have been outraged had their right of
personal combat been questioned. The simian submits with odd
readiness to the loss of this privilege. What outrages him is to
make him stop wagging his tongue. He becomes most excited and
passionate about the right of free speech, even going so far in his
emotion as to declare it is sacred.

He looks upon other creatures pityingly because they are dumb.
If one of his own children is born dumb, he counts it a tragedy.
Even that mere hesitation in speech known as stammering he
deems a misfortune.

So precious to a simian is the privilege of making sounds with
his tongue that when he wishes to punish severely those men he
calls criminals, he forbids them to chatter, and forces them by
threats to be silent. It is felt that this punishment is entirely too
cruel, however, and that even the worst offenders should be allowed
to talk part of each day.

Whatever a simian does, there must always be some talking
about it. He can't even make peace without a kind of chatter called
a peace conference. Super-cats would not have had to " make "
peace: they would have just walked off and stopped fighting.

In a world of super-cat-men, I suppose there would have been
fewer sailors; and people would have cared less for seaside resorts,
or for swimming. Cats hate getting wet, so men descended from
them might have hated it. They would have felt that even going in
wading was a sign of great hardihood, and only the most daring
young fellows, showing off, would have done it.

Among them there would have been no anti-vivisection societies;
No Young Cats Christian Associations or Red Cross work;
No vegetarians;

No early-closing laws;
Much more hunting and trapping;
No riding to hounds; that's pure simian. Just think how it would
have entranced the old-time monkeys to foresee such a game! A
game where they'd all prance off on captured horses, tearing pell-

Punctilious,
  haughty,
    inflammable

mell through the woods in gay red
coats, attended by yelping packs of
servant-dogs. It is excellent sport — but
how cats would scorn to hunt in that
way!

They would not have knighted explorers — they would have all been
explorers.

Imagine that you are strolling through
a super-cat city at night. Over yonder
is the business quarter, its evening
shops blazing with jewels. The great
stockyards lie to the east where you
hear those sad sounds: that low mooing as of innumerable herds, waiting
slaughter. Beyond lie the silent aqua-
riums and the crates of fresh mice.

(They raise mice instead of hens in the country, in Super-cat
Land.) To the west is a beautiful but weirdly bacchanalian park,
with long groves of catnip, where young super-cats have their fling,
and where a few crazed catnip addicts live on till they die, unable
to break off their strangely undignified orgies. And here where you
stand is the sumptuous residence district. Houses with spacious
grounds everywhere: no densely packed buildings. The streets
have been swept up — or lapped up — until they are spotless. Not
a scrap of paper is lying around anywhere; no rubbish, no dust.
Few of the pavements are left bare, as ours are, and those few are
polished; the rest have deep soft velvet carpets. No footfalls are
heard.

There are no lights in these streets, though these people are
abroad much at night. All you see are stars overhead and the
glowing eyes of cat ladies, of lithe silken ladies who pass you, or of

stiff-whiskered men. Beware of those men and the gleam of their split-pupiled stare. They are haughty, punctilious, inflammable; self-absorbed too, however. They will probably not even notice you; but if they do, you are lost. They take offense in a flash, abhor strangers, despise hospitality, and would think nothing of killing you or me on their way home to dinner.

Follow one of them. Enter this house. Ah, what splendor! No servants, though a few abject monkeys wait at the back doors and submissively run little errands. But of course they are never let inside; they would seem out of place. Gorgeous couches, rich colors, silken walls, an oriental magnificence. In here is the ball-room. But wait: what is this in the cor-

One of their poets

ner? A large triumphal statue — of a cat overcoming a dog. And look at this dining-room, its exquisite appointments, its daintiness: faucets for hot and cold milk in the pantry, and a gold bowl of cream.

Someone is entering. Hush! If I could but describe her! Languorous, slender, and passionate. Sleepy eyes that see everything. An indolent purposeful step. An unimaginable grace. If you were her lover, my boy, you would learn how fierce love can be, how capricious and sudden, how hostile, how ecstatic, how violent!

Think what the state of the arts would have been in such cities. They would have had few comedies on their stage; no farces. Cats care little for fun. In the circus, superlative acrobats. No clowns.

In drama and singing they would have surpassed us probably. Even in the stage of arrested development as mere animals in which we see cats, they wail with a passionate intensity at night in our yards. Imagine how a Caruso descended from such beings would sing.

In literature they would not have begged for happy endings.

They would have been personally more self-assured than we, far freer of cheap imitativeness of each other in manners and art, and hence more original in art; more clearly aware of what they really desired, not cringingly watchful of what was expected of them; less widely observant perhaps, more deeply thoughtful.

Their artists would have produced less, however, even though they felt more. A super-cat artist would have valued the pictures he drew for their effects on himself; he wouldn't have cared a rap whether anyone else saw them or not. He would not have bothered, usually, to give any form to his conceptions. Simply to have had the sensation would have for him been enough. But since simians love to be noticed, it does not content them to have a conception; they must wrestle with it until it takes a form in which others can see it. They doom the artistic impulse to toil with its nose to the grindstone, until their idea is expressed in a book or a statue. Are they right? I have doubts. The artistic impulse seems not to wish to produce finished work. It certainly deserts us half-way, after the idea is born; and if we go on, art is labor. With the cats, art is joy.

But the dominant characteristic of this fine race is cunning. And hence I think it would have been through their craftiness, chiefly, that they would have felt the impulse to study and the wish to advance. Craft is a cat's delight; craft they never can have too much of. So it would have been from one triumph of cunning to another that they would have marched. That would have been the greatest driving force of their civilization.

This would have meant great progress in invention and science — or in some fields of science, the economic for instance. But it would have retarded them in others. Craft studies the world calculatingly, from without, instead of understandingly from within. Especially would it have cheapened the feline philosophies; for not simply how to know but how to circumvent the universe would have been their desire. Mankind's curiosity is disinterested; it seems purer by contrast. That is to say, made as we are, it seems purer to us. What we call disinterested, however, super-cats might call aimless. (Aimlessness is one of the regular simian traits.)

I don't mean to be prejudiced in favor of the simian side. Curiosity may be as debasing, I grant you, as craft. And craft might turn into artifices of a kind which would be noble and fine. Just as the ignorant and fitful curiosity of some little monkey is hardly to be compared to the astronomer's magnificent search, so the craft and cunning we see in our pussies would bear small relation to the high-minded planning of some ruler of the race we are imagining.

And yet — craft *is* self-defeating in the end. Transmute it into its finest possible form, let it be as subtle and civilized as you please, as yearning and noble, as enlightened, it still sets itself over against the wholeness of things; its role is that of the part at war with the whole. Milton's Lucifer had the mind of a fine super-cat.

That craft may defeat itself in the end, however, is not the real point. That doesn't explain why the lions aren't ruling the planet. The trouble is, it would defeat itself in the beginning. It would have too bitterly stressed the struggle for existence. Conflict and struggle make civilizations virile, but they do not by themselves make civilizations. Mutual aid and support are needed for that. There the felines are lacking. They do not co-operate well; they have small group-devotion. Their lordliness, their strong self-regard, and their coolness of heart have somehow thwarted the chance of their racial progress.

VII

THERE are many other beasts that one might once have thought had a chance.

Some, like horses and deer, were not bold enough; or were stupid, like buffaloes.

Some had over-trustful characters, like the seals; or exploitable characters, like cows, and chickens, and sheep. Such creatures sentence themselves to be captives, by their lack of ambition.

Dogs? They have more spirit. But they have lost their chance of kingship through worshipping us. The dog's finer qualities can't be praised too warmly; there is a purity about his devotion which makes mere men feel speechless; but with all love for dogs, one must grant they are vassals, not rulers. They are too parasitic — the one willing servant class of the world. And we have betrayed them by making under-simians of them. We have taught them some of our own ways of behaving and frowned upon theirs. Loving us, they let us stop their developing in tune with their natures; and they've patiently tried ever since to adopt ways of ours. They have done it, too; but of course they can't get far; it's not their own road. Dogs have more love than integrity. They've been true to us, yes, but they haven't been true to themselves.

Pigs? The pig is remarkably intelligent and brave — but he's gross; and grossness delays one's achievement, it takes so much time. The snake too, though wise, has a way of eating himself into stupors. If super-snake-men had had banquets they would have been too vast to describe. Each little snake family could have eaten a herd of cattle at Christmas.

Goats, then? Bears or turtles? Wolves, whales, crows? Each had brains and pride, and would have been glad to rule the world if they could; but each had their defects, and their weaknesses for such a position.

The elephant? Ah! Evolution has had its tragedies, hasn't it, as well as its triumphs; and well should the elephant know it. He had the best chance of all. Wiser even than the lion or the wisest of apes, his wisdom furthermore was benign where theirs was sinister. Consider his dignity, his poise and skill. He was plastic, too. He had learned to eat many foods and endure many climates. Once, some say, this race explored the globe. Their bones are found everywhere, in South America even; so the elephants' Columbus may have found some road here before ours. They are cosmopolitans, these suave and well-bred beings. They have rich emotional natures, long memories, loyalty; they are steady and sure; and not narrow, not self-absorbed, for they seem interested in everything. What was it, then, that put them out of the race?

Could it have been a quite natural belief that they had already won?

And when they saw that they hadn't, and that the monkey-men were getting ahead, were they too great-minded and decent to exterminate their puny rivals?

It may have been their tolerance and patience that betrayed them. They wait too long before they resent an imposition or insult. Just as ants are too energetic and cats too shrewd for their own highest good, so the elephants suffer from too much patience. Their exhibitions of it may seem superb — such power and such restraint, combined, are noble — but a quality carried to excess

defeats itself. Kings who won't lift their scepters must yield in the
end; and, the worst of it is, to upstarts who snatch at their crowns.

I fancy the elephants would have been gentler masters than we:
more live-and-let-live in allowing other species to stay here. Our
way is to kill good and bad, male and female and babies, till the
few last survivors lie hidden away from our guns. All species must
surrender unconditionally — those are our terms — and come and
live in barns alongside us; or on us, as parasites. The creatures that
want to live a life of their own, we call wild. If wild, then, no matter how harmless, we treat them as outlaws, and those of us who are
specially well brought up shoot them for fun. Some might be our
friends. We don't wish it. We keep them all terrorized. When one
of us conquering monkey-men enters the woods, most animals that
scent him slink away, or race off in a panic. It is not that we have
planned this deliberately; but they know what we're like. Race by
race they have been slaughtered. Soon all will be gone. We give
neither freedom nor life-room to those we defeat.

If we had been as strong as the elephants, we might have been
kinder. When great power comes naturally to people, it is used
more urbanely. We use it as parvenus do, because that's what we
are. The elephant, being born to it, is easy-going, confident, tolerant. He would have been a more humane king.

A race descended from elephants would have had to build on
a large scale. Imagine a crowd of huge, wrinkled, slow-moving
elephant-men getting into a vast elephant omnibus.

And would they have ever tried airships?

The elephant is stupid when it comes to learning how to use
tools. So are all other species except our own. Isn't it strange? A
tool, in the most primitive sense, is any object, lying around, that
can obviously be used as an instrument for this or that purpose.
Many creatures use objects as *materials,* as birds use twigs for
nests. But the step that no animal takes is learning freely to use
things as instruments. When an elephant plucks off a branch and
swishes his flanks, and thus keeps away insects, he is using a tool.
But he does it only by a vague and haphazard association of ideas.

If he once became a conscious user of tools he would of course go much further.

We ourselves, who are so good at it now, were slow enough in beginning. Think of the long epochs that passed before it entered our heads.

And all that while the contest for leadership blindly went on, without any species making use of this obvious aid. The lesson to be learned was simple; the reward was the rule of a planet. Yet only one species, our own, has ever had that much brains.

It makes you wonder what other obvious lessons may still be unlearned.

It is not necessarily stupid, however, to fail to use tools. To use tools involves using reason, instead of sticking to instinct. Now, sticking to instinct has its disadvantages, but so has using reason. Whichever faculty you use, the other atrophies and partly deserts you. We are trying to use both. But we still don't know which has the more value.

A sudden vision comes to me of one of the first far-away ape-men who tried to use reason instead of instinct as a guide for his conduct. I imagine him, perched in his tree, torn between those two voices, wailing loudly at night by a river, in his puzzled distress.

My poor far-off brother!

The First Thinker

VIII

W<small>E</small> have been considering which species was on the whole most finely equipped to be rulers, and thereafter achieve a high civilization; but that wasn't the problem. The real problem was which would *do* it — a different matter.

To do it there was need of a species that had at least these two qualities: some quenchless desire, to urge them on and on; and also adaptability of a thousand kinds to their environment.

The rhinoceros cares little for adaptability. He slogs through the world. But we! We are experts. Adaptability is what we depend on. We talk of our mastery of nature, which sounds very grand; but the fact is we respectfully adapt ourselves first to her ways. " We attain no power over nature till we learn natural laws, and our lordship depends on the adroitness with which we learn and conform."

Adroitness, however, is merely an ability to win; back of it there must be some spur to make us use our adroitness. Why don't we all die or give up when we're sick of the world? Because the love of life is reinforced, in most energized beings, by some longing that pushes them forward, in defeat and in darkness. All creatures wish to live, and to perpetuate their species, of course; but those two wishes alone evidently do not carry any race far. In addition to these, a race, to be great, needs some hunger, some itch, to spur it up the hard path we lately have learned to call evolution. The love of toil in the ants, and of craft in cats, are examples (imaginary or not). What other such lust could exert great driving force?

With us is it curiosity? Endless interest in one's environment?

Many animals have some curiosity, but " some " is not enough; and in but few is it one of the master passions. By a master passion I mean a passion that is really your master: some appetite which habitually, day in, day out, makes its subjects forget fatigue or danger, and sacrifice their ease to its gratification. That is the kind of hold that curiosity has on the monkeys.

IX

IMAGINE a prehistoric prophet observing these beings, and fore-
casting what kind of civilizations their descendants would build.
Anyone could have foreseen certain parts of the simians' history:
could have guessed that their curiosity would unlock for them, one
by one, nature's doors, and — idly — bestow on them stray bits of
valuable knowledge; could have pictured them spreading inquir-
ingly all over the globe, stumbling on their inventions — and idly
passing on and forgetting them.

To have to learn the same thing over and over again wastes the
time of a race. But this is continually necessary with simians, because of their disorder. " Disorder," a prophet would have sighed;
" that is one of their handicaps; one that they will never get rid
of, whatever it costs. Having so much curiosity makes a race scatter-
brained.

" Yes," he would have dismally continued, " it will be a queer
mixture: these simians will attain to vast stores of knowledge, in
time, that is plain. But after spending centuries groping to discover
some art, in after centuries they will now and then find it's forgotten. How incredible it would seem on other planets to hear of
lost arts!

" There is a strong streak of triviality in them, which you don't
see in cats. They won't have fine enough characters to concentrate
on the things of most weight. They will talk and think far more
of trifles than of what is important. Even when they are reasonably
civilized, this will be so. Great discoveries sometimes will fail to be
heard of, because too much else is; and many will thus disappear,
and these men will not know it." [1]

Let me interrupt this lament to say a word for myself and my
ancestors. It is easy to blame us as undiscriminating, but we are at
least full of zest. And it's well to be interested, eagerly and intensely,
in so many things, because there is often no knowing which may
turn out important. We don't go around being interested on pur-

[1] We did rescue Mendel's from the dust-heap; but perhaps it was an
exception.

pose, hoping to profit by it, but a profit may come. And anyway it is generous of us not to be too self-absorbed. Other creatures go to the other extreme to an amazing extent. They are ridiculously oblivious of what is going on. The smallest ant in the garden will ignore the largest woman who visits it. She is a huge and most dangerous super-mammoth in relation to him, and her tread shakes the earth; but he has no time to be bothered, investigating suchlike phenomena. He won't even get out of her way. He has his work to do, hang it.

Birds and squirrels have less of this glorious independence of spirit. They watch you closely — if you move around. But not if you keep still. In other words, they pay no more attention than they can help, even to mammoths.

We, of course, observe everything, or try to. We could spend our lives looking on. Consider our museums for instance: they are a sign of our breed. It makes us smile to see birds, like the magpie, with a mania for this collecting — but only monkeyish beings could reverence museums as we do, and pile such heterogeneous trifles and quantities in them. Old furniture, egg-shells, watches, bits of stone. . . . And next door, a " menagerie." Though our victory over all other animals is now æons old, we still bring home captives and exhibit them caged in our cities. And when a species dies out — or is crowded (by us) off the planet — we even collect the bones of the vanquished and show them like trophies.

Curiosity is a valuable trait. It will make the simians learn many things. But the curiosity of a simian is as excessive as the toil of an ant. Each simian will wish to know more than his head can hold, let alone ever deal with; and those whose minds are active will wish to know everything going. It would stretch a god's skull to accomplish such an ambition, yet simians won't like to think it's beyond their powers. Even small tradesmen and clerks, no matter how thrifty, will be eager to buy costly encyclopedias, or books of all knowledge. Almost every simian family, even the dullest, will think it is due to themselves to keep all knowledge handy.

Their idea of a liberal education will therefore be a great hodge-podge; and he who narrows his field and digs deep will be viewed as an alien. If more than one man in a hundred should thus dare to concentrate, the ruinous effects of being a specialist will be sadly discussed. It may make a man exceptionally useful, they will have to admit; but still they will feel badly, and fear that civilization will suffer.

One of their curious educational ideas — but a natural one — will be shown in the efforts they will make to learn more than one "language." They will set their young to spending a decade or more of their lives in studying duplicate systems — whole systems — of chatter. Those who thus learn several different ways to say the same things will command much respect, and those who learn many will be looked on with awe — by true simians. And persons without this accomplishment will be looked down on a little, and will actually feel quite apologetic about it themselves.

Consider how enormously complicated a complete language must be, with its long and arbitrary vocabulary, its intricate system of sounds; the many forms that single words may take, especially if they are verbs; the rules of grammar, the sentence structure, the idioms, slang, and inflections. Heavens, what a genius for tongues these simians have! [1] Where another race, after the most frightful discord and pains, might have slowly constructed one language before this earth grew cold, this race will create literally hundreds, each complete in itself, and many of them with quaint little systems of writing attached. And the owners of this linguistic gift are so humble about it, they will marvel at bees, for their hives, and at beavers' mere dams.

To return, however, to their fear of being too narrow, in going to the other extreme they will run to incredible lengths. Every civilized simian, every day of his life, in addition to whatever older facts he has picked up, will wish to know all the news of all the world. If he felt any true concern to know it, this would be rather fine of him: it would imply such a close solidarity on the part of this genus. (Such a close solidarity would seem crushing, to others; but that is another matter.) It won't be true concern, however, it

---

[1] You remember what Kipling says in the *Jungle Books*, about how disgusted the quiet animals were with the Bandarlog, because they were eternally chattering, would never keep still. Well, this is the good side of it.

will be merely a blind inherited instinct. He'll forget what he's read, the very next hour, or moment. Yet there he will faithfully sit, the ridiculous creature, reading of bombs in Spain or floods in Tibet, and especially insisting on all the news he can get of the kind our race loved when they scampered and fought in the forest, news that will stir his most primitive simian feelings — wars, accidents, love-affairs, and family quarrels.

To feed himself with this largely purposeless provender, he will pay thousands of simians to be reporters of such events day and

night; and they will report them on such a voluminous scale as to smother or obscure more significant news altogether. Great printed sheets will be read by everyone every day; and even the laziest of this lazy race will not think it labor to perform this toil. They won't like to eat in the morning without their papers, such slaves they will be to this droll greed for knowing. They won't even think it is droll, it is so in their blood.

Their swollen desire for investigating everything about them, including especially other people's affairs, will be quenchless. Few will feel that they really are " fully informed "; and all will give much of each day all their lives to the news.

Books, too, will be used to slake this unappeasable thirst. They will actually hold books in deep reverence. Books! Bottled chatter! Things that some other simian has formerly said. They will dress them in costly bindings, keep them under glass, and take an affecting pride in the number they read. Libraries — storehouses of books

— will dot their world. The destruction of one will be a crime against civilization. (Meaning, again, a simian civilization.) Well, it is an offense, to be sure — a barbaric offense. But so is defacing forever a beautiful landscape; and they won't even notice that sometimes; they won't shudder anyway, the way they instinctively do at the loss of a " library."

All this is inevitable and natural, and they cannot help it. There even are ways one can justify excesses like this. If their hunger for books ever seems indiscriminate to them when they themselves stop to examine it, they will have their excuses. They will argue that some bits of knowledge they once had thought futile had later on come in most handy, in unthought-of ways. True enough! For their scientists. But not for their average men: they will simply be like obstinate housekeepers who clog up their homes, preserving odd boxes and wrappings, and stray lengths of string, to exult if but one is of some trifling use ere they die. It will be in this spirit that simians will cherish their books and pile them up everywhere into great indiscriminate mounds; and these mounds will seem signs of culture and sagacity to them.

Those who know many facts will feel wise! They will despise those who don't. They will even believe, many of them, that knowledge is power. Unfortunate dupes of this saying will keep on reading, ambitiously, till they have stunned their native initiative and made their thoughts weak; and will then wonder dazedly what in the world is the matter, and why the great power they were expecting to gain fails to appear. Again, if they ever forget what they read, they'll be worried. Those who can forget — those with fresh eyes who have swept from their minds such facts as the exact month and day that their children were born, or the numbers on houses, or the names (the mere meaningless labels) of the people they meet — will be urged to go live in sanitariums or see memory doctors!

By nature their itch is rather for knowing than for understanding or thinking. Some of them will learn to think, doubtless, and even to concentrate, but their eagerness to acquire those accomplishments will not be strong or insistent. Creatures whose main-

spring is curiosity will enjoy the accumulating of facts, far more
than the pausing at times to reflect on those facts. If they do not
reflect on them, of course they'll be slow to find out about the
ideas and relationships lying behind them; and they will be curious
about those ideas; so you would suppose they'd reflect. But deep
thinking is painful. It means they must channel the spready rivers
of their attention. That cannot be done without discipline and
drills for the mind; and they will abhor doing that; their minds
will work better when they are left free to run off at tangents.

Compare them in this with other species. Each has its own kind
of strength. To be compelled to be so quick-minded as the simians
would be torture to cows. Cows could dwell on one idea, week by
week, without trying at all; but they'd all have brain-fever in an
hour at a simian tea. A super-cow people would revel in long,
thoughtful books on abstruse philosophical subjects, and would sit
up late reading them. Most of the ambitious simians who try it —
out of pride — go to sleep. The typical simian brain is supremely
distractible, and it's really too jumpy by nature to endure much
reflection.

Therefore many more of them will be well-informed than sagacious.

This will result in their knowing most things far too soon, at
too early a stage of civilization to use them aright. They will learn
to make valuable explosives at a stage in their growth when they
will use them not only in industries, but for killing brave men.
They will devise ways to mine coal efficiently, in enormous
amounts, at a stage when they won't know enough to conserve it,
and will waste their few stores. They will use up a lot of it in a
simian habit [1] called travel. This will consist in queer little hurried runs over the globe, to see ten thousand things in the hope
of thus filling their minds.

Their minds will be full enough. Their intelligence will be active
and keen. It will have a constant tendency, however, to outstrip
their wisdom. Their intelligence will enable them to build great
industrial systems before they have the wisdom and goodness to
run them aright. They will form greater political empires than
they will have strength to guide. They will endlessly quarrel about

[1] Even in a wild state, the monkey is restless and does not live in lairs.

which is the best scheme of government, without stopping to realize that learning to govern comes first. (The average simian will imagine he knows without learning.)

The natural result will be industrial and political wars. In a world of unmanageable structures, wild smashes must come.

X

INVENTIONS will come so easily to simians (in comparison with all other creatures) and they will take such childish pleasure in monkeying around, making inventions, that their many devices will be more of a care than a comfort. In their homes a large part of their time will have to be spent keeping their numerous ingenuities in good working order — their elaborate bell-ringing arrangements, their locks and their clocks. In the field of science, to be sure, this fertility in invention will lead to a long list of important and beautiful discoveries: telescopes and the calculus, radiographs, and the spectrum. Discoveries great enough, almost, to make angels of them. But here again their simianness will cheat them of half of their dues, for they will neglect great discoveries of the truest importance, and honor extravagantly those of less value and splendor if only they cater especially to simian traits.

To consider examples: A discovery that helps them to talk, just to talk, more and more, will be hailed by these beings as one of the highest of triumphs. Talking to each other over wires will come in this class. The lightning when harnessed and tamed will be made to trot round conveying the most trivial cacklings all day and night.

Huge seas of talk of every sort and kind, in print, speech, and writing, will roll unceasingly over their civilized realms, involving an unbelievable waste in labor and time, and sapping the intelligence talk is supposed to upbuild. In a simian civilization great halls will be erected for lectures, and great throngs will actually pay to go inside at night to hear some self-satisfied talk-maker chatter for hours. Almost any subject will do for a lecture, or talk; yet very few subjects will be counted important enough for the average man to do any *thinking* on them, off by himself.

In their futurist books they will dream of an even worse state, a more dreadful indulgence in communication than the one just described. This they'll hope to achieve by a system called mental telepathy. They will long to communicate wordlessly, mind impinging on mind, until all their minds are awash with messages every moment, and withdrawal from the stream is impossible anywhere on earth. This will foster the brotherhood of man. (Conglomerateness being their ideal.) Super-cats would have invented more barriers instead of more channels.

Discoveries in surgery and medicine will also be overpraised. The reason will be that the race will so need these discoveries. Unlike the great cats, simians tend to undervalue the body. Having less self-respect, less proper regard for their egos, they care less than the cats do for the casing of the ego — the body. The more civilized they grow, the more they will let their bodies deteriorate. They will let their shoulders stoop, their lungs shrink, and their stomachs grow fat. No other species will be quite so deformed and distorted. Athletics they will watch, yes, but on the whole sparingly practice. Their snuffy old scholars will even be proud to decry them. Where once the simians swung high through forests, or scampered like deer, their descendants will plod around farms, or mince along city streets, moving constrictedly, slowly, their litheness half gone.

They will think of Nature as " something to go out and look at." They will try to live wholly apart from her and forget they're her sons. Forget? They will even deny it, and declare themselves sons of God. In spite of her wonders they will regard Nature as somehow too humble to be the true parent of such prominent people as simians. They will lose all respect for the dignity of fair Mother Earth, and whisper to each other she is an evil and indecent old person. They will snatch at her gifts, pry irreverently into her mysteries, and ignore half the warnings they get from her about how to live.

Ailments of every kind will abound among such folk, inevitably, and they will resort to extraordinary expedients in their search for relief. Although squeamish as a race about inflicting much pain in cold blood, they will systematically infect other animals with their own rank diseases, or cut out other animals' organs, or kill and dissect them, hoping thus to learn how to offset their neglect of themselves. Conditions among them will be such that this will really be necessary. Few besides impractical sentimentalists will therefore oppose it. But the idea will be to gain health by legerdemain, by a trick, instead of by taking the trouble to live healthy lives.

Strange barrack-like buildings called hospitals will stand in their cities, where their trick-men, the surgeons, will slice them right open when ill; and thousands of zealous young pharmacists will mix little drugs, which thousands of wise-looking simians will firmly prescribe. Each generation will change its mind as to these drugs, and laugh at all former opinions; but each will use some of them, and each will feel assured that in this respect they know the last word.

And, in obstinate blindness, this people will wag their poor heads and attribute their diseases not to simianness but to civilization.

The advantages that any man or race has can sometimes be handicaps. Having hands, which so aids a race, for instance, can also be harmful. The simians will do so many things with their hands, it will be bad for their bodies. Instead of roaming far and wide over the country, getting vigorous exercise, they will use their hands to catch and tame horses, build carriages, motors, and then when they want a good outing they will " go for a ride," with their bodies slumped down, limp and sluggish, and losing their spring.

Then, too, their brains will do harm, and great harm, to their bodies. The brain will give them such an advantage over all other animals that they will insensibly be led to rely too much on it, to give it too free a rein, and to find the mirrors in it too fascinating. This organ, this outgrowth, this new part of them, will grow overactive, and its many fears and fancies will naturally injure the body. The interadjustment is delicate and intimate, the strain is continuous. When the brain fails to act with the body, or, worse, works against it, the body will sicken, no matter what cures doctors try.

As in bodily self-respect, so in racial self-respect they'll be wanting. They will have plenty of racial pride and prejudice, but that is not the same thing. That will make them angry when simians of one color mate with those of another. But a general deterioration in physique will cause much less excitement.

They will *talk* about improving the race — they will talk about everything — but they won't use their chances to *do* it. Whenever a new discovery makes life less hard, for example, these heedless beings will seldom preserve this advantage, or use their new wealth to take more time thereafter for thought, or to gain health and strength or do anything else to make the race better. Instead, they will use the new ease just to increase in numbers; and they will keep on at this until misery once more has checked them. Life will then be as hard as ever, naturally, and the chance will be gone.

They will have a proverb: " The poor ye have always with you " — said by one who knew simians.

Their ingenious minds will have an answer to this. They will argue it is well that life should be Spartan and hard, because of the discipline and its strengthening effects on the character. But the good effects of this sort of discipline will be mixed with sad wreckage. And only creatures incapable of disciplining themselves could thus argue. It is an odd expedient to get yourself into trouble just for discipline's sake.

The fact is, however, the argument won't be sincere. When their nations grow so over-populous and their families so large it means misery, that will not be a sign of their having felt ready for discipline. It will be a sign of their not having practiced it in their sexual lives.

XI

THE SIMIANS are always being stirred by desire and passion. It constantly excites them, constantly runs through their minds. Wild or tame, primitive or cultured, this is a brand of the breed. Other species have times and seasons for sexual matters, but the simian folk are thus preoccupied all the year round.

This superabundance of desire is not necessarily good or bad, of itself. But to shape it for the best it will have to be studied — and faced. This they will not do. Some of them won't like to study it, deeming it bad — deeming it bad, yet yielding constantly to it. Others will hesitate because they will deem it so sacred, or will secretly fear that study might show them it ought to be curbed.

Meantime, this part of their nature will be coloring all their activities. It will beautify their arts, and erotically confuse their

religions. It will lend a little interest to even their dull social functions. It will keep alive degrading social evils in all their great towns.
Through these latter evils, too, their politics will be corrupted; especially their best and most democratic attempts at self-government. Self-government works best among those who have learned
to self-govern.

In the far distant ages that lie before us what will be the result
of this constant preoccupation with desire? Will it kill us or save
us? Will this trait and our insatiable curiosity interact on each
other? That might further eugenics. That might give us a better
chance to breed finely than all other species.

We already owe a great deal to passion — more than men ever
realize. Wasn't it Darwin who once even risked the conjecture that
the vocal organs themselves were developed for sexual purposes,
the object being to call or charm one's mate. Hence — perhaps —
only animals that were continuously concerned with their matings
would be at all likely to form an elaborate language. And without
an elaborate language, growth is apt to be slow.

If we owe this to passion, what follows? Does it mean, for example, that the more different mates that each simian once learned
to charm, the more rapidly language, and with it civilization, advanced?

XII

A DOCTOR, who was making a study of monkeys, once told me that
he was trying experiments that bore on the polygamy question.
He had a young monkey named Jack who had mated with a female
named Jill; and in another cage another newly wedded pair, Arabella and Archer. Each pair seemed absorbed in each other, and
devoted and happy. They even hugged each other at meal-time and
exchanged bits of food.

After a time their transports grew less fiery, and their affections
less fixed. Archer got a bit bored. He was decent about it, though,
and when Arabella cuddled beside him he would more or less
perfunctorily embrace her. But when he forgot, she grew cross.

The same thing occurred a little later in the Jack and Jill cage, only there it was Jill who became a little tired of Jack.

Soon each pair was quarreling. They usually made up, pretty soon, and started loving again. But it petered out; each time more quickly.

Meanwhile the two families had become interested in watching each other. When Jill had repulsed Jack and he had moped about it awhile, he would begin staring at Arabella, over opposite, and trying to attract her attention. This got Jack in trouble all around. Arabella indignantly made faces at him and then turned her back; and as for Jill, she grew furious and tore out his fur.

Archer felt bored

But in the next stage they even stopped hating each other. Each pair grew indifferent.

Then the doctor put Jack in with Arabella, and Archer with Jill. Arabella promptly yielded to Jack. New devotion. More transports. Jill and Archer were shocked. Jill clung to the bars of her cage, quivering, and screaming remonstrance; and even blasé Archer chattered angrily at some of the scenes. Then the doctor hung curtains between the cages to shut out the view. Jill and Archer, left to each other, grew interested. They soon were inseparable.

The four monkeys, thus redistributed, were now happy once more, and full of new liveliness and spirit. But before very long, each pair quarreled — and made up — and quarreled — and then grew indifferent, and had cynical thoughts about life.

At this point the doctor put them back with their original mates.

And — they met with a rush! Gave cries of recognition and joy, like faithful souls reunited. And when they were tired, they affectionately curled up together; and hugged each other even at meal-time, and exchanged bits of food.

This was as far as the doctor had got at the time that I met him; and as I have lost touch with him since, I don't know how things were afterwards. His theory at the time was that variety was good for fidelity.

"So many of us feel this way, it may be in the blood," he concluded. "Some creatures, such as wolves, are more serious; or perhaps more cold-blooded. Never mate but once. Well — we're not wolves. We can't make wolves our models. Of course we are not monkeys either, but at any rate they are our cousins. Perhaps wolves can be continent without any trouble at all, but it's harder for simians; it may affect their nervous systems injuriously. If we want to know how to behave, according to the way Nature made us, I say that with all due allowances we should study the monkeys."

To be sure, these particular monkeys were living in idleness. This corresponds to living in high social circles with us, where men do not have to work, and lack some of the common incentives to home-building. The experiment was not conclusive.

Still, even in low social circles —

XIII

ARE we or are we not simians? It is no use for any man to try to think anything else out until he has decided first of all where he stands on that question. It is not only in love-affairs; let us lay all that aside for the moment. It is in ethics, economics, art, education, philosophy, what not. If we are fallen angels, we should go this road; if we are super-apes, that.

"Our problem is not to discover what we ought to do if we were different, but what we ought to do being what we are. There is no end to the beings we can imagine different from ourselves; but they do not exist," and we cannot be sure they would be better than we if they did. For, when we imagine them, we must imagine their entire environment; they would have to be a part of some whole that does not now exist. And that new whole, that new reality, being merely a figment of our little minds, "would probably be inferior to the reality that is. For there is this to be said in favor of reality: that we have nothing to compare it with. Our fantasies are always incomplete, because they are fantasies. And reality is complete. We cannot compare their incompleteness with its completeness." [1]

Too many moralists begin with a dislike of reality: a dislike of men as they are. They are free to dislike them — but not at the same time to be moralists. Their feeling leads them to ignore the obligation which should rest on all teachers, " to discover the best that man can do, not to set impossibilities before him and tell him that if he does not perform them he is damned."

Man is moldable; very; and it is desirable that he should aspire. But he is apt to be hasty about accepting any and all general ideals without figuring out whether they are suitable for simian use.

One result of his habit of swallowing whole most of the ideals that occur to him is that he has swallowed a number that strongly conflict. Any ideal whatever strains our digestions if it is hard to assimilate; but when two at once act on us in different ways, it is unbearable. In such a case the poets will prefer the ideal that's idealest; the hard-headed instinctively choose the one adapted to simians.

Whenever this is argued, extremists spring up on each side. One extremist will say that, being mere simians, we cannot transcend much, and will seem to think that, having limitations, we should preserve them forever. The other will declare that we are not merely simians, never were just plain animals; or, if we were, souls were somehow smuggled into us, since which time we have been different. We have all been perfect at heart since that date, equipped with beautiful spirits, which only a strange perverse obstinacy leads us to soil.

What this obstinacy is is the problem that confronts theologians. They won't think of it as simianness; they call it original sin. They regard it as the voice of some devil, and say good men should not listen to it. The scientists say it isn't a devil, it is part of our nature, which should of course be civilized and guided, but should not be stamped out. (It might mutilate us dangerously to become under-simianized. Look at Mrs. Humphry Ward and George Washington. Worthy souls, but no flavor.)

[1] From an anonymous article entitled " Tolstoy and Russia " in the London *Times*, September 26, 1918.

In every field of thought, then, two schools appear, that are divided on this: Must we forever beat heart high-grade simians? Or are we at heart something else?

For example, in education we have in the main two great systems. One depends upon discipline. The other on exciting the interest. The teacher who does not recognize or allow for our simian nature keeps little children at work for long periods at dull and dry tasks. Without some such discipline, he fears that his boys will lack strength. The other system believes they will learn more when their interest is roused; and when their minds, which are mobile by nature, are allowed to keep moving.

Or in politics: the best government for simians seems to be based on a parliament: a talk-room, where endless vague thoughts can be expressed. This is the natural child of those primeval sessions that gave pleasure to apes. It is neither an ideal nor a rational arrangement, of course. Small executive committees would be better. But not if we are simians.

Or in industry: Why do factory workers produce more in eight hours a day than in ten? It is absurd. Super-sheep could not do it. But that is the way men are made. To preach to such beings about the dignity of labor is futile. The dignity of labor is not a simian conception at all. True simians hate to have to work steadily; they call it grind and confinement. They are always ready to pity the toilers who are condemned to this fate, and to congratulate those who escape it or who can do something else. When they see some performer in spangles risk his life, at a circus, swinging around on trapezes, high up in the air, and when they are told he must do it daily, do they pity *him*? No! Super-elephants would say, and quite properly: " What a horrible life! " But it naturally seems stimulating to simians. Boys envy the fellow. On the other hand, whenever we are told about factory life, we instinctively shudder to think of enduring such evils. We see some old workman, filling cans with a whirring machine; and we hear the humanitarians telling us, indignant and grieving, that he actually must stand in that nice, warm, dry room every day, safe from storms and wild beasts, and with nothing to do but fill cans; and at once we groan: " How deadly! What monotonous toil! Shorten his hours! " His work would seem blissful to super-spiders — but to us it's intolerable. The factory system is meant for other species than ours.

Our monkey-blood is also apparent in our judgments of crime. If a crime is committed on impulse, we partly forgive it. Why? Because, being simians, with a weakness for yielding to impulses, we like to excuse ourselves by feeling not accountable for them. Elephants would have probably taken an opposite stand. They aren't creatures of impulse and would be shocked at crimes due to such causes; their fault is the opposite one of pondering too long over injuries, and becoming vindictive in the end, out of all due proportion. If a young super-elephant were to murder another on impulse, they would consider him a dangerous character and string him right up. But if he could prove that he had long thought of doing it, they would tend to forgive him. "Poor fellow, he brooded," they would say. "That's upsetting to anyone."

As to modesty and decency, if we are simians we have done well, considering; but if we are something else — fallen angels — we have indeed fallen far. Not being modest by instinct, we invent artificial ideals, which are doubtless well-meaning but are inherently of course second-rate, so that even at our best we smell prudish. And as for our worst, when we, as we say, let ourselves go, we dirty the life-force unspeakably, with chuckles and leers. But a race so indecent by nature as the simians are would naturally have a hard time behaving as though they were not; and the strain of pretending that their thoughts were all pretty and sweet would naturally send them to smutty extremes for relief. The standards of purity we have adopted are far too strict — for simians.

XIV

We were speaking awhile ago of the fertility with which simians breed. This is partly due to the constant love-interest they take in each other, but it is also reinforced by their reliance on numbers. That reliance will be deep, since to their numbers they will owe much success. It will be thus that they will drive out other species and garrison the globe. Such a race would naturally come to esteem fertility. It will seem profane not to.

As time goes on, however, the advantage of numbers will end;
and in their higher stages large numbers will be a great drawback.
The resources of a planet are limited, at each stage of the arts. Also,
there is only a limited space on a planet. Yet it will come hard to
them to think of ever checking their increase. They will bring more
young into existence than they can either keep well or feed. The
earth will be covered with them everywhere, as far as eye can see.
North and south, east and west, there will always be simians huddling. Their cities will be far more distressing than cities of vermin
— for vermin are healthy and calm and successful in life.

Ah, those masses of people — unintelligent, superstitious, un-
civilized! What a dismal drain they will be on the race's strength!
Not merely will they lessen its ultimate chance of achievement;
their hardships will always distress and preoccupy minds — fine,
generous minds — that might have done great things if free; that
might have done something constructive, at least, for their era, instead of being burned out attacking mere anodyne-problems.

Nature will do what it can to lessen the strain, providing an appropriate remedy for their bad behavior in plagues. Many epochs
will pass before the simians will learn or dare to control them — for
they won't think they can, any more than they dare control propagation. They will reverently call their propagation and plagues " acts
of God." When they get tired of reverence and stop their plagues,
it will be too soon. Their inventiveness will be — as usual — ahead
of their wisdom; and they will unfortunately end the good effects
of plagues (as a check) before they are advanced enough to keep
down their numbers themselves.

Meanwhile, when, owing to the pressure of other desires, any
group of primates does happen to become less prolific, they will
feel ashamed, talk of race suicide, and call themselves decadent.
And they will often be right: for though some regulation of the
birth-rate is an obvious good, and its diminution often desirable
in any planet's history, yet among simians it will be apt to come
from second-rate motives. Greed, selfishness, or fear-thoughts will
be the incentives, the bribes. Contrivances, rather than continence,
will be the method. How audacious, and how disconcerting to
Nature, to baffle her thus! Even into her shrine they must thrust
their bold paws to control her. Another race viewing them in the

garlanded chambers of love, unpacking their singular devices, might think them grotesque; but the busy little simians will be blind to such quaint incongruities.

Still, there is a great gift that their excess of passion will bestow on this race: it will give them romance. It will teach them what little they ever will learn about love. Other animals have little romance; there is none in the rut, that seasonal madness that drives them to mate with perhaps the first comer. But the simians will attain to a fine discrimination in love, and this will be their path to the only spiritual heights they can reach. For in love their inmost selves will draw near, in the silence of truth; learning little by little what the deepest sincerity means, and what clean hearts and minds and what crystal-clear sight it demands. Such intercommunication of spirit with spirit is at the beginning of all true understanding. It is the beginning of silent cosmic wisdom: it may lead to knowing the ways of that power called God.

XV

Not content with the whole of a planet and themselves, too, to study, this race's children will also study the heavens. How few kinds of creatures would ever have felt that impulse, and yet how natural it will seem to these! How boundless and magnificent is the curiosity of these tiny beings, who sit and peer out at the night from their small whirling globe, considering deeply the huge cold seas of space, and learning with wonderful skill to measure the stars.

In studies so vast, however, they are tested to the core. In these great journeys the traveler must pay dear for his flaws. For it always is when you most finely are exerting your strength that every weakness you have most tells against you.

One weakness of the primates is the character of their self-consciousness. This useful faculty, that can probe so deep, has one naïve defect — it relies too readily on its own findings. It doesn't suspect enough its own unconfessed predilections. It assumes that it can be completely impartial — but isn't. To instance an obvious way in which it will betray them: beings that are intensely self-conscious and aware of their selves will also instinctively feel that their universe is. What active principle animates the world, they will ask. A great blind force? It is possible. But they will recoil from admitting any such possibility. A self-aware purposeful force, then? That is better! (More simian.) " A blind force can't have been the creator of all. It's unthinkable." Any theory *their* brains find " unthinkable " cannot be true.

(This is not to argue that it really is a blind force — or the opposite. It is merely an instance of how little impartial they are.)

A second typical weakness of this race will come from their fears. They are not either self-sufficing or gallant enough to travel great roads without cringing — clear-eyed, unafraid. They are finely made, but not nobly made — in that sense. They will therefore have a too urgent need of religion. Few primates have the courage to face — alone — the still inner mysteries: Infinity, Space, and Time. They will think it too terrible, they will feel it would turn them to water, to live through unearthly moments of vision without creeds or beliefs. So they'll get beliefs first. Ah, poor creatures! The cart before the horse! Ah, the blasphemy (pitiful!) of their seeking high spiritual temples, with god-maps or bibles about them, made below in advance! Think of their entering into the presence of Truth, declaring so loudly and boldly they know her already, yet far from willing to stand or fall by her flames — to rise like a phœnix or die as an honorable cinder! — but creeping in, clad in their queer blindfolded beliefs, designed to shield them from her stern, bright tests! Think of Truth sadly — or merrily — eying such worms!

XVI

IMAGINE you are watching the Bandarlog at play in the forest. As you behold them and comprehend their natures, now hugely brave and boastful, now full of dread, the most weakly emotional of any intelligent species, ever trying to attract the notice of some greater animal, not happy, indeed, unless noticed — is it not plain they are bound to invent things called gods? Don't think for the moment of whether there are gods or not; think of how sure these beings would be to invent them. (Not wait to find them.) Having small self-reliance, they cannot bear to face life alone. With no self-sufficingness, they must have the countenance of others. It is these pressing needs that will hurry the primates to build, out of each shred of truth they can possibly twist to their purpose, and out of imaginings that will impress them because they are vast, deity after deity to prop up their souls.

What a strange company they will be, these gods, in their day, each of them an old bearded simian up in the sky, who begins by fishing the universe out of a void, like a conjurer taking a rabbit out of a hat! (A hat which, if it resembled a void, wasn't there.) And after creating enormous suns and spheres, and filling the farthest heavens with vaster stars, one god will turn back and long for the smell of roast flesh, another will call desert tribes to "holy" wars, and a third will grieve about divorce or dancing.

All gods that any groups of simians ever conceive of, from the woodenest little idol in the forest to the mightiest Spirit, no matter how much they may differ, will have one trait in common: a readiness to drop any cosmic affair at short notice, focus their minds on the far-away pellet called Earth, and become immediately wholly concerned, ay, engrossed, with any individual worshipper's woes or desires — a readiness to notice a fellow when he is going to bed. This will bring indescribable comfort to simian hearts; and a god that neglects this duty won't last very long, no matter how competent he may be in other respects.

But one must reciprocate. For the maker of the Cosmos, as they see him, wants noticing too; he is fond of the deference and attention that simians pay him, and naturally he will be angry if it is withheld — or if he is not, it will be most magnanimous of him. Hence prayers and hymns. Hence queer vague attempts at communing with this noble kinsman.

To desire communion with gods is a lofty desire, but hard to attain through an ignobly definite creed. Dealing with the highest, most wordless states of being, the simians will attempt to conceive them in material form. They will have beliefs, for example, as to the furnishings and occupations in heaven. And why? Why, to help men to have religious conceptions without themselves being seers — which in any true sense of "religious" is an impossible plan.

In their efforts to be concrete they will make their creeds amusingly simian. Consider the simian amorousness of Jupiter, and the

brawls on Olympus. Again, in the old Jewish Bible, what tempts
the first pair? The Tree of Knowledge, of course. It appealed to
the curiosity of their nature, and who could control *that!*

And Satan in the Bible is distinctly a simian's devil. The snake,
it is known, is the animal monkeys most dread. Hence when men
give their devil a definite form they make him a snake. A race of
super-chickens would have pictured their devil a hawk.

XVII

W HAT are the handicaps this race will have in building religions?
The greatest is this: they have such small psychic powers. The over-
activity of their minds will choke the birth of such powers, or dull
them. The race will be less in touch with Nature, some day, than
its dogs. It will substitute the compass for its once innate sense of
direction. It will lose its gifts of natural intuition, premonition, and
rest, by encouraging its use of the mind to be cheaply incessant.

This lack of psychic power will cheat them of insight and poise;
for minds that are wandering and active, not receptive and still, can
seldom or never be hushed to a warm inner peace.

One service these restless minds, however, will do: they eventually will see through the religions they themselves invented.

But ages will be thrown away in repeating this process.

A simian creed will not be very hard thus to pierce. When forming a religion, they will be in far too much haste, to wait to apply
a strict test to their holy men's visions. Furthermore they will have
so few visions that any will awe them; so naturally they will accept
any vision as valid. Then their rapid and fertile inventiveness will
come into play, and spin the wildest creeds from each vision living
dust ever dreamed.

They will next expect everybody to believe whatever a few men
have seen, on the slippery ground that if you simply try believing
it, you will then feel it's true. Such religions are vicarious; their
prophets alone will see God, and the rest will be supposed to be
introduced to Him by the prophets. These " believers " will have
no white insight at all of their own.

Now, a second-hand believer who is warmed at one remove — if
at all — by the breath of the spirit will want to have exact defini-

tions in the beliefs he accepts. Not having had a vision to go by, he needs plain commandments. He will always try to crystallize creeds. And that, plainly, is fatal. For as time goes on, new and remoter aspects of truth are discovered, which can seldom or never be fitted into creeds that are changeless.

Over and over again this will be the process: A spiritual personality will be born; see new truth; and be killed. His new truth not only will not fit into too rigid creeds, but whatever false finality is in them it must contradict. So the seer will be killed.

His truth being mighty, however, it will kill the creeds too.

There will then be nothing left to believe in — except the dead seer.

For a few generations he may then be understandingly honored. But his priests will feel that is not enough: he must be honored uncritically; so uncritically that, whatever his message, it must be deemed the Whole Truth. Some of his message they themselves will have garbled; and it was not, at best, final; but still it will be made into a fixed creed and given his name. Truth will be given his name. All men who thereafter seek truth must find only his kind, else they won't be his " followers." (To be his co-seekers won't do.) Priests will always hate any new seers who seek further for truth. Their feeling will be that their seer found it, and thus ended all that. Just believe what he says. The job's over. No more truth need be sought.

It's a comforting thing to believe cosmic search nicely settled.

Thus the mold will be hardened. So new truths, when they come, can but break it. Then men will feel distraught and disillusioned, and civilizations will fall.

Thus each cycle will run. So long as men intertwine falsehoods with every seer's visions, both perish, and every civilization that is built on them must perish too.

XVIII

If men can ever learn to accept all their truths as not final, and if they can ever learn to build on something better than dogma, they may not be found saying, discouragedly, every once in so often, that every civilization carries in it the seeds of decay. It will carry

such seeds with great certainty, though, when they're put there, by
the very race, too, that will later deplore the results. Why shouldn't
creeds totter when they are jerry-built creeds?

On stars where creeds come late in the life of a race; where they
spring from the riper, not cruder, reactions of spirit; where they
grow out of nobly developed psychic powers that have put their
possessors in tune with cosmic music; and where no cheap halluci-
nations discredit their truths; they perhaps run a finer, more beautiful course than the simians', and open the eyes of the soul to far
loftier visions.

XIX

It has always been a serious matter for men when a civilization
decayed. But it may at some future day prove far more serious still.
Our hold on the planet is not absolute. Our descendants may lose it.

Germs may do them out of it. A chestnut fungus springs up,
defies us, and kills all our chestnuts. The boll weevil very nearly
baffles us. The fly seems unconquerable. Only a strong civilization,
when such foes are about, can preserve us. And our present efforts
to cope with such beings are fumbling and slow.

We haven't the habit of candidly facing this danger. We read
our biological history, but we don't take it in. We blandly assume
we were always "intended" to rule, and that no other outcome
could even be considered by Nature. This is one of the remnants
of ignorance certain religions have left; but it's odd that men who
don't believe in Easter should still believe this. For the facts are,
of course, this is a hard and precarious world, where every mistake
and infirmity must be paid for in full.

If mankind ever is swept aside as a failure, however, what a
brilliant and enterprising failure he at least will have been. I felt
this with a kind of warm suddenness only today, as I finished these
dreamings and drove through the gates of the park. I had been
shutting my modern surroundings out of my thoughts, so completely, and living as it were in the wild world of ages ago, that
when I let myself come back suddenly to the twentieth century
and stare at the park and the people, the change was tremendous.
All around me were the well-dressed descendants of primitive ani-

mals, whizzing about in bright motors, past tall, soaring buildings. What gifted, energetic achievers they suddenly seemed!

I thought of a photograph I had once seen of a ship being torpedoed. There it was, the huge, finely made structure, awash in the sea, with tiny black spots hanging on to its side — crew and passengers. The great ship, even while sinking, was so mighty, and those atoms so helpless. Yet, it was those tiny beings that had created that ship. They had planned it and built it and guided its bulk through the waves. They had also invented a torpedo that could rend it asunder.

It is possible that our race may be an accident, in a meaningless universe, living its brief life uncared-for, on this dark, cooling star; but even so — and all the more — what marvelous creatures we are! What fairy-story, what tale from the Arabian Nights of the jinns, is a hundredth part as wonderful as this true fairy-story of simians! It is so much more heartening, too, than the tales we invent. A universe capable of giving birth to many such accidents is — blind or not — a good world to live in, a promising universe.

And if there are no other such accidents, if we stand alone, if all the uncountable armies of planets are empty, or peopled by animals only, with no keys to thought, then we have done something so mighty, what may it not lead to! What powers may we not develop before the Sun dies! We once thought we lived on God's footstool; it may be a throne.

This is no world for pessimists. An amœba on the beach, blind and helpless, a mere bit of pulp — that amœba has grandsons today who read Kant and play symphonies. Will those grandsons in turn have descendants who will sail through the void, discover the foci of forces, the means to control them, and learn how to marshal the planets and grapple with space? Would it after all be any more startling than our rise from the slime?

No sensible amœba would have ever believed for a minute that any of his most remote children would build and run dynamoes. Few sensible men of today stop to feel, in their hearts, that we live in the very same world where that miracle happened.

This world, and our racial adventure, are magical still.

XX

Yᴇᴛ although for high-spirited marchers the march is sufficient, there still is that other way of looking at it that we dare not forget. Our adventure may satisfy us; does it satisfy Nature? She is letting us camp for a while here among the wrecked graveyards of mightier dynasties, not one of which met her tests. Their bones are the message the epochs she murdered have left us: we have learned to decipher their sickening warning at last. '

Yes, and even if we are permitted to have a long reign, and are not laid away with the failures, are we a success?

We need so much spiritual insight, and we have so little. Our airships may some day float over the hills of Arcturus, but how will that help us if we cannot find the soul of the world? Is that soul alive and loving? Or cruel? Or callous? Or dead?

We have no sure vision. Hopes, guesses, beliefs — that is all.

There are sounds we are deaf to, there are strange sights invisible to us. There are whole realms of splendor, it may be, of which we are heedless, and which we are as blind to as ants to the call of the sea.

Life is enormously flexible — look at all that we've done to our dogs — but we carry our hairy past with us wherever we go. The wise St. Bernards and the selfish toy lap-dogs are brothers, and some things are possible for them, and others are not. So with us. There are definite limits to simian civilizations, due in part to some primitive traits that help keep us alive, and in part to the mere fact that every being has to be something, and when one is a simian one is not also everything else. Our main-springs are fixed, and our principal traits are deep-rooted. We cannot now relive the ages whose imprint we bear.

We have but to look back on our past to have hope in our future; but — it will be only our future, not some other race's. We shall win our own triumphs, yet know that they would have been different had we cared above all for creativeness, beauty, or love.

So we run about, busy and active, marooned on this star, always violently struggling, yet with no clearly seen goal before us. Men, animals, insects — what tribe of us asks any object, except to keep trying to satisfy its own master appetite? If the ants were earth's lords they would make no more use of their lordship than to learn and enjoy every possible method of toiling. Cats would spend their span of life, say, trying new kinds of guile. And we, who crave so much to know, crave so little but knowing. Some of us wish to know Nature most; those are the scientists. Others, the saints and philosophers, wish to know God. Both are alike in their hearts, yes, in spite of their quarrels. Both seek to assuage, to no end, the old simian thirst.

If we wanted to *be* Gods — but ah, can we grasp that ambition?

Julian Huxley

PHILOSOPHIC ANTS:
A BIOLOGIC FANTASY[1]

PHILOSOPHIC — ANTS?

Amœba has her picture in the book,
   Proud Protozoon! — Yet beware of pride.
   All she can do is fatten and divide;
She cannot even read, or sew, or cook. . . .

The Worm can crawl — but has no eyes to look;
   The Jelly-fish can swim — but lacks a bride;
   The Fly's a very Ass personified;
And speech is absent even from the Rook.

The Ant herself cannot philosophize —
   While Man does that, and sees, and keeps a wife,
And flies, and talks, and is extremely wise . . .
   Will our Philosophy to later Life
Seem but a crudeness of the planet's youth,
Our Wisdom but a parasite of Truth?

[1] Read before the Heretics Club, Cambridge, May 1922.

[542]

> " *Incomprehensibility; that's what I say.*"
> — LEWIS CARROLL (amended)

ACCORDING to a recent study by Mr. Shapley (*Proc. Nat. Acad. Sci.*, Philadelphia, Vol. VI, p. 204), the normal rate of progression of ants — or at least of the species of ant which he studied — is a function of temperature. For each rise of ten degrees centigrade, the ants go about double as fast. So complete is the dependence that the ants may be employed as a thermometer, measurement of their rate of locomotion giving the temperature to within one degree centigrade.

*   *   *   *   *   *   *

The simple consequence — easy of apprehension by us, but infinite puzzlement to ants — is that on a warm day an ant will get through a task four or five times as heavy as she will on a cold one. She does more, thinks more, lives more: more Bergsonian duration is hers.

There was a time, we learn in the myrmecine annals, when ants were simple unsophisticated folk, barely emerged from entomological barbarism. Some stayed at home to look after the young brood and tend the houses, others went afield to forage. It was not long before they discovered that the days differed in length. At one season of the year they found the days insufferably long; they must rest five or six times if they were, by continuing work while light lasted, to satisfy their fabulous instinct for toil. At the opposite season they needed no rest at all, for they only carried through a fifth of the work. This irregularity vexed them; and what is more, time varied from day to day, and this hindered them in the accurate execution of any plans.

But as the foragers talked with the household servants, and with those of their own number who through illness or accident were forced to stay indoors, they discovered that the home-stayers noticed a much slighter difference in time between the seasons.

It is easy for us to see this as due to the simple fact that the temperature of the nest varies less, summer and winter, than does that of the outer air; but it was a hard nut for them, and there was much head-scratching. It was of course made extremely difficult by the fact that they were not sensitive to gradual changes in temperature as such, the change being as it were taken up in the altered rate of living. But as their processes of thought kept pace in alteration with their movements, they found it simplest and most natural to believe in the fixity and uniformity of their own life and its processes, and to refer all changes to the already obvious mutability of external nature.

The Wise Ants were summoned; they were ordered by the Queen to investigate the matter; and so, after consultation, decided to apply the test of experiment. Several of their numbers, at stated intervals throughout the year, stayed in and went out on alternate days, performing identical tasks on the two occasions. The task was the repeated recitation of the most efficacious of the myrmecine sacred formulæ.

The rough-and-ready calculations of the workers were speedily corroborated. "Great is God, and we are the people of God!" could be recited out of doors some twenty thousand times a day in summer, less than four thousand times in winter; while the corresponding indoor figures were about fifteen thousand and six thousand.

There was the fact; now for the explanation. After many conclaves a most ingenious hypothesis was put forward, which found universal credence. Let me give it in an elegant and logical form.

(1) It was well known — indeed, self-evident — that the Ant race was the offspring and special care of the Power who made and ruled the universe.

(1.1) Therefore a great deal of the virtue and essence of that Power inhered in the race of Ants. Ants, indeed, were made in the image of God.

(1.2) It was, alas, common knowledge that this Power, although omnipotent and omniscient, was confronted by another power, the power of disorder, of irregularity, who prevented tasks, put temptations in the way of workers, and was in fact the genius of Evil.

(2) Further, it was a received tradition among them that there had been a fall from the grace of a Golden Age, when

there were no neuters, but all enjoyed married bliss; and the ant-cows gave milk and honey from their teats.

(2.1) And that this was forfeited by a crime (unmentionable, I regret to say, in modern society) on the part of a certain Queen of Ants in the distant past. The Golden Age was gone; the poor neuters — obligate spinsters — were brought into being; work became the order of the day. Ant-lions with flaming jaws were set round that kingdom of Golden Age, from which all ants were thenceforth expelled.

(2.2.1) This being so, it was natural to conclude that the fall from grace involved a certain loss of divine qualities.

(2.2.2) The general conclusion to be drawn was that in the race of ants there still resided a certain quantity of these virtues that give regularity to things and events; although not sufficient wholly to counterbalance the machinations of the power of evil and disorder.

(2.2.3) That where a number of ants had their home and were congregated together, there the virtue resided in larger bulk and with greater effect, but that abroad, where ants were scattered and away from hearth, home, and altar, the demon of irregularity exerted greater sway.

This doctrine held the field for centuries.

* * * * * * *

But at last a philosopher arose. He was not satisfied with the current explanation, although this had been held for so long that it had acquired the odor and force of a religious dogma. He decided to put the matter to the test. He took a pupa (*anglice*, " ant's egg ") and on a windless day suspended it from a twig outside the nest. There he had it swung back and forth, counting its swings. He then (having previously obtained permission from the Royal Sacerdotal College) suspended the pupa by the same length of thread from the roof of the largest chamber of the nest — a dome devoted to spiritual exercise — and repeated the swinging and the counting. The living pendulum-bob achieved the same daily number of oscillations inside the nest as outside, although it was full summer and the foragers found the day quite twice as long as did the home-stayers. The trial was repeated with another pupa and other lengths of thread; the result was always the same.

It was then that he laid the foundations of ant science by his bold pronouncement that neither the combat of spiritual powers nor the expansion or contraction of the store of divine grace had anything to do with the strange alteration of diurnal length; but that the cause of it lay in the Ants themselves, who varied with the varying of something for which he invented the word *Temperature*, not in a contraction or expansion of Time.

This he announced in public, thinking that a tested truth must be well received and would of necessity some day prove useful to society. But the consequence was a storm of protest, horror, and execration.

Did this impious creature think to overthrow the holy traditions with impunity? Did he not realize that to impugn one sentence, one word, one letter of the Sacred Books was to subvert the whole? Did he think that a coarse, simple, verifiable experiment was to weigh against the eternal verity of subtle and mysterious Revelation? No! and again a thousand times No!!

He was brought before the Wise Ants and cross-questioned by them. It was finally decided that he was to abjure his heretical opinion and to recant in public, reciting aloud to the four winds of heaven: " The Ant is the norm of all " —

Μύρμηξ παντὸς νόμος.

He said it. But Truth stirred within him, and under his breath he muttered: " *Eppur si muove* . . ." This was overheard, and he was condemned (loneliness being much hated and dreaded by ants) to a solitary banishment.

Later philosophers, however, by using this same pendulum method, were enabled to find that the movements of sap in plants differed in rate according to the length of day, and later discovered that the expansion of water in hollow stems also followed these changes. By devising machines for registering these movements, they were enabled to prophesy with considerable success the amount of work to be got through on a given day, and so to render great aid to the smooth working of the body politic. Thus, gradually, the old ideas fell into desuetude among the educated classes

— which, however, did not prevent the common people from remaining less than half-convinced and from regarding the men of science with suspicion and disapproval.

*   *   *   *   *   *   *

We happen to be warm-blooded — to have had the particular problem faced by our philosophic ants solved for us during the passage of evolutionary time, not by any taking of thought on our part or on the part of our ancestors, but by the casual processes of variation and natural selection. But a succession of similar problems presses upon us. Relativity is in the air; it is so much in the air that it becomes almost stifling at times; but even so, its sphere so far has been the inorganic sciences, and biological relativity, though equally important, has been little mentioned.

We have all heard the definition of life as " one damn thing after another "; it would perhaps be more accurate to substitute some term such as *relatedness* for *thing.*

When I was a small boy, my mother wrote down in a little book a number of my infant doings and childish sayings, the perusal of which I find an admirable corrective to any excessive moral or intellectual conceit. What, for instance, is to be thought of a scientist of whom the following incident is recorded, even if the record refers to the age of four years?

I (for convenience one must assign the same identity to oneself at different ages, although again it is but a relative sameness that persists) — I had made some particularly outrageous statement which was easily proved false; to which proof, apparently without compunction, I answered: " Oh, well, I always exagg-erate when it's a fine day. . . ."

The converse of this I came across recently in a solemn treatise of psychology: a small girl of five or six, in the course of an " essay " in school, affirmed that the sun was shining and the day was fine; while as a matter of fact it had been continuously overcast and gloomy; on being pressed for a reason, she explained that she felt so happy that particular morning that she had been sure it was a fine day.

If the weather can affect one's statements of fact, and one's emotions can affect the apparent course of meteorological events, where is the line to be drawn? What is real? The only things of which we have immediate cognizance are, of course, happenings in our minds; and the precise nature and quality of each of these happenings depends on two things — on the constitution and state of our mind and its train on the one hand; on the other hand upon events or relations between events outside that system. That sounds very grand; but all it means after all is that you need a cause to produce an effect, a machine to register as well as a something to be registered.

As further consequence, since this particular machine (if I may be permitted to use the odious word in a purely metaphorical sense), this mind of ours, is never the same for two succeeding instants, but continually varies both in the quantity of its activity and the quality of its state, it follows that variations in mental happenings depend very largely on variations in the machine that registers, not by any means solely upon variations in what is to be registered.

Few (at least among Englishmen) would dispute the thesis that food, properly cooked and served, and of course adapted to the hour, is attractive four times in the day. But to a large proportion among us, even sausages and marmalade at nine, or roast beef and potatoes on a Sabbath noon, would prove not only not attractive but positively repellent if offered us on a small steamer on a rough day. I will not labor the point.

We all know how the size of sums of money appears to vary in a remarkable way according as they are being paid in or paid out. We all know to our cost the extraordinary superiority of the epochs when our more elderly relatives were youthful. The fact remains that we are always prone to regard the registering machine as a constant, and to believe that all the variation comes from outside. It is easy to discount the inner variation in ourselves when we are seasick, or in others when they are old and reminiscent, but not only is this discounting sometimes far more difficult, it is sometimes not even attempted.

What, for instance, are we to say to those who profess to find a harmony in the universe, those to whom poverty and discomfort and hard work appear the merest accidents, to whom even disease, pain, loss, death, and disaster are " somehow good "? You and I would probably retort that we have a rooted dislike to discomfort, that we should most strongly deny that the loss of a friend or even of a leg was anything but bad, that a toothache was not damnably unpleasant. But I think that if they were philosophically inclined (which they probably would not be), they might justifiably retort that the difference between their universe and ours was due to a difference in their mental machinery, which they had succeeded in adjusting so that it registered in a different and a better way.

It is at least clear that something of the sort can happen in the intellectual sphere. To the uneducated, the totality of things, if ever reflected upon, is a compound of fog and chaos; advance is painfully slow, and interlarded with unpleasant falls into pits and holes of illogicality and inconsequence; to those who have taken the trouble to push on, however, an orderly system at last reveals itself.

The problem of the origin and relationship of species gave such mental distress to those zoologists of the first half of the nineteenth century who were conscientious enough to struggle with it that many of them ended by a mental suppression of the problem and a refusal to discuss it further. The publication of Darwin's *Origin of Species* was to them what psychoanalysis is (or may be) to a patient with a repressed complex. Or, again, no one can read accounts of the physicists' recent work on the structure of the atom without experiencing an extraordinary feeling of satisfaction. Instead of wallowing in unrelated facts, we fly on wings of principle; not only can we better cut our way through the jungle of things, but we are allowed a privilege that has universally been considered one of the attributes of gods — the calm and untroubled understanding of things and processes.

> The Gods are happy.
> They turn on all sides
> Their shining eyes,
> And see below them
> The earth and men.

This being so, what is to prevent us from believing that, once certain adjustments are made in the mental sausage-machine, we shall discover that what we once found impossibly tough meat will

pass smoothly through and become done up into the most satisfactory of sausages? In other words, that the values are there if we
choose to make them — an Euckenish doctrine which, for all that
it arouses instinctive suspicion, may none the less be true.

But even when we have made all possible discounts of this kind,
evolved the smoothest-running machinery, converted the raw and
meaty material of being into every conceivable kind of tidy sausage,
the fact remains that there are feats beyond the power of our machine — beyond its power because of the very quality of its being.

We live at a certain rhythm in time, at a certain level of size
and space; beyond certain limits, events in the outer world are not
directly appreciable by the ordinary channels of sense, although a
symbolic picture of them may be presented to us by the intellect.

When we are listening to the organ, sometimes there come notes
which are on the border-line between sound and feeling: their
separate vibrations are distinguishable and pulse through us, and
the more the vibrations are separable, the more they are felt as
mechanical shocks, the less as sound. However, we know perfectly
well that all sounds as a matter of fact depend on vibratory disturbance, and that it is only some peculiarity of the registering machinery, in ear or brain, which enables us to hear a note as continuous.

Still more remarkable are the facts of vision. As I write I see the
tulips in my garden, red against the green grass: the red is a continuous sensation; but the physicists appear to be justified in telling
us that the eye is being bombarded every second with a series of
waves, not the few hundred or thousand that give us sound, but
the half-billion or so which conspire to illuminate our vision.

With sound, we alter the frequency of the waves and we get a
difference of tone which seems to be merely a difference of more or
less; but alter the frequency of light-waves, and the whole quality
of the sensation changes, as when I look from the tulips to the sky.
The change of registering mechanism is here more profound than
the change in outer event.

Or again, to choose an example that depends more on size than
rhythm, how very difficult it is to remember that the pressure of
air on our bodies is not the uniform gentle embrace of some homogeneous substance, but the bombardment of an infinity of particles.

The particles are not even all alike: some are of oxygen, others of nitrogen, of carbonic acid gas, of water vapor. They are not all traveling at uniform speeds; collisions are all the time occurring, and the molecules are continuously changing their rate of travel as they clash and bump.

We have only to look down a microscope to convince ourselves of the alteration in our experience that it would mean if we were to become sufficiently diminished. The tiniest solid particles in fluids can be seen to be in a continuous state of agitation — inexplicable until it was pointed out that this mysterious " Brownian " movement was the inevitable result of impacts by the faster-moving molecules of the fluid. Many living things that we can still see are small enough to live permanently in such agitation; the longest diameter of many bacteria is but half a micron (a two-thousandth of a millimeter), and there are many ultra-microscopic organisms which, owing to their closer approximation to molecular dimensions, must pass their lives in erratic excursions many times more violent than any visible Brownian motion.

If we could shrink, like Alice, at the persuasion of some magic mushroom, the rain of particles on our skin, now as unfelt as midges by a rhinoceros, would at last begin to be perceptible. We should find ourselves surrounded by an infinity of motes; titillated by a dance of sand-grains; bruised by a rain of marbles; pounded by flights of fives-balls. What is more, the smaller we became, the more individuality and apparent free will should we detect in the surrounding particles. As we got still smaller, we should, now and again, find the nearly uniform bombardment replaced by a concerted attack on one side or the other, and we should be hurled for perhaps double our own length in one direction. If we could conceivably enter into a single inorganic molecule, we should find ourselves one of a moving host of similar objects; and we should further perceive that these objects were themselves complex, some like double stars, others star-clusters, others single suns, and all again built of lesser units held in a definite plan, in an architecture reminding us (if we still had memory) of a solar system *in petto*. If we were lucky enough to be in a complicated fluid like sea water, we should be intrigued by the relations of the different kinds of particles. They would be continually coming up to other particles of different kinds and would then sometimes enter into intimate union with them. If we could manage to follow their history, we should find that after a time they would separate, and seek new partners, of the same or of different species. Some kinds of the units, or people, as we should be inclined to call them, would spend most of their existence in the married state, others would apparently prefer to remain single, or, if they married, would within no long time obtain divorce.

We should be forcibly reminded of life in some cosmopolitan city like London or New York. If there existed a registrar to note down the events of these little beings' existence, and we were privileged to inspect the register, we should find that each had its own history, different from that of every other in its course and its matrimonial adventures.

If we were near the surface we should find that the outer beings always arranged themselves in a special and coherent layer, apparently to protect themselves against the machinations of the different beings inhabiting the region beyond; for every now and again one would seem to be pulled from the water and be lost among the more scattered inhabitants of the air.

If we could not revert to our old size, we might remember, as we listened to the scientist enunciating the simple formulæ of the gas-laws, or giving numerical expression to vapor-pressures and solubilities, that this simplicity and order which he enabled us to find in inorganic nature was only simplicity when viewed on a large enough scale, and that it was needful to deal in millions and billions before chance aberrations faded into insignificance, needful to experience molecules from the standpoint of a unit almost infinitely bigger before individual behavior could be neglected and merged in the orderly average. And we might be tempted to wonder how the personal idiosyncrasies of our human units might appear to a being as much larger than we as we are larger than a molecule — whether kings and beggars would not fare alike, and all the separate, striving, feeling, conflicting personalities, with their individual histories, their ancestors, successes, marriages, friendships, pains, and pleasures, be merged in some homogeneous and simple effect, altering in response to circumstances, with changes capable of expression in some formula as simple as Boyle's or Avogadro's Law.

Almost more startling might be the effect of altering the rhythm at which we live, or rather at which we experience events.

If only I were Mr. H. G. Wells, I could make a mint of money by a story based on this idea of rhythm of living.[1] Let us see. . . . First there would be Mercaptan the distinguished inventor, who would lead me (lay, uninstructed, Watsonish me, after the fashion of narrators) into his laboratory. There on the table would be the machine — all but complete: handles, coils of wire, quartz terminals, gauges of rock crystal in which oscillated colored fluids, platinum cogwheels . . . dot . . . dot . . . dot . . . dot. . . . He hardly dared to make the final connections, all clear and calculable though they were. He had put so much of himself into it: so many hopes . . . fears . . . dots. . . .

Then there would be the farewell dinner-party — first the inventor's voice on the wireless telephone, summoning Wagrom the explorer, Glosh of the *Evening Post*, Stewartson Ampill the novelist, and the rest of our old friends; then the warm friendly light of the candles, the excellent port, the absence of women, the reminiscences, the asterisks, the . . .

Mercaptan refuses to allow the rest to come into the laboratory, in case something should go wrong. He straps the machine on his shoulders, makes a final connection; his life processes begin to work faster, faster, ever faster. The first effect of course was a change of color. The blue oblong of the window became green — yellow — orange — red. Meanwhile each wave-length of the ultra-violet became blue, and itself ran down the gamut of color. Then came the turn of the X-rays — by their dim light he groped about, till they, too, became relatively too slow for his retina. That ought to make him blind, of course — but no! Mr. Wells had thought that all out; and he came into a state of nearly maximum speed where he perceived a brilliant, phosphorescent light given out by all objects, generated by disturbances of a wave-length unimaginably, undiscov-

---

[1] The reading of this paper brought a string of informants eager to let me know that Mr. Wells had already written a story on this theme. I was grateful to them for having caused me to read *The New Accelerator*, which by some strange chance I had managed to miss; but Mr. Wells's treatment is so wholly different from that which I have sketched that I feel no scruples in letting it stand; and, if amends are needed, at least I make him a present of the germ of a new tale, and so feel that honor should be satisfied.

erably small. Meanwhile he had passed through an amazing experience — he had heard the veritable music of the spheres! That had happened when in his acceleration he had, so to speak, caught up with the light-waves, until they were tuned to his ear's organ of Corti; and all that had been visible in his ordinary life was now to be appreciated by hearing. Unfortunately, as his ears possessed no lens, this universal music was to him of course merely a hideous babel of sound.

At last, as the workings of his body approached the rapidity of light's own oscillations, he entered on a new phase — surrounded on every side by an ocean of waves which lapped softly against his body — waves, waves, and still more waves. . . .

He was in that region not unlike that from which life has escaped when it ceased to be infinitely little, a region in which none of the events that make up our ordinary life, none of the bodies that are our normal environment, have existence any more — all reduced to a chaos of billows ceaselessly and meaninglessly buffeting his being.

" *Mi ritrovai in una selva oscura.*"

Life is a wood, dark and trackless enough, to be sure; but Mercaptan could not even see that it was a wood — for the trees.

Yet it was soothing: the very meaninglessness of the wave-rocking released one of responsibility, and it was delicious to float upon this strange etheric sea.

Then his scientific mind reasserted itself. He realized that he had magnified his rate of life and was consuming his precious days at an appalling speed. The lever was thrown into reverse, and he passed gradually back to what he had been accustomed to think of as reality.

Back to it; and then beyond it, slowing his vital rhythm. This time he was able by an ingenious arrangement to eliminate much of the disturbing effect of his rhythm-change on his vision. It was an idea of which he was very proud: every alternate light-wave was cut out when he doubled the capacity of each process of life, and so on in automatic correspondence. As a result he was enabled to get a picture of the outer world very similar to that obtained in the ordinary accelerations of slow processes that are made possible by running slow-taken cinema records at high speed. He saw the snowdrops lift their matutinal heads and drop them again at evening —

an instant later; the spring was an alarming burst of living energy, the trees' budding and growth of leaves became a portent, like the bristling of hairs on the backs of vegetable cats. As his rate changed and he comprehended more and more in each pulse, the flowers faded and fell before he could think of plucking them, autumnal apples rotted in his grasp, day was a flash and night a wink of the eye, the two blending at last in a continuous half-light.

After a time ordinary objects ceased to be distinguishable; then the seasons shared the fate of day and night. The lever was now nearly hard over, and the machine was reaching its limits. He was covering nearly a thousand of men's years with each of his own seconds.

The cinema effect was almost useless to him now, and he discarded this apparatus. Now followed what he had so eagerly awaited, something deducible in general but unpredictable in all particulars. As the repeated separate impacts of the ether waves had condensed, at his old ordinary rate, to form the continuous sensation of light, so now the events of nature coalesced to give new objects, new kinds of sensation. Especially was this so with life: the repeated generations seemed to act like separate repeated waves of light, blending to give a picture of the species changing and evolving before his eyes.

Other experiences he could explain less well. He was conscious of strange sensations that he thought were probably associated with changes in energy-distribution, in entropy; others which he seemed to perceive directly, by some form of telepathy, concerning the type of mental process occurring around him. It was all strange; but of one thing he was sure — that if only he could find a way of nourishing and maintaining himself in this new state, he would be able, as a child does in the first few years of life, to correlate his puzzling new sensations, and that when he had done this he would obtain a different and more direct view of reality than any he had ever obtained or thought of obtaining before.

As the individual light-waves were summed to give light, as the microcosm of gas-molecules canceled out to give a uniformity of pressure, so now the repetition of the years coalesced into what could be described as visible time, a sensation of cosmic rate; the repeated pullulations of living things fused into something perceived as organic achievement: and the infinite variety of organisms, their conflicts and interactions, resolved itself, through the mediation of his sense-organs and brain at their new rhythm, into a direct perception of life as a whole, an entity with a pressure on its environment, a single slowly evolving form, a motion and direction.

He put the lever to its limit; the rhythm of the cosmos altered again in relation to his own. He had an extraordinary sense of being on the verge of a revelation. The universe — that was the same; but what he experienced of it was totally different. He had immediate experience of the waxing and waning of suns, of the condensation of nebulæ, the slowing down and speeding up of evolutionary processes.

The curious, apparently telepathic sense which he had had of the mental side of existence was intensified. Through it the world began to be perceived as a single Being, with all its parts in interaction. The shadowy lineaments of this being were half seen by his mental vision — vast, colossal, slowly changing; but they appeared only to disappear again, like a picture in the fire.

Strive as he might, he could not see its real likeness. Now it appeared benign; at its next dim reappearance there would be a feeling of capricious irresponsibility about it: at another instant it was cold, remote; once or twice terrible, impending over and filling everything with a black demoniacal power which brought only horror with it.

If he could but accelerate the machine! He wanted to *know* — to know whether this phantom were a reality, to know above all if it were a thing of evil or of good; and he could not know unless he could advance that last final step necessary to fuse the rhythm of separate events into the sensation of the single whole.

He sat straining all his faculties; the machine whirred and rocked, but in vain. And at last, feeling desperately hungry, for he had forgotten to take food with him, he gradually brought back the lever to its neutral point.

* * * * * * *

Of course, Mr. Wells would have done it much better than this.

* * * * * * *

And then there would have to be an ending. I think the news-paperman would take his opportunity to slink off into the labora-tory and get on the machine with the idea of making a scoop for his paper . . . and then he would put the lever in too violently, and be thrown backwards. His head hit the corner of a bench, and he remained stunned; but, by evil chance, the handles of the ma-chine still made connection with his body after the fall. The machine was making him adjust his rhythm to that of light; so that he was living at an appalling rate. He had gone into the laboratory late at night. Next morning they found him — dead; and dead of senile decay — gray-haired, shriveled, atrophic.

Then of course the machine is smashed up; and Mr. Wells be-gins to write another book.

＊　　＊　　＊　　＊　　＊　　＊　　＊

I have spent so much time in frivolous discussion of rhythm and size and commonplaces that I have not pointed out another funda-mental fact of biological relativity — to wit, that we are but paro-chial creatures endowed only with sense-organs giving information about the agencies normally found in our own little environment. Mind without the objects of mind is the very Chimæra bombinat-ing *in vacuo.*

Out of all the ether waves we are sensitive to an octave as light, and some few others as heat. X-rays and ultra-violet destroy us, but we know nothing about them until they begin to give us pain; while the low swell of Hertzian waves passes by and through us harmless and unheeded. Electrical sense again we have none.

Imagine what it would be for inhabitants of another planet where changes in Hertzian waves were the central, pivotal changes in environment, where accordingly life had become sensitive to " wireless " and to nought else save perhaps touch — imagine such beings broadcast upon the face of the Earth. With a little practice and ingenuity they would no doubt be able to decipher the mes-sages floating through our atmosphere, would feel the rhythms of the Black Hamitic Band transmitting jazz to a million homes, and be able to follow, night by night, the soporific but benevolent fairy-stories of Uncle Archibald. I wonder what they would make of it all. They would at intervals, of course, be bumping into things and people. But would touch and radio-sense alone make our world intelligible? I wonder. . . .

When we begin trying to quit our anthropocentry and discover what the world might be like if only we had other organs of body and mind for its assaying, we must flounder and bump in a not dissimilar fashion.

Even the few senses that we do possess are determined by our environment. Sweet things are pleasant to us: sugar is sweet; so is " sugar of lead " — lead acetate; sugar is nutritious, lead acetate a poison. The biologist will conclude, and with perfect reason, that if sugar was as rare as lead acetate in nature, lead acetate as common as sugar, we should then abominate and reject sweet things as emphatically as we now do filth or acids or over-hot liquids.

But I must pause and find a moral for my tale; for all will agree that a moral has been so long out of fashion that it is now fast becoming fashionable again.

Every schoolboy, as Macaulay would say, knows William of Occam's Razor — that philosophical tool of admirable properties: " *Entia non multiplicanda præter necessitatem.*"

We want another razor — a Relativist Razor; and with that we will carry out barbering operations worthy of another Shaving of Shagpat: we will shave the Absolute.

The hoary Absolute, enormous and venerable, gray-bearded and gray-locked — he sits enthroned, wielding tremendous power, filling young minds with fear and awe.

Up, barbers, and at him! Heat the water of your enthusiasm; lather those disguising appurtenances. See the tufts collapse into the white foam — feel the hairy jungles melt away before your steel! And at the end, when the last hair falls, you will wipe away the lather, and look upon that face and see — ah, what indeed?

I will not be so banal as to attempt to describe that sight in detail. You will have seen it already in your mind's eye; " or else " (to quote Mr. Belloc) — " or else you will not; I cannot be positive which." If not, you never will; if yes, what need to waste more of the compositor's time? But of him who forges that razor, who arms those barbers, who gives them courage for their colossal task, of him shall a new Lucretius sing.

BIBLIOGRAPHY

Belloc, H.: *The Bad Child's Book of Beasts.*
Bergson, H.: *Time and Free-Will.*
Carroll, L.: *Alice in Wonderland.*
——: *Alice Through the Looking Glass.*
Einstein, see Kant.
Hegel, see Einstein.
Kant, see Hegel.
Lear, E.: *Nonsense Songs and Stories.*
Lucretius: *De Rerum Natura.*
Macaulay, Lord: *Essays.*
Maxwell, Clerk: *Collected Papers.*
Mee, A.: *Children's Encyclopædia.*
Meredith, G.: *The Shaving of Shagpat.*
Occam, W. de: *Opera Omnia.*
Shapley: *Proc. Nat. Ac. Sci.,* VI, 204.
Swift, J.: *Gulliver's Travels.*
Wells, H. G.: *The New Accelerator.*
Wheeler, W. M.: *Ants* (Columbia University Series).

GEESE: AN APPRECIATION
AND A MEMORY

Oɴᴇ November evening, in the neighborhood of Lyndhurst, I saw
a flock of geese marching in a long procession, led, as their custom
is, by a majestical gander; they were coming home from their
feeding-ground in the forest, and when I spied them were approaching their owner's cottage. Arrived at the wooden gate of the garden
in front of the cottage, the leading bird drew up square before it,
and with repeated loud screams demanded admittance. Pretty
soon, in response to the summons, a man came out of the cottage,
walked briskly down the garden path, and opened the gate, but
only wide enough to put his right leg through; then, placing his
foot and knee against the leading bird, he thrust him roughly back;
as he did so three young geese pressed forward and were allowed
to pass in; then the gate was slammed in the face of the gander and
the rest of his followers, and the man went back to the cottage.
The gander's indignation was fine to see, though he had most prob-

ably experienced the same rude treatment on many previous occasions. Drawing up to the gate again, he called more loudly than before; then deliberately lifted a leg, and placing his broad webbed foot like an open hand against the gate, actually tried to push it open! His strength was not sufficient; but he continued to push and to call until the man returned to open the gate and let the birds go in.

It was an amusing scene, and the behavior of the bird struck me as characteristic. It was this lofty spirit of the goose and strict adhesion to his rights, as well as his noble appearance and the stately formality and deliberation of his conduct, that caused me very long ago to respect and admire him above all our domestic birds. Doubtless from the æsthetic point of view other domesticated species are his superiors in some things: the mute swan, "floating double," graceful and majestical, with arched neck and ruffled scapulars; the oriental pea-fowl in his glittering mantle; the helmeted guinea-fowl, powdered with stars, and the red cock with his military bearing — a shining Elizabethan knight of the feathered world, singer, lover, and fighter. It is hardly to be doubted that, mentally, the goose is above all these; and to my mind his, too, is the nobler figure; but it is a very familiar figure, and we have not forgotten the reason of its presence among us. He satisfies a material want only too generously, and on this account is too much associated in the mind with mere flavors. We keep a swan or a peacock for ornament; a goose for the table — he is the Michaelmas and Christmas bird. A somewhat similar debasement has fallen on the sheep in Australia. To the man in the bush he is nothing but a tallow-elaborating organism, whose destiny it is to be cast, at maturity, into the melting-vat, and whose chief use is to lubricate the machinery of civilization. It a little shocks, and at the same time amuses, our colonial to find that great artists in the parent country admire this most unpoetic beast, and waste their time and talents in painting it.

Some five or six years ago, in the *Alpine Journal*, Sir Martin Conway gave a lively and amusing account of his first meeting with A. D. M'Cormick, the artist who subsequently accompanied him to the Karakoram Himalayas. "A friend," he wrote, "came to me bringing in his pocket a crumpled-up water sketch or impression of a lot of geese. I was struck by the breadth of the treatment, and I remembered saying that the man who could see such monumental magnificence in a flock of geese ought to be the kind of man to paint mountains, and render somewhat of their majesty."

I will venture to say that he looked at the sketch or impression with the artist's clear eye, but had not previously so looked at the living creature; or had not seen it clearly, owing to the mist of images — if that be a permissible word — that floated between it and his vision — remembered flavors and fragrances, of rich meats, and of sage and onions and sweet apple sauce. When this interposing mist is not present, who can fail to admire the goose — that stately bird-shaped monument of cloudy gray or crystal white marble, to be seen standing conspicuous on any village green or common in England? For albeit a conquered bird, something of the ancient wild and independent spirit survives to give him a prouder bearing than we see in his fellow feathered servants. He is the least timid of our domestic birds, yet even at a distance he regards your approach in an attitude distinctly reminiscent of the graylag goose, the wariest of wildfowl, stretching up his neck and standing motionless and watchful, a sentinel on duty. Seeing him thus, if you deliberately go near him he does not slink or scuttle away, as other domestic birds of meaner spirits do, but boldly advances to meet and challenge you. How keen his senses are, how undimmed by ages of captivity the ancient instinct of watchfulness is in him, everyone must know who has slept in lonely country houses. At some late hour of the night the sleeper was suddenly awakened by the loud screaming of the geese; they had discovered the approach of some secret prowler, a fox perhaps, or a thievish tramp or gypsy, before a dog barked. In many a lonely farmhouse throughout the land you will be told that the goose is the better watch-dog.

When we consider this bird purely from the æsthetic point of view — and here I am speaking of geese generally, all of the thirty species of the sub-family Anserinæ, distributed over the cold and temperate regions of the globe — we find that several of them possess a rich and beautiful coloring, and, if not so proud, often a more graceful carriage than our domestic bird, or its original, the wild graylag goose. To know these birds is to greatly admire them, and we may now add that this admiration is no new thing on the earth. It is the belief of distinguished Egyptologists that a fragmentary fresco, discovered at Medum, dates back to a time at least four thousand years before the Christian era, and is probably the oldest picture in the world. It is a representation of six geese, of three different species, depicted with marvelous fidelity and a thorough appreciation of form and coloring.

Among the most distinguished in appearance and carriage of the handsome exotic species is the Magellanic goose, one of the five or six species of the antarctic genus Chloëphaga, found in Patagonia and the Magellan Islands. One peculiarity of this bird is that the sexes differ in coloring, the male being white, with gray mottlings, whereas the prevailing color of the female is a ruddy brown — a fine rich color set off with some white, gray, intense cinnamon, and beautiful black mottlings. Seen on the wing the flock presents a somewhat singular appearance, as of two distinct species associating together, as we may see when by chance gulls and rooks, or sheldrakes and black scoters, mix in one flock.

This fine bird has long been introduced into this country, and as it breeds freely, it promises to become quite common. I can see it any day; but these exiles, pinioned and imprisoned in parks, are not quite like the Magellanic geese I was intimate with in former years, in Patagonia and in the southern pampas of Buenos Aires, where they wintered every year in incredible numbers, and were called " bustards " by the natives. To see them again, as I have seen them, by day and all day long in their thousands, and to listen again by night to their wild cries, I would willingly give up, in exchange, all the invitations to dine which I shall receive, all the novels I shall read, all the plays I shall witness, in the next three years; and some other miserable pleasures might be thrown in. Listening to the birds when, during migration, on a still, frosty night, they flew low, following the course of some river, flock succeeding flock all night long; or heard from a herdsman's hut on the pampas, when thousands of the birds had encamped for the night on the plain hard by, the effect of their many voices (like that of their appearance when seen flying) was singular, as well as beautiful, on account of the striking contrasts in the various sounds they uttered. On clear, frosty nights they are most loquacious, and their voices may be heard by the hour, rising and falling,

now few, and now many taking part in the endless confabulation
— a talkee-talkee and concert in one; a chatter as of many mag-
pies; the solemn deep, *honk-honk,* the long, grave note changing
to a shuddering sound; and, most wonderful, the fine silvery
whistle of the male, steady or tremulous, now long and now short,
modulated a hundred ways — wilder and more beautiful than the
night-cry of the widgeon, brighter than the voice of any shore
bird, or any warbler, thrush, or wren, or the sound of any wind
instrument.

It is probable that those who have never known the Magellanic
goose in a state of nature are best able to appreciate its fine qualities in its present semi-domestic state in England. At all events the
enthusiasm with which a Londoner spoke of this bird in my presence some time ago came to me rather as a surprise. It was at the
studio in St. John's Wood of our greatest animal-painter, one Sunday evening, and the talk was partly about birds, when an elderly
gentleman said that he was pleased to meet someone who would
be able to tell him the name of a wonderful bird he had lately seen
in St. James's Park. His description was vague; he could not say
what its color was, nor what sort of beak it had, nor whether its
feet were webbed or not; but it was a large tall bird, and there were
two of them. It was the way this bird had comported itself towards
him that had so taken him. As he went through the park at the
side of the enclosure, he caught sight of the pair some distance
away on the grass, and the birds, observing that he had stopped in
his walk to regard them, left off feeding, or whatever they were
doing, and came to him. Not to be fed — it was impossible to believe that they had any such motive; it was solely and purely a
friendly feeling towards him which caused them immediately to
respond to his look, and to approach him, to salute him, in their
way. And when they had approached within three or four yards
of where he stood, advancing with a quiet dignity, and had then
uttered a few soft low sounds, accompanied with certain graceful
gestures, they turned and left him; but not abruptly, with their
backs towards him — oh, no, they did nothing so common; they
were not like other birds — they were perfect in everything; and,
moving from him, half paused at intervals, half turning first to one
side then the other, inclining their heads as they went. Here our

old friend rose and paced up and down the floor, bowing to this side and that and making other suitable gestures, to try to give us some faint idea of the birds' gentle courtesy and exquisite grace. It was, he assured us, most astonishing; the birds' gestures and motions were those of a human being, but in their perfection immeasurably superior to anything of the kind to be seen in any court in Europe or the world.

The birds he had described, I told him, were no doubt Upland Geese.

"Geese!" he exclaimed, in a tone of surprise, and disgust. "Are you speaking seriously? Geese! Oh, no, nothing like geese — a sort of ostrich."

It was plain that he had no accurate knowledge of birds; if he had caught sight of a kingfisher or green woodpecker, he would probably have described it as a sort of peacock. Of the goose, he only knew that it is a ridiculous, awkward creature, proverbial for its stupidity, although very good to eat; and it wounded him to find that anyone could think so meanly of his intelligence and taste as to imagine him capable of greatly admiring any bird called a goose, or any bird in any way related to a goose.

I will now leave the subject of the beautiful antarctic goose, the "bustard" of the horsemen of the pampas, and "sort of ostrich" of our Londoner, to relate a memory of my early years, and of how I first became an admirer of the familiar domestic goose. Never since have I looked on it in such favorable conditions.

Two miles from my home there stood an old mud-built house, thatched with rushes, and shaded by a few ancient half-dead trees. Here lived a very old woman with her two unmarried daughters, both withered and gray as their mother; indeed, in appearance, they were three amiable sister witches, all very, very old. The high ground on which the house stood sloped down to an extensive reed- and rush-grown marsh, the source of an important stream; it was a paradise of wildfowl, swan, roseate spoonbill, herons white and herons gray, ducks of half a dozen species, snipe, and painted snipe, and stilt, plover, and godwit; the glossy ibis, and the great crested blue ibis with a powerful voice. All these interested, I might say fascinated, me less than the tame geese that spent most of their time in or on the borders of the marsh in the company of the wild birds. The three old women were so fond of their geese that they would not part with one for love or money; the most they would ever do would be to present an egg, in the laying season, to some visitor as a special mark of esteem.

It was a grand spectacle when the entire flock, numbering upwards of a thousand, stood up on the marsh and raised their necks on a person's approach. It was grand to hear them, too, when, as often happened, they all burst out in a great screaming concert. I can hear that mighty uproar now!

With regard to the character of the sound . . . the poet Cowper thought not meanly of the domestic gray goose as a vocalist, when heard on a common or even in a farmyard. But there is a vast difference in the effect produced on the mind when the sound is heard amid its natural surroundings in silent desert places. Even hearing them as I did, from a distance, on that great marsh, where they existed almost in a state of nature, the sound was not comparable to that of the perfectly wild bird in his native haunts. The cry of the wild graylag was described by Robert Gray in his *Birds of the West of Scotland*. Of the bird's voice he writes: " My most recent experiences (August 1870) in the Outer Hebrides remind me of a curious effect which I noted in connection with the call-note of this bird in these quiet solitudes. I had reached South Uist, and taken up my quarters under the hospitable roof of Mr. Birnie, at Grogarry . . . and in the stillness of the Sabbath morning following my arrival was aroused from sleep by the cries of the graylags as they flew past the house. Their voices, softened by distance, sounded not unpleasantly, reminding me of the clanging of church bells in the heart of a large town."

It is a fact, I think, that to many minds the mere wildness represented by the voice of a great wild bird in his lonely haunts is so grateful that the sound itself, whatever its quality may be, delights, and is more than the most beautiful music. A certain distinguished man of letters and Church dignitary was once asked, a friend tells me, why he lived away from society, buried in the loneliest village on the dreary east coast; at that spot where, standing on the flat desolate shore you look over the North Sea and have no land between you and far Spitzbergen. He answered that he made his home there because it was the only spot in England in which, sitting in his own room, he could listen to the cry of the pink-footed goose. Only those who have lost their souls will fail to understand.

The geese I have described, belonging to the three old women, could fly remarkably well, and eventually some of them, during their flights down-stream, discovered at a distance of about eight miles from home the immense, low, marshy plain bordering the sea-like Plata River. There were no houses and no people in that endless green, wet land, and they liked it so well that they visited it more and more often, in small flocks of a dozen to twenty birds, going and coming all day long, until all knew the road. It was observed that when a man on foot or on horseback appeared in sight of one of these flocks, the birds at this distance from home were as wary as really wild birds, and watched the stranger's approach in alarm, and when he was still at a considerable distance rose and flew away beyond sight.

The old dames grieved at this wandering spirit in their beloved birds, and became more and more anxious for their safety. But by this time the aged mother was fading visibly into the tomb, though so slowly that long months went by while she lay on her bed, a weird-looking object — I remember her well — leaner, grayer, more ghostlike, than the silent, lean, gray heron on the marsh hard by. And at last she faded out of life, aged, it was said by her descendants, a hundred and ten years; and after she was dead, it was found that of that great company of noble birds there remained only a small remnant of about forty, and these were probably incapable of sustained flight. The others returned no more; but whether they met their death from duck- and swan-shooters in the marshes or had followed the great river down to the sea, forgetting their home, was never known. For about a year after they had ceased going back, small flocks were occasionally seen in the marshes, very wild and strong on the wing, but even these, too, vanished at last.

It is probable that, but for powder and shot, the domestic goose of Europe, by occasionally taking to a feral life in thinly settled countries, would ere this have become widely distributed over the earth.

And one wonders if in the long centuries running to thousands of years, of tame flightless existence, the strongest impulse of the wild migrant has been wholly extinguished in the domestic goose?

We regard him as a comparatively unchangeable species, and it is probable that the unexercised faculty is not dead but sleeping, and would wake again in favorable circumstances. The strength of the wild bird's passion has been aptly described by Miss Dora Sigerson in her little poem, " The Flight of the Wild Geese." The poem, oddly enough, is not about geese, but about men — wild Irishmen who were called Wild Geese; but the bird's powerful impulse and homing faculty are employed as an illustration, and admirably described:

Flinging the salt from their wings, and despair from their hearts
They arise on the breast of the storm with a cry and are gone.
When will you come home, wild geese, in your thousand
    strong? . . .
Not the fierce wind can stay your return or tumultuous sea . . .
Only death in his reaping could make you return no more.

Now arctic and antarctic geese are alike in this their devotion to their distant breeding-ground, the cradle and true home of the species or race; and I will conclude this chapter with an incident related to me many years ago by a brother who was sheep-farming in a wild and lonely district on the southern frontier of Buenos Aires. Immense numbers of upland geese in great flocks used to spend the cold months on the plains where he had his lonely hut; and one morning in August in the early spring of that southern country, some days after all the flocks had taken their departure to the south, he was out riding and saw at a distance before him on the plain a pair of geese. They were male and female — a white and a brown bird. Their movements attracted his attention and he rode to them. The female was walking steadily on in a southerly direction, while the male, greatly excited, and calling loudly from time to time, walked at a distance ahead, and constantly turned back to see and call to his mate, and at intervals of a few minutes he would rise up and fly, screaming, to a distance of some hundreds of yards; then finding that he had not been followed, he would return and alight at a distance of forty or fifty yards in advance of the other bird and begin walking on as before. The female had one wing broken, and, unable to fly, had set out on her long journey to the Magellanic Islands on her feet; and her mate, though called to by that mysterious imperative voice in his breast, yet would not forsake her; but flying a little distance to show her the way, and returning again and again, and calling to her with his wildest and most piercing cries, urged her still to spread her wings and fly with him to their distant home.

And in that sad, anxious way they would journey on to the inevitable end, when a pair or family of carrion eagles would spy them from a great distance — the two travelers left far behind by their fellows, one flying, the other walking; and the first would be left to continue the journey alone.

Since this appreciation was written a good many years ago I have seen much of geese, or, as it might be put, have continued my relations with them and have written about them too in my *Adventures Among Birds* (1913). In recent years it has become a custom of mine to frequent Wells-next-the-Sea in October and November just to welcome the wild geese that come in numbers annually to winter at that favored spot. Among the incidents related in that last book of mine about the wild geese, there were two or three about the bird's noble and dignified bearing and its extraordinary intelligence, and I wish here to return to that subject just to tell yet one more goose story, only in this instance it was about the domestic bird.

It happened that among the numerous letters I received from readers of *Birds and Man* on its first appearance, there was one which particularly interested me, from an old gentleman, a retired schoolmaster in the cathedral city of Wells. He was a delightful letter-writer, but by and by our correspondence ceased and I heard no more of him for three or four years. Then I was at Wells, spending a few days looking up and inquiring after old friends in the place, and remembering my pleasant letter-writer I went to call on him. During our conversation he told me that the chapter which had impressed him most in my book was the one on the goose, especially all that related to the lofty dignified bearing of the bird, its independent spirit and fearlessness of its human masters, in which it differs so greatly from all other domestic birds. He knew it well; he had been feelingly persuaded of that proud spirit in the bird, and had greatly desired to tell me of an adventure he had met with, but the incident reflected so unfavorably on himself, as a humane and fair-minded or sportsmanlike person, that he had refrained. However, now that I had come to see him he would make a clean breast of it.

It happened that in January some winters ago, there was a very great fall of snow in England, especially in the south and west. The snow fell without intermission all day and all night, and on the following morning Wells appeared half buried in it. He was then living with a daughter who kept house for him in a cottage standing in its own grounds on the outskirts of the town. On attempting to leave the house he found they were shut in by the snow, which had banked itself against the walls to the height of the eaves. Half an hour's vigorous spade-work enabled him to get out from the kitchen door into the open, and the sun in a blue sky shining on a dazzling white and silent world. But no milkman was going his rounds, and there would be no baker nor butcher nor any other tradesman to call for orders. And there were no provisions in the house! But the milk for breakfast was the first thing needed, and so with a jug in his hand he went bravely out to try and make his way to the milk-shop which was not far off.

A wall and hedge bounded his front garden on one side, and this was now entirely covered by an immense snowdrift, sloping up to a height of about seven feet. It was only when he paused to look at this vast snow-heap in his garden that he caught sight of a goose, a very big snow-white bird without a gray spot in its plumage, standing within a few yards of him, about four feet from the ground. Its entire snowy whiteness with snow for a background had prevented him from seeing it until he looked directly at it. He stood still, gazing in astonishment and admiration at this noble bird, standing so motionless with its head raised high that it was like the figure of a goose carved out of some crystalline white stone and set up at that spot on the glittering snowdrift. But it was no statue; it had living eyes which without the least turning of the head watched him and every motion he made. Then all at once the thought came into his head that here was something, very good succulent food in fact, sent, he almost thought providentially, to provision his house; for how easy it would be for him as he passed the bird to throw himself suddenly upon and capture it! It had belonged to someone, no doubt, but that great snowstorm and the

furious northeast wind had blown it far, far from its native place
and it was now lost to its owner forever. Practically it was now a
wild bird for him to take without any qualms and to nourish himself on its flesh while the snow siege lasted. Standing there, jug in
hand, he thought it out, and then took a few steps towards the
bird in order to see if there was any sign of suspicion in it; but
there was none, only he could see that the goose without turning
its head was all the time regarding him out of the corner of one
eye. Finally he came to the conclusion that his best plan was to
go for the milk and on his return to set the jug down by the gate
when coming in, then to walk in a careless, unconcerned manner
towards the door, taking no notice of the goose until he got abreast
of it, and then turn suddenly and hurl himself upon it. Nothing
could be easier; so away he went and in about twenty minutes was
back again with the milk, to find the bird in the same place, standing as before motionless in the same attitude. It was not disturbed
at his coming in at the gate, nor did it show the slightest disposition to move when he walked towards it in his studied careless
manner. Then, when within three yards of it, came the supreme
moment, and wheeling suddenly round he hurled himself with violence upon his victim, throwing out his arms to capture it, and so
great was the impulse he had given himself that he was buried to
the ankles in the drift. But before going into it, in that brief moment, the fraction of a second, he saw what happened; just as his
hands were about to touch it the wings opened and the bird was
lifted from its stand and out of his reach as if by a miracle. In the
drift he was like a drowning man, swallowing snow into his lungs
for water. For a few dreadful moments he thought it was all over
with him; then he succeeded in struggling out and stood trembling
and gasping and choking, blinded with snow. By and by he recovered and had a look round, and lo! there stood his goose on the
summit of the snow-bank about three yards from the spot where
it had been! It was standing as before, perfectly motionless, its
long neck and head raised, and was still in appearance the snow-
white figure of a carved bird, only it was more conspicuous and
impressive now, being outlined against the blue sky, and, as before, it was regarding him out of the corner of one eye. He had
never, he said, felt so ashamed of himself in his life! If the bird

had screamed and fled from him it would not have been so bad, but there it had chosen to remain, as if despising his attempt at harming it too much even to feel resentment. A most uncanny bird! it seemed to him that it had divined his intention from the first and had been prepared for his every movement; and now it appeared to him to be saying mentally: "Have you got no more plans to capture me in your clever brain, or have you quite given it up?"

Yes, he had quite, quite given it up!

And then the goose, seeing there were no more plans, quietly unfolded its wings and rose from the snowdrift and flew away over the town and the cathedral away on the further side, and towards the snow-covered Mendips; he standing there watching it until it was lost to sight in the pale sky.

✍ *H. M. Tomlinson* ❧

THE DERELICT

In a tramp steamer, which was overloaded, and in midwinter, I had crossed to America for the first time. What we experienced of the western ocean during that passage gave me so much respect for it that the prospect of the return journey, three thousand miles of those seas between me and home, was already a dismal foreboding. The shipping posters of New York, showing stately liners too lofty even to notice the Atlantic, were arguments good enough for steerage passengers, who do, I know, reckon a steamer's worth by the number of its funnels; but the pictures did nothing to lessen my regard for that dark outer world I knew. And having no experience of ships installed with racquet-courts, Parisian cafés, swimming-baths, and pergolas, I was naturally puzzled by the inconsequential behavior of the first-class passengers at the hotel. They were leaving by the liner which was to take me, and, I gathered, were going to cross a bridge to England in the morning. Of course, this might have been merely the innocent profanity of the simple-minded.

Embarking at the quay next day, I could not see that our ship had either a beginning or an end. There was a blank wall which ran out of sight to the right and left. How far it went, and what it enclosed, were beyond me. Hundreds of us in a slow procession mounted stairs to the upper floor of a warehouse, and from thence a bridge led us to a door in the wall half-way in its height. No funnels could be seen. Looking straight up from the embarkation gangway, along what seemed the parapet of the wall was a row of far-off indistinguishable faces peering straight down at us. There was no evidence that this building we were entering, of which the high black wall was a part, was not an important and permanent feature of the city. It was in keeping with the magnitude of New York's skyscrapers, which this planet's occasionally non-irritant skin permits to stand there to afford man an apparent reason to be gratified with his own capacity and daring.

But with the knowledge that this wall must be afloat there came no sense of security when, going through that little opening in its altitude, I found myself in a spacious decorated interior which hinted nothing of a ship, for I was puzzled as to direction. My last ship could be surveyed in two glances; she looked, and was, a comprehensible ship, no more than a manageable handful for an able master. In that ship you could see at once where you were and what to do. But in this liner you could not see where you were, and would never know which way to take unless you had a good memory. No understanding came to me in that hall of a measured and shapely body, designed with a cunning informed by ages of sea-lore to move buoyantly and surely among the ranging seas, to balance delicately, a quick and sensitive being, to every precarious slope, to recover a lost poise easily and with the grace natural to a quick creature controlled by an alert mind.

There was no shape at all to this structure. I could see no line the run of which gave me warrant that it was comprised in the rondure of a ship. The lines were all of straight corridors, which, for all I knew, might have ended blindly on open space, as streets which traverse a city and are bare in vacancy beyond the dwellings. It was possible we were encompassed by walls, but only one wall was visible. There we idled, all strangers, and to remain strangers, in a large hall roofed by a dome of colored glass. Quite properly, palms stood beneath. There were offices and doors everywhere. On a broad staircase a multitude of us wandered aimlessly up and down. Each side of the stairway were electric lifts, intermittent and brilliant apparitions. I began to understand why the saloon passengers thought nothing of the voyage. They were encountering nothing unfamiliar. They had but come to another hotel for a few days.

I attempted to find my cabin, but failed. A uniformed guide took care of me. But my cabin, curtained, upholstered, and warm, with mirrors and plated ware, sunk somewhere deeply among carpeted and silent streets down each of which the perspective of glow-lamps looked interminable, left me still questioning. The long walk had given me a fear that I was remote from important affairs which might be happening beyond. My address was 323. The street door — I was down a side turning, though — bore that number. A visitor could make no mistake, supposing he could find the street and my side turning. That was it. There was a very great deal in this place for everybody to remember, and most of us were strangers. No doubt, however, we were afloat, if the lifebelts in the rack meant anything. Yet the cabin, insulated from all noise, was not soothing, but disturbing. I had been used to a ship in which you could guess all that was happening even when in your bunk; a sensitive and communicative ship.

A steward appeared at my door, a stranger out of nowhere, and asked whether I had seen a bag not mine in the cabin. He might have been created merely to put that question, for I never saw him again on the voyage. This liner was a large province having irregular and shifting bounds, permitting incontinent entrance and disappearance. All this should have inspired me with an idea of our vastness and importance, but it did not. I felt I was one of a multitude included in a nebulous mass too vague to hold together unless we were constantly wary.

In the saloon there was the solid furniture of rare woods, the ornate decorations, and the light and shadows making vague its limits and giving it an appearance of immensity, to keep the mind from the thought of our real circumstances. At dinner we had valentine music, dreamy stuff to accord with the shaded lamps which displayed the tables in a lower rosy light. It helped to extend the mys-

terious and romantic shadows. The pale, disembodied masks of the
waiters swam in the dusk above the tinted light. I had for a companion a vivacious American lady from the Middle West, and she
looked round that prospect we had of an expensive café, and said:
" Well, but I am disappointed. Why, I've been looking forward
to seeing the ocean, you know. And it isn't here."

" Smooth passage," remarked a man on the other side. " No sea
at all worth mentioning." Actually, I know there was a heavy beam
sea running before a half-gale. I could guess the officer in charge
somewhere on the exposed roof might have another mind about it;
but it made no difference to us in our circle of rosy intimate light
bound by those vague shadows which were alive with ready servitude.

" And I've been reading *Captains Courageous* with this voyage in
view. Isn't this the month when the forties roar? I want to hear
them roar, just once, you know, and as gently as any sucking dove."
We all laughed. " We can't even tell we're in a ship."

She began to discuss Kipling's book. " There's some fine seas in
that. Have you read it? But I'd like to know where that ocean is he
pretends to have seen. I do believe the realists are no more reliable
than the romanticists. Here we are a thousand miles out, and none
of us has seen the sea yet. Tell me, does not a realist have to mag-
nify his awful billows just to get them into his reader's view? "

I murmured something feeble and sociable. I saw then why sailors
never talk directly of the sea. I, for instance, could not find my key
at that moment — it was in another pocket somewhere — so I had
no iron to touch. Talking largely of the sea is something like the
knowing talk of young men about women; and what is a simple
sailor-man that he should open his mouth on mysteries?

Only on the liner's boat-deck, where you could watch her four
funnels against the sky, could you see to what extent the liner was
rolling. The arc seemed to be considerable then, but slowly described. But the roll made little difference to the promenaders below. Sometimes they walked a short distance on the edges of their
boots, leaning over as they did so, and swerving from the straight,
as though they had turned giddy. The shadows formed by the weak
sunlight moved slowly out of ambush across the white deck, but
often moved indecisively, as though uncertain of a need to go; and

then slowly went into hiding again. The sea whirling and leaping past was far below our wall side. It was like peering dizzily over a precipice when watching those green and white cataracts.

The passengers, wrapped and comfortable on the lee deck, chatted as blithely as at a garden party, while the band played medleys of national airs to suit our varied complexions. The stewards came round with loaded trays. A diminutive and wrinkled dame in costly furs frowned through her golden spectacles at her book, while her maid sat attentively by. An American actress was the center of an eager group of grinning young men; she was unseen, but her voice was distinct. The two Vanderbilts took their brisk constitutional among us as though the liner had but two real passengers though many invisible nobodies. The children, who had not ceased laughing and playing since we left New York, waited for the slope of the deck to reach its greatest, and then ran down towards the bulwarks precipitously. The children, happy and innocent, completed for us the feeling of comfortable indifference and security which we found when we saw there was more ship than ocean. The liner's deck canted slowly to leeward, went over more and more, beyond what it had done yet, and a pretty little girl with dark curls riotous from under her red tam-o'-shanter, ran down and brought up against us violently with both hands, laughing heartily. We laughed too. Looking seawards, I saw receding the broad green hill, snow-capped, which had lifted us and let us down. The sea was getting up.

Near sunset, when the billows were mounting express along our run, sometimes to leap and snatch at our upper structure, and were rocking us with some ease, there was a commotion forward. Books and shawls went anywhere as the passengers ran. Something strange was to be seen upon the waters.

It looked like a big log out there ahead, over the starboard bow. It was not easy to make out. The light was failing. We overhauled it rapidly, and it began to shape as a ship's boat. " Oh, it's gone," exclaimed someone then. But the forlorn object lifted high again, and sank once more. Whenever it was glimpsed, it was set in a patch of foam.

That flotsam, whatever it was, was of man. As we watched it intently, and before it was quite plain, we knew intuitively that hope was not there, that we were watching something past its doom. It

drew abeam, and we saw what it was, a derelict sailing ship, mast-
less and awash. The alien wilderness was around us now, and we saw
a sky that was overcast and driven, and seas that were uplifted,
which had grown incredibly huge, swift, and perilous, and they had
colder and more somber hues.

The derelict was a schooner, a lifeless and soddened hulk, so
heavy and uncontesting that its foundering seemed at hand. The
waters poured back and forth at her waist, as though holding her
body captive for the assaults of the active seas which came over her
broken bulwarks, and plunged ruthlessly about. There was something ironic in the indifference of her defenseless body to these
unending attacks. It mocked this white and raging post-mortem
brutality, and gave her a dignity that was cold and superior to all
the eternal powers could now do. She pitched helplessly head first
into a hollow, and a door flew open under the break of her poop; it
surprised and shocked us, for the dead might have signed to us then.
She went astern of us fast, and a great comber ran at her, as if it had
but just spied her, and thought she was escaping. There was a high
white flash, and a concussion we heard. She had gone. But she appeared again far away, on a summit in desolation, black against the
sunset. The stump of her bowsprit, the accusatory finger of the
dead, pointed at the sky.

I turned, and there beside me was the lady who had wanted to
find the sea. She was gazing at the place where the wreck was last
seen, her eyes fixed, her mouth a little open in awe and horror.

April 1910

THREE FRIENDS: LEWIS, O'NEILL, DREISER

SINCLAIR LEWIS

LATE one afternoon eleven years ago, our mutual friend, T. R.
Smith, then managing editor of the *Century Magazine*, telephoned
Mencken and myself at our office and bade us come up to his flat
that evening for a drink. When we got there, we found with Smith
a tall, skinny, paprika-headed stranger to whom we were introduced
as one Lewis. The fellow was known to neither of us save as the
author of a negligible serial that had appeared in the *Saturday Evening Post* and that had subsequently been gathered between book
covers and, to me specifically, as the author of a play called *Hobohemia*, produced the year before down in Greenwich Village and
exquisitely — if I may be permitted so critically indelicate a word
— epizootic.

Barely had we taken off our hats and coats and before Smith had an opportunity even to fish out his *de luxe* corkscrew from behind his *de luxe* sets of the works of the more esoteric Oriental and Po-lack amorists, when the tall, skinny, paprika-headed stranger simul-taneously coiled one long arm around Mencken's neck and the other around mine, wellnigh strangling us and putting resistance out of the question, and — yelling at the top of his lungs — began: "So you guys are critics, are you? Well, let me tell you something. I'm the best writer in this here gottdamn country and if you, Georgie, and you, Hank, don't know it now, you'll know it gott-damn soon. Say, I've just finished a book that'll be published in a week or two and it's the gottdamn best book of its kind that this here gottdamn country has had and don't you guys forget it! I worked a year on the gottdamn thing and it's the goods, I'm a-tell-ing you! Listen, when it comes to writing a novel, I'm so far ahead of most of the men you two think are good that I'll be gott-damned if it doesn't make me sick to think of it! Just wait till you read the gottdamn thing. You've got a treat coming, Georgie and Hank, and don't you boys make no mistake about *that!*"

Projected from Smith's flat by the self-endorsing uproar — it kept up for fully half an hour longer — Mencken and I jumped into a taxicab, directed the driver to speed us post-haste to a tavern where we might in some peace recover our equilibrium and our ear-drums, and looked at each other. "Of all the idiots I've ever laid eyes on, that fellow is the worst!" groaned Mencken, gasping for breath. Regaining my own breath some moments later, all that I could add was that if any such numskull could ever write anything worth reading, maybe there was something in Christian Science too.

Three days later I got the following letter from Mencken, who had returned to Baltimore:

DEAR GEORGE: Grab hold of the bar-rail, steady yourself, and pre-pare yourself for a terrible shock! I've just read the advance sheets of the book of that *Lump* we met at Schmidt's and, by God, he has done the job! It's a genuinely excellent piece of work. Get it as soon as you can and take a look. I begin to believe that perhaps there isn't a God after all. There is no justice in the world. Yours in Xt.,

M.

The book was *Main Street*.

As is sufficiently known, it not only became a best-seller over-night, but it promptly established its author as one of the most observant, penetrating, and significant writers in America.

It was more than a year before I ran across our friend again. I had dropped in late one night at a beer conference of four or five literary compeers in a mughouse off Union Square, where we were then in the custom of gathering. We were in the midst of a quiet, if some-what malty, conversazione when the door flew open and our friend entered. Who had bidden him to come or how he had learned of our meeting-place, no one knew. Jamming down his hat on one of the wall-pegs, he yelled for a Seidel, grabbed a chair and pulled it up to the table, bounced himself up and down on it for three min-utes as if it were a mechanical gymnasium horse, and began loudly to sing something in pig-German, accompanying his melodic gifts with gestures that swept two glasses, three Schweitzer cheese sand-wiches and one sizable order of Bismarck herring off the table. The song concluded and paying not the slightest heed to our grunts and maledictions, he next yelled for a fresh Seidel (fondly embracing the waiter, whom he addressed familiarly and endearingly as leetle Owgoost), complained bitterly of the slowness of the service, de-manded of the assemblage if it did not regard him as the best gott-damn writer in this here gottdamn country, got down at one big gulp three-quarters of the contents of the delivered pipkin, pushed his chair from him, mounted to his feet, cleared his throat several times, and launched into the following declamation:

" Ladies und chentlemens: It is gewiss a great pleasure, gottin-himmel, für me to have been envited to shpeak to you dis eefining. In rising to address mit you, mit my impromptu shpeech in mine vest pocket, I am reminded uff der shtory uff der zwei Irishers, Pat und Mike, who vas riding on der choo-choo car. Pat und Mike, I forgot me to tell you, vas sailors in der navy. It seems Pat had der unter berth und by and by he heard such a noise von der ober berth und he called oop asking warum? Und Mike he answered: ' Shure und begorra how can Oi ivver get a night's shlape at all, at all? Oi've been tryin' to get into this damn hammock ivver since eight bells! ' Now, ladies und chentlemens, shtanding up here before you great folks, I feel me a whole lot like Mike und maybe after I've sprechen

along für a while, I may feel me so darn shmall I'll be able to crawl
me into a choo-choo hammock mineself mit no trouble at all,
at all."

At this point, he paused just long enough to shout for another
Seidel and to drop what he evidently desired us to believe were rich
German and Irish dialects. Then — " Gentlemen," he proceeded,
aiming an imaginary hunk of chewed plug-cut at a remote corner
of the wall, " it strikes me that each year at this annual occasion
when friend and foe get together and lay down the battle-ax and let
the waves of good-fellowship waft them up the flowery slopes of
amity, it behooves us, standing together eye to eye and shoulder to
shoulder as fellow-citizens of the greatest city in the world, to consider where we are both as regards ourselves and the common weal.
It is true that even with our two hundred and fifty-two or practically
two hundred and fifty-three thousand population, there are by the
last census almost a score of larger cities in the United States. But,
gentlemen, if by the next census we do not stand at least tenth,
then I'll be the first to request any knocker to remove my shirt and
to eat the same, with the compliments of yours truly! It may be true
that New York, Chicago, and Philadelphia will continue to keep
ahead of us in size. But aside from these three cities, which are so
overgrown that no decent white man, nobody who loves his wife
and kiddies and God's great out-o'-doors and likes to shake the hand
of his neighbor in greeting, would want to live in them — and let
me tell you right here and now, I wouldn't trade a corner lot in this
fine city of ours for the whole of any one of them — aside from
these three, gentlemen, it's evident to anyone with a head for facts
that this grand city of ours is the finest example of American life
and prosperity to be found anywhere on God's earth! I don't mean
to say we're perfect. We've got a lot to do in the way of extending
the paving of motor boulevards, for, believe me, it's the fellow with
four to ten thousand a year, say, and an automobile and a nice little
family in a bungalow on the edge of the town that makes the wheels
of progress go round! That, gentlemen, take it from yours truly, is
the type of fellow that's ruling America today; in fact, it's the ideal
type to which the entire world must tend if there's to be a decent,
well-balanced, Christian, go-ahead future for this little old planet.

Once in a while I just naturally sit back and size up this Solid American Citizen with a whale of a lot of satisfaction."

For at least twenty-five minutes more he kept on in this vein, occasionally lapsing for a few seconds into dubious German, Irish, or French dialect and interrupting himself only with admonitions to leetle Owgoost. Finally exhausted, he dropped with a bang into his chair, spilling half the contents of his Seidel over himself, and waited for some sign of approval of his great comedic gifts. There bloomed only a grim silence, save for a quiet remark from one end of the table that the lock on the outer door, evidently defective, had better promptly be replaced with a triple-Siegel. Not in the least disconcerted by the captious lull, our visitor pulled himself together, mopped up the hop moisture from his trousers, and — getting to his legs — lifted the remains of his Seidel above his head and clamorously proposed a toast to the novel he was then working on.

Concluding by this time that there was nothing to be done about it, the assembled literati decided to make the best of things. One got up and raised his Seidel " To our distinguished guest, Sinclair Lewisohn." Another " To Upton Sinclair, author of *Main Street*." A third observed that it was an honor to have Alfred Henry Lewis present, while a fourth ventured to inquire if the guest could by any chance be May Sinclair.

" Well, anyway, what did you guys think of my speech? " demanded leetle Owgoost's best customer.

The answer was a volume of inelegant mouth-noises.

A few months later the speech was found to be the keynote of one of the sharpest, most bitingly satirical, and best novels ever written by an American. Its name, if you haven't already identified it, was *Babbitt*.

I began to meet our friend more frequently. He would stop in at my apartment in the late afternoon for a Florestan cocktail, sometimes so moody that he didn't speak five words and at other times so excited and voluble that he would stand up and, apropos of nothing at all, make speeches at me for an hour on end. These speeches, generally couched in dialect of one species or another, were invariably on one of two subjects: himself — in terms of a facetious self-appraisal predicated upon critics who did not sufficiently appre-

ciate him, and myself — consisting for the most part in deplorings
of the unhappy facts that I didn't drink enough, that I didn't have
the sense to recognize *Hobohemia* for a swell play, that Mencken
and I were nice enough fellows all right but that we ought to get
married, and that something ought to be done about our recognizing Stuart Sherman anyway. At other times I would call on him
in whatever hotel room he was occupying that week. He never used
a chair in any such room, but always favored a far end of the bed,
the rest of the bed usually being taken up by a varying and various
assortment of individuals who gave one the impression that he had
run down into the street and herded them in indiscriminately a few
minutes before. Who most of them were I never had the faintest
idea. Many of them looked like a comic-strip artist's idea of anar-
chists; they all talked at once about everything under the sun; and
they all drank his liquor very proficiently. He called them all by
diminutives of their Christian names, always duly announced in introducing each one of them that each was a grand guy, and confidently and enthusiastically predicted to me on each and every occasion that no less than six of those present were virtuosi of one sort
or another who one day would take the critics off their feet. None
of them — there were at least eighty or ninety he thus eulogized in
the period of my visits — has yet been heard of.

He had been living in London for several weeks with Paul de
Kruif, his collaborator, working on *Arrowsmith* — originally called
" Dr. Martin Arrowsmith " — before I got there on my annual
spring trip. The day I arrived I went to a lunch party, where I found
myself seated between John Drinkwater and Philip Guedalla,
neither of whom I had previously met. I had not sat down before
Guedalla said to me: " You are an American and I have a message
for you. If your country doesn't recall Sinclair Lewis at once, there
will be war between England and the United States! " It did not
take a confidant of the oracles to imagine what had been happening.
Our friend Red, as his nickname goes, had all too evidently been
living up to his sobriquet, if not its communistic implications, at
least in its taurian. It developed that the moment he had set foot on
the English shore he had begun to make speeches. These speeches
— according to Guedalla amounting up to the hour to a total of

something like two or three hundred and delivered in dialect on every conceivable occasion at the rate of a dozen or so daily, or rather nightly — had mainly to do, it appeared, with the shameful failure of the English critics, excepting only Hugh Walpole, to take a proper interest in American literature. Our friend, despite the German, French, Italian, Cockney, and Way Down East dialects in which he couched his diatribes, may have minced words but certainly not meanings. He not only, while calling loudly for 'arf and 'arf or a spot of whisky old top, named names, but dates, places, and weather conditions. Every now and then, by way of prolonging international amity for a little while longer, it had been necessary for de Kruif, a veritable Sandow of a man, to grab hold of his colleague, pull him down into a chair, and sit on him.

On one occasion, I was informed, our genial friend, being entertained by a lady of title and being congratulated by those present on his literary gifts, had indicated his whole-hearted concurrence in the wisdom of the encomiums by running around the room and imprinting a very moist buss on the lips of all the female guests. On another, during a gathering of celebrated English men of letters, he had — after, as is his custom, promptly addressing everyone by contractions of their given names — wound his arms around two of the sedate valetudinarians present and insisted that he be allowed to teach them the American jazz dances. On a third, invited to a dinner in his honor by an English woman essayist and novelist, he had brought along with him two strange Germans, a Russian, three Americans whom he had picked up at the American Express Company that afternoon, and two taxicab-drivers, both boiled.

With the completion of *Arrowsmith*, which further established him as one of the most important American novelists of his time, our friend returned to his native land and, finding himself in need of some ready money, applied himself to the writing of a deliberately commercial novel, *Mantrap*, that would need only a cameraman standing behind it and a peroxide blonde in front of it to make a popular moving picture. Always forthright and completely honest with himself, whatever the effect of the forthrightness and honesty may be on the delicate sensibilities of such as leetle Owgoost, Englishmen, Pulitzer Prize committees, and suddenly kissed dowagers, he made no bones of what he was doing, but frankly announced to anyone who would listen that he was, to use his own locution, turning out a swell piece of cheese to grab off some easy gravy.

His literary cheese duly manufactured, he disappeared from New York for a number of months, traveling the West to gather material for his next piece of work. The night that he got back, he was put to bed with a high temperature, but the next morning — the temperature having dropped to 102 — he telephoned Mencken and me to come to dinner with him that night, assuring us that he was in great shape and never felt better in his life. We arrived at about quarter to seven and found that he was still in bed, now with a temperature of 103. No sooner had we entered his bedroom and hardly had we begun to denounce him for a mule for having asked us to dine with him when he was obviously a pretty sick man, than he jumped out of bed, the tails of his short white old-fashioned nightgown flapping about him, and — striking an attitude — began:

" Brothers and sisters, don't you listen for one second to these wishy-washy fellows that carry water on both shoulders, that love to straddle the fence, that are scared of the sternness of the good old-time Methodist doctrine and tell you that details don't mean anything, that dogmas and discipline don't mean anything. They do! Let me tell you, brothers and sisters, that justification means something! Baptism means something! It means something that the wicked and worldly — and here I point to some of our fellow-citizens — stand for this horrible stinking tobacco and this insane alcohol, which turns men into murderers, but we Methodists must keep ourselves pure and clean and undefiled. But tonight, on this first day of getting acquainted with you, brothers and sisters, I don't want to go into these details; I want to get right down to the fundamental thing that details merely carry out — and what is that fundamental thing? What is it? I'll tell you, brothers and sisters. It is the Lord Jehovah and His love for each and every one of us, big or small, rich or poor, drunk or sober. Love! Love! Love! How beauteous the very word! Not carnal love, not love of the flesh, but the divine presence. Love is the rainbow that stands out in all its glorious many-colored hues illuminating again the dark clouds of life. It is the bright morning and the evening star that, in glad refulgence, there on the awed horizon, call all our hearts — and that goes for yours, Georgie, and yours, Hank — to an uplifted rejoicing in God's marvelous firmament! Round about the cradle of the babe, sleeping so quietly while o'er him stands in almost agonized adoration his loving mother, shines the miracle of Love, and at the last sad end, comforting the fond hearts that bear its immortal permanence, round even the quiet tomb, shines Love. What is great art — and I am not speaking of ordinary pictures but of those celebrated Old Masters with their great moral lessons — what is the mother of art, the inspiration of the poet, the patriot, the philosopher, and the great man of affairs, be he business man or statesman — yes, brothers and sisters and Georgie and Hank, what inspires their every effort? Love! Love! Do you not sometimes hear, stealing o'er the plains at dawn, coming as it were from some far distant secret place, a sound of melody? (Shut up, you two bums, and listen!) When our dear sister here plays the offertory, do you not seem sometimes to catch the distant rustle of the wings of cherubim? And what is music, lovely music, what is sweet melody? 'Tis the voice of Love! 'Tis the magician that makes royal kings and queens out of plain folks like us! 'Tis the perfume of the wondrous rose, 'tis the strength of the athlete, strong and mighty to endure mid the heat and dust of the valorous conquest. Ah, Love, Love! Without it, we are less than beasts; with it, earth is heaven and we are as the gods! Yes, brothers and sisters and you two lice, that is what Love — created by the Almighty and conveyed through all the generations by His Church, particularly, it seems to me, by the great, broad, wholesome, democratic, liberal brotherhood of the Methodist Church — that is what Love means to us!"

His temperature having now evidently shot up again, he let out a loud whoop, informed us that we were both low infidels bent for hell, fell back into bed, and, exhausted, was sound asleep a few moments later.

At dinner in a near-by restaurant shortly afterwards, Mencken contented himself with a single word of comment. It was: "Bughouse!" At dinner in the same restaurant not very much later as times goes, we were congratulatingly buying our friend drinks on the elaboration of the boudoir harangue — where it figured almost word for word — into his now famous and finely ironic novel *Elmer Gantry*.

One can always tell a new novel coming on when the oratorical mood in any one, single thematic direction assails our friend. *The Man Who Knew Coolidge* was nothing more than a series of such orations gathered together, with not a word changed. They had been delivered in a variety of places and at a variety of times, including the corner of Fifth Avenue and Fifty-sixth Street at high noon, a beer-house in Hoboken at eleven o'clock at night, another beer-house in Union Hill, New Jersey, at two in the morning, the bathroom of my apartment, the men's lavatory at the Rennert Hotel in Baltimore, a publisher's tea at the Sherry-Netherland, several taxicabs, two New York theater lobbies on opening nights, and the steps of St. Ignatius' Church. *Dodsworth*, a year later, was heralded both before and directly after our friend's European material-seeking trip by innumerable vaudeville performances in the British dialect, aided and abetted by a monocle that he had purchased for the further embellishment of his histrionic talents.

One afternoon a year or so ago, our hero called me up and somewhat mysteriously hinted that I had better be at his house in West Tenth Street at seven o'clock that evening if I didn't want to miss something good. Since he is generally about as mysterious as a traffic cop, my curiosity was aroused and at seven promptly I was on the scene. Three other male guests, as mysteriously summoned, they told me, were already there: one a writer, one a labor leader (our friend at the time was planning a labor novel), and one an intermittent producer of theater plays. After a cocktail or two we were bidden to sit to dinner. In the middle of the meal our host arose and excused himself. Returning a few minutes later, he informed us that he had to have a minor operation performed and had just telephoned the surgeon to come over. We had been invited, it appeared, to stand around and be company while the operation was going on. Protests being of no avail, we had to entertain Lewis while the surgical performance was in progress. "Looking at you guys gives me such a pain," he observed, "that the other one in comparison won't seem so bad."

When some months later the news was flashed over the wires that our friend had been awarded the Nobel Prize, the immense gratification that a number of us felt was slightly modified by qualms as to how the fellow would conduct himself in the presence of Swedish royalty. It was our firm conviction, based upon years of close intimacy, that he would in all likelihood run right up to the Queen, call her by her first name, and lodge an aqueous smack upon her lips, and that when he was presented to His Majesty he would promptly and affectionately whack him on the back, put his arm around him, and call him " you old son-of-a-gun." Consequently, on the night the award was announced, some of us gathered together with him and solemnly engaged to offer him sage counsel and instruction in the finer shades of the punctilio.

" For example," we asked him, " what are you going to say to the King when you meet him? "

" What am I going to say? " he roared, waving his arms in the air and knocking over two lamps. " What am I going to say? Well, just you guys listen! ' Your Gracious Majesty and Officers of the Coldstream Guards: It is a great pleasure, let me tell you, for a little feller from Sauk Center to meet you big Swedes. I feel proud and honored, believe me, boys, and when I get back home and tell the folks of the swell reception you've given me, they're going to be not only proud of me but of you too. After all, we're all brothers in Kiwanis, whether we're Swedes, Americans, or Bohunks, and our hearts are in the right place. So what do you all say to going out, King, and having a little drink? ' "

Yet once again our old friend fooled us. Just as his whistle, however wet and riotous it may be when he is not in the grip of literary labor pains, is ever of an unremitting and almost Pythagorean aridity when he really sets himself down to work, so his conduct at Stockholm turned out to be so formal and proper — indeed, so dismayingly formal and proper — that His August Majesty, together with several members of his court, privy to the eccentricities of American comportment, actually inquired of our hero if he was not, at least on one of his parents' side, partly British.

EUGENE O'NEILL

In all the many years of our friendship, I have heard Eugene
O'Neill laugh aloud once and only once. We were walking, after
dinner one evening in July, up the long, lonely road just beyond
the château he was then living and working in at Saint-Antoine-du-
Rocher in Touraine. In the country, men who live in cities generally find themselves talking out of character. If they are sober, sedate fellows in the city, they become orally frisky in the country;
if they are flippant in the city, they become more or less solemn
and even wistful at the smell of flowers and manure. Their discourse alters with the scene. O'Neill, who in the city — for he is
essentially a man of cities despite his inability to write save a cow
is mooing or a sea is swishing beneath his window — has the mien
and the conversational *élan* of an embalmer, presently proceeded
thus: " When Princeton, after kicking my tail out of place as an
undergraduate because I was too accurate a shot with an Anheuser-
Busch beer-bottle and hit a window in Woodrow Wilson's house
right where it lived, some years later suddenly got proud of its old
beer-bottle heaver but magnanimously allowed Yale to claim the
hoodlum for its own with an honorary degree, I found myself in
New Haven late one night viewing a number of old boys of the
class of 1880 or thereabouts having a hot reunion with themselves.
Three of them in particular, that I ran across on one of the street
corners, were so grandly stewed that I had to stand still and watch
them. One of them, it appeared, was president of a big bank in
New York; another was vice-president of one of the big railroads;
and the third was a United States Senator. After playing leap-frog
for about ten minutes, during which one of them fell down and
rolled half-way into a sewer, the three, singing barber-shop at the
top of their lungs, wobbled across the street to the opposite corner,
where there was a mail-box. With a lot of grunts and after much
steaming and puffing, the bank president and the vice-president
of the big railroad got down on their knees and hoisted their old
classmate, the Senator, up on their shoulders in a line with the
slit in the mail-box. Whereupon the Senator proceeded to use the

mail-box for a purpose generally reserved for telegraph poles and the sides of barns."

The boisterous roar that followed his recollection of the scene marked, as I have said, the only time within my knowledge of O'Neill that he has laughed outright at anything. In all the years I have known him, the most that has ever issued from him has been a quiet little chuckle and I have only, in all that time, heard him chuckle twice, once in New York when he indulged in a reminiscence of the wonderful free-lunch that he and his brother Jim used to get with a five-cent glass of beer (and live on) in a saloon opposite the old Madison Square Garden, and once at Le Plessis, in France, when he handed me a newspaper article in Spanish, treating of the time he once spent in Buenos Aires during his sailor days, asked me to translate it for him, and I inserted several imaginary paragraphs describing in rich detail his great proficiency as a tango dancer. He is constitutionally the antithesis of l'homme qui rit. Nothing even faintly amuses him, unless it be the remembrance of his dead brother's gift for Rabelaisian monkeyshines, the singing (in a voice capable of just three notes, all sour) of old barroom ballads, or remembered tales of his father, the late James O'Neill, who, during the years when he was a matinée idol, used to parade Fourteenth Street at high noon daily — after at least three hours spent in dolling himself up — by way of giving the girls a treat, and who always made it a practice on Sundays to get to church half an hour late by way of staging an effective entrance for himself.

Contrary to finding amusement in the world, O'Neill finds endlessly the materials for indignation. The body of his dramatic writing reflects him more closely, I venture to say, than that of any other playwright in the present-day American theater. Let the dramatic critic of some yokel newspaper in some yokel town that he has never even heard of write that he isn't all he should be as a dramatist, and he lets out a vituperative blast of such volume, that, once done, he finds himself completely exhausted. Several times I myself have been denounced, if somewhat more politely, for expressed opinions on his work. Once, he let me read the manuscript of his play Welded, in which he had great faith. When I reported to him that all I could discern in it was some very third-rate Strindberg, he sharply observed that I couldn't conceivably understand any such play, as I had never been married, put on his hat, walked out, and didn't let me hear from him for two months afterwards. When, several years later, he sent me the manuscript of *Lazarus Laughed* and I wrote to him that I didn't care for it, he replied in the next mail that my judgment of it couldn't be taken seriously by him because I was lacking in all religious feeling and was therefore prejudiced against any such play, and that it was really a masterpiece whatever I thought about it. On this occasion he was so disgusted with my critical gifts that he didn't write to me again for three months. The same thing happened in the case of *Dynamo*, which in a preliminary manuscript reading struck me as being close to caricature. Even after the play was produced and almost unanimously condemned, he stuck to his loyalty toward it and to his conviction that all the critics were dolts. "It maybe wasn't all it should have been," he subsequently admitted to me, "because I was going through a lot of trouble in family matters when I was writing it." And — I happened to be visiting him at the time — he sulked for the rest of the day and condescended only to exchange a curt good-night with me at bedtime. If a newspaper or any other kind of photographer snaps him without his formal permission, he seethes. If he gets a letter with something in it that displeases him, he mutters sourly over it for twenty-four hours. The petty nuisances and annoyances that every man suffers and quickly dismisses from mind and attention cause him something bordering on acute agony.

After many years of being very hard up, his plays gradually began to make him money. But real money came only with the tremendous success, both as a performed play and published book, of *Strange Interlude*, which netted him close to a half-million dollars. Since boyhood he had had just two wishes: one, to have some shirts tailored by a first-class London shirt-maker and, two, to own a carriage dog such as he had seen loping after the rigs of the rich in his youngster days. His greatest satisfaction in *Strange Interlude* was that it had made the gratification of the two wishes possible.

He has a dislike of meeting people that amounts almost to a terror. Even with his few close friends he is generally so taciturn that it is sometimes necessary to go over and poke him to make certain that he is neither asleep nor dead. He sits glumly for hours at a time without opening his mouth, brooding deeply over some undecipherable concern which, upon ultimate revelation, turns out to be a worried speculation as to whether his wife has ordered spaghetti, his favorite dish, for dinner for him that night. Having sat at different tables with him countless times, I have, with rare exception, heard him during the course of a meal say more than two words and they have invariably been — in reply to an inquiry as to whether he would care for any more of this or that — " Why sure." The way to lose O'Neill's friendship is to ask him for oral expressions of opinion on anything (if he feels like expressing an opinion, he will write a letter, and a satisfactorily long one), or to introduce him to any man other than one who knows a great deal about professional sports and who will confine his conversation to that subject. The one great admiration that he has temporarily achieved for any man in the last four years was for Sparrow Robertson, the chief sporting writer of the Paris *Herald*, whom he met just once and found to be " a grand bird." He has a great respect for Sean O'Casey, but beyond that an aversion to most men of his own profession, asserting that the majority of them are not worth the powder to blow them up, and of all those whom he has met in later years only W. S. Maugham and H. R. Lenormand have any interest for him. He goes to a theater about once in every five years and then only in Europe, because he has heard that some play of his is being done there in a language that he cannot understand. I have known him on only one occasion really to admit that he had been in a theater. That was when the Russian Tairoff did *All God's Chillun* in Russian in Paris several years ago. He professed to have found it the best production of any of his plays that he had ever seen. " But," I protested, " you don't know a word of Russian. How could you tell? " He looked at me pityingly. " You should have seen the way Tairoff's wife, in the role of the girl, brushed those books off the table in that scene in the last act! " he replied with grave seriousness.

Displaying outwardly all the glow and effervescence of a magnum of ice water, he is internally given to huge enthusiasms of all sorts and varieties. Whatever piece of work he happens currently to be working on arouses him to such a pitch of incalescence over its virtues that he will go around all day wreathed in broad, mysterious smiles. And when O'Neill thus smiles, it is as if any other man stood gleefully on his head, waved his arms and legs, and let out a bellow that shook the heavens. Familiar with all his longer as well as with a number of his shorter plays since their manuscript infancy, I recall only one time when doubt over a script that he was writing assailed him. In all the other cases he was as excited over their merits as a child of the wealthy anticipating on Christmas Eve the gifts he was certain to get. The one exception was a trilogy which he had undertaken. "Would to God," he wrote me, "that this damned trilogy of mine were off of my neck! I'm beginning to hate it and curse the day I ever conceived such an idea. The notion haunts me that I've bitten off a good deal more than I can chew. On my return, the first two acts of the first play struck me as not right, so I've started to rewrite them. And so it goes on! It looks as if the rest of my life was doomed to be spent rewriting the damned thing. I honestly feel very low about it and am anxious to get done with it and free my mind from the obsession of it and get on to something else. When these two acts are done, for better or worse, I'm going to call quits. I don't think I can go through the ordeal of typing it myself now. I'm too fed up. Think it wiser to get it typed. It would bore me so that before the end I would probably burn it."

But not so usually. Confidence generally permeates his being, warming him to the very toes. He says nothing, or at best very little, but the mysterious smiles embroider his features. Of *The Straw*, he informed me: "I have complete confidence in my own valuation of it." *Where the Cross Is Made* was "great fun to write, theatrically very thrilling, an amusing experiment in treating the audience as insane." "I would like to stand or fall" — in each instance — "by *Bound East for Cardiff*, *The Long Voyage Home*, *The Moon of the Caribbees*, *Beyond the Horizon*, *The Straw*, and *Gold*," he wrote me. Each of these plays, he duly announced, was "my sincerest effort and was written purely for its own sake." Of *All God's Chillun Got Wings* — "Well, I've got it done and I'm immensely pleased with it!" Of *Desire Under the Elms* — "Its poetical vision illuminating even the most sordid and mean blind alleys of life — that is my justification as a dramatist!" Of *Marco Millions* — "There's a whole lot of poetical beauty in it and fine

writing." *The Great God Brown* was " a devastating, crucifying new
one." *Lazarus Laughed* was " far the best play I've ever written."
Of *Dynamo* — " I thoroughly disagree with you about the play. It
is *not* far, far below me. I'm sure of that! Wait and see! It will come
into its own some day when it isn't judged as a symbolical trilogy
with a message to good Americans about what's wrong with them
and what to do about it. I think you're wrong this time — as wrong
as about *Lazarus Laughed*. Not that you're not right about the ex-
cessiveness of the stage directions, but then I thought you knew
that my scripts get drastically weeded out in that respect when I
read proof and that I always let them slide as they first occur to me
until then. A slovenly method, perhaps, but the way I've always
worked. Then again, I don't think it's fair to take the speeches of
a lot of admittedly inarticulate characters in a particular play as
expressions of the general underlying theme of a trilogy — which I
obviously never intended them to be." Indeed, even in the case of
the later trilogy, *Mourning Becomes Electra*, about which there
were the preliminary doubts already recorded, I received, when the
play at length was finished, this comment: " It has been one hell
of a job! Let's hope the result in some measure justifies the labor
I've put in. To get enough of Clytemnestra in Christine, of Electra
in Lavinia, of Orestes in Orin, etc., and yet keep them American
primarily; to conjure a Greek fate out of the Mannons themselves
(without calling in the aid of even a Puritan Old Testament God)
that would convince a modern audience without religion or moral
ethics; to prevent the surface melodrama of the plot from overwhelming the real drama; to contrive murders that escape cops and
courtroom scenes; and finally to keep myself out of it and shun the
many opportunities for effusions of personal writing anent life and
fate — all this has made the going tough and the way long! And
even now it's done I don't know quite what I've got. All I *do* know
is that after reading it all through, in spite of my familiarity with
every page, it leaves me moved and disturbed spiritually, and I have
a feeling of there being real size in it, quite apart from its length; a
sense of having had a valid dramatic experience with intense tortured passions beyond the ambition or scope of other modern plays.
As for the separate parts, each play, each set, seem better than I
hoped. And that's that."

Wherever he happens to be at the moment happens enthusiastically also to be the place of all places for him to be and forever live in. Provincetown was " ideal, quiet and the only place where I could ever work." When in Bermuda, he wrote me: " I didn't start this letter with any view of boring you by an expounding of inner principles. It was rather to recommend Bermuda to you as a place to ' take the waters ' in case you're planning a spring vacation. The climate is grand. The German bottled beer and English bottled ale are both excellent. And the swimming is wonderful, if you like such, which I do above everything. It has proved a profitable winter resort for me. I've gotten more work done than in the corresponding season up north in many years." When at Belgrade Lakes, in Maine, he sent me a postcard: " There's tranquillity here. A place to think and work if ever there was one! Ideal for me." " Well, after a week in London," he wrote, " I am strong for it! It seems to me that if it were possible for me to live contented in any city this would be the one. There is something so self-assuredly nerveless about it. Of course, the weather has been unexpectedly fine — warm and sunny every day — and that helps. In short, I've been happier here since I left New York than ever in my life before." While he was living in Guéthary in the Basque country, I received the following: " The Basque country and the Basques hit me right where I belong! According to present plans and inclinations it is here that I shall settle down to make a home for the rest of my days. Europe has meant a tremendous lot to me, more than I ever hoped it could. I've felt a deep sense of peace here, a real enjoyment in just living from day to day, that I've never known before. For more than the obvious financial reasons, I've come to the conclusion that anyone doing creative work is a frightful sap to waste the amount of energy required to beat life in the U. S. A. when over here one can have just that more strength to put into one's job." When he was in Indo-China, this arrived: " This is the place! There is nothing more beautiful and interesting in the world. It is grand! " Settled for several years in Touraine, he wrote: " This is the place for me! The most beautiful part of France. Here is the ideal place to live and work! " During a motor trip through Spain, I received three postcards from him at different times. One, from Madrid, conveyed this message: " I've never seen a more beautiful spot. It would be a great place to work in." One, from Granada, this: "Spain is most interesting and I'm darn glad we picked it out for a vacation. Granada is quiet, peaceful and immensely attractive. What a place to live and work in!" And, from Malaga, this: "This is the best place I have ever struck in Europe — really good stuff! It'd be a swell place to live and work in." Returned to New York again, he said to me: "Why I ever left here, damned if I know. There's life and vitality here. It's the place for ideas! This is the spot for me and my work!" His present passion is for a small island off the Georgia coast. "The best place to live and work I've ever found!"

O'Neill and Sinclair Lewis are alike in one respect. Both have naturally a boyish quality, an innocent artlessness in a number of directions, that will doubtless remain with them to their last years. In it lies much of their charm. Lewis is as excited over a party as any débutante, and a trip to Hoboken on the ferry works him up to a degree of delight comparable only to Robert Fulton's first sensation when he saw his steamboat actually working. O'Neill, for all his solemn exterior, gets an unparalleled pleasure from splashing around in a swimming-pool and making funny gurgling noises, from putting on the fancily colored dressing-gowns he bought several years ago in China, from singing raucous duets with a crony — "Rosie, You Are My Posy" and "'Twas Christmas in the Harem" are two of his favorites — from lying on the ground and letting Blemie, his pet dog, crawl over him, the meanwhile tickling him on the bottom, from watches with bells in them, from the idea that one day he may master the accordion and be as proficient a performer as the vaudeville headliner, Phil Baker, and from drinking enormous glasses of Coca-Cola and making everyone believe it is straight whisky. When his very lovely wife, Carlotta, comes down to dinner in some particularly striking gown, his face lights up like a county fair. She knows well the effect it has on him and quietly lays in a constantly replenished wardrobe for his relish. "Do you like it?" she will delicately ask on each occasion. And, though his infinite satisfaction is clearly to be perceived, like a little boy who doesn't want to give in and admit anything too quickly, he will invariably mumble: "Well, it's pretty, but I like blue better."

Years ago, he was a drinker of parts. In fact, there were times when he went on benders that lasted a whole month and times when he slept next to the bung-hole of a whisky barrel at Jimmy the Priest's and when Jimmy, the proprietor, coming to work the next morning, found the barrel one-eighth gone. About four or five years ago, however, he hoisted himself onto the water-wagon and has since sat thereon with an almost Puritanical splendor and tenacity. Like many another reformed bibber, he now views the wine-cup with a superior dudgeon and is on occasion not averse to delivering himself of eloquent harangues against it and its evils. It is not easy to forget his pious indignation when Barrett Clark once ventured to mention his old drinking bouts to him. "Altogether too much damned nonsense has been written since the beginning of time about the dissipation of artists!" he exploded. "Why, there are fifty times more real drunkards among the Bohemians who play at art, and probably more than that among the people who never think about art at all. The artist drinks, when he drinks at all [note the whimsy of that *at all*], for relaxation, forgetfulness, excitement, for any purpose except his art!" So today it is Coca-Cola, followed by Kalak, with a vengeance.

O'Neill is very slow in making friends. He tests a potential friendship much after the technique of a fisherman trying out various personal and metaphysical lines, flies, and worms to determine what kind of fish the stranger is and to what degree, personally or philosophically, he resembles a sucker. Once he has made a friend for himself, that man remains a friend, in his eyes, until hell freezes. In all the world I suppose that there are not more than five men at the very most whom O'Neill really regards as friends, and at least three of these are relics of his early more or less disreputable days in Greenwich Village and the adjacent gin-mills. I had known him for exactly ten years before we got to the point where we called each other by our first names.

He has done much of his more recent writing in an enormous chair that he had manufactured for himself in England. It is a cross between a dentist's and a barber's chair, with all sorts of pull-in and pull-out contrivances attached to it and with a couple of small shelves for reference books. A board is so arranged that it can be maneuvered in front of him and on it he rests his pad. Stripped to the waist — he never works, if he can help it, with anything on above his navel — and with his legs stretched out to their full length, he writes everything in longhand and his chirography is so minute that it takes a magnifying glass for average eyes comfortably to read it.

I have never known him to tell a smoking-car story and, if someone happens to venture one while he is around, he sits silent and wide-eyed at its conclusion, as if he couldn't possibly understand it and wonders just what the point is. As for himself, he has just one story and will repeat it, to his apparent own infinite amusement, on the slightest provocation. It is the venerable one known as "The Old Bean," and concerns the braggadocio of an old souse who, despite all the dire catastrophes that befall him, imagines that the tremendous shrewdness of his intellect allows him on all occasions to get the best of everyone else. It is a long story, lasting at least an hour if related at top speed, and I have heard it from him regularly twice a year. Once, telling it to me again and embroidering its details, it occupied the entire time it took us to walk the seven miles from Le Plessis to Tours. The sole other occasion for unwonted loquacity on his part is the reminiscence of his vagrant New York days at the dive known as the Hell Hole and at Jimmy the Priest's, where, with a pot-companion named Joe Smith, he shared a room — which they always referred to as "the garbage flat" — for the fine sum of three dollars a month. His particular comrades at Jimmy's, in addition to Joe, included a number of odoriferous colored gentlemen, a press-agent for Paine's Fireworks named Jimmy Beith, and one Major Adams, a red-nosed inebriate of sixty-odd who had been cashiered years before from the British army. This fraternity, hardly ever with more than fifty cents at a time in its combined treasury, subsisted on raw whisky for breakfast and on what free lunch it could cabbage off the end of the bar during the rest of the day. From time to time other habitués of the place were accepted into the fold, including an old sea captain named Chris Christopherson, whom O'Neill in later years incorporated name and all into his play *Anna Christie,* a sailor named Driscoll, whose name suggested to him the Driscoll of *Bound East for Cardiff, The Moon of the Caribbees,* and *In the Zone,* and a septuagenarian miser who had lived in a small, bare room above the saloon for twenty-two years, who never could persuade himself to throw away a newspaper, and who could hardly find room enough to sleep on the floor for the enormous stacks of accumulated copies of the New York *Times*. The favorite tipple of the brotherhood, when one or another of the members — usually O'Neill, who at intervals would contrive to cozen a dollar out of his father — managed in some way to get hold of the price, was, aside from the breakfast rye, Benedictine drunk by the tumblerful. But such treats were rare and makeshifts were necessary. Alcohol mixed with camphor was found — after one got used to the taste — to have a pretty effect. Varnish diluted with water was also discovered to have its points. And there were days when even wood alcohol mixed in small doses with sarsparilla, with just a soupçon of benzine to give it a certain bouquet, was good enough, in the brothers' view, for any man who wasn't a sissy.

For weeks on end, the brotherhood would sit, or lie, in Jimmy's without stirring out for even a moment's breath of air. That is, all save the Major, who had a hobby for collecting old and wholly useless books of all descriptions, which he never read, and for attending funerals. If he came home any evening without at least three frowzy books garnered from God knows where or without having attended at least two funerals of persons entirely unknown to him, he would mope for the rest of the night and would regain his cheer only after he had drunk a half-dozen or so toasts to His Majesty the King, in beakers of varnish. It was apparently not the royal toasts, however, that caused the Major's demise, but something ponderously diagnosed by a hastily summoned neighborhood medico as " malicious liver complaint." The Major's funeral was a gala affair, with the remaining brotherhood so melancholiously but none the less richly in its cups that no fewer than three of the mourners lost their balance and tumbled into the grave on top of their late brother's coffin.

Nor was it the nature of the brotherhood's refreshments that unwound the mortal coil of Brother Beith. Learning one night, while full of Pond's Extract mixed with one-eighth whisky and three-eighths gasoline, that his dear wife, whom he had forgotten all about in the fifteen years he hadn't laid eyes on her, had run off with a fellow in South Africa, he committed suicide by jumping out of one of Jimmy's upper windows. Beith's suicide, together with certain personal emotional misfortunes in an encounter with Cupid, weighed upon O'Neill's mind and — now it may be told — a month or so after Beith took his life the man who was to become the first of American dramatists attempted, with an overdose of veronal, to follow suit. When, one afternoon at two o'clock — the conventional hour for rising and having whisky breakfast — O'Neill failed to stir, failed even to respond to the brothers' nudges, pokes, and peremptory kicks, an ambulance was quickly summoned and our friend was carted off at a gallop to Bellevue. With the brothers grouped solicitously about his cot, two internes worked over him for an hour before he again gave signs of life. Three hours later, the dose of veronal not having been so large as he believed, O'Neill was back in the world once more and, with a whoop of joy, the brothers put on their hats and moved mysteriously toward the door. " We'll be back soon," they observed significantly — and were gone. Four hours later they reappeared, all beautifully and magnificently drunk. It developed that they had rushed to O'Neill's father and had got fifty dollars from him to pay the hospital fee for his son's resuscitation. " You dirty bums! " groaned O'Neill, with what vocal strength he could muster. " How much you got left? " Thirty-two dollars, they reluctantly informed him. " All right, divide! " he insisted. And with his sixteen dollars safe in hand, he rolled over, grinned satisfiedly, and went happily and peacefully to sleep.

We were sitting one late summer afternoon about two years ago in my rooms in the avenue Maréchal Foch, in Paris, looking out at the merry-go-round of motor-cars in the Étoile and at the Arc de Triomphe in the sinking sun. I asked him — his reflective mood seemed to inspire the question — what he would like more than anything else out of life.

" The Nobel Prize? " I hinted out of the side of my apéritif glass.

" On careful consideration — and no sour grapes about it because I have had no hopes — I think the Nobel Prize, until you become very old and childlike, costs more than it's worth. It's an anchor around one's neck that one would never be able to shake off," he answered, gulping his tea.

"A more intelligent critical appraisal of your work?" I smiled.

His ears, as is their wont when critics and criticism are mentioned, stood setter-like and challenging on end. "I expect denunciation! It's generally sure to come. But I'm getting awfully callous to the braying, for or against. When they knock me, what the devil! they're really boosting me with their wholesale condemnations, for the reaction against such nonsense will come soon enough. These tea-pot turmoils at least keep me shaken up and convinced I'm on my way to something. I know enough history to realize that no one worth a damn ever escaped them — so it gives me hope. When I'm generally approved of, I begin to look in the mirror very skeptically and contemplate taking up some other career I might succeed at. So it's all tonic."

He finished his tea.

"I'll tell you what I want and it's the God's truth. I want just what I've now at last and for the first time in my life got! Life has certainly changed for me in the last year or so and for the first time in God knows how long I feel as if it had something to give me as a living being quite outside of the life in my work. The last time I saw you I told you I was happy. A rash statement, but I now make it again with a tenfold emphasis. And, believe me, it has stood tests that would have wrecked it if it wasn't the genuine article. I feel younger and more pepped up with the old zest for living and working than I've ever felt since I started working. I may seem to slop over a bit, but you don't know into what a bog of tedium and life-sickness I was sinking. I was living on my work as a fellow does on his nerves sometimes, and sooner or later my work would certainly have been sapped of its life because you can't keep on that way forever, even if you put up the strongest of bluffs to yourself and the world in general. Now I feel as if I'd tapped a new life and could rush up all the reserves of energy in the world to back up my work. Honestly, it's a sort of miracle to me, I'd become so resigned to the worst. So be a little indulgent and don't mind my unloading a little of the pop-eyed wonder of it at you!"

At this point Carlotta, his wife, came in, put her arm around him, and kissed him.

"Where've you been?" he asked, his face suddenly lapsing again into that perverse little-boy expression.

Carlotta gave him another little kiss.

"I've been shopping for dresses, Genie dear," she said. "Blue ones."

THEODORE DREISER

IT was seventeen years ago that a morning's mail brought to me the brief note from Theodore Dreiser that led that same evening to what was really, save for a casual word some seven years earlier, my first meeting with him. "I urge you please to come down to my place at eight o'clock tonight. I have asked a dozen or so others as well. I want to present to you a significant and very important idea that I have in mind." My curiosity aroused by the cryptical subpœna, I appeared at the little flat in West Tenth Street in which he was then living and was ushered by him into a tiny room packed like soda crackers with at least twenty men, all of them talking at once and nine-tenths of them smoking the smelliest cigars that my nose in all its wide experience had engaged. In the group there was only one man whom I had ever seen before, George Luks, the painter. Who the rest were I had not the faintest idea and haven't to this day, as Dreiser made no gesture toward an introduction further than to announce "Nathan" upon my entrance and as the great news seemed to be completely lost in the enveloping din.

"The others will be in any minute now," he informed me. "Then we can get down to business. In the meantime, find yourself a seat on the floor."

Shortly thereafter four or five more men came in. They, too, were strangers to me, as they seemed to be to one another. As Luks, whom Huneker had once introduced me to, was occupied elsewhere and, as I say, I didn't know anyone else, I duly found myself a place on the floor, sat myself simultaneously on it and a small sticky piece of cake that had evidently been lying there for a couple of days, and awaited the significant and very important Dreiserian evangel. After numerous injunctions praying the assemblage to shut up and listen to what he had to say, Dreiser took his position in the center of the mob, blew violently for several minutes at the thick cloud of smoke that hid the congress from his view, took out his handkerchief and, catching two ends of it with his fingers, began slowly to roll and unroll it, and proceeded:

"I've asked you all here to tell you of a plan I've thought of and to get your views on it. It's this: There are a lot of writing geniuses in America who are so poor that they can't go ahead with what they've got in them and who need help. Unless they get help, these geniuses, so far undiscovered, will never be heard of. It's my idea that what we all ought to do is to go around and try to interest rich men in these geniuses and get them to subsidize them. Let me hear your opinions."

He had hardly got the word *opinions* out of his mouth than Luks, a low fellow given, it was whispered, to an occasional indulgence in alcoholic liquor, let out such a loud and derisory hoot that poor Dreiser was a full minute in regaining his equilibrium. Fixing the offender with his characteristic cold one-eyed stare, he bade the reason for the unseemly interruption.

"Who are these neglected great geniuses?" Luks demanded. "Just you name me *one!*"

"That's not the point," returned Dreiser.

"Well, if that isn't the point," shouted Luks, "for God's sake what is? Name *one* neglected genius, old boy, and hurry up about it, as this floor is damned hard and my backside is getting sore."

"There are a lot of them," Dreiser insisted, but his confidence began perceptibly to show signs of weakening.

"All right," hammered Luks, taking a swig out of a pocket-flask that he had thoughtfully brought with him. "All right, old boy, but just you go ahead and relieve our minds by naming *one* of them!"

Dreiser continued slowly to roll and unroll the handkerchief, the meanwhile still fixing Luks with that cold left eye.

"I'm waiting, old boy," chuckled Luks, wiping off his mouth with the back of his hand. "Just you name *one!*"

We waited, but Dreiser made no move.

"Well, I guess the meeting's over," said Luks. "Let's get the hell out of here!"

And the meeting was over.

As some men's hobby is collecting postage stamps or Buxbeutel and others' discovering out-of-the-way little restaurants or recondite cocktail mixtures, Dreiser's — like Lewis's — is discovering and collecting geniuses. Since the days of my early acquaintance with him, he has discovered and collected about him more geniuses than ever were heard of in the world before. The only trouble with Dreiser's geniuses is that, for some strange reason, no one ever considers them geniuses but himself, conceivably due to the fact, among other things, that they never seem to have done or to do anything. But though they never produce anything to suggest their dower of genius, Dreiser is in each instance sure that they are geniuses. Who they are or where they hail from, none of Dreiser's friends has ever been able to learn. What is more, their names are for the most part and remain for the most part meaningless. They do not write books or poems or plays; they do not paint or carve out marble; they do not compose music or play the piano, violin or xylophone. At least, if they do, only Dreiser seems to be privy to the news. But that they all are blessed with the divine fire to an incalculable degree, he will confidently assure anyone who will lend him an ear. I myself have met no less than two or three hundred of these great geniuses either in Dreiser's company or upon receipt of letters of introduction from him. But just what direction their genius took or what masterpieces they were responsible for I have never quite been able to make out, although I have listened patiently and politely to their voluble and enthusiastic tributes to their own talents. Looking back over all the theoretical Flauberts, Beethovens, Sardous, and Raphaels of Dreiser's faith, there is only one, in point of fact, whose name appears even faintly to have ever been heard of outside of Dreiser's rooms. That one is the recently deceased Charles Fort, a writer happy in the conviction that all science was simply so much blather, and in whose enormous metaphysical and literary prowess Dreiser had fervently and steadfastly believed for all of fifteen years. What has become of his other many pets I do not, as recorded, know.

When first I met him, Dreiser, as I have said, was living in a couple of two-by-four rooms in West Tenth Street. He was miserably hard up and was existing, he told me, on something like ten dollars a week. But he never whined, never grumbled. In all that time, indeed, I heard him complain only once and that was because whoever lived in the cellar under him — his rooms were on the first floor of a seedy and dilapidated three-story house — made so much noise at night that he couldn't work. He subsequently learned that the cellar was occupied by two Italians engaged in the august profession of counterfeiting. The police some time afterwards backed up a patrol-wagon late one night to apprehend the knaves, but the latter, while the police were gumshoeing around the front of the house, quietly departed out of the rear entrance. Thereafter Dreiser was able to pursue belles-lettres in peace.

Although his rooms looked like a brace of dry-goods boxes that had been left on a wharf during several months of severe storms, he had exercised himself to give them a tone. The aforesaid tone was accomplished by covering the two windows with red hangings which excluded all light, illuminating the *mise en scène* with candles, and maintaining a small phonograph in constant operation upon three mournful Russian musical records. There, for hours on end, he would, sit in the dim candlelight, rolling and unrolling his handkerchief, and listening in rapt taciturnity and open-eyed wonder to the dolesome emanations from the wax — at intervals of every five or ten minutes opening his mouth only to ejaculate: " Beautiful, beautiful! "

Now and again in those days, Mencken and I would seek to lighten our friend's obstinate moodiness with facetiæ of one species or another, but never with the faintest degree of success. It was one of our juvenile monkeyshines to fill the mail-box outside his door with a variety of objects, including small American flags accompanied by scrawls issuing Black Hand threats, letters ostensibly written by the President urging him to come at once to the White House for a confidential talk, menus of Armenian restaurants affectionately inscribed to him by Robert W. Chambers, Elinor Glyn, and Harold Bell Wright, frankfurters tied with red, white, and blue ribbons, beer-bottle labels, photographs of the Czar bearing the inscription: " To Theodore, gentleman and scholar — well, anyway, scholar," and other such nonsenses. Dreiser's invariable retort was to go out, buy a ten-cent Street and Smith paper-back by Bertha M. Clay and present it to us with the sour remark that it

was the only kind of literature either of us could understand. This
was his single form of humorous repartee. I still have, among the
works of the Mlle. Clay that he presented to us, such masterpieces
as *Redeemed by Love*, or *Love Works Wonders*, *For a Woman's
Honor*, *The Gipsy's Daughter*, *A Heart's Idol*, *Another Man's
Wife*, *Gladys Greye*, and *His Perfect Trust*.

On one occasion, knowing how badly he needed money, Mencken
and I consulted an acquaintance connected with the moving pictures in an effort to get him some kind of offer that might bring
him easy funds and permit him to pursue in comfort the novel
that he was then working on. We finally got an offer for him
of two thousand dollars. All that he would have to do was to
pose before the camera in his own person, seated at a desk writing. The picture dealt with a novelist and it was the idea to show
a well-known novelist at work by way of an introduction. He was
not to figure in the story; after the short series of shots his job
would be done and the two thousand dollars would be his. Not
without a feeling of satisfaction over our achievement, since it
involved no invasion of Dreiser's dignity, we hurried down to tell
him of it. Firmly convinced, despite our protestations, that we
were up to another joke at his expense, he grew excessively indignant, cursed us out roundly, and refused us the honor of personal contact with him until further notice.

It was fully six months before I saw him again. We found ourselves seated next to each other at a small stag dinner given by
T. R. Smith in a private room at the Beaux Arts restaurant. Dreiser,
who had succumbed to the geniality of the wassail bowl, was in
high spirits, roaring with laughter over any and everything, pulling
chairs out from under the guests, offering toasts to the glory of
Jehovah, and making loud Swiss music on the table glasses with his
knife. " So here you are again, by God! " he bellowed, clapping me
lustily on the back and mussing up my hair. " So here you are
again. Well, well, well! Look who's here, fellows! It certainly is
an awful sight. Yes, sir, it certainly is! Take a look, all of you. My
God, what a face! So here you are again! It certainly is a great thrill;
yes, sir, it certainly is! Ho, ho, ho, so here you are again! " And so
on for fully fifteen minutes; all to the accompaniment of rever-
berating yowls of pleasure and chuckles of self-satisfaction over his

great sardonic humor. So tickled was he, indeed, over his imagined complete retaliation for the moving-picture episode that we became friends again in his eyes and have so remained, without further interruption, until this day.

Only once was that friendship even mildly threatened, and that was when Mencken and I, then editing *The Smart Set*, after publishing a number of his manuscripts of the usual more or less despondent nature, suggested to him that he do a story for us of a somewhat different character. " What kind of story? " he wanted to know. " Why not a society story? " suggested Mencken, swallowing a grin. " Something very swell and tony. Get out of the tenements and dirty undershirt atmosphere for a change. It'll do you good." Oblivious of Mencken's jocosity, Dreiser allowed that he might try his hand at some such story and, lo and behold, about two days later the result arrived. The scene was laid in Cincinnati and the occasion was a great ball given by the leader of the élite in that city. The very air quivered with *ton*. There were " no less than dozens of butlers " and the heroine, " an heiress of the *beau monde*, swept down the great staircase attired in a very trig green satin." Other ladies present were also attired in " trig green satin " and the climax of the " trig affair " came when the hostess confronted the " fashionable multimillionaire, Mr. Diamondberg " and accused him, in the middle of the ballroom, of having swindled her husband out of a street-railway franchise. When we sent the story back to him, he was surly over our failure to appreciate its elegances and held me equally responsible with Mencken for having wasted his time and energy.

As, gradually, money came to him from his writings and life became easier for him, his nature expanded in many directions. His attitude toward his work did not change, for nothing, I believe, could ever change that. If he had ten dollars in his pocket or ten hundred thousand, nothing or no one could influence him once he took pen in hand. Even in the poor days when at times he was forced by necessity to write on order, he wrote with complete honesty, the best he knew how, and — whether it was liked and accepted or not — with a sincerity that was not to be mistaken. If he has ever done hack work, he at least did not regard it as such. Even the story about the heiress of the *beau monde* attired in trig green satin was an honest job so far as he himself viewed it. But if affluence altered his attitude toward his work no whit, it altered — and why not? — his manner of living. The first large round sum of money that came to him, the proceeds of the sale of *An American Tragedy* to the moving pictures, resulted in the installing of himself in an elaborate duplex studio apartment, with a brace of colored girls in white caps and aprons to add a note to the scene, with monthly soirées and receptions involving the activities of Hungarian violinists, Russian coloratura sopranos and an international and marvelous assortment of dubious pianistic professors, and with a cut-glass punch-bowl, banked with lettuce sandwiches, caviar sandwiches, and *petits fours*, glistening in splendor on the dining-room table. There also followed the purchase of an estate up the Hudson, with a remodeled house large enough to hold a good part of the Authors' League of America, and with a swimming-pool, a small lodge-house for visiting bachelors, and a set of very dégagé after-dinner coffee-cups. There appeared on the scene, as well, what is known as "a man," a colored gentleman whose profession embraced the taking of cards at the door, the pressing of trousers, the service of beverages, and a close scrutiny of the behavior of any visiting poets. "Is it possible that that host of ours was Dreiser, *Theodore Dreiser?*" Fannie Hurst once demanded of me in ironic perplexity upon leaving one of the studio gatherings. "Say what you will, I won't believe it!"

Dreiser's simplicity, however, for all the great change in his external surroundings, is still his simplicity of the days when he hadn't a cent. His friends are still the friends of those days; his cast of mind is still exactly the same; his diversions are still composed of such innocent adventures as going to the movies, having an occasional dinner in some side-street Italian or Chinese speakeasy, or taking a trip to Coney Island, Asbury Park, or Atlantic City. "What I am still looking for," he has told me, "in the midst of all this success that seems to have come to me, is some little, greasy one-horse publisher who wouldn't know a mahogany desk if he saw one but who has a high and very real love for literature and who, though he may be poor in money, will have time to talk sincerely with me about my work, and understand the kind of man I am, and let me talk with him through the nights of all that is in my mind and heart.

I am sick of these business-men publishers with their offices that look like the Île de France and with their minds that look on books as if they were so many boxes of merchandise."

A Socialist — " Equitist " he calls it — in philosophy, and a very indignant one to boot, with a passion for writing letters to newspapers and magazines inveighing against the rank injustices of the capitalistic system, he is so absolutely earnest in his convictions that I honestly believe that if the issue were brought to a head he would be the first to give every cent he owned in the world into the common fund. " I really don't need or want money," he has said to me, " though under the existing order of things you may be damned sure I want and get every dollar that is coming to me. But I could still live on ten dollars a week and probably be just as happy on it." The trip to Russia that he undertook several years ago made a tremendous impression upon him. Among the things other than economic, governmental, and the like that moved him deeply and set him to a profound ponderation was Russian art. Immediately upon his return, he sought me out and bade my help in introducing one of the greatest phenomena of this art to America. " It's wonderful! " he proclaimed. " There's nothing in the whole world like it! It will be a revelation to this country! " I asked him what it was. " The Russian ballet," he gravely informed me. " But," I protested, " Americans already know almost as much about the Russian ballet as the Russians. It has been shown here time and again." Dreiser looked at me, disbelief all over him. " You don't say so! " he remarked. " Well, isn't that odd, now! " He was very much disappointed.

One always finds Dreiser surprised and amazed at what has long been familiar to most persons. When he sees something for the first time, it is discovered to the world so far as he is concerned. Once, returning from a trip through the West, he hotly demanded why no one had ever remarked on the majesty of the Grand Canyon. " It's gorgeous, beautiful, that's what it is! " he announced. " People should be told about it." Going to Europe for the first time at forty, he subsequently delivered himself of a book full of wide-eyed marvelings at various Continental cities, peoples, and customs that had already been written about by hundreds of men before him and that were subjects of long-standing knowledge to almost everybody else.

Even more greatly so than O'Neill is Dreiser fundamentally a lugubrious fellow. Despite his fitful excursions into a swollen humor, his nature is cast o'er with melancholy, and even his occasional search for diversion of one kind or another has implicit in it a tendency toward and taste for the glum, the depressing, and the morbid. While I will not go so far as to say that his favorite form of melody is the requiem, it is pretty safe to say that nothing really appeals to him in the way of music save that which, in the bumpkin expression, is described as "sad." In the movies, to which he often goes, only the more drab and despairful Russian films make any impression upon him, although there is a single qualification here in the instance of the comedy films of Laurel and Hardy, which he peculiarly delights in. He cannot stand high lights and, wherever he lives, his rooms have the aspect of an undertaker's boudoir. When he goes to a restaurant, he prefers one that is so dimly illuminated that he can hardly make out whether he is eating spaghetti or chop suey. He spends many hours in drug-stores examining the stocks of pills, medicaments, embrocations, and tinctures, which he lays in by the wholesale, never traveling out of reach of a pharmacy without carrying with him a suitcase chock-full of his grim purchases. Any man with whiskers is immediately accepted by him as a distinguished and very learned person. His taste in reading is for novels in which everyone dies a horrible death and in which the groans fill at least one hundred and fifty of the book's pages.

Of all the writers whom I know intimately, Dreiser is the only one who actually enjoys the physical business of writing. Whereas the rest of these men hate the actual business of putting their thoughts and inspirations upon paper, complain bitterly of the dreadful chore that literary composition is, and do all sorts of things to try to divert themselves from the misery that envelops them when they sit down to their desks, Dreiser would rather write than do anything else. He looks forward to the day's job as another writer looks impatiently ahead to the hour when it will be finished. "I am a writer; I like to write; and I am wretched when I don't write," he has told me. "If I don't produce three thousand words a day, I'm unhappy." He writes, writes, writes. Commonly regarded as being mainly devoted to the novel form, he has written in more various literary forms than any other American of repute. Aside from novels, he has turned out poetry, long plays, short plays, short stories, travel books, special articles on all kinds of subjects, political and economic feuilletons, special newspaper assignments, Sunday-supplement feature stories, pamphlets, essays, personality sketches, magazine articles, newspaper editorials, dramatic criticism, fashion articles, autobiography, novelettes, and magazine fillers. He has written on women violinists, interior decoration, carrier pigeons in war-time — " Their Use on Warships and Capabilities in Carrying Swift Information " — life-stories of successful men, electricity in the household, American portrait-painters, Japanese home life, the horseless age, American women playwrights, American female harp-players, the Society for the Prevention of Cruelty to Animals, the food problem, the subway, the history of the horse, the rural free mail delivery, Hollywood, Ty Cobb, movie actors, antique furniture, American foreign relations, chicken ranches, baseball, railroad wrecks, street-car strikes, insects, matrimonial problems, Marshall Field, Thomas A. Edison, Philip Armour, Chauncey Depew, Mrs. Clara Shortridge Foltz — " A Modern Portia " — cats and dogs, babies, metal workers, photography, " Artistic and Literary People in the Picturesque Bronx," the cashregister business, sweat-shops, the right to kill, applied religion, the Authors' League of America, and diseases. . . .

Almost any kind of movement or cause finds in him a ready-made and excitedly eager sympathizer. Ever since he helped to organize something known as the National Child Rescue Campaign back in 1907, he has either been helping to organize or serving on committees to rectify one or another national, political, economic, social, or literary ill. His name has figured on more letter-heads proposing crusades for or against any and everything than even Mr. Lincoln Steffens's or Mrs. Charles Sabin's. He has been on anti-censorship committees, Sacco-Vanzetti committees, Mooney committees, assistance for starving Armenians committees, baby milk committees, free-library committees, committees for a better understanding of the Soviet, bread-line committees, committees for a better understanding of Socialism, committees for a truer understanding of Communism, committees to raise funds for monuments, tenement investigation committees, committees for better movies, committees to reopen wrongful convictions of alleged criminals, literary committees, committees to protest against the sewage conditions at Far Rockaway, anti-noise committees, committees to beautify Greenwich Village, civil-liberties committees, committees to look after the welfare of poets' widows, Indiana state-anthem committees, committees to erect statues to his late brother, tree-saving committees, sailors' aid committees, committees in protest against the deportation of alleged radicals, committees to investigate the white-slave traffic, committees to investigate the condition of mine-workers and mill-hands, committees protesting the lynching of Negro Lotharios, committees against child labor, committees against the high cost of living, pro-Ben Lindsey committees, pro-Jurgen committees, anti-Prohibition committees, and scores of others. If he has ever turned down anyone who asked him to serve on a committee, provided only that it did not involve him in the necessity of attending a banquet, there is no record of the fact.

As to criticism of his writings, favorable or unfavorable, he has for the last twenty years displayed a sublime and complete indifference. Indignant over many things, what is said against him personally or professionally is of not the slightest concern to him. When some friend of his wrathfully brings to his notice some particularly ignorant, prejudiced, and nasty critical comment on his work, he quietly rolls and unrolls his handkerchief, chuckles softly, and says: " Oh, yes? " That is his invariable rejoinder, amplified only on rare occasions with an adagio ejaculation of the mot de Cambronne. In all the long time that I have known him, I recall only three instances when anything printed about him invaded his composure in the remotest degree. On each of these occasions what was said about his writings did not interest him in the least; it was the reflection on him personally that mildly tried his temper. The first instance was when James L. Ford asserted in the New York Herald that any man who wrote the kind of stuff that Dreiser wrote should be shot, and that it was impossible for any person in decent society longer to speak to him. The second instance was when the New York Times, in an article on Zola's death, pointed out that

Zola " had died falling in his own vomit " and that " it would be well for an American writer named Dreiser, a disciple of Zola, to take note." The third instance was when a reviewer on a Montreal paper — I believe it was the *Star* — observed that only a man who had plumbed the depths of perversion could write such a novel as *The Genius*.

One night about a year ago, on the eve of his sixtieth birthday, we sat together over the rosy waters contemplating the literary scene. I telescope a few snatches from his conversation: " Take Shaw. The old fellow makes a sad idiot of himself trying to convince himself through other people that he's still young and spry. I had lunch with him in his flat when I was last in London and guess what the bug did! After each course he jumped up from the table, grabbed hold of two chairs, placed them some five and a half feet apart, adjusted his chin on one and his feet on the other, and then — in a horizontal position — chinned himself up and down on them for a couple of minutes. When lunch was over and I was safely out of the place, he probably had to go to bed and rest up for twelve hours from the exertion of having impressed me, as he believed, with his remarkable youthful vitality. . . . Take Wells. A notable man, but so persistently damned British in his point of view that I can no longer carry on any correspondence with him. We corresponded for quite a time, but it got so not long ago that his unyielding British prejudices made it impossible for me to get any satisfaction out of trying to exchange opinions with him. . . . Take George Moore. I had a visit with him several years ago and hoped to have a long chat on literature with the old fellow. And what do you imagine he spent the whole three hours talking about? About his prostate gland! . . . The trouble with literary men is that they leave widows. When you once wrote that a widow is the financial remains of a love-affair, you said a mouthful, my boy! I tried lately to get together a collection of short stories by poor So-and-So, who died some ten years ago, write an introduction to them, and so not only help perpetuate his reputation but get a little money for his widow. And what did the old girl do? She accused me of a plan to make money for myself, together with a reputation, at her dead husband's expense. A fact! All widows of literary men ought to be buried with them. They're generally all

the same. I've run up against any number of them in my time and
they always imagine that any friend of their late lamenteds is some
kind of ghoul. . . . Andreyev is the world's greatest dramatist. His
Devil in the Mind is a tremendous play. I know it is, because I
happen to know a man who's exactly like his central character. . . .
David Graham Phillips was as overestimated as hell. But Harold
Frederick and Will Payne were two real geniuses of Phillips's day
who were never properly appreciated. . . . Don't talk to me of
current American literature. The profound amours of amateur
emotions — that's what the bulk of it is. . . . I don't believe in
saints, but there's one man on this earth who strikes me as being
one, and he's Abraham Cahan. . . . Plagiarism? The hell with it!
Take Gross, the Chicago merchant who was a friend of mine, and
Rostand, who stole his play and made it into *Cyrano de Bergerac.*
I thoroughly believe Rostand swiped my friend's play and I helped
my friend out in his lawsuit. But Rostand made it into a beautiful
thing, didn't he, so what the odds? . . . Critics are getting too rich.
More of them ought to starve to death. Every time I hear of a
critic who is hardly getting enough to eat I laugh until I bust my
galluses. Nothing personal, however, nothing personal, mind you.
Ha-ha-ha. . . ."

Carl Van Vechten

LA TIGRESSE

I

New York, which Henry James once referred to as " the long, shrill city," of all the cities of the world I have lived in, delights me most.[1] Some cities I always dislike; some, like Florence or Cincinnati, I find agreeable for a week or a month at a time, but there is a shifting grace about Manhattan like the changeless, changing pattern woven by the waves of the sea, which is persistently and perennially attractive. Moreover, there are overtones which awaken memories. When one is in Paris one is in Paris; when one is in Amsterdam one is in Amsterdam; when one is in Munich one is assuredly nowhere but in Munich, but it is possible to be in New York and a great many other places simultaneously. Shut away from your sight

[1] This is still my feeling.

[616]

the buildings that surround the Public Library and you are in Imperial Rome. Further up Fifth Avenue certain millionaires have reminded us that there are châteaux on the Loire.[1] The Giralda Tower of Seville [1] looms in leafy Madison Square, " Diana's wooded park," as O. Henry lovingly described it, and near by a fair copy of the Venetian campanile pierces the sky. A little removed on Fourth Avenue there is a very good imitation of the Torre del Mangia in Siena. Where Canal Street strikes off from the Bowery in the heart of Jewry the sweeping colonnades which preface the Manhattan Bridge unmistakably suggest the colonnades of St. Peter's at Rome. The Arch of Titus guards Washington Square. The chalets which serve as stations for the elevated railroads remind us that the Swiss Family Robinson lived in a tree. The Town Hall of Verona decorates Herald Square.[2] There are buildings on Lafayette Street and on East Forty-third Street obviously inspired by Venice. On East Broadway, between brick tenements and lofty buildings, smart brick houses with white doorways topped by fan windows, marble steps, and hand-wrought iron railings with polished brass finials, carry us back to London or New York of the fifties. At certain seasons of the year violets [3] or roast chestnuts are vended on the street corners after the manner of Paris. A veritable Egyptian pyramid caps a building on Nassau Street. Here and there one catches a glimpse of a Dutch façade. The " diners " awaken thoughts of London coffee stalls, including Neil Lyons's immortal Arthur's. The lovely eighteenth-century City Hall, perhaps the most beautiful single building in New York, is surrounded by skyscrapers, like a Taj Mahal in a valley dominated by mountain peaks. Now the war has set a camouflaged battleship with fighting turrets in the center of Union Square, otherwise a wilderness of moving-picture houses, saloons, and burlesque theaters, and at several points, at street intersections or in parks, Iowa farmhouses have been erected in which the Salvation Army or the Knights of Columbus dispense hot

---

[1] No longer, alas!

[2] More than half of this charming structure has been demolished to make way for a taller office building.

[3] Since the performance in 1926 of a play by Edouard Bourdet called *The Captive*, in which a Lesbian presents her friend with violets, florists, as well as street vendors, have found it practically impossible to sell these lovely flowers in New York, so sex-conscious, apparently, is the female population.

coffee, doughnuts, and the *Saturday Evening Post* to soldiers and sailors. If these incongruities cause no comment, it is because the note of incongruity is the true note of the island. Nothing is incongruous because everything is. In a city where one finds a Goya Apartment House and a Hotel Seville it is no surprise to discover that an avenue has been christened after Santa Claus! New York, indeed, is the only city over which airships may float without appearing to fly in the face of tradition. I might safely say, I think, that if a blue hippopotamus took to laying eggs on the corner of Forty-seventh Street and Broadway every day at noon, after a week the rite would pass unobserved.

So in New York it is possible to eat in seventy or eighty different styles: in Spanish restaurants on Pearl Street,[1] on the sidewalk, after the fashion of certain European cities, on Second Avenue,[1] in Rumanian style on Forsythe Street, the food of the Syrians on Washington Street, Turkish or Armenian fashion on Lexington Avenue, Swedish fashion on Thirty-sixth Street, Russian fashion on Thirty-seventh, German on Fourteenth, Japanese on Nineteenth, Hawaiian on Forty-seventh, Jewish on Canal, Indian on Forty-second, Greek on Sixth Avenue, and French, Chinese, Negro, and American almost anywhere!

So cosmopolitan is New York in the matter of cookery that no bizarre appetite should go unsatisfied: gefüllte fish or venison, sharks' fins or bear steak, snails or pirogue, grouse or tel kadayif are all to be found somewhere.

In these strange restaurants, all so foreign to the spirit of America, and yet all somehow so *right* in Manhattan, bearing nostalgic breaths of the homelands to those who frequent them, strange adventures occur, a thousand unchronicled episodes happen in a night. It is well to remember in this regard that New York is the city where John Masefield worked as a barman, where Harry Thaw shot Stanford White on a roof garden of White's own designing, where P. T. Barnum first exhibited white elephants and aged Negro women, and where later he became the impresario of Tom Thumb and Jenny Lind, where Adah Isaacs Menken, the lady who wrote *Infelicia*, dedicated to Charles Dickens, and who, in her im-

---

[1] No longer, alas.

personation of Mazeppa, was bound to the back of a horse which
dashed madly over the canvas crags of a New York stage, lived at
what later became the Maison Favre,[1] where Nick Carter worked,
where Van Bibber sailed in swan boats, where Steve Brodie jumped
off the Brooklyn Bridge, where Chuck Connors ruled Chinatown,
where Gorky was refused hotel accommodations and Marie Lloyd
was held at Ellis Island because they had neglected to marry their
consorts, where Theodore Roosevelt, returning from a journey
around the world, drove up Broadway in a triumphal procession
like an emperor in his chariot, where Emma Goldman,[2] William
Dean Howells,[2] Theodore Dreiser, Victor Maurel,[2] and David
Belasco [2] make their homes and do their work.

II

It was a sweet sight, the tall, ungainly young blond French savage
in his naval uniform, very naïve, standing to sing in the crowded
café. We had earlier invited him to sit at our table to consume a
little of the popular red wine of California, so that when someone
suggested that he sing *Madelon* he got up to do so at once as if
there were no other course open to him after having accepted
our hospitality. His high-pitched and unresonant organ produced
sounds wholly unrelated to the art, or even the pastime, of singing
as it is generally understood, but he knew the words and he continued to deliver stanza after stanza in his quaint schoolboy manner, lifting now his right arm, now his left.

Quand Madelon vient nous servir à boire . . .

The buzz of conversation in the café ceased and began again,
ceased and began again. Jean-Baptiste (why are all French peasants
named Jean-Baptiste?) continued:

Quand Madelon vient nous servir à boire . . .

---

[1] This picturesque French pension, located at 528 Seventh Avenue behind
the Metropolitan Opera House, is now no more. The actual table d'hôte,
presided over by Madame Favre herself, was a great haunt of celebrities in
pre-war days. I occupied the first floor front during the years 1907–10.
[2] No longer, alas!

Was this the twenty-first time? When he came to the stanza about
the caporal,

> Un caporal enkepi de fantasie . . .

we felt we had listened long enough for the sake of politeness and
went on with our conversation, but Jean-Baptiste continued to
sing:

> Ma-de-lon, Ma-de-lon, Ma-de-lon. . . .

It is a better war-song than America or England has produced,
Peter Whiffle was saying. Both words and music are far better than
those of *Over There* or *Tipperary*.

It is very long, was my comment.

> Elle rit, c'est tout l'mal qu'elle sait faire . . .

sang Jean-Baptiste and suddenly, quite as suddenly as he had commenced, he finished, and sat down to drink more of the good red
wine of California in the most complete silence. He had sung all
the stanzas he knew and unless someone asked him to repeat them,
which doubtless he would willingly have done, he could do no
more for us. Eventually, however, Peter Whiffle, observing that the
boy seemed out of our circle, brought him back in again with a
question: Qu'est-ce que vous faites au pays?

Jean-Baptiste became garrulous: Sometimes we have rabbit stew.
When my sister was married we had rabbit stew. For weeks beforehand in preparation we caught cats on the roads, in the fields, in
the barns. My brother caught cats and I caught cats and my father
caught cats: we all caught cats. We caught forty cats, perhaps fifty
cats. Some were huge tomcats, some were females with kittens
inside them. Some were black and some were white and some were
yellow and some were tabbies. One cat scratched a big gash in my
brother's face which bled. My father and I shut the cats in a
room — my brother was afraid to help us after he had been
scratched — and we went in after them with cudgels and beat about
us, beat the cats on the head. How they did howl and screech and
fight, but we were a match for them. For an hour we chased them
around the room, beating them, till all the cats lay dead on the
floor. Then my brother and my mother skinned the cats and made a

magnificent rabbit stew for my sister's wedding. . . . Jean-Baptiste
lapsed into complete silence again, reverting to his glass of red wine.

It was growing late. A few sailors with their girls sat about at the
tables chatting and drinking. The proprietor, a great figure of a
man with shaggy eyebrows and the mustache of a villain of a tank
melodrama, glowered from behind the counter. A young fellow
occasionally tapped melodies out of the piano, American tunes of
the day and night, and some of the sailors tried to dance, hobbling
about clumsily, destroying rhythm and women's footwear.

The place brought a vague memory back which I sought to establish more vividly. Some past fragrance blew into my nostrils. . . .
I tried to remember my nights in seaport towns, Spezia? Hardly.
Nor Liverpool, nor Dieppe. Antwerp? There is a certain street in
Antwerp where sailors are deprived simultaneously of their virility
and of their money, a long winding street near the wharves. In
the evening the windows, with tiny, square, bulging Belgian panes,
are brilliantly lighted, but each of these windows is carefully curtained and only a chance shadow occasionally exposes a lewd movement in the interior to the passer-by. A fat figure decorates a doorstep now and again, and in the street one jostles a slovenly hussy or
passes a sleek procurer with greasy mustache and eager eyes. Here
and there a café interrupts the rhythm, a café where fat Belgian
molls and drunken sailors, English, French, Swedish, and American
sailors, make some pretense of gayety. . . . No, the present scene
was not like this. Perhaps it was the perfume of one of the women,
and perhaps it was the way the sailors danced, but suddenly it all
came back to me how once I had spent a quiet and delightful
evening in a bourgeois café, a haunt of French sailors, near the
Quai de Cronstadt in Toulon. There had been some singing, a
great deal of talking, an immense amount of smoking and drinking,
and it was all extremely cheerful.

The entrance of a pleasant-looking little woman, obviously a
personality, interrupted my reverie. She wore a plaid skirt with a
blue flannel blouse. Her frowzy hair was surmounted by an unfashionable turban. Her figure was inclined to stoutness. She was
forty and she had a number of gold teeth, but her eyes were dark
and piercing and her smile, as she turned to bow to one of my
companions, was divine. I must have looked a question.

That is La Tigresse, he said.

La Tigresse?

I don't know her real name. Everyone here calls her that. She lives upstairs and usually appears about this hour in the morning. She is very remarkable when she sings.

We invited her to sing at once, but some time elapsed before she did so. Passing from group to group, she asked sailors questions about their homes, about their lives at sea, about the women they met, about Paris. When she finally came to sit with us, I was struck at once by her essential dignity, her reserve, her poise. She spoke feelingly of the war and its effect on her beautiful France and she touched on more trivial topics, but whatever she talked about she was always interesting and charming, always to a certain extent a personage. She had, indeed, completely aroused my curiosity before she sang at all.

It was two o'clock. The crowd had thinned to three groups. The patron yawned behind the counter. The pianist had left. Suddenly La Tigresse arose and, backing into the center of the floor, began to sing, without accompaniment, *Quand je danse avec l'homme frisé*, which related the history of a preposterous béguin in a frank and ribald manner. The tune itself had the self-conscious impertinence of the can-can from *Orphée aux Enfers*. Her hips swayed, her eyes flashed fire, her voice bawled out the tones. Singing, indeed, the woman became an artist. What fervor! What animation! What power of characterization! What sensuous appeal! With one song she had already evoked an atmosphere and she continued to hold us with her magic, singing now comic songs about a simple couple from Brussels visiting Paris, now tragedies of the waterfront, and then the dark and gloomy Seine flowed under the nocturnal bridges before our eyes and the vice and sordid misery of the rats who haunt the quays came between us and the reality of the café. Lower and lower she dragged us with unfailing effect, through the streets of Ménilmontant and Belleville. Bibi and Toto and Bubu and other bad boys stalked across her red and purple canvas. They loved and killed and died. In contrast to these sordid histories, she sketched lighter pictures of Paris smiling, tiny midinettes, saucy grisettes, and flamboyant cocottes, Madeleine of the Olympia Bar, Célestine of Maxim's, or Marguerite of Pagé's, or the love adven-

tures of little Mimi Pinson on her way to work, overtaken by a shaft
from Eros, shot from the window of a warehouse by a beau gars.
All of these were painted with sympathy and understanding. The
characteristic gesture was never wanting, nor were humor and
pathos. I don't know how much she would have delighted me in
the theater, but here, a little under the influence of the good red
California wine, in this small, semi-deserted room, with a few
French sailors as a background, hers seemed the finest and most
finished art. We ordered a bottle of champagne, and when it
bubbled in the glasses, La Tigresse sat down to help us drink it.

" Who are you? " I asked, in some awe.

" La Tigresse. Have you never seen my name on the posters in
Paris? " She spoke freely of her triumphs in the small halls behind
the Gare Montparnasse and her advance to the Scala and even
La Cigale, where her successful representation of a femme cocher
had caused the defection of the beautiful Idette Bremonval.

And now she was here, forgotten, singing in a cheap American
haunt of French sailors and taken by them with less gusto than
they would have awarded to the commonest Coney Island diva.
Our applause, I thought, must have come to her as a great boon,
giving her a delight she had not experienced for some time, and
yet from her appearance and manner as she sat at our table I could
not make out that she was in any way excited.

" The woman is a find," I said to Peter Whiffle later. " She should
have a great success if we could arrange some drawing-room appearances for her." As we discussed the possibilities of her making
a more public audition a great pity surged over my heart, a pity for
her warm but unfashionable apparel, the signs of her poverty.

We went back again and again to hear La Tigresse. She always
came into the café around one o'clock to remain until the place
was empty. Sometimes she simply tied a skirt around her nightgown, stuck a few pins in her hair, drew on stockings and low
shoes, threw a black shawl over her broad shoulders, and descended
from her bedroom; sometimes she wore the costume in which I had
seen her originally; but each night she had a new repertory, each
night she delighted us with new songs.

Peter and I agreed that something must be done. We were
aware that French songs, no matter how good or how well sung,

would make no effect in our music halls. I recalled, indeed, the
lamentable failure of Yvette Guilbert to establish herself with the
public of the Colonial Theatre on Broadway one sad Monday
afternoon. A " recital " in Æolian Hall did not seem practical. We
believed, however, that La Tigresse in her plaid skirt and blue
flannel blouse might take on at once in somebody's drawing-room
after dinner. This was to be her rehabilitation. In time, indeed,
she might be able to return to Paris, to her old place in the halls
there. So we dreamed and planned.

One night after La Tigresse had been particularly wonderful —
she had led three apaches to the guillotine and four or five women
to bed — we determined to speak to the patron about her, and we
called this grave-faced peasant, this brawny fellow from the south
of France, over to our table.

" It's about La Tigresse . . ." I began, rather awkwardly.

" La Tigresse? . . . Well, there she is."

" Yes, what can be done about her? "

" What do you mean: what can be done about her? "

" We want to get her some work."

" Work! La Tigresse won't work. She doesn't want work."

We looked rather astonished, and I persisted: But surely if she
were better known she could make some money. . . . Then she
could buy herself some decent clothes. . . . She . . .

At last the patron understood, and understanding, he began to
laugh. Huge guffaws shook his enormous frame as he rocked back
and forth. He shouted and puffed with merriment. Tears ran down
his cheeks and mingled with the pomade of his mustache.

We stared at him in amazement and so did the few others who
remained in the café. At last he felt calm enough to speak.

" You think she's poor," he gasped, " La Tigresse . . . ? "

We nodded. " Isn't she? "

" Good God! I'm prosperous. I do a good business. I've put
away some money, but I'd like to have all the money that woman
has! She was very successful in Paris and she saved her earnings.
Later when twilight was beginning to descend on her talent " — it
is often very easy for even the proprietor of a café to be somewhat
poetic when he is speaking French — " she met an old South
American. He gives her all the money she wants and asks very

little in return. He sees her only three or four times a year because he is always traveling and La Tigresse detests to travel. She has a pearl necklace. She has a car. God, it's funny to think that someone believes La Tigresse to be poor! "

" Then why," I demanded, " does she dress as she does? Why does she sing for us? Why does she come here at all? "

" It is her life. It is what she is accustomed to. It is what she likes. She was brought up in the bars of Toulon and her childhood was pleasant. So she comes here to revive the memory. The types are similar, as similar as one can find in New York. Her clothes are no disguise. She is comfortable in them. She always wears them. They are what she is used to. What would you have? "

III

THE NIGHT was cold. It was after three and the streets were deserted. The cold steel-blue of the sky was sprinkled with stars. It was very still.

Peter Whiffle spoke the first word.

" What a wonderful thing to do," he was saying, as much to himself as to me, " to revert to type in this way, or rather to refuse to relinquish type, to cling to it, to live with it, to caress and love it. She sees no reason for making herself uncomfortable merely because she is rich, and she is right. You've heard of men who, after they made their pile, bought the old farm back for sentimental reasons, but they never went to live on it. Nobody has ever done this before."

" It's all very well for La Tigresse," I replied, as we continued to walk. " If you know what you want you can find it somewhere in New York. But how are you and I going to revert to type, supposing we want to? What is our type? How are we going to settle back in our middle life into the pleasures of our youth? They have been too many. They have been too various."

Peter turned this over. " I don't want to settle back and I don't believe you do either. If you do, you'll find a nice little wooden house, very much like the one you were born in, I should fancy, down Union Square way. It's dedicated just now to the uses of the Salvation Army war activities, but the doughnuts would probably do more to make you remember the old home than the building itself."

"It's too late to go there tonight," I announced, "and tomorrow . . . Well, I'll think it over."

"You bet you'll think it over!" retorted Peter.

February 17, 1919

Maurice Baring

HIGH-BROWS AND
LOW-BROWS

It has been my misfortune to have been considered a high-brow among low-brows and a low-brow among high-brows; and while such a position has many disadvantages it has one advantage: it enables one to discuss the relative merits of the two categories with a certain impartiality. Let us take the case of the high-brow first. And first of all let us define our terms.

The question has often been debated before. It is constantly being discussed, and you will notice that whenever it is mentioned by the intellectual the first thing he makes clear is that he, although he may be passionately interested in the things of the mind, is not a high-brow; other people are high-brows, not he himself.

If a high-brow means a scholar — but what do we mean by a scholar? Someone once defined a business-man as one who can read a balance sheet as easily as a musician can read the page of a full score, and a scholar as a man who could read Greek with his feet on the fender. If a high-brow means a scholar, or if a high-brow means a lower genus to which I claim to belong, people who are not and never will be scholars, who cannot read the classics comfortably without a crib, and who have read very few serious books and have not remembered what they have read, who have no sense of quantity, make false concords as easily as some people fall off a log, and are lax in grammar, but who, nevertheless, like reading books; if a high-brow means the first of these two categories, and to be pro-high-brow implies admiration for it, then I am on the side of the high-brows; and if it means belonging to the second category, then I am a high-brow myself: very high-brow of very high-brow.

At the same time there are bad high-brows as well as good high-brows; let us face the fact.

And even among high-brows, Class A, the scholars, there are some who are sometimes very severe on Class B, the non-scholars, who like reading: they treat these more severely than they treat the quite ignorant. I know this because I have suffered from them.

But let us first consider the case of the good high-brow: the real high-brow. I have known a great many. It is these people I mean to defend and to praise. I admire them immensely. I mean the people who read Greek for fun, and who can write Latin verse as easily as some people can guess crossword puzzles, who remember the history they have read and who can quote Thucydides and Lucretius, and can do a quadratic equation, and addition and subtraction in their head, and can count their change at a booking-office. When people say of such people "high-brows" and sniff, I am annoyed; and when the high-brows themselves are ashamed of their knowledge and of their culture, I am angry.

When people hide or deny their culture — and I mean deny it, not modestly conceal it — and laugh at the cultured when they are still more cultured themselves, I see red; because I regard this culture as the bulwark of our civilization, rapidly, alas! being undermined by the relentless tide of education, and our most precious heritage, which we are fast losing.

Things were very different in the eighteenth century. In the eighteenth century Dr. Johnson said that any man who wore a sword and a wig was ashamed of being illiterate, and that Greek was like lace: a man had as much of it as he could. Dr. Johnson was talking of ordinary men of the world; the men who went to clubs and drank three bottles of claret. They were small bottles, what we call pints. The same cannot be said of men who wear plus-fours or polo boots. If they have Latin and Greek they hide it, and if taxed with it they would probably deny it.

When people quote Latin in the House of Commons, the quotation is now greeted with cries of " Translate "; in the eighteenth century there would have been no need of translation, and those who did not know what the quotation meant would have concealed their ignorance decently. This is due to the spread of what is called Education. More people are taught things, but they are taught less. In fact, they are taught hardly anything; in former times they were taught little, but that little they learnt. It was beaten into them.

I am speaking of England.

In Scotland everything is different. The Scotch people are highly educated. You will notice I say Scotch, and not Scottish. If I were writing for one of the daily morning or evening newspapers the sub-editor would automatically cut out the word *Scotch* and substitute the word *Scottish*, and yet if you look out the word *Scottish* in the dictionary you will see that the word *Scottish* was originally used only technically for matters of law, or institutions, such as the Scottish Archers, but the ordinary English adjective, meaning native of Scotland, was Scotch, and the word Scotch was used by Shakspere, Dr. Johnson, Sir Walter Scott, and Stevenson,[1] and we still say: " I would like some Scotch whisky to drink," or " A Scotch and splash, miss," and we do not say: " A Scottish and splash, miss." This use of the word *Scottish* is a piece of pedantry first started by some dons, by the kind of high-brows who are going to be attacked later on in this lecture, and then popularized by the press when the standard style of writing Pitman's instead of Cranmer's English was adopted by the board schools.

They adopted many other things of the same kind. Pedants of this kind and their disciples in the press swoon when a split infinitive is used, and make a sentence perform acrobatic feats so as to avoid the use of one. But why in Heaven's name should one not

---

[1] See *Kidnapped*, Chapter xvii — " which we have no name for either in Scotch or English."

use the split infinitive if the emphasis of the sentence demands it? Why should you not say: " I wish to emphatically deny," if you want to emphatically deny, when to say: " I wish to deny emphatically " breaks the torrent of your wrath? Good writers can be quoted as using a split infinitive, and in Milton's lines:

> Alas! what boots it with incessant care
> To tend the homely slighted shepherd's trade
> And strictly meditate the thankless Muse?

strictly meditate is a moral split infinitive, because the word *to* is understood, and *meditate* is governed by *to*.[1]

Dr. Swift is said to have used a split infinitive, but I can't find it. As the poet says:

> What are you doing? As I live!
> You're splitting an infinitive!
> Go, get your little pot of glue,
> And mend the wretched creature, do!

All this is a digression suggested by the word *Scotch* or *Scottish*. And I was saying that the Scotch were well educated: their education has done them no harm in the practical affairs of life, and our best doctors, our best engineers, our best gardeners, and our best mechanics are Scotch.[2]

I remember a year or two after the Great War a firm in the north of England advertised for a young man who had taken honors in classics; they were tired of the products of the modern side.

All this may annoy my friend Mr. Wells. Mr. Wells thinks that not only the Latin and Greek languages, but Latin and Greek history and architecture ought to be eliminated; that they are so much antiquated ivy, choking and rotting the vital growths and strong shoots of the young idea; that the classical ideal is all wrong; what is wanted is modern stuff and modern art. I have nothing against modern art, but I want to know exactly what people mean when they talk of modern art. If they mean the products due to the fresh impressions and to the ardent vision of the young, I am with them;

---

[1] This statement is controversial.
[2] I know there is another side to this question.

but if they mean that modern art must have no roots in the past, and no connection with anything that has gone before, I think they are talking nonsense.

The laws of strategy, someone said in the war, are subject to the laws of common sense, and so are the laws of art.

When people make a thing, it is made with a special purpose and for special use, whether it is a house, a boat, a house-boat, a spoon, or a ship. A house is made to live in, a house-boat to catch cold in, a spoon to feed with, a ship to sail or to row in, a church to pray in, a theater to hear plays in; a railway station is a place for people to get into a train from or for people to get out of a train into. (My prepositions are at the end of my sentence; and I mean them to be.) Given that fact, these things are subject to certain laws. A spoon that is flat cannot hold foodstuffs; it may be beautiful as a work of art, but it is not a spoon. A ship which has masts on its keel and a spherical rudder at the end of the bowsprit may be interesting, but cannot be serviceable. A theater in which there is no room for the audience is not a theater, and so on. Now, the people who understand the laws of supply and demand with regard to concrete objects of use and who made these things for use, most economically and most practically, so that while they were as closely appropriate to their functions they were also as pleasing to the eye as possible — the people who accomplished this feat as well as possible were the Greeks; so that when we admire a modern work of art because it is appropriate and fulfills its object, we are admiring the spirit and the example of the Greeks, whether we know it or not. The Pennsylvania Railway Station, the Pierpont Morgan Library, and any skyscraper in New York are Greek in that they fulfill their purpose as economically and as beautifully as possible; and to admire American architecture and deny that Greek architecture is beautiful is a contradiction, a nonsense.

" But," someone will say, " I don't care a button for the Parthenon; but I do admire Epstein's Underground Station." The answer is that if Epstein's Underground Station fulfills its purpose as a station for underground trains, it fulfills one of the aims of Greek architecture; if the ornament on it strikes you as beautiful, it fulfills the other; that is all it aims at, for it is not trying to be useless or ugly. It is striving to be useful and beautiful: if it strikes some peo-

ple as ugly, that is either their fault for not being able to understand Epstein's meaning, or Epstein's fault for not making his
meaning clear or impressive; but the aim in both is the same.

In the case of a new work of art, the expression of a new-
fashioned way of looking at things (which may turn out to be an
old-fashioned but forgotten way), you need time before you can
tell whether the artist has had enough skill to make his meaning
plain to a sufficient number of people; if so, his work of art will
live . . . for a time, perhaps a long time, perhaps for centuries. Or
whether he has not; if so, it will be forgotten in a comparatively
short time.

Nobody writes masterpieces, said Anatole France, but some people write what may become masterpieces with the aid of Time,

> " *Qui est un galant homme.*"

Mozart aimed at writing tuneful music, and when his first works
were produced they were thought harsh. Wagner aimed at weaving
webs of beautiful sound, and for a long time these webs were
thought to be hideous, until they reached the great public, which
never had the slightest difficulty in detecting and enjoying the intricate conglomeration of his recurring snatches of tune.

Whistler's nocturnes were abused by Ruskin and hissed at
Christie's when they were put up for auction; but Whistler, as is
plain to small children now, was not trying to destroy the art of the
old masters; he was trying to do what they had done before him:
to depict nature as well as he could as he saw her.

So the theory that because modern art is good ancient art must
be destroyed is based on nothing at all. And when people, as I have
heard them do, in one breath praise masterpieces of Russian fiction
and deplore time spent on the classics, they are in one breath com-
mending and abusing works that have been produced according to
precisely the same standard, and which follow the same laws, and
which are good or bad for the same reasons.

I now perceive that I have not yet defined the good high-brow.
I will do so at once. I mean by the good high-brow the man who is
well educated and glad of the fact without thrusting it down other
people's throats, who, without being ashamed of his knowledge, his
intellectual or artistic superiority, or his gifts and aptitudes, does

not use them as a rod to beat others with, and does not think that
because he is the fortunate possessor of certain rare gifts or talents,
he is therefore a better or a more useful man: such is the good high-
brow. I have known many. The late Vice-Provost of Eton was a
good high-brow; the late Lord Balfour was a good high-brow; and
there are hosts of others who are dead, and there are some still alive.
My point is that the more of these there are, the better for the nation, the better for all of us. When there shall be no more of them,
it will mean the extinction of our civilization. My point is also that
to abuse these people, to despise them, to laugh at them, to be
ashamed of them, and, worse still, to be ashamed of being one of
them if you happen to be one of them, is to sin against Light, to
deny your birthright, and to be false to yourself and to everything
else.

It is an unforgivable sin, and the worst form of snobbishness;
that is to say, of cowardice.

Now we come to the bad high-brow, which no high-brow will
admit that he can be; but, as a Master of Trinity once said, we are
none of us infallible, not even the youngest of us. And the moment
we fall into the temptation of despising the interests and the recre-
ations of others, however futile they may seem to us, we become
bad high-brows.

The worst kind of high-brow is he who calls other people high-
brows. It is bad when high-brows despise people for going racing;
but it is worse when they despise them for not going racing, for
one suspects insincerity at once.

The worst faults of the bad high-brow are not (putting aside his
knowledge, learning, scholarship, or culture, which are not faults
at all, but the gifts of Heaven, if they are genuine, and the curse of
the devil if they are false) his pride, arrogance, and narrow-minded-
ness; but his envy of others who are either high-brows like himself
and possibly better ones, or, worse still, his envy of others who are
not high-brows at all, but people who are amusing themselves in
their own way. If you want to know what envy is, said Lord
Beaconsfield, you should live among artists; but were he alive now
he would have said you must live among high-brows. But the bad
high-brow is not a new thing: he is as old as the hills. Aristophanes
knew him and satirized him; Molière knew him, male and female,

and shot some of his most pointed arrows at the species, fixing them to remain forever before our delighted gaze.

In fact, the bad high-brow has had his full meed of satire and censure, and we may be sure that as long as satirists exist, and as long as he exists, he will always get it.

The bad low-brow gets his share too. Tony Lumpkin was essentially a low-brow, and so was Mr. G. P. Huntley's Algy, who was awfully good at algebra, and all the well-dressed swells satirized by different generations of comedy artists (musical or not), from Sothern's Lord Dundreary, and Nelly Farren, to the days of Vesta Tilley or Nelson Keys; by writers such as Mr. Anstey, Mr. Belloc, Mr. P. G. Wodehouse, and Mr. A. P. Herbert.

Mr. Wodehouse excels at drawing the contrast and the conflict between the high-brow and the low-brow, between the male low-brow and the female high-brow, and especially between the male English high-brow and the American female high-brow.

For in America most high-brows are female and most low-brows are male. In fact, they are just Brows. Of course when American high-brows are male, they excel all other Brows in the height of their brows, just as American skyscrapers are the highest in the world; that is because America is such a big country; and also because Americans generally export that kind.

I was once traveling from St. Petersburg to Moscow, and in the same carriage with me there happened to be two high-brows — a Russian student and a Japanese student. The Russian student was expansive and talkative, and the Japanese was civil but reserved. The Russian could not talk Japanese, and the Japanese could, besides Japanese, only talk English. When the Russian talked to the Japanese, the Japanese made a noise like a siphon; but the Russian, not contented with that, insisted on my interpreting his questions to the Japanese:

"Ask him if he knows English," said the Russian.

I did. The Japanese made a hissing noise. I thought that meant yes.

"Ask him," continued the Russian, "if he has read any English books."

The Japanese said he had read the English lyric, but not the English epic.

" Ask him if he has read the great English modern authors," said the Russian.

" Which? " I asked.

" Lord Byron, Oscar Wilde, Jerome K. Jerome, Mrs. Humphry Ward, Herbert Spencer, and Jack London," said the Russian, all in one breath.

I put the question. The Japanese smiled, and said he had read the English novel.

" Which one? " asked the Russian (through me).

" All of it," answered the Japanese (through me).

" All of which one? "

" All the English novel."

" Dickens? "

A negative hiss.

" Thackeray? "

Another negative hiss.

" George Eliot? "

A double hiss.

" George Meredith? "

A vacant look.

" Marie Corelli? "

A raised eyebrow.

" Conan Doyle? "

Silence, which implied definite disapproval.

" Thomas Hardy? "

Complete silence.

I began to give it up.

The Japanese then opened a bag and produced a book printed in Japanese.

He pointed to it and said:

" The English novel."

But as it was printed in Japanese and began at the end, we were not much wiser.

He then produced another book, and, pointing to it, said:

" The English lyric."

It seemed to be rather a long lyric.

We then gave it up, and the Russian explained to me what was worth reading in English literature. He said that the greatest Eng-

lish writer after Lord Byron was Oscar Wilde. That Jerome K.
Jerome's *Three Men in a Boat* was a very funny book, but that
Jerome K. Jerome's masterpiece was *Mark Clever*. (I had not read
it, to his immense surprise. I have read it since, and I do think it is
a very good book.) But the greatest English story-teller was Mrs.
Humphry Ward. Her greatest book was *Marcella*, but *Sir George
Tressady* was very good, too. There was no English drama. It was
a pity.

"Shakspere?" I said. And then I thought we might try the Japanese with Shakspere, but he only hissed.

"Shakspere," said the Russian, "never existed. There was no
such man."

"But his plays exist," I said.

"They are reactionary," said the Russian. "We are past all that.
We no longer understand it. They are no longer acted."

I begged his pardon, there was one of them being acted in Moscow at the present moment — *Julius Cæsar* — I had seen it.

"All that," said the Russian, "is nothing. Shakspere is nothing;
besides which he never existed."

"Have you ever read *Hamlet*?" I asked.

"*Gamlet*," he corrected me. Yes, he had read *Gamlet* at school.
"We read that at school," he explained, "and then we forget it;
it does not interest us — it is outside of our movement."

I asked what his movement was. He said that in politics he was
an amorphist, but that his movement was towards the left phase
of the middle right in literature, but towards the left phase of the
left in music, and towards the left phase of the right in painting.
He thought there should be no words in the drama: only gym-
nastics and facial expression. Then he corrected himself and said:

"No," with great vehemence. "No facial expression. Masks, like
the Greeks."

I asked him if he liked Greek plays. He said no, the Greeks were
antisocial, except the *Antigone* of Sophocles, which was good left.
I asked him whether he had heard of Bernard Shaw. At first he did
not understand. Then he said: "*Sheu?*" pronounced like the
French *le*. He understood. Yes, he had seen a play of his in St.
Petersburg. It is what they called left-center. Very old-fashioned.
The play was called *Mistress Ooaren*.

All this time the Japanese looked on and smiled and said nothing. Then we neared a station, and the Japanese took a French book from his bag and pointed to it, saying: "The French novel." It was called Le Roman russe, by the Count Melchior de Vogüé. Over and over again it has been my fortune to be told about English literature by foreign high-brows in trains, and to be initiated in the secrets of the literature of my country. I once met a Serbian professor who told me that he had written a book about Shakspere. He spoke French (not Shakspere — the Serb). Shakspere was a well-known case, he said, of self-hallucination. He knew, because he was a mind-doctor. Hamlet was a well-known case of a man who thinks he sees ghosts.

"But," I said, "the other people in the play saw the ghost."

"They caught his infection," he said.

"But they saw it first," I objected.

"It was Suggestion," he said; "it often happens. The infection comes from the brain of the man who thinks he sees a ghost before he has seen the ghost, and his coming hallucination infects other brains. Shakspere was hallucinated or he could not have described the case so accurately. All his characters are hallucinated — Macbeth, King Lear, Brutus (he saw a ghost)."

I said enough things had happened to King Lear to make him go mad.

"Not in that way," he said. "Ophelia is mad; Lady Macbeth is mad; Othello is mad; Shylock is mad; Timon of Athens is very mad; Antonio is mad; Romeo is mad. The cases are all accurately described by one who has the illness himself."

"Was Falstaff mad?" I asked.

"Falstaff," said the doctor, "is a case of what we call metaphenomania. He was a metaphenomaniac; he could not help altering facts and changing the facets of appearances."

"What we call a liar?" I suggested.

The doctor said that was an unscientific way of putting it, but it was true. Then he got out.

Of foreign high-brows, Germans are the most learned, but the most comfortable; perhaps because they drink beer. Russians are the most uncompromising, because their opinions upon matters of literature and art, music and games depend upon their politics.

The French are the most lucid, the English the most arrogant. There is a story about an English high-brow who was a great mathematician and philosopher when he grew up; but he was, to start with, a little boy, and, like other little boys, he went to school. The first night he went to bed in his dormitory he noticed that all the other boys knelt down to say their prayers; but he, having been brought up among the ruthless, thought that to say one's prayers was a piece of old-fashioned and pernicious superstition, and he went to bed without saying his prayers; and all the other boys threw boots at his head and called him a heathen and other rude names; but at the end of the term none of the boys said their prayers.

I now perceive that I have nearly finished this lecture, and I have not defined either the good or the bad low-brow, which I ought to have done at the very beginning. I will now do so at the end, because it is never too late to end.

A good low-brow is a man who, although he enjoys outdoor sports and games, and likes racing, gambling, eating, drinking, smoking, telling lies, the society and affection of the female beautiful, the female vivacious and the male vivacious and hospitable, the sporting newspapers, colored pictures, moving pictures, musical comedy, music-halls, frivolous conversation, new stories and old stories, does not want to shoot pianists, painters, writers, poets, men of science, philosophers, inventors, mathematicians, thinkers, and professional chess-players. He is just as nice to them as he is to the beautiful and to the vivacious and to book-makers. He lives and lets live, and he endures high-brows, if not gladly, with patience; whereas a bad low-brow is one who would like all books and plays to be potted and translated into American; who can only tell anecdotes that you have heard before, and which are unrefined without being witty, and repeat limericks that were made up long ago at the Shanghai Bar, and these he quotes wrongly, spoiling the rhythm.

It is a mistake to think that all high-brows belong to the learned professions; soldiers, sailors, and tinkers are often high-brows; poets and painters are often the lowest of low-brows.

All dons are high-brows. Some high-brows are sailors. Therefore some sailors are dons.

That I believe to be a good example of false logic.

Ernest Newman

THE ELASTIC LANGUAGE

I

Of all the wonders of all the arts, surely harmony in music is the most wonderful. It may be that some day each of the other arts will be brought to a standstill from the sheer impossibility of putting to new uses the material that in the course of many centuries will have been manipulated in every conceivable manner. Architecture and sculpture, perhaps, will be the first to give out: there must be some natural limit to the possible number of vital permutations and combinations of straight lines and curves, and it may not be too fantastic to believe that the circle of really new things to be said in these two arts is steadily shrinking from generation to generation. Of painting I will not venture to speak; but in poetry and prose there is even now an unmistakable impatience on the part of criticism with everything that does not justify its existence by being something quite different from everything of its kind that has appeared before; and there must surely be a limit to the number of changes that can be rung upon words, upon the ten or a dozen elemental emotions that are the substance of all artistic thinking, and upon the few standard patterns upon which all plots are constructed. But to musical novelty no man can see an end, because the language of music is not a fixed but a fluid one. I am aware that John Stuart Mill used to be haunted in his youth by the idea that music before long would reach the limit of its resources, because there are only thirteen notes in the octave, and thirteen units are capable of only a certain number of permutations and combinations. But he forgot, in the first place, that what may be called the extensive material of music — the mere number of units spread out, as it were, on a table — is not thirteen notes only, but as many multiples of thirteen as there are octaves in our instruments or our orchestras. That fact of itself enormously increases the mathematical possibilities of the scale. The intensive resources of music also are seemingly illimitable. They are of two orders. Not only do the many timbres of our instruments permit of an infinite rearrangement of colors, but we are just beginning to realize that color in music has, in addition to its aural quality, a quasi-spatial quality. That is to say, we are now learning to use color not exclusively on the flat, as in the older music, but in depths of foreground and background. A combination of tones on the pianoforte, for instance, that sounds hideously discordant when all the notes are played with equal force, may take on a curious beauty when some of the upper notes, let us say, are played *pianissimo* against a *forte* in the left hand. Debussy in his later work has made some very interesting experiments in this " spacing " of piano color. The problem is one not merely of the different timbres of the various registers of the piano, but of the overtones in the harmonies. Since each note sounded is not merely the note we call C or G or A, but is accompanied by all the harmonics of itself, while each of these harmonics in turn generates harmonics of its own, it is evident that every chord is accompanied by an almost infinite number of satellite tones, ranging from the bass of the chord to the top of the piano scale. At present our theory in these things is stronger than our practice. We know that all these satellite tones are there, but in actual hearing we can distinguish only one or two of them, and that only by a conscious effort of the ear and brain. But there can be little doubt that our hearing for overtones will become more acute in the course of time; and when it is fairly well developed, a whole new field of harmonic effect will be opened to composers. Tenuous high notes can be used to reinforce subtly the main harmonics of the basic harmony, or, by stressing some of the harmonics that are, as we say, slightly out of tune, we can give fascinating piquancy to the flavor of the chord. It was along this line that Debussy experimented. It is clear that it will open up to music a field of harmonic resource as vast as that opened up for the art by Monteverdi and the others who first began to use unprepared discords as a positive, instead of a negative, element in the harmonic palette.

But my concern today is not with these developments of the future, but with the other intensive resource of music with which history has made us familiar — harmony as a language that, instead of remaining fixed, as a spoken language becomes after a certain time, is infinitely elastic both in its vocabulary and in the combinations of that vocabulary. We shall best appreciate this advantage of music, perhaps, by seeing how greatly the expressive resources of the spoken language would be increased could words undergo that rearrangement of their letters that the notes of a chord can undergo. Everyone will remember the delicious mistake of the typist (or compositor) who a few weeks ago made Mr. J. C. Squire speak of Mr. Hotario Bottomley. That is the verbal equivalent of a change in the distribution of the notes in a chord; the thing is not the same, and yet it is the same. Now if we could consistently manipulate the letters of words in this way, rearranging them, adding or omitting one or two, we could create new words that would abbreviate and concentrate expression by combining two images in the one symbol. At present we only discover these possible rearrangements by the mistakes of compositors and others. A typist of mine once wrote " platitune " for " platitude." Here, I think, is a word that might well be incorporated into the language. A platitune would be a platitudinous melody. Two concepts would be simultaneously expressed by the one symbol. Let us take another case. The other day, passing a surgery, I noticed that owing to the

lapse of the initial letter the place was described as an " urgery."
It struck me that here again is a word that our language would be
all the richer for. When the policeman brought a Saturday night
accident case into the hospital, the surgeon could say: "Take him
to the urgery," thus conveying, in the minimum of words, the
double fact that it was a matter for surgery and that the case was
urgent. A little while ago one of the correspondents at the front,
who had intended to speak of our men as having overcome a weakened German resistance, was made to say that they overcame a
" weakneed " German resistance. If the word *weak-kneed* had not
already been in existence, here would have been a chance to adopt
it: yet our purists, who would raise no objection to increasing the
resources of the language by hyphenating *weak* and *kneed* into a
double-barrelled word, would protest against such a telescoping of
the two as we get in *weakneed*, that, from its mere spelling, lets
us know that the German resistance was not merely weak, but
weaker than it once was — again a duality of concept expressed in
a single term.

If words, instead of being the inelastic things they are at present,
were as elastic as the constituent elements of musical harmony, we
should not only be able to endow the same letters with many new
meanings; often the new word would set us upon the track of a new
truth. Let us suppose that a musician is improvising at the piano,
or even playing a piece already written. In the last chord he strikes
a wrong note. What does he do, if he is a man of resource? Instead
of rising from the piano stool in confusion, or making matters worse
by hastily playing the right chord after the wrong one, thus adver-
tising his error, he calmly accepts the wrong chord as the starting-
point for a new train of thought, and improvises until it suits him
to revert to the original idea. It is on record that Liszt or someone
actually did this at a recital, and, of course, only those who knew
thoroughly the work he was playing were aware that anything had
gone wrong. And in the process of composing on paper, something
in a man's brain will make him unconsciously put down a combination that was not the one he had been consciously working up to,
but that sets him off on a train of thought that opens out new possibilities for his original idea. Let me now give what I take to be
an equivalent of this process in the language of words. When the

war broke out, I wrote an article in the *Musical Times* in which I pointed out that a great war was always a liberator of a new nervous energy, the chances being that the energy would have a touch of disease in it. I instanced the early French Romantics, many of whom attributed their own excessively excitable nervous systems to the fact that they were born during the convulsions of the Napoleonic wars. "What else can you expect of us," said Alfred de Musset, "conceived as we were between two battles?" This came out in my proof, "conceived as we were between two bottles." This was a new light on the subject for me; and I thought the emendation so much nearer the probable truth than the original that I asked the editor of the *Musical Times* to let the error stand. Dr. McNaught was compelled to decline, on the ground that they had some clergymen among their subscribers. Now if words were harmonies, and literature what music is, this printer's error would have been not an error but a discovery. From it a whole new thesis could have been developed, as Liszt developed a new piece of music out of a wrong note struck accidentally.

II

IT is because harmony is not only a language but the most elastic of languages that it cannot be taught. What passes for harmony-teaching in schools and textbooks is not harmony-teaching at all, but the teaching of harmonic analysis. The tradition is kept up that there is a grammar of harmony that students can and must learn; but that tradition survives only because teachers can use it to their own profit. Harmony-teaching is not an art but an industry, and a highly profitable industry to the professors, the schools, and the writers of textbooks. They tell the students that it is essential they should learn, while they are young, the grammar of harmony. But there is no grammar of harmony. Grammar is only a set of rules by which all the members of a community speaking a common language agree, for convenience' sake, to be bound. It may be said that the main rules of grammar are necessarily the same in all languages — that the agreement of the noun with its verb, for instance, is not an artificial but a natural relation, a basic necessity for intelligible expression because it is a basic necessity of coherent thinking. But the different languages show different rules for the agreement of noun and verb: in Greek, plural neuter nouns take a singular verb; in Russian, the genitive is used instead of the accusative after a negation; and so on. Any grammatical rule whatever, however irrational it may seem, will work perfectly well so long as everyone agrees to abide by it. But there are no such " rules " in harmony, and no " grammar " in the sense that this word carries in connection with language. The textbooks tell the guileless student that this or that is " correct " or " incorrect," " good " or " bad "; but the truth is that anything is correct and good that sounds so. There is perhaps not an example in the textbooks of what the student is warned to avoid as " bad " that could not be shown to be a constituent of some admired effect in someone or other's music. The excellent Ebenezer Prout, in one of those learned treatises of his that have saddened the lives of three or four generations of students, after having cudgelled his brain to think of something really horrible against which to warn the budding composer, evolved the following:

which he marks " very bad," the reason being that it leaps and leaps in the same direction beyond the limit of an octave. Apparently he did not know, or if he knew had forgotten, that one of Brahms's most beautiful songs opens with this very sequence of notes:

Wie Me-lo - di - en   zieht es mir lei - se durch den Sinn.

There is, I repeat, no body of accepted practice that can be taught as the " grammar " of harmony. All that the textbooks are useful for is to teach harmonic analysis. Just as the textbook of prosody tells the student what spondees and dactyls are, and teaches him to recognize a hexameter or an iambic pentameter when he sees one, so the harmony books can tell him that a certain combination of notes is the second inversion of the chord of the dominant seventh;

but just as no amount of knowledge of prosody will help anyone in the slightest degree to think poetically unless he is a born poet, so no amount of knowledge of textbook harmony will teach anyone who is not a born harmonist to think harmonically; and just as a poet could weave the subtlest rhythmical patterns without ever having even heard of the terms *dactyl* or *spondee*, so a born musician can write abstruse harmony without being able to name a number of the chords that he uses instinctively.

If the writing of harmony, indeed, had been dependent upon the theory of harmony, we should have very little music today, for the plain truth is that there is *no* theory of harmony. There is any number of theories of harmony, but there is not a single theory, as Dr. Shirlaw shows in the remarkably sound and learned volume that he has recently published,[1] that has won, or is likely to win, general acceptance. Dr. Shirlaw, who has an incomparable knowledge of his subject, passes in review the chief theoretical treatises on harmony that have appeared in Europe since the sixteenth century. I cordially and maliciously commend the book to the attention of all teachers and students — particularly to the former, who, by the time they have reached its 484th page, will, if they are honest with themselves, have grave doubts as to the truth of many of the things they have been telling their pupils with the air of a revelation from heaven. If the use of harmony as a language had been in any way dependent on a knowledge on the composers' part of the nature of the material they were manipulating, music could never have been written. Attempts have been made to deduce our scales and harmonies from the harmonic series thrown off by a vibrating string or a sounding pipe; but at some point or other — the justification of the minor harmony, for example — each demonstrator has either become hopelessly entangled in contradictions or has had to call in metaphysics to fill the gap that acoustics could not bridge. Theory has always failed utterly to explain the practice of its own day. The seventeenth- and eighteenth-century composers who were also theorists were constantly using chords rightly and accounting

[1] *The Theory of Harmony: An Enquiry into the Natural Principles of Harmony, with an Examination of the Chief Systems of Harmony from Rameau to the Present Day;* by Matthew Shirlaw, Mus.D., F.R.C.O. Novello & Co.

for them wrongly. Thinking, as they had been taught to do by the theorists of the past, in terms of intervals rather than of chords, they tied themselves into the most ludicrous knots of analysis because they could not perceive that this or that chord was simply the inversion of another. In our own day we have seen a leading theorist — the late Ebenezer Prout — issue a textbook of harmony based on a certain acoustical theory (which textbook was largely used in schools), and then, in a new edition of the work, throw over the former theory and formulate a new one, which, however, as Dr. Shirlaw shows, is no more consistent, no more capable of explaining the facts, than the old one was; and the new textbook, faulty as it is, in turn becomes gospel to thousands of innocent teachers and students.

A popular theory is that harmony has been evolved from melody. It could be argued with equal, perhaps superior, force that melody has been evolved from unconscious harmony: that is to say, man did not first invent a scale and then discover how to make harmonies from it, but a subconscious feeling for harmony — a feeling it may have taken thousands of years to develop — guided him in the construction of the scale. Nothing in the whole history of the subject is more remarkable than the way in which the unconscious instincts of men have guided them to the truth of harmony where the reasoning of the theorists would have led them away from it. The folk-singer who was irresistibly attracted to the third of the scale, by reason of its peculiarly satisfactory relation to the tonic, at a time when theorists were maundering about the abstract virtues of the fourth and fifth, had not the slightest inkling that he was acoustically justified in his preference (the third being sounded as the first harmonic after the octave and the fifth in every tone that man or instrument can make); he merely obeyed an instinct. It may almost be said that he was not so much using harmony as harmony was using him. So has it always been. The interval of the tritone (the augmented fourth), against which the mediæval theorists fulminated as the theologians did against the devil, came gradually and unconsciously to be recognized (as the essence of the flavor of the chord of the dominant seventh) as one of the seminal factors in modern harmony.

III

HARMONY as a language owes its wonderful elasticity to the fact that it is a natural language — the only truly natural language that man has ever spoken. All other languages are arbitrary: there is not the slightest reason in nature why we should call a dog a dog, or a cat a cat, or why nouns should be declined and verbs conjugated in the way they are. But harmony is not an invented or a manufactured language, but a natural language. It is not so much we who speak it as nature that speaks it through us. It is the universal thing it is, conveying the same concepts, embodying the same logic, to all the nations that after a long process of evolution have learned how to limit and simplify their melodic scales, because nature herself has given us, in the overtones and undertones of each musical sound, at any rate the basic material of our music — a material that is necessarily the same wherever there are sounds and ears to hear them.

Man, that is to say, is by nature a harmonic animal just as he is by nature an ambulatory or an ethical animal. All the grace and ease and variety of his present bodily movements, all the subtleties and nobilities of his present ethical sense, are only the coming into visible being of certain potentialities that were in him from the first. Harmony has no more developed at haphazard than a tree has. Its actual historic evolution, indeed, has been precisely like that of a tree: from some two or three chords that were and are the trunk of music there have grown, step by step, all the chords in use today; and chords that at one time seemed to be twigs thrown off from a branch have in the course of generations become in their turn substantial branches, from which have sprung still smaller branches, from which again have come seemingly isolated and final twigs that in turn, we may be sure, will become parent stems of still other twigs. It is a pity that someone does not write a real history of harmony. Dr. Charles Macpherson has just attempted something of the kind in an excellent little volume published by Messrs. Kegan Paul & Co.;[1] but the subject deserves a much more extended treatment. It would be interesting to have the pedigrees of all the most

[1] *A Short History of Harmony*. The Music-Lover's Library.

complicated chords of today traced back through one ancestor after
another to their first parent, and the passage in this or that composer's work signalized in which it makes its first significant appearance. A genealogical tree of this kind would not only have its historical value. It would also show how supremely natural a language
harmony is, and how it owes the universality of its meaning to the
fact that through all the ages, in man qua man, sound qua sound
has been incessantly striving to realize in detail its own primal
dynamic force, as a tree strives to realize in trunk and branch and
twig and leaf the primal dynamic force concentrated in its seed.

  I referred before to the fallacy that will be found in so many
treatises on music — that man began by making scales, and having
written for a long time melodies in these scales, found that certain
notes were agreeable when sounded together, and so was led by
slow stages to the discovery of harmony. It is only historically and
externally that melody precedes harmony; psychologically, it is
hardly too much to say, harmony has from the first — even before
harmony was written — been man's guide in the making of his
scales and his melodies. Harmony, it would seem, has always been
working subconsciously in him; and the history of harmony is the
history of the subconscious emerging further and further into consciousness. Without the scale we now use, harmony of any extended
range and complexity would have been impossible; and we can
hardly doubt that the process described in the histories, by which
the Greek and the mediæval scales have insensibly settled into the
modern scale, was at bottom the effort of man's subconscious harmonic sense to find an outlet — much in the same way that a tuber,
in a dark room, unconsciously throws out feelers towards the chink
through which comes a ray of light. The mediæval musicians, in
their constant manipulations of the ecclesiastical scales so as to
get a semitone before the final of the mode, and so on, were unconsciously obeying an obscure harmonic " pull " within them towards the perfect cadence, and towards the dominant-tonic relationship that is the basis of modern tonality and of modern music.
It is a fact of unshakable significance that the basic elements of our
music — the three or four trunks, as it were, from which the forest
has grown — are given us in the relations of the first few overtones

of the harmonic series. Long before science had an inkling of that fact, the musical sense in man was unconsciously making use of it; and for a long period the great masters of vocal polyphony wove their beautiful tissues out of the simple chord-groups suggested by these elementary relationships. Even today, with our harmony the bold, free thing that it is, there is no escape, so far as we can see, from the original bonds that nature has laid upon us. The importance of the fifth and the fourth in our modern tonality is apparently the inevitable outcome of the importance of the fifth and the fourth in the harmonic series; and one of the reasons why the "whole-tone" scale is at present so intractable to the larger uses is the absence from it of these essential pivotal points upon which the harmony can swing and return without losing itself.

As Dr. Macpherson shows, the bulk of our serviceable modern harmony has been evolved from simpler and still simpler elements by three main processes — (1) the *contraction* of the steps by which the seminal chords normally follow each other, (2) an *expansion* of these steps, (3) *chromatic distortion*, for which, perhaps, "chromatic sophistication" would be a better term, for it implies simply the subtilization of plain chords by chromatic alteration, the altered forms becoming in their turn diatonic elements in other and, at first sight, unrelated keys. In Dr. Macpherson's little book will be found a demonstration of the historical processes by which some of our seemingly complex modern harmonies have thus been evolved from simple germs. And in this evolution we seem to see the same unconscious forces at work as in the organic world. Rich as she is in varieties, nature is chiefly interested in the type. Oddities appear and disappear, being infertile. The record of harmonic evolution is strewn with innovations that came to nothing because they were too far removed from the main line of life of the time to be successfully grafted upon it. What I have ventured to call by the name of "serviceable harmony" — harmony, that is to say, that is sufficiently malleable and flexible for contemporary musical thought to do whatever it likes with it — has always come about by gradual and logical development from pre-existing harmony, not by a sudden leap from it. In our own day we have seen the limitations of freak harmony demonstrated by Debussy and Scriabine; their systems, admirable as they are for special purposes, are not generally serviceable for all that a modern composer of comprehensive genius has to say; and for the full utilization of them we shall have to wait until the really vital parts of them have been absorbed into the general body of harmony, and become a natural, unconscious language for all musicians. The process of evolution by which new relationships are always being established between the basic elements of harmony is most aptly illustrated in Wagner, and, in a smaller degree, in Strauss. The harmonies of *Tristan* are for the most part nothing more than natural and inevitable sophistications of the simpler harmonies of earlier music. That is why, in spite of their novelty, any ordinarily musical person could follow them without difficulty; and it is because Wagner derives all his twigs and leaves from a basic trunk or two that there is not a single harmony in the whole of his music that has not justified itself and become part of the current musical tongue of the world. Strauss sometimes wastes himself in experiments that are doomed to infertility; but he also has expanded the harmonic idiom in just the way that Wagner did: the best of his novel harmonies " argue out " logically because they are only sophistications of simpler combinations. And the sign of the great man is that, as with Wagner and Strauss, he is the master of his own harmony, instead of being the servant of it, as Debussy and Scriabine often are. The harmonic innovations in *Tristan* were not spirits that Wagner had raised but could not lay again. His thought moves freely and naturally among them; they came into being ready clothed with the new melodic and rhythmic figuration that was most appropriate to them, whereas Debussy had to give up in despair the problem of fusing his new harmony into an indivisible whole with his melody and his rhythm — especially the latter. These experimentalists do invaluable service in suggesting possible fields of new harmonic subtlety which it will be the business of more broadly based composers to cultivate; but the great stream of real progress — if I may alter the, metaphor — will always flow along the main bed that time has channeled so deep. If any of us lives another fifty years, it will be interesting to see the result when a new harmonic sophistication gives us something as much subtler than *Tristan* as *Tristan* is subtler than *Figaro*. It may be that in time, as some hold, the limits of the possibilities of our present scale will be reached, and composers will have to resort to quarter-tones; but judging from the past, it will be many generations yet before the last change has been rung upon the thirteen notes of the scale from which all the music we know has grown.

H. L. Mencken

MEMORANDUM

I<small>T</small> must have been in 1913 or thereabout that I first met him — a very tall, very slim young fellow, but lately out of college, with a faint and somewhat puzzling air of the exotic about him. I recall especially his mustache: so immensely black that it seemed beyond the poor talents of nature, and yet so slender, so struggling that it was palpably real. How he got into my office in Baltimore I don't remember: I was fat in those days, and lazy and very busy, and I did not see any visitors that I could avoid. No doubt he fetched me by raising the name of Joseph Conrad. He was, it appeared, in communication with Conrad; he had a Conrad letter in his pocket. Astounding and interesting! He unfolded a scheme to gather all the Conrad books together — they were printed, as I recall it, by eleven different publishers — and reissue them decently in one series. We were, of course, on good terms at once. It is a curious fact that we are on good terms still, despite innumerable transactions between us, steadily increasing in complexity and many of them involving money. I can recall no other New Yorker with whom I have communed peacefully so long.

That was before he set up shop on his own account. He worked for Doubleday, Page & Company, his backers in the Conrad enterprise, and a bit later for Mitchell Kennerley. I saw him two or three times a year, as he reached Baltimore on his rounds. A highly serious young man. He had a great many ideas, and was surely not backward about exposing them. One and all, they related to the single subject: the making of books. He believed that taste was improving in America: that good books would find a larger public year after year. He believed that Americans were beginning to notice books as works of art: the way they were printed, the paper in them, the binding, even the dust covers. He carried around specimens of somewhat startling novelties in that line, chiefly out of Leipzig and Munich. He outlined projects for duplicating them, improving on them, going far ahead of them. It appeared quickly that a young man with so many notions would not long survive as a hireling. One day he told me that he planned to set up shop for himself. I dare say my eyebrows lifted: it was surely not a propitious time for ventures involving the intellect. The World War was less than a year old; doubts and fears consumed the Republic; people were reading newspapers, not books. He cheerfully threw in additional difficulties. He had, it appeared, no money, or very little. He hadn't even an office: a small space in his father's quarters would be enough. Worst of all, he had a girl, and would have a wife come Whitsun.

So the ship put out in October 1915, with a jury mast, sails out of the rag-bag, and a crew of one boy and one girl. The girl, in fact, was not yet aboard; she was shipped early the following spring. For a number of months I heard nothing from the skipper. He was hard at work, vastly at work, almost desperately at work. Then I caught a glimpse of the ship. It had two masts now, and new sails, and a new and challenging ensign under the main-truck: on a field of white a spectral dog, leaping into space. This dog, I learned, was a borzoi; I know no more about it to this day. The ship now began to appear off my coast more frequently. It sprouted a third mast, and then a fourth. Sailors began to show on the deck, apparently well

filled with proteins and carbohydrates. A smoke-stack arose, and
belched smoke. Deck grew upon deck. I began to hear a band, and
the shuffle of dancing in the evening. There were stewards, officers
in blue and brass, a purser, a boots. A bar opened. In an imperial
suite lolled the sybarite, Joe Hergesheimer. In 1917 I engaged passage myself, taking a modest room on D deck. It seemed only polite
to pay my respects to the skipper. I found him immersed in books
up to his neck — big books and little books, books sober and staid
and books of an almost voluptuous gaudiness, books of all ages and
in all languages, books in the full flush of beauty, ready for the customer, and books stripped down to their very anatomical elements.
And all the talk I heard, to the end of that first voyage, was of books,
books, books.

It was five or six years, perhaps, before I ever heard him mention
any other subject. No, that is too sweeping. Once — it must have
been toward the end of 1915 — he told me about the bride-elect:
her willingness to make the voyage in that first crazy bark, her interest in books — nay, in type, paper, ink. Presently I had a view of
her: she seemed too young and too charming for it to be true. But
I believed it later when I found her on deck, magnificently navigat-
ing the craft while the skipper took to the land and visited the trade
in Buffalo, Detroit, and St. Paul. He went off talking books, and he
came back talking books. Always books. One day, quite by accident,
I discovered that he was also interested in music. We launched into
Brahms instantly — but in ten minutes we were back to books. I
tried Beethoven; he lasted longer. Bach; longer still. But even old
Johann Sebastian, in the end, yielded to books.

That was in the days of hard struggle. Of late, with the waters
calm, the decks crowded with passengers, and the holds full of —
books! — I have noticed a growing expansiveness. There is more
time to listen to the band, even to grab a clarinet and essay a few
toots. One night, lately, we put in a solid hour belaboring Richard
Strauss; not a type clicked, not a rose fluttered upon William Heinemann's grave. There have been conferences, too, on the subject of
Moselle, its snares and mysteries, and on the hotels of London,
Paris, and Berlin, and on dogs, and even on the Coolidge statecraft.
If I were younger and less bilious in my prejudices, there would
be discourse, I suspect, on golf: I have seen the grotesque clubs of

the game in a corner. There is a son to think of. There is a large and complicated organization, ever growing, ever presenting problems. There is the *American Mercury*. It has changed both of us, if only by enormously multiplying our contacts, East, West, North, South. But to Alfred, I believe, it is still visible primarily as a book. Into it have gone all the ideas that buzzed in his head back in 1915. It is a sort of service stripe for him, marking off his first ten years as a publisher.

THE HILLS OF ZION

I⊤ was hot weather when they tried the infidel Scopes at Dayton, but I went down there very willingly, for I had good reports of the sub-Potomac bootleggers, and moreover I was eager to see something of evangelical Christianity as a going concern. In the big cities of the Republic, despite the endless efforts of consecrated men, it is laid up with a wasting disease. The very Sunday-school superintendents, taking jazz from the stealthy radio, shake their fireproof legs; their pupils, moving into adolescence, no longer respond to the proliferating hormones by enlisting for missionary service in Africa, but resort to necking and petting instead. I know of no evangelical church from Oregon to Maine that is not short of money: the graft begins to peter out, like wire-tapping and three-card monte before it. Even in Dayton, though the mob was up to do execution upon Scopes, there was a strong smell of antinomianism. The nine churches of the village were all half empty on Sunday, and weeds choked their yards. Only two or three of the resident pastors managed to sustain themselves by their ghostly science; the rest had to take orders for mail-order pantaloons or work in the adjacent strawberry fields; one, I heard, was a barber. On the courthouse green a score of sweating theologians debated the darker passages of Holy Writ day and night, but I soon found that they were all volunteers, and that the local faithful, while interested in their exegesis as an intellectual exercise, did not permit it to impede the indigenous debaucheries. Exactly twelve minutes after I reached the village I was taken in tow by a Christian man and introduced to the favorite tipple of the Cumberland Range: half corn liquor and half coca-cola. It seemed a dreadful dose to me, spoiled as I was by the bootleg light wines and beers of the Eastern seaboard, but I found that the Dayton illuminati got it down with gusto, rubbing their tummies and rolling their eyes. I include among them the chief local proponents of the Mosaic cosmogony. They were all hot for Genesis, but their faces were far too florid to belong to teetotalers, and when a pretty girl came tripping down the main street, which was very often, they reached for the places where their neckties should have been with all the amorous enterprise of movie actors. It seemed somehow strange.

An amiable newspaper woman of Chattanooga, familiar with those uplands, presently enlightened me. Dayton, she explained, was simply a great capital like any other great capital. That is to say, it was to Rhea County what Atlanta was to Georgia or Paris to France. That is to say, it was predominantly epicurean and sinful. A country girl from some remote valley of the county, coming into town for her semi-annual bottle of Lydia Pinkham's Vegetable Compound, shivered on approaching Robinson's drug-store quite as a country girl from up-state New York might shiver on approaching the Metropolitan Opera House or the Ritz Hotel. In every village lout she saw a potential white-slaver. The hard sidewalks hurt her feet. Temptations of the flesh bristled to all sides of her, luring her to hell. This newspaper woman told me of a session with just such a visitor, holden a few days before. The latter waited outside one of the town hot-dog and coca-cola shops while her husband negotiated with a hardware merchant across the street. The newspaper woman, idling along and observing that the stranger was badly used by the heat, invited her to step into the shop for a glass of coca-cola. The invitation brought forth only a gurgle of terror. Coca-cola, it quickly appeared, was prohibited by the country lady's pastor, as a levantine and hell-sent narcotic. He also prohibited coffee and tea — and pies! He had his doubts about white bread and boughten meat. The newspaper woman, interested, inquired about ice-cream. It was, she found, not specifically prohibited, but going into a coca-cola shop to get it would be clearly sinful. So she offered to get a saucer of it and bring it out to the sidewalk. The visitor vacillated — and came near being lost. But God saved her in the nick of time. When the newspaper woman emerged from the place she was in full flight up the street! Later on, her husband, mounted on a mule, overtook her four miles out the mountain pike.

This newspaper woman, whose kindness covered city infidels as well as Alpine Christians, offered to take me back in the hills to a place where the old-time religion was genuinely on tap. The Scopes jury, she explained, was composed mainly of its customers, with a few Dayton sophisticates added to leaven the mass. It would thus be instructive to climb the heights and observe the former at their ceremonies. The trip, fortunately, might be made by automobile. There was a road running out of Dayton to Morgantown, in the mountains to the westward, and thence beyond. But foreigners, it appeared, would have to approach the sacred grove cautiously, for the upland worshippers were very shy, and at the first sight of a strange face they would adjourn their orgy and slink into the forest. They were not to be feared, for God had long since forbidden them to practice assassination, or even assault, but if they were alarmed a rough trip would go for naught. So, after dreadful bumpings up a long and narrow road, we parked our car in a little wood-path a mile or two beyond the tiny village of Morgantown and made the rest of the approach on foot, deployed like skirmishers. Far off in a dark, romantic glade a flickering light was visible, and out of the silence came the rumble of exhortation. We could distinguish the figure of the preacher only as a moving mote in the light: it was like looking down the tube of a dark-field microscope. Slowly and cautiously we crossed what seemed to be a pasture, and then we crouched down along the edge of a cornfield and stealthily edged further and further. The light now grew larger and we could begin to make out what was going on. We went ahead on all fours, like snakes in the grass.

From the great limb of a mighty oak hung a couple of crude torches of the sort that car inspectors thrust under Pullman cars when a train pulls in at night. In the guttering glare was the preacher, and for a while we could see no one else. He was an immensely tall and thin mountaineer in blue jeans, his collarless shirt open at the neck and his hair a tousled mop. As he preached he paced up and down under the smoking flambeaux, and at each turn he thrust his arms into the air and yelled: " Glory to God! " We

crept nearer in the shadow of the cornfield and began to hear more
of his discourse. He was preaching on the Day of Judgment. The
high kings of the earth, he roared, would all fall down and die; only
the sanctified would stand up to receive the Lord God of Hosts. One
of these kings he mentioned by name, the King of what he called
Greece-y. The King of Greece-y, he said, was doomed to hell. We
crawled forward a few more yards and began to see the audience.
It was seated on benches ranged round the preacher in a circle.
Behind him sat a row of elders, men and women. In front were the
younger folk. We crept on cautiously, and individuals rose out of
the ghostly gloom. A young mother sat suckling her baby, rocking
as the preacher paced up and down. Two scared little girls hugged
each other, their pigtails down their backs. An immensely huge
mountain woman, in a gingham dress, cut in one piece, rolled on
her heels at every " Glory to God! " To one side, and but half
visible, was what appeared to be a bed. We found afterwards that
half a dozen babies were asleep upon it.

The preacher stopped at last, and there arose out of the darkness
a woman with her hair pulled back into a little tight knot. She began
so quietly that we couldn't hear what she said, but soon her voice
rose resonantly and we could follow her. She was denouncing the
reading of books. Some wandering book-agent, it appeared, had
come to her cabin and tried to sell her a specimen of his wares. She
refused to touch it. Why, indeed, read a book? If what was in it
was true, then everything in it was already in the Bible. If it was
false, then reading it would imperil the soul. This syllogism from
Caliph Omar complete, she sat down. There followed a hymn, led
by a somewhat fat brother wearing silver-rimmed country spectacles.
It droned on for half a dozen stanzas, and then the first speaker resumed the floor. He argued that the gift of tongues was real and
that education was a snare. Once his children could read the Bible,
he said, they had enough. Beyond lay only infidelity and damnation. Sin stalked the cities. Dayton itself was a Sodom. Even Morgantown had begun to forget God. He sat down, and a female
aurochs in gingham got up. She began quietly, but was soon leaping
and roaring, and it was hard to follow her. Under cover of the turmoil we sneaked a bit closer.

A couple of other discourses followed, and there were two or three hymns. Suddenly a change of mood began to make itself felt. The last hymn ran longer than the others, and dropped gradually into a monotonous, unintelligible chant. The leader beat time with his book. The faithful broke out with exultations. When the singing ended there was a brief palaver that we could not hear, and two of the men moved a bench into the circle of light directly under the flambeaux. Then a half-grown girl emerged from the darkness and threw herself upon it. We noticed with astonishment that she had bobbed hair. " This sister," said the leader, " has asked for prayers." We moved a bit closer. We could now see faces plainly, and hear every word. What followed quickly reached such heights of barbaric grotesquerie that it was hard to believe it real. At a signal all the faithful crowded up to the bench and began to pray — not in unison, but each for himself! At another they all fell on their knees, their arms over the penitent. The leader kneeled facing us, his head alternately thrown back dramatically or buried in his hands. Words spouted from his lips like bullets from a machine-gun — appeals to God to pull the penitent back out of hell, defiances of the demons of the air, a vast impassioned jargon of apocalyptic texts. Suddenly he rose to his feet, threw back his head and began to speak in the tongues — blub-blub-blub, gurgle-gurgle-gurgle. His voice rose to a higher register. The climax was a shrill, inarticulate squawk, like that of a man throttled. He fell headlong across the pyramid of suppliants.

A comic scene? Somehow, no. The poor half-wits were too horribly in earnest. It was like peeping through a knothole at the writhings of people in pain. From the squirming and jabbering mass a young woman gradually detached herself — a woman not uncomely, with a pathetic home-made cap on her head. Her head jerked back, the veins of her neck swelled, and her fists went to her throat as if she were fighting for breath. She bent backward until she was like half a hoop. Then she suddenly snapped forward. We caught a flash of the whites of her eyes. Presently her whole body began to be convulsed — great throes that began at the shoulders and ended at the hips. She would leap to her feet, thrust her arms in air, and then hurl herself upon the heap. Her praying flattened out into a mere delirious caterwauling, like that of a tomcat on a petting party. I describe the thing discreetly, and as a strict behav-

iorist. The lady's subjective sensations I leave to infidel patholo-
gists, privy to the works of Ellis, Freud, and Moll. Whatever they
were, they were obviously not painful, for they were accompanied
by vast heavings and gurglings of a joyful and even ecstatic nature.
And they seemed to be contagious, too, for soon a second penitent,
also female, joined the first, and then came a third, and a fourth,
and a fifth. The last one had an extraordinary violent attack. She
began with mild enough jerks of the head, but in a moment she
was bounding all over the place, like a chicken with its head cut off.
Every time her head came up, a stream of hosannas would issue
out of it. Once she collided with a dark, undersized brother, hith-
erto silent and stolid. Contact with her set him off as if he had been
kicked by a mule. He leaped into the air, threw back his head, and
began to gargle as if with a mouthful of BB shot. Then he loosed
one tremendous, stentorian sentence in the tongues, and collapsed.

By this time the performers were quite oblivious of the profane
universe and so it was safe to go still closer. We left our hiding and
came up to the little circle of light. We slipped into the vacant seats
on one of the rickety benches. The heap of mourners was directly
before us. They bounced into us as they cavorted. The smell that
they radiated, sweating there in that obscene heap, half suffocated
us. Not all of them, of course, did the thing in the grand manner.
Some merely moaned and rolled their eyes. The female ox in gingham flung her great bulk on the ground and jabbered an unintelligible prayer. One of the men, in the intervals between fits, put on
his spectacles and read his Bible. Beside me on the bench sat the
young mother and her baby. She suckled it through the whole orgy,
obviously fascinated by what was going on, but never venturing to
take any hand in it. On the bed just outside the light half a dozen
other babies slept peacefully. In the shadows, suddenly appearing
and as suddenly going away, were vague figures, whether of believers
or of scoffers I do not know. They seemed to come and go in
couples. Now and then a couple at the ringside would step out and
vanish into the black night. After a while some came back, the
males looking somewhat sheepish. There was whispering outside the
circle of vision. A couple of Fords lurched up the road, cutting holes
in the darkness with their lights. Once someone out of sight loosed
a bray of laughter.

All this went on for an hour or so. The original penitent, by this time, was buried three deep beneath the heap. One caught a glimpse, now and then, of her yellow bobbed hair, but then she would vanish again. How she breathed down there I don't know; it was hard enough six feet away, with a strong five-cent cigar to help. When the praying brothers would rise up for a bout with the tongues, their faces were streaming with perspiration. The fat harridan in gingham sweated like a longshoreman. Her hair got loose and fell down over her face. She fanned herself with her skirt. A powerful old gal she was, plainly equal in her day to a bout with obstetrics and a week's washing on the same morning, but this was worse than a week's washing. Finally she fell into a heap, breathing in great, convulsive gasps.

Finally we got tired of the show and returned to Dayton. It was nearly eleven o'clock — an immensely late hour for those latitudes — but the whole town was still gathered in the courthouse yard, listening to the disputes of theologians. The Scopes trial had brought them in from all directions. There was a friar wearing a sandwich sign announcing that he was the Bible champion of the world. There was a Seventh Day Adventist arguing that Clarence Darrow was the beast with seven heads and ten horns described in Revelation xiii, and that the end of the world was at hand. There was an evangelist made up like Andy Gump, with the news that atheists in Cincinnati were preparing to descend upon Dayton, hang the eminent Judge Raulston, and burn the town. There was an ancient who maintained that no Catholic could be a Christian. There was the eloquent Dr. T. T. Martin, of Blue Mountain, Miss., come to town with a truck-load of torches and hymnbooks to put Darwin in his place. There was a singing brother bellowing apocalyptic hymns. There was William Jennings Bryan, followed everywhere by a gaping crowd. Dayton was having a roaring time. It was better than the circus. But the note of devotion was simply not there; the Daytonians, after listening awhile, would slip away to Robinson's drug-store to regale themselves with coca-cola, or to the lobby of the Aqua Hotel, where the learned Raulston sat in state, judicially picking his teeth. The real religion was not present. It began at the bridge over the town creek, where the road makes off for the hills.

THE NATURE OF SLANG

SLANG is defined by the Oxford Dictionary as " language of a highly colloquial type, considered as below the level of standard educated speech, and consisting either of new words or of current words employed in some special sense." The origin of the word is unknown. Ernest Weekley, in his *Etymological Dictionary of Modern English*, 1921, suggests that it may have some relation to the verb *to sling*, and cites two Norwegian dialect words, based upon the cognate verb *slenge* or *slengje*, that appear to be its brothers: *slengjeord*, a neologism, and *slengjenamn*, a nickname. But he is not sure, so he adds the note that " some regard it as an argotic perversion of the French *langue*, language." A German philologian, O. Ritter, believes that it may be derived, not from *langue*, but from *language* itself, most probably by a combination of blending and shortening, as in *thiev*(*s' lang*)*uage*, *beggar*(*s' lang*)*uage*, and so on. *Webster's New International*, 1934, follows somewhat haltingly after Weekley. The Oxford Dictionary, 1919, evades the question by dismissing *slang* as " a word of cant origin, the ultimate source of which is not apparent." When it first appeared in English, about the middle of the eighteenth century, it was employed as a synonym of *cant*, and so designated " the special vocabulary used by any set of persons of a low or disreputable character "; and half a century later it began to be used interchangeably with *argot*, which means the vocabulary special to any group, trade, or profession. But during the past fifty years the three terms have tended to be more or less clearly distinguished. The jargon of criminals is both a kind of slang and a kind of argot, but it is best described as cant, a word derived from the Latin cantus, and going back, in its present sense, to c. 1540. One of the principal aims of cant is to make what is said unintelligible to persons outside the group, a purpose that is absent from most forms of argot and slang. Argot often includes slang, as when a circus man calls his patrons suckers and speaks of refunding money to one full of complaints as squaring the beef, but when he calls the circus grounds the lot and the manager's quarters the white wagon, he is simply using the special language of his trade, and it is quite as respectable as the argot of lawyers or diplomats. The essence of slang is that it is of general dispersion, but still stands outside the accepted canon of the language. It is, says George H. McKnight, " a form of colloquial speech created in a spirit of defiance and aiming at freshness and novelty. . . . Its figures are consciously far-fetched and are intentionally drawn from the most ignoble of sources. Closely akin to profanity in its spirit, its aim is to shock." Among the impulses leading to its invention, adds Henry Bradley, " the two more important seem to be the desire to secure increased vivacity and the desire to secure increased sense of intimacy in the use of language." " It seldom attempts," says the London Times, " to supply deficiencies in conventional language; its object is nearly always to provide a new and different way of saying what can be perfectly well said without it." What chiefly lies behind it is simply a kind of linguistic exuberance, an excess of word-making energy. It relates itself to the standard language a great deal as dancing relates itself to music. But there is also something else. The best slang is not only ingenious and amusing; it also embodies a kind of social criticism. It not only provides new names for a series of everyday concepts, some new and some old; it also says something about them. " Words which produce the slang effect," observes Frank K. Sechrist, " arouse associations which are incongruous or incompatible with those of customary thinking."

Everyone, including even the metaphysician in his study and the eremite in his cell, has a large vocabulary of slang, but the vocabulary of the vulgar is likely to be larger than that of the cultured, and it is harder worked. Its content may be divided into two categories: (a) old words, whether used singly or in combination, that have been put to new uses, usually metaphorical, and (b) new words that have not yet been admitted to the standard vocabulary. Examples of the first type are *rubberneck*, for a gaping and prying person, and *iceberg*, for a cold woman; examples of the second are *hoosegow, flimflam, blurb, bazoo,* and *blah.* There is a constant movement of slang terms into accepted usage. *Nice,* as an adjective of all work, signifying anything satisfactory, was once in slang use only, and the purists denounced it, but today no one would question " a *nice* day," " a *nice* time," or " a *nice* hotel." The French word *tête* has been a sound name for the human head for many centuries, but its origin was in *testa,* meaning a pot, a favorite slang word of the soldiers of the decaying Roman Empire, exactly analogous to our *block, nut,* and *bean.* The verb-phrase *to hold up* is now perfectly good American, but so recently as 1901 the late Brander Matthews was sneering at it as slang. In the same way many other verb-phrases — e.g., *to cave in, to fill the bill,* and *to fly off the handle* — once viewed askance, have gradually worked their way to a relatively high level of the standard speech. On some indeterminate tomorrow *to stick up* and *to take for a ride* may follow them. " Even the greatest purist," says Robert Lynd, " does not object today to the inclusion of the word *bogus* in a literary English vocabulary, though a hundred years ago *bogus* was an American slang word meaning an apparatus for coining false money. *Carpetbagger* and *bunkum* are other American slang words that have naturalized themselves in English speech, and *mob* is an example of English slang that was once as vulgar as *incog* or *photo.*" Sometimes a word comes in below the salt, gradually wins respectability, and then drops to the level of slang and is worked to death. An example is offered by *strenuous.* It was first used by John Marston, the dramatist, in 1599, and apparently he invented it, as he invented *puffy, chilblained, spurious,* and *clumsy.* Strange as it may seem to us today, all these words were frowned on by the purists of the time as uncouth and vulgar, and Ben Jonson attacked them with violence in his *Poetaster,* written in 1601. In particular, Ben was upset by *strenuous.* But it made its way despite him, and during the next three centuries it was used by a multitude of impeccable authors, including Milton, Swift, Burke, Hazlitt, and Macaulay. And then Theodore Roosevelt invented and announced the Strenuous Life, the adjective struck the American fancy and passed into slang, and in a little while it was so horribly threadbare that all persons of careful speech sickened of it, and to this day it bears the ridiculous connotation that hangs about most slang and is seldom used seriously.

All neologisms, of course, are not slang. At about the time the word *hoosegow*, derived from the Spanish, came into American slang use, the word *rodeo*, also Spanish, came into the standard vocabulary. The distinction between the two is not hard to make out. *Hoosegow* was really not needed. We had plenty of words to designate a jail, and they were old and good words. *Hoosegow* came in simply because there was something arresting and outlandish about it — and the users of slang have a great liking for pungent novelties. *Rodeo*, on the other hand, designated something for which there was no other word in American — something, indeed, of which the generality of Americans had just become aware — and so it was accepted at once. Many neologisms have been the deliberate inventions of quite serious men: e.g., *gas, kodak, vaseline.* *Scientist* was concocted in 1840 by William Whewell, professor of moral theology and casuistical divinity at Cambridge. *Ampere* was proposed solemnly by the Electric Congress which met in Paris in 1881, and was taken into all civilized languages instantly. *Radio* was suggested for wireless telegrams by an international convention held in Berlin in 1906, and was extended to wireless broadcasts in the United States about 1920, though the English prefer *wireless* in the latter sense. But such words as these were never slang; they came into general and respectable use at once, along with *argon, X-ray, carburetor, stratosphere, bacillus,* and many another of the sort. These words were all sorely needed; it was impossible to convey the ideas behind them without them, save by clumsy circumlocutions. It is one of the functions of slang, also, to serve a short cut, but it is seldom if ever really necessary. Instead, as W. D. Whitney once said, it is only a wanton product of " the exuberance of mental activity, and the natural delight of language-making." This mental activity, of course, is the function of a relatively small class. " The unconscious genius of the people," said Paul Shorey, " no more invents slang than it invents epics. It is coined in the sweat of their brow by smart writers who, as they

would say, are *out for the coin*." Or, if not out for the coin, then
at least out for notice, *kudos*, admiration, or maybe simply for
satisfaction of the " natural delight of language-making." Some of
the best slang emerges from the argot of college students, but
everyone who has observed the process of its gestation knows that
the general run of students have nothing to do with the matter,
save maybe to provide an eager welcome for the novelties set before
them. College slang is actually made by the campus wits, just as
general slang is made by the wits of the newspapers and theaters.
The idea of calling an engagement-ring a *handcuff* did not occur
to the young gentlemen of Harvard by mass inspiration; it occurred
to a certain definite one of them, probably after long and deliberate
cogitation, and he gave it to the rest and to his country.

Toward the end of 1933 W. J. Funk of the Funk and Wagnalls
Company, publishers of the *Standard Dictionary* and the *Literary
Digest*, undertook to supply the newspapers with the names of the
ten most fecund makers of the American slang then current. He
nominated T. A. (Tad) Dorgan, the cartoonist; Sime Silverman,
editor of the theatrical weekly, *Variety*; Gene Buck, the song-
writer; Damon Runyon, the sports-writer; Walter Winchell and
Arthur (Bugs) Baer, newspaper columnists; George Ade, Ring
Lardner, and Gelett Burgess. He should have added Jack Conway
and Johnny O'Connor of the staff of *Variety*; James Gleason,
author of *Is Zat So?*; Rube Goldberg, the cartoonist; Johnny Stanley and Johnny Lyman, Broadway figures; Wilson Mizner and
Milt Gross. Conway, who died in 1928, is credited with the invention of *palooka* (a third-rater), *belly-laugh*, *Arab* (for Jew), *S.A.*
(sex appeal), *high-hat*, *pushover*, *boloney* (for buncombe, later
adopted by Alfred E. Smith), *headache* (wife), and the verbs *to
scram*, *to click* (meaning to succeed), and *to laugh that off*.
Winchell, if he did not actually invent *whoopee*, at least gave it
the popularity it enjoyed, c. 1930. He is also the father of *Chicago-
rilla*, *Joosh* (for Jewish), *pash* (for passion), and *shafts* (for legs),
and he has devised a great many nonce words and phrases, some
of them euphemistic and others far from it; e.g., for married:
welded, *sealed*, *lohengrined*, *merged*, and *middle-aisled*; for divorced: *Reno-vated*; for contemplating divorce: *telling it to a
judge*, *soured*, *curdled*, *in husband trouble*, *this-and-that-way*, and

on the verge; for in love: *on the merge, on fire, uh-huh, that way, cupiding,* Adam-and-Eveing, and *man-and-womaning it;* for expecting young: *infanticipating, baby-bound,* and *storked.* I add a few other characteristic specimens of his art: *go-ghetto, debutramp, phffft, foofff* (a pest), *Wildeman* (a homosexual), *heheheh* (a mocking laugh), *Hard-Times Square* (Times Square), *blessed-event* (the birth of young), *the Hardened Artery* (Broadway), *radiodor* (a radio announcer), *moom-pitcher* (moving picture), *girl-mad, Park Rowgue* (a newspaper reporter), and *intelligentlemen.* Most of these, of course, had only their brief days, but a few promise to survive. Dorgan, who died in 1929, was the begetter of *apple-sauce, twenty-three skiddoo, ball-and-chain* (for wife), *cake-eater, dumb Dora, dumbell* (for stupid person), *nobody home,* and *you said it.* He also gave the world " Yes, we have no bananas," though he did not write the song, and he seems to have originated *the cat's pajamas,* which was followed by a long series of similar superlatives. The sports-writers, of course, are all assiduous makers of slang, and many of their inventions are taken into the general vocabulary. Thus those who specialize in boxing have contributed, in recent years, *kayo, cauliflower-ear, prelim, shadow-boxing, slug-fest, title-holder, punch-drunk, brother-act, punk, to side-step,* and *to go the limit;* those who cover baseball have made many additions to the list of baseball terms; and those who follow the golf tournaments have given currency to *birdie, fore, par, bunker, divot, fairway, to tee off, stance,* and *onesome, twosome, threesome,* and so on — some of them received into the standard speech, but the majority lingering in the twilight of slang.

George Philip Krapp attempts to distinguish between slang and sound idiom by setting up the doctrine that the former is " more expressive than the situation demands." " It is," he says, " a kind of hyperesthesia in the use of language. *To laugh in your sleeve* is idiom because it arises out of a natural situation; it is a metaphor derived from the picture of one raising his sleeve to his face to hide a smile, a metaphor which arose naturally enough in early periods when sleeves were long and flowing; but *to talk through your hat* is slang, not only because it is new, but also because it is a grotesque exaggeration of the truth." The theory, unluckily, is combated by many plain facts. *To hand it to him, to get away with it,* and even *to hand him a lemon* are certainly not metaphors that transcend the practicable and probable, and yet all are undoubtedly slang. On the other hand, there is palpable exaggeration in such phrases as " he is not worth the powder it would take to kill him," in such adjectives as *breakbone* (fever), and in such compounds as *fire-eater*, and yet it would be absurd to dismiss them as slang. Between *blockhead* and *bonehead* there is little to choose, but the former is sound English, whereas the latter is American slang. So with many familiar similes, e.g., *like greased lightning, as scarce as hen's teeth:* they are grotesque hyperboles, but hardly slang.

The true distinction, in so far as any distinction exists at all, is that indicated by Whitney, Bradley, Sechrist, and McKnight. Slang originates in the effort of ingenious individuals to make the language more pungent and picturesque — to increase the store of terse and striking words, to widen the boundaries of metaphor, and to provide a vocabulary for new shades of difference in meaning. As Dr. Otto Jespersen has pointed out, this is also the aim of poets (as, indeed, it is of prose-writers), but they are restrained by consideration of taste and decorum, and also, not infrequently, by historical or logical considerations. The maker of slang is under no such limitations: he is free to confect his neologism by any process that can be grasped by his customers, and out of any materials available, whether native or foreign. He may adopt any of the traditional devices of metaphor. Making an attribute do duty for the whole gives him *stiff* for corpse, *flat-foot* for policeman, *smoke-eater* for fireman, *skirt* for woman, *lunger* for consumptive, and *yes-man* for sycophant. Hidden resemblances give him *morgue* for a newspaper's file of clippings, *bean* for head, and *sinker* for a doughnut. The substitution of far-fetched figures for literal description gives him *glad-rags* for fine clothing, *bonehead* for ignoramus, *booze-foundry* for saloon, and *cart-wheel* for dollar, and the contrary resort to a brutal literalness gives him *kill-joy, low-life,* and *hand-out.* He makes abbreviations with a free hand — *beaut* for beauty, *gas* for gasoline, and so on. He makes bold avail of composition, as in *attaboy* and *whatdyecallem,* and of onomatopœia, as in *biff, zowie, honky-tonk,* and *wow.* He enriches the ancient counters of speech with picturesque synonyms, as in *guy, gink, duck, bird,* and *bozo* for fellow. He transfers proper names to common usage, as in *ostermoor* for mattress, and then sometimes gives them remote figurative significances, as in *ostermoors* for whiskers. Above all, he enriches the vocabulary of action with many new verbs and verb-phrases: e.g., *to burp, to neck, to gang, to frame up, to hit the pipe, to give him the works,* and so on. If, by the fortunes that condition language-making, his neologism acquires a special and limited meaning, not served by any existing locution, it enters into sound idiom and is presently wholly legitimatized; if, on the contrary, it is adopted by the populace as a counter-word and employed with such banal imitativeness that it soon loses any definite significance whatever, then it remains slang and is avoided by the finical. An example of the former process is afforded by *tommy-rot.* It first appeared as English schoolboy slang, but its obvious utility soon brought it into good usage. In one of Jerome K. Jerome's books, *Paul Kelver,* there is the following dialogue:

"The wonderful songs that nobody ever sings, the wonderful pictures that nobody ever paints, and all the rest of it. It's *tommy-rot!*"
"I wish you wouldn't use slang."
"Well, you know what I mean. What is the proper word? Give it to me."
"I suppose you mean *cant.*"
"No, I don't. *Cant* is something that you don't believe in yourself. It's *tommy-rot;* there isn't any other word."

Nor were there any other words for *hubbub, fireworks, foppish, fretful, sportive, dog-weary, to bump,* and *to dwindle* in Shakspere's time; he adopted and dignified them because they met genuine needs. Nor was there any other satisfactory word for *graft* when it came in, nor for *rowdy,* nor for *boom,* nor for *joy-ride,* nor for *slacker,* nor for *trust-buster.* Such words often retain a humorous quality; they are used satirically and hence appear but seldom in wholly serious discourse. But they have standing in the language nevertheless, and only a prig would hesitate to use them as George Saintsbury used *the best of the bunch* and *joke-smith.* So recently as 1929 the *Encyclopaedia Britannica* listed *bootlegger, speakeasy, dry, wet, crook, fake, fizzle, hike, hobo, poppycock, racketeer,* and *O.K.* as American slang terms, but today most of them are in perfectly good usage. What would one call a racketeer if *racketeer* were actually forbidden? It would take a phrase of four or five words at least, and they would certainly not express the idea clearly.

On the other hand, many an apt and ingenious neologism, by falling too quickly into the gaping maw of the proletariat, is spoiled forthwith and forever. Once it becomes, in Oliver Wendell Holmes's phrase, " a cheap generic term, a substitute for differentiated specific expressions," it quickly acquires such flatness that the fastidious flee it as a plague. The case of *strenuous* I have already mentioned. One recalls, too, many capital verb-phrases thus ruined by unintelligent appreciation: e.g., *to freeze on to, to have the goods, to cut no ice, to fall for,* and *to get by;* and some excellent substantives: e.g., *dope* and *dub,* and compounds: e.g., *come-on* and *easy-mark,* and simple verbs: e.g., *to neck* and *to vamp.* These are all quite as sound in structure as the great majority of our most familiar words and phrases — *to cut no ice,* for example, is certainly as good as *to butter no parsnips* — but their adoption by the ignorant and their endless use and misuse in all sorts of situations have left them tattered and obnoxious, and soon or late they will probably go the way, as Brander Matthews once said, of all the other "temporary phrases which spring up, one scarcely knows how, and flourish unaccountably for a few months, and then disappear forever, leaving no sign." Matthews was wrong in two particulars here. They do not arrive by any mysterious parthenogenesis, but come from sources which, in many cases, may be determined. And they last, alas, a good deal more than a month. *Shoo-fly* afflicted the American people for four or five years, and " I *don't* think," *aber nit, over the left, good night,* and *oh yeah* were scarcely less long-lived. There are, indeed, slang terms that have survived for centuries, never dropping quite out of use and yet never attaining to good usage. Among verbs, *to do* for to cheat has been traced to 1789, *to frisk* for to search to 1781, *to grease* for to bribe to 1557, and *to blow* for to boast to c. 1400. Among nouns, *gas* for empty talk has been traced to 1847, *jug* for prison to 1834, *lip* for insolence to 1821, *sap* for fool to 1815, *murphy* for potato to 1811, *racket* to 1785, *bread-basket* for stomach to 1753, *hush-money* to 1709, *hick* to 1690, *gold-mine* for profitable venture to 1664, *grub* for food to 1659, *rot-gut* to 1597, and *bones* for dice to c. 1386. Among the

adjectives, *lousy* in the sense of inferior goes back to 1690; when it
burst into American slang in 1910 or thereabout it was already more
than two centuries old. *Booze* has never got into standard English,
but it was known to slang in the first years of the fourteenth century. When *nuts* in the sense revealed by " Chicago was *nuts* for
the Giants " came into popularity in the United States *c.* 1920, it
was treated by most of the newspaper commentators on current
slang as a neologism, but in truth it had been used in precisely the
same sense by R. H. Dana, Jr., in *Two Years Before the Mast*, 1840,
and by Mark Twain in *Following the Equator*, 1897. Sometimes
an old slang word suddenly acquires a new meaning. An example
is offered by *to chisel*. In the sense of to cheat, as in " He *chiseled*
me out of three dollars," it goes back to the first years of the nineteenth century, but with the advent of the N.R.A., in the late Summer of 1933, it took on the new meaning of to evade compliance
with the law by concealment or stealth. It has been credited to
Franklin D. Roosevelt, but I believe that its true father was General Hugh S. Johnson, J.D.

  With the possible exception of the French, the Americans now
produce more slang than any other people, and put it to heavier use
in their daily affairs. But they entered upon its concoction relatively
late, and down to the second decade of the nineteenth century they
were content to take their supply from England. American slang,
says George Philip Krapp, " is the child of the new nationalism,
the new spirit of joyous adventure that entered American life after
the close of the War of 1812." There was, during the colonial and
early republican periods, a great production of neologisms, but very
little of it was properly describable as slang. I find *to boost*, defined
as to raise up, to lift up, to exalt, in the glossary appended to David
Humphreys's *The Yankey in England*, 1815, but all the other slang
terms listed — e.g., *duds* for clothes, *spunk* for courage, and *uppish*
— are in Francis Grose's *Classical Dictionary of the Vulgar Tongue*,
published in London thirty years before. The Rev. John Wither-
spoon's denunciation of slang in *The Druid*, 1781, is a denunciation of English slang, though he is discussing the speech habits of
Americans. But with the great movement into the West, following
the War of 1812, the American vulgate came into its own, and soon
the men of the ever-receding frontier were pouring out a copious

stream of neologisms, many of them showing the audacious fancy of true slang. When these novelties penetrated to the East they produced a sort of linguistic shock, and the finicky were as much upset by the " tall talk " in which they were embodied as English pedants are today by the slang of Hollywood. That some of them were extremely extravagant is a fact: I need point only to *blustiferous, clam-jamphrie, conbobberation, helliferocious, mollagausauger, peedoodles, ripsniptiously, slangwhanger, sockdolager, to exflunctify, to flummuck, to giraffe, to hornswoggle, to obflisticate,* and *to puckerstopple.* Most of these, of course, had their brief days and then disappeared, but there were others that got into the common vocabulary and still survive: e.g., *blizzard, to hornswoggle, sockdolager,* and *rambunctious,* the last-named the final step in a process which began with *robustious* and ran through *rumbustious* and *rambustious* in England before Americans took a hand in it. With them came many verb-phrases: e.g., *to pick a crow with, to cut one's eye-teeth, to go the whole hog.* This " tall talk," despite the horror of the delicate, was a great success in the East, and its salient practitioners — for example, David Crockett — were popular heroes. Its example encouraged the production of like neologisms everywhere, and by 1840 the use of slang was very widespread. It is to those days before the Civil War that we owe many of the colorful American terms for strong drink, still current: e.g., *panther-sweat, nose-paint, red-eye, corn-juice, forty-rod, mountain-dew, coffin-varnish, bust-head, stagger-soup, tonsil-paint, squirrel-whisky,* and so on, and for drunk: e.g., *boiled, canned, cockeyed, frazzled, fried, oiled, ossified, pifflicated, pie-eyed, plastered, snozzled, stewed, stuccoed, tanked, woozy.* " Perhaps the most striking difference between British and American slang," says Krapp, " is that the former is more largely merely a matter of the use of queer-sounding words, like *bally* and *swank,* whereas American slang suggests vivid images and pictures." This was hardly true in the heyday of " tall talk," but that it is true now is revealed by a comparison of current English and American college slang. The vocabulary of Oxford and Cambridge seems inordinately obvious and banal to an American undergraduate. At Oxford it is made up in large part of a series of childish perversions of common and proper nouns, effected by adding -er or inserting gg. Thus, breakfast becomes *brekker,* collection becomes *collecker*, the Queen Street Cinema becomes the *Queener*, St. John's becomes *Jaggers* and the Prince of Wales becomes the *Pragger-Wagger*. The rest of the vocabulary is equally feeble. To match the magnificent American *lounge-lizard* the best the Oxonians can achieve is *a bit of a lad*, and in place of the multitudinous American synonyms for *girl* there are only *bint* (Arabic for woman) and a few other such flabby terms. All college slang, of course, borrows heavily from the general slang vocabulary. For example, *chicken*, which designated a young girl on most American campuses until 1921 or thereabout, was used by Steele in 1711, and, in the form of *no chicken*, by Swift in 1720. It had acquired a disparaging significance in the United States by 1788, as the following lines show:

> From visiting bagnios, those seats of despair,
> Where *chickens* will call you *my duck* and *my dear*
> In hopes that your purse may fall to their share,
>   Deliver me!

Like the vulgar language in general, popular American slang has got very little sober study from the professional philologians. The only existing glossary of it by a native scholar — *A Dictionary of American Slang*, by Maurice H. Weseen, associate professor of English at the University of Nebraska — is an extremely slipshod and even ridiculous work. There are several collections by laymen, but most of them are still worse. The best, and by far, is *Slang Today and Yesterday*, by Eric Partridge, which deals principally with English slang, but also has a valuable section on American slang. All the dictionaries of Americanisms, of course, include words reasonably describable as slang, but they appear only incidentally, and not in large numbers. Thornton, for example, bars out a great deal of interesting and amusing material by confining his researches to written records. In England the literature of the subject is far more extensive. It began in the sixteenth century with the publication of several vocabularies of thieves' argot, and has been enriched in recent years by a number of valuable works, notably the Partridge volume just cited, *Slang, Phrase and Idiom in Colloquial English and Their Use*, by Thomas R. G. Lyell, and the monumental *Slang and Its Analogues*, by John S. Farmer and W. E. Henley. Before the completion of the last-named, the chief authorities on English slang were A *Dictionary of Slang, Jargon and Cant*, by Albert Barrère and Charles G. Leland, and A *Dictionary of Modern Cant, Slang and Vulgar Words*, by J. C. Hotten. Relatively little attention is paid to slang in the philological journals, but it is frequently discussed in the magazines of general circulation and in the newspapers. When the English papers denounce Americanisms, which is very often, it is commonly slang that arouses their most violent dudgeon. This dudgeon, of course, is grounded upon its very success: the American movies and talkies have implanted American slang in England even more copiously than they have implanted more decorous American neologisms. As the *Spectator* was saying lately, its influence " on the British Empire continues, ever more rapidly, to increase — a portent frequently mentioned and almost as frequently deplored." Sometimes it is belabored as intolerably vulgar, indecent, and against God, as when the *Christian World* blamed it for the prevalence of " dishonest and debased thought" and ascribed its use to " a sneaking fear and dislike of calling beautiful things by their beautiful names and of calling ugly things by their ugly names "; sometimes it is sneered at as empty and puerile, signifying nothing, as when Allan Monkhouse demanded piously: " What is the good of all this? " and answered: " Such words are the ghosts of old facetiousness, and the world would be better without them "; and sometimes efforts are made to dispose of it by proving that it is all stolen from England, as when Dr. C. T. Onions, one of the editors of the Oxford Dictionary, offered to show a London reporter that the dictionary listed any American slang term he could name. Alas, for Dr. Onions, after making good with *to grill, fresh, to figure* (in the sense of to conclude), *bunkum* (he apparently forgot its clearly American origin), and *rake-off* (he had to fall back upon an American example), he came to grief with *baloney* and *nerts*. One of the favorite forms of this latter enterprise is a letter to the editor announcing the discovery that this or that locution, lately come into popularity by way of the talkies, is to be found in Shakspere, or the Authorized Version of the Bible, or maybe even in *Piers Plowman*. There are also the specialists who devote themselves to demonstrating that American slang is simply a series of borrowings from the Continental languages, particularly French — for example, that *and how* is a translation of *et comment*, that *you're telling me* is from *à qui le dites-vous*, and that *to get one's goat* is from *prendre sa chèvre*. But not all Englishmen, of course, oppose and deride the American invasion, whether of slang or of novelties on high levels. Not a few agree with Horace Annesley Vachell that " American slanguage is not a tyranny, but a beneficent autocracy. . . . *Lounge-lizard*, for example, is excellent. . . . It is humiliating to reflect that English slang at its best has to curtsey to American slang." To which " Jackdaw " adds in *John O'London's Weekly:* " We do but pick up the crumbs that fall from Jonathan's table."

During the World War there was some compensatory borrowing of English army slang and argot by the American troops, but it did not go very far. Indeed, the list of loan-words that came into anything approaching general use in the A.E.F. was about limited to *ace, blimp, cootie, Frog, Jack Johnson, Jerry, blotto, over the top,* and *whizz-bang.* Some of the favorites of the British soldiers — e.g., *fag, blighty, cheerio, to strafe, funk-hole,* and *righto* — were seldom if ever used by the Americans. The greater part of the American vocabulary came from the regular army, and some of it was of very respectable antiquity: e.g., *hand-shaker, Holy Joe* (for chaplain), *slum* (stew), *corned willie* (corned-beef hash), *outfit, belly-robber, dog-robber* (an officer's servant or orderly), *doughboy, jawbone* (meaning credit, or anything spurious or dubious), *mud-splasher* (artilleryman), *buck-private, top-kick, gold-fish* (canned salmon), *gob, leatherneck, padre, chow,* and *punk* (bread). A few novelties came in — e.g., *tin-hat* and *a.w.o.l.* — and there was some fashioning of counter-words and phrases from French materials — e.g., *boocoo* or *boocoop* (beaucoup), *toot sweet* (tout de suite), and *trez beans* (très bien) — but neither class was numerous. Naturally enough, a large part of the daily conversation of the troops was obscene, or, at all events, excessively vulgar. Their common name for cavalryman, for example, could hardly be printed here. The English called the military police *red-caps,* but the American name was *M.P.'s.* The British used *O.C.* for Officer Commanding; the Americans used *C.O.* for Commanding Officer. The British were fond of a number of Americanisms — e.g., *cold-feet, kibosh, nix, pal,* and *to chew the rag* — but whether they were borrowed from the A.E.F. or acquired by some less direct route I do not know. About *gob, leatherneck,* and *doughboy* there have been bitter etymological wrangles. *Gob* has been traced variously to a Chinese word (*gobshite*), of unknown meaning and probably mythical; to *gobble,* an allusion to the somewhat earnest methods of feeding prevailing among sailors; and to *gob,* an archaic English dialect word signifying expectoration. The English coast-guardsmen, who are said to be free spitters, are often called *gobbies.* In May 1928 Admiral H. A. Wiley, then commander-in-chief of the United States fleet, forbade the use of *gob* in ships' newspapers, calling it " undignified and unworthy." But the gobs continue to cherish it. *Leatherneck,* I have been told, originated in the fact that the collar of the Marines used to be lined with leather. But the Navy prefers to believe that it has something to do with the fact that a sailor, when he washes, strips to the waist and renovates his whole upper works, whereas a Marine simply rolls up his sleeves and washes in the scantier manner of a civilian. It is the theory of all gobs that all Marines are dirty fellows. But the step from unwashed necks to leather seems to me to be somewhat long and perilous. The term *devil-dogs,* often applied to the Marines during the World War, was supposed to be a translation of the German *teufelhunde.* During the fighting around Château Thierry, in June and July 1918, the Marines were heavily engaged, and the story went at the time that the Germans, finding them very formidable, called them *teufelhunde.* But I have been told by German officers who were in that fighting that no such word was known in the German army. *Doughboy* is an old English navy term for dumpling. It was formerly applied to the infantry only, and its use is said to have originated in the fact that the infantrymen once pipe-clayed parts of their uniforms, with the result that they became covered with a doughy mass when it rained.

Three
American Poets

I HAVE asked a good many people if they had ever noticed that the seventh of Elinor Wylie's sonnets in One Person lacks a line, and I have never yet found one who had, not even William Rose Benét, who saw it through the press. The final sonnet has two deliberate extra lines, to emphasize the end of the series. It is as if you had heard a bell tolling somewhere, five strokes at a time and then an interval, and your ear had come, perhaps unconsciously, to count five each time and to expect five the next, and then had heard six, and you had suddenly known that this was the last of the tolling. But I cannot believe that Elinor Wylie, one of the most accurate of poets, meant to leave out what would have been either the fourth or the fifth line of her seventh sonnet. The sense of the octave is continuous. If she wrote another line, and then somehow lost it in transcription, it must have been parenthetic. Of course that is possible. Although she had prepared the sonnets for the printer of *Angels and Earthly Creatures*, she died before they were in type, and so had no chance to miss the line if it existed. It is hardly possible that she intended to run the fourth and fifth line together on a single rhyme, as the sonnet now stands. I think it most likely that her delicate ear lost count in the intense excitement which ruled and drove her through the whole series.

That it was an intense and genuine excitement I saw with my own eyes. Early in June 1928 I stopped off in London on my way to Paris, and Elinor Wylie, then living in Chelsea, gave a party for me. She asked me to stay after the other guests had gone, because she wanted to show me something she had written. I suppose that the hero of her sonnets had already heard them, and I understood that Edith Olivier had too, but I think no one else before me. Sitting very erect, white, and thin on a sofa in her drawing-room, Elinor Wylie said to me — she always spoke of saying her poems, not reading them — a dozen or so of these unforgettable sonnets, all she had done. Her excitement must have affected me, for I can now specifically remember only the ninth sonnet, with its reference to Shelley. If the seventh was among those she said, and among those which she let me read from her typed copy, I noticed the missing line no more than she. I so promptly missed the line when I read the published sonnets that I wonder whether I heard or read the seventh in Chelsea. But I cannot be sure, for the total impression was overwhelming.

As I listened to her I had a strange sensation that I was seeing something I had experienced or read about. What was it? It kept tantalizing me, nagging at my attention. Then it came over me that I was remembering Peacock's words about Shelley, in the matter of Mary Godwin. " Nothing that I had ever read in tale or history could present a more striking image of a sudden, violent, irresistible, uncontrollable passion than that under which I found him laboring when, at his request, I went up from the country to call on him in London." I could make a very romantic story out of this episode if I were disposed to mysterious imaginings. For it was a joke between Elinor Wylie and me that I was a kind of Peacock to her Shelley. Now, the romantic story might run, a transmigrated Shelley had summoned a transmigrated Peacock to be a confidant again when history was repeated. It is a pleasant fancy, but it seems to me less moving than the plainer facts. This was no old love reborn but a new love, fresh as Eden.

After all, history never really repeats itself. When Shelley met Mary Godwin he was not yet twenty-two. When Elinor Wylie met her One Person she was forty-two, at the end not at the beginning of her seven years of poetry. Whatever tumult of the emotions Shelley went through, his mind was swarming with doctrines which supported him as much as they confused him. In Elinor Wylie's mind there was little of such support, such confusion. In Chelsea and in Soho, later, she told me the whole story. She and her hero were both married. She had no intention of letting her life, or anybody's, be broken up. The circumstances which kept the lovers apart would go on doing it. Her love must remain her secret — though she had to tell a few close friends. But now for the first time her senses were involved, and love tore at her flesh. To that extent this was first love for her — actually, not merely as any new love seems the first. All the ardors of a young girl had come to a woman who had lived long enough to greet them with incredulous surprise and yet know how to measure them by experience. For her they had a splendor, a bearing, an omen which they could not have had for a young girl, who would have been timid and pitiful, and perhaps would have felt them less because she could not comprehend them. With her they would have been lost in inarticulate sighs and tears. But Elinor Wylie, with the heart of sixteen, had the tongue of maturity and a beautiful expressive art. " For once in the world, youth knew and age could."

Simple in emotion, magnificent in expression, *One Person* belongs with the best love-poetry in any language. If the expression were, here and there, simpler and less crowded with shining thought, these sonnets would have almost no rivals. As it is, I know none which are definitely better, and I find it hard to believe that there are any which will outlive them.

I often hear complaints that poetry is no longer read. This is far from true. Poets may not be much read, particularly minor poets in individual volumes. But poetry has still a huge audience. During the eight years when I was editor of the Literary Guild no book ever selected was so popular, to judge by the number of copies sold, as my brother Mark Van Doren's *Anthology of World*

Poetry. And other successful anthologies of verse continue to be bought and read year after year as few prose works are. I suspect this is because readers are more interested in poems than in poets. They want to find their own feelings put in beautiful words, but they do not care who put them there. And they do not always have the patience to hunt for meanings. I believe that fine poems are frequently overlooked for want of what I may call stage directions. The reader is too often not quite sure who is speaking or what about. The poets seem to be too proud to tell, or contemptuous, or indifferent. For instance, in *Bells for John Whitesides' Daughter*, that exquisite elegy by the sensitive and witty John Crowe Ransom, I am willing to bet that many readers are not sure that the child, in her "brown study, lying so primly propped," is dead. That she is dead is what gives the poem its aching point. Of course the bells ought to prove it, but "brown study" is an extraordinary understatement for pale death. In Ransom's *Epitaph* many readers must have had to puzzle out, if they ever did, that the "intrepid Generalissimo" is Christ. And how clear is it, in Wallace Stevens's brilliant *Sunday Morning*, that here are merely a lady's reasons for not going to church and her reflections upon comparative religion?

Recent poets are so reticent that, in supplying these stage directions for poems which I admire very much, I feel embarrassingly, guiltily matter-of-fact. But if poets will leave their stage directions out, there will be readers who are mystified. Mystification is not a purpose of poetry.

C.V.D.

⊰ *Elinor Wylie* ⊱

ONE PERSON

Although these words are false, none shall prevail
To prove them in translation less than true
Or overthrow their dignity, or undo
The faith implicit in a fabulous tale;
The ashes of this error shall exhale
Essential verity, and two by two
Lovers devout and loyal shall renew
The legend, and refuse to let it fail.

Even the betrayer and the fond deceived,
Having put off the body of this death,
Shall testify with one remaining breath,
From sepulchers demand to be believed:
These words are true, although at intervals
The unfaithful clay contrive to make them false.

[683]

I

Now shall the long homesickness have an end
Upon your heart, which is a part of all
The past no human creature may recall
Save you, who are persuasive to unbend
The brows of death, and name him for a friend:
This ecstasy is supernatural;
I have survived to see the heavens fall
Into my hands, which on your hands depend.

Time has prepared us an enduring bed
Within the earth of this beloved land;
And, lying side by side and hand in hand,
We sleep coeval with the happy dead
Who are ourselves, a little earlier bound
To one another's bosom in the ground.

II

What other name had half expressed the whole
Of that incomparable and touching grace
Which spells the shape of danger in your face?
It is the very pattern of your soul;
The eagle's home, above the moon's control,
Above the seas, the high precipitate place;
The stairway cut from planetary space;
The crystal steps which climb a steeper goal.

The shadow of its light is only this:
That all your beauty is the work of wars
Between the upper and the nether stars;
Its symmetry is perfect and severe
Because the barbarous force of agonies
Broke it, and mended it, and made it clear.

III

" Children and dogs are subject to my power,"
You said, and smiled, and I beside you smiled,
Perceiving my unwisdom of a child,
My courage of a wolf new-taught to cower:
Upon the grass, beneath the falling flower,
I saw my spirit silent and beguiled
Standing at gaze; a brute no longer wild;
An infant wearied by the difficult hour.

And am I not your child who has come home?
And am I not your hound for faithfulness?
Put forth your hand, put forth your hand to bless
A creature stricken timorous and dumb,
Who now regards you with a lover's eyes
And knows that you are merciful and wise.

IV

Now am I Orson to your Valentine
Forever, and I choose it shall be so;
For how should the uncivil brier grow
Germane in nature to the noble vine?
The savage should be servant to the fine;
The falcon fly superior to the crow;
O dear my lord, believe me that I know
How far your virtues have outnumbered mine.

And you have levied final tribute now —
Your chivalry demanding the pretense —
You have constrained your vassal to avow
That we are equals, lest a violence
Be suffered by our love, and so I must
Deny the intrinsic difference in our dust.

V

The little beauty that I was allowed —
The lips new-cut and colored by my sire,
The polished hair, the eyes' perceptive fire —
Has never been enough to make me proud:
For I have moved companioned by a cloud,
And lived indifferent to the blood's desire
Of temporal loveliness in vain attire:
My flesh was but a fresh-embroidered shroud.

Now do I grow indignant at the fate
Which made me so imperfect to compare
With your degree of noble and of fair;
Our elements are the farthest skies apart;
And I enjoin you, ere it is too late,
To stamp your superscription on my heart.

VI

I have believed that I prefer to live
Preoccupied by a Platonic mind;
I have believed me obdurate and blind
To those sharp ecstasies the pulses give:
The clever body five times sensitive
I never have discovered to be kind
As the poor soul, deceived and half-divined,
Whose hopes are water in a witch's sieve.

Oh now both soul and body are unfit
To apprehend this miracle, my lord!
Not all my senses, striving in accord
With my pure essence, are aware of it
Save as a power remote and exquisite,
Not seen or known, but fervently adored.

VII

Would I might make subliminal my flesh
And so contrive a gentle atmosphere
To comfort you because I am not there;
Or else incorporate and carve afresh
A lady, from the chilly heaven and clear
Which flows around you like a stream of air,
To warm and wind you in her body's mesh.

So would I cherish you a loving twice;
Once in a mist made matter; once again
In my true substance made ethereal:
And yet I cannot succor you at all
Whose letter cries, " My hands are cold as ice,"
The while I kiss the colder air in vain.

VIII

O love, how utterly am I bereaved
By Time, who sucks the honey of our days,
Sets sickle to our Aprils, and betrays
To killing winter all the sun achieved!
Our parted spirits are perplexed and grieved
Severed by cold, and change that never stays;
And what the clock, and what the season says
Is rumor neither valued nor believed.

Thus absence chills us to apparent death
And withers up our virtue, but together
We grow beyond vagaries of the weather
And make a summer of our mingled breath
Wherein we flourish, and forget to know
We must lie murdered by predestined snow.

IX

A subtle spirit has my path attended,
In likeness not a lion but a pard;
And when the arrows flew like hail, and hard,
He licked my wounds, and all my wounds were mended;
And happy I, who walked so well-defended,
With that translucid presence for a guard,
Under a sky reversed and evil-starred;
A woman by an archangel befriended.

Now must I end the knightly servitude
Which made him my preserver, and renounce
That heavenly aid forever and at once;
For it were neither courteous nor good
If we, who are but perishable things,
Should hang another weight between his wings.

X

When I perceive the sable of your hair
Silvered, and deep within those caverns are
Your eyesockets, a double-imaged star,
And your fine substance fretted down by care,
Then do I marvel that a woman dare
Prattle of mortal matters near and far
To one so wounded in demonic war
Against some prince of Sirius or Altair.

How is it possible that this hand of clay,
Though white as porcelain, can contrive a touch
So delicate it shall not hurt too much?
What voice can my invention find to say
So soft, precise, and scrupulous a word
You shall not take it for another sword?

XI

" Before I die, let me be happy here."
The glass of heaven was split, and by that token
I knew the bubble of my heart had broken;
The cool and chaste, the iridescent sphere,
Filled, in that vernal season of the year,
With sapling's blood, the beechen and the oaken
And the green willow's; when the word was spoken
This innocence did faint and disappear.

So have I lost my only wedding dower,
The veins of spring, enclosed within my heart,
Traced small in silver like a celestial chart;
And I am vanished in the leaf and flower,
Since, at your voice, my body's core and pith
Dissolves in air, and is destroyed forthwith.

XII

In our content, before the autumn came
To shower sallow droppings on the mold,
Sometimes you have permitted me to fold
Your grief in swaddling-bands, and smile to name
Yourself my infant, with an infant's claim
To utmost adoration as of old,
Suckled with kindness, fondled from the cold,
And loved beyond philosophy or shame.

I dreamt I was the mother of a son
Who had deserved a manger for a crib;
Torn from your body, furbished from your rib,
I am the daughter of your skeleton,
Born of your bitter and excessive pain:
I shall not dream you are my child again.

XIII

Oh, mine is Psyche's heavy doom reversed
Who meet at noon, part by diminished light,
But never feel the subtle balm of night
Fall merciful upon a body pierced
By extreme love; and I considered first
That you, a god more prodigally bright
Than the lessor Eros, had enriched my sight,
Made your own morning, and the stars immersed.

But secondly I saw my soul arise
And, in the hushed obscure, presume to creep
Tiptoe upon your spirit laid asleep,
And slant the impious beam across your eyes;
And I believe I have my just deserts
Lacking the shadow of peace upon our hearts.

XIV

My fairer body and perfected spirit,
Beyond metempsychosis, and beyond
The faults you must forgive me to be fond,
Are yours in any death that I may merit;
Mortality has wearied us who wear it,
And they are wiser creatures who have shunned
This miry world, this slough of man's despond,
To fortify the skies we shall inherit.

I have entreated you to grant me Time
To memorize the pure appointed task;
Today it is Eternity I ask
In which to learn the lesson of this rhyme:
Its liberal periods are not too wide.
To educate me fitly for your bride.

XV

My honored lord, forgive the unruly tongue
That utters blasphemies; forgive the brain
Borne on a whirlwind of unhallowed pain:
Remember only the intrepid song;
The flag defended and the gauntlet flung;
The love that speech can never render plain;
The mind's resolve to turn and strive again;
The fortitude that has endured so long.

My cherished lord, in charity forgive
A starveling hope that may at times desire
To warm its frozen fingers at your fire;
'Tis by such trifles that your lovers live,
And so rise up, and in the starlight cold
Frighten the foxes from your loneliest fold.

XVI

I hereby swear that to uphold your house
I would lay my bones in quick destroying lime
Or turn my flesh to timber for all time;
Cut down my womanhood; lop off the boughs
Of that perpetual ecstasy that grows
From the heart's core; condemn it as a crime
If it be broader than a beam, or climb
Above the stature that your roof allows.

I am not the hearthstone nor the cornerstone
Within this noble fabric you have builded;
Not by my beauty was its cornice gilded;
Not on my courage were its arches thrown:
My lord, adjudge my strength, and set me where
I bear a little more than I can bear.

XVII

Upon your heart, which is the heart of all
My late discovered earth and early sky,
Give me the dearest privilege to die;
Your pity for the velvet of my pall;
Your patience for my grave's inviolate wall;
And for my passing bell, in passing by,
Your voice itself, diminished to a sigh
Above all other sounds made musical.

Meanwhile I swear to you I am content
To live without a sorrow to my name;
To live triumphant, and to die the same,
Upon the fringes of this continent,
This map of paradise, this scrap of earth
Whereon you burn like flame upon a hearth.

XVIII

Let us leave talking of angelic hosts
Of nebulæ, and lunar hemispheres,
And what the days, and what the Uranian years
Shall offer us when you and I are ghosts;
Forget the festivals and pentecosts
Of metaphysics, and the lesser fears
Confound us, and seal up our eyes and ears
Like little rivers locked below the frosts.

And let us creep into the smallest room
That any hunted exile has desired
For him and for his love when he was tired;
And sleep oblivious of any doom
Which is beyond our reason to conceive;
And so forget to weep, forget to grieve,
And wake, and touch each other's hands, and turn
Upon a bed of juniper and fern.

John Crowe Ransom

BELLS FOR JOHN WHITESIDES' DAUGHTER

There was such speed in her little body,
And such lightness in her footfall,
It is no wonder that her brown study
Astonishes us all.

Her wars were bruited in our high window.
We look among orchard trees and beyond,
Where she took arms against her shadow,
Or harried unto the pond

The lazy geese, like a snow cloud
Dripping their snow on the green grass,
Tricking and stopping, sleepy and proud,
Who cried in goose, Alas,

For the tireless heart within the little
Lady with rod that made them rise
From their noon apple dreams, and scuttle
Goose-fashion under the skies!

But now go the bells, and we are ready;
In one house we are sternly stopped
To say we are vexed at her brown study,
Lying so primly propped.

HERE LIES A LADY

Here lies a lady of beauty and high degree.
Of chills and fever she died, of fever and chills,
The delight of her husband, her aunts, an infant of three,
And of medicos marveling sweetly on her ills.

For either she burned, and her confident eyes would blaze,
And her fingers fly in a manner to puzzle their heads —
What was she making? Why, nothing; she sat in a maze
Of old scraps of laces, snipped into curious shreds —

Or this would pass, and the light of her fire decline
Till she lay discouraged and cold as a thin stalk white and blown,
And would not open her eyes, to kisses, to wine;
The sixth of these states was her last; the cold settled down.

Sweet ladies, long may ye bloom, and toughly I hope ye may thole,
But was she not lucky? In flowers and lace and mourning,
In love and great honor we bade God rest her soul
After six little spaces of chill, and six of burning.

EPITAPH

Napoleon took many captures and is dead,
Julius brought unto Rome many victories,
Nor did Alexander expire on a wastrel's bed;
But this was a somewhat greater captain than these.

He took a city too, O Eminences.
It was a city reared stubborn against a foe,
Furnished it was with no frail few defences,
But it fell to the intrepid Generalissimo.

Its two towers compacted of a tough masonry,
The right tower squat against the thunderbolts of Heaven,
The left tower sheer on the brink like a mighty tree
From the bottom of Hell, and terrible to the craven.

He was a lone besieger of a grim defence,
He was scarred, and weary of circling it round after round,
He battered incessantly upon its fundaments,
At last he bestrode it thundering to the ground.

A lone besieger, so Cæsar's ghost had said,
Leading no soldiers; but he had known black magic,
And mustered invisible regiments to his aid,
For he triumphed; and the envious Cæsars took it as tragic.

TWO IN AUGUST

Two that could not have lived their single lives
As can some husbands and wives
Did something strange: they tensed their vocal cords
And attacked each other with silences and words
Like catapulted stones and arrowed knives.

Dawn was not yet; night is for loving or sleeping,
Sweet dreams or safekeeping;
Yet he of the wide brows that were used to laurel
And she, the famed for gentleness, must quarrel,
Furious both of them, and scared, and weeping.

How sleepers groan, twitch, wake to such a mood
Is not well understood,
Nor why two entities grown almost one
Should rend and murder trying to get undone,
With individual tigers in their blood.

In spring's luxuriant weather had the bridal
Transpired, nor had the growing parts been idle,
Nor was it easily dissolved;
Therefore they tugged but were still intervolved,
With pain prodigious. The exploit was suicidal.

She in terror fled from the marriage chamber
Circuiting the dark room like a string of amber
Round and round and back,
And would not light one lamp against the black,
And heard the clock that clanged: Remember, Remember.

And he must tread barefooted the dim lawn,
Soon he was up and gone;
High in the trees the night-mastered birds were crying
With fear upon their tongues, no singing nor flying
Which are their lovely attitudes by dawn.

Whether those bird-cries were of heaven or hell
There is no way to tell;
In the long ditch of darkness the man walked
Under the hackberry trees where the birds talked
With words too sad and strange to syllable.

Wallace Stevens

SUNDAY MORNING

I

Complacencies of the peignoir, and late
Coffee and oranges in a sunny chair,
And the green freedom of a cockatoo
Upon a rug mingle to dissipate
The holy hush of ancient sacrifice,
She dreams a little, and she feels the dark
Encroachment of that old catastrophe,
As a calm darkens among water-lights.
The pungent oranges and bright, green wings
Seem things in some procession of the dead,
Winding across wide water, without sound.
The day is like wide water, without sound,
Stilled for the passing of her dreaming feet
Over the seas, to silent Palestine,
Dominion of the blood and sepulcher.

II

Why should she give her bounty to the dead?
What is divinity if it can come
Only in silent shadows and in dreams?
Shall she not find in comforts of the sun,
In pungent fruit and bright, green wings, or else
In any balm or beauty of the earth,
Things to be cherished like the thought of heaven?
Divinity must live within herself:
Passions of rain, or moods in falling snow;
Grievings in loneliness, or unsubdued
Elations when the forest blooms; gusty
Emotions on wet roads on autumn nights;
All pleasures and all pains, remembering
The bough of summer and the winter branch.
These are the measures destined for her soul.

III

Jove in the clouds had his inhuman birth.
No mother suckled him, no sweet land gave
Large-mannered motions to his mythy mind.
He moved among us, as a muttering king,
Magnificent, would move among his hinds,
Until our blood, commingling, virginal,
With heaven, brought such requital to desire
The very hinds discerned it, in a star.
Shall our blood fail? Or shall it come to be
The blood of paradise? And shall the earth
Seem all of paradise that we shall know?
The sky will be much friendlier then than now,
A part of labor and a part of pain,
And next in glory to enduring love,
Not this dividing and indifferent blue.

IV

She says: " I am content when wakened birds,
Before they fly, test the reality
Of misty fields, by their sweet questionings;
But when the birds are gone, and their warm fields
Return no more, where, then, is paradise? "
There is not any haunt of prophecy,
Nor any old chimæra of the grave,
Neither the golden underground, nor isle
Melodious, where spirits gat them home,
Nor visionary south, nor cloudy palm
Remote on heaven's hill, that has endured
As April's green endures; or will endure
Like her remembrance of awakened birds,
Or her desire for June and evening, tipped
By the consummation of the swallow's wings.

V

She says: " But in contentment I still feel
The need of some imperishable bliss."
Death is the mother of beauty; hence from her,
Alone, shall come fulfillment to our dreams
And our desires. Although she strews the leaves
Of sure obliteration on our paths,
The path sick sorrow took, the many paths
Where triumph rang its brassy phrase, or love
Whispered a little out of tenderness,
She makes the willow shiver in the sun
For maidens who were wont to sit and gaze
Upon the grass, relinquished to their feet.
She causes boys to pile new plums and pears
On disregarded plate. The maidens taste
And stray impassioned in the littering leaves.

VI

Is there no change of death in paradise?
Does ripe fruit never fall? Or do the boughs
Hang always heavy in that perfect sky,
Unchanging, yet so like our perishing earth,
With rivers like our own that seek for seas
They never find, the same receding shores
That never touch with inarticulate pang?
Why set the pear upon those river-banks
Or spice the shores with odors of the plum?
Alas, that they should wear our colors there,
The silken weavings of our afternoons,
And pick the strings of our insipid lutes!
Death is the mother of beauty, mystical,
Within whose burning bosom we devise
Our earthly mothers waiting, sleeplessly.

VII

Supple and turbulent, a ring of men
Shall chant in orgy on a summer morn
Their boisterous devotion to the sun,
Not as a god, but as a god might be,
Naked among them, like a savage source.
Their chant shall be a chant of paradise,
Out of their blood, returning to the sky;
And in their chant shall enter, voice by voice,
The windy lake wherein their lord delights,
The trees, like serafin, and echoing hills,
That choir among themselves long afterward.
They shall know well the heavenly fellowship
Of men that perish and of summer morn.
And whence they came and whither they shall go
The dew upon their feet shall manifest.

VIII

She hears, upon that water without sound,
A voice that cries: " The tomb in Palestine
Is not the porch of spirits lingering.
It is the grave of Jesus, where he lay."
We live in an old chaos of the sun,
Or old dependency of day and night,
Or island solitude, unsponsored, free,
Of that wide water, inescapable.
Deer walk upon our mountains, and the quail
Whistle about us their spontaneous cries;
Sweet berries ripen in the wilderness;
And, in the isolation of the sky,
At evening, casual flocks of pigeons make
Ambiguous undulations as they sink,
Downward to darkness, on extended wings.

PETER QUINCE AT THE CLAVIER

I

Just as my fingers on these keys
Make music, so the selfsame sounds
On my spirit make a music, too.

Music is feeling, then, not sound;
And thus it is that what I feel,
Here in this room, desiring you,

Thinking of your blue-shadowed silk,
Is music. It is like the strain
Waked in the elders by Susanna.

Of a green evening, clear and warm,
She bathed in her still garden, while
The red-eyed elders watching, felt

The basses of their beings throb
In witching chords, and their thin blood
Pulse pizzicati of Hosanna.

II

In the green water, clear and warm,
Susanna lay.
She searched
The touch of springs,
And found
Concealed imaginings.
She sighed,
For so much melody.

Upon the bank, she stood
In the cool
Of spent emotions,
She felt, among the leaves,
The dew
Of old devotions.

She walked upon the grass,
Still quavering.
The winds were like her maids,
On timid feet,
Fetching her woven scarves,
Yet wavering.

A breath upon her hand
Muted the night.
She turned —
A cymbal crashed,
And roaring horns.

III

Soon, with a noise like tambourines,
Came her attendant Byzantines.

They wondered why Susanna cried
Against the elders by her side;

And as they whispered, the refrain
Was like a willow swept by rain.

Anon, their lamps' uplifted flame
Revealed Susanna and her shame.

And then, the simpering Byzantines
Fled, with a noise like tambourines.

IV

Beauty is momentary in the mind —
The fitful tracing of a portal;
But in the flesh it is immortal.

The body dies; the body's beauty lives.
So evenings die, in their green going,
A wave, interminably flowing.
So gardens die, their meek breath scenting
The cowl of winter, done repenting.
So maidens die, to the auroral
Celebration of a maiden's choral.

Susanna's music touched the bawdy strings
Of those white elders; but, escaping,
Left only Death's ironic scraping.
Now, in its immortality, it plays
On the clear viol of her memory,
And makes a constant sacrament of praise.

Short Stories

VERY many of the best short stories have been written by men or women who are better known for their longer works, and few writers have been able to reach anything like a first rank with short stories alone. Maupassant wrote novels, though they are not so good as his short stories, and Chekhov wrote superb plays. It is true that the ancient literatures are often nearly at their best in fables, parables, popular tales, but these are for the most part dramatized maxims or elaborated metaphors and belong as much to ethics as to fiction. Modern short stories, for all there has been so much talk about their techniques and triumphs, are hardly more than by-products of modern literature. Thousands of readers know *Madame Bovary* for scores who know Flaubert's *Legend of St. Julian the Hospitaller*, which is surely inferior only in length. I remember once, in a group of which half the members had genuine literary taste, asking what was the finest short story anybody knew. Ford Madox Ford instantly said *St. Julian*, and after some discussion nobody disagreed with him. Though unforgettable short stories have been written by Balzac, Turgenev, Tolstoi, Henry James, Anatole France, not to mention D. H. Lawrence, Somerset Maugham, Theodore Dreiser, James Joyce, all of these are thought of primarily as novelists.

I suppose that mere bulk makes some of the difference. Not that readers value a narrative more highly because it is long, but that they remember it more clearly because they have lived longer with its characters and events. Somerset Maugham, an expert critic, suggests that the element of time is what marks the short story off from the novel. " I think it possible that the short story should occupy itself with a single moment of time. . . . There is something static in the short story; the novel is dynamic. In the latter one thing leads to another; in the former it stays put. . . . The short story does not aim at the development of character; nor does it aim at the discovery of character. . . . The short-story writer can only show what his people are at the moment he chooses to interfere in their fates." But these admirable distinctions do not seem to me to make it clear why novels are so often preferred to short stories. The matter of time is incidental to the preference. The real point, I think, is that readers are more interested in the characters of fiction as a whole than in what happens to them. A novel, with its multiplication of happenings, can build up a character until it appears to have a life beyond all the incidents of the story. Reading the novel, you imagine other incidents in the character's past or future and feel that you know how he would behave in any one of them. But in a short story you have seldom learned more about the character than what was revealed in a single incident which, to make the story effective, commonly has had to be intense and so to be exclusive of all the phases of character not needed for a single effect. That is to say, in a short story there is not room for much character.

Length, however, is relative. I have here put *The Woman Who Rode Away*, by D. H. Lawrence, unhesitatingly among the short stories although it is almost as long as *My Mortal Enemy*, which I did not hesitate to put among the novels. *My Mortal Enemy* may be a novel in outline, but it is a novel. Myra is developed or discovered on every page. Veil after veil falls away, trait after trait comes out, and nothing is left but that last central mystery which sets off each person from any other. In *The Woman Who Rode Away* the heroine has no quality but her formless discontent, she has the sense at the very beginning of the adventure that she is already dead, and she numbly accepts, without change or growth, what happens as she waits for her dark end. She barely realizes that things are happening specifically to her, as does the reader. The interest lies in the happenings themselves, and all of them belong to one moment in her life. Lawrence was writing a short story. Yet I think it is fair to say that he was a better short-story writer for being a novelist too. At least he never, like many writers of short stories only, was satisfied with dexterous ingenuity in the manipulation of happenings. Somewhere about each of his stories there is something large, if only in the overtones.

What handicaps most short stories is the lack of something large about them. Maupassant and Chekhov are almost the only writers who have been able to achieve this through pure realism, by seeing simple facts so lucidly and presenting them so vividly that they come to readers like immediate experience and are somehow symptoms of all life without having to be symbols. Katherine Mansfield does this now and then, as in *The Doll's House*. The story seems to concern itself with nothing in the world but the episode which it relates. At the same time, nobody can read it without reflecting how cruel fortunate children can be to the unfortunate, and further reflecting that while they are more outspoken than their elders, they are not actually more cruel. The inevitable reflection enlarges the story.

All the other stories I have here selected make use of fancy in one way or another for this enlargement. *The Inmost Light* by Arthur Machen revives in London the ancient belief that men may traffic, like Roger Bacon and Paracelsus and Faust, in forbidden learning with forbidden and horrible consequences. *The Story of a Panic* by E. M. Forster fancies that Pan comes again, to bewilder smug visitors in Italy. *The Woman Who Rode Away* imagines that the descendants of Montezuma still keep up the rites of human sacrifice in the mountains of Chihuahua. *The Riddle* by Walter de la Mare is as fantastic as any folk-tale of the old

witch in the wood. A. E. Coppard's *Adam and Eve and Pinch Me*
is the story of a dream — is it a dream? — in which time is jumbled
and events still to come confuse the present. Zona Gale's *Bridal
Pond* is the legend of a vision so real to the man who had it that
it upsets his wits and gave him a strange reason for his madness.
Max Beerbohm's *Enoch Soames*, one of the most original stories
ever written, tells how Soames, that dim diabolist, sold himself to
the devil for a chance to find out what the name Soames would
mean a hundred years later, and found that he was remembered
only as a character in a story to be written by Max Beerbohm.

I have no natural inclination toward fanciful stories, and I did
not expect, when I began making this selection, that I should
choose so many of that kind. I have chosen these only because they
seemed the best before me. If there is a conclusion to be drawn it
it probably that fancy — which is a mode of poetry — can enlarge
the happenings of a story more easily than plain realism can, and
does it oftener.

                                                                        C.V.D.

~ *Max Beerbohm* ~

ENOCH SOAMES

WHEN a book about the literature of the 1890's was given by Mr. Holbrook Jackson to the world, I looked eagerly in the index for SOAMES, ENOCH. I had feared he would not be there. He was not there. But everybody else was. Many writers whom I had quite forgotten, or remembered but faintly, lived again for me, they and their work, in Mr. Holbrook Jackson's pages. The book was as thorough as it was brilliantly written. And thus the omission found by me was an all the deadlier record of poor Soames's failure to impress himself on his decade.

I dare say I am the only person who noticed the omission. Soames had failed so piteously as all that! Nor is there a counterpoise in the thought that if he had had some measure of success he might have passed, like those others, out of my mind, to return only at the historian's beck. It is true that had his gifts, such as they were, been acknowledged in his lifetime, he would never have made the bargain I saw him make — that strange bargain whose results have kept him always in the foreground of my memory. But it is from those very results that the full piteousness of him glares out.

Not my compassion, however, impels me to write of him. For his sake, poor fellow, I should be inclined to keep my pen out of the ink. It is ill to deride the dead. And how can I write about Enoch Soames without making him ridiculous? Or rather, how am I to hush up the horrid fact that he was ridiculous? I shall not be able to do that. Yet, sooner or later, write about him I must. You will see, in due course, that I have no option. And I may as well get the thing done now.

In the summer term of '93 a bolt from the blue flashed down on Oxford. It drove deep, it hurtlingly embedded itself in the soil. Dons and undergraduates stood around, rather pale, discussing nothing but it. Whence came it, this meteorite? From Paris. Its name? Will Rothenstein. Its aim? To do a series of twenty-four portraits in lithograph. These were to be published from the Bodley Head, London. The matter was urgent. Already the Warden of A, and the Master of B, and the Regius Professor of C, had meekly " sat." Dignified and doddering old men, who had never consented to sit to anyone, could not withstand this dynamic little stranger. He did not sue: he invited; he did not invite: he commanded. He was twenty-one years old. He wore spectacles that flashed more than any other pair ever seen. He was a wit. He was brimful of ideas. He knew Whistler. He knew Edmond de Goncourt. He knew everyone in Paris. He knew them all by heart. He was Paris in Oxford. It was whispered that, so soon as he had polished off his selection of dons, he was going to include a few undergraduates. It was a proud day for me when I — I was included. I liked Rothenstein not less than I feared him; and there arose between us a friendship that has grown ever warmer, and been more and more valued by me, with every passing year.

At the end of term he settled in — or, rather meteoritically into — London. It was to him I owed my first knowledge of that forever enchanting little world-in-itself Chelsea, and my first acquaintance with Walter Sickert and other august elders who dwelt there. It was Rothenstein that took me to see, in Cambridge Street, Pimlico, a

young man whose drawings were already famous among the few —
Aubrey Beardsley by name. With Rothenstein I paid my first visit
to the Bodley Head. By him I was inducted into another haunt of
intellect and daring, the domino room of the Café Royal.

There, on that October evening — there, in that exuberant vista
of gilding and crimson velvet set amidst all those opposing mirrors
and upholding caryatids, with fumes of tobacco ever rising to the
painted and pagan ceiling, and with the hum of presumably cynical conversation broken into so sharply now and again by the clatter
of dominoes shuffled on marble tables, I drew a deep breath, and
" This indeed," said I to myself, " is life."

It was the hour before dinner. We drank vermouth. Those who
knew Rothenstein were pointing him out to those who knew him
only by name. Men were constantly coming in through the swing-
doors and wandering slowly up and down in search of vacant tables,
or of tables occupied by friends. One of these rovers interested me
because I was sure he wanted to catch Rothenstein's eye. He had
twice passed our table, with a hesitating look; but Rothenstein, in
the thick of a disquisition on Puvis de Chavannes, had not seen
him. He was a stooping, shambling person, rather tall, very pale,
with longish and brownish hair. He had a thin vague beard — or,
rather, he had a chin on which a large number of hairs weakly curled
and clustered to cover its retreat. He was an odd-looking person; but
in the nineties odd apparitions were more frequent, I think, than
they are now. The young writers of that era — and I was sure this
man was a writer — strove earnestly to be distinct in aspect. This
man had striven unsuccessfully. He wore a soft black hat of clerical
kind but of Bohemian intention, and a gray waterproof cape which,
perhaps because it was waterproof, failed to be romantic. I decided
that dim was the mot juste for him. I had already essayed to write,
and was immensely keen on the mot juste, that Holy Grail of the
period.

The dim man was now again approaching our table, and this
time he made up his mind to pause in front of it. " You don't remember me," he said in a toneless voice.

Rothenstein brightly focused him. " Yes, I do," he replied after a
moment, with pride rather than effusion — pride in a retentive
memory. " Edwin Soames."

" Enoch Soames," said Enoch.

" Enoch Soames," repeated Rothenstein in a tone implying that it was enough to have hit on the surname. " We met in Paris two or three times when you were living there. We met at the Café Groche."

" And I came to your studio once."

" Oh yes; I was sorry I was out."

" But you were in. You showed me some of your paintings, you know. . . . I hear you're in Chelsea now."

" Yes."

I almost wondered that Mr. Soames did not, after this monosyllable, pass along. He stood patiently there, rather like a dumb animal, rather like a donkey looking over a gate. A sad figure, his. It occurred to me that *hungry* was perhaps the *mot juste* for him; but — hungry for what? He looked as if he had little appetite for anything. I was sorry for him; and Rothenstein, though he had not invited him to Chelsea, did ask him to sit down and have something to drink.

Seated, he was more self-assertive. He flung back the wings of his cape with a gesture which — had not those wings been waterproof — might have seemed to hurl defiance at things in general. And he ordered an absinthe. " *Je me tiens toujours fidèle,*" he told Rothenstein, " *á la sorcière glauque.*"

" It is bad for you," said Rothenstein dryly.

" Nothing is bad for one," answered Soames. " *Dans ce monde il n'y a ni de bien ni de mal.*"

" Nothing good and nothing bad? How do you mean? "

" I explained it all in the preface to *Negations.*"

" *Negations?* "

" Yes; I gave you a copy of it."

" Oh, yes, of course. But did you explain — for instance — that there was no such thing as bad or good grammar? "

" N-no," said Soames. " Of course in Art there is the good and the evil. But in Life — no." He was rolling a cigarette. He had weak white hands, not well washed, and with finger-tips much stained by nicotine. " In Life there are illusions of good and evil, but " — his voice trailed away to a murmur in which the words *vieux jeu* and *rococo* were faintly audible. I think he felt he was not doing himself justice, and feared that Rothenstein was going to point out fallacies. Anyhow, he cleared his throat and said: " *Parlons d'autre chose.*"

It occurs to you that he was a fool? It didn't to me. I was young and had not the clarity of judgment that Rothenstein already had. Soames was quite five or six years older than either of us. Also, he had written a book.

It was wonderful to have written a book.

If Rothenstein had not been there, I should have revered Soames. Even as it was, I respected him. And I was very near indeed to reverence when he said he had another book coming out soon. I asked if I might ask what kind of book it was to be.

" My poems," he answered. Rothenstein asked if this was to be the title of the book. The poet meditated on this suggestion, but said he rather thought of giving the book no title at all. " If a book is good in itself — " he murmured, waving his cigarette.

Rothenstein objected that absence of title might be bad for the sale of a book. " If," he urged, " I went into a bookseller's and said simply: ' Have you got? ' or ' Have you a copy of? ' how would they know what I wanted? "

" Oh, of course I should have my name on the cover," Soames answered earnestly. " And I rather want," he added, looking hard at Rothenstein, " to have a drawing of myself as frontispiece." Rothenstein admitted that this was a capital idea, and mentioned that he was going into the country and would be there for some time. He then looked at his watch, exclaimed at the hour, paid the waiter, and went away with me to dinner. Soames remained at his post of fidelity to the glaucous witch.

" Why were you so determined not to draw him? " I asked.

" Draw him? Him? How can one draw a man who doesn't exist? "

" He is dim," I admitted. But my *mot juste* fell flat. Rothenstein repeated that Soames was non-existent.

Still, Soames had written a book. I asked if Rothenstein had read *Negations*. He said he had looked into it, " but," he added crisply, " I don't profess to know anything about writing." A reservation very characteristic of the period! Painters would not then allow that anyone outside their own order had a right to any opinion about painting. This law (graven on the tablets brought down by Whistler from the summit of Fujiyama) imposed certain limitations. If

other arts than painting were not utterly unintelligible to all but
the men who practiced them, the law tottered — the Monroe Doctrine, as it were, did not hold good. Therefore no painter would
offer an opinion of a book without warning you at any rate that his
opinion was worthless. No one is a better judge of literature than
Rothenstein; but it wouldn't have done to tell him so in those days;
and I knew that I must form an unaided judgment on *Negations*.

Not to buy a book of which I had met the author face to face
would have been for me in those days an impossible act of self-
denial. When I returned to Oxford for the Christmas term I had
duly secured *Negations*. I used to keep it lying carelessly on the
table in my room, and whenever a friend took it up and asked what
it was about I would say: " Oh, it's rather a remarkable book. It's
by a man whom I know." Just " what it was about " I never was able
to say. Head or tail was just what I hadn't made of that slim green
volume. I found in the preface no clue to the exiguous labyrinth of
contents, and in that labyrinth nothing to explain the preface.

" Lean near to life. Lean very near — nearer.

" Life is web, and therein nor warp nor woof is, but web only.

" It is for this I am Catholick in church and in thought, yet do let
swift Mood weave there what the shuttle of Mood wills."

These were the opening phrases of the preface, but those which
followed were less easy to understand. Then came " Stark: A
Conte," about a midinette who, so far as I could gather, murdered,
or was about to murder, a mannequin. It was rather like a story by
Catulle Mendès in which the translator had either skipped or cut
out every alternate sentence. Next, a dialogue between Pan and St.
Ursula — lacking, I felt, in " snap." Next, some aphorisms (entitled
ἀφορίσματα). Throughout, in fact, there was a great variety of form;
and the forms had evidently been wrought with much care. It was
rather the substance that eluded me. Was there, I wondered, any
substance at all? It did now occur to me: suppose Enoch Soames
was a fool! Up cropped a rival hypothesis: suppose *I* was! I inclined
to give Soames the benefit of the doubt. I had read *L'Après-midi
d'un faune* without extracting a glimmer of meaning. Yet Mallarmé
— of course — was a Master. How was I to know that Soames wasn't
another? There was a sort of music in his prose, not indeed arresting, but perhaps, I thought, haunting, and laden perhaps with mean-

ings as deep as Mallarmé's own. I awaited his poems with an open mind.

And I looked forward to them with positive impatience after I had had a second meeting with him. This was on an evening in January. Going into the aforesaid domino room, I passed a table at which sat a pale man with an open book before him. He looked from his book to me, and I looked back over my shoulder with a vague sense that I ought to have recognized him. I returned to pay my respects. After exchanging a few words, I said with a glance to the open book, " I see I am interrupting you," and was about to pass on, but " I prefer," Soames replied in his toneless voice, " to be interrupted," and I obeyed his gesture that I should sit down.

I asked him if he often read here. " Yes; things of this kind I read here," he answered, indicating the title of his book — The Poems of Shelley.

" Anything that you really " — and I was going to say " admire? " But I cautiously left my sentence unfinished, and was glad that I had done so, for he said, with unwonted emphasis: " Anything second-rate."

I had read little of Shelley, but " Of course," I murmured, " he's very uneven."

" I should have thought evenness was just what was wrong with him. A deadly evenness. That's why I read him here. The noise of this place breaks the rhythm. He's tolerable here." Soames took up the book and glanced through the pages. He laughed. Soames's laugh was a short, single, and mirthless sound from the throat, unaccompanied by any movement of the face or brightening of the eyes. " What a period! " he uttered, laying the book down. And " What a country! " he added.

I asked rather nervously if he didn't think Keats had more or less held his own against the drawbacks of time and place. He admitted that there were " passages in Keats," but did not specify them. Of " the older men," as he called them, he seemed to like only Milton. " Milton," he said, " wasn't sentimental." Also: " Milton had a dark insight." And again: " I can always read Milton in the reading-room."

" The reading-room? "

" Of the British Museum. I go there every day."

" You do? I've only been there once. I'm afraid I found it rather
a depressing place. It — it seemed to sap one's vitality."

" It does. That's why I go there. The lower one's vitality, the
more sensitive one is to great art. I live near the Museum. I have
rooms in Dyott Street."

"And you go round to the reading-room to read Milton? "

" Usually Milton." He looked at me. " It was Milton," he cer-
tificatively added, " who converted me to Diabolism."

" Diabolism? Oh, yes? Really? " said I, with that vague discomfort and that intense desire to be polite which one feels when a man
speaks of his own religion. " You — worship the Devil? "

Soames shook his head. " It's not exactly worship," he qualified,
sipping his absinthe. " It's more a matter of trusting and encouraging. "

" Ah, yes. . . . But I had rather gathered from the preface to
Negations that you were a — a Catholic."

" *Je l'étais à cette époque.* Perhaps I still am. Yes, I'm a Catholic
Diabolist."

This profession he made in an almost cursory tone. I could see
that what was upmost in his mind was the fact that I had read
Negations. His pale eyes had for the first time gleamed. I felt as one
who is about to be examined, *viva voce,* on the very subject in which
he is shakiest. I hastily asked him how soon his poems were to be
published. " Next week," he told me.

" And are they to be published without a title? "

" No. I found a title, at last. But I shan't tell you what it is," as
though I had been so impertinent as to inquire. " I am not sure that
it wholly satisfies me. But it is the best I can find. It suggests something of the quality of the poems. . . . Strange growths, natural
and wild, yet exquisite," he added, " and many-hued, and full of
poisons."

I asked him what he thought of Baudelaire. He uttered the snort
that was his laugh, and " Baudelaire," he said, " was a *bourgeois
malgré lui.*" France had only one poet: Villon; " and two-thirds of
Villon were sheer journalism." Verlaine was " an *épicier malgré
lui.*" Altogether, rather to my surprise, he rated French literature
lower than English. There were " passages " in Villiers de l'Isle-

Adam. But "I," he summed up, "owe nothing to France." He nodded at me. "You'll see," he predicted.

I did not, when the time came, quite see that. I thought the author of *Fungoids* did — unconsciously, of course — owe something to the young Parisian decadents, or to the young English ones who owed something to *them*. I still think so. The little book — bought by me in Oxford — lies before me as I write. Its pale gray buckram cover and silver lettering have not worn well. Nor have its contents. Through these, with a melancholy interest, I have again been looking. They are not much. But at the time of their publication I had a vague suspicion that they *might* be. I suppose it is my capacity for faith, not poor Soames's work, that is weaker than it once was. . . .

To a Young Woman

> *Thou art, who hast not been!*
>   Pale tunes irresolute
>   And traceries of old sounds
>   Blown from a rotted flute
> Mingle with noise of cymbals rouged with rust,
> Nor not strange forms and epicene
>   Lie bleeding in the dust,
>   Being wounded with wounds.
>
>   For this it is
> That in thy counterpart
>   Of age-long mockeries
> *Thou hast not been nor art!*

There seemed to me a certain inconsistency as between the first and last lines of this. I tried, with bent brows, to resolve the discord. But I did not take my failure as wholly incompatible with a meaning in Soames's mind. Might it not rather indicate the depth of his meaning? As for the craftsmanship, "rouged with rust" seemed to me a fine stroke, and "nor not" instead of "and" had a curious felicity. I wondered who the Young Woman was, and what she had made of it all. I sadly suspect that Soames could not have made more of it than she. Yet, even now, if one doesn't try to make any sense at all of the poem, and reads it just for the sound, there is a certain grace of cadence. Soames was an artist — in so far as he was anything, poor fellow!

It seemed to me, when first I read *Fungoids*, that, oddly enough, the Diabolistic side of him was the best. Diabolism seemed to be a cheerful, even a wholesome, influence in his life.

NOCTURNE

Round and round the shutter'd Square
I stroll'd with the Devil's arm in mine.
No sound but the scrape of his hoofs was there
And the ring of his laughter and mine.
    We had drunk black wine.

*I scream'd: " I will race you, Master! "
" What matter," he shriek'd, " tonight
Which of us runs the faster?
There is nothing to fear tonight
    In the foul moon's light! "*

Then I look'd him in the eyes,
And I laugh'd full shrill at the lie he told
And the gnawing fear he would fain disguise.
It was true, what I'd time and again been told:
    He was old — old.

There was, I felt, quite a swing about that first stanza — a joyous and rollicking note of comradeship. The second was slightly hysterical perhaps. But I liked the third: it was so bracingly unorthodox, even according to the tenets of Soames's peculiar sect in the faith. Not much " trusting and encouraging " here! Soames triumphantly exposing the Devil as a liar, and laughing " full shrill," cut a quite heartening figure, I thought — then! Now, in the light of what befell, none of his poems depresses me so much as " Nocturne."

I looked out for what the metropolitan reviewers would have to say. They seemed to fall into two classes: those who had little to say and those who had nothing. The second class was the larger, and the words of the first were cold; insomuch that

Strikes a note of modernity throughout. . . . These tripping numbers. — *Preston Telegraph.*

was the only lure offered in advertisements by Soames's publisher.
I had hopes that when next I met the poet I could congratulate him
on having made a stir; for I fancied he was not so sure of his intrinsic greatness as he seemed. I was but able to say, rather coarsely,
when next I did see him, that I hoped *Fungoids* was " selling splendidly." He looked at me across his glass of absinthe and asked if I
had bought a copy. His publisher had told him that three had been
sold. I laughed, as at a jest.

" You don't suppose I care, do you? " he said, with something
like a snarl. I disclaimed the notion. He added that he was not a
tradesman. I said mildly that I wasn't, either, and murmured that
an artist who gave truly new and great things to the world had always to wait long for recognition. He said he cared not a sou for
recognition. I agreed that the act of creation was its own reward.

His moroseness might have alienated me if I had regarded myself as a nobody. But ah! hadn't both John Lane and Aubrey
Beardsley suggested that I should write an essay for the great new
venture that was afoot — *The Yellow Book*? And hadn't Henry
Harland, as editor, accepted my essay? And wasn't it to be in the
very first number? At Oxford I was still *in statu pupillari*. In London I regarded myself as very much indeed a graduate now — one
whom no Soames could ruffle. Partly to show off, partly in sheer
goodwill, I told Soames he ought to contribute to *The Yellow
Book*. He uttered from the throat a sound of scorn for that publication.

Nevertheless, I did, a day or two later, tentatively ask Harland
if he knew anything of the work of a man called Enoch Soames.
Harland paused in the midst of his characteristic stride around the
room, threw up his hands towards the ceiling, and groaned aloud:
he had often met " that absurd creature " in Paris, and this very
morning had received some poems in manuscript from him.

" Has he *no* talent? " I asked.

" He has an income. He's all right." Harland was the most joyous
of men and most generous of critics, and he hated to talk of anything about which he couldn't be enthusiastic. So I dropped the
subject of Soames. The news that Soames had an income did take
the edge off solicitude. I learned afterwards that he was the son
of an unsuccessful and deceased bookseller in Preston, but had

inherited an annuity of three hundred pounds from a married aunt,
and had no surviving relatives of any kind. Materially, then, he was
" all right." But there was still a spiritual pathos about him, sharpened for me now by the possibility that even the praises of the
Preston Telegraph might not have been forthcoming had he not
been the son of a Preston man. He had a sort of weak doggedness
which I could not but admire. Neither he nor his work received the
slightest encouragement; but he persisted in behaving as a personage: always he kept his dingy little flag flying. Wherever congregated the *jeunes féroces* of the arts, in whatever Soho restaurant
they had just discovered, in whatever music-hall they were most
frequenting, there was Soames in the midst of them, or, rather,
on the fringe of them, a dim but inevitable figure. He never sought
to propitiate his fellow-writers, never bated a jot of his arrogance
about his own work or of his contempt for theirs. To the painters
he was respectful, even humble; but for the poets and prosaists of
The Yellow Book, and later of *The Savoy,* he had never a word
but of scorn. He wasn't resented. It didn't occur to anybody that
he or his Catholic Diabolism mattered. When, in the autumn of
'96, he brought out (at his own expense, this time) a third book,
his last book, nobody said a word for or against it. I meant, but
forgot, to buy it. I never saw it, and am ashamed to say I don't even
remember what it was called. But I did, at the time of its publication, say to Rothenstein that I thought poor old Soames was really
a rather tragic figure, and that I believed he would literally die for
want of recognition. Rothenstein scoffed. He said I was trying to
get credit for a kind heart which I didn't possess; and perhaps this
was so. But at the private view of the New English Art Club, a few
weeks later, I beheld a pastel portrait of " Enoch Soames, Esq."
It was very like him, and very like Rothenstein to have done it.
Soames was standing near it, in his soft hat and his waterproof
cape, all through the afternoon. Anybody who knew him would
have recognized the portrait at a glance, but nobody who didn't
know him would have recognized the portrait from its bystander:
it " existed " so much more than he; it was bound to. Also, it had
not that expression of faint happiness which on this day was dis-
cernible, yes, in Soames's countenance. Fame had breathed on him.
Twice again in the course of the month I went to the New English,

and on both occasions Soames himself was on view there. Looking back, I regard the close of that exhibition as having been virtually the close of his career. He had felt the breath of Fame against his cheek — so late, for such a little while; and at its withdrawal he gave in, gave up, gave out. He, who had never looked strong or well, looked ghastly now — a shadow of the shade he had once been. He still frequented the domino room, but, having lost all wish to excite curiosity, he no longer read books there. " You read only at the Museum now? " asked I, with attempted cheerfulness. He said he never went there now. " No absinthe there," he muttered. It was the sort of thing that in the old days he would have said for effect; but it carried conviction now. Absinthe, erst but a point in the " personality " he had striven so hard to build up, was solace and necessity now. He no longer called it " la sorcière glauque." He had shed away all his French phrases. He had become a plain, unvarnished, Preston man.

Failure, if it be a plain, unvarnished, complete failure, and even though it be a squalid failure, has always a certain dignity. I avoided Soames because he made me feel rather vulgar. John Lane had published, by this time, two little books of mine, and they had had a pleasant little success of esteem. I was a — slight but definite — " personality." Frank Harris had engaged me to kick up my heels in The Saturday Review, Alfred Harmsworth was letting me do likewise in The Daily Mail. I was just what Soames wasn't. And he shamed my gloss. Had I known that he really and firmly believed in the greatness of what he as an artist had achieved, I might not have shunned him. No man who hasn't lost his vanity can be held to have altogether failed. Soames's dignity was an illusion of mine. One day in the first week of June 1897 that illusion went. But on the evening of that day Soames went too.

I had been out most of the morning, and, as it was too late to reach home in time for luncheon, I sought " the Vingtième." This little place — Restaurant du Vingtième Siècle, to give it its full title — had been discovered in '96 by the poets and prosaists, but had now been more or less abandoned in favor of some later find. I don't think it lived long enough to justify its name; but at that time there it still was, in Greek Street, a few doors from Soho Square, and almost opposite to that house where, in the first years of the century, a little girl, and with her a boy named De Quincey, made nightly encampment in darkness and hunger among dust and rats and old legal parchments. The Vingtième was but a small · whitewashed room, leading out into the street at one end and into a kitchen at the other. The proprietor and cook was a Frenchman, known to us as Monsieur Vingtième; the waiters were his two daughters, Rose and Berthe; and the food, according to faith, was good. The tables were so narrow, and were set so close· together that there was space for twelve of them, six jutting from either wall.

Only the two nearest to the door, as I went in, were occupied. On one side sat a tall, flashy, rather Mephistophelean man whom I had seen from time to time in the domino room and elsewhere. On the other side sat Soames. They made a queer contrast in that sunlit room — Soames sitting haggard in that hat and cape which nowhere at any season had I seen him doff, and this other, this keenly vital man, at sight of whom I more than ever wondered whether he were a diamond-merchant, a conjurer, or the head of a private detective agency. I was sure Soames didn't want my company; but I asked, as it would have seemed brutal not to, whether I might join him, and took the chair opposite to his. He was smoking a cigarette, with an untasted salmi of something on his plate and a half-empty bottle of Sauterne before him; and he was quite silent. I said that the preparations for the Jubilee made London impossible. (I rather liked them, really.) I professed a wish to go right away till the whole thing was over. In vain did I attune myself to his gloom. He seemed not to hear me nor even to see me. I felt that his behavior made me ridiculous in the eyes of the other man. The gangway between the two rows of tables at the Vingtième was hardly more than two feet wide (Rose and Berthe, in their ministrations, had always to edge past each other, quarreling in whispers as they did so), and anyone at the table abreast of yours was practically at yours. I thought our neighbor was amused at my failure to interest Soames, and so, as I could not explain to him that my insistence was merely charitable, I became silent. Without turning my head, I had him well within my range of vision. I hoped I looked less vulgar than he in contrast with Soames. I was sure he was not an Englishman, but what was his nationality?

Though his jet-black hair was enbrosse, I did not think he was French. To Berthe, who waited on him, he spoke French fluently, but with a hardly native idiom and accent. I gathered that this was his first visit to the Vingtième; but Berthe was offhand in her manner to him: he had not made a good impression. His eyes were handsome, but — like the Vingtième's tables — too narrow and set too close together. His nose was predatory, and the points of his mustache, waxed up beyond his nostrils, gave a fixity to his smile. Decidedly, he was sinister. And my sense of discomfort in his presence was intensified by the scarlet waistcoat which tightly, and so unseasonably in June, sheathed his ample chest. This waistcoat wasn't wrong merely because of the heat, either. It was somehow all wrong in itself. It wouldn't have done on Christmas morning. It would have struck a jarring note at the first night of *Hernani*. I was trying to account for its wrongness when Soames suddenly and strangely broke silence. " A hundred years hence! " he murmured, as in a trance.

" We shall not be here! " I briskly but fatuously added.

" We shall not be here. No," he droned, " but the Museum will still be just where it is. And the reading-room, just where it is. And people will be able to go and read there." He inhaled sharply, and a spasm as of actual pain contorted his features.

I wondered what train of thought poor Soames had been following. He did not enlighten me when he said, after a long pause: " You think I haven't minded."

" Minded what, Soames? "

" Neglect. Failure."

" Failure? " I said heartily. " Failure? " I repeated vaguely. " Neglect — yes, perhaps; but that's quite another matter. Of course you haven't been — appreciated. But what then? Any artist who — who gives — " What I wanted to say was: " Any artist who gives truly new and great things to the world has always to wait long for recognition "; but the flattery would not out: in the face of his misery, a misery so genuine and so unmasked, my lips would not say the words.

And then — he said them for me. I flushed. " That's what you were going to say, isn't it? " he asked.

" How did you know? "

"It's what you said to me three years ago, when *Fungoids* was published." I flushed the more. I need not have done so at all, for "It's the only important thing I ever heard you say," he continued. "And I've never forgotten it. It's a true thing. It's a horrible truth. But — d'you remember what I answered? I said: 'I don't care a sou for recognition.' And you believed me. You've gone on believing I'm above that sort of thing. You're shallow. What should you know of the feelings of a man like me? You imagine that a great artist's faith in himself and in the verdict of posterity is enough to keep him happy. . . . You've never guessed at the bitterness and loneliness, the " — his voice broke; but presently he resumed, speaking with a force that I had never known in him. "Posterity! What use is it to *me*? A dead man doesn't know that people are visiting his grave — visiting his birthplace — putting up tablets to him — unveiling statues of him. A dead man can't read the books that are written about him. A hundred years hence! Think of it! If I could come back to life *then* — just for a few hours — and go to the reading-room, and *read*! Or better still: if I could be projected, now, at this moment, into that future, into that reading-room, just for this one afternoon! I'd sell myself body and soul to the Devil for that! Think of the pages and pages in the catalogue: ' SOAMES, ENOCH ' endlessly — endless editions, commentaries, prolegomena, biographies " — but here he was interrupted by a sudden loud creak of the chair at the next table. Our neighbor had half risen from his place. He was leaning towards us, apologetically intrusive.

"Excuse — permit me," he said softly. "I have been unable not to hear. Might I take a liberty? In this little restaurant-sans-façon " — he spread wide his hands — "might I, as the phrase is, ' cut in '? "

I could but signify our acquiescence. Berthe had appeared at the kitchen door, thinking the stranger wanted his bill. He waved her away with his cigar, and in another moment had seated himself beside me, commanding a full view of Soames.

"Though not an Englishman," he explained, "I know my London well, Mr. Soames. Your name and fame — Mr. Beerbohm's too — very known to me. Your point is: who am *I*? " He glanced quickly over his shoulder, and in a lowered voice said: " I am the Devil."

I couldn't help it: I laughed. I tried not to, I knew there was nothing to laugh at, my rudeness shamed me, but — I laughed with increasing volume. The Devil's quiet dignity, the surprise and disgust of his raised eyebrows, did but the more dissolve me. I rocked to and fro, I lay back aching. I behaved deplorably.

"I am a gentleman, and," he said with intense emphasis, "I thought I was in the company of *gentlemen*."

"Don't!" I gasped faintly. "Oh, don't!"

"Curious, *nicht wahr?*" I heard him say to Soames. "There is a type of person to whom the very mention of my name is — oh-so-awfully-funny! In your theaters the dullest *comédien* needs only to say: 'The Devil!' and right away they give him 'the loud laugh that speaks the vacant mind.' Is it not so?"

I had now just breath enough to offer my apologies. He accepted them, but coldly, and readdressed himself to Soames.

"I am a man of business," he said, "and always I would put things through 'right now,' as they say in the States. You are a poet. *Les affaires* — you detest them. So be it. But with me you will deal, eh? What you have said just now gives me furiously to hope."

Soames had not moved, except to light a fresh cigarette. He sat crouched forward, with his elbows squared on the table, and his head just above the level of his hands, staring up at the Devil. "Go on," he nodded. I had no remnant of laughter in me now.

"It will be the more pleasant, our little deal," the Devil went on, "because you are — I mistake not? — a Diabolist."

"A Catholic Diabolist," said Soames.

The Devil accepted the reservation genially. "You wish," he resumed, "to visit now — this afternoon as-ever-is — the reading-room of the British Museum, yes? But of a hundred years hence, yes? *Parfaitement.* Time — an illusion. Past and future — they are as ever present as the present, or at any rate only what you call 'just-round-the-corner.' I switch you on to any date. I project you — pouf! You wish to be in the reading-room just as it will be on the afternoon of June 3, 1997? You wish to find yourself standing in that room, just past the swing-doors, this very minute, yes? And to stay there till closing time? Am I right?"

Soames nodded.

The Devil looked at his watch. " Ten past two," he said. " Closing time in summer same then as now: seven o'clock. That will give
you almost five hours. At seven o'clock — pouf — you find yourself again here, sitting at this table. I am dining tonight *dans le
monde* — *dans le higlif*. That concludes my present visit to your
great city. I come and fetch you here, Mr. Soames, on my way
home."

" Home? " I echoed.

" Be it never so humble! " said the Devil lightly.

" All right," said Soames.

" Soames! " I entreated. But my friend moved not a muscle.

The Devil had made as though to stretch forth his hand across
the table and touch Soames's forearm; but he paused in his gesture.

" A hundred years hence, as now," he smiled, " no smoking allowed in the reading-room. You would better therefore — "

Soames removed the cigarette from his mouth and dropped it
into his glass of Sauterne.

" Soames! " again I cried. " Can't you " — but the Devil had
now stretched forth his hand across the table. He brought it slowly
down on — the table-cloth. Soames's chair was empty. His cigarette
floated sodden in his wineglass. There was no other trace of him.

For a few moments the Devil let his hand rest where it lay, gazing at me out of the corners of his eyes, vulgarly triumphant.

A shudder shook me. With an effort I controlled myself and
rose from my chair. " Very clever," I said condescendingly. " But
— *The Time Machine* is a delightful book, don't you think? So
entirely original! "

" You are pleased to sneer," said the Devil, who had also risen,
" but it is one thing to write about an impossible machine; it is a
quite other thing to be a Supernatural Power." All the same, I had
scored.

Berthe had come forth at the sound of our rising. I explained to
her that Mr. Soames had been called away, and that both he and I
would be dining here. It was not until I was out in the open air that
I began to feel giddy. I have but the haziest recollection of what I
did, where I wandered, in the glaring sunshine of that endless afternoon. I remember the sound of carpenters' hammers all along Piccadilly, and the bare chaotic look of the half-erected " stands."

Was it in the Green Park, or in Kensington Gardens, or where was
it that I sat on a chair beneath a tree, trying to read an evening
paper? There was a phrase in the leading article that went on repeating itself in my fagged mind — " Little is hidden from this
august Lady full of the garnered wisdom of sixty years of Sovereignty." I remember wildly conceiving a letter (to reach Windsor
by express messenger told to await answer):

MADAM: Well knowing that Your Majesty is full of the garnered
wisdom of sixty years of Sovereignty, I venture to ask your advice
in the following delicate matter. Mr. Enoch Soames, whose poems
you may or may not know . . .

Was there no way of helping him — saving him? A bargain was a
bargain, and I was the last man to aid or abet anyone in wriggling
out of a reasonable obligation. I wouldn't have lifted a little finger
to save Faust. But poor Soames! — doomed to pay without respite
an eternal price for nothing but a fruitless search and a bitter dis-
illusioning. . . .

Odd and uncanny it seemed to me that he, Soames, in the flesh,
in the waterproof cape, was at this moment living in the last decade of the next century, poring over books not yet written, and
seeing and seen by men not yet born. Uncannier and odder still,
that tonight and evermore he would be in hell. Assuredly, truth
was stranger than fiction.

Endless that afternoon was. Almost I wished I had gone with
Soames — not indeed to stay in the reading-room, but to sally
forth for a brisk sightseeing walk around a new London. I wandered
restlessly out of the park I had sat in. Vainly I tried to imagine
myself an ardent tourist from the eighteenth century. Intolerable
was the strain of the slow-passing and empty minutes. Long before
seven o'clock I was back at the Vingtième.

I sat there just where I had sat for luncheon. Air came in listlessly through the open door behind me. Now and again Rose or
Berthe appeared for a moment. I had told them I would not order
any dinner till Mr. Soames came. A hurdy-gurdy began to play,
abruptly drowning the noise of a quarrel between some Frenchmen further up the street. Whenever the tune was changed I heard

the quarrel still raging. I had bought another evening paper on my way. I unfolded it. My eyes gazed ever away from it to the clock over the kitchen door. . . .

Five minutes, now, to the hour! I remembered that clocks in restaurants are kept five minutes fast. I concentrated my eyes on the paper. I vowed I would not look away from it again. I held it upright, at its full width, close to my face, so that I had no view of anything but it. . . . Rather a tremulous sheet? Only because of the draft, I told myself.

My arms gradually became stiff; they ached; but I could not drop them — now. I had a suspicion, I had a certainty. Well, what then? . . . What else had I come for? Yet I held tight that barrier of newspaper. Only the sound of Berthe's brisk footstep from the kitchen enabled me, forced me, to drop it, and to utter:

" What shall we have to eat, Soames? "

" Il est souffrant, ce pauvre Monsieur Soames? " asked Berthe.

" He's only — tired." I asked her to get some wine — Burgundy — and whatever food might be ready. Soames sat crouched forward against the table, exactly as when last I had seen him. It was as though he had never moved — he who had moved so unimaginably far. Once or twice in the afternoon it had for an instant occurred to me that perhaps his journey was not to be fruitless — that perhaps we had all been wrong in our estimate of the works of Enoch Soames. That we had been horribly right was horribly clear from the look of him. But " Don't be discouraged," I falteringly said. " Perhaps it's only that you — didn't leave enough time. Two, three centuries hence, perhaps — "

" Yes," his voice came. " I've thought of that."

" And now — now for the more immediate future! Where are you going to hide? How would it be if you caught the Paris express from Charing Cross? Almost an hour to spare. Don't go on to Paris. Stop at Calais. Live in Calais. He'd never think of looking for you in Calais."

" It's like my luck," he said, " to spend my last hours on earth with an ass." But I was not offended. " And a treacherous ass," he strangely added, tossing across to me a crumpled bit of paper which he had been holding in his hand. I glanced at the writing on it — some sort of gibberish, apparently. I laid it impatiently aside.

" Come, Soames! Pull yourself together! This isn't a mere mat-
ter of life and death. It's a question of eternal torment, mind you!
You don't mean to say you're going to wait limply here till the
Devil comes to fetch you? "

" I can't do anything else. I've no choice."

" Come! This is ' trusting and encouraging ' with a vengeance!
This is Diabolism run mad! " I filled his glass with wine. " Surely,
now that you've seen the brute — "

" It's no good abusing him."

" You must admit there's nothing Miltonic about him, Soames."

" I don't say he's not rather different from what I expected."

" He's a vulgarian, he's a swell-mobsman, he's the sort of man
who hangs about the corridors of trains going to the Riviera and
steals ladies' jewel-cases. Imagine eternal torment presided over by
him! "

" You don't suppose I look forward to it, do you? "

" Then why not slip quietly out of the way? "

Again and again I filled his glass, and always, mechanically, he
emptied it; but the wine kindled no spark of enterprise in him. He
did not eat, and I myself ate hardly at all. I did not in my heart
believe that any dash for freedom could save him. The chase would
be swift, the capture certain. But better anything than this passive,
meek, miserable waiting. I told Soames that for the honor of the
human race he ought to make some show of resistance. He asked
what the human race had ever done for him. " Besides," he said,
" can't you understand that I'm in his power? You saw him touch
me, didn't you? There's an end of it. I've no will. I'm sealed."

I made a gesture of despair. He went on repeating the word
sealed. I began to realize that the wine had clouded his brain. No
wonder! Foodless he had gone into futurity, foodless he still was.
I urged him to eat at any rate some bread. It was maddening to
think that he, who had so much to tell, might tell nothing. " How
was it all," I asked, " yonder? Come! Tell me your adventures."

" They'd make first-rate ' copy,' wouldn't they? "

" I'm awfully sorry for you, Soames, and I make all possible allowances; but what earthly right have you to insinuate that I should
make ' copy,' as you call it, out of you? "

The poor fellow pressed his hands to his forehead. " I don't know," he said. "I had some reason, I know. . . . I'll try to remember."

"That's right. Try to remember everything. Eat a little more bread. What did the reading-room look like?"

"Much as usual," he at length muttered.

"Many people there?"

"Usual sort of number."

"What did they look like?"

Soames tried to visualize them. "They all," he presently remembered, "looked very like one another."

My mind took a fearsome leap. "All dressed in Jaeger?"

"Yes. I think so. Grayish-yellowish stuff."

"A sort of uniform?" He nodded. "With a number on it, perhaps? — a number on a large disk of metal sewn onto the left sleeve? DKF 78,910 — that sort of thing?" It was even so. "And all of them — men and women alike — looking very well cared-for? Very Utopian? And smelling rather strongly of carbolic? And all of them quite hairless?" I was right every time. Soames was only not sure whether the men and women were hairless or shorn. "I hadn't time to look at them very closely," he explained.

"No, of course not. But — "

"They stared at me, I can tell you. I attracted a great deal of attention." At last he had done that! "I think I rather scared them. They moved away whenever I came near. They followed me about at a distance, wherever I went. The men at the round desk in the middle seemed to have a sort of panic whenever I went to make inquiries."

"What did you do when you arrived?"

Well, he had gone straight to the catalogue, of course — to the S volumes, and had stood long before SN–SOF, unable to take this volume out of the shelf, because his heart was beating so. . . . At first, he said, he wasn't disappointed — he only thought there was some new arrangement. He went to the middle desk and asked where the catalogue of *twentieth*-century books was kept. He gathered that there was still only one catalogue. Again he looked up his name, stared at the three little pasted slips he had known so well. Then he went and sat down for a long time. . . .

"And then," he droned, " I looked up the *Dictionary of National*

Biography and some encyclopedias. . . . I went back to the middle
desk and asked what was the best modern book on late nineteenth-
century literature. They told me Mr. T. K. Nupton's book was
considered the best. I looked it up in the catalogue and filled in a
form for it. It was brought to me. My name wasn't in the index,
but — Yes! " he said with a sudden change of tone. " That's what
I'd forgotten. Where's that bit of paper? Give it me back."

I, too, had forgotten that cryptic screed. I found it fallen on the
floor, and handed it to him.

He smoothed it out, nodding and smiling at me disagreeably.
" I found myself glancing through Nupton's book," he resumed.
" Not very easy reading. Some sort of phonetic spelling. . . . All
the modern books I saw were phonetic."

" Then·I don't want to hear any more, Soames, please."

" The proper names seemed all to be spelt in the old way. But for
that, I mightn't have noticed my own name."

" Your own name? Really? Soames, I'm very glad."

" And yours."

" No! "

" I thought I should find you waiting here tonight. So I took the
trouble to copy out the passage, Read it."

I snatched the paper. Soames's handwriting was characteristically
dim. It, and the noisome spelling, and my excitement, made me
all the slower to grasp what T. K. Nupton was driving at.

The document lies before me at this moment. Strange that the
words I here copy out for you were copied out for me by poor
Soames just seventy-eight years hence. . . .

From p. 234 of *Inglish Littracher 1890–1900* bi T. K. Nupton,
publishd bi th Stait, 1992:

" Fr egzarmpl, a riter ov th time, naimd Max Beerbohm, hoo woz
stil alive in th twentieth cenchri, rote a stauri in wich e pautraid an
immajnari karrakter kauld ' Enoch Soames ' — a thurd-rait poit hoo
beleevz imself a grate jeneus an maix a bargin with th Devvl in
auder ter no wot posterriti thinx ov im! It iz a sumwot labud sattire
but not without vallu az showing hou seriusli the yung men ov th
aiteen-ninetiz took themselvz. Nou that the littreri profeshn haz
bin auganized az a departmnt of publik servis, our riters hav found

their levvl an hav lernt ter doo their duti without thort ov th morro.
' Th laibrer iz werthi ov hiz hire,' an that iz aul. Thank hevvn we
hav no Enoch Soameses amung us todai! "

I found that by murmuring the words aloud (a device which I
commend to my reader) I was able to master them, little by little.
The clearer they became, the greater was my bewilderment, my
distress and horror. The whole thing was a nightmare. Afar, the
great grisly background of what was in store for the poor dear art
of letters; here, at the table, fixing on me a gaze that made me hot
all over, the poor fellow whom — whom evidently . . . but no:
whatever down-grade my character might take in coming years, I
should never be such a brute as to —
     Again I examined the screed. " Immajnari " — but here Soames
was, no more imaginary, alas! than I. And " Iabud " — what on
earth was that? (To this day, I have never made out that word.)
" It's all very — baffling," I at length stammered.
     Soames said nothing, but cruelly did not cease to look at me.
     " Are you sure," I temporized, " quite sure you copied the thing
out correctly? "
     " Quite."
     " Well, then it's this wretched Nupton who must have made
— must be going to make — some idiotic mistake. . . . Look here,
Soames! you know me better than to suppose that I . . . After all,
the name ' Max Beerbohm ' is not at all an uncommon one, and
there must be several Enoch Soameses running around — or rather,
' Enoch Soames ' is a name that might occur to anyone writing a
story. And I don't write stories: I'm an essayist, an observer, a re-
corder. . . . I admit that it's an extraordinary coincidence. But
you must see — "
     " I see the whole thing," said Soames quietly. And he added, with
a touch of his old manner, but with more dignity than I had ever
known in him: " Parlons d'autre chose."
     I accepted that suggestion very promptly. I returned straight
to the more immediate future. I spent most of the long evening in
renewed appeals to Soames to slip away and seek refuge somewhere.
I remember saying at last that if indeed I was destined to write
about him, the supposed " stauri " had better have at least a happy

ending. Soames repeated those last three words in a tone of intense scorn. " In Life and in Art," he said, " all that matters is an *inevitable* ending."

" But," I urged, more hopeful than I felt, " an ending that can be avoided *isn't* inevitable."

" You aren't an artist," he rasped. " And you're so hopelessly not an artist that, so far from being able to imagine a thing and make it seem true, you're going to make even a true thing seem as if you'd made it up. You're a miserable bungler. And it's like my luck."

I protested that the miserable bungler was not I — was not going to be I — but T. K. Nupton; and we had a rather heated argument, in the thick of which it suddenly seemed to me that Soames saw he was in the wrong: he had quite physically cowered. But I wondered why — and now I guessed with a cold throb just why — he stared so, past me. The bringer of that " inevitable ending " filled the doorway.

I managed to turn in my chair and to say, not without a semblance of lightness: " Aha, come in! " Dread was indeed rather blunted in me by his looking so absurdly like a villain in a melodrama. The sheen of his tilted hat and of his shirt-front, the repeated twists he was giving to his mustache, and most of all the magnificence of his sneer, gave token that he was there only to be foiled.

He was at our table in a stride. " I am sorry," he sneered witheringly, " to break up your pleasant party, but — "

" You don't: you complete it," I assured him. " Mr. Soames and I want to have a little talk with you. Won't you sit? Mr. Soames got nothing — frankly nothing — by his journey this afternoon. We don't wish to say that the whole thing was a swindle — a common swindle. On the contrary, we believe you meant well. But of course the bargain, such as it was, is off."

The Devil gave no verbal answer. He merely looked at Soames and pointed with rigid forefinger to the door. Soames was wretchedly rising from his chair when, with a desperate quick gesture, I swept together two dinner-knives that were on the table and laid their blades across each other. The Devil stepped sharp back against the table behind him, averting his face and shuddering.

" You are not superstitious! " he hissed.

" Not at all," I smiled.

" Soames! " he said as to an underling, but without turning his face, " put those knives straight! "

With an inhibitive gesture to my friend, " Mr. Soames," I said emphatically to the Devil, " is a *Catholic Diabolist* "; but my poor friend did the Devil's bidding, not mine; and now, with his master's eyes again fixed on him, he arose, he shuffled past me. I tried to speak. It was he that spoke. " Try," was the prayer he threw back at me as the Devil pushed him roughly out through the door, " try to make them know that I did exist! "

In another instant I too was through that door. I stood staring all ways — up the street, across it, down it. There was moonlight and lamplight, but there was not Soames nor that other.

Dazed, I stood there. Dazed, I turned back, at length, into the little room; and I suppose I paid Berthe or Rose for my dinner and luncheon, and for Soames's; I hope so, for I never went to the Vingtième again. Ever since that night I have avoided Greek Street altogether. And for years I did not set foot even in Soho Square, because on that same night it was there that I paced and loitered, long and long, with some such dull sense of hope as a man has in not straying far from the place where he has lost something. . . . " Round and round the shutter'd Square " — that line came back to me on my lonely beat, and with it the whole stanza, ringing in my brain and bearing in on me how tragically different from the happy scene imagined by him was the poet's actual experience of that prince in whom of all princes we should put not our trust.

But — strange how the mind of an essayist, be it never so stricken, roves and ranges! — I remember pausing before a wide doorstep and wondering if perchance it was on this very one that the young De Quincey lay ill and faint while poor Ann flew as fast as her feet would carry her to Oxford Street, the " stony-hearted stepmother " of them both, and came back bearing that " glass of port wine and spices " but for which he might, so he thought, actually have died. Was this the very doorstep that the old De Quincey used to revisit in homage? I pondered Ann's fate, the cause of her sudden vanishing from the ken of her boy friend; and presently I blamed myself for letting the past override the present. Poor vanished Soames!

And for myself, too, I began to be troubled. What had I better do? Would there be a hue and cry — Mysterious Disappearance of an Author, and all that? He had last been seen lunching and dining in my company. Hadn't I better get a hansom and drive straight to Scotland Yard? . . . They would think I was a lunatic. After all, I reassured myself, London was a very large place, and one very dim figure might easily drop out of it unobserved — now especially, in the blinding glare of the near Jubilee. Better say nothing at all, I thought.

And I was right. Soames's disappearance made no stir at all. He was utterly forgotten before anyone, so far as I am aware, noticed that he was no longer hanging around. Now and again some poet or prosaist may have said to another: " What has become of that man Soames? " but I never heard any such question asked. The solicitor through whom he was paid his annuity may be presumed to have made inquiries, but no echo of these resounded. There was something rather ghastly to me in the general unconsciousness that Soames had existed, and more than once I caught myself wondering whether Nupton, that babe unborn, were going to be right in thinking him a figment of my brain.

In that extract from Nupton's repulsive book there is one point which perhaps puzzles you. How is it that the author, though I have here mentioned him by name and have quoted the exact words he is going to write, is not going to grasp the obvious corollary that I have invented nothing? The answer can be only this: Nupton will not have read the later passages of this memoir. Such lack of thoroughness is a serious fault in anyone who undertakes to do scholar's work. And I hope these words will meet the eye of some contemporary rival to Nupton and be the undoing of Nupton.

I like to think that some time between 1992 and 1997 somebody will have looked up this memoir and will have forced on the world his inevitable and startling conclusions. And I have reasons for be-lieving that this will be so. You realize that the reading-room into which Soames was projected by the Devil was in all respects pre-cisely as it will be on the afternoon of June 3, 1997. You realize, therefore, that on that afternoon, when it comes round, there the selfsame crowd will be, and there Soames too will be, punctually, he and they doing precisely what they did before. Recall now Soames's account of the sensation he made. You may say that the mere difference of his costume was enough to make him sensational in that uniformed crowd. You wouldn't say so if you had ever seen him. I assure you that in no period could Soames be anything but dim. The fact that people are going to stare at him, and follow him around, and seem afraid of him, can be explained only on the hypothesis that they will somehow have been prepared for his ghostly visitation. They will have been awfully waiting to see whether he really would come. And when he does come the effect will of course be — awful.

An authentic, guaranteed, proven ghost, but — only a ghost, alas! Only that. In his first visit Soames was a creature of flesh and blood, whereas the creatures into whose midst he was projected were but ghosts, I take it — solid, palpable, vocal, but unconscious and automatic ghosts, in a building that was itself an illusion. Next time that building and those creatures will be real. It is of Soames that there will be but the semblance. I wish I could think him destined to revisit the world actually, physically, consciously. I wish he had this one brief escape, this one small treat, to look forward to. I never forget him for long. He is where he is, and forever. The more rigid moralists among you may say he has only himself to blame. For my part, I think he has been very hardly used. It is well that vanity should be chastened; and Enoch Soames's vanity was, I admit, above the average and called for special treatment. But there was no need for vindictiveness. You say he contracted to pay the price he is paying; yes; but I maintain that he was induced to do so by fraud. Well informed in all things, the Devil must have known that my friend would gain nothing by his visit to futurity. The whole thing was a very shabby trick. The more I think of it, the more detestable the Devil seems to me.

Of him I have caught sight several times, here and there, since that day at the Vingtième. Only once, however, have I seen him at close quarters. This was in Paris. I was walking, one afternoon, along the rue d'Antin, when I saw him advancing from the opposite direction — overdressed as ever, and swinging an ebony cane, and altogether behaving as though the whole pavement belonged to him. At thought of Enoch Soames and the myriads of other sufferers eternally in this brute's dominion, a great cold wrath filled me, and I drew myself up to my full height. But — well, one is so used to nodding and smiling in the street to anybody whom one knows that the action becomes almost independent of oneself: to prevent it requires a very sharp effort and great presence of mind. I was miserably aware, as I passed the Devil, that I nodded and smiled to him. And my shame was the deeper and hotter because he, if you please, stared straight at me with the utmost haughtiness.

To be cut — deliberately cut — by *him!* I was, I still am, furious at having had that happen to me.

Arthur Machen

THE INMOST LIGHT

I

ONE evening in autumn, when the deformities of London were veiled in faint blue mist, and its vistas and far-reaching streets seemed splendid, Mr. Charles Salisbury was slowly pacing down Rupert Street, drawing nearer to his favorite restaurant by slow degrees. His eyes were downcast in study of the pavement, and thus it was that as he passed in at the narrow door, a man who had come up from the lower end of the street jostled against him.

" I beg your pardon — wasn't looking where I was going. Why, it's Dyson! "

" Yes, quite so. How are you, Salisbury? "

" Quite well. But where have you been, Dyson? I don't think I can have seen you for the last five years? "

" No; I dare say not. You remember I was getting rather hard up when you came to my place at Charlotte Street? "

" Perfectly. I think I remember you telling me that you owed five weeks' rent, and that you had parted with your watch for a comparatively small sum."

" My dear Salisbury, your memory is admirable. Yes, I was hard up. But the curious thing is that soon after you saw me I became harder up. My financial state was described by a friend as ' stone broke.' I don't approve of slang, mind you, but such was my condition. But suppose we go in; there might be other people who would like to dine — it's human weakness, Salisbury."

" Certainly; come along. I was wondering as I walked down whether the corner table were taken. It has a velvet back, you know."

" I know the spot; it's vacant. Yes, as I was saying, I became even harder up."

" What did you do then? " asked Salisbury, disposing of his hat, and settling down in the corner of the seat, with a glance of fond anticipation at the menu.

" What did I do? Why, I sat down and reflected. I had a good classical education, and a positive distaste for business of any kind: that was the capital with which I faced the world. Do you know, I have heard people describe olives as nasty! What lamentable Philistinism! I have often thought, Salisbury, that I could write genuine poetry under the influence of olives and red wine. Let us have Chianti; it may not be very good, but the flasks are simply charming."

" It is pretty good here. We may as well have a big flask."

" Very good. I reflected, then, on my want of prospects, and I determined to embark in literature."

" Really; that was strange. You seem in pretty comfortable circumstances, though."

" Though! What a satire upon a noble profession. I am afraid, Salisbury, you haven't a proper idea of the dignity of an artist. You see me sitting at my desk — or at least you can see me if you care to call — with pen and ink, and simple nothingness before me, and if you come again in a few hours you will (in all probability) find a creation! "

" Yes, quite so. I had an idea that literature was not remunerative."

" You are mistaken; its rewards are great. I may mention, by the way, that shortly after you saw me I succeeded to a small income. An uncle died, and proved unexpectedly generous."

" Ah, I see. That must have been convenient."

" It was pleasant — undeniably pleasant. I have always considered it in the light of an endowment of my researches. I told you I was a man of letters; it would, perhaps, be more correct to describe myself as a man of science."

" Dear me, Dyson, you have really changed very much in the last few years. I had a notion, don't you know, that you were a sort of idler about town, the kind of man one might meet on the north side of Piccadilly every day from May to July."

" Exactly. I was even then forming myself, though all unconsciously. You know my poor father could not afford to send me to the university. I used to grumble, in my ignorance, at not having completed my education. That was the folly of youth, Salisbury; my university was Piccadilly. There I began to study the great science which still occupies me."

" What science do you mean? "

" The science of the great city; the physiology of London; literally and metaphysically the greatest subject that the mind of man can conceive. What an admirable salmi this is; undoubtedly the final end of the pheasant. Yet I feel sometimes positively overwhelmed with the thought of the vastness and complexity of London. Paris a man may get to understand thoroughly with a reasonable amount of study; but London is always a mystery. In Paris you may say: ' Here live the actresses, here the Bohemians, and the Ratés '; but it is different in London. You may point out a street, correctly enough, as the abode of washerwomen; but in that second floor a man may be studying Chaldee roots, and in the garret over the way a forgotten artist is dying by inches."

" I see you are Dyson, unchanged and unchangeable," said Salisbury, slowly sipping his Chianti. " I think you are misled by a too fervid imagination; the mystery of London exists only in your fancy. It seems to me a dull place enough. We seldom hear of a really

artistic crime in London, whereas I believe Paris abounds in that
sort of thing."

"Give me some more wine. Thanks. You are mistaken, my dear
fellow, you are really mistaken. London has nothing to be ashamed
of in the way of crime. Where we fail is for want of Homers, not
Agamemnons. _Carent quia vate sacro_, you know."

"I recall the quotation. But I don't think I quite follow you."

"Well, in plain language, we have no good writers in London
who make a specialty of that kind of thing. Our common reporter
is a dull dog; every story that he has to tell is spoilt in the telling.
His idea of horror and of what excites horror is so lamentably deficient. Nothing will content the fellow but blood, vulgar red blood,
and when he can get it he lays it on thick and considers that he
has produced a telling article. It's a poor notion. And, by some
curious fatality, it is the most commonplace and brutal murders
which always attract the most attention and get written up the
most. For instance, I dare say that you never heard of the Harlesden
case?"

"No; no, I don't remember anything about it."

"Of course not. And yet the story is a curious one. I will tell it
you over our coffee. Harlesden, you know, or I expect you don't
know, is quite on the out-quarters of London; something curiously
different from your fine old crusted suburb like Norwood or Hampstead, different as each of these is from the other. Hampstead, I
mean, is where you look for the head of your great China house
with his three acres of land and pine houses, though of late there
is the artistic substratum; while Norwood is the home of the prosperous middle-class family who took the house ' because it was near
the Palace,' and sickened of the Palace six months afterwards; but
Harlesden is a place of no character. It's too new to have any character as yet. There are the rows of red houses and the rows of white
houses and the bright green Venetians, and the blistering doorways,
and the little back yards they call gardens, and a few feeble shops,
and then, just as you think you're going to grasp the physiognomy
of the settlement, it all melts away."

"How the dickens is that? The houses don't tumble down before
one's eyes, I suppose!"

" Well, no, not exactly that. But Harlesden as an entity disappears. Your street turns into a quiet lane, and your staring houses into elm trees, and the back gardens into green meadows. You pass instantly from town to country; there is no transition as in a small country town, no soft gradations of wider lawns and orchards, with houses gradually becoming less dense, but a dead stop. I believe the people who live there mostly go into the City. I have seen once or twice a laden bus bound thitherwards. But however that may be, I can't conceive a greater loneliness in a desert at midnight than there is there at midday. It is like a city of the dead; the streets are glaring and desolate, and as you pass, it suddenly strikes you that this too is part of London. Well, a year or two ago there was a doctor living there; he had set up his brass plate and his red lamp at the very end of one of those shining streets, and from the back of the house the fields stretched away to the north. I don't know what his reason was in settling down in such an out-of-the-way place; perhaps Dr. Black, as we will call him, was a far-seeing man and looked ahead. His relations, so it appeared afterwards, had lost sight of him for many years and didn't even know he was a doctor, much less where he lived. However, there he was settled in Harlesden, with some fragments of a practice, and an uncommonly pretty wife. People used to see them walking out together in the summer evenings soon after they came to Harlesden, and, so far as could be observed, they seemed a very affectionate couple. These walks went on through the autumn, and then ceased, but, of course, as the days grew dark and the weather cold, the lanes near Harlesden might be expected to lose many of their attractions. All through the winter nobody saw anything of Mrs. Black; the doctor used to reply to his patients' inquiries that she was a ' little out of sorts, would be better, no doubt, in the spring.' But the spring came, and the summer, and no Mrs. Black appeared, and at last people began to rumor and talk amongst themselves, and all sorts of queer things were said at ' high teas,' which you possibly have heard are the only form of entertainment known in such suburbs. Dr. Black began to surprise some very odd looks cast in his direction, and the practice, such as it was, fell off before his eyes. In short, when the neighbors whispered about the matter, they whispered that Mrs. Black was dead, and that the doctor had made away with her. But this wasn't the case; Mrs. Black was seen alive in June. It was a Sunday afternoon, one of those few exquisite days that an English climate offers, and half London had strayed out into the fields, north, south, east, and west, to smell the scent of the white may, and to see if the wild roses were yet in blossom in the hedges. I had gone out myself early in the morning, and had had a long ramble, and somehow or other as I was steering homeward I found myself in this very Harlesden we have been talking about. To be exact, I had a glass of beer in the General Gordon, the most flourishing house in the neighborhood, and as I was wandering rather aimlessly about, I saw an uncommonly tempting gap in a hedgerow and resolved to explore the meadow beyond. Soft grass is very grateful to the feet after the infernal grit strewn on suburban sidewalks, and after walking about for some time I thought I should like to sit down on a bank and have a smoke. While I was getting out my pouch, I looked up in the direction of the houses, and as I looked I felt my breath caught back, and my teeth began to chatter, and the stick I had in one hand snapped in two with the grip I gave it. It was as if I had had an electric current down my spine, and yet for some moment of time which seemed long, but which must have been very short, I caught myself wondering what on earth was the matter. Then I knew what had made my very heart shudder and my bones grind together in an agony. As I glanced up I had looked straight towards the last house in the row before me, and in an upper window of that house I had seen for some short fraction of a second a face. It was the face of a woman, and yet it was not human. You and I, Salisbury, have heard in our time, as we sat in our seats in church in sober English fashion, of a lust that cannot be satiated and of a fire that is unquenchable, but few of us have any notion what these words mean. I hope you never may, for as I saw that face at the window, with the blue sky above me and the warm air playing in gusts about me, I knew I had looked into another world — looked through the window of a commonplace, brand-new house and seen hell open before me. When the first shock was over, I thought once or twice that I should have fainted; my face streamed with a cold sweat, and my breath came and went in sobs, as if I had been half drowned. I managed to get up at last and walk round to the street, and there I saw the name ' Dr. Black ' on the post by the front gate. As fate or my luck would have it, the door opened and a man came down the steps as I passed by. I had no doubt it was the doctor himself. He was of a type rather common in London; long and thin, with a pasty face and a dull black mustache. He gave me a look as we passed each other on the pavement, and though it was merely the casual glance which one foot-passenger bestows on another, I felt convinced in my mind that here was an ugly customer to deal with. As you may imagine, I went my way a good deal puzzled and horrified, too, by what I had seen; for I had paid another visit to the General Gordon and had got together a good deal of the common gossip of the place about the Blacks. I didn't mention the fact that I had seen a woman's face in the window; but I heard that Mrs. Black had been much admired for her beautiful golden hair, and round what had struck me with such a nameless terror, there was a mist of flowing yellow hair, as it was an aureole of glory round the visage of a satyr. The whole thing bothered me in an indescribable manner; and when I got home I tried my best to think of the impression I had received as an illusion, but it was no use. I knew very well I had seen what I have tried to describe to you, and I was morally certain that I had seen Mrs. Black. And then there was the gossip of the place, the suspicion of foul play, which I knew to be false, and my own conviction that there was some deadly mischief or other going on in that bright red house at the corner of Devon Road: how to construct a theory of a reasonable kind out of these two elements? In short, I found myself in a world of mystery; I puzzled my head over it and filled up my leisure moments by gathering together odd threads of speculation, but I never moved a step towards any real solution, and as the summer days went on, the matter seemed to grow misty and indistinct, shadowing some vague terror, like a nightmare of last month. I suppose it would before long have faded into the background of my brain — I should not have forgotten it, for such a thing could never be forgotten — but one morning as I was looking over the paper my eye was caught by a heading over some two dozen lines of small type. The words I had seen were simply: 'The Harlesden Case,' and I knew what I was going to read. Mrs. Black was dead. Black had called in another medical man to certify as to cause of death, and something or other had aroused the strange doctor's suspicions and there had been an inquest and post-mortem. And the result? That, I will confess, did astonish me considerably; it was the triumph of the unexpected. The two doctors who made the autopsy were obliged to confess that they could not discover the faintest trace of any kind of foul play; their most exquisite tests and reagents failed to detect the presence of poison in the most infinitesimal quantity. Death, they found, had been caused by a somewhat obscure and scientifically interesting form of brain disease. The tissue of the brain and the molecules of the gray matter had undergone a most extraordinary series of changes; and the younger of the two doctors, who has some reputation, I believe, as a specialist in brain trouble, made some remarks in giving his evidence which struck me deeply at the time, though I did not then grasp their full significance. He said: 'At the commencement of the examination I was astonished to find appearances of a character entirely new to me, notwithstanding my somewhat large experience. I need not specify these appearances at present, it will be sufficient for me to state that as I proceeded in my task I could scarcely believe that the brain before me was that of a human being at all.' There was some surprise at this statement, as you may imagine, and the coroner asked the doctor if he meant to say that the brain resembled that of an animal. 'No,' he replied, 'I should not put it in that way. Some of the appearances I noticed seemed to point in that direction, but others, and these were the more surprising, indicated a nervous organization of a wholly different character from that either of man or the lower animals.' It was a curious thing to say, but of course the jury brought in a verdict of death from natural causes, and, so far as the public was concerned, the case came to an end. But after I had read what the doctor said I made up my mind that I should like to know a good deal more, and I set to work on what seemed likely to prove an interesting investigation. I had really a good deal of trouble, but I was successful in a measure. Though why — my dear fellow, I had no notion at the time. Are you aware that we have been here nearly four hours? The waiters are staring at us. Let's have the bill and be gone."

The two men went out in silence and stood a moment in the cool air, watching the hurrying traffic of Coventry Street pass before

them to the accompaniment of the ringing bells of hansoms and
the cries of the newsboys; the deep far murmur of London surging
up ever and again from beneath these louder noises.

" It is a strange case, isn't it? " said Dyson at length. " What do
you think of it? "

" My dear fellow, I haven't heard the end, so I will reserve my
opinion. When will you give me the sequel? "

" Come to my rooms some evening; say next Thursday. Here's
the address. Good night; I want to get down to the Strand." Dyson
hailed a passing hansom, and Salisbury turned northward to walk
home to his lodgings.

II

MR. SALISBURY, as may have been gathered from the few remarks
which he had found it possible to introduce in the course of the
evening, was a young gentleman of a peculiarly solid form of intellect, coy and retiring before the mysterious and the uncommon,
with a constitutional dislike of paradox. During the restaurant dinner he had been forced to listen in almost absolute silence to a
strange tissue of improbabilities strung together with the ingenuity
of a born meddler in plots and mysteries, and it was with a feeling
of weariness that he crossed Shaftesbury Avenue and dived into the
recesses of Soho, for his lodgings were in a modest neighborhood
to the north of Oxford Street. As he walked he speculated on the
probable fate of Dyson, relying on literature, unbefriended by a
thoughtful relative, and could not help concluding that so much
subtlety united to a too vivid imagination would in all likelihood
have been rewarded with a pair of sandwich-boards or a super's
banner. Absorbed in this train of thought, and admiring the perverse dexterity which could transmute the face of a sickly woman
and a case of brain disease into the crude elements of romance,
Salisbury strayed on through the dimly lighted streets, not noticing
the gusty wind which drove sharply round corners and whirled the
stray rubbish of the pavement into the air in eddies, while black
clouds gathered over the sickly yellow moon. Even a stray drop or
two of rain blown into his face did not rouse him from his meditations, and it was only when with a sudden rush the storm tore

down upon the street that he began to consider the expediency of finding some shelter. The rain, driven by the wind, pelted down with the violence of a thunderstorm, dashing up from the stones and hissing through the air, and soon a perfect torrent of water coursed along the kennels and accumulated in pools over the choked-up drains. The few stray passengers who had been loafing rather than walking about the street had scuttered away, like frightened rabbits, to some invisible places of refuge, and though Salisbury whistled loud and long for a hansom, no hansom appeared. He looked about him, as if to discover how far he might be from the haven of Oxford Street, but strolling carelessly along, he had turned out of his way, and found himself in an unknown region, and one to all appearance devoid even of a public house where shelter could be bought for the modest sum of twopence. The street lamps were few and at long intervals, and burned behind grimy glasses with the sickly light of oil, and by this wavering glimmer Salisbury could make out the shadowy and vast old houses of which the street was composed. As he passed along, hurrying, and shrinking from the full sweep of the rain, he noticed the innumerable bell-handles, with names that seemed about to vanish of old age graven on brass plates beneath them, and here and there a richly carved penthouse overhung the door, blackening with the grime of fifty years. The storm seemed to grow more and more furious; he was wet through, and a new hat had become a ruin, and still Oxford Street seemed as far off as ever; it was with deep relief that the dripping man caught sight of a dark archway which seemed to promise shelter from the rain if not from the wind. Salisbury took up his position in the driest corner and looked about him; he was standing in a kind of passage contrived under part of a house, and behind him stretched a narrow footway leading between blank walls to regions unknown. He had stood there for some time, vainly endeavoring to rid himself of some of his superfluous moisture and listening for the passing wheel of a hansom, when his attention was aroused by a loud noise coming from the direction of the passage behind and growing louder as it drew nearer. In a couple of minutes he could make out the shrill, raucous voice of a woman, threatening and renouncing and making the very stones echo with her accents, while now and then a man grumbled and expostulated.

Though to all appearance devoid of romance, Salisbury had some relish for street rows, and was, indeed, somewhat of an amateur in the more amusing phases of drunkenness; he therefore composed himself to listen and observe with something of the air of a subscriber to grand opera. To his annoyance, however, the tempest seemed suddenly to be composed, and he could hear nothing but the impatient steps of the woman and the slow lurch of the man as they came towards him. Keeping back in the shadow of the wall, he could see the two drawing nearer; the man was evidently drunk and had much ado to avoid frequent collision with the wall as he tacked across from one side to the other, like some bark beating up against a wind. The woman was looking straight in front of her, with tears streaming from her blazing eyes, but suddenly as they went by, the flame blazed up again, and she burst forth into a torrent of abuse, facing round upon her companion.

"You low rascal, you mean, contemptible cur," she went on, after an incoherent storm of curses, "you think I'm to work and slave for you always, I suppose, while you're after that Green Street girl and drinking every penny you've got? But you're mistaken, Sam — indeed, I'll bear it no longer. Damn you, you dirty thief, I've done with you and your master too, so you can go your own errands, and I only hope they'll get you into trouble."

The woman tore at the bosom of her dress, and taking something out that looked like paper, crumpled it up and flung it away. It fell at Salisbury's feet. She ran out and disappeared in the darkness, while the man lurched slowly into the street, grumbling indistinctly to himself in a perplexed tone of voice. Salisbury looked out after him and saw him maundering along the pavement, halting now and then and swaying indecisively, and then starting off at some fresh tangent. The sky had cleared, and white fleecy clouds were fleeting across the moon, high in the heaven. The light came and went by turns, as the clouds passed by, and, turning round as the clear, white rays shone into the passage, Salisbury saw the little ball of crumpled paper which the woman had cast down. Oddly curious to know what it might contain, he picked it up and put it in his pocket and set out afresh on his journey.

III ·

SALISBURY was a man of habit. When he got home, drenched to the skin, his clothes hanging lank about him, and a ghastly dew besmearing his hat, his only thought was of his health, of which he took studious care. So, after changing his clothes and encasing himself in a warm dressing-gown, he proceeded to prepare a sudorific in the shape of hot gin and water, warming the latter over one of those spirit-lamps which mitigate the austerities of the modern hermit's life. By the time this preparation had been exhibited and Salisbury's disturbed feelings had been soothed by a pipe of tobacco, he was able to get into bed in a happy state of vacancy, without a thought of his adventure in the dark archway or of the weird fancies with which Dyson had seasoned his dinner. It was the same at breakfast the next morning, for Salisbury made a point of not thinking of anything until that meal was over; but when the cup and saucer were cleared away and the morning pipe was lit, he remembered the little ball of paper and began fumbling in the pockets of his wet coat. He did not remember into which pocket he had put it, and as he dived now into one and now into another, he experienced a strange feeling of apprehension lest it should not be there at all, though he could not for the life of him have explained the importance he attached to what was in all probability mere rubbish. But he sighed with relief when his fingers touched the crumpled surface in an inside pocket, and he drew it out gently and laid it on the little desk by his easy-chair with as much care is if it had been some rare jewel. Salisbury sat smoking and staring at his find for a few minutes, an odd temptation to throw the thing in the fire and have done with it struggling with as odd a speculation as to its possible contents, and as to the reason why the infuriated woman should have flung a bit of paper from her with such vehemence. As might be expected, it was the latter feeling that conquered in the end, and yet it was with something like repugnance that he at last took the paper and unrolled it and laid it out before him. It was a piece of common dirty paper, to all appearance torn out of a cheap exercise-book, and in the middle were a few lines written in a queer cramped hand. Salisbury bent his head and stared eagerly at it for a moment, drawing a long breath, and then fell back in his chair gazing blankly before him, till at last with a sudden revulsion he burst into a peal of laughter, so long and loud and uproarious that the landlady's baby in the floor below awoke from sleep and echoed his mirth with hideous yells. But he laughed again and again, and took the paper up to read a second time what seemed such meaningless nonsense.

"Q. has had to go and see his friends in Paris," it began. "Traverse Handel S. 'Once around the grass, and twice around the lass, and thrice around the maple tree.'"

Salisbury took up the paper and crumpled it as the angry woman had done, and aimed it at the fire. He did not throw it there, however, but tossed it carelessly into the well of the desk and laughed again. The sheer folly of the thing offended him, and he was ashamed of his own eager speculation, as one who pores over the high-sounding announcements in the agony column of the daily paper and finds nothing but advertisement and triviality. He walked to the window and stared out at the languid morning life of his quarter; the maids in slatternly print dresses washing doorsteps, the fishmonger and the butcher on their rounds, and the tradesmen standing at the doors of their small shops, drooping for lack of trade and excitement. In the distance a blue haze gave some grandeur to the prospect, but the view as a whole was depressing and would only have interested a student of the life of London, who finds something rare and choice in its every aspect. Salisbury turned away in disgust, and settled himself in the easy-chair, upholstered in a bright shade of green and decked with yellow gimp, which was the pride and attraction of the apartments. Here he composed himself to his morning's occupation — the perusal of a novel that dealt with sport and love in a manner that suggested the collaboration of a stud-groom and a ladies' college. In an ordinary way, however, Salisbury would have been carried on by the interest of the story up to lunch-time, but this morning he fidgeted in and out of his chair, took the book up and laid it down again, and swore at last to himself and at himself in mere irritation. In point of fact the jingle of the paper found in the archway had "got into his head," and do what he would he could not help muttering over and over: "Once around the grass, and twice around the lass, and thrice around the maple tree." It became a positive pain, like the foolish burden of a music-hall song, everlastingly quoted, and sung at all hours of the day and night, and treasured by the street boys as an unfailing resource for six months together. He went out into the streets and tried to forget his enemy in the jostling of the crowds and the roar and clatter of the traffic, but presently he would find himself stealing quietly aside and pacing some deserted byway, vainly puzzling his brains, and trying to fix some meaning to phrases that were meaningless. It was a positive relief when Thursday came, and he remembered that he had made an appointment to go and see Dyson; the flimsy reveries of the self-styled man of letters appeared entertaining when compared with this ceaseless iteration, this maze of thought from which there seemed no possibility of escape. Dyson's abode was in one of the quietest of the quiet streets that lead down from the Strand to the river, and when Salisbury passed from the narrow stairway into his friend's room, he saw that the uncle had been beneficent indeed. The floor glowed and flamed with all the colors of the East; it was, as Dyson pompously remarked, "a sunset in a dream," and the lamplight, the twilight of London streets, was shut out with strangely worked curtains, glittering here and there with threads of gold. In the shelves of an oak armoire stood jars and plates of old French china, and the black and white of etchings not to be found in the Haymarket or in Bond Street stood out against the splendor of a Japanese paper. Salisbury sat down on the settle by the hearth and sniffed and mingled fumes of incense and tobacco, wondering and dumb before all this splendor after the green rep and the oleographs, the gilt-framed mirror, and the lusters of his own apartment.

"I am glad you have come," said Dyson. "Comfortable little room, isn't it? But you don't look very well, Salisbury. Nothing disagreed with you, has it?"

"No; but I have been a good deal bothered for the last few days. The fact is I had an odd kind of — of — adventure, I suppose I may call it, that night I saw you, and it has worried me a good deal. And the provoking part of it is that it's the merest nonsense — but, however, I will tell you all about it, by and by. You were going to let me have the rest of that odd story you began at the restaurant."

" Yes. But I am afraid, Salisbury, you are incorrigible. You are a slave to what you call matter of fact. You know perfectly well that in your heart you think the oddness in that case is of my making, and that it is all really as plain as the police reports. However, as I have begun, I will go on. But first we will have something to drink, and you may as well light your pipe."

Dyson went up to the oak cupboard and drew from its depths a rotund bottle and two little glasses, quaintly gilded.

" It's Benedictine," he said. " You'll have some, won't you? "

Salisbury assented, and the two men sat sipping and smoking reflectively for some minutes before Dyson began.

" Let me see," he said at last, " we were at the inquest, weren't we? No, we had done with that. Ah, I remember. I was telling you that on the whole I had been successful in my inquiries, investigation, or whatever you like to call it, into the matter. Wasn't that where I left off? "

" Yes, that was it. To be precise, I think ' though ' was the last word you said on the matter."

" Exactly. I have been thinking it all over since the other night, and I have come to the conclusion that that ' though ' is a very big ' though ' indeed. Not to put too fine a point on it, I have had to confess that what I found out, or thought I found out, amounts in reality to nothing. I am as far away from the heart of the case as ever. However, I may as well tell you what I do know. You may remember my saying that I was impressed a good deal by some remarks of one of the doctors who gave evidence at the inquest. Well, I determined that my first step must be to try if I could get something more definite and intelligible out of that doctor. Somehow or other I managed to get an introduction to the man, and he gave me an appointment to come and see him. He turned out to be a pleasant, genial fellow; rather young and not in the least like the typical medical man, and he began the conference by offering me whisky and cigars. I didn't think it worth while to beat about the bush, so I began by saying that part of his evidence at the Harlesden inquest struck me as very peculiar, and I gave him the printed report, with the sentences in question underlined. He just glanced at the slip and gave me a queer look. ' It struck you as peculiar, did it? ' said he. ' Well, you must remember that the Harlesden case was very peculiar. In fact, I think I may safely say that in some features it was unique — quite unique.' 'Quite so,' I replied, 'and that's exactly why it interests me and why I want to know more about it. And I thought that if anybody could give me any information it would be you. What is your opinion of the matter?'

"It was a pretty downright sort of question, and my doctor looked rather taken aback.

"'Well,' he said, 'as I fancy your motive in inquiring into the question must be mere curiosity, I think I may tell you my opinion with tolerable freedom. So, Mr., Mr. Dyson? if you want to know my theory, it is this: I believe that Dr. Black killed his wife.'

"'But the verdict,' I answered, 'the verdict was given from your own evidence.'

"'Quite so; the verdict was given in accordance with the evidence of my colleague and myself, and, under the circumstances, I think the jury acted very sensibly. In fact, I don't see what else they could have done. But I stick to my opinion, mind you, and I say this also: I don't wonder at Black's doing what I firmly believe he did. I think he was justified.'

"'Justified! How could that be?' I asked. I was astonished, as you may imagine, at the answer I had got. The doctor wheeled round his chair and looked steadily at me for a moment before he answered.

"'I suppose you are not a man of science yourself? No; then it would be of no use my going into detail. I have always been firmly opposed myself to any partnership between physiology and psychology. I believe that both are bound to suffer. No one recognizes more decidedly than I do the impassable gulf, the fathomless abyss that separates the world of consciousness from the sphere of matter. We know that every change of consciousness is accompanied by a rearrangement of the molecules in the gray matter; and that is all. What the link between them is, or why they occur together, we do not know, and most authorities believe that we never can know. Yet I will tell you that as I did my work, the knife in my hand, I felt convinced, in spite of all theories, that what lay before me was not the brain of a dead woman — not the brain of a human being at all. Of course I saw the face; but it was quite placid, devoid of all expression. It must have been a beautiful face, no doubt, but I

can honestly say that I would not have looked in that face when
there was life behind it for a thousand guineas, no, nor for twice
that sum.'

" 'My dear sir,' I said, ' you surprise me extremely. You say that
it was not the brain of a human being. What was it, then? '

" 'The brain of a devil.' He spoke quite coolly and never moved
a muscle. ' The brain of a devil,' he repeated, ' and I have no doubt
that Black found some way of putting an end to it. I don't blame
him if he did. Whatever Mrs. Black was, she was not fit to stay in
this world. Will you have anything more? No? Good night, good
night.'

" It was a .queer sort of opinion to get from a man of science,
wasn't it? When he was saying that he would not have looked on
that face when alive for a thousand guineas, or two thousand
guineas, I was thinking of the face I had seen, but I said nothing.
I went again to Harlesden and passed from one shop to another,
making small purchases and trying to find out whether there was
anything about the Blacks which was not already common property,
but there was very little to hear. One of the tradesmen to whom
I spoke said he had known the dead woman well; she used to buy
of him such quantities of grocery as were required for their small
household, for they never kept a servant, but had a charwoman in
occasionally, and she had not seen Mrs. Black for months before
she died. According to this man, Mrs. Black was ' a nice lady,'
always kind and considerate and so fond of her husband, and he of
her, as everyone thought. And yet, to put the doctor's opinion on
one side, I knew what I had seen. And then after thinking it all
over and putting one thing with another, it seemed to me that the
only person likely to give me much assistance would be Black himself, and I made up my mind to find him. Of course he wasn't to
be found in Harlesden; he had left, I was told, directly after the
funeral. Everything in the house had been sold, and one fine day
Black got into the train with a small portmanteau and went nobody
knew where. It was a chance if he were ever heard of again, and it
was by a mere chance that I came across him at last. I was walking
one day along Gray's Inn Road, not bound for anywhere in particular, but looking about me, as usual, and holding onto my hat,
for it was a gusty day in early March and the wind was making

the treetops in the Inn rock and quiver. I had come up from the
Holborn end, and I had almost got to Theobald's Road when I
noticed a man walking in front of me, leaning on a stick, and to all
appearance very feeble. There was something about his look that
made me curious, I don't know why, and I began to walk briskly
with the idea of overtaking him, when of a sudden his hat blew
off and came bounding along the pavement to my feet. Of course
I rescued the hat and gave it a glance as I went towards its owner.
It was a biography in itself; a Piccadilly maker's name in the inside,
but I don't think a beggar would have picked it out of the gutter.
Then I looked up and saw Dr. Black of Harlesden waiting for me.
A queer thing, wasn't it? But, Salisbury, what a change! When I
saw Dr. Black come down the steps of his house at Harlesden he
was an upright man, walking firmly with well-built limbs; a man,
I should say, in the prime of his life. And now before me there
crouched this wretched creature, bent and feeble, with shrunken
cheeks, and hair that was whitening fast, and limbs that trembled
and shook together, and misery in his eyes. He thanked me for
bringing him his hat, saying: 'I don't think I should ever have
got it, I can't run much now. A gusty day, sir, isn't it?' and with
this he was turning away, but by little and little I contrived to
draw him into the current of conversation, and we walked together
eastward. I think the man would have been glad to get rid of me;
but I didn't intend to let him go, and he stopped at last in front
of a miserable house in a miserable street. It was, I verily believe,
one of the most wretched quarters I have ever seen: houses that
must have been sordid and hideous enough when new, that had
gathered foulness with every year, and now seemed to lean and
totter to their fall. 'I live up there,' said Black, pointing to the
tiles, 'not in the front — in the back. I am very quiet there. I won't
ask you to come in now, but perhaps some other day — ' I caught
him up at that and told him I should be only too glad to come and
see him. He gave me an odd sort of glance, as if he were wondering
what on earth I or anybody else could care about him, and I left
him fumbling with his latch-key. I think you will say I did pretty
well when I tell you that within a few weeks I had made myself
an intimate friend of Black's. I shall never forget the first time I
went to his room; I hope I shall never see such abject, squalid misery

again. The foul paper, from which all pattern or trace of a pattern
had long vanished, subdued and penetrated with the grime of the
evil street, was hanging in moldering pennons from the wall. Only
at the end of the room was it possible to stand upright, and the
sight of the wretched bed and the odor of corruption that pervaded
the place made me turn faint and sick. Here I found him munching
a piece of bread; he seemed surprised to find that I had kept my
promise, but he gave me his chair and sat on the bed while we
talked. I used to go to see him often, and we had long conversations
together, but he never mentioned Harlesden or his wife. I fancy
that he supposed me ignorant of the matter, or thought that if I
had heard of it, I should never connect the respectable Dr. Black
of Harlesden with a poor garreteer in the backwoods of London.
He was a strange man, and as we sat together smoking, I often wondered whether he were mad or sane, for I think the wildest dreams
of Paracelsus and the Rosicrucians would appear plain and sober
fact compared with the theories I have heard him earnestly advance in that grimy den of his. I once ventured to hint something
of the sort to him. I suggested that something he had said was in
flat contradiction to all science and all experience. 'No,' he answered, 'not all experience, for mine counts for something. I am no
dealer in unproved theories; what I say I have proved for myself,
and at a terrible cost. There is a region of knowledge which you will
never know, which wise men seeing from afar off shun like the
plague, as well they may, but into that region I have gone. If you
knew, if you could even dream of what may be done, of what one
or two men have done in this quiet world of ours, your very soul
would shudder and faint within you. What you have heard from
me has been but the merest husk and outer covering of true science
— that science which means death, and that which is more awful
than death, to those who gain it. No, when men say that there are
strange things in the world, they little know the awe and the terror
that dwell always with them and about them.' There was a sort of
fascination about the man that drew me to him, and I was quite
sorry to have to leave London for a month or two; I missed his odd
talk. A few days after I came back to town I thought I would look
him up, but when I gave the two rings at the bell that used to summon him, there was no answer. I rang and rang again and was just

turning to go away when the door opened and a dirty woman asked
me what I wanted. From her look I fancy she took me for a plain-
clothes officer after one of her lodgers, but when I inquired if Mr.
Black were in, she gave me a stare of another kind. 'There's no
Mr. Black lives here,' she said. 'He's gone. He's dead this six weeks.
I always thought he was a bit queer in his head, or else had been
and got into some trouble or other. He used to go out every morning from ten till one, and one Monday morning we heard him
come in and go into his room and shut the door, and a few minutes
after, just as we was a-sitting down to our dinner, there was such
a scream that I thought I should have gone right off. And then we
heard a stamping, and down he came, raging and cursing most
dreadful, swearing he had been robbed of something that was worth
millions. And then he just dropped down in the passage, and we
thought he was dead. We got him up to his room and put him on
his bed, and I just sat there and waited, while my 'usband he went
for the doctor. And there was the winder wide open, and a little tin
box he had lying on the floor open and empty, but of course nobody could possible have got in at the winder, and as for him having
anything that was worth anything, it's nonsense, for he was often
weeks and weeks behind with his rent, and my 'usband he threatened often and often to turn him into the street, for, as he said,
we've got a living to myke like other people — and, of course, that's
true; but, somehow, I didn't like to do it, though he was an odd
kind of man, and I fancy had been better off. And then the doctor
came and looked at him and said as he couldn't do nothing, and
that night he died as I was a-sitting by his bed; and I can tell you
that, with one thing and another, we lost money by him, for the
few bits of clothes as he had were worth next to nothing when they
came to be sold.' I gave the woman half a sovereign for her trouble
and went home thinking of Dr. Black and the epitaph she had
made him, and wondering at his strange fancy that he had been
robbed. I take it that he had very little to fear on that score, poor fellow; but I suppose that he was really mad, and died in a sudden
access of his mania. His landlady said that once or twice when she
had had occasion to go into his room (to dun the poor wretch for
his rent, most likely), he would keep her at the door for about a
minute, and that when she came in she would find him putting

away his tin box in the corner by the window; I suppose he had become possessed with the idea of some great treasure and fancied
himself a wealthy man in the midst of all his misery. *Explicit*, my
tale is ended, and you see that though I knew Black, I know nothing of his wife or of the history of her death. — That's the Harlesden case, Salisbury, and I think it interests me all the more deeply
because there does not seem the shadow of a possibility that I or
anyone else will ever know more about it. What do you think
of it? "

" Well, Dyson, I must say that I think you have contrived to
surround the whole thing with a mystery of your own making. I
go for the doctor's solution: Black murdered his wife, being himself in all probability an undeveloped lunatic."

" What? Do you believe, then, that this woman was something
too awful, too terrible to be allowed to remain on the earth? You
will remember that the doctor said it was the brain of a devil? "

" Yes, yes, but he was speaking, of course, metaphorically. It's
really quite a simple matter if you only look at it like that."

" Ah, well, you may be right; but yet I am sure you are not. Well,
well, it's no good discussing it any more. A little more Benedictine?
That's right; try some of this tobacco. Didn't you say that you had
been bothered by something — something which happened that
night we dined together? "

" Yes, I have been worried, Dyson, worried a great deal. I —
But it's such a trivial matter — indeed, such an absurdity — that I
feel ashamed to trouble you with it."

" Never mind, let's have it, absurd or not."

With many hesitations, and with much inward resentment of
the folly of the thing, Salisbury told his tale, and repeated reluctantly the absurd intelligence and the absurder doggerel of the
scrap of paper, expecting to hear Dyson burst out into a roar of
laughter.

" Isn't it too bad that I should let myself be bothered by such
stuff as that? " he asked, when he had stuttered out the jingle of
once, and twice, and thrice.

Dyson had listened to it all gravely, even to the end, and meditated for a few minutes in silence.

" Yes," he said at length, " it was a curious chance, your taking

shelter in that archway just as those two went by. But I don't
know that I should call what was written on the paper nonsense;
it is bizarre certainly, but I expect it has a meaning for somebody.
Just repeat it again, will you, and I will write it down. Perhaps we
might find a cipher of some sort, though I hardly think we shall."

Again had the reluctant lips of Salisbury slowly to stammer out
the rubbish that he abhorred, while Dyson jotted it down on a slip
of paper.

"Look over it, will you?" he said, when it was done; "it may be
important that I should have every word in its place. Is that all
right?"

"Yes; that is an accurate copy. But I don't think you will get
much out of it. Depend upon it, it is mere nonsense, a wanton
scribble. I must be going now, Dyson. No, no more; that stuff of
yours is pretty strong. Good night."

"I suppose you would like to hear from me, if I did find out anything?"

"No, not I; I don't want to hear about the thing again. You may
regard the discovery, if it is one, as your own."

"Very well. Good night."

IV

A GOOD many hours after Salisbury had returned to the company
of the green rep chairs, Dyson still sat at his desk, itself a Japanese
romance, smoking many pipes and meditating over his friend's
story. The bizarre quality of the inscription which had annoyed
Salisbury was to him an attraction, and now and again he took it up
and scanned thoughtfully what he had written, especially the
quaint jingle at the end. It was a token, a symbol, he decided, and
not a cipher, and the woman who had flung it away was in all
probability entirely ignorant of its meaning; she was but the agent
of the "Sam" she had abused and discarded, and he too was again
the agent of someone unknown; possibly of the individual styled Q,
who had been forced to visit his French friends. But what to make
of "Traverse Handel S." Here was the root and source of the
enigma, and not all the tobacco of Virginia seemed likely to suggest any clue here. It seemed almost hopeless, but Dyson regarded

himself as the Wellington of mysteries and went to bed feeling assured that sooner or later he would hit upon the right track. For the next few days he was deeply engaged in his literary labors, labors which were a profound mystery even to the most intimate of his friends, who searched the railway bookstalls in vain for the result of so many hours spent at the Japanese bureau in company with strong tobacco and black tea. On this occasion Dyson confined himself to his room for four days, and it was with genuine relief that he laid down his pen and went out into the streets in quest of relaxation and fresh air. The gas-lamps were being lighted, and the fifth edition of the evening papers was being howled through the streets, and Dyson, feeling that he wanted quiet, turned away from the clamorous Strand and began to trend away to the northwest. Soon he found himself in streets that echoed to his footsteps, and crossing a broad new thoroughfare and verging still to the west, Dyson discovered that he had penetrated to the depths of Soho. Here again was life; rare vintages of France and Italy, at prices which seemed contemptibly small, allured the passer-by; here were cheeses, vast and rich, here olive oil, and here a grove of Rabelaisian sausages; while in a neighboring shop the whole press of Paris appeared to be on sale. In the middle of the roadway a strange miscellany of nations sauntered to and fro, for there cab and hansom rarely ventured; and from window over window the inhabitants looked forth in pleased contemplation of the scene. Dyson made his way slowly along, mingling with the crowd on the cobble-stones, listening to the queer babel of French and German, and Italian and English, glancing now and again at the shop-windows with their leveled batteries of bottles, and had almost gained the end of the street when his attention was arrested by a small shop at the corner, a vivid contrast to its neighbors. It was the typical shop of the poor quarter; a shop entirely English. Here were vended tobacco and sweets, cheap pipes of clay and cherry-wood; penny exercise-books and penholders jostled for precedence with comic songs, and story papers with appalling cuts showed that romance claimed its place beside the actualities of the evening paper, the bills of which fluttered at the doorway. Dyson glanced up at the name above the door and stood by the kennel trembling, for a sharp pang, the pang of one who has made a discovery, had for a moment left him incapable of motion. The name' over the shop was Travers. Dyson looked up again, this time at the corner of the wall above the lamp-post, and read in white letters on a blue ground the words: " Handel Street, W. C." and the legend was repeated in fainter letters just below. He gave a little sigh of satisfaction, and without more ado walked boldly into the shop and stared full in the face of the fat man who was sitting behind the counter. The fellow rose to his feet and returned the stare a little curiously, and then began in stereo-typed phrase:

" What can I do for you, sir? "

Dyson enjoyed the situation and a dawning perplexity on the man's face. He propped his stick carefully against the counter and leaning over it, said slowly and impressively:

" Once around the grass, and twice around the lass, and thrice around the maple tree."

Dyson had calculated on his words producing an effect, and he was not disappointed. The vender of the miscellanies gasped, open-mouthed like a fish, and steadied himself against the counter. When he spoke, after a short interval, it was in a hoarse mutter, tremulous and unsteady.

" Would you mind saying that again, sir? I didn't quite catch it."

" My good man, I shall most certainly do nothing of the kind. You heard what I said perfectly well. You have got a clock in your shop, I see; an admirable timekeeper, I have no doubt. Well, I give you a minute by your own clock."

The man looked about him in a perplexed indecision, and Dyson felt that it was time to be bold.

" Look here, Travers, the time is nearly up. You have heard of Q, I think. Remember, I hold your life in my hands. Now! "

Dyson was shocked at the result of his own audacity. The man shrank and shriveled in terror, the sweat poured down a face of ashy white, and he held up his hands before him.

" Mr. Davies, Mr. Davies, don't say that — don't for heaven's sake. I didn't know you at first, I didn't indeed. Good God! Mr. Davies, you wouldn't ruin me? I'll get it in a moment."

" You had better not lose any more time."

The man slunk piteously out of his own shop and went into a back parlor. Dyson heard his trembling fingers fumbling with a bunch of keys, and the creak of an opening box. He came back presently with a small package neatly tied up in brown paper in his hands, and, still full of terror, handed it to Dyson.

" I'm glad to be rid of it," he said, " I'll take no more jobs of this sort."

Dyson took the parcel and his stick and walked out of the shop with a nod, turning round as he passed the door. Travers had sunk into his seat, his face still white with terror, with one hand over his eyes, and Dyson speculated a good deal as he walked rapidly away as to what queer chords those could be on which he had played so roughly. He hailed the first hansom he could see and drove home, and when he had lit his hanging lamp and laid his parcel on the table, he paused for a moment, wondering on what strange thing the lamplight would soon shine. He locked his door, and cut the strings, and unfolded the paper layer after layer, and came at last to a small wooden box, simply but solidly made. There was no lock, and Dyson had simply to raise the lid, and as he did so he drew a long breath and started back. The lamp seemed to glimmer feebly like a single candle, but the whole room blazed with light — and not with light alone, but with a thousand colors, with all the glories of some painted window; and upon the walls of his room and on the familiar furniture, the glow flamed back and seemed to flow again to its source, the little wooden box. For there upon a bed of soft wool lay the most splendid jewel, a jewel such as Dyson had never dreamed of, and within it shone the blue of far skies, and the green of the sea by the shore, and the red of the ruby, and deep violet rays, and in the middle of all it seemed aflame as if a fountain of fire rose up, and fell, and rose again with sparks like stars for drops. Dyson gave a long deep sigh, and dropped into his chair, and put his hands over his eyes to think. The jewel was like an opal, but from a long experience of the shop-windows he knew there was no such thing as an opal one-quarter or one-eighth of its size. He looked at the stone again, with a feeling that was almost awe, and placed it gently on the table under the lamp, and watched the wonderful flame that shone and sparkled in its center, and then turned to the box, curious to know whether it might contain other marvels. He lifted the bed of wool on which the opal had reclined, and saw beneath, no more jewels, but a little old pocketbook, worn and shabby with use. Dyson opened it at the first leaf, and dropped the book again appalled. He had read the name of the owner, neatly written in blue ink:

STEVEN BLACK, M.D.,
Oranmore,
Devon Road,
Harlesden.

It was several minutes before Dyson could bring himself to open the book a second time; he remembered the wretched exile in his garret, and his strange talk; and the memory, too, of the face he had seen at the window, and of what the specialist had said, surged up in his mind, and as he held his finger on the cover, he shivered, dreading what might be written within. When at last he held it in his hand and turned the pages, he found that the first two leaves were blank, but the third was covered with clear, minute writing, and Dyson began to read with the light of the opal flaming in his eyes.

V

" EVER since I was a young man " — the record began — " I devoted all my leisure and a good deal of time that ought to have been given to other studies to the investigation of curious and obscure branches of knowledge. What are commonly called the pleasures of life had never any attractions for me, and I lived alone in London, avoiding my fellow-students, and in my turn avoided by them as a man self-absorbed and unsympathetic. So long as I could gratify my desire of knowledge of a peculiar kind, knowledge of which the very existence is a profound secret to most men, I was intensely happy, and I have often spent whole nights sitting in the darkness of my room and thinking of the strange world on the brink of which I trod. My professional studies, however, and the necessity of obtaining a degree, for some time forced my more obscure employment into the background, and soon after I had qualified I met Agnes, who became my wife. We took a new house in this remote suburb, and I began the regular routine of a sober practice, and for some months lived happily enough, sharing in the life about me, and only thinking at odd intervals of that occult science which had once fascinated my whole being. I had learnt enough of the paths I had begun to tread to know that they were beyond all expression difficult and dangerous, that to persevere meant in all probability the wreck of a life, and that they led to regions so terrible that the mind of man shrinks appalled at the very thought. Moreover, the quiet and the peace I had enjoyed since my marriage had wiled me away to a great extent from places where I knew no peace could dwell. But suddenly — I think indeed it was the work of a single night, as I lay awake on my bed gazing into the darkness — suddenly, I say, the old desire, the former longing, returned, and returned with a force that had been intensified ten times by its absence; and when the day dawned and I looked out of the window and saw with haggard eyes the sunrise in the east, I knew that my doom had been pronounced; that as I had gone far, so now I must go farther with unfaltering steps. I turned to the bed where my wife was sleeping peacefully, and lay down again, weeping bitter tears, for the sun had set on our happy life and had risen with a dawn of terror to us both. I will not set down here in minute detail what followed; outwardly I went about the day's labor as before, saying nothing to my wife. But she soon saw that I had changed; I spent my spare time in a room which I had fitted up as a laboratory, and often I crept upstairs in the gray dawn of the morning, when the light of many lamps still glowed over London; and each night I had stolen a step nearer to that great abyss which I was to bridge over, the gulf between the world of consciousness and the world of matter. My experiments were many and complicated in their nature, and it was some months before I realized whither they all pointed, and when this was borne in upon me in a moment's time, I felt my face whiten and my heart still within me. But the power to draw back, the power to stand before the doors that now opened wide before me and not to enter in, had long ago been absent; the way was closed, and I could only pass onward. My position was as utterly hopeless as that of the prisoner in an utter dungeon, whose only light is that of the dungeon above him; the doors were shut and escape was impossible. Experiment after experiment gave the same result, and I knew, and shrank even as the thought passed through my mind, that in the work I had to do there must be elements which no laboratory could furnish, which no scales could ever measure. In that work, from which even I doubted to escape with life, life itself must enter; from some human being there must be drawn that essence which men call the soul, and in its place (for in the scheme of the world there is no vacant chamber) — in its place would enter in what the lips can hardly utter, what the mind cannot conceive without a horror more awful than the horror of death itself. And when I knew this, I knew also on whom this fate would fall; I looked into my wife's eyes. Even at that hour, if I had gone out and taken a rope and hanged myself, I might have escaped, and she also, but in no other way. At last I told her all. She shuddered, and wept, and called on her dead mother for help, and asked me if I had no mercy, and I could only sigh. I concealed nothing from her; I told her what she would become, and what would enter in where her life had been; I told her of all the shame and of all the horror. You who will read this when I am dead — if indeed I allow this record to survive — you who have opened the box and have seen what lies there, if you could understand what lies hidden in that opal! For one night my wife consented to what I asked of her, consented with the tears running down her beautiful face, and hot shame flushing red over her neck and breast, consented to undergo this for me. I threw open the window, and we looked together at the sky and the dark earth for the last time; it was a fine starlight night, and there was a pleasant breeze blowing, and I kissed her on her lips, and her tears ran down upon my face. That night she came down to my laboratory, and there, with shutters bolted and barred down, with curtains drawn thick and close, so that the very stars might be shut out from the sight of that room, while the crucible hissed and boiled over the lamp, I did what had to be done, and led out what was no longer a woman. But on the table the opal flamed and sparkled with such light as no eyes of man have ever gazed on, and the rays of the flame that was within it flashed and glittered, and shone even to my heart. My wife had only asked one thing of me; that when there came at last what I had told her, I would kill her. I have kept that promise."

There was nothing more. Dyson let the little pocketbook fall, and turned and looked again at the opal with its flaming inmost light, and then with unutterable irresistible horror surging up in his heart, grasped the jewel and flung it on the ground and trampled it beneath his heel. His face was white with terror as he turned away, and for a moment stood sick and trembling, and then with a start he leapt across the room and steadied himself against the door. There was an angry hiss, as of steam escaping under great pressure, and as he gazed, motionless, a volume of heavy yellow smoke was slowly issuing from the very center of the jewel and wreathing itself in snakelike coils above it. And then a thin white flame burst forth from the smoke and shot up into the air and vanished; and on the ground there lay a thing like a cinder, black and crumbling to the touch.

❧ *E. M. Forster* ☙

THE STORY OF A PANIC

I

Eustace's career — if career it can be called — certainly dates from
that afternoon in the chestnut woods above Ravello. I confess at
once that I am a plain, simple man, with no pretensions to literary
style. Still, I do flatter myself that I can tell a story without exag-
gerating, and I have therefore decided to give an unbiased account
of the extraordinary events of eight years ago.

Ravello is a delightful place with a delightful little hotel in which
we met some charming people. There were the two Miss Robinsons, who had been there for six weeks with Eustace, their nephew,
then a boy of about fourteen. Mr. Sandbach had also been there
some time. He had held a curacy in the north of England, which he
had been compelled to resign on account of ill health, and while

he was recruiting at Ravello he had taken in hand Eustace's education — which was then sadly deficient — and was endeavoring to fit him for one of our great public schools. Then there was Mr. Leyland, a would-be artist, and, finally, there was the nice landlady, Signora Scafetti, and the nice English-speaking waiter, Emmanuele — though at the time of which I am speaking Emmanuele was away, visiting a sick father.

To this little circle I, my wife, and my two daughters made, I venture to think, a not unwelcome addition. But though I liked most of the company well enough, there were two of them to whom I did not take at all. They were the artist, Leyland, and the Miss Robinsons' nephew, Eustace.

Leyland was simply conceited and odious, and as those qualities will be amply illustrated in my narrative, I need not enlarge upon them here. But Eustace was something besides: he was indescribably repellent.

I am fond of boys as a rule, and was quite disposed to be friendly. I and my daughters offered to take him out — " No, walking was such a fag." Then I asked him to come and bathe — " No, he could not swim."

" Every English boy should be able to swim," I said; " I will teach you myself."

" There, Eustace dear," said Miss Robinson; " here is a chance for you."

But he said he was afraid of the water! — a boy afraid! — and of course I said no more.

I would not have minded so much if he had been a really studious boy, but he neither played hard nor worked hard. His favorite occupations were lounging on the terrace in an easy-chair and loafing along the highroad, with his feet shuffling up the dust and his shoulders stooping forward. Naturally enough, his features were pale, his chest contracted, and his muscles undeveloped. His aunts thought him delicate; what he really needed was discipline.

That memorable day we all arranged to go for a picnic up in the chestnut woods — all, that is, except Janet, who stopped behind to finish her water-color of the Cathedral — not a very successful attempt, I am afraid.

I wander off into these irrelevant details because in my mind I cannot separate them from an account of the day; and it is the same with the conversation during the picnic: all is imprinted on my brain together. After a couple of hours' ascent we left the donkeys that had carried the Miss Robinsons and my wife, and all proceeded on foot to the head of the valley — Vallone Fontana Caroso is its proper name, I find.

I have visited a good deal of fine scenery before and since, but have found little that has pleased me more. The valley ended in a vast hollow, shaped like a cup, into which radiated ravines from the precipitous hills around. Both the valley and the ravines and the ribs of hill that divided the ravines were covered with leafy chestnut, so that the general appearance was that of a many-fingered green hand, palm upwards, which was clutching convulsively to keep us in its grasp. Far down the valley we could see Ravello and the sea, but that was the only sign of another world.

" Oh, what a perfectly lovely place! " said my daughter Rose. " What a picture it would make! "

" Yes," said Mr. Sandbach. " Many a famous European gallery would be proud to have a landscape a tithe as beautiful as this upon its walls."

" On the contrary," said Leyland, " it would make a very poor picture. Indeed, it is not paintable at all."

" And why is that? " said Rose, with far more deference than he deserved.

" Look, in the first place," he replied, " how intolerably straight against the sky is the line of the hill. It would need breaking up and diversifying. And where we are standing the whole thing is out of perspective. Besides, all the coloring is monotonous and crude."

" I do not know anything about pictures," I put in, " and I do not pretend to know; but I know what is beautiful when I see it, and I am thoroughly content with this."

" Indeed, who could help being contented! " said the elder Miss Robinson; and Mr. Sandbach said the same.

" Ah! " said Leyland, " you all confuse the artistic view of Nature with the photographic."

Poor Rose had brought her camera with her, so I thought this

positively rude. I did not wish any unpleasantness; so I merely
turned away and assisted my wife and Miss Mary Robinson to put
out the lunch — not a very nice lunch.

"Eustace, dear," said his aunt, "come and help us here."

He was in a particularly bad temper that morning. He had, as
usual, not wanted to come, and his aunts had nearly allowed him to
stop at the hotel to vex Janet. But I, with their permission, spoke
to him rather sharply on the subject of exercise; and the result was
that he had come, but was even more taciturn and moody than
usual.

Obedience was not his strong point. He invariably questioned
every command, and only executed it grumbling. I should always
insist on prompt and cheerful obedience, if I had a son.

"I'm — coming — Aunt — Mary," he at last replied, and dawdled
to cut a piece of wood to make a whistle, taking care not to arrive
till we had finished.

"Well, well, sir!" said I, "you stroll in at the end and profit by
our labors." He sighed, for he could not endure being chaffed. Miss
Mary, very unwisely, insisted on giving him the wing of the
chicken, in spite of all my attempts to prevent her. I remember
that I had a moment's vexation when I thought that, instead of
enjoying the sun and the air and the woods, we were all engaged
in wrangling over the diet of a spoilt boy.

But after lunch he was a little less in evidence. He withdrew to
a tree-trunk and began to loosen the bark from his whistle. I was
thankful to see him employed, for once in a way. We reclined and
took a *dolce far niente.*

Those sweet chestnuts of the South are puny striplings compared
with our robust Northerners. But they clothed the contours of the
hills and valleys in a most pleasing way, their veil being only broken
by two clearings, in one of which we were sitting.

And because these few trees were cut down, Leyland burst into
a petty indictment of the proprietor.

"All the poetry is going from Nature," he cried; "her lakes and
marshes are drained, her seas banked up, her forests cut down.
Everywhere we see the vulgarity of desolation spreading."

I have had some experience of estates, and answered that cutting
was very necessary for the health of the larger trees. Besides, it was

unreasonable to expect the proprietor to derive no income from his lands.

" If you take the commercial side of landscape, you may feel pleasure in the owner's activity. But to me the mere thought that a tree is convertible into cash is disgusting."

" I see no reason," I observed politely, " to despise the gifts of Nature because they are of value."

It did not stop him. " It is no matter," he went on, " we are all hopelessly steeped in vulgarity. I do not except myself. It is through us, and to our shame, that the Nereids have left the waters and the Oreads the mountains, that the woods no longer give shelter to Pan."

" Pan! " cried Mr. Sandbach, his mellow voice filling the valley as if it had been a great green church, " Pan is dead. That is why the woods do not shelter him." And he began to tell the striking story of the mariners who were sailing near the coast at the time of the birth of Christ, and three times heard a loud voice saying: " The great god Pan is dead."

" Yes. The great god Pan is dead," said Leyland. And he abandoned himself to that mock misery in which artistic people are so fond of indulging. His cigar went out, and he had to ask me for a match.

" How very interesting," said Rose. " I do wish I knew some ancient history."

" It is not worth your notice," said Mr. Sandbach. " Eh, Eustace? "

Eustace was finishing his whistle. He looked up, with the irritable frown in which his aunts allowed him to indulge, and made no reply.

The conversation turned to various topics and then died out. It was a cloudless afternoon in May, and the pale green of the young chestnut leaves made a pretty contrast with the dark blue of the sky. We were all sitting at the edge of the small clearing for the sake of the view, and the shade of the chestnut saplings behind us was manifestly insufficient. All sounds died away — at least, that is my account; Miss Robinson says that the clamor of the birds was the first sign of uneasiness that she discerned. All sounds died away, except that, far in the distance, I could hear two boughs of a great chestnut grinding together as the tree swayed. The grinds grew shorter and shorter, and finally that sound stopped also. As I looked over the green fingers of the valley, everything was absolutely motionless and still; and that feeling of suspense which one so often experiences when Nature is in repose began to steal over me.

Suddenly we were all electrified by the excruciating noise of Eustace's whistle. I never heard any instrument give forth so earsplitting and discordant a sound.

"Eustace, dear," said Miss Mary Robinson, "you might have thought of your poor Aunt Julia's head."

Leyland, who had apparently been asleep, sat up.

"It is astonishing how blind a boy is to anything that is elevating or beautiful," he observed. "I should not have thought he could have found the wherewithal out here to spoil our pleasure like this."

Then the terrible silence fell upon us again. I was now standing up and watching a cat's-paw of wind that was running down one of the ridges opposite, turning the light green to dark as it traveled. A fanciful feeling of foreboding came over me; so I turned away, to find, to my amazement, that all the others were also on their feet, watching it too.

It is not possible to describe coherently what happened next; but I, for one, am not ashamed to confess that, though the fair blue sky was above me, and the green spring woods beneath me, and the kindest of friends around me, yet I became terribly frightened, more frightened than I ever wish to become again, frightened in a way I never have known either before or after. And in the eyes of the others, too, I saw blank, expressionless fear, while their mouths strove in vain to speak and their hands to gesticulate. Yet all around us were prosperity, beauty, and peace, and all was motionless, save the cat's-paw of wind, now traveling up the ridge on which we stood.

Who moved first has never been settled. It is enough to say that in one second we were tearing away along the hillside. Leyland was in front, then Mr. Sandbach, then my wife. But I only saw for a brief moment; for I ran across the little clearing and through the woods and over the undergrowth and the rocks and down the dry torrent-beds into the valley below. The sky might have been black as I ran, and the trees short grass, and the hillside a level road; for I saw nothing and heard nothing and felt nothing, since all the channels of sense and reason were blocked. It was not the spiritual fear that one has known at other times; but brutal overmastering physical fear, stopping up the ears, and dropping clouds before the eyes, and filling the mouth with foul tastes. And it was no ordinary humiliation that survived; for I had been afraid, not as a man, but as a beast.

II

I CANNOT describe our finish any better than our start; for our fear passed away as it had come, without cause. Suddenly I was able to see, and hear, and cough, and clear my mouth. Looking back, I saw that the others were stopping too; and in a short time we were all together, though it was long before we could speak, and longer before we dared to.

No one was seriously injured. My poor wife had sprained her ankle, Leyland had torn one of his nails on a tree-trunk, and I myself had scraped and damaged my ear. I never noticed it till I had stopped.

We were all silent, searching one another's faces. Suddenly Miss Mary Robinson gave a terrible shriek. " Oh, merciful heavens! Where is Eustace? " And then she would have fallen if Mr. Sandbach had not caught her.

" We must go back, we must go back at once," said my Rose, who was quite the most collected of the party. " But I hope — I feel he is safe."

Such was the cowardice of Leyland that he objected. But, finding himself in a minority, and being afraid of being left alone, he gave in. Rose and I supported my poor wife, Mr. Sandbach and Miss Robinson helped Miss Mary, and we returned slowly and silently, taking forty minutes to ascend the path that we had descended in ten.

Our conversation was naturally disjointed, as no one wished to offer an opinion on what had happened. Rose was the most talkative; she startled us all by saying that she had very nearly stopped where she was.

" Do you mean to say that you weren't — that you didn't feel compelled to go? " said Mr. Sandbach.

" Oh, of course, I did feel frightened " — she was the first to use the word — " but I somehow felt that if I could stop on, it would be quite different, that I shouldn't be frightened at all, so to speak." Rose never did express herself clearly; still, it is greatly to her credit that she, the youngest of us, should have held on so long at that terrible time.

" I should have stopped, I do believe," she continued, " if I had not seen Mamma go."

Rose's experience comforted us a little about Eustace. But a feeling of terrible foreboding was on us all as we painfully climbed the chestnut-covered slopes and neared the little clearing. When we reached it our tongues broke loose. There, at the further side, were the remains of our lunch, and close to them, lying motionless on his back, was Eustace.

With some presence of mind I at once cried out: " Hey, you young monkey! Jump up! " But he made no reply, nor did he answer when his poor aunts spoke to him. And, to my unspeakable horror, I saw one of those green lizards dart out from under his shirt-cuff as we approached.

We stood watching him as he lay there so silently, and my ears began to tingle in expectation of the outbursts of lamentations and tears.

Miss Mary fell on her knees beside him and touched his hand, which was convulsively entwined in the long grass.

As she did so, he opened his eyes and smiled.

I have often seen that peculiar smile since, both on the possessor's face and on the photographs of him that are beginning to get into the illustrated papers. But, till then, Eustace had always worn a peevish, discontented frown; and we were all unused to this disquieting smile, which always seemed to be without adequate reason.

His aunts showered kisses on him, which he did not reciprocate, and then there was an awkward pause. Eustace seemed so natural and undisturbed; yet, if he had not had astonishing experiences himself, he ought to have been all the more astonished at our extraordinary behavior. My wife, with ready tact, endeavored to behave as if nothing had happened.

"Well, Mr. Eustace," she said, sitting down as she spoke, to ease her foot, "how have you been amusing yourself since we have been away?"

"Thank you, Mrs. Tytler, I have been very happy."

"And where have you been?"

"Here."

"And lying down all the time, you idle boy?"

"No, not all the time."

"What were you doing before?"

"Oh, standing or sitting."

"Stood and sat doing nothing! Don't you know the poem ' Satan finds some mischief still for — ' "

"Oh, my dear madam, hush! hush!" Mr. Sandbach's voice broke in; and my wife, naturally mortified by the interruption, said no more and moved away. I was surprised to see Rose immediately take her place and, with more freedom than she generally displayed, run her fingers through the boy's tousled hair.

"Eustace! Eustace!" she said hurriedly, "tell me everything — every single thing."

Slowly he sat up — till then he had lain on his back.

"Oh, Rose — " he whispered, and, my curiosity being aroused, I moved nearer to hear what he was going to say. As I did so, I caught sight of some goats' footmarks in the moist earth beneath the trees.

"Apparently you have had a visit from some goats," I observed. "I had no idea they fed up here."

Eustace laboriously got onto his feet and came to see; and when he saw the footmarks he lay down and rolled on them, as a dog rolls in dirt.

After that there was a grave silence, broken at length by the solemn speech of Mr. Sandbach.

"My dear friends," he said, "it is best to confess the truth bravely. I know that what I am going to say now is what you are all now feeling. The Evil One has been very near us in bodily form. Time may yet discover some injury that he has wrought among us.

But at present, for myself at all events, I wish to offer up thanks for a merciful deliverance."

With that he knelt down, and, as the others knelt, I knelt too, though I do not believe in the Devil being allowed to assail us in visible form, as I told Mr. Sandbach afterwards. Eustace came too, and knelt quietly enough between his aunts after they had beckoned to him. But when it was over he at once got up and began hunting for something.

" Why! Someone has cut my whistle in two," he said. (I had seen Leyland with an open knife in his hand — a superstitious act which I could hardly approve.)

" Well, it doesn't matter," he continued.

" And why doesn't it matter? " said Mr. Sandbach, who has ever since tried to entrap Eustace into an account of that mysterious hour.

" Because I don't want it any more."

" Why? "

At that he smiled; and, as no one seemed to have anything more to say, I set off as fast as I could through the wood and hauled up a donkey to carry my poor wife home. Nothing occurred in my absence, except that Rose had again asked Eustace to tell her what had happened; and he, this time, had turned away his head and had not answered her a single word.

As soon as I returned, we all set off. Eustace walked with difficulty, almost with pain, so that when we reached the other donkeys, his aunts wished him to mount one of them and ride all the way home. I make it a rule never to interfere between relatives, but I put my foot down at this. As it turned out, I was perfectly right, for the healthy exercise, I suppose, began to thaw Eustace's sluggish blood and loosen his stiffened muscles. He stepped out manfully, for the first time in his life, holding his head up and taking deep drafts of air into his chest. I observed with satisfaction to Miss Mary Robinson that Eustace was at last taking some pride in his personal appearance.

Mr. Sandbach sighed, and said that Eustace must be carefully watched, for we none of us understood him yet. Miss Mary Robinson being very much — over much, I think — guided by him, sighed too.

"Come, come, Miss Robinson," I said, "there's nothing wrong with Eustace. Our experiences are mysterious, not his. He was astonished at our sudden departure, that's why he was so strange when we returned. He's right enough — improved, if anything."

"And is the worship of athletics, the cult of insensate activity, to be counted as an improvement?" put in Leyland, fixing a large, sorrowful eye on Eustace, who had stopped to scramble onto a rock to pick some cyclamen. "The passionate desire to rend from Nature the few beauties that have been still left her — that is to be counted as an improvement too?"

It is mere waste of time to reply to such remarks, especially when they come from an unsuccessful artist, suffering from a damaged finger. I changed the conversation by asking what we should say at the hotel. After some discussion it was agreed that we should say nothing, either there or in our letters home. Importunate truth-telling, which brings only bewilderment and discomfort to the hearers, is, in my opinion, a mistake; and, after a long discussion, I managed to make Mr. Sandbach acquiesce in my view.

Eustace did not share in our conversation. He was racing about, like a real boy, in the wood to the right. A strange feeling of shame prevented us from openly mentioning our fright to him. Indeed, it seemed almost reasonable to conclude that it had made but little impression on him. So it disconcerted us when he bounded back with an armful of flowering acanthus, calling out:

"Do you suppose Gennaro'll be there when we get back?"

Gennaro was the stopgap waiter, a clumsy, impertinent fisher-lad, who had been had up from Minori in the absence of the nice English-speaking Emmanuele. It was to him that we owed our scrappy lunch; and I could not conceive why Eustace desired to see him, unless it was to make mock with him of our behavior.

"Yes, of course he will be there," said Miss Robinson. "Why do you ask, dear?"

"Oh, I thought I'd like to see him."

"And why?" snapped Mr. Sandbach.

"Because, because I do, I do; because, because I do." He danced away into the darkening wood to the rhythm of his words.

"This is very extraordinary," said Mr. Sandbach. "Did he like Gennaro before?"

"Gennaro has only been here two days," said Rose, "and I know that they haven't spoken to each other a dozen times."

Each time Eustace returned from the wood his spirits were higher. Once he came whooping down on us as a wild Indian, and another time he made believe to be a dog. The last time he came back with a poor dazed hare, too frightened to move, sitting on his arm. He was getting too uproarious, I thought; and we were all glad to leave the wood and start upon the steep staircase path that leads down into Ravello. It was late and turning dark; and we made all the speed we could, Eustace scurrying in front of us like a goat.

Just where the staircase path debouches on the white highroad, the next extraordinary incident of this extraordinary day occurred. Three old women were standing by the wayside. They, like ourselves, had come down from the woods, and they were resting their heavy bundles of fuel on the low parapet of the road. Eustace stopped in front of them and, after a moment's deliberation, stepped forward and — kissed the left-hand one on the cheek!

"My good fellow!" exclaimed Mr. Sandbach, "are you quite crazy?"

Eustace said nothing, but offered the old woman some of his flowers and then hurried on. I looked back; and the old woman's companions seemed as much astonished at the proceeding as we were. But she herself had put the flowers in her bosom and was murmuring blessings.

This salutation of the old lady was the first example of Eustace's strange behavior, and we were both surprised and alarmed. It was useless talking to him, for he either made silly replies or else bounded away without replying at all.

He made no reference to Gennaro on the way home, and I hoped that that was forgotten. But when we came to the Piazza, in front of the Cathedral, he screamed out: "Gennaro! Gennaro!" at the top of his voice, and began running up the little alley that led to the hotel. Sure enough, there was Gennaro at the end of it, with his arms and legs sticking out of the nice little English-speaking waiter's dress suit, and a dirty fisherman's cap on his head — for, as the poor landlady truly said, however much she superintended his toilet, he always managed to introduce something incongruous into it before he had done.

Eustace sprang to meet him, and leapt right up into his arms and put his own arms round his neck. And this in the presence, not only of us, but also of the landlady, the chambermaid, the facchino, and of two American ladies who were coming for a few days' visit to the little hotel.

I always make a point of behaving pleasantly to Italians, however little they may deserve it; but this habit of promiscuous intimacy was perfectly intolerable and could only lead to familiarity and mortification for all. Taking Miss Robinson aside, I asked her permission to speak seriously to Eustace on the subject of intercourse with social inferiors. She granted it; but I determined to wait till the absurd boy had calmed down a little from the excitement of the day. Meanwhile Gennaro, instead of attending to the wants of the two new ladies, carried Eustace into the house, as if it was the most natural thing in the world.

"*Ho capito*," I heard him say as he passed me. "*Ho capito*" is the Italian for "I have understood"; but, as Eustace had not spoken to him, I could not see the force of the remark. It served to increase our bewilderment, and by the time we sat down at the dinner-table, our imaginations and our tongues were alike exhausted.

I omit from this account the various comments that were made, as few of them seem worthy of being recorded. But for three or four hours seven of us were pouring forth our bewilderment in a stream of appropriate and inappropriate exclamations. Some traced a connection between our behavior in the afternoon and the behavior of Eustace now. Others saw no connection at all. Mr. Sandbach still held to the possibility of infernal influences, and also said that he ought to have a doctor. Leyland only saw the development of "that unspeakable Philistine, the boy." Rose maintained, to my surprise, that everything was excusable; while I began to see that the young gentleman wanted a sound thrashing. The poor Miss Robinsons swayed helplessly about between these diverse opinions; inclining now to careful supervision, now to acquiescence, now to corporal chastisement, now to Eno's Fruit Salt.

Dinner passed off fairly well, though Eustace was terribly fidgety, Gennaro as usual dropping the knives and spoons, and hawking and clearing his throat. He only knew a few words of English, and we were all reduced to Italian for making known our wants. Eustace, who had picked up a little somehow, asked for some oranges. To my annoyance, Gennaro in his answer made use of the second person singular — a form only used when addressing those who are both intimates and equals. Eustace had brought it on himself; but an impertinence of this kind was an affront to us all, and I was determined to speak, and to speak at once.

When I heard him clearing the table I went in, and, summoning up my Italian, or rather Neapolitan — the Southern dialects are execrable — I said: " Gennaro! I heard you address Signor Eustace with ' *Tu.*' "

" It is true."

" You are not right. You must use ' *Lei* ' or ' *Voi* ' — more polite forms. And remember that, though Signor Eustace is sometimes silly and foolish — this afternoon for example — yet you must always behave respectfully to him; for he is a young English gentleman, and you are a poor Italian fisher-boy."

I know that speech sounds terribly snobbish, but in Italian one can say things that one would never dream of saying in English. Besides, it is no good speaking delicately to persons of that class. Unless you put things plainly, they take a vicious pleasure in misunderstanding you.

An honest English fisherman would have landed me one in the eye in a minute for such a remark, but the wretched downtrodden Italians have no pride. Gennaro only sighed and said: " It is true."

" Quite so," I said, and turned to go. To my indignation I heard him add: " But sometimes it is not important."

" What do you mean? " I shouted.

He came close up to me with horrid gesticulating fingers.

" Signor Tytler, I wish to say this: If Eustazio asks me to call him ' Voi,' I will call him ' Voi.' Otherwise, no."

With that he seized up a tray of dinner things and fled from the room with them; and I heard two more wineglasses go on the courtyard floor.

I was now fairly angry, and strode out to interview Eustace. But he had gone to bed, and the landlady, to whom I also wished to speak, was engaged. After more vague wonderings, obscurely expressed owing to the presence of Janet and the two American ladies, we all went to bed, too, after a harassing and most extraordinary day.

III*

BUT the day was nothing to the night.

I suppose I had slept for about four hours, when I woke suddenly thinking I heard a noise in the garden. And immediately, before my eyes were open, cold terrible fear seized me — not fear of something that was happening, like the fear in the wood, but fear of something that might happen.

Our room was on the first floor, looking out onto the garden — or terrace, it was rather: a wedge-shaped block of ground covered with roses and vines, and intersected with little asphalt paths. It was bounded on the small side by the house; round the two long sides ran a wall, only three feet above the terrace level, but with a good twenty-feet drop over it into the olive yards, for the ground fell very precipitously away.

Trembling all over, I stole to the window. There, pattering up and down the asphalt paths, was something white. I was too much alarmed to see clearly; and in the uncertain light of the stars the thing took all manner of curious shapes. Now it was a great dog, now an enormous white bat, now a mass of quickly traveling cloud. It would bounce like a ball, or take short flights like a bird, or glide slowly like a wraith. It gave no sound — save the pattering sound of what, after all, must be human feet. And at last the obvious explanation forced itself upon my disordered mind; and I realized that Eustace had got out of bed, and that we were in for something more.

I hastily dressed myself and went down into the dining-room, which opened upon the terrace. The door was already unfastened. My terror had almost entirely passed away, but for quite five minutes I struggled with a curious cowardly feeling, which bade me not interfere with the poor strange boy, but leave him to his ghostly patterings and merely watch him from the window, to see he took no harm.

But better impulses prevailed and, opening the door, I called out:

"Eustace! What on earth are you doing? Come in at once."

He stopped his antics and said: "I hate my bedroom. I could not stop in it, it is too small."

"Come! Come! I'm tired of affectation. You've never complained of it before."

"Besides I can't see anything — no flowers, no leaves, no sky; only a stone wall." The outlook of Eustace's room certainly was limited; but, as I told him, he had never complained of it before.

"Eustace, you talk like a child. Come in! Prompt obedience, if you please."

He did not move.

"Very well; I shall carry you in by force," I added, and made a few steps towards him. But I was soon convinced of the futility of pursuing a boy through a tangle of asphalt paths, and went in instead, to call Mr. Sandbach and Leyland to my aid.

When I returned with them he was worse than ever. He would not even answer us when we spoke, but began singing and chattering to himself in a most alarming way.

"It's a case for the doctor now," said Mr. Sandbach, gravely tapping his forehead.

He had stopped his running and was singing, first low, then loud — singing five-finger exercises, scales, hymn tunes, scraps of Wagner — anything that came into his head. His voice — a very untuneful voice — grew stronger and stronger, and he ended with a tremendous shout which boomed like a gun among the mountains and awoke everyone who was still sleeping in the hotel. My poor wife and the two girls appeared at their respective windows, and the American ladies were heard violently ringing their bell.

"Eustace," we all cried, "stop! Stop, dear boy, and come into the house."

He shook his head and started off again — talking this time. Never have I listened to such an extraordinary speech. At any other time it would have been ludicrous, for here was a boy, with no sense of beauty and a puerile command of words, attempting to tackle themes which the greatest poets have found almost beyond their power. Eustace Robinson, aged fourteen, was standing in his nightshirt saluting, praising, and blessing, the great forces and manifestations of Nature.

He spoke first of night and the stars and planets above his head, of the swarms of fireflies below him, of the invisible sea below the fireflies, of the great rocks covered with anemones and shells that were slumbering in the invisible sea. He spoke of the rivers and waterfalls, of the ripening bunches of grapes, of the smoking cone of Vesuvius and the hidden fire-channels that made the smoke, of the myriads of lizards who were lying curled up in the crannies of the sultry earth, of the showers of white rose-leaves that were tangled in his hair. And then he spoke of the rain and the wind by which all things are changed, of the air through which all things live, and of the woods in which all things can be hidden.

Of course, it was all absurdly highfaluting: yet I could have kicked Leyland for audibly observing that it was "a diabolical caricature of all that was most holy and beautiful in life."

"And then" — Eustace was going on in the pitiable conversational doggerel which was his only mode of expression — "and then there are men, but I can't make them out so well." He knelt down by the parapet and rested his head on his arms.

"Now's the time," whispered Leyland. I hate stealth, but we darted forward and endeavored to catch hold of him from behind. He was away in a twinkling, but turned round at once to look at us. As far as I could see in the starlight, he was crying. Leyland rushed at him again, and we tried to corner him among the asphalt paths, but without the slightest approach to success.

We returned, breathless and discomfited, leaving him to his madness in the further corner of the terrace. But my Rose had an inspiration.

"Papa," she called from the window, "if you get Gennaro, he might be able to catch him for you."

I had no wish to ask a favor of Gennaro, but, as the landlady had by now appeared on the scene, I begged her to summon him from the charcoal-bin in which he slept, and make him try what he could do.

She soon returned, and was shortly followed by Gennaro, attired in a dress coat, without either waistcoat, shirt, or vest, and a ragged pair of what had been trousers, cut short above the knees for purposes of wading. The landlady, who had quite picked up English ways, rebuked him for the incongruous and even indecent appearance which he presented.

" I have a coat and I have trousers. What more do you desire? "

" Never mind, Signora Scafetti," I put in. " As there are no ladies here, it is not of the slightest consequence." Then, turning to Gennaro, I said: " The aunts of Signor Eustace wish you to fetch him into the house."

He did not answer.

" Do you hear me? He is not well. I order you to fetch him into the house."

" Fetch! Fetch! " said Signora Scafetti, and shook him roughly by the arm.

" Eustazio is well where he is."

" Fetch! Fetch! " Signora Scafetti screamed, and let loose a flood of Italian, most of which, I am glad to say, I could not follow. I glanced up nervously at the girls' window, but they hardly know as much as I do, and I am thankful to say that none of us caught one word of Gennaro's answer.

The two yelled and shouted at each other for quite ten minutes, at the end of which Gennaro rushed back to his charcoal-bin and Signora Scafetti burst into tears, as well she might, for she greatly valued her English guests.

" He says," she sobbed, " that Signor Eustace is well where he is, and that he will not fetch him. I can do no more."

But I could, for, in my stupid British way, I have got some insight into the Italian character. I followed Mr. Gennaro to his place of repose and found him wriggling down onto a dirty sack.

" I wish you to fetch Signor Eustace to me," I began.

He hurled at me an unintelligible reply.

" If you fetch him, I will give you this." And out of my pocket I took a new ten-lira note.

This time he did not answer.

" This note is equal to ten lire in silver," I continued, for I knew that the poor-class Italian is unable to conceive of a single large sum.

" I know it."

" That is, two hundred soldi."

" I do not desire them. Eustazio is my friend."

I put the note into my pocket.

" Besides, you would not give it me."

" I am an Englishman. The English always do what they promise."

" That is true." It is astonishing how the most dishonest of nations trust us. Indeed, they often trust us more than we trust one another. Gennaro knelt up on his sack. It was too dark to see his face, but I could feel his warm garlicky breath coming out in gasps, and I knew that the eternal avarice of the South had laid hold upon him.

" I could not fetch Eustazio to the house. He might die there."

" You need not do that," I replied patiently. " You need only bring him to me; and I will stand outside in the garden." And to this, as if it were something quite different, the pitiable youth consented.

" But give me first the ten lire."

" No " — for I knew the kind of person with whom I had to deal. Once faithless, always faithless.

We returned to the terrace, and Gennaro, without a single word, pattered off towards the pattering that could be heard at the remoter end. Mr. Sandbach, Leyland, and myself moved away a little from the house and stood in the shadow of the white climbing roses, practically invisible.

We heard " Eustazio " called, followed by absurd cries of pleasure from the poor boy. The pattering ceased, and we heard them talking. Their voices got nearer, and presently I could discern them through the creepers, the grotesque figure of the young man, and the slim little white-robed boy. Gennaro had his arm round Eustace's neck, and Eustace was talking away in his fluent, slipshod Italian.

" I understand almost everything," I heard him say. " The trees, hills, stars, water, I can see all. But isn't it odd! I can't make out men a bit. Do you know what I mean? "

" *Ho capito*," said Gennaro gravely, and took his arm off Eustace's shoulder. But I made the new note crackle in my pocket; and he heard it. He stuck his hand out with a jerk; and the unsuspecting Eustace gripped it in his own.

" It is odd! " Eustace went on — they were quite close now —
" It almost seems as if — as if — "

I darted out and caught hold of his arm, and Leyland got hold of
the other arm, and Mr. Sandbach hung onto his feet. He gave shrill
heart-piercing screams; and the white roses, which were falling early
that year, descended in showers on him as we dragged him into the
house.

As soon as we entered the house he stopped shrieking; but floods
of tears silently burst forth and spread over his upturned face.

" Not to my room," he pleaded. " It is so small."

His infinitely dolorous look filled me with strange pity, but what
could I do? Besides, his window was the only one that had bars to it.

" Never mind, dear boy," said kind Mr. Sandbach. " I will bear
you company till the morning."

At this his convulsive struggles began again. " Oh, please, not
that. Anything but that. I will promise to lie still and not to cry
more than I can help, if I am left alone."

So we laid him on the bed and drew the sheets over him and left
him sobbing bitterly, and saying: " I nearly saw everything, and
now I can see nothing at all."

We informed the Miss Robinsons of all that had happened, and
returned to the dining-room, where we found Signora Scafetti and
Gennaro whispering together. Mr. Sandbach got pen and paper
and began writing to the English doctor at Naples. I at once drew
out the note and flung it down on the table to Gennaro.

" Here is your pay," I said sternly, for I was thinking of the
Thirty Pieces of Silver.

" Thank you very much, sir," said Gennaro, and grabbed it.

He was going off, when Leyland, whose interest and indifference
were always equally misplaced, asked him what Eustace had meant
by saying he could " not make out men a bit."

" I cannot say. Signor Eustazio " (I was glad to observe a little
deference at last) " has a subtle brain. He understands many
things."

" But I heard you say you understood," Leyland persisted.

" I understand, but I cannot explain. I am a poor Italian fisher-
lad. Yet, listen: I will try." I saw to my alarm that his manner was
changing, and tried to stop him. But he sat down on the edge of

the table and started off, with some absolutely incoherent remarks.

"It is sad," he observed at last. "What has happened is very sad. But what can I do? I am poor. It is not I."

I turned away in contempt. Leyland went on asking questions. He wanted to know who it was that Eustace had in his mind when he spoke.

"That is easy to say," Gennaro gravely answered. "It is you, it is I. It is all in this house, and many outside it. If he wishes for mirth, we discomfort him. If he asks to be alone, we disturb him. He longed for a friend, and found none for fifteen years. Then he found me, and the first night I — I who have been in the woods and understood things too — betray him to you, and send him in to die. But what could I do?"

"Gently, gently," said I.

"Oh, assuredly he will die. He will lie in the small room all night, and in the morning he will be dead. That I know for certain."

"There, that will do," said Mr. Sandbach. "I shall be sitting with him."

"Filomena Giusti sat all night with Caterina, but Caterina was dead in the morning. They would not let her out, though I begged, and prayed, and cursed, and beat the door, and climbed the wall. They were ignorant fools, and thought I wished to carry her away. And in the morning she was dead."

"What is all this?" I asked Signora Scafetti.

"All kinds of stories will get about," she replied, "and he, least of anyone, has reason to repeat them."

"And I am alive now," he went on, "because I had neither parents nor relatives nor friends, so that, when the first night came, I could run through the woods and climb the rocks and plunge into the water, until I had accomplished my desire!"

We heard a cry from Eustace's room — a faint but steady sound, like the sound of wind in a distant wood heard by one standing in tranquillity.

"That," said Gennaro, "was the last noise of Caterina. I was hanging onto her window then, and it blew out past me."

And, lifting up his hand, in which my ten-lira note was safely packed, he solemnly cursed Mr. Sandbach, and Leyland, and myself, and Fate, because Eustace was dying in the upstairs room.

Such is the working of the Southern mind; and I verily believe that
he would not have moved even then, had not Leyland, that unspeakable idiot, upset the lamp with his elbow. It was a patent self-
extinguishing lamp, bought by Signora Scafetti, at my special request, to replace the dangerous thing that she was using. The result
was that it went out; and the mere physical change from light to
darkness had more power over the ignorant animal nature of Gennaro than the most obvious dictates of logic and reason.

I felt, rather than saw, that he had left the room and shouted out
to Mr. Sandbach: "Have you got the key of Eustace's room in
your pocket?" But Mr. Sandbach and Leyland were both on the
floor, having mistaken each other for Gennaro, and some more
precious time was wasted in finding a match. Mr. Sandbach had
only just time to say that he had left the key in the door, in case the
Miss Robinsons wished to pay Eustace a visit, when we heard a
noise on the stairs, and there was Gennaro, carrying Eustace down.

We rushed out and blocked up the passage, and they lost heart
and retreated to the upper landing.

"Now they are caught," cried Signora Scafetti. "There is no
other way out."

We were cautiously ascending the staircase, when there was a
terrific scream from my wife's room, followed by a heavy thud on
the asphalt path. They had leapt out of her window.

I reached the terrace just in time to see Eustace jumping over the
parapet of the garden wall. This time I knew for certain he would
be killed. But he alighted in an olive tree, looking like a great white
moth, and from the tree he slid onto the earth. And as soon as his
bare feet touched the clods of earth he uttered a strange loud cry,
such as I should not have thought the human voice could have
produced, and disappeared among the trees below.

"He has understood and he is saved," cried Gennaro, who was
still sitting on the asphalt path. "Now instead of dying he will
live!"

"And you, instead of keeping the ten lire, will give them up," I
retorted, for at this theatrical remark I could contain myself no
longer.

"The ten lire are mine," he hissed back, in a scarcely audible
voice. He clasped his hand over his breast to protect his ill-gotten

gains, and, as he did so, he swayed forward and fell upon his face on the path. He had not broken any limbs, and a leap like that would never have killed an Englishman, for the drop was not great. But those miserable Italians have no stamina. Something had gone wrong inside him, and he was dead.

The morning was still far off, but the morning breeze had begun, and more rose-leaves fell on us as we carried him in. Signora Scafetti burst into screams at the sight of the dead body, and, far down the valley towards the sea, there still resounded the shouts and the laughter of the escaping boy.

❧ *D. H. Lawrence* ❧

THE WOMAN WHO RODE AWAY

I

Sʜᴇ had thought that this marriage, of all marriages, would be an adventure. Not that the man himself was exactly magical to her. A little, wiry, twisted fellow, twenty years older than herself, with brown eyes and graying hair, who had come to America a scrap of a wastrel, from Holland, years ago, as a tiny boy, and from the gold-mines of the west had been kicked south into Mexico, and now was more or less rich, owning silver-mines in the wilds of the Sierra Madre: it was obvious that the adventure lay in his circumstances rather than his person. But he was still a little dynamo of energy, in spite of accidents survived, and what he had accomplished he had accomplished alone. One of those human oddments there is no accounting for.

When she actually *saw* what he had accomplished, her heart quailed. Great green-covered, unbroken mountain-hills, and, in the midst of the lifeless isolation, the sharp pinkish mounds of the dried mud from the silver-works. Under the nakedness of the works, the walled-in, one-story adobe house, with its garden inside, and its deep inner veranda with tropical climbers on the sides. And when you looked up from this shut-in flowered patio, you saw the huge pink cone of the silver-mud refuse, and the machinery of the extracting-plant against heaven above. No more.

To be sure, the great wooden doors were often open. And then she could stand outside, in the vast open world. And see great, void, tree-clad hills piling behind one another, from nowhere into nowhere. They were green in autumn-time. For the rest, pinkish, stark dry, and abstract.

And in his battered Ford car her husband would take her into the dead, thrice-dead little Spanish town forgotten among the mountains. The great, sun-dried dead church, the dead portales, the hopeless covered market-place, where, the first time she went, she saw a dead dog lying between the meat-stalls and the vegetable array, stretched out as if forever, nobody troubling to throw it away. Deadness within deadness.

Everybody feebly talking silver and showing bits of ore. But silver was at a standstill. The great war came and went. Silver was a dead market. Her husband's mines were closed down. But she and he lived on in the adobe house under the works, among the flowers that were never very flowery to her.

She had two children, a boy and a girl. And her eldest, the boy, was nearly ten years old before she aroused from her stupor of subjected amazement. She was now thirty-three, a large, blue-eyed, dazed woman, beginning to grow stout. Her little, wiry, tough, twisted, brown-eyed husband was fifty-three, a man as tough as wire, tenacious as wire, still full of energy, but dimmed by the lapse of silver from the market, and by some curious inaccessibility on his wife's part.

He was a man of principles, and a good husband. In a way, he doted on her. He never quite got over his dazzled admiration of her. But essentially he was still a bachelor. He had been thrown out on the world, a little bachelor, at the age of ten. When he married he was over forty, and had enough money to marry on. But his capital was all a bachelor's. He was boss of his own works, and marriage was the last and most intimate bit of his own works.

He admired his wife to extinction, he admired her body, all her points. And she was to him always the rather dazzling Californian girl from Berkeley whom he had first known. Like any sheik, he kept her guarded among those mountains of Chihuahua. He was jealous of her as he was of his silver-mine; and that is saying a lot.

At thirty-three she really was still the girl from Berkeley, in all but physique. Her conscious development had stopped mysteriously with her marriage, completely arrested. Her husband had never become real to her, neither mentally nor physically. In spite of his late sort of passion for her, he never meant anything to her, physically. Only morally he swayed her, downed her, kept her in an invincible slavery.

So the years went by, in the adobe house strung round the sunny patio, with the silver-works overhead. Her husband was never still. When the silver went dead, he ran a ranch lower down, some twenty miles away, and raised pure-bred hogs, splendid creatures. At the same time he hated pigs. He was a squeamish waif of an idealist, and really hated the physical side of life. He loved work, work, work, and making things. His marriage, his children, were something he was making, part of his business, but with a sentimental income this time.

Gradually her nerves began to go wrong: she must get out. She must get out. So he took her to El Paso for three months. And at least it was the United States.

But he kept his spell over her. The three months ended: back she was, just the same, in her adobe house among those eternal green or pinky-brown hills, void as only the undiscovered is void. She taught her children, she supervised the Mexican boys who were her servants. And sometimes her husband brought visitors, Spaniards or Mexicans or occasionally white men.

He really loved to have white men staying on the place. Yet he had not a moment's peace when they were there. It was as if his wife were some peculiar secret vein of ore in his mines, which no one must be aware of except himself. And she was fascinated by the young gentlemen, mining engineers, who were his guests at times. He, too, was fascinated by a real gentleman. But he was an old-timer miner with a wife, and if a gentleman looked at his wife, he felt as if his mine were being looted, the secrets of it pried out.

It was one of these young gentlemen who put the idea into her mind. They were all standing outside the great wooden doors of the patio, looking at the outer world. The eternal, motionless hills were all green, it was September, after the rains. There was no sign of anything, save the deserted mine, the deserted works, and a bunch of half-deserted miner's dwellings.

"I wonder," said the young man, "what there is behind those great blank hills."

"More hills," said Lederman. "If you go that way, Sonora and the coast. This way is the desert — you came from there — and the other way, hills and mountains."

"Yes, but what *lives* in the hills and the mountains? *Surely* there is something wonderful? It looks *so* like nowhere on earth: like being on the moon."

"There's plenty of game, if you want to shoot. And Indians, if you call *them* wonderful."

"Wild ones?"

"Wild enough."

"But friendly?"

"It depends. Some of them are quite wild, and they don't let anybody near. They kill a missionary at sight. And where a missionary can't get, nobody can."

"But what does the government say?"

"They're so far from everywhere, the government leaves 'em alone. And they're wily; if they think there'll be trouble, they send a delegation to Chihuahua and make a formal submission. The government is glad to leave it at that."

"And do they live quite wild, with their own savage customs and religion?"

"Oh, yes. They use nothing but bows and arrows. I've seen them in town, in the Plaza, with funny sort of hats with flowers round them, and a bow in one hand, quite naked except for a sort of shirt, even in cold weather — striding round with their savage's bare legs."

"But don't you suppose it's wonderful, up there in their secret villages?"

"No. What would there be wonderful about it? Savages are savages, and all savages behave more or less alike: rather low-down and dirty, unsanitary, with a few cunning tricks, and struggling to get enough to eat."

"But surely they have old, old religions and mysteries — it must be wonderful, surely it must."

"I don't know about mysteries — howling and heathen practices, more or less indecent. No, I see nothing wonderful in that kind of stuff. And I wonder that you should, when you have lived in London or Paris or New York — "

"Ah, everybody lives in London or Paris or New York," said the young man, as if this were an argument.

And his peculiar vague enthusiasm for unknown Indians found a full echo in the woman's heart. She was overcome by a foolish romanticism more unreal than a girl's. She felt it was her destiny to wander into the secret haunts of these timeless, mysterious, marvelous Indians of the mountains.

She kept her secret. The young man was departing, her husband was going with him down to Torreón, on business — would be away for some days. But before the departure she made her husband talk about the Indians: about the wandering tribes, resembling the Navajo, who were still wandering free; and the Yaquis of Sonora; and the different groups in the different valleys of Chihuahua State.

There was supposed to be one tribe, the Chilchuis, living in a high valley to the south, who were the sacred tribe of all the Indians. The descendants of Montezuma and of the old Aztec or Totonac kings still lived among them, and the old priests still kept up the ancient religion, and offered human sacrifices — so it was said. Some scientists had been to the Chilchui country, and had come back gaunt and exhausted with hunger and bitter privation, bringing various curious, barbaric objects of worship, but having seen nothing extraordinary in the hungry, stark village of savages.

Though Lederman talked in this offhand way, it was obvious he felt some of the vulgar excitement at the idea of ancient and mysterious savages.

" How far away are they? " she asked.

" Oh — three days on horseback — past Cuchitee and a little lake there is up there."

Her husband and the young man departed. The woman made her crazy plans. Of late, to break the monotony of her life, she had harassed her husband into letting her go riding with him, occasionally, on horseback. She was never allowed to go out alone. The country truly was not safe, lawless and crude.

But she had her own horse, and she dreamed of being free as she had been as a girl, among the hills of California.

Her daughter, nine years old, was now in a tiny convent in the little half-deserted Spanish mining-town five miles away.

" Manuel," said the woman to her house-servant, " I'm going to ride to the convent to see Margarita and take her a few things. Perhaps I shall stay the night in the convent. You look after Freddy and see everything is all right till I come back."

" Shall I ride with you on the master's horse, or shall Juan? " asked the servant.

" Neither of you. I shall go alone."

The young man looked her in the eyes, in protest. Absolutely impossible that the woman should ride alone!

" I shall go alone," repeated the large, placid-seeming fair-complexioned woman, with peculiar overbearing emphasis. And the man silently, unhappily yielded.

" Why are you going alone, Mother? " asked her son, as she made up parcels of food.

" Am I never to be let alone? Not one moment of my life? " she cried, with sudden explosion of energy. And the child, like the servant, shrank into silence.

She set off without a qualm, riding astride on her strong roan horse, and wearing a riding suit of coarse linen, a riding skirt over her linen breeches, a scarlet necktie over her white blouse, and a black felt hat on her head. She had food in her saddle-bags, an army canteen with water, and a large, native blanket tied on behind the saddle. Peering into the distance, she set off from her home. Manuel and the little boy stood in the gateway to watch her go. She did not even turn to wave them farewell.

But when she had ridden about a mile, she left the wild road and

took a small trail to the right, that led into another valley, over steep
places and past great trees, and through another deserted mining-
settlement. It was September, the water was running freely in the
little stream that had fed the now abandoned mine. She got down
to drink, and let the horse drink too.

She saw natives coming through the trees, away up the slope.
They had seen her and were watching her closely. She watched
in turn. The three people, two women and a youth, were making a
wide detour, so as not to come too close to her. She did not care.
Mounting, she trotted ahead up the silent valley, beyond the silver-
works, beyond any trace of mining. There was still a rough trail,
that led over rocks and loose stones into the valley beyond. This
trail she had already ridden, with her husband. Beyond that she
knew she must go south.

Curiously, she was not afraid, although it was a frightening country, the silent, fatal-seeming mountain slopes, the occasional distant, suspicious, elusive natives among the trees, the great carrion
birds occasionally hovering, like great flies, in the distance, over
some carrion or some ranch-house or some group of huts.

As she climbed, the trees shrank and the trail ran through a
thorny scrub, that was trailed over with blue convolvulus and an
occasional pink creeper. Then these flowers lapsed. She was nearing
the pine trees.

She was over the crest, and before her another silent, void, green-
clad valley. It was past midday. Her horse turned to a little runlet
of water, so she got down to eat her midday meal. She sat in silence
looking at the motionless unliving valley, and at the sharp-peaked
hills, rising higher to rock and pine trees, southwards. She rested
two hours in the heat of the day, while the horse cropped around
her.

Curious that she was neither afraid nor lonely. Indeed, the loneliness was like a drink of cold water to one who is very thirsty. And a
strange elation sustained her from within.

She traveled on, and camped at night in a valley beside a stream,
deep among the bushes. She had seen cattle and had crossed several
trails. There must be a ranch not far off. She heard the strange wailing shriek of a mountain lion, and the answer of dogs. But she sat
by her small camp-fire in a secret hollow place and was not really

afraid. She was buoyed up always by the curious, bubbling elation within her.

It was very cold before dawn. She lay wrapped in her blanket looking at the stars, listening to her horse shivering, and feeling like a woman who has died and passed beyond. She was not sure that she had not heard, during the night, a great crash at the center of herself, which was the crash of her own death. Or else it was a crash at the center of the earth, and meant something big and mysterious.

With the first peep of light she got up, numb with cold, and made a fire. She ate hastily, gave her horse some pieces of oil-seed cake, and set off again. She avoided any meeting — and since she met nobody, it was evident that she in turn was avoided. She came at last in sight of the village of Cuchitee, with its black houses with their reddish roofs, a somber, dreary little cluster below another silent, long-abandoned mine. And beyond, a long, great mountain-side, rising up green and light to the darker, shaggier green of pine trees. And beyond the pine trees stretches of naked rock against the sky, rock slashed already and brindled with white stripes of snow. High up, the new snow had already begun to fall.

And now, as she neared, more or less, her destination, she began to go vague and disheartened. She had passed the little lake among yellowing aspen trees whose white trunks were round and suave like the white round arms of some woman. What a lovely place! In California she would have raved about it. But here she looked and saw that it was lovely, but she didn't care. She was weary and spent with her two nights in the open, and afraid of the coming night. She didn't know where she was going, or what she was going for. Her horse plodded dejectedly on, towards that immense and forbidding mountain slope, following a stony little trail. And if she had had any will of her own left, she would have turned back, to the village, to be protected and sent home to her husband.

But she had no will of her own. Her horse splashed through a brook, and turned up a valley, under immense yellowing cotton-wood trees. She must have been near nine thousand feet above sea-level, and her head was light with the altitude and with weari-ness. Beyond the cottonwood trees she could see, on each side, the steep sides of mountain slopes hemming her in, sharp-plumaged with overlapping aspen, and, higher up, with sprouting, pointed spruce and pine tree. Her horse went on automatically. In this tight valley, on this slight trail, there was nowhere to go but ahead, climbing.

Suddenly her horse jumped, and three men in dark blankets were on the trail before her.

"*Adiós!*" came the greeting, in the full, restrained Indian voice.

"*Adiós!*" she replied, in her assured, American woman's voice.

"Where are you going?" came the quiet question, in Spanish. The men in the dark sarapes had come closer and were looking up at her.

"On ahead," she replied coolly, in her hard, Saxon Spanish.

These were just natives to her: dark-faced, strongly-built men in dark sarapes and straw hats. They would have been the same as the men who worked for her husband, except, strangely, for the long black hair that fell over their shoulders. She noted this long black hair with a certain distaste. These must be the wild Indians she had come to see.

"Where do you come from?" the same man asked. It was always the one man who spoke. He was young, with quick, large, bright black eyes that glanced sideways at her. He had a soft black mustache on his dark face, and a sparse tuft of beard, loose hairs on his chin. His long black hair, full of life, hung unrestrained on his shoulders. Dark as he was, he did not look as if he had washed lately.

His two companions were the same, but older men, powerful and silent. One had a thin black line of mustache, but was beardless. The other had the smooth cheeks and the sparse dark hairs marking the lines of his chin with the beard characteristic of the Indians.

"I come from far away," she replied, with half-jocular evasion.

This was received in silence.

"But where do you live?" asked the young man, with that same quiet insistence.

"In the north," she replied airily.

Again there was a moment's silence. The young man conversed quietly, in Indian, with his two companions.

"Where do you want to go, up this way?" he asked suddenly, with challenge and authority, pointing briefly up the trail.

"To the Chilchui Indians," answered the woman laconically.

The young man looked at her. His eyes were quick and black, and inhuman. He saw, in the full evening light, the faint sub-smile of assurance on her rather large, calm, fresh-complexioned face; the weary, bluish lines under her large blue eyes; and in her eyes, as she looked down at him, a half-childish, half-arrogant confidence in her own female power. But in her eyes, also, a curious look of trance.

"*Usted es Señora?* You are a lady?" the Indian asked her.

"Yes, I am a lady," she replied complacently.

"With a family?"

"With a husband and two children, boy and girl," she said.

The Indian turned to his companions and translated, in the low, gurgling speech, like hidden water running. They were evidently at a loss.

"Where is your husband?" asked the young man.

"Who knows?" she replied airily. "He has gone away on business for a week."

The black eyes watched her shrewdly. She, for all her weariness, smiled faintly in the pride of her own adventure and the assurance of her own womanhood, and the spell of the madness that was on her.

"And what do you want to do?" the Indian asked her.

"I want to visit the Chilchui Indians — to see their houses and to know their gods," she replied.

The young man turned and translated quickly, and there was a silence almost of consternation. The grave elder men were glancing at her sideways, with strange looks, from under their decorated hats. And they said something to the young man, in deep chest voices.

The latter still hesitated. Then he turned to the woman.

"Good!" he said. "Let us go. But we cannot arrive until tomorrow. We shall have to make a camp tonight."

"Good!" she said. "I can make a camp."

Without more ado, they set off at a good speed up the stony trail. The young Indian ran alongside her horse's head, the other two ran behind. One of them had taken a thick stick, and occasionally he struck her horse a resounding blow on the haunch, to urge him forward. This made the horse jump, and threw her back in the saddle, which, tired as she was, made her angry.

" Don't do that! " she cried, looking round angrily at the fellow. She met his black, large, bright eyes, and for the first time her spirit really quailed. The man's eyes were not human to her, and they did not see her as a beautiful white woman. He looked at her with a black, bright, inhuman look and saw no woman in her at all. As if she were some strange, unaccountable *thing*, incomprehensible to him, but inimical. She sat in her saddle in wonder, feeling once more as if she had died. And again he struck her horse, and jerked her badly in the saddle.

All the passionate anger of the spoilt white woman rose in her. She pulled her horse to a standstill and turned with blazing eyes to the man at her bridle.

" Tell that fellow not to touch my horse again," she cried.

She met the eyes of the young man, and in their bright black inscrutability she saw a fine spark, as in a snake's eye, of derision. He spoke to his companion in the rear, in the low tones of the Indian. The man with the stick listened without looking. Then, giving a strange low cry to the horse, he struck it again on the rear, so that it leaped forward spasmodically up the stony trail, scattering the stones, pitching the weary woman in her seat.

The anger flew like a madness into her eyes, she went white at the gills. Fiercely she reined in her horse. But before she could turn, the young Indian had caught the reins under the horse's throat, jerked them forward, and was trotting ahead rapidly, leading the horse.

The woman was powerless. And along with her supreme anger there came a slight thrill of exultation. She knew she was dead.

The sun was setting, a great yellow light flooded the last of the aspens, flared on the trunks of the pine trees, the pine needles bristled and stood out with dark lustre, the rocks glowed with unearthly glamour. And through this effulgence the Indian at her horse's head trotted unweariedly on, his dark blanket swinging, his bare legs glowing with a strange transfigured ruddiness in the powerful light, and his straw hat with its half-absurd decorations of flowers and feathers shining showily above his river of long black hair. At times he would utter a low call to the horse, and then the other Indian, behind, would fetch the beast a whack with the stick.

The wonder-light faded off the mountains, the world began to grow dark, a cold air breathed down. In the sky half a moon was struggling against the glow in the west. Huge shadows came down from steep rocky slopes. Water was rushing. The woman was conscious only of her fatigue, her unspeakable fatigue, and the cold wind from the heights. She was not aware how moonlight replaced daylight. It happened while she traveled unconscious with weariness.

For some hours they traveled by moonlight. Then suddenly they came to a standstill. The men conversed in low tones for a moment.

" We camp here," said the young man.

She waited for him to help her down. He merely stood holding the horse's bridle. She almost fell from the saddle, so fatigued.

They had chosen a place at the foot of rocks that still gave off a little warmth of the sun. One man cut pine boughs, another erected little screens of pine boughs against the rock for shelter and put boughs of balsam pine for beds. The third made a small fire, to heat tortillas. They worked in silence.

The woman drank water. She did not want to eat — only to lie down.

" Where do I sleep? " she asked.

The young man pointed to one of the shelters. She crept in and lay inert. She did not care what happened to her, she was so weary, and so beyond everything. Through the twigs of spruce she could see the three men squatting round the fire on their hams, chewing the tortillas they picked from the ashes with their dark fingers, and drinking water from a gourd. They talked in low, muttering tones, with long intervals of silence. Her saddle and saddle-bags lay not far from the fire, unopened, untouched. The men were not interested in her nor her belongings. There they squatted with their hats on their heads, eating, eating mechanically, like animals, the dark sarape with its fringe falling to the ground before and behind, the powerful dark legs naked and squatting like an animal's, showing the dirty white shirt and the sort of loin-cloth which was the only other garment, underneath. And they showed no more sign of interest in her than if she had been a piece of venison they were bringing home from the hunt and had hung inside a shelter. After a while they carefully extinguished the fire and went inside their own shelter. Watching through the screen of boughs, she had a moment's thrill of fear and anxiety, seeing the dark forms cross and pass silently in the moonlight. Would they attack her now?

But no! They were as if oblivious of her. Her horse was hobbled; she could hear it hopping wearily. All was silent, mountain-silent, cold, deathly. She slept and woke and slept in a semi-conscious numbness of cold and fatigue. A long, long night, icy and eternal, and she aware that she had died.

II

YET when there was a stirring, and a clink of flint and steel, and the form of a man crouching like a dog over a bone, at a red splutter of fire, and she knew it was morning coming, it seemed to her the night had passed too soon.

When the fire was going, she came out of her shelter with one real desire left: for coffee. The men were warming more tortillas.

" Can we make coffee? " she asked.

The young man looked at her, and she imagined the same faint spark of derision in his eyes. He shook his head.

" We don't take it," he said. " There is no time."

And the elder men, squatting on their haunches, looked up at her in the terrible paling dawn, and there was not even derision in their eyes. Only that intense, yet remote, inhuman glitter which was terrible to her. They were inaccessible. They could not see her as a woman at all. As if she were not a woman. As if, perhaps, her whiteness took away all her womanhood and left her as some giant, female white ant. That was all they could see in her.

Before the sun was up, she was in the saddle again, and they were climbing steeply, in the icy air. The sun came, and soon she was very hot, exposed to the glare in the bare places. It seemed to her they were climbing to the roof of the world. Beyond against heaven were slashes of snow.

During the course of the morning they came to a place where the horse could not go farther. They rested for a time with a great slant of living rock in front of them, like the glossy breast of some earth-beast. Across this rock, along a wavering crack, they had to go. It seemed to her that for hours she went in torment, on her hands and knees, from crack to crevice, along the slanting face of this pure rock-mountain. An Indian in front and an Indian behind walked slowly erect, shod with sandals of braided leather. But she in her riding boots dared not stand erect.

Yet what she wondered, all the time, was why she persisted in clinging and crawling along these mile-long sheets of rock. Why she did not hurl herself down and have done! The world was below her.

When they emerged at last on a stony slope, she looked back and saw the third Indian coming carrying her saddle and saddle-bags on his back, the whole hung from a band across his forehead. And he had his hat in his hand, as he stepped slowly, with the slow, soft, heavy tread of the Indian, unwavering in the chinks of rock, as if along a scratch in the mountain's iron shield.

The stony slope led downwards. The Indians seemed to grow excited. One ran ahead at a slow trot, disappearing round the curve of stones. And the track curved round and down, till at last, in the full blaze of the mid-morning sun, they could see a valley below them, between walls of rock, as in a great wide chasm let in the mountains. A green valley, with a river, and trees, and clusters of low flat sparkling houses. It was all tiny and perfect, three thousand feet below. Even the flat bridge over the stream, and the square with the houses around it, the bigger buildings piled up at opposite ends of the square, the tall cottonwood trees, the pastures and stretches of yellow-sere maize, the patches of brown sheep or goats in the distance, on the slopes, the railed enclosures by the stream-side. There it was, all small and perfect, looking magical, as any place will look magical seen from the mountains above. The unusual thing was that the low houses glittered white, whitewashed, looking like crystals of salt, or silver. This frightened her.

They began the long, winding descent at the head of the barranca, following the stream that rushed and fell. At first it was all rocks; then the pine trees began, and soon the silver-limbed aspens. The flowers of autumn, big pink daisy-like flowers, and white ones,

and many yellow flowers, were in profusion. But she had to sit
down and rest, she was so weary. And she saw the bright flowers
shadowily, as pale shadows hovering, as one who is dead must see
them.

At length came grass and pasture-slopes between mingled aspen
and pine trees. A shepherd, naked in the sun save for his hat and
his cotton loin-cloth, was driving his brown sheep away. In a grove
of trees they sat and waited, she and the young Indian. The one
with the saddle had also gone forward.

They heard a sound of someone coming. It was three men, in
fine sarapes of red and orange and yellow and black, and with brilliant feather head-dresses. The oldest had his gray hair braided with
fur, and his red and orange-yellow sarape was covered with curious
black markings, like a leopard-skin. The other two were not gray-
haired, but they were elders too. Their blankets were in stripes, and
their head-dresses not so elaborate.

The young Indian addressed the elders in a few quiet words.
They listened without answering or looking at him or at the woman,
keeping their faces averted and their eyes turned to the ground,
only listening. And at length they turned and looked at the woman.

The old chief, or medicine-man, whatever he was, had a deeply
wrinkled and lined face of dark bronze, with a few sparse gray
hairs round the mouth. Two long braids of gray hair, braided with
fur and colored feathers, hung on his shoulders. And yet it was only
his eyes that mattered. They were black and of extraordinary piercing strength, without a qualm of misgiving in their demonish,
dauntless power. He looked into the eyes of the white woman with
a long, piercing look, seeking she knew not what. She summoned
all her strength to meet his eyes and keep up her guard. But it was
no good. He was not looking at her as one human being looks at
another. He never even perceived her resistance or her challenge,
but looked past them both, into she knew not what.

She could see it was hopeless to expect any human communication with this old being.

He turned and said a few words to the young Indian.

" He asks what do you seek here? " said the young man in Spanish.

" I? Nothing! I only came to see what it was like."

This was again translated, and the old man turned his eyes on her once more. Then he spoke again, in his low muttering tone, to the young Indian.

" He says, why does she leave her house with the white men? Does she want to bring the white man's God to the Chilchui? "

" No," she replied, foolhardy. " I came away from the white man's God myself. I came to look for the God of the Chilchui."

Profound silence followed when this was translated. Then the old man spoke again, in a small voice almost of weariness.

" Does the white woman seek the gods of the Chilchui because she is weary of her own God? " came the question.

" Yes, she does. She is tired of the white man's God," she replied, thinking that was what they wanted her to say. She would like to serve the gods of the Chilchui.

She was aware of an extraordinary thrill of triumph and exultance passing through the Indians, in the tense silence that followed when this was translated. Then they all looked at her with piercing black eyes, in which a steely covetous intent glittered incomprehensible. She was the more puzzled, as there was nothing sensual or sexual in the look. It had a terrible glittering purity that was beyond her. She was afraid, she would have been paralyzed with fear, had not something died within her, leaving her with a cold, watchful wonder only.

The elders talked a little while, then the two went away, leaving her with the young man and the oldest chief. The old man now looked at her with a certain solicitude.

" He says, are you tired? " asked the young man.

" Very tired," she said.

" The men will bring you a carriage," said the young Indian.

The carriage, when it came, proved to be a litter consisting of a sort of hammock of dark woolen frieze, slung onto a pole which was borne on the shoulders of two long-haired Indians. The woolen hammock was spread on the ground, she sat down on it, and the two men raised the pole to their shoulders. Swinging rather as if she were in a sack, she was carried out of the grove of trees, following the old chief, whose leopard-spotted blanket moved curiously in the sunlight.

They had emerged in the valley-head. Just in front were the maize-fields, with ripe ears of maize. The corn was not very tall,

in this high altitude. The well-worn path went between it, and all
she could see was the erect form of the old chief, in the flame and
black sarape, stepping soft and heavy and swift, his head forward,
looking to neither right nor left. Her bearers followed, stepping
rhythmically, the long blue-black hair glistening like a river down
the naked shoulders of the man in front.

They passed the maize and came to a big wall or earthwork made
of earth and adobe bricks. The wooden doors were open. Passing
on, they were in a network of small gardens, full of flowers and
herbs and fruit trees, each garden watered by a ditch of running
water. Among each cluster of trees and flowers was a small, glittering white house, windowless, and with closed door. The place was
a network of little paths, small streams, and little bridges among
square, flowering gardens.

Following the broadest path — a soft narrow track between
leaves and grass, a path worn smooth by centuries of human feet,
no hoof of horse nor any wheel to disfigure it — they came to the
little river of swift bright water, and crossed on a log bridge. Everything was silent — there was not a human being anywhere. The
road went on under magnificent cottonwood trees. It emerged suddenly outside the central plaza or square of the village.

This was a long oblong of low white houses with flat roofs, and
two bigger buildings, having as it were little square huts piled on
top of bigger long huts, stood at either end of the oblong, facing
each other rather askew. Every little house was a dazzling white,
save for the great round beam-ends which projected under the flat
eaves, and for the flat roofs. Round each of the bigger buildings,
on the outside of the square, was a stockyard fence, inside which
was a garden with trees and flowers, and various small houses.

Not a soul was in sight. They passed silently between the houses
into the central square. This was quite bare and arid, the earth
trodden smooth by endless generations of passing feet, passing
across from door to door. All the doors of the windowless houses
gave onto this blank square, but all the doors were closed. The firewood lay near the threshold, a clay oven was still smoking, but
there was no sign of moving life.

The old man walked straight across the square to the big house at the end, where the two upper stories, as in a house of toy bricks, stood each one smaller than the lower one. A stone staircase, outside, led up to the roof of the first story.

At the foot of this staircase the litter-bearers stood still and lowered the woman to the ground.

" You will come up," said the young Indian who spoke Spanish.

She mounted the stone stairs to the earthen roof of the first house, which formed a platform round the wall of the second story. She followed around this platform to the back of the big house. There they descended again, into the garden at the rear.

So far they had seen no one. But now two men appeared, bareheaded, with long braided hair, and wearing a sort of white shirt gathered into a loin-cloth. These went along with the three newcomers, across the garden where red flowers and yellow flowers were blooming, to a long, low white house. There they entered without knocking.

It was dark inside. There was a low murmur of men's voices. Several men were present, their white shirts showing in the gloom, their dark faces invisible. They were sitting on a great log of smooth old wood that lay along the far wall. And, save for this log, the room seemed empty. But no, in the dark at one end was a couch, a sort of bed, and someone lying there, covered with furs.

The old Indian in the spotted sarape, who had accompanied the woman, now took off his hat and his blanket and his sandals. Laying them aside, he approached the couch and spoke in a low voice. For some moments there was no answer. Then an old man with the snow-white hair hanging round his darkly visible face, roused himself like a vision and leaned on one elbow, looking vaguely at the company, in tense silence.

The gray-haired Indian spoke again, and then the young Indian, taking the woman's hand, led her forward. In her linen riding habit and black boots and hat and her pathetic bit of a red tie, she stood there beside the fur-covered bed of the old, old man, who sat reared up, leaning on one elbow, remote as a ghost, his white hair streaming in disorder, his face almost black, yet with a far-off intentness, not of this world, leaning forward to look at her.

His face was so old, it was like dark glass, and the few curling

hairs that sprang white from his lips and chin were quite incredible.
The long white locks fell unbraided and disorderly on either side
of the glassy dark face. And, under a faint powder of white eyebrows,
the black eyes of the old chief looked at her as if from the far, far
dead, seeing something that was never to be seen.

At last he spoke a few deep, hollow words, as if to the dark air.

" He says, do you bring your heart to the God of the Chilchui? "
translated the young Indian.

" Tell him yes," she said, automatically.

There was a pause. The old Indian spoke again, as if to the air.
One of the men present went out. There was a silence as if of
eternity, in the dim room that was lighted only through the open
door.

The woman looked round. Four old men with gray hair sat on the
log by the wall facing the door. Two other men, powerful and impassive, stood near the door. They all had long hair, and wore white
shirts gathered into a loin-cloth. Their powerful legs were naked
and dark. There was a silence like eternity.

At length the man returned, with white and dark clothing on his
arm. The young Indian took them, and, holding them in front of
the woman, said:

" You must take off your clothes and put these on."

" If all you men will go out," she said.

" No one will hurt you," he said quietly.

" Not while you men are here," she said.

He looked at the two men by the door. They came quickly forward and suddenly gripped her arms as she stood, without hurting
her, but with great power. Then two of the old men came, and
with curious skill slit her boots down with keen knives, and drew
them off, and slit her clothing so that it came away from her. In a
few moments she stood there white and uncovered. The old man on
the bed spoke, and they turned her round for him to see. He spoke
again, and the young Indian deftly took the pins and comb from
her fair hair, so that it fell over her shoulders in a bunchy tangle.

Then the old man spoke again. The Indian led her to the bed-
side. The white-haired, glossy-dark old man moistened his finger-
tips at his mouth, and most delicately touched her on the breasts
and on the body, then on the back. And she winced strangely each

time, as the finger-tips drew along her skin, as if Death itself were touching her.

And she wondered, almost sadly, why she did not feel shamed in her nakedness. She only felt sad and lost. Because nobody felt ashamed. The elder men were all dark and tense with some other deep, gloomy, incomprehensible emotion, which suspended all her agitation, while the young Indian had a strange look of ecstasy on his face. And she, she was only utterly strange and beyond herself, as if her body were not her own.

They gave her the new clothing: a long white cotton shift, that came to her knees; then a tunic of thick blue woolen stuff, embroidered with scarlet and green flowers. It was fastened over one shoulder only, and belted with a braid sash of scarlet and black wool.

When she was thus dressed, they took her away, barefoot, to a little house in the stockaded garden. The young Indian told her she might have what she wanted. She asked for water to wash herself. He brought it in a jar, together with a long wooden bowl. Then he fastened the gate-door of her house, and left her a prisoner. She could see through the bars of the gate-door of her house the red flowers of the garden, and a humming-bird. Then from the roof of the big house she heard the long, heavy sound of a drum, unearthly to her in its summons, and an uplifted voice calling from the housetop in a strange language, with a far-away emotionless intonation, delivering some speech or message. And she listened as if from the dead.

But she was very tired. She lay down on a couch of skins, pulling over her the blanket of dark wool, and she slept, giving up everything.

When she woke it was late afternoon, and the young Indian was entering with a basket tray containing food, tortillas and corn mush with bits of meat, probably mutton, and a drink made of honey, and some fresh plums. He brought her also a long garland of red and yellow flowers with knots of blue buds at the end. He sprinkled the garland with water from a jar, then offered it to her, with a smile. He seemed very gentle and thoughtful, and on his face and in his dark eyes was a curious look of triumph and ecstasy, that frightened her a little. The glitter had gone from the black eyes, with their curving dark lashes, and he would look at her with this strange soft glow of ecstasy that was not quite human, and terribly impersonal, and which made her uneasy.

" Is there anything you want? " he said, in his low, slow, melodious voice, that always seemed withheld, as if he were speaking aside to somebody else, or as if he did not want to let the sound come out to her.

" Am I going to be kept a prisoner here? " she asked.

" No, you can walk in the garden tomorrow," he said softly. Always this curious solicitude.

" Do you like that drink? " he said, offering her a little earthenware cup. " It is very refreshing."

She sipped the liquor curiously. It was made with herbs and sweetened with honey, and had a strange, lingering flavor. The young man watched her with gratification.

" It has a peculiar taste," she said.

" It is very refreshing," he replied, his black eyes resting on her always with that look of gratified ecstasy. Then he went away. And presently she began to be sick, and to vomit violently, as if she had no control over herself.

Afterwards she felt a great soothing languor steal over her, her limbs felt strong and loose and full of languor, and she lay on her couch listening to the sounds of the village, watching the yellowing sky, smelling the scent of burning cedar-wood, or pine-wood. So distinctly she heard the yapping of tiny dogs, the shuffle of far-off feet, the murmur of voices, so keenly she detected the smell of smoke, and flowers, and evening falling, so vividly she saw the one bright star infinitely remote, stirring above the sunset, that she felt as if all her senses were diffused on the air, that she could distinguish the sound of evening flowers unfolding, and the actual crystal sound of the heavens, as the vast belts of the world-atmosphere slid past one another, and as if the moisture ascending and the moisture descending in the air resounded like some harp in the cosmos.

She was a prisoner in her house and in the stockaded garden, but she scarcely minded. And it was days before she realized that she never saw another woman. Only the men, the elderly men of the big house, that she imagined must be some sort of temple, and the men priests of some sort. For they always had the same colors, red, orange, yellow, and black, and the same grave, abstracted demeanor.

Sometimes an old man would come and sit in her room with her, in absolute silence. None spoke any language but Indian, save the one younger man. The older man would smile at her, and sit with her for an hour at a time, sometimes smiling at her when she spoke in Spanish, but never answering save with this slow, benevolent-seeming smile. And they gave off a feeling of almost fatherly solicitude. Yet their dark eyes, brooding over her, had something away in their depths that was awesomely ferocious and relentless. They would cover it with a smile, at once, if they felt her looking. But she had seen it.

Always they treated her with this curious impersonal solicitude, this utterly impersonal gentleness, as an old man treats a child. But underneath it she felt there was something else, something terrible. When her old visitor had gone away, in his silent, insidious, fatherly fashion, a shock of fear would come over her; though of what she knew not.

The young Indian would sit and talk with her freely, as if with great candor. But with him, too, she felt that everything real was unsaid. Perhaps it was unspeakable. His big dark eyes would rest on her almost cherishingly, touched with ecstasy, and his beautiful, slow, languorous voice would trail out its simple, ungrammatical Spanish. He told her he was the grandson of the old, old man, son of the man in the spotted sarape; and they were caciques, kings from the old, old days, before even the Spaniards came. But he himself had been in Mexico City, and also in the United States. He had worked as a laborer, building the roads in Los Angeles. He had traveled as far as Chicago.

"Don't you speak English, then?" she asked.

His eyes rested on her with a curious look of duplicity and conflict, and he mutely shook his head.

"What did you do with your long hair when you were in the United States?" she asked. "Did you cut it off?"

Again, with the look of torment in his eyes, he shook his head.

"No," he said, in a low, subdued voice, "I wore a hat, and a handkerchief tied round my head."

And he relapsed into silence, as if of tormented memories.

" Are you the only man of your people who has been to the United States? " she asked him.

" Yes. I am the only one who has been away from here for a long time. The others come back soon, in one week. They don't stay away. The old men don't let them."

" And why did you go? "

" The old men want me to go — because I shall be the cacique — "

He talked always with the same naïveté, an almost childish candor. But she felt that this was perhaps just the effect of his Spanish. Or perhaps speech altogether was unreal to him. Anyhow, she felt that all the real things were kept back.

He came and sat with her a good deal — sometimes more than she wished — as if he wanted to be near her. She asked him if he was married. He said he was — with two children.

" I should like to see your children," she said.

But he answered only with that smile, a sweet, almost ecstatic smile, above which the dark eyes hardly changed from their enigmatic abstraction.

It was curious, he would sit with her by the hour, without ever making her self-conscious, or sex-conscious. He seemed to have no sex, as he sat there so still and gentle and apparently submissive, with his head bent a little forward, and the river of glistening black hair streaming maidenly over his shoulders.

Yet when she looked again, she saw his shoulders broad and powerful, his eyebrows black and level, the short, curved, obstinate black lashes over his lowered eyes, the small, fur-like line of mustache above his blackish, heavy lips, and the strong chin, and she knew that in some other mysterious way he was darkly and powerfully male. And he, feeling her watching him, would glance up at her swiftly with a dark, lurking look in his eyes, which immediately he veiled with that half-sad smile.

The days and the weeks went by, in a vague kind of contentment. She was uneasy sometimes, feeling she had lost the power over herself. She was not in her own power, she was under the spell of some other control. And at times she had moments of terror and horror. But then these Indians would come and sit with her, casting their insidious spell over her by their very silent presence, their silent, sexless, powerful physical presence. As they sat they seemed to take her will away, leaving her will-less and victim to her own indifference. And the young man would bring her sweetened drink, often the same emetic drink, but sometimes other kinds. And after drinking, the languor filled her heavy limbs, her senses seemed to float in the air, listening, hearing. They had brought her a little female dog, which she called Flora. And once, in the trance of her senses, she felt she *heard* the little dog conceive, in her tiny womb, and begin to be complex, with young. And another day she could hear the vast sound of the earth going round, like some immense arrow-string booming.

But as the days grew shorter and colder, when she was cold, she would get a sudden revival of her will, and a desire to go out, to go away. And she insisted to the young man she wanted to go out.

So one day they let her climb to the topmost roof of the big house where she was and look down the square. It was the day of the big dance, but not everybody was dancing. Women with babies in their arms stood in their doorways, watching. Opposite, at the other end of the square, there was a throng before the other big house, and a small, brilliant group on the terrace-roof of the first story, in front of wide open doors of the upper story. Through these wide open doors she could see fire glinting in darkness, and priests in head-dresses of black and yellow and scarlet feathers, wearing robe-like blankets of black and red and yellow, with long green fringe, were moving about. A big drum was beating slowly and regularly, in the dense, Indian silence. The crowd below waited —

Then a drum started on a high beat, and there came the deep, powerful burst of men singing a heavy, savage music, like a wind roaring in some timeless forest, many mature men singing in one breath, like the wind; and long lines of dancers walked out from under the big house. Men with naked, golden-bronze bodies and streaming black hair, tufts of red and yellow feathers on their arms, and kilts of white frieze with a bar of heavy red and black and green embroidery round their waists, bending slightly forward and stamping the earth in their absorbed, monotonous stamp of the dance, a fox-fur, hung by the nose from their belt behind, swaying with the sumptuous swaying of a beautiful fox-fur, the tip of the tail writh-

ing above the dancer's heels. And after each man, a woman with
a strange elaborate head-dress of feathers and seashells, and wearing a short black tunic, moving erect, holding up tufts of feathers
in each hand, swaying her wrists rhythmically and subtly beating
the earth with her bare feet.

So the long line of the dance unfurling from the big house opposite. And from the big house beneath her, strange scent of incense,
strange tense silence, then the answering burst of inhuman male
singing, and the long line of the dance unfurling.

It went on all day, the insistence of the drum, the cavernous,
roaring, storm-like sound of male singing, the incessant swinging
of the fox-skins behind the powerful, gold-bronze, stamping legs
of the men, the autumn sun from a perfect blue heaven pouring on
the rivers of black hair, men's and women's, the valley all still, the
walls of rock beyond, the awful huge bulking of the mountain
against the pure sky, its snow seething with sheer whiteness.

For hours and hours she watched, spellbound, and as if drugged.
And in all the terrible persistence of the drumming and the primeval, rushing deep singing, and the endless stamping of the dance of
fox-tailed men, the tread of heavy, bird-erect women in their black
tunics, she seemed at last to feel her own death; her own obliteration. As if she were to be obliterated from the field of life again.
In the strange towering symbols on the heads of the changeless, absorbed women she seemed to read once more the *Mene, Mene,
Tekel, Upharsin*. Her kind of womanhood, intensely personal and
individual, was to be obliterated again, and the great primeval symbols were to tower once more over the fallen individual independence of woman. The sharpness and the quivering nervous consciousness of the highly-bred white woman was to be destroyed again,
womanhood was to be cast once more into the great stream of impersonal sex and impersonal passion. Strangely, as if clairvoyant,
she saw the immense sacrifice prepared. And she went back to her
little house in a trance of agony.

After this, there was always a certain agony when she heard the
drums at evening, and the strange uplifted savage sound of men
singing round the drum, like wild creatures howling to the invisible
gods of the moon and the vanished sun. Something of the chuck-
ling, sobbing cry of the coyote, something of the exultant bark of

the fox, the far-off wild melancholy exultance of the howling wolf, the torment of the puma's scream, and the insistence of the ancient fierce human male, with his lapses of tenderness and his abiding ferocity.

Sometimes she would climb the high roof after nightfall and listen to the dim cluster of young men round the drum on the bridge just beyond the square, singing by the hour. Sometimes there would be a fire, and, in the fire-glow, men in their white shirts, or naked save for a loin-cloth, would be dancing and stamping like specters, hour after hour in the dark cold air, within the fire-glow, forever dancing and stamping like turkeys, or dropping squatting by the fire to rest, throwing their blankets round them.

" Why do you all have the same colors? " she asked the young Indian. " Why do you all have red and yellow and black, over your white shirts? And the women have black tunics? "

He looked into her eyes, curiously, and the faint, evasive smile came onto his face. Behind the smile lay a soft, strange malignancy.

" Because our men are the fire and the daytime, and our women are the spaces between the stars at night," he said.

" Aren't the women even stars? " she said.

" No. We say they are the spaces between the stars, that keep the stars apart."

He looked at her oddly, and again the touch of derision came into his eyes.

" White people," he said, " they know nothing. They are like children, always with toys. We know the sun, and we know the moon. And we say, when a white woman sacrifice herself to our gods, then our gods will begin to make the world again, and the white man's gods will fall to pieces."

" How sacrifice herself? " she asked quickly.

And he, as quickly covered, covered himself with a subtle smile.

" She sacrifice her own gods and come to our gods, I mean that," he said, soothingly.

But she was not reassured. An icy pang of fear and certainty was at her heart.

" The sun he is alive at one end of the sky," he continued, " and the moon lives at the other end. And the man all the time have to keep the sun happy in his side of the sky, and the woman have to keep the moon quiet at her side of the sky. All the time she have to work at this. And the sun can't ever go into the house of the moon, and the moon can't ever go into the house of the sun, in the sky. So the woman, she asks the moon to come into her cave, inside her. And the man, he draws the sun down till he has the power of the sun. All the time he do this. Then when the man gets a woman, the sun goes into the cave of the moon, and that is how everything in the world starts."

She listened, watching him closely, as one enemy watches another who is speaking with double meaning.

" Then," she said, " why aren't you Indians masters of the white men? "

" Because," he said, " the Indian got weak, and lost his power with the sun, so the white men stole the sun. But they can't keep him — they don't know how. They got him, but they don't know what to do with him, like a boy who catch a big grizzly bear and can't kill him and can't run away from him. The grizzly bear eats the boy that catch him, when he want to run away from him. White men don't know what they are doing with the sun, and white women don't know what they do with the moon. The moon she got angry with white women, like a puma when someone kills her little ones. The moon, she bites white women — here inside," and he pressed his side. " The moon, she is angry in a white woman's cave. The Indian can see it — and soon," he added, " the Indian women get the moon back and keep her quiet in their house. And the Indian men get the sun, and the power over all the world. White men don't know what the sun is. They never know."

He subsided into a curious exultant silence.

" But," she faltered, " why do you hate us so? Why do you hate me? "

He looked up suddenly with a light on his face, and a startling flame of a smile.

" No, we don't hate," he said softly, looking with a curious glitter into her face.

" You do," she said, forlorn and hopeless.

And after a moment's silence he rose and went away.

Winter had now come, in the high valley, with snow that melted in the day's sun, and nights that were bitter cold. She lived on, in a kind of daze, feeling her power ebbing more and more away from her, as if her will were leaving her. She felt always in the same relaxed, confused, victimized state, unless the sweetened herb drink would numb her mind altogether and release her senses into a sort of heightened, mystic acuteness and a feeling as if she were diffusing out deliciously into the harmony of things. This at length became the only state of consciousness she really recognized: this exquisite sense of bleeding out into the higher beauty and harmony of things. Then she could actually hear the great stars in heaven, which she saw through her door, speaking from their motion and brightness, saying things perfectly to the cosmos, as they· trod in perfect ripples, like bells on the floor of heaven, passing one another and grouping in the timeless dance, with the spaces of dark between. And she could hear the snow on a cold, cloudy day twittering and faintly whistling in the sky, like birds that flock and fly away in autumn, suddenly calling farewell to the invisible moon, and slipping out of the plains of the air, releasing peaceful warmth. She herself would call to the arrested snow to fall from the upper air. She would call to the unseen moon to cease to be angry, to make peace again with the unseen sun like a woman who ceases to be angry in her house. And she would smell the sweetness of the moon relaxing to the sun in the wintry heaven, when the snow fell in a faint, cold-perfumed relaxation, as the peace of the sun mingled again in a sort of unison with the peace of the moon.

She was aware too of the sort of shadow that was on the Indians of the valley, a deep, stoical disconsolation, almost religious in its depth.

"We have lost our power over the sun, and we are trying to get him back. But he is wild with us, and shy like a horse that has got away. We have to go through a lot." So the young Indian said to her, looking into her eyes with a strained meaning. And she, as if bewitched, replied:

"I hope you will get him back."

The smile of triumph flew over his face.

"Do you hope it?" he said.

"I do," she answered fatally.

"Then all right," he said. "We shall get him."

And he went away in exultance.

She felt she was drifting on some consummation, which she had no will to avoid, yet which seemed heavy and finally terrible to her.

It must have been almost December, for the days were short, when she was taken again before the aged man, and stripped of her clothing, and touched with the old finger-tips.

The aged cacique looked her in the eyes, with his eyes of lonely, far-off, black intentness, and murmured something to her.

" He wants you to make the sign of peace," the young man translated, showing her the gesture. " Peace and farewell to him."

She was fascinated by the black, glass-like, intent eyes of the old cacique; that watched her without blinking, like a basilisk's, overpowering her. In their depths also she saw a certain fatherly compassion, and pleading. She put her hand before her face, in the required manner, making the sign of peace and farewell. He made the sign of peace back again to her, then sank among his furs. She thought he was going to die, and that he knew it.

There followed a day of ceremonial, when she was brought out before all the people, in a blue blanket with white fringe, and holding blue feathers in her hands. Before an altar of one house she was perfumed with incense and sprinkled with ash. Before the altar of the opposite house she was fumigated again with incense by the gorgeous, terrifying priests in yellow and scarlet and black, their faces painted with scarlet paint. And then they threw water on her. Meanwhile she was faintly aware of the fire on the altar, the heavy, heavy sound of a drum, the heavy sound of men beginning powerfully, deeply, savagely to sing, the swaying of the crowd of faces in the plaza below, and the formation for a sacred dance.

But at this time her commonplace consciousness was numb, she was aware of her immediate surroundings as shadows, almost immaterial. With refined and heightened senses she could hear the sound of the earth winging on its journey, like a shot arrow, the ripple-rustling of the air, and the boom of the great arrow-string. And it seemed to her there were two great influences in the upper air, one golden towards the sun, and one invisible silver; the first traveling like rain ascending to the gold presence sunwards, the second like rain silverily descending the ladders of space towards the hovering, lurking clouds over the snowy mountain-top. Then between them, another presence, waiting to shake himself free of moisture, of heavy white snow that had mysteriously collected about him. And in summer, like a scorched eagle, he would wait to shake himself clear of the weight of heavy sunbeams. And he was colored like fire. And he was always shaking himself clear, of snow or of heavy heat, like an eagle rustling.

Then there was a still stranger presence, standing watching from the blue distance, always watching. Sometimes running in upon the wind, or shimmering in the heat-waves. The blue wind itself, rushing as it were out of the holes in the earth into the sky, rushing out of the sky down upon the earth. The blue wind, the go-between, the invisible ghost that belonged to two worlds, that played upon the ascending and the descending chords of the rains.

More and more her ordinary personal consciousness had left her, she had gone into that other state of passional cosmic consciousness, like one who is drugged. The Indians, with their heavily religious natures, had made her succumb to their vision.

Only one personal question she asked the young Indian:

" Why am I the only one that wears blue? "

" It is the color of the wind. It is the color of what goes away and is never coming back, but which is always here, waiting like death among us. It is the color of the dead. And it is the color that stands away off, looking at us from the distance, that cannot come near to us. When we go near, it goes farther. It can't be near. We are all brown and yellow and black hair, and white teeth and red blood. We are the ones that are here. You with blue eyes, you are the messengers from the far-away, you cannot stay, and now it is time for you to go back."

" Where to? " she asked.

" To the 'way-off things like the sun and the blue mother of rain, and tell them that we are the people on the world again, and we can bring the sun to the moon again, like a red horse to a blue mare; we are the people. The white women have driven back the moon in the sky, won't let her come to the sun. So the sun is angry. And the Indian must give the moon to the sun."

" How? " she said.

" The white woman got to die and go like a wind to the sun, tell him the Indians will open the gate to him. And the Indian women will open the gate to the moon. The white women don't let the

moon come down out of the blue corral. The moon used to come
down among the Indian women, like a white goat among the
flowers. And the sun want to come down to the Indian men, like
an eagle to the pine trees. The sun, he is shut out behind the white
man, and the moon she is shut out behind the white woman, and
they can't get away. They are angry, everything in the world gets
angrier. The Indian says, he will give the white woman to the sun,
so the sun will leap over the white man and come to the Indian
again. And the moon will be surprised, she will see the gate open,
and she not know which way to go. But the Indian woman will call
to the moon: *Come! Come! Come back into my grasslands. The
wicked white woman can't harm you any more.* Then the sun will
look over the heads of the white men, and see the moon in the
pastures of our women, with the Red Men standing around like
pine trees. Then he will leap over the heads of the white men, and
come running past to the Indians through the spruce trees. And we,
who are red and black and yellow, we who stay, we shall have the
sun on our right hand and the moon on our left. So we can bring
the rain down out of the blue meadows, and up out of the black;
and we can call the wind that tells the corn to grow, when we ask
him, and we shall make the clouds to break, and the sheep to have
twin lambs. And we shall be full of power, like a spring day. But
the white people will be a hard winter, without snow — "

" But," said the white woman, " I don't shut out the moon —
how can I? "

" Yes," he said, " you shut the gate, and then laugh, think you
have it all your own way."

She could never quite understand the way he looked at her. He
was always so curiously gentle, and his smile was so soft. Yet there
was such a glitter in his eyes, and an unrelenting sort of hate came
out of his words, a strange, profound, impersonal hate. Personally
he liked her, she was sure. He was gentle with her, attracted by her
in some strange, soft, passionless way. But impersonally he hated
her with a mystic hatred. He would smile at her, winningly. Yet if,
the next moment, she glanced around at him unawares, she would
catch that gleam of pure after-hate in his eyes.

" Have I got to die and be given to the sun? " she asked.

"Some time," he said, laughing evasively. "Some time we all die."

They were gentle with her, and very considerate with her. Strange men, the old priests and the young cacique alike, they watched over her and cared for her like women. In their soft, insidious understanding there was something womanly. Yet their eyes, with that strange glitter, and their dark, shut mouths that would open to the broad jaw, the small, strong, white teeth, had something very primitively male and cruel.

One wintry day, when snow was falling, they took her to a great dark chamber in the big house. The fire was burning in a corner on a high raised dais under a sort of hood or canopy of adobe-work. She saw in the fire-glow the glowing bodies of the almost naked priests, and strange symbols on the roof and walls of the chamber. There was no door or window in the chamber, they had descended by a ladder from the roof. And the fire of pine-wood danced continually, showing walls painted with strange devices, which she could not understand, and a ceiling of poles making a curious pattern of black and red and yellow, and alcoves or niches in which were curious objects she could not discern.

The older priests were going through some ceremony near the fire, in silence, intense Indian silence. She was seated on a low projection of the wall, opposite the fire, two men seated beside her. Presently they gave her a drink from a cup, which she took gladly, because of the semi-trance it would induce.

In the darkness and in the silence she was accurately aware of everything that happened to her: how they took off her clothes, and, standing her before a great, weird device on the wall, colored blue and white and black, washed her all over with water and the amole infusion; washed even her hair, softly, carefully, and dried it on white cloths, till it was soft and glistening. Then they laid her on a couch under another great indecipherable image of red and black and yellow, and now rubbed all her body with sweet-scented oil, and massaged all her limbs, and her back, and her sides, with a long, strange, hypnotic massage. Their dark hands were incredibly powerful, yet soft with a watery softness she could not understand. And the dark faces, leaning near her white body, she saw were darkened with red pigment, with lines of yellow round the cheeks. And the dark eyes glittered absorbed, as the hands worked upon the soft white body of the woman.

They were so impersonal, absorbed in something that was beyond her. They never saw her as a personal woman; she could tell that. She was some mystic object to them, some vehicle of passions too remote for her to grasp. Herself in a state of trance, she watched their faces bending over her, dark, strangely glistening with the transparent red paint, and lined with bars of yellow. And in this weird, luminous-dark mask of living face, the eyes were fixed with an unchanging steadfast gleam, and the purplish-pigmented lips were closed in a full, sinister, sad grimness. The immense fundamental sadness, the grimness of ultimate decision, the fixity of revenge, and the nascent exultance of those that are going to triumph — these things she could read in their faces, as she lay and was rubbed into a misty glow, by their uncanny dark hands. Her limbs, her flesh, her very bones at last seemed to be diffusing into a roseate sort of mist, in which her consciousness hovered like some sun-gleam in a flushed cloud.

She knew the gleam would fade, the cloud would go gray. But at present she did not believe it. She knew she was a victim; that all this elaborate work upon her was the work of victimizing her. But she did not mind. She wanted it.

Later they put a short blue tunic on her and took her to the upper terrace and presented her to the people. She saw the plaza below her full of dark faces and of glittering eyes. There was no pity; only the curious hard exultance. The people gave a subdued cry when they saw her, and she shuddered. But she hardly cared.

Next day was the last. She slept in a chamber of the big house. At dawn they put on her a big blue blanket with a fringe and led her out into the plaza, among the throng of silent, dark-blanketed people. There was pure white snow on the ground, and the dark people in their dark-brown blankets looked like inhabitants of another world.

A large drum was slowly pounding, and an old priest was declaring from a housetop. But it was not till noon that a litter came forth, and the people gave that low, animal cry which was so moving. In the sack-like litter sat the old, old cacique, his white hair braided with black braid and large turquoise stones. His face was like a piece of obsidian. He lifted his hand in token, and the litter stopped in front of her. Fixing her with his old eyes, he spoke to her for a few moments, in his hollow voice. No one translated.

Another litter came, and she was placed in it. Four priests moved ahead, in their scarlet and yellow and black, with plumed head-dresses. Then came the litter of the old cacique. Then the light drums began, and two groups of singers burst simultaneously into song, male and wild. And the golden-red, almost naked men, adorned with ceremonial feathers and kilts, the rivers of black hair down their backs, formed into two files and began to tread the dance. So they threaded out of the snowy plaza, in two long, sump-tuous lines of dark red-gold and black and fur, swaying with a faint tinkle of bits of shell and flint, winding over the snow between the two bee-clusters of men who sang around the drum.

Slowly they moved out, and her litter, with its attendance of feathered, lurid, dancing priests, moved after. Everybody danced the tread of the dance-step, even, subtly, the litter-bearers. And out of the plaza they went, past smoking ovens, on the trail to the great cottonwood trees, that stood like gray-silver lace against the blue sky, bare and exquisite above the snow. The river, diminished, rushed among fangs of ice. The checker-squares of gardens within fences were all snowy, and the white houses now looked yellowish.

The whole valley glittered intolerably with pure snow, away to the walls of the standing rock. And across the flat cradle of snow-bed wound the long thread of the dance, shaking slowly and sump-tuously in its orange and black motion. The high drums thudded quickly, and on the crystalline frozen air the swell and roar of the chant of savages was like an obsession.

She sat looking out of her litter with big, transfixed blue eyes, under which were the wan markings of her drugged weariness. She knew she was going to die, among the glisten of this snow, at the hands of this savage, sumptuous people. And as she stared at the blaze of blue sky above the slashed and ponderous mountain, she thought: " I am dead already. What difference does it make, the transition from the dead I am to the dead I shall be, very soon! " Yet her soul sickened and felt wan.

The strange procession trailed on, in perpetual dance, slowly across the plain of snow, and then entered the slopes between the pine trees. She saw the copper-dark men dancing the dance-tread, onwards, between the copper-pale tree-trunks. And at last she, too, in her swaying litter entered the pine trees.

They were traveling on and on, upwards, across the snow under the trees, past the superb shafts of pale, flaked copper, the rustle and shake and tread of the threading dance, penetrating into the forest, into the mountain. They were following a stream-bed; but the stream was dry, like summer, dried up by the frozenness of the head-waters. There were dark, red-bronze willow bushes with wattles like wild hair, and pallid aspen trees looking like cold flesh against the snow. Then jutting dark rocks.

At last she could tell that the dancers were moving forward no more. Nearer and nearer she came upon the drums, as to a lair of mysterious animals. Then through the bushes she emerged into a strange amphitheater. Facing was a great wall of hollow rock, down the front of which hung a great, dripping, fang-like spoke of ice. The ice came pouring over the rock from the precipice above, and then stood arrested, dripping out of high heaven, almost down to the hollow stones where the stream-pool should be below. But the pool was dry.

On either side the dry pool the lines of dancers had formed, and the dance was continuing without intermission, against a background of bushes.

But what she felt was that fanged inverted pinnacle of ice, hanging from the lip of the dark precipice above. And behind the great rope of ice she saw the leopard-like figures of priests climbing the hollow cliff face, to the cave that, like a dark socket, bored a cavity, an orifice, half-way up the crag.

Before she could realize, her litter-bearers were staggering in the footholds, climbing the rock. She, too, was behind the ice. There it hung, like a curtain that is not spread, but hangs like a great fang. And near above her was the orifice of the cave sinking dark into the rock. She watched it as she swayed upwards.

On the platform of the cave stood the priests, waiting in all their gorgeousness of feathers and fringed robes, watching her ascent. Two of them stooped to help her litter-bearer. And at length she was on the platform of the cave, far in behind the shaft of ice, above the hollow amphitheater among the bushes below, where men were dancing, and the whole populace of the village was clustered in silence.

The sun was sloping down the afternoon sky, on the left. She knew that this was the shortest day of the year, and the last day of her life. They stood her facing the iridescent column of ice, which fell down marvelously arrested, away in front of her.

Some signal was given, and the dance below stopped. There was now absolute silence. She was given a little to drink, then two priests took off her mantle and her tunic, and in her strange pallor she stood there, between the lurid robes of the priests, beyond the pillar of ice, beyond and above the dark-faced people. The throng below gave the low, wild cry. Then the priests turned her round, so she stood with her back to the open world, her long blond hair to the people below. And they cried again.

She was facing the cave, inwards. A fire was burning and flickering in the depths. Four priests had taken off their robes and were almost as naked as she was. They were powerful men in the prime of life, and they kept their dark, painted faces lowered.

From the fire came the old, old priest, with an incense-pan. He was naked and in a state of barbaric ecstasy. He fumigated his victim, reciting at the same time in a hollow voice. Behind him came another robeless priest, with two flint knives.

When she was fumigated, they laid her on a large flat stone, the four powerful men holding her by the outstretched arms and legs. Behind stood the aged man, like a skeleton covered with dark glass, holding a knife and transfixedly watching the sun; and behind him again was another naked priest, with a knife.

She felt little sensation, though she knew all that was happening. Turning to the sky, she looked at the yellow sun. It was sinking. The shaft of ice was like a shadow between her and it. And she realized that the yellow rays were filling half the cave, though they had not reached the altar where the fire was, at the far end of the funnel-shaped cavity.

Yes, the rays were creeping round slowly. As they grew ruddier, they penetrated farther. When the red sun was about to sink, he would shine full through the shaft of ice deep into the hollow of the cave, to the innermost.

She understood now that this was what the men were waiting for. Even those that held her down were bent and twisted round, their black eyes watching the sun with a glittering eagerness, and awe, and craving. The black eyes of the aged cacique were fixed like black mirrors on the sun, as if sightless, yet containing some terrible answer to the reddening winter planet. And all the eyes of the priests were fixed and glittering on the sinking orb, in the reddening, icy silence of the winter afternoon.

They were anxious, terribly anxious, and fierce. Their ferocity wanted something, and they were waiting the moment. And their ferocity was ready to leap out into a mystic exultance, of triumph. But still they were anxious.

Only the eyes of that oldest man were not anxious. Black, and fixed, and as if sightless, they watched the sun, seeing beyond the sun. And in their black, empty concentration there was power, power intensely abstract and remote, but deep, deep to the heart of the earth, and the heart of the sun. In absolute motionlessness he watched till the red sun should send his ray through the column of ice. Then the old man would strike, and strike home, accomplish the sacrifice and achieve the power.

The mastery that man must hold, and that passes from race to race.

⤝§ *Katherine Mansfield* §⤜

THE DOLL'S HOUSE

WHEN dear old Mrs. Hay went back to town after staying with the Burnells she sent the children a doll's house. It was so big that the carter and Pat carried it into the courtyard, and there it stayed, propped up on two wooden boxes beside the feed-room door. No harm could come to it; it was summer. And perhaps the smell of paint would have gone off by the time it had to be taken in. For, really, the smell of paint coming from that doll's house ("Sweet of old Mrs. Hay, of course; most sweet and generous!") — but the smell of paint was quite enough to make anyone seriously ill, in Aunt Beryl's opinion. Even before the sacking was taken off. And when it was. . . .

There stood the doll's house, a dark, oily, spinach green, picked out with bright yellow. Its two solid little chimneys, glued onto the roof, were painted red and white, and the door, gleaming with yellow varnish, was like a little slab of toffee. Four windows, real windows, were divided into panes by a broad streak of green. There was actually a tiny porch, too, painted yellow, with big lumps of congealed paint hanging along the edge.

But perfect, perfect little house! Who could possibly mind the smell? It was part of the joy, part of the newness.

" Open it quickly, someone! "

The hook at the side was stuck fast. Pat pried it open with his penknife, and the whole house-front swung back, and — there you were, gazing at one and the same moment into the drawing-room and dining-room, the kitchen and two bedrooms. That is the way for a house to open! Why don't all houses open like that? How much more exciting than peering through the slit of a door into a mean little hall with a hatstand and two umbrellas! That is — isn't it? — what you long to know about a house when you put your hand on the knocker. Perhaps it is the way God opens houses at dead of night when He is taking a quiet turn with an angel. . . .

" O-oh! " The Burnell children sounded as though they were in despair. It was too marvelous; it was too much for them. They had never seen anything like it in their lives. All the rooms were papered. There were pictures on the walls, painted on the paper, with gold frames complete. Red carpet covered all the floors except the kitchen; red plush chairs in the drawing-room, green in the dining-room; tables, beds with real bedclothes, a cradle, a stove, a dresser with tiny plates and one big jug. But what Kezia liked more than anything, what she liked frightfully, was the lamp. It stood in the middle of the dining-room table, an exquisite little amber lamp with a white globe. It was even filled all ready for lighting, though, of course, you couldn't light it. But there was something inside that looked like oil, and that moved when you shook it.

The father and mother dolls, who sprawled very stiff as though they had fainted in the drawing-room, and their two little children asleep upstairs, were really too big for the doll's house. They didn't look as though they belonged. But the lamp was perfect. It seemed to smile at Kezia, to say: " I live here." The lamp was real.

The Burnell children could hardly walk to school fast enough the next morning. They burned to tell everybody, to describe, to

— well — to boast about their doll's house before the school-bell rang.

" I'm to tell," said Isabel, " because I'm the eldest. And you two can join in after. But I'm to tell first."

There was nothing to answer. Isabel was bossy, but she was always right, and Lottie and Kezia knew too well the powers that went with being eldest. They brushed through the thick buttercups at the road edge and said nothing.

" And I'm to choose who's to come and see it first. Mother said I might."

For it had been arranged that while the doll's house stood in the courtyard they might ask the girls at school, two at a time, to come and look. Not to stay to tea, of course, or to come traipsing through the house. But just to stand quietly in the courtyard while Isabel pointed out the beauties, and Lottie and Kezia looked pleased. . . .

But hurry as they might, by the time they had reached the tarred palings of the boys' playground the bell had begun to jangle. They only just had time to whip off their hats and fall into line before the roll was called. Never mind. Isabel tried to make up for it by looking very important and mysterious and by whispering behind her hand to the girls near her: " Got something to tell you at playtime."

Playtime came and Isabel was surrounded. The girls of her class nearly fought to put their arms round her, to walk away with her, to beam flatteringly, to be her special friend. She held quite a court under the huge pine trees at the side of the playground. Nudging, giggling together, the little girls pressed up close. And the only two who stayed outside the ring were the two who were always outside, the little Kelveys. They knew better than to come anywhere near the Burnells.

For the fact was the school the Burnell children went to was not at all the kind of place their parents would have chosen if there had been any choice. But there was none. It was the only school for miles. And the consequence was all the children in the neighborhood, the Judge's little girls, the doctor's daughters, the storekeeper's children, the milkman's, were forced to mix together. Not to speak of there being an equal number of rude, rough little boys as well. But the line had to be drawn somewhere. It was drawn at the Kelveys. Many of the children, including the Burnells, were not allowed even to speak to them. They walked past the Kelveys with their heads in the air, and as they set the fashion in all matters of behavior, the Kelveys were shunned by everybody. Even the teacher had a special voice for them, and a special smile for the other children when Lil Kelvey came up to her desk with a bunch of dreadfully common-looking flowers.

They were the daughters of a spry, hardworking little washer-woman, who went about from house to house by the day. This was awful enough. But where was Mr. Kelvey? Nobody knew for certain. But everybody said he was in prison. So they were the daughters of a washerwoman and a jailbird. Very nice company for other people's children! And they looked it. Why Mrs. Kelvey made them so conspicuous was hard to understand. The truth was they were dressed in " bits " given to her by the people for whom she worked. Lil, for instance, who was a stout, plain child, with big freckles, came to school in a dress made from a green art-serge tablecloth of the Burnells', with red plush sleeves from the Logans' curtains. Her hat, perched on top of her high forehead, was a grown-up woman's hat, once the property of Miss Lecky, the post-mistress. It was turned up at the back and trimmed with a large scarlet quill. What a little guy she looked! It was impossible not to laugh. And her little sister, our Else, wore a long white dress, rather like a nightgown, and a pair of little boy's boots. But what-ever our Else wore, she would have looked strange. She was a tiny wishbone of a child, with cropped hair and enormous solemn eyes — a little white owl. Nobody had ever seen her smile; she scarcely ever spoke. She went through life holding on to Lil, with a piece of Lil's skirt screwed up in her hand. Where Lil went our Else followed. In the playground, on the road going to and from school, there was Lil marching in front and our Else holding on behind. Only when she wanted anything, or when she was out of breath, our Else gave Lil a tug, a twitch, and Lil stopped and turned round. The Kelveys never failed to understand each other.

Now they hovered at the edge; you couldn't stop them listening. When the little girls turned round and sneered, Lil, as usual, gave her silly, shamefaced smile, but our Else only looked.

And Isabel's voice, so very proud, went on telling. The carpet made a great sensation, but so did the beds with real bedclothes, and the stove with an oven door.

When she finished, Kezia broke in. " You've forgotten the lamp, Isabel."

" Oh, yes," said Isabel, " and there's a teeny little lamp, all made of yellow glass, with a white globe, that stands on the dining-room table. You couldn't tell it from a real one."

" The lamp's best of all," cried Kezia. She thought Isabel wasn't making half enough of the little lamp. But nobody paid any attention. Isabel was choosing the two who were to come back with them that afternoon and see it. She chose Emmie Cole and Lena Logan. But when the others knew they were all to have a chance, they couldn't be nice enough to Isabel. One by one they put their arms round Isabel's waist and walked her off. They had something to whisper to her, a secret. " Isabel's my friend."

Only the little Kelveys moved away forgotten; there was nothing more for them to hear.

Days passed, and as more children saw the doll's house, the fame of it spread. It became the one subject, the rage. The one question was: " Have you seen Burnells' doll's house? Oh, ain't it lovely! " " Haven't you seen it? Oh, I say! "

Even the dinner hour was given up to talking about it. The little girls sat under the pines eating their thick mutton sandwiches and big slabs of johnny-cake spread with butter. While always, as near as they could get, sat the Kelveys, our Else holding on to Lil, listening too, while they chewed their jam sandwiches out of a newspaper soaked with large red blobs. . . .

" Mother," said Kezia, " can't I ask the Kelveys just once? "

" Certainly not, Kezia."

" But why not? "

" Run away, Kezia; you know quite well why not."

At last everybody had seen it except them. On that day the subject rather flagged. It was the dinner hour. The children stood together under the pine trees, and suddenly, as they looked at the Kelveys eating out of their paper, always by themselves, always listening, they wanted to be horrid to them. Emmie Cole started the whisper.

" Lil Kelvey's going to be a servant when she grows up."

" O-oh, how awful! " said Isabel Burnell, and she made eyes at Emmie.

Emmie swallowed in a very meaning way and nodded to Isabel as she'd seen her mother do on those occasions. " It's true — it's true — it's true," she said.

Then Lena Logan's little eyes snapped. " Shall I ask her? " she whispered.

" Bet you don't," said Jessie May.

" Pooh, I'm not frightened," said Lena. Suddenly she gave a little squeal and danced in front of the other girls. " Watch! Watch me! Watch me now! " said Lena. And sliding, gliding, dragging one foot, giggling behind her hand, Lena went over to the Kelveys.

Lil looked up from her dinner. She wrapped the rest quickly away. Our Else stopped chewing. What was coming now?

" Is it true you're going to be a servant when you grow up, Lil Kelvey? " shrilled Lena.

Dead silence. But instead of answering, Lil only gave her silly, shamefaced smile. She didn't seem to mind the question at all. What a sell for Lena! The girls began to titter.

Lena couldn't stand that. She put her hands on her hips; she shot forward. " Yah, yer father's in prison! " she hissed, spitefully.

This was such a marvelous thing to have said that the little girls rushed away in a body, deeply, deeply excited, wild with joy. Someone found a long rope, and they began skipping. And never did they skip so high, run in and out so fast, or do such daring things as on that morning.

In the afternoon Pat called for the Burnell children with the buggy and they drove home. There were visitors. Isabel and Lottie, who liked visitors, went upstairs to change their pinafores. But Kezia thieved out at the back. Nobody was about; she began to swing on the big white gates of the courtyard. Presently, looking along the road, she saw two little dots. They grew bigger, they were coming towards her. Now she could see that one was in front and one close behind. Now she could see that they were the Kelveys.

Kezia stopped swinging. She slipped off the gate as if she was going to run away. Then she hesitated. The Kelveys came nearer, and beside them walked their shadows, very long, stretching right across the road with their heads in the buttercups. Kezia clambered back on the gate; she had made up her mind; she swung out.

"Hullo," she said to the passing Kelveys.

They were so astounded that they stopped. Lil gave her silly smile. Our Else stared.

"You can come and see our doll's house if you want to," said Kezia, and she dragged one toe on the ground. But at that Lil turned red and shook her head quickly.

"Why not?" asked Kezia.

Lil gasped, then she said: "Your ma told our ma you wasn't to speak to us."

"Oh, well," said Kezia. She didn't know what to reply. "It doesn't matter. You can come and see our doll's house all the same. Come on. Nobody's looking."

But Lil shook her head still harder.

"Don't you want to?" asked Kezia.

Suddenly there was a twitch, a tug at Lil's skirt. She turned round. Our Else was looking at her with big, imploring eyes; she was frowning; she wanted to go. For a moment Lil looked at our Else very doubtfully. But then our Else twitched her skirt again. She started forward. Kezia led the way. Like two little stray cats they followed across the courtyard to where the doll's house stood.

"There it is," said Kezia.

There was a pause. Lil breathed loudly, almost snorted; our Else was still as a stone.

"I'll open it for you," said Kezia kindly. She undid the hook and they looked inside.

"There's the drawing-room and the dining-room, and that's the — "

"Kezia!"

Oh, what a start they gave!

"Kezia!"

It was Aunt Beryl's voice. They turned round. At the back door stood Aunt Beryl, staring as if she couldn't believe what she saw.

"How dare you ask the little Kelveys into the courtyard?" said her cold, furious voice. "You know as well as I do you're not allowed to talk to them. Run away, children, run away at once. And don't come back again," said Aunt Beryl. And she stepped into the yard and shooed them out as if they were chickens.

"Off you go immediately!" she called, cold and proud.

They did not need telling twice. Burning with shame, shrinking together, Lil huddling along like her mother, our Else dazed, somehow they crossed the big courtyard and squeezed through the white gate.

"Wicked, disobedient little girl!" said Aunt Beryl bitterly to Kezia, and she slammed the doll's house to.

The afternoon had been awful. A letter had come from Willie Brent, a terrifying, threatening letter, saying if she did not meet him that evening in Pulman's Bush, he'd come to the front door and ask the reason why! But now that she had frightened those little rats of Kelveys and given Kezia a good scolding, her heart felt lighter. That ghastly pressure was gone. She went back to the house humming.

When the Kelveys were well out of sight of Burnells', they sat down to rest on a big red drainpipe by the side of the road. Lil's cheeks were still burning; she took off the hat with the quill and held it on her knee. Dreamily they looked over the hay paddocks, past the creek, to the group of wattles where Logan's cows stood waiting to be milked. What were their thoughts?

Presently our Else nudged up close to her sister. But now she had forgotten the cross lady. She put out a finger and stroked her sister's quill; she smiled her rare smile.

"I seen the little lamp," she said, softly.

Then both were silent once more.

Walter de la Mare

THE RIDDLE

So these seven children, Ann, and Matilda, James, William and Henry, Harriet and Dorothea, came to live with their grandmother. The house in which their grandmother had lived since her childhood was built in the time of the Georges. It was not a pretty house, but roomy, substantial, and square; and an elm tree outstretched its branches almost to the windows.

When the children were come out of the cab (five sitting inside and two beside the driver), they were shown into their grandmother's presence. They stood in a little black group before the old lady, seated in her bow-window. And she asked them each their names, and repeated each name in her kind, quavering voice. Then to one she gave a work-box, to William a jack-knife, to Dorothea a painted ball; to each a present according to age. And she kissed all her grandchildren to the youngest.

"My dears," she said, "I wish to see all of you bright and gay in my house. I am an old woman, so that I cannot romp with you; but Ann must look to you, and Mrs. Fenn too. And every morning and every evening you must all come in to see your granny; and bring me smiling faces, that call back to my mind my own son Harry. But all the rest of the day, when school is done, you shall do just as you please, my dears. And there is only one thing, just one, I would have you remember. In the large spare bedroom that looks out on the slate roof there stands in the corner an old oak chest; ay, older than I, my dears, a great deal older; older than my grandmother. Play anywhere else in the house, but not there." She spoke kindly to them all, smiling at them; but she was very aged, and her eyes seemed to see nothing of this world.

And the seven children, though at first they were gloomy and strange, soon began to be happy and at home in the great house. There was much to interest and amuse them there; all was new to them. Twice every day, morning and evening, they came in to see their grandmother, who every day seemed more feeble; and she spoke pleasantly to them of her mother, and her childhood, but never forgetting to visit her store of sugar-plums. And so the weeks passed by.

It was evening twilight when Henry went upstairs from the nursery by himself to look at the oak chest. He pressed his fingers into the carved fruit and flowers, and spoke to the dark-smiling heads at the corners; and then, with a glance over his shoulder, he opened the lid and looked in. But the chest concealed no treasure, neither gold nor baubles, nor was there anything to alarm the eye. The chest was empty, except that it was lined with silk of old-rose, seeming darker in the dusk, and smelling sweet of pot-pourri. And while Henry was looking in, he heard the softened laughter and the clinking of the cups downstairs in the nursery; and out at the window he saw the day darkening. These things brought strangely to his memory his mother, who in her glimmering white dress used to read to him in the dusk; and he climbed into the chest; and the lid closed gently down over him.

When the other six children were tired with their playing, they filed into their grandmother's room as usual for her good-night and her sugar-plums. She looked out between the candles at them as if she were unsure of something in her thoughts. The next day Ann told her grandmother that Henry was not anywhere to be found. "Dearie me, child. Then he must be gone away for a time," said the old lady. She paused. " But remember, all of you, do not meddle with the oak chest."

But Matilda could not forget her brother Henry, finding no pleasure in playing without him. So she would loiter in the house thinking where he might be. And she carried her wood doll in her bare arms, singing under her breath all she could make up about him. And when in a bright morning she peeped in on the chest, so sweet-scented and secret it seemed that she took her doll with her into it — just as Henry himself had done.

So Ann, and James, and William, Harriet and Dorothea were left at home to play together. " Some day maybe they will come back to you, my dears," said their grandmother, " or maybe you will go to them. Heed my warning as best you may."

Now Harriet and William were friends together, pretending to be sweethearts; while James and Dorothea liked wild games of hunting, and fishing, and battles.

On a silent afternoon in October Harriet and William were talking softly together, looking out over the slate roof at the green fields, and they heard the squeak and frisk of a mouse behind them in the room. They went together and searched for the small, dark hole from whence it had come out. But finding no hole, they began to finger the carving of the chest, and to give names to the dark-smiling heads, just as Henry had done. " I know! Let's pretend you are Sleeping Beauty, Harriet," said William, " and I'll be the Prince that squeezes through the thorns and comes in." Harriet looked gently and strangely at her brother; but she got into the box and lay down, pretending to be fast asleep; and on tiptoe William leaned over, and seeing how big was the chest, he stepped in to kiss the Sleeping Beauty and to wake her from her quiet sleep. Slowly the carved lid turned on its noiseless hinges. And only the clatter of James and Dorothea came in sometimes to recall Ann from her book.

But their old grandmother was very feeble, and her sight dim, and her hearing extremely difficult.

Snow was falling through the still air upon the roof; and Dorothea was a fish in the oak chest, and James stood over the hole in the ice, brandishing a walking-stick for a harpoon, pretending to be an Eskimo. Dorothea's face was red, and her wild eyes sparkled through her tousled hair. And James had a crooked scratch upon his cheek. " You must struggle, Dorothea, and then I shall swim back and drag you out. Be quick, now! " He shouted with laughter as he was drawn into the open chest. And the lid closed softly and gently down as before.

Ann, left to herself, was too old to care overmuch for sugar-plums, but she would go solitary to bid her grandmother good-night; and the old lady looked wistfully at her over her spectacles. " Well, my dear," she said with trembling head; and she squeezed Ann's fingers between her own knuckled finger and thumb. " What lonely old people we are, to be sure! " Ann kissed her grandmother's soft, loose cheek. She left the old lady sitting in her easy-chair, her hands upon her knees, and her head turned sidelong towards her.

When Ann was gone to bed she used to sit reading her book by candlelight. She drew up her knees under the sheets, resting her book upon them. Her story was about fairies and gnomes, and the gently flowing moonlight of the narrative seemed to illumine the white pages, and she could hear in fancy fairy voices, so silent was the great many-roomed house and so mellifluent were the words of the story. Presently she put out her candle, and, with a confused babel of voices close to her ear, and faint swift pictures before her eyes, she fell asleep.

And in the dead of the night she arose out of bed in dream, and with her eyes wide open, yet seeing nothing of reality, moved silently through the vacant house. Past the room where her grand-mother was snoring in brief, heavy slumber, she stepped light and surely, and down the wide staircase. And Vega the far-shining stood over against the window above the slate roof. Ann walked in the strange room as if she were being guided by the hand to-wards the oak chest. There, just as if she was dreaming it was her bed, she laid herself down in the old rose silk, in the fragrant place. But it was so dark in the room that the movement of the lid was indistinguishable.

Through the long day the grandmother sat in her bow-window. Her lips were pursed, and she looked with dim, inquisitive scrutiny upon the street where people passed to and fro, and vehicles rolled by. At evening she climbed the stair and stood in the doorway of the large spare bedroom. The ascent had shortened her breath. Her magnifying spectacles rested upon her nose. Leaning her hand on the door-post she peered in towards the glimmering square of window in the quiet gloom. But she could not see far, because her sight was dim and the light of day feeble. Nor could she detect the faint fragrance, as of autumnal leaves. But in her mind was a tangled skein of memories — laughter and tears, and little children now old-fashioned, and the advent of friends, and long farewells. And gossiping fitfully, inarticulately, with herself, the old lady went down again to her window-seat.

A. E. Coppard

ADAM AND EVE AND PINCH ME

. . . And in the whole of his days, vividly at the end of the afternoon — he repeated it again and again to himself — the kind country spaces had *never* absorbed *quite* so rich a glamour of lights, so miraculous a bloom of clarity. He could feel streaming in his own mind, in his bones, the same crystalline brightness that lay upon the land. Thoughts and images went flowing through him as easily and amiably as fish swim in their pools; and as idly, too, for one of his speculations took up the theme of his family name. There was such an agreeable oddness about it, just as there was about all the luminous sky today, that it touched him as just a little remarkable. What *did* such a name connote, signify, or symbolize? It was a rann of a name, but it had euphony! Then again, like the fish, his ambulating fancy flashed into other shallows, and he giggled as he paused, peering at the buds in the brake. Turning back towards his house again he could see, beyond its roofs, the spire of the church tinctured richly as the vane: all round him was a new grandeur upon the grass of the fields, and the spare trees had shadows below that seemed to support them in the manner of a plinth, more real than themselves, and the dikes and any chance heave of the level fields were underlined, as if for special emphasis, with long shades of mysterious blackness.

With a little drift of emotion that had at other times assailed him in the wonder and ecstasy of pure light, Jaffa Codling pushed through the slit in the back hedge and stood within his own garden. The gardener was at work. He could hear the voices of the children about the lawn at the other side of the house. He was very happy, and the place was beautiful, a fine white many-windowed house rising from a lawn bowered with plots of mold, turreted with shrubs, and overset with a vast walnut tree. This house had deep clean eaves, a roof of faint-colored slates that, after rain, glowed dully, like onyx or jade, under the red chimneys, and halfway up at one end was a balcony set with black balusters. He went to a French window that stood open and stepped into the dining-room. There was no one within, and on that lonely instant a strange feeling of emptiness dropped upon him. The clock ticked almost as if it had been caught in some indecent act; the air was dim and troubled after that glory outside. Well, now, he would go up at once to his study and write down for his new book the ideas and images he had accumulated — beautiful rich thoughts they were — during that wonderful afternoon. He went to mount the stairs and he was passed by one of the maids; humming a silly song, she brushed past him rudely, but he was an easy-going man — maids were unteachably tiresome — and reaching the landing, he sauntered towards his room. The door stood slightly open and he could hear voices within. He put his hand upon the door . . . it would not open any further. What the devil . . . he pushed — like the bear in the tale — and he pushed, and he pushed — was there something against it on the other side? He put his shoulder to it . . . some wedge must be there, and that was extraordinary. Then his whole apprehension was swept up and whirled as by an avalanche — Mildred, his wife, was in there; he could hear her speaking to a man in fair soft tones and the rich phrases that could be used only by a woman yielding a deep affection to him. Codling kept still. Her words burned on his mind and thrilled him as if spoken to himself. There was a movement in the room, then utter silence. He again thrust savagely at the partly open door, but he could not stir it. The silence within continued. He beat upon the door with his fists, crying: " Mildred, Mildred! " There was no response, but he could hear the rocking armchair commence to swing to and fro. Pushing his hand round the edge of the door, he tried to thrust his head into the opening. There was not space for this, but he could just peer into the corner of a mirror hung near, and this is what he saw: the chair at one end of its swing, a man sitting in it, and upon one arm of it Mildred, the beloved woman, with her lips upon the man's face, caressing him with her hands. Codling made another effort to get into the room — as vain as it was violent. " Do you hear me, Mildred? " he shouted. Apparently neither of them heard him; they rocked to and fro while he gazed stupefied. What, in the name of God . . . What this . . . was she bewitched . . . were there such things after all as magic, devilry!

He drew back and held himself quite steadily. The chair stopped swaying, and the room grew awfully still. The sharp ticking of the clock in the hall rose upon the house like the tongue of some perfunctory mocker. Couldn't they hear the clock? . . . Couldn't they hear his heart? He had to put his hand upon his heart, for, surely, in that great silence inside there, they would hear its beat, growing so loud now that it seemed almost to stun him! Then in a queer way he found himself reflecting, observing, analyzing his own actions and intentions. He found some of them to be just a little spurious, counterfeit. He felt it would be easy, so perfectly easy, to flash in one blast of anger and annihilate the two. He would do nothing of the kind. There was no occasion for it. People didn't really do that sort of thing, or, at least, not with a genuine passion. There was no need for anger. His curiosity was satisfied, quite satisfied, he was certain, he had not the remotest interest in the man. A welter of unexpected thoughts swept upon his mind as he stood there. As a writer of books he was often stimulated by the emotions and impulses of other people, and now his own surprise was beginning to intrigue him, leaving him, oh, quite unstirred emotionally, but interesting him profoundly.

He heard the maid come stepping up the stairway again, humming her silly song. He did not want a scene or to be caught eavesdropping and so turned quickly to another door. It was locked. He sprang to one beyond it; the handle would not turn. "Bah! what's up with 'em?" But the girl was now upon him, carrying a tray of coffee-things. "Oh, Mary!" he exclaimed casually, "I . . ." To his astonishment the girl stepped past him as if she did not hear or see him, tapped upon the door of his study, entered, and closed the door behind her. Jaffa Codling then got really angry. Hell! were the blasted servants in it! He dashed to the door again and tore at the handle. It would not even turn, and though he wrenched with fury at it, the room was utterly sealed against him. He went away for a chair with which to smash the effrontery of that door. No, he wasn't angry, either with his wife or this fellow — Gilbert, she had called him — who had a strangely familiar aspect as far as he had been able to take it in; but when one's servants . . . faugh!

The door opened and Mary came forth smiling demurely. He was a few yards further along the corridor at that moment. "Mary!" he shouted, "leave the door open!" Mary carefully closed it and turned her back on him. He sprang after her with bad words bursting from him as she went towards the stairs and flitted lightly down, humming all the way as if in derision. He leaped downwards after her, three steps at a time, but she trotted with amazing swiftness into the kitchen and slammed the door in his face. Codling stood, but kept his hands carefully away from the door, kept them behind him. "No, no," he whispered cunningly, "there's something fiendish about door-handles today. I'll go and get a bar, or a butt of timber," and, jumping out into the garden for some such thing, the miracle happened to him. For it was nothing else than a miracle, the unbelievable, the impossible, simple and laughable if you will, but having as much validity as any miracle can ever invoke. It was simple and laughable because by all the known physical laws he should have collided with his gardener, who happened to pass the window with his wheelbarrow as Codling jumped out onto the path. And it was unbelievable that they should not, and impossible that they *did* not collide; and it was miraculous, because Codling stood for a brief moment in the garden path, and the wheelbarrow of Bond, its contents, and Bond himself passed apparently through the figure of Codling as if he were so much air, as if he were not a living, breathing man but just a common ghost. There was no impact, just a momentary breathlessness. Codling stood and looked at the retreating figure going on utterly unaware of him. It is interesting to record that Codling's first feelings were mirthful. He giggled. He was jocular. He ran along in front of the gardener and let him pass through him once more; then after him again; he scrambled into the man's barrow and was wheeled about by this incomprehensible thick-headed gardener who was dead to all his master's efforts to engage his attention. Presently he dropped the wheelbarrow and went away, leaving Codling to cogitate upon the occurrence. There was no room for doubt, some essential part of him had become detached from the obviously not less vital part. He felt he was essential because he was responding to the experience, he was reacting in the normal way to normal stimuli, although he happened for the time being to be invisible to his fellows and unable to communicate with them. How had it come about — this queer thing? How could he discover what part of him had cut loose, as it were? There was no question of this being death; death wasn't funny, it wasn't a joke; he had still all his human instincts. You didn't get angry with a faithless wife or joke with a fool of a gardener if you were dead, certainly not! He had realized enough of himself to know he was the usual man of instincts, desires, and prohibitions, complex and contradictory; his family history for a million or two years would have denoted that, not explicitly — obviously impossible — but suggestively. He had found himself doing things he had no desire to do, doing things he had a desire *not* to do, thinking thoughts that had no contiguous meanings, no meanings that could be related to his general experience. At odd times he had been chilled — ay, and even agreeably surprised — at the immense potential evil in himself. But still, this was no mere Jekyl and Hyde affair; that a man and his own ghost should separately inhabit the same world was a horse of quite another color. The other part of him was alive and active somewhere . . . as alive . . . as alive . . . yes, as *he* was, but dashed if he knew where! What a lark when they got back to each other and compared notes! In his tales he had brooded over so many imagined personalities, followed in the track of so many psychological enigmas, that he had felt at times a stranger to himself. What if, after all, that brooding had given him the faculty of projecting this figment of himself into the world of men. Or was he some unrealized latent element of being without its natural integument, doomed now to drift over the ridge of the world forever? Was it his personality, his spirit? Then how was the dashed thing working? Here was he with the most wonderful happening in human experience, and he couldn't differentiate or disinter things. He was like a new Adam flung into some old Eden.

There was Bond tinkering about with some plants a dozen yards in front of him. Suddenly his three children came round from the other side of the house, the youngest boy leading them, carrying in his hand a small sword which was made, not of steel, but of some more brightly shining material; indeed, it seemed at one moment to be of gold, and then again of flame, transmuting everything in its neighborhood into the likeness of flame, the hair of the little girl Eve, a part of Adam's tunic; and the fingers of the boy Gabriel as he held the sword were like pale tongues of fire. Gabriel, the youngest boy, went up to the gardener and gave the sword into his hands, saying: " Bond, is this sword any good? " Codling saw the gardener take the weapon and examine it with a careful sort of smile; his great gnarled hands became immediately transparent, the blood could be seen moving diligently about the veins. Codling was so interested in the sight that he did not gather in the gardener's reply. The little boy was dissatisfied and repeated his question: " No, but, Bond, *is* this sword any good? " Codling rose, and stood by invisible. The three beautiful children were grouped about the great angular figure of the gardener in his soiled clothes, looking up now into his face, and now at the sword, with anxiety in all their puckered eyes. " Well, Marse Gabriel," Codling could hear him reply, " as far as a sword goes, it may be a good un, or it may be a bad un, but, good as it is, it can never be anything but a bad thing." He then gave it back to them; the boy Adam held the haft of it, and the girl Eve rubbed the blade with curious fingers. The younger boy stood looking up at the gardener with unsatisfied gaze. " But, Bond, *can't* you say if this sword's any good? " Bond turned to his spade and trowels. " Mebbe the shape of it's wrong, Marse Gabriel, though it seems a pretty handy

size." Saying this he moved off across the lawn. Gabriel turned to
his brother and sister and took the sword from them; they all
followed after the gardener and once more Gabriel made inquiry:
"Bond, is this sword any good?" The gardener again took it
and made a few passes in the air like a valiant soldier at exercise.
Turning then, he lifted a bright curl from the head of Eve and
cut it off with a sweep of the weapon. He held it up to look at
it critically and then let it fall to the ground. Codling sneaked behind him and, picking it up, stood stupidily looking at it. " Mebbe,
Marse Gabriel," the gardener was saying, " it ud be better made
of steel, but it has a smartish edge on it." He went to pick up the
barrow, but Gabriel seized it with a spasm of anger and cried out:
" No, no, Bond, will you say, just yes or no, Bond, is this sword
any good? " The gardener stood still and looked down at the little
boy, who repeated his question — " just yes or no, Bond! " " No,
Marse Gabriel! " " Thank you, Bond! " replied the child with dignity, " that's all we wanted to know," and, calling to his mates to
follow him, he ran away to the other side of the house.

Codling stared again at the beautiful lock of hair in his hand, and
felt himself grow so angry that he picked up a strange-looking flow-
erpot at his feet and hurled it at the retreating gardener. It struck
Bond in the middle of the back and, passing clean through him,
broke on the wheel of his barrow, but Bond seemed to be quite unaware of this catastrophe. Codling rushed after, and, taking the gardener by the throat, he yelled: " Damn you, will you tell me what
all this means? " But Bond proceeded calmly about his work un-
noticing, carrying his master about as if he were a clinging vapor,
or a scarf hung upon his neck. In a few moments Codling dropped
exhausted to the ground. " What . . . oh hell . . . what, what
am I to do? " he groaned, " What has happened to me? What
shall I do? What can I do? " He looked at the broken flower-
pot. " Did I invent that? " He pulled out his watch. " That's a
real watch, I hear it ticking, and it's six o'clock." Was he dead or
disembodied or mad? What was this infernal lapse of identity?
And who the devil, yes, who was it upstairs with Mildred? He
jumped to his feet and hurried to the window; it was shut; to the
door, it was fastened; he was powerless to open either. Well! well!
this was experimental psychology with a vengeance, and he began

to chuckle again. He'd have to write to McDougall about it. Then he turned and saw Bond wheeling across the lawn towards him again. "Why is that fellow always shoving that infernal green barrow around?" he asked, and, the fit of fury seizing him again, he rushed towards Bond, but, before he reached him, the three children danced into the garden again, crying, with great excitement: "Bond, oh, Bond!" The gardener stopped and set down the terrifying barrow; the children crowded about him, and Gabriel held out another shining thing, asking: "Bond, is this box any good?" The gardener took the box and at once his eyes lit up with interest and delight. "Oh, Marse Gabriel, where'd ye get it? Where'd ye get it?" "Bond," said the boy impatiently, "is the box any good?" "Any good?" echoed the man. "Why, Marse Gabriel, Marse Adam, Miss Eve, look yere!" Holding it down in front of them, he lifted the lid from the box and a bright-colored bird flashed out and flew round and round above their heads. "Oh," screamed Gabriel with delight, "it's a kingfisher!" "That's what it is," said Bond, "a kingfisher!" "Where?" asked Adam. "Where?" asked Eve. "There it flies — round the fountain — see it? See it!" "No," said Adam. "No," said Eve.

"Oh, do, do see it," cried Gabriel, "here it comes, it's coming!" and, holding his hands on high, and standing on his toes, the child cried out as happy as the bird which Codling saw flying above them.

"I can't see it," said Adam.

"Where is it, Gaby?" asked Eve.

"Oh, you stupids," cried the boy, "there it goes. There it goes . . . there . . . it's gone!"

He stood looking brightly at Bond, who replaced the lid.

"What shall we do now?" he exclaimed eagerly. For reply, the gardener gave the box into his hand and walked off with the barrow. Gabriel took the box over to the fountain. Codling, unseen, went after him, almost as excited as the boy; Eve and her brother followed. They sat upon the stone tank that held the falling water. It was difficult for the child to unfasten the lid; Codling attempted to help him, but he was powerless. Gabriel looked up into his father's face and smiled. Then he stood up and said to the others:

"Now, do watch it this time."

They all knelt carefully beside the water. He lifted the lid and, behold, a fish like a gold carp, but made wholly of fire, leaped from the box into the fountain. The man saw it dart down into the water, he saw the water bubble up behind it, he heard the hiss that the junction of fire and water produces, and saw a little track of steam follow the bubbles about the tank until the figure of the fish was consumed and disappeared. Gabriel, in ecstasies, turned to his sister with blazing happy eyes, exclaiming:

" There! Evey! "

" What was it? " asked Eve, nonchalantly. " I didn't see anything."

" More didn't I," said Adam.

" Didn't you see that lovely fish? "

" No," said Adam.

" No," said Eve.

" Oh, stupids," cried Gabriel, " it went right past the bottom of the water."

" Let's get a fishin' hook," said Adam.

" No, no, no," said Gabriel, replacing the lid of the box. " Oh no."

Jaffa Codling had remained on his knees staring at the water so long that when he looked around him again, the children had gone away. He got up and went to the door, and that was closed; the windows, fastened. He went moodily to a garden bench and sat on it with folded arms. Dusk had begun to fall into the shrubs and trees, the grass to grow dull, the air chill, the sky to muster its gloom. Bond had overturned his barrow, stalled his tools in the lodge, and gone to his home in the village. A curious cat came round the house and surveyed the man who sat chained to his seven-horned dilemma. It grew dark and fearfully silent. Was the world empty now? Some small thing, a snail perhaps, crept among the dead leaves in the hedge, with a sharp, irritating noise. A strange flood of mixed thoughts poured through his mind until at last one idea disentangled itself, and he began thinking with tremendous fixity of little Gabriel. He wondered if he could brood or meditate or " will " with sufficient power to bring him into the garden again. The child had just vaguely recognized him for a moment at the waterside. He'd try that dodge, telepathy was a mild kind of a trick after so much of the miraculous. If he'd lost his blessed body, at least the part that ate and smoked and talked to Mildred. . . . He stopped as his mind stumbled on a strange recognition. . . . What a joke, of course . . . idiot . . . not to have seen *that*! He stood up in the garden with joy . . . of course, *he* was upstairs with Mildred, it was himself, the other bit of him, that Mildred had been talking to. What a howling fool he'd been!

He found himself concentrating his mind on the purpose of getting the child Gabriel into the garden once more, but it was with a curious mood that he endeavored to establish this relationship. He could not fix his will into any calm intensity of power, or fixity of purpose, or pleasurable mental ecstasy. The utmost force seemed to come with a malicious threatening splenetic " entreaty." That damned snail in the hedge broke the thread of his meditation; a dog began to bark sturdily from a distant farm; the faculties of his mind became joggled up like a child's picture puzzle, and he brooded unintelligibly upon such things as skating and steam engines, and Elizabethan drama so lapped about with themes like jealousy and chastity. Really now, Shakspere's Isabella was the most consummate snob in . . . He looked up quickly to his wife's room and saw Gabriel step from the window to the balcony as if he were fearful of being seen. The boy lifted up his hands and placed the bright box on the rail of the balcony. He looked up at the faint stars for a moment or two and then carefully released the lid of the box. What came out of it and rose into the air appeared to Codling to be just a piece of floating light, but as it soared above the roof, he saw it grow to be a little ancient ship, with its hull and fully set sails and its three masts all of faint primrose flame color. It cleaved through the air, rolling slightly as a ship through the wave, in widening circles above the house, making a curving ascent until it lost the shape of a vessel and became only a moving light hurrying to some sidereal shrine. Codling glanced at the boy on the balcony, but in that brief instant something had happened, the ship had burst like a rocket and released three colored drops of fire which came falling slowly, leaving beautiful gray furrows of smoke in their track. Gabriel leaned over the rail with outstretched palms, and, catching the green star and the blue one as they drifted down to him, he ran with a rill of laughter back into the house. Codling sprang forward just in time

to catch the red star; it lay vividly blasting his own palm for a monstrous second, and then, slipping through, was gone. He stared at
the ground, at the balcony, the sky, and then heard an exclamation
. . . his wife stood at his side.

" Gilbert! How you frightened me! " she cried. " I thought you
were in your room; come along in to dinner." She took his arm and
they walked up the steps into the dining-room together. " Just a
moment," said her husband, turning to the door of the room. His
hand was upon the handle, which turned easily in his grasp, and he
ran upstairs to his own room. He opened the door. The light was
on, the fire was burning brightly, a smell of cigarette smoke about,
pen and paper upon his desk, the Japanese book-knife, the gilt
matchbox, everything all right, no one there. He picked up a book
from his desk . . . Monna Vanna. His bookplate was in it — Ex
Libris — Gilbert Cannister. He put it down beside the green dish;
two yellow oranges were in the green dish, and two most deliberately green Canadian apples rested by their side. He went to the
door and swung it backwards and forwards quite easily. He sat on
his desk trying to piece the thing together, glaring at the print and
the book-knife and the smart matchbox, until his wife came up behind him exclaiming: " Come along, Gilbert! "

" Where are the kids, old man? " he asked her, and before she replied, he had gone along to the nursery. He saw the two cots, his
boy in one, his girl in the other. He turned whimsically to Mildred,
saying: " There are only two, are there? " Such a question did not
call for reply, but he confronted her as if expecting some assuring
answer. She was staring at him with her bright beautiful eyes.

" Are there? " he repeated.

" How strange you should ask me that now! " she said. . . . " If
you're a very good man . . . perhaps . . ."

" Mildred! "

She nodded brightly.

He sat down in the rocking-chair, but got up again, saying to her
gently: " We'll call him Gabriel."

" But suppose — "

" No, no," he said, stopping her lovely lips, " I know all about
him." And he told her a pleasant little tale.

❧ Zona Gale ❧

BRIDAL POND

THE JUDGE had just said: "Case dismissed," and a sharp situation concerning cheese had thus become negligible when, before the next case on the calendar could be called, Jens Jevins came forward and said loudly:

"I wish to confess to the murder of my wife."

Now the courtroom was still, the fierce heat forgotten, and the people stupefied, for Jens Jevins was the richest farmer in the township. No one tried to silence or delay him.

He faced now the Judge and now the people, his face and neck the color of chicken-skin, his tossed hair like a raveled fabric, his long right arm making always the same gesture. His clothes were good, and someone had pressed them.

"I planned to kill Agna for a long time. There was a time when for a week I slept with a pistol under my pillow, hoping for the strength to shoot her in her sleep. When I could tell by her breathing that it was time, I'd get up on my elbow and look at her, but I never had the courage to use the pistol on her — no, though I sat up in bed sometimes for half an hour with my finger on the trigger. Something would delay me — our dog would bark, or the kitchen clock would strike, or I would imagine my father shaking his head at me; and once she woke and asked me whether I had locked the porch door.

" Most of that week the room was as bright as morning, because the moon shone in, but as it rose later and hung higher, the room grew dark. And it seemed wrong to shoot Agna in the dark. Then I thought of a better plan."

The courtroom was held as a ball of glass, in which black figures hang in arrested motion. The silence was not vacant, but rich and winy, like a rest in music. It was the rest in the tread of a giant, one step, one step, and men crushed and powerless. The Judge, the bailiff, the spectators were crushed and powerless, all with staring eyes, and their short breath caught through the mouth. Jens and Agna Jevins, they were known to all, and he so prosperous; and she a small complaining woman, who took prizes, with whom all must have talked on bright mornings, after she had lain asleep, close to death.

" At the south of our lot," Jens Jevins continued, and conversationally, quite quietly, as if he were talking to some surveyors, " there is a long slope and then a pond, where in my father's time they took out clay to make bricks. This place is not fenced; is separated from the highway by a few alders — some of you know," he said, with an air of surprise, remembering the spectators as living beings who had experienced his highway and the sight of his pond. " I would go down there sometimes on spring evenings when the boys were catching frogs, and last week I went down, and they were catching frogs. And it was the night the Alexander boy fell in — well over his head he went, for the pond is above seven feet deep there, and sixteen farther out. I, that was standing near, was able to seize on him — I mention this because pulling him out put in my head the idea of what to do to Agna.

" So the next night I waited till late, and I said to her that we might walk down and watch the boys catch frogs. She was glad to go and mentioned that I didn't often invite her to take evening walks any more, and we went down the slope. But I hadn't waited long enough, the boys were still there. She and I stood on the rim of the pond, and I edged her towards the place where the Alexander boy went in, and saw how easy it would be to send her down and keep her from climbing out. Only the boys were still there.

" It was dusk, and the cars from town came down the highway and took the turn beyond our alders, and it looked as if they were all coming straight on to us, till they swung the corner. She says: ' What if one didn't see the turn and came crashing on to us? ' and she shivered and said her shoulders were chilly, though the night was warm, and she wanted to go back to the house. So we went back and I read the evening paper aloud, about a young couple that had got married that day at Sun Prairie and had had a great doings. She said she wished we were starting over, and I said: ' I don't ' and went to bed.

" But in the night I woke up and thought of what she'd said. What if we were starting over? And what if I'd murdered her early — say, on the honeymoon? I saw that I couldn't have done it then. I wondered how I could do it now."

Now the Judge found his voice, and leaned down as if he were ill or drunk, and said from his throat: " Why did you want to do it? "

Jens Jevins looked astonished. " I didn't want to do it," he said, " but there was thirty-seven years of it already and there might be twenty more."

Having answered, he continued:

" I began to see that what wasn't tragedy now would have been tragedy then. I thought of us driving through the country, if we'd been in the days of machines, like the Sun Prairie couple. Agna and me, you understand — and her young again. Her in the same blue dress, in the seat beside me. Me in a new suit, and shoes with the new not off the soles. Us talking and laughing, our valises stowed in the back. Going along the road. Along the road that swung round by our place and turned the corner by the alder trees. Dark it might be, or maybe a fog would have come down. We'd be talking and laughing, and the road strange, and I'd miss the turn, and the car'd come skimming between the alders and across the base of the slope and making for the clay hole. Spite of all I could do, setting the brakes, on it'd come, heading for the clay hole. In the dark or maybe in the fog. And we wouldn't know we'd left the road till I'd see a light from somewhere lapping on the pond, and then it'd be too late. Straight in and down — in and down. Nothing I could do. Agna in her blue dress. On the day of our wedding.

" But now it was thirty years and past, and twenty more to come. I woke her up. I says: ' I can't sleep. It's warm. Let's go down and walk out somewheres.' She laughed and grumbled some, but she went with me. She was always one to go with me. We put on little and went down the slope to the pond. It was deep dark — the light of a star was deep in the water. We heard the frogs and smelled the first wild grape. I took her to the place were the Alexander boy had slipped in and where it was hard for anybody to climb out. I waited a minute. Another car was coming along the road. ' When it turns the corner,' I thought, ' when it turns! ' Its lights shone straight and strong, they blinded us; they came on and on, towards us. Agna says: ' It's coming, it's coming! . . .' For the lights made no turn at the corner. The lights shot out from the alders. I could hear the talking and laughing in the car. In less than a flash of time the car shook the ground around us and went crashing down and down into the deep of the water. But first the lights of the water, or of the dashboard, or of the sky, or of heaven struck full on their faces, that were still laughing. Well, there on that seat, I tell you, I saw me in my wedding suit, that was new, and beside me Agna, that was young again.

" There was a cry from Agna, that was young, and from me where I stood — and I saw what I'd done — reached back into the past and killed her that it was tragedy to kill. It was so that it had found me out. God had done it to me — just that way. I see it so. . . . All night I've walked in the woods, waiting for the time to tell. Now you know — now you know."

Jens Jevins stood, head down, abruptly distracted, listless. The hundred voices in the room burst their silence. And after the first words, crude and broken, the women were saying: " Walked all night in the woods? But somebody has just pressed his clothes for him! "

Now the sound of running feet and the cries of men reached the room, and as these increased, none knew whether to run down into the street or to stay in the courtroom, where Jens Jevins might say something more. But now a great gasping voice cried from the stair: "Car gone into Jevins's clay hole!" . . . and immediately the room was emptied of all but those who must stay, and Jevins, who seemed not to have heard.

As one man, and he breathing his horror, the town of Tarnham ran down the highway and did not take the turn, but kept straight on and flowed over the green and spangled slope and surrounded the Jevins pond. Some highway men, placing signs, had seen the corner of a top protruding from the water.

And now policemen and firemen were lifting from the water, slowly and with sickening lurchings and saggings, a black coupé, new by the signs, and within it the seated figures of man and woman. And all about them, on sides and back of the car, were gay ribbon streamers, white and pink, and lettering said: "Yes, we're just married." And such signs were also pasted on paper, and from the car was dangling a water-soaked old shoe. A young chap he was, with his hands still on the wheel, and the emergency brake set, and a rose on his coat lapel; and his young bride, in her neat gown of blue, had her hands folded in her lap, over a little silver bag.

Now the sheriff came leading Jens Jevins and pushed through the crowd, and the people moved respectfully, for the tale of the courtroom had not yet gone about. The sheriff and Jens Jevins went to the two figures, taken from the car and covered on the grass, and Jens said in a loud voice: "There we are!" And now he shouted in agony: "Agna, Agna! Jens!" and cast himself on the ground beside the two still figures.

The people were stupefied, not knowing what to feel, with the men and women from the courtroom murmuring his story. Jens Jevins — and he so prosperous and known to them all! They had seen him yesterday buying and selling. Could his wife have been in the car, too — the complaining woman, who took prizes?

No, for here she came walking down the slope from the house, wondering at the crowd gathered about their pond. She looked questioning, in her neat black dress and her striped scarf, and they made way for her; and a neighbor who had been in the courtroom cried: "Mrs. Jevins, Mrs. Jevins! The car that you saw last night go into the water had a bride and groom!"

But Agna Jevins said: "What car? I saw no car go into the water."

"What! You were not out here in the night and saw this car . . . ?"

"I?" cried Agna Jevins. "I was in bed the whole night, and Jens too. What car . . ."

They told her. She covered her eyes and said: "God forgive me, I heard a cry and thought of saying so to Jens, but he was sleeping soundly."

Jens and the sheriff moved toward her, and when he came up to her, Jens began speaking softly: "All our friends, Agna, thinking of us through the night. And who could have imagined that we were spending the whole night so, side by side; and with the sunrise, we still so near to each other, saying nothing. Who could have told us in our early youth: ' You will rest on that night in a bed of ooze, and none shall know or care that you lie passionless and forgotten '? Who could have known that our wedding day and our death night would be one, because of a pond beyond alders, pleasant and secured? We have died with our dream and our happiness upon us; neither trouble nor weariness has touched us, nor the slow rust of unending days. I have no need to send you to your death, for we have died in the safety of our youth and not in the deep of days already dead. . . ."

They led him to his house.

Weeping, Mrs. Jevins said: "It must have come on him all of a rush. For I pressed his clothes and got his breakfast and he went out of the house. And nothing had changed."

The legend grew that Jens Jevins had had a vision of that happening of the night, and that it had sent him off his head.

Biography

I T is a fair guess that if Stephen Crane and Frank Norris had
not died so young the course of modern American literature might
have been changed. All the seeds of the new fiction were in them
and Theodore Dreiser, who was only two months younger than
Crane and little over a year younger than Norris. When Crane
died the year *Sister Carrie* was published, and Norris two years
later, it meant not only that their own work stopped but that
Dreiser was left alone to do the work of three. Norris, who had discovered Dreiser's first novel and had argued it into print, might
have helped bring it back to life after its studied neglect by the
publishers, but he died too soon. Crane, whose *Maggie* had had
comparable misfortunes, would surely have valued Dreiser, but he
died before there was a chance for him to read *Sister Carrie*. Without the recognition and encouragement of his natural peers, Dreiser
was almost silent for a decade, and the decade in fiction was given

up largely to historical or sentimental romances. Yet there was a good deal of anti-romance in the air. Journalists were turning over scandal after scandal with lively muckrakes, and a school of biographers tried to get at the disregarded truth about the national heroes. The novel inclined to naturalism, though the novelists who practiced it had none of them the gift of Crane, the scope of Norris, or the patient genius of Dreiser. But the new fiction, lacking its three best writers, was handicapped and delayed. If Crane and Norris had lived . . .

They did not, and modern American literature, which may be said to have begun with Crane in the nineties, took twenty years to get under way in verse and twenty-five in prose. By that time Crane had been more or less forgotten, except for the vague legend of his Bohemianism and *The Red Badge of Courage*, which had its enthusiasts much as Keats's poems had for a generation after his death. Keats had to wait twenty-seven years for a biographer; Crane, in more rapid times, only twenty-three. Perhaps the luckiest thing that ever happened to Crane was Thomas Beer. For Beer not only found out all that could be found out about Crane but also wrote his biography in complete sympathy and with skill and grace. It was too late to revive Crane's collected works, and impossible, whatever effort was made. Much of what he wrote was mere journalism, brightened by an occasional flash but not preserved. All that would really last was *The Red Badge* and a volume of selected stories. This Beer understood, and he was able to reconstruct the man as he lived. Now there are three lasting Crane books: two by him and this one about him.

C.V.D.

⤚ *Thomas Beer* ⤙

STEPHEN CRANE

A STUDY IN AMERICAN LETTERS

INTRODUCTION

On a rainy day of March of the year 1923, listening to the author of this biography telling me of his earnest labors for the memory of a man who was certainly unique in his generation, I exclaimed to myself with wonder: " And so it has come to pass after all — this thing which I did not expect to see! " In truth I had never expected the biography of Stephen Crane to appear in my lifetime. My immense pleasure was affected by the devastating touch of time which like a muddy flood covers under a mass of daily trivialities things of value: moments of affectionate communion with kindred spirits, words spoken with the careless freedom of perfect confidence, the deepest emotions of joy and sorrow — together with such things of merely historical importance as the recollection

of dates, for instance. After hearing from Mr. Beer of his difficulties in fixing certain dates in the history of Stephen Crane's
life I discovered that I was unable to remember with any kind of
precision the initial date of our friendship. Indeed life is but a
dream — especially for those of us who have never kept a diary or
possessed a notebook in their lives.

In this extremity I had recourse to another friend of Stephen
Crane, who had appreciated him intuitively almost as soon as I
did myself and who is a woman of excellent memory. My wife's
recollection is that Crane and I met in London in October 1897,
and that he came to see us for the first time in our Essex home in
the following November.

I have mentioned in a short paper written two years ago that it
was Mr. S. S. Pawling, partner in the publishing firm of Mr. Heinemann, who brought us together. It was done at Stephen Crane's
own desire.

I was told by Mr. Pawling that when asked whom he wanted to
meet Crane mentioned two names, of which one was of a notable
journalist (who had written some novels) whom he knew in
America, I believe, and the other was mine. At that time the only
facts we knew about each other were that we both had the same
publisher in England. The only other fact I knew about Stephen
Crane was that he was quite a young man. I had of course read
his *Red Badge of Courage*, of which people were writing and talking at that time. I certainly did not know that he had the slightest
notion of my existence, or that he had seen a single line (there
were not many of them then) of my writing. I can safely say that
I earned this precious friendship by something like ten months of
strenuous work with my pen. It took me just that time to write
The Nigger of the Narcissus working at what I always considered
a very high pressure. It was on the ground of the authorship of that
book that Crane wanted to meet me. Nothing could have been
more flattering than to discover that the author of *The Red Badge
of Courage* appreciated my effort to present a group of men held
together by a common loyalty and a common perplexity in a
struggle not with human enemies but with the hostile conditions
testing their faithfulness to the conditions of their own calling.

Apart from the imaginative analysis of his own temperament

tried by the emotions of a battlefield Stephen Crane dealt in his book with the psychology of the mass — the army; while I — in mine — had been dealing with the same subject on a much smaller scale and in more specialized conditions — the crew of a merchant ship, brought to the test of what I may venture to call the moral problem of conduct. This may be thought a very remote connection between these two works, and the idea may seem too far-fetched to be mentioned here; but that was my undoubted feeling at the time. It is a fact that I considered Crane, by virtue of his creative experience with *The Red Badge of Courage*, as eminently fit to pronounce a judgment on my first consciously planned attempt to render the truth of a phase of life in the terms of my own temperament with all the sincerity of which I was capable.

I had, of course, my own opinion as to what I had done; but I doubted whether anything of my ambitiously comprehensive aim would be understood. I was wrong there; but my doubt was excusable since I myself would have been hard put to it if requested to give my complex intentions the form of a concise and definite statement. In that period of misgivings which so often follows an accomplished task I would often ask myself who in the world could be interested in such a thing. It was after reading *The Red Badge*, which came into my hands directly after its publication in England, that I said to myself: "Here's a man who may understand — if he ever sees the book; though of course that would not mean that he would like it." I do not mean to say that I looked towards the author of *The Red Badge* as the only man in the world. It would have been stupid and ungrateful. I had the moral support of one or two intimate friends and the solid fact of Mr. W. H. Henley's acceptance of my tale for serial publication in the *New Review* to give me confidence, while I awaited the larger verdict.

It seems to me that in trying to recall my memories of Stephen Crane I have been talking so far only about myself; but that is unavoidable, since this introduction, which I am privileged to write, can only trace what is left on earth of our personal intercourse, which was even more short and fleeting than it may appear from the record of dates, October 1897 — May 1900. And out of that beggarly tale of months must be deducted the time of his absence from England during the Spanish-American War and of

his visit to the United States shortly before the beginning of his
last illness. Even when he was in England our intercourse was not
so close and frequent as the warmth of our friendship would have
wished it to be. We both lived in the country and, though not
very far from each other, in different counties. I had my work to
do, always in conditions which made it a matter of urgency. He
had his own tasks and his own visions to attend to. I do not think
that he had more friendships to claim him than I, but he certainly had more acquaintances and more calls on his time.

This was only natural. It must be remembered that as an anthor
he was my senior, as I used to remind him now and then with
affected humility which always provoked his smiles. He had a quiet
smile that charmed and frightened one. It made you pause by
something revelatory it cast over his whole physiognomy, not like
a ray but like a shadow. I often asked myself what it could be,
that quality that checked one's carefree mood, and now I think I
have had my answer. It was the smile of a man who knows that
his time will not be long on this earth.

I would not for a moment wish to convey the impression of
melancholy in connection with my memories of Stephen Crane.
I saw his smile first over the tablecloth in a restaurant. We shook
hands with intense gravity and a direct stare at each other, after
the manner of two children told to make friends. It was under
the encouraging gaze of Sidney Pawling, who, a much bigger man
than either of us and possessed of a deep voice, looked like a
grown-up person entertaining two strange small boys — protecting
and slightly anxious as to the experiment. He knew very little of
either of us. I was a new author and Crane was a new arrival. It
was the meeting of *The Red Badge* and *The Nigger* in the presence of their publisher; but as far as our personalities went we were
three strangers breaking bread together for the first time. Yet it
was as pleasantly easy a meal as any I can remember. Crane talked
in his characteristic deliberate manner about Greece, at war. I had
already sensed the man's intense earnestness underlying his quiet
surface. Every time he raised his eyes that secret quality (for his
voice was careless) of his soul was betrayed in a clear flash. Most
of the true Stephen Crane was in his eyes, most of his strength
at any rate, though it was apparent also in his other features, as

for instance in the structure of his forehead, the deep solid arches under the fair eyebrows.

Some people saw traces of weakness in the lower part of his face. What I could see there was a hint of the delicacy of sentiment, of the inborn fineness of nature which this man, whose life had been anything but a stroll through a rose-garden, had managed to preserve like a sacred heritage. I say heritage, not acquisition, for it was not and could not have been acquired. One could depend on it on all occasions; whereas the cultivated kind is apt to show ugly gaps under very slight provocation. The coarseness of the professedly delicate must be very amusing to the misanthrope. But Crane was no enemy of his kind. That sort of thing did not amuse him. As to his own temper, it was proof against anger and scorn, as I can testify, having seen him both angry and scornful, always quietly, on fitting occasions. Contempt and indignation never broke the surface of his moderation, simply because he had no surface. He was all through of the same material, incapable of affectation of any kind, of any pitiful failure of generosity for the sake of personal advantage, or even from sheer exasperation, which must find its relief.

Many people imagined him a fiery individuality. Certainly he was not cold-blooded. But his was an equable glow, morally and temperamentally. I would have said the same of his creative power (I have seen him sit down before a blank sheet of paper, dip his pen, write the first line at once, and go on without haste and without pause for a couple of hours), had he not confided to me that his mentality did flag at times. I do not think it was anything more than every writer is familiar with at times. Another man would have talked of his " failing inspiration." It is very characteristic of Crane that I have never heard him use that word when talking about his work.

His phraseology was generally of a very modest cast. That unique and exquisite faculty, which Edward Garnet, another of his friends, found in his writing, " of disclosing an individual scene by an odd simile " was not apparent in his conversation. It was interesting of course, but its charm consisted mainly in the freshness of his impressions set off by an acute simplicity of view and expressed with an amusing deliberation. Superabundance of words was not his

failing when communing with those whom he liked and felt he
could trust. With the other kind of "friends" he followed the
method of a sort of suspended silence. On a certain occasion (it
was at Brede Place) after two amazingly conceited idiots had gone
away I said to him: "Stevie, you brood like a distant thunder-
cloud." He had retired early to the other end of the room, and
from there had sent out, now and then, a few words, more like the
heavy drops of rain that precede the storm than growls of thunder.
Poor Crane, if he could look black enough at times, never thun-
dered; though I have no doubt he could have been dangerous if
he had liked. There always seemed to be something (not timidity)
which restrained him, not from within but, I could not help fancy-
ing, from outside, with an effect as of a whispered *memento mori*
in the ear of a reveler not lost to the sense of grace.

That of course was a later impression. It must be stated clearly
that I know very little of Stephen Crane's life. We did not feel
the need to tell each other formally the story of our lives. That did
not prevent us from being very intimate and also very open with
each other from the first. Our affection would have been "everlasting," as he himself qualified it, had not the jealous death intervened with her cruel capriciousness by striking down the younger
man. Our intimacy was really too close to admit of indiscretions;
not that he did not speak amusingly of his experiences and of his
hardships, and warmly of the men that helped him in his early
days, like Mr. Hamlin Garland for instance, or men kindly encouraging to him, like Mr. Howells. Many other names he used
to utter lovingly have been forgotten by me after so many years.

It is a fact that I heard more of his adventures than of his trials,
privations, and difficulties. I know he had many. He was the least
recriminatory of men (though one of the most sensitive, I should
say), but, in any case, nothing I could have learned would have
shaken the independent judgment I had formed for myself of his
trustworthiness as a man and a friend. Though the word is discred-
ited now and may sound pretentious, I will say that there was in
Crane a strain of chivalry which made him safe to trust with one's
life. To be recognizably a man of honor carries no immunity against
human weaknesses, but comports more rigid limitations in personal
relations than the status of an "honorable man," however recog-

nizable that too may be. Some men are " honorable " by courtesy, others by the office they hold, or simply by belonging to some popular assembly, the election to which is not generally secured by a dignified accuracy of statement and a scrupulous regard for the feelings of others. Many remain honorable (because of their great circumspection in the conduct of their affairs) without holding within themselves any of these restraints which are inherent in the character of a man of honor, however weak or luckless he may be.

I do not know everything about the strength of Crane's circumspection, but I am not afraid of what the biography which follows may disclose to us; though I am convinced that it will be free from hypocritical reservations. I think I have understood Stephen Crane, and from my too short acquaintance with his biographer I am confident he will receive the most humane and sympathetic treatment. What I discovered very early in our acquaintance was that Crane had not the face of a lucky man. That certitude came to me at our first meeting while I sat opposite him listening to his simple tales of Greece, while M. S. Pawling presided at the initiatory feast — friendly and debonair, looking solidly anchored in the stream of life, and very reassuring, like a big, prosperous ship to the sides of which we two in our tossing little barks could hook on for safety. He was interested in the tales too; and the best proof of it is that when he looked at his watch and jumped up, saying: " I must leave you two now," it was very near four o'clock. Nearly a whole afternoon wasted, for an English business man.

No such consideration of waste or duty agitated Crane and myself. The sympathy that, even in regard of the very few years allotted to our friendship, may be said to have sprung up instantaneously between us was the most undemonstrative case of that sort in the last century. We not only did not tell each other of it (which would have been missish) but even without entering formally into a previous agreement to remain together we went out and began to walk side by side in the manner of two tramps without home, occupation, or care for the next night's shelter. We certainly paid no heed to direction. The first thing I noticed were the Green Park railings, when to my remark that he had seen no war before he went to Greece Crane made answer: " No. But the *Red Badge*

is all right." I assured him that I never had doubted it; and, since
the title of the work had been pronounced for the first time, feeling I must do something to show I had read it, I said shyly: " I
like your General." He knew at once what I was alluding to, but
said not a word. Nothing could have been more tramp-like than
our silent pacing, elbow to elbow, till, after we had left Hyde Park
Corner behind us, Crane uttered with his quiet earnestness the
words: " I like your young man — I can just see him." Nothing
could have been more characteristic of the depth of our three-
hour-old intimacy than that each of us should have selected for
praise the merest by-the-way vignette of a minor character.

This was positively the only allusion we made that afternoon
to our immortal works. Indeed, we talked very little of them at
any time, and then always selecting some minor point for particular
mention; which, after all, is not a bad way of showing an affectionate appreciation of a piece of work done by a friend. A stranger
would have expected more, but, in a manner of speaking, Crane
and I had never been strangers. We took each other's work for
granted from the very first, I mean from the moment we had exchanged those laudatory remarks alongside the Green Park railings.
Henceforth mutual recognition kept to that standard. It consisted
often of an approving grunt, sometimes of the mention of some
picked-out paragraph, or of a line or only of a few words that had
caught our fancy and would, for a time, be applied more or less
aptly to the turns of our careless or even serious talks.

Thus, for instance, there was a time when I persecuted poor
Crane with the words " barbarously abrupt." They occur in that
marvelous story *The Open Boat* and are applied by him to the
waves of the sea (as seen by men tossing in a small dinghy) with
an inspired audacity of epithet which was one of Crane's gifts that
gave me most delight. How amazingly apt these words are where
they stand, anybody can see by looking at that story, which is altogether a big thing and has remained an object of my confirmed
admiration. I was always telling Crane that this or that was " barbarously abrupt," or begging him not to be so " barbarously abrupt "
himself, with a keen enjoyment of the incongruity; for no human
being could be less abrupt than Crane. As to his humanity (in
contradistinction to barbarity), it was a shining thing without a

flaw. It is possible that he may have grown at length weary of my little joke, but he invariably received it with a smile, thus proving his consistent humanity toward his kind. But, after all, he, too, liked that story of his, of four men in a very small boat, which by the deep and simple humanity of presentation seems somehow to illustrate the essentials of life itself, like a symbolic tale. It opens with a phrase that anybody could have uttered, but which, in relation to what is to follow, acquires the poignancy of a meaning almost universal. Once, much later in our acquaintance, I made use of it to him. He came on a flying visit to Pent Farm, where we were living then. I noticed that he looked harassed. I, too, was feeling for the moment as if things were getting too much for me. He lay on the couch and I sat on a chair opposite. After a longish silence in which we both could have felt how uncertain was the issue of life envisaged as a deadly adventure in which we were both engaged like two men trying to keep afloat in a small boat, I said suddenly across the width of the mantelpiece:

"None of them knew the color of the sky."

He raised himself sharply. The words had struck him as familiar, though I believe he failed to place them at first. "Don't you know that quotation?" I asked. (These words form the opening sentence of his tale.) The startled expression passed off his face. "Oh, yes," he said quietly, and lay down again. Truth to say, it was a time when neither he nor I had the leisure to look up idly at the sky. The waves just then were too "barbarously abrupt."

I do not mean to say that it was always so. Now and then we were permitted to snatch a glance at the color of the sky. But it is a fact that in the history of our essentially undemonstrative friendship (which is nearly as difficult to recapture as a dream) that first long afternoon is the most carefree instant, and the only one that had a character of enchantment about it. It was spread out over a large portion of central London. After the Green Park the next thing I remember is the Kensington Gardens, where under the lofty and historical trees I was vouchsafed a glimpse of the low mesquit bush overspreading the plum-colored infinities of the great Texas plains. Then after a long tramp amongst an orderly multitude of grimy brick houses — from which the only things I carried off were the impressions of the colored rocks of Mexico (or was it Arizona?), and my first knowledge of a locality called the Painted Desert — there came suddenly Oxford Street. I don't know whether the inhabitants of London were keeping indoors or had gone into the country that afternoon, but I don't remember seeing any people in the streets except for a figure, now and then, unreal, flitting by, obviously negligible. The wheeled traffic, too, was stopped; yet, it seems, not entirely, because I remember Crane seizing my arm and jerking me back on the pavement with the calm remark: "You will get run over." I love to think that the dear fellow had saved my life and it seemed to amuse him. As to London's enormous volume of business, all I know is that one A B C. shop had remained open. We went through the depressing ceremony of having tea there; but our interest in each other mitigated its inherent horrors and gave me a good idea of Crane's stoicism. At least I suppose we had tea, otherwise they would not have let us sit there so long. To be left alone was all we wanted. Neither of us had then a club to entertain the other in. It will give a good notion of our indomitable optimism (on that afternoon) when I say that it was there, in those dismal surroundings, we reached the conclusion that though the world had grown old and weary, yet the scheme of creation remained as obscure as ever, and (from our own particular point of view) there was still much that was interesting to expect from gods and men.

As if intoxicated by this draft of hope we rolled out of that A B C. shop, but I kept my head sufficiently to guess what was coming and to send a warning telegram to my wife in our Essex home. Crane then was, I believe, staying temporarily in London. But he seemed to have no care in the world; and so we resumed our tramping — east and north and south again, steering through uncharted mazes the streets, forgetting to think of dinner but taking a rest here and there, till we found ourselves, standing in the middle of Piccadilly Circus, blinking at the lights like two authentic night-birds. By that time we had been (in Tottenham Court Road) joined by Balzac. How he came in I have no idea. Crane was not given to literary curiosities of that kind. Somebody he knew, or something he had read, must have attracted lately his attention to Balzac. And now suddenly at ten o'clock in the evening he demanded insistently to be told in particular detail all about the _Comédie Humaine_, its contents, its scope, its plan, and its general significance, together with a critical description of Balzac's style. I told him hastily that it was just black on white; and for the rest, I said, he would have to wait till we got across to Monico and had eaten some supper. I hoped he would forget Balzac and his *Comédie*. But not a bit of it; and I had no option but to hold forth over the remnants of a meal, in the rush of hundreds of waiters and the clatter of tons of crockery, caring not what I said (for what could Stephen want with Balzac?), in the comfortable assurance that the Monstrous Shade, even if led by some strange caprice to haunt the long room of Monico's, did not know enough English to understand a single word I said. I wonder what Crane made of it all. He did not look bored, and it was eleven o'clock before we parted at the foot of that monumentally heavy abode of frivolity, the Pavilion, with just a handshake and a good-night — no more — without making any arrangements for meeting again, as though we had lived in the same town from childhood and were sure to run across each other next day.

It struck me directly I left him that we had not even exchanged addresses; but I was not uneasy. Sure enough, before the month was out there arrived a postcard (from Ravensbrook) asking whether he might come to see us. He came, was received as an old friend, and before the end of the day conquered my wife's sympathy, as undemonstrative and sincere as his own quiet friendliness. The friendship that sprang up between them was confirmed by the interest Crane displayed in our first child, a boy who came on the scene not quite two months afterwards. How strong was that interest on the part of Stephen Crane and his wife in the boy is evidenced by the fact that at the age of six weeks he was invited to come for a long visit to Ravensbrook. He was in fact impatiently expected there. He arrived in state, bringing with him not only his parents but also a young aunt, and was welcomed like a prince. This visit, during which I suffered from a sense of temporary extinction, is commemorated by a group photograph taken by an artist summoned with his engine (regardless of expense) to Ravensbrook. Though the likenesses are not bad it is a very awful thing. Nobody looks like him or herself in it. The best yet are the Crane dogs, a very important part of the establishment and quite conscious of it, belonging apparently to some order of outlandish poodles, amazingly sedate and yet the most restless animals I have ever met. They pervaded, populated, and filled the whole house. Whichever way one looked at any time, down the passage, up the stairs, into the drawing-room, there was always a dog in sight. Had I been asked on the first day how many there were I would have guessed about thirty. As a matter of fact there were only three, but I think they never sat down, except in Crane's study, where they had their entrée at all hours.

A scratching would be heard at the door, Crane would drop his pen with alacrity to throw it open — and the dogs would enter sedately in single file, taking a lot of time about it, too. Then the room would resound for a while with grunts, sniffs, yawns, heavy flops, followed by as much perhaps as three whole minutes of silence. Then the dogs would get up, one after another, never all together, and direct their footsteps to the door in an impressive and ominous manner. The first arrival waited considerately for the others before trying to attract attention by means of scratching on the bottom panel. Then, never before, Crane would raise his head, go meekly to the door — and the procession would file out at the slowest possible pace. The recurrent sedateness of the proceedings, the utter unconsciousness of the dogs, dear Stephen's absurd gravity while playing his part in those ceremonies, without ever a muscle of his face moving, were irresistibly, exasperatingly funny. I tried to preserve my gravity (or at least to keep calm), with fair success. Only one afternoon on the fifth or sixth repetition I could not help bursting into a loud interminable laugh and then the dear fellow asked me in all innocence what was the matter. I managed to conceal my nervous irritation from him and he never learned the secret of that laugh in which there was a beginning of hysteria.

If the definition that man is a laughing animal be true then Crane was neither one nor the other; indeed, he was but a hurried visitor on this earth on which he had so little reason to be joyous. I might say that I never heard him laugh except in connection with the baby. He loved children; but his friendship with our child was of the kind that put our mutual sentiment, by comparison, somewhere within the arctic region. The two could not be compared; at least I have never detected Crane stretched full length and sustained on his elbows on a grass plot, in order to gaze at me; on the other hand this was his usual attitude of communion with the small child

— with him who was called *the Boy*, and whose destiny it was to see
more war before he came of age than the author of *The Red Badge*
had time to see in all the allotted days of his life. In the gravity of its
disposition the baby came quite up to Crane; yet those two would
sometimes find something to laugh at in each other. Then there
would be silence, and glancing out of the low window of my room
I would see them, very still, staring at each other with a solemn understanding that needed no words or perhaps was beyond words altogether. I could not object on any ground to their profound intimacy, but I do not see why Crane should have developed such an
unreasonable suspicion as to my paternal efficiency. He seemed to
be everlastingly taking the boy's part. I could not see that the baby
was being oppressed, hectored over, or in any way deprived of its
rights, or ever wounded in its feelings by me; but Crane seemed always to nurse some vague unexpressed grievance as to my conduct.
I was inconsiderate. For instance — why could I not get a dog for
the boy? One day he made me quite a scene about it. He seemed to
imply I should drop everything and go look for a dog. I sat under
the storm and said nothing. At last he cried: " Hang it all, a boy
ought to have a dog." It was an appeal to first principles, but for an
answer I pointed at the window and said: " Behold the boy." . . .
He was sitting on a rug spread on the grass, with his little red stock-
ing-cap very much over one eye (a fact of which he seemed unaware), and propped round with many pillows on account of his
propensity to roll over on his side helplessly. My answer was irresistible. This is one of the few occasions on which I heard Stephen
Crane laugh outright. He dropped his preaching on the dog theme
and went out to the boy while I went on with my work. But he was
strangely incorrigible. When he came back after an hour or so, his
first words were: " Joseph, I will teach your boy to ride." I closed
with the offer at once — but it was not to be. He was not given the
time.

The happiest mental picture my wife and I preserve of Crane is
on the occasion of our first visit to Brede Place when he rode to
meet us at the park gate. He looked at his best on horseback. On
that day he must have been feeling well. As usual, he was happy in
the saddle. As he went on trotting by the side of the open trap I said
to him: " If you give the boy your seat I will be perfectly satisfied."

I knew this would please him; and indeed his face remained wreathed in smiles all the way to the front door. He looked about him at that bit of the world, down the green slopes and up the brown fields, with an appreciative serenity and the confident bearing of a man who is feeling very sure of the present and of the future. All because he was looking at life from the saddle, with a good morning's work behind him. Nothing more is needed to give a man a blessed moment of illusion. The more I think of that morning, the more I believe it was just that: that it had really been given me to see Crane perfectly happy for a couple of hours; and that it was under this spell that, directly we arrived, he led me impatiently to the room in which he worked when at Brede. After we got there he said to me: " Joseph, I will give you something." I had no idea what it would be, till I saw him sit down to write an inscription in a very slim volume. He presented it to me with averted head. It was *The Black Riders*. He had never spoken to me of his verse before. It was while holding the book in my hand that I learned that they were written years before in America. I expressed my appreciation of them that afternoon in the usual half a dozen, or dozen, words which we allowed ourselves when completely pleased with each other's work. When the pleasure was not so complete, the words would be many. And that was a great waste of breath and time. I must confess that we were no critics, I mean temperamentally. Crane was even less of a critic than myself. Criticism is very much a matter of a vocabulary, very consciously used; with us it was the intonation that mattered. The tone of a grunt could convey an infinity of meaning between us.

The articulate literary conscience at our elbow was Edward Garnett. He, of course, was worth listening to. His analytical appreciation (or appreciative analysis) of Crane's art, in the London Academy of 17th December, 1898,[1] goes to the root of the matter with Edward's almost uncanny insight, and a well-balanced sympathy with the blind, pathetic striving of the artist towards a complete realization of his individual gift. How highly Edward Garnett rated Crane's gift is recorded in the conclusions of that admirable and, within the limits of its space, masterly article of some two columns,

[1] Extended and republished in the volume *Friday Nights*. New York: Alfred A. Knopf; 1922.

where at the end are set down such affirmative phrases as: " The chief impressionist of the age . . . Mr. Crane's talent is unique " . . . and where he hails him as " the creator of fresh rhythms and phrases," while the very last words state confidently that: " Undoubtedly, of the young school it is Mr. Crane who is the genius — the others have their talents."

My part here being not that of critic but of private friend, all I will say is that I agreed warmly at the time with that article which from the quoted phrases might be supposed a merely enthusiastic pronouncement, but on reading will be found to be based on that calm sagacity which Edward Garnett, for all his fiery zeal in the cause of letters, could always summon for the judgment of matters emotional — as all response to the various forms of art must be in the main. I had occasion to reread it last year in its expanded form in a collection of literary essays of great, now almost historical, interest in the record of American and English imaginative literature. I found there a passage or two, not bearing precisely on Crane's work but giving a view of his temperament, on which of course his art was based; and of the conditions moral and material under which he had to put forth his creative faculties and his power of steady composition. On those matters, as a man who had the opportunity to look at Crane's life in England, I wish to offer a few remarks before closing my contribution to the memory of my friend.

I do not know that he was ever dunned for money and had to work under a threat of legal proceedings. I don't think he was ever dunned in the sense in which such a phrase is used about a spendthrift unscrupulous in incurring debts. No doubt he was sometimes pressed for money. He lived by his pen, and the prices he obtained were not great. Personally he was not extravagant; and I will not quarrel with him for not choosing to live in a garret. The tenancy of Brede Place was held by him at a nominal rent. That glorious old place was not restored then, and the greatest part of it was uninhabitable. The Cranes had furnished in a modest way six or seven of the least dilapidated rooms, which even then looked bare and half-empty. Certainly there was a horse, and at one time even two, but that luxury was not so very expensive at that time. One man looked after them. Riding was the only exercise open to Crane; and if he did work so hard, surely he was entitled to some relaxation, if only for the preservation of his unique talent.

His greatest extravagance was hospitality, of which I, too, had my share; often in the company, I am sorry to say, of men who after sitting at his board chose to speak of him and of his wife slightingly. Having some rudimentary sense of decency, their behavior while actually under the Cranes' roof often produced on me a disagreeable impression. Once I ventured to say to him: "You are too good-natured, Stephen." He gave me one of his quiet smiles, that seemed to hint so poignantly at the vanity of all things, and after a period of silence remarked: "I am glad those Indians are gone." He was surrounded by men who, secretly envious, hostile to the real quality of his genius (and a little afraid of it), were also in antagonism with the essential fineness of his nature. But enough of them. *Pulvis et umbra sunt.* I mean even those that may be alive yet. They were ever hardly anything else; one would have forgotten them if it were not for the legend (if one may dignify perfidious and contemptible gossip by that name) they created in order to satisfy that same obscure instinct of base humanity, which in the past would often bring against any exceptional man the charge of consorting with the devil. It was just as vague, just as senseless, and in its implications just as lying as the mediæval kind. I have heard one of these " friends " hint before several other Philistines that Crane could not write his tales without getting drunk!

Putting aside the gross palpable stupidity of such a statement — which the creature gave out as an instance of the artistic temperament — I am in a position to disclose what may have been the foundation of this piece of gossip. I have seen repeatedly Crane at work. A small jug of still smaller ale would be brought into the study at about ten o'clock; Crane would pour out some of it into a glass and settle himself at the long table at which he used to write in Brede Place. I would take a book and settle myself at the other end of the same table, with my back to him; and for two hours or so not a sound would be heard in that room. At the end of that time Crane would say suddenly: "I won't do any more now, Joseph." He would have covered three of his large sheets with his regular, legible, perfectly controlled handwriting, with no more than half a dozen erasures — mostly single words — in the whole lot. It seemed to me always a perfect miracle in the way of mastery over material and expression. Most of the ale would be still in the glass, and how flat by that time I don't like to think! The most amusing part was to see Crane, as if moved by some obscure sense of duty, drain the last drop of that untempting remnant before we left the room to stroll to and fro in front of the house while waiting for lunch. Such is the origin of some of these gleeful whispers making up the Crane legend of " unrestrained temperament." I have known various sorts of temperaments — some perfidious and some lying — but " unrestrained temperament " is mere parrot talk. It has no meaning. But it was suggestive. It was founded on Crane's visits to town, during which I more than once met him there. We used to spend afternoons and evenings together and I did not see any of his supposed revels in progress; nor yet have I ever detected any after effects of them on any occasion. Neither have I ever seen anybody who would own to having been a partner in those excesses — if only to the extent of standing by charitably — which would have been a noble part to play. I dare say all those " excesses " amounted to very little more than the one in which he asked me to join him in the following letter. It is the only note I have kept from the very few which we exchanged. The reader will see why it is one of my most carefully preserved possessions.

RAVENSBROOK.
OXTED.
17 March. (1899)

" MY DEAR CONRAD: I am enclosing you a bit of MS. under the supposition that you might like to keep it in remembrance of my warm and endless friendship for you. I am still hoping that you will consent to Stokes' invitation to come to the Savage on Saturday night. Cannot you endure it? Give my affectionate remembrances to Mrs. Conrad and my love to the boy.

Yours always,
STEPHEN CRANE.

P.S. You must accept says Cora — and I — our invitation to come home with me on Sat. night.

I joined him. We had a very amusing time with the Savages. Afterwards Crane refused to go home till the last train. Evidence of what somebody has called his " unrestrained temperament," no doubt. So we went and sat at Gatti's, I believe, unless it was in a Bodega which existed then in that neighborhood, and talked. I have a vivid memory of this awful debauch because it was on that evening that Crane told me of a subject for a story — a very exceptional thing for him to do. He called it "The Predecessor." I could not recall now by what capricious turns and odd associations of thought he reached the enthusiastic conclusion that it would make a good play, and that we must do it together. He wanted me to share in a certain success — "a dead-sure thing," he said. His was an unrestrainedly generous temperament. But let that pass. I must have been specially predisposed, because I caught the infection at once. There and then we began to build up the masterpiece, interrupting each other eagerly, for, I don't know how it was, the air around us had suddenly grown thick with felicitous suggestions. We carried on this collaboration as far as the railway time-table would let us, and then made a break for the last train. Afterwards we did talk of our collaboration now and then, but no attempt at it was ever made. Crane had other stories to write; I was immersed deeply in *Lord Jim*, of which I had to keep up the installments in *Blackwood*; difficulties in presenting the subject on the stage rose one after another before our experience. The general subject consisted in a man personating his "predecessor" (who had died) in the hope of winning a girl's heart. The scenes were to include a ranch at the foot of the Rocky Mountains, I remember, and the action I fear would have been frankly melodramatic. Crane insisted that one of the situations should present the man and the girl on a boundless plain standing by their dead ponies after a furious ride (a truly Crane touch). I made some objections. A boundless plain in the light of a sunset could be got into a back-cloth, I admitted; but I doubted whether we could induce the management of any London theater to deposit two stuffed horses on its stage.

Recalling now those earnestly fantastic discussions it occurs to me that Crane and I must have been unconsciously penetrated by a prophetic sense of the technique and of the very spirit of filmplays, of which even the name was unknown then to the world. But if gifted with prophetic sense we must have been strangely ignorant of ourselves, since it must be obvious to anyone who has read a page of our writings that a collaboration between us two could never come to anything in the end — could never even have been begun. The project was merely the expression of our affection for each other. We were fascinated for a moment by the will-of-the-wisp of close artistic communion. It would in no case have led us into a bog. I flatter myself we both had too much regard for each other's gifts not to be clear-eyed about them. We would not have followed the lure very far. At the same time it cannot be denied that there were profound, if not extensive, similitudes in our temperaments which could create for a moment that fascinating illusion. It is not to be regretted, for it had, at any rate, given us some of the most light-hearted moments in the clear but sober atmosphere of our intimacy. From the force of circumstances there could not be much sunshine in it. " None of them saw the color of the sky! " And alas! it stood already written that it was the younger man who would fail to make a landing through the surf. So I am glad to have that episode to remember, a brotherly serio-comic interlude, played under the shadow of coming events. But I would not have alluded to it at all if it had not come out in the course of my most interesting talk with the author of this biography that Crane had thought it worth while to mention it in his correspondence, whether seriously or humorously, I know not. So here it is without the charm which it had for me but which cannot be reproduced in the mere relation of its outward characteristics: a clear gleam on us two, succeeded by the Spanish-American War into which Crane disappeared like a willful man walking away into the depths of an ominous twilight.

The cloudy afternoon when we two went rushing all over London together was for him the beginning of the end. The problem was to find sixty pounds that day, before the sun set, before dinner, before the "six forty " train to Oxted, at once, that instant — lest peace should be declared and the opportunity of seeing a war be missed. I had not sixty pounds to lend him. Sixty shillings was nearer my mark. We tried various offices but had no luck, or rather we had the usual luck of money-hunting enterprises. The man was either gone out to see about a dog, or would take no interest in the Spanish-American War. In one place the man wanted to know what was the hurry. He would have liked to have forty-eight hours to think the matter over. As we came downstairs Crane's white-faced excitement frightened me. Finally it occurred to me to take him to Messrs.

William Blackwood & Sons' London office. There he was received in a most friendly way. Presently I escorted him to Charing Cross, where he took the train for home with the assurance that he would have the means to start " for the war " next day. That is the reason I cannot to this day read his tale *The Price of the Harness* without a pang. It has done nothing more deadly than pay his debt to Messrs. Blackwood; yet now and then I feel as though that afternoon I had led him by the hand to his doom. But, indeed, I was only the blind agent of the fate that had him in her grip! Nothing could have held him back. He was ready to swim the ocean.

Thirteen years afterwards I made use, half consciously, of the shadow of the primary idea of the " Predecessor," in one of my short tales which were serialized in the *Metropolitan Magazine*. But in that tale the dead man in the background is not a Predecessor but merely an assistant on a lonely plantation; and instead of the ranch, the mountains, and the plains, there is a cloud-capped island, a bird-haunted reef, and the sea. All this the mere distorted shadow of what we two used to talk about in a fantastic mood; but now and then, as I wrote, I had the feeling that he had the right to come and look over my shoulder. But he never came. I received no suggestions from him, subtly conveyed without words. There will never be any collaboration for us now. But I wonder, were he alive, whether he would be pleased with the tale. I don't know. Perhaps not. Or perhaps, after picking up the volume with that detached air I remember so well, and turning over page after page in silence, he would suddenly read aloud a line or two and then, looking straight into my eyes as was his wont on such occasions, say with all the intense earnestness of affection that was in him: " I — like — that, Joseph."

JOSEPH CONRAD

I: *SUNNY BLUE*

THE BIRTH of his fourteenth child so distracted Jonathan Townley Crane, D.D., that a letter went unfinished until the next day, when he neatly changed its date from November 1 to November 2, 1871 and concluded: " I was interrupted yesterday and did not send this to the Post Office. Mrs. Crane sends her regards. The new baby is a boy and we have named him Stephen for his ancestor who signed the Declaration."

This naming of the new baby must have been important in the gentle, elderly man's mind. Master Edmund Crane, aged thirteen, took the letter to the post and tumbled on the steep front steps of 14 Mulberry Place, Newark, New Jersey, dreadfully bruising his knee. So Jonathan Crane wrote, a week later: " Mrs. Crane is still alarmed for Ed's knee which continues painful but the baby is very good and quiet. We have named him Stephen because it is an old name in the Crane family." And the family was old in the State of New Jersey, largely lettered on grants of land and the documents of two wars; there were Cranes in the colony when Anne was Queen of England; the Crane who figured in the Continental Congress had his coat armor painted on the flaps of his saddle-bag. Plainly, the good and quiet baby was named with care.

He was good and quiet and frail. In the spring of 1872 Jonathan Crane halted a sermon in the Central Methodist Church with a blunt statement that Stephen was ill and needed him. There were eight older children living, but Stephen had arrived in this surprising and belated fashion. Sermons and the writing of controversial pamphlets were suspended when Stephen took cold. He took cold with regularity, and his first appearances in the solid society of Mulberry Place were made as an attachment to a monstrous red silk handkerchief which he liked immensely as a plaything and dropped into the aisle of his father's church, cutting the drift of a sermon with wails until somebody brought it back and his parent could go on talking slowly of the necessity of foreign missions and the danger of frivolous amusements to the youth of his sect.

Jonathan Crane came of Presbyterian stock, but it appears that,

as an undergraduate of Princeton, he was disturbed about a point
in Presbyterian dogma: did the souls of unbaptized infants go to
hell? It seemed hardly just. Methodism offered an escape from the
problem and gave his controversial abilities fuller scope. He delighted in argument but argument must be kept within the bounds
of breeding. Once some cruder Christian flung at him in debate:
" Brother Crane never forgets that he is a gentleman! " and Jonathan Crane retorted: " Why should I, sir? "

He wrote a good, severe prose, and some of his ideas remain interesting. He had, like Somerset Maugham, deep doubts as to the
intentions of missionaries. The Word must be spread, but " by all
means the candidates for the post of missionary should be strictly
examined as to their motives in undertaking these duties. We hear
grave reports of some who domineer and oppress these childish
intellects committed to their care and it can not be doubted that
some of our brethren seek to exalt their own station and that some
are more interested to clothe the naked bodies of the heathen than
to enlighten their minds." And he had doubts about the sanctity of
small towns: " I am much more concerned that we should live
truthfully and kindly here than that we should be busy in condemn-
ing the luxuries and sins of New York City." And he had doubts
about the Christian Temperance Union League when four ladies
from Ohio came to consult his wife on the subject in 1873: " Mrs.
Crane is much impressed by this project. I do not think it exactly
practical . . . but they mean very well. Little Stephen has a bad
cold this week."

Stephen had become the pet of the family. Only his mother
could brush the fair, soft hair which curled a little and he was always
shown to callers at the plain brick house. In 1873 young Richard
Watson Gilder brought a Miss Rutherford to see Mrs. Crane, and
Stephen fell in love with the girl. He was discovered as an ornament
of her red skirt when Mr. Gilder was squiring her round the corner
of Market Street. Enchanted by the conquest, she came back the
next day with a toy for the baby, but Stephen sat disdainfully in a
corner and wouldn't look. Whenever Miss Rutherford wore red,
though, he was hers completely.

The family taught him his letters and he showed a bright interest
in the career of his biggest brother, Jonathan Townley Crane, Jun-

ior, cub reporter of the *Newark Advertiser*. Mrs. Crane was the domestic dictionary and Townley would ask her how to spell adjectives of his articles. The baby attended the process and becomes a personage with his first recorded question. He was making symbols on a piece of paper in good imitation of the journalist and lifted up his voice to ask: " Ma, how do you spell O? "

In 1874 Dr. Crane's time at the church in Newark was up; the family moved to Bloomington on the Raritan across from Bound Brook, and Stephen was held on a white horse which he remembered twenty years later as a savage beast. But it was no part of Mrs. Crane's theory that a child of hers should be afraid of anything. He was told to stay on the horse and not to be scared. Somebody threw a ball of hard rubber too swiftly into his delicate hands with thin bones; Mrs. Crane wiped his sapphire eyes and told him that he mustn't cry. She took him to the religious frolics at Ocean Grove, where he saw the waves from the beach and had an atrocious dream of black riders on black horses charging at him from the long surf up the shore and so woke screaming, night after night. But, always, he must not cry.

His brothers took him to bathe in the Raritan from a sandbar that jutted into the clear river near the house, although both Miss Frances Willard and Anthony Comstock had lately assured the world that it was a disgusting and unchristian thing for any boy to be seen in an undressed condition outside his own home. However, he was taken to swim in spite of the joint edict, and his brothers were delighted by his ambition. He was left paddling in the shallows, but he wouldn't stay there. He must get out where Will or Ed was splashing and somebody would fish him out just as his head disappeared. Stevie came up strangling but not afraid. He missed the river, it seems, when the Cranes spent a year in Paterson, and made a manful effort to climb down into the Hudson from a pier of Jersey City when his father was preaching there in 1877. The straggling port and a return to Paterson disagreed with him and there is a legend that some doctor advised Jonathan Crane to find duties in high air. So in 1879 the man of sixty left his native state and took charge of Methodism in Port Jervis, over the border.

Port Jervis was then a pretty town, splashed in white houses about the hills that were making northwestern New York known

as a game-preserve. Stephen improved and could be sent to school
on his eighth birthday. He could read and write and was already
learned in the moral adventures of Goody Twoshoes. The school at
once annoyed him. Here he was debased and hemmed in by a pack
of infants aged five and six. Humiliation dragged him forward and
" they tell me that I got through two grades in six weeks which
sounds like the lie of a fond mother at a teaparty but I do remember
that I got ahead very fast and that father was pleased with me. He
used to take me driving with him to little places near Port Jervis
where he was going to preach or bury somebody. Once we got
mixed up in an Irish funeral near a place named Slate Hill. Everybody was drunk and father was scandalized. . . . He was so simple
and good that I often think he didn't know much of anything about
humanity. Will, one of my brothers, gave me a toy gun and I tried
to shoot a cow with it over at Middletown when father was preaching there and that upset him wonderfully. He liked all kinds of animals and never drove a horse faster than two yards an hour even if
some Christian was dying elsewhere. But it is a big job to be presiding elder in a Methodist Conference. He worked himself to death,
my people thought."

Jonathan Crane had worked long and hard. He had once been
president of the Pennington Seminary and was fond of boys, who,
he said, " should be handled with great kindness and care as they
have often notions about justice in conduct far beyond their years."
So he was much distressed when a lad named nothing less than
Samuel Weller wrote from Newark to say that he had been discharged from the shop of a good Methodist for denying hell. The
old man took his daughter Agnes down to Newark and hunted other
work for Samuel Weller, caught cold on the way back to Port Jervis, and died suddenly, having preached the day before.

He died and terror closed on his last child. People came from
everywhere to lament Jonathan Crane. Some country wife stood in
the kitchen and sang long hymns. Townley and George and Will
and Edmund were in black clothes; his mother sat in the darkened
parlor surrounded by whispering women and, somehow, one of
Stephen's hands brushed the cold silver handle of the coffin; the
full horror of Christian death smashed on the lank child's consciousness. " We tell kids that heaven is just across the gaping grave

and all that bosh and then we scare them to glue with flowers and white sheets and hymns. We ought to be crucified for it! . . . I have forgotten nothing about this, not a damned iota, not a shred."

There followed penitential confusions. Mrs. Crane lived for some months in Roseville, outside Newark, and Stephen endured scarlet fever in a boarding-house, but his mother had learned to like Port Jervis, and Stephen had been well there. So he was brought back to the hills and played games patterned on *Black Dick of the Pony Express* and *The Terror of the Sagebrush* with other children. It was a good time — " a bully time " — afterwards. He could make up a game more quickly than the rest of the gang, and brother Edmund gave him a quarter to get his long curls cropped, against Mrs. Crane's orders. She made for him mittens of the brightest red and he had red-topped boots in winter when snow thickened on the paths after sumach's bloody flare had died from the hills. He was very well and happy. Wind whipped up color in his pointed face, and his mother let him go racing in the wake of grown men whose heels rang sharply on frozen earth, running past the house toward the wild glow of fires that reddened the whole night.

2

THE TACTFUL Matthew Arnold, on pilgrimage among us in 1883, told William Forester that Americans should get done with the Civil War as a topic; it was a bore. The surgeon answered: " But so many of us fought in it." The critic playfully retorted: " That's no excuse. War is seldom fruitful or important." He then gave Dr. Forester a signed copy of his note on the translation of Homer's *Iliad*, a poem dealing with the siege of Troy, and went somewhere else. As he recedes in the Victorian mist, it sometimes seems that Matthew Arnold was singularly obtuse, for war happens to be a department of æsthetic available, as is religion, to everybody.

The Civil War ceased physically in 1865 and its political end may be reasonably expected about the year 3000. As heroic legend its history has been curious and remains unwritten because of that spiritual censorship which strictly forbids the telling of truth about any American record until the material of such an essay is scattered and gone. How did the men who scorched their youth and scarred their

bodies think of those four years, before the easy sentiment of senility clouded down? One knows that in 1868 General Custer's wife
noted: " My husband's troopers seem to have absolutely no unkind
feeling toward the Secessionists at all and they never talk about
their triumphs and exploits. They are always teasing each other
about how badly they fought and how many times they ran away.
It is distressing to see and hear how little exalted their views are."
And one knows that in 1869 at a banquet of the Grand Army a man
lifted his glass and toasted: " Everyone that ran at Shiloh, like I
did! "

The distress of Mrs. Custer and the boredom of Matthew Arnold
meet to supply a conjecture. The war did become a bore to foreigners and literary critics and the common man's attitude toward
the myth of a pure, courageous host bent on the Lord's work was
truly shocking. The swift cynicism of the American which is the
basis of our popular thought rounded promptly on romantic views
of the Rebellion. Duval, the leading ballad singer of New York was
hissed from the stage in June of 1865 when he tried to please an
audience speckled with soldiers by chanting: *Home Have Come
Our Boys in Blue.* The gunbearing animals shouted: " Dry up! "
and " Sing something funny! " A pamphlet without signature was
issued in Philadelphia before 1866 began and, along with a wholly
accurate account of the war's two last months, buyers were invited
to believe that General Grant told masculine stories to his staff and
that General Sheridan drank whisky before all men out of a silver
flask. Both rumors have unofficially persisted to this day. There were
songs current attributing mistresses to the popular Northern generals, doubtless due to an adolescent habit of making heroes in all
things strenuous, and a New York publisher found that John Esten
Cooke's frankly Southern novels, *Surry of Eagle's Nest* and *Mohun*
sold most readily in the North although Cooke had not one flattering word to say of the Union forces, and the Virginian himself
wrote that " I am surprised by the number of handsome letters
that come to hand from former soldiers of the enemy."

The war left almost nothing printed that the literate peasants and
clerks who fought would recognize as the truth of their acts. In
Cooke's *Mohun* one finds a rather vivid picture of collapsing Richmond with its intrigues, its profiteers, and its frantic pleasures, but

the mind of the Virginian gentleman, trained on Lever and Dickens, shrank from the detail of the battlefield, and his tales merely build a Pantheon for the South with central niches rightly reserved to the figures of Lee and Stonewall Jackson. He was honest and not too extravagant, but he was no realist. There is no Northern fiction worth a glance, and narrative reminiscences such as Warren Goss's *Recollections of a Private* were rare. Goss, the best of the narrators, was remorselessly pruned by his publisher even though his book succeeded among boys and soldiers on the ground of its frankness.

The realists sat on fences and the steps of stores in the sprawled depth of the nation and made a topic of the war when political campaigns and labor held no thrill. They might be flogged by acute orators into the ready ferocity of election days and Grand Army rallies, but in 1870 James Russell Lowell found that stories of the battle-line " obscene and horrible " were being told before young boys by the commonplace veterans of Cambridge, Massachusetts, and it is pretty evident that the realists on shady corners preferred war in form. A lad growing up in Ohio saw two men not yet middle-aged come to blows about the rightful ownership of a pair of boots lost in the baking trenches before Vicksburg, and a queerly sensitive child in upper New York may have heard and seen equal ironies. " An American," the sulphurous John Skidmore wrote in 1880, " has only three subjects — his work, the Rebellion and women. Owing to our freedom of speech he can only talk about the first subject in the company of ladies and Mr. Lowell is right in saying that our national conversation is dull as the ladies are most averse to hearing anything truthful about the war." The realists, one imagines, were restricted to the fence and the cornfield. But in 1883 a Miss Olive Brett came upon Stephen Crane digging her small nephew from the sands at Ocean Grove and was told that Johnny was a corpse foolishly planted by the burial squad while he still had a canteen full of whisky on him and that Stephen was his provident comrade retrieving supplies. This is not a child's fancy of battle; Stephen had been listening to some realist; Miss Brett was properly horrified and directly spanked him.

Now, Stephen's brother William is remembered by men who knew him as an undergraduate at Wesleyan as an expert in the strategy of Chancellorsville and Gettysburg. His brother Edmund

yearly gave the boy volume after volume of Harry Castleman's
"Frank" series. There were *Frank on a Gunboat* and *Frank on
the Red River* and *Frank at Mobile Bay* — unpretentious and
straightforward tales about a boy in the war written, apparently,
for boys. There is no known biography of Harry Castleman, but
this oddity makes him interesting. Stephen adored these works.
Mrs. Crane let him look at the monstrous flat tomes of the Harper's
history of the Rebellion with their crude and romantic pictures,
and on rainy days, when the pictures palled, he poured all the buttons from his mother's store into battalions and regiments that
marched and countermarched about his bony knees in an endless
conflict, incomprehensible to the family. It was a private war.

There were other books, of course. When he was ten his sister
Agnes gave him *Sir Wilfrid's Seven Flights*, a thing printed for
children by the moral Routledge, but certainly the least moral book
ever issued by his house with that aim, as the hero is a rake and all
his adventures end in some frustrated scene. Sir Wilfrid sees El
Dorado buried in its own golden sand and flings back the gift of
eternal wisdom rather than live forever with the revived Rhodope
in her kingdom beneath the pyramids. Stephen liked it and a paragraph of the stiff, ornate prose Tom Hood claimed to have written
came to the surface of his thought eighteen years later. *Sir Wilfrid's Seven Flights* must have affected him badly; in the summer
of 1882 the kind Miss Brett tried to read him *A Christmas Carol*
by Charles Dickens and Stephen went to sleep.

In 1883 Mrs. Crane moved to a small house in Asbury Park,
New Jersey. Asbury Park was advertised widely in the nation as a
resort quite free from sin, but there was some mistake about that
since Stephen was riding the retired circus pony his brother Townley had found for him along a road behind the seaside town in
May of 1884 and he saw a white girl stabbed by her Negro lover
on the edge of a roadmaker's camp. He galloped the pony home
and said nothing to Mrs. Crane although he was sweating with
fright.

A strain of secrecy had developed in the slim boy or he knew
that his mother's health was failing. Mary Crane had passed sixty
now, and no longer insisted that Stephen must be brave. She worried in the other extreme and told friends: "Stevie is like the

wind in Scripture. He bloweth whither he listeth." He rode the pony into the ocean, to the admiration of other children, and clung to its bare back while it did tricks. He also pulled a somewhat older boy, Wallis McHarg, out of the surf and then told Wallis he would punch his jaw if the rescued dared to tell Mrs. Crane they had been swimming on Sunday.

" My mother was a very religious woman but I don't think that she was as narrow as most of her friends or her family — " She was Mary Helen Peck, the child and sister of famous Methodist preachers; " My brothers tell me that she got herself into trouble before I was old enough to follow proceedings by taking care of a girl who had an accidental baby. Inopportune babies are not part of Methodist ritual but mother was always more of a Christian than a Methodist and she kept this girl at our house in Asbury until she found a home somewhere. Mother's friends were mostly women and they had the famous feminine aversion to that kind of baby. It is funny that women's interest in babies trickles clean off the mat if they have never met papa socially. . . . After my father died, mother lived in and for religion. We had very little money. Mother wrote articles for Methodist papers and reported for the [New York] Tribune and the [Philadelphia] Press. Every August she went down to Ocean Grove and reported proceedings at the Methodist holy show there. . . . My brother Will used to try to argue with her on religious subjects such as hell but he always gave it up. Don't understand that mother was bitter or mean but it hurt her that any of us should be slipping from Grace and giving up eternal damnation or salvation or those things. You could argue just as well with a wave. . . . She was always starting off when she felt well enough to some big prayer meeting or experience meeting and she spoke very well. Her voice was something like Ellen Terry's but deeper. She spoke as slowly as a big clock ticks and her effects were impromptu. . . . It is in me to think that she did some good work for the public schools. One of my sisters was a teacher and mother tried for years to get women placed on the school boards and to see that whisky was not sold to boys under age. . . . I used to like church and prayer meetings when I was a kid but that cooled off and when I was thirteen or about that, my brother Will told me not to believe in Hell after my uncle had been boring me about the lake of fire and the rest of the side-shows. . . . Once when I was fourteen an organ grinder on the beach at Asbury gave me a nice long drink out of a nice red bottle for picking up his hat for him. I felt ecstatic walking home and then I was an Emperor and some Rajahs and Baron de Blowitz all at the same time. I had been sulky all morning and now I was perfectly willing to go to a prayer meeting and Mother was tickled to death. And, mind you, all because this nefarious Florentine gave me a red drink out of a bottle. I have frequently wondered how much mothers ever know about their sons, after all. She would not have found it much of a joke. . . ."

She was a woman of intense pride. She had been educated more thoroughly than were most American girls of her period, and her dignity on the platform of meetings is remembered. Her last years were stimulated by a project: the sale of alcohol to children in New Jersey had become a scandal and she proposed to stop it. It seems that her work was effective and that the women of other sects admired her. She has been somewhat wildly described as a religious maniac, but what is known of her shows a fine mind trained in a formula.

But the child of her age was to have everything and be every-thing. She worried over him when he had troubles with algebra at school and his brilliance in other studies delighted her. For he was brilliant; the sensitive brain absorbed and recorded swiftly; he seemed to learn without effort and his memory of words was prodigious. A boy of fourteen who can use *irascible, pyrotechnic, impartial,* and *memorial* correctly in an impromptu essay written for a prize of a quarter between two hot games of baseball is not as other American boys of fourteen. He had a passion for outland-ish words and even invented one, a verb, *higgle.* It appears that to higgle is to behave in the manner of a school-teacher. . . .

Baseball was now more important than verbs. The game had crystallized by advertisement and professional playing into the na-tional sport and nuisance. Stephen's thin fingers began to thicken at the knuckles. Being fifteen he wrote to Wallis McHarg that he was going to be a professional ball-player. " But ma says it's not a serious occupation and Will says I have to go to college first." Wallis, aged sixteen, was sympathetic but wrote from Chicago that

Stephen had better go to college. There was an alternative measure. Why should not Wallis and Stephen enlist in the army? That would end all difficulties with mothers and so forth. But baseball had driven out war from Stephen's imagination and he hung about taller boys playing on the beach and endured the fate of umpires willingly if he might be let in for an inning. Before he was sent off to boarding-school he had a sort of small fame in Asbury Park and thereabouts: no one could pitch a ball that he would not catch barehanded.

Baseball made him eminent in the Hudson River Institute at Claverack, New York. He arrived there in February of 1887 with six pipes which he smoked with some uneasiness and several volumes of Harry Castleman's romances. The school was in high repute at the time and was semi-military, but, curiously, the child who had once been fascinated by the image of war could not drill well. He had turned into a wiry lad whose mouth rose at the corners in a charming, remembered grin when he was amused. Some of the boys thought him sullen because he seldom talked, but baseball answered for the social defect and there was enough muscle on his long arms to get him safely through an immense fight in the spring of 1888. The fight began with Stephen's assertion that Lord Tennyson's poems were " swill." He lost a bit of a front tooth in making good his opinion.

His schooldays were to stay in mind with fragrance although " I never learned anything there. American private schools are not as bad as our public schools, perhaps, but there is no great difference. I tried to learn French because my mother thought it important but no foreign language will ever be my friend. . . . But heaven was sunny blue and no rain fell on the diamond when I was playing baseball. I was very happy, there."

The summer of 1888 was happy with a new excitement. He went to work for his brother Townley, collecting items for Townley's press bureau at Asbury Park. The Jersey shore was populous now, and fresh colonies sprang up along the endless beach. So a calamitous bicycle replaced the pony and Stephen plowed along hot roads, hunting news of arrivals and departures and the small excitements of clambakes and sailing parties. A matron from Elizabeth was told then that " our papers " would be glad to know how long she was stopping at Avon-by-the-Sea and the *Philadelphia Press* accepted half a column on the history of a traveled merry-go-round which had come all the way from San Francisco to please the children of Asbury Park. The half-column contains seven split infinitives. No earthly criticism could or ever did make Stephen Crane respect an infinitive. But he was now a reporter and the boys at Claverack were impressed by accounts of a gloveless prizefight seen secretly in a barn behind Atlantic City.

He met odd people; he saw, in the riff-raff of cheap entertainers and idlers, those amazing types who are still so feebly represented in American fiction, the attendants on shooting-galleries and carrousels, the mercenary pilgrims of a tiny circus that broke up at Asbury. Stephen begged five dollars from his mother to start a lost cowboy back to Wyoming and the man gave him a real revolver alleged to have slain six Indians. A private education was in progress; it became plain that the world was a wide place filled with creatures who didn't conform to the rules prescribed for boys. And a Canadian lady, nameless in the record, gave him a paper-bound copy of Count Tolstoi's *Sevastopol*.

In February of 1890 a young civil engineer, Porter Cheney, was convalescent after typhoid in the house of a relative at Easton, Pennsylvania, where Lafayette College supplied what excitement there was. Cheney spent his afternoons in a poolroom behind a tobacco-store and a lean, fair boy played pool very badly against him while they talked about camping trips in the New York hills and about books. Cheney took his companion for some remarkable lounger who had no duties anywhere. At times the boy fell abstracted and stood trying to balance a cue on the small tip of his arched nose, without much success. He burned cigarettes between the fingers of his left hand, seldom putting them to his mouth, and asserted that Count Tolstoi was the world's foremost writer. There was a lesser fellow named Flaubert who had written a novel much too long called *Salammbô*. We are annually told that *Salammbô* is a firework which failed to explode, but one wonders if that failure was complete. Those catalogues of jewels, tribes, gods, and those terminal paragraphs in which the view is switched so swiftly from one shape to a thousand, from death to a setting sun or the sound of something far away? If imitation is flattery, the dead

firework has been flattered. Well, he had read *Salammbô* and did
not think very well of the Carthaginian Princess, but this was better writing than the English could do. No, he didn't like Robert
Louis Stevenson and he didn't know anything about Henry James.
The engineer was impressed, somehow, and described this lad to
his sister in several letters. The faculty of Lafayette remembered
Stephen as a tow-headed, pleasant boy who preferred boxing to
study. Stephen took home the pin of a fraternity, Delta Upsilon,
and in June of 1890 captained a mixed team of lads and grown
men against a like team from Atlantic City. The score was 9 to 0
in Stephen's favor.

Summer of 1890 held other significant details in American civilization. Anthony Comstock, agent of the Society for the Suppression of Vice, invaded the shop of Eugene Caret, a new art-dealer
on Broadway, and bade him take from a show-window the photograph of a statue by Rodin. Monsieur Caret was so scared that he
sold his stock and retired from New York City by the next liner.
He was later bewildered to hear that the Metropolitan Museum
had bought a copy of *L'Age d'Airan* and that it was public to any
stare, without a figleaf, in the main court of the Museum. In July
Miss Frances Willard committed written mayhem on the person
of Richard Watson Gilder for allowing the word " rape " to be
printed in the *Century* because a magazine meant to be read by
" Christian women " had no right to soil their eyes with such im-
mundicities. Mr. Gilder carefully assured the great reformer that
the American public was not wholly composed of susceptible
Christian women, but he got back no answer. Frances Willard had
spoken and that was enough. In August the editor of the *Atlantic
Monthly* informed a young man in Topeka, Kansas, that " New
York has now become the capital of art and letters in the United
States." The issue of *Scribner's* for August contained " A Walk
Up the Avenue " by Richard Harding Davis, already known as the
author of *Gallagher*. Herewith Davis mounted into celebrity as
gracefully as he might have swung his fine body in its handsome
dress to the cushions of a waiting cab. He rode, a figure of pleasant
sophistication and fresh good humor, among passengers who lacked
those qualities precisely, and boys laboring with manuscript looked
up and saw a star.

Townley Crane got for Stephen the post of correspondent to the *New York Tribune* in the town of Syracuse, and Syracuse University was pleasant enough after Mrs. Crane consented to a change from engineering to " belles-lettres." Stephen wanted to be a writer and his mother was willing. He must be good and always independent, always honest. She wrote these orders in one of her last letters. There was little left for Mary Crane but a trip to a congress of women in Boston, a few days of illness, and a painless end in a hospital. Stephen would make for her kindness a small monument and would miss her silently.

He lounged at Syracuse in the back room of a restaurant and other freshmen were impressed by a classmate who sold sketches to the *Detroit Free Press* and who assured them that the police court was the most interesting place in Syracuse. He got notice from the faculty by telling a professor that he disagreed with Saint Paul's theory of sin and seriously shocked the wife of another authority by declining to meet Miss Frances Willard at her house for the reason that he thought Miss Willard a fool. A boy who had no reverence for sacred characters must have been notable in a Methodist university, and spring made him famous. The baseball team had never had such a shortstop and, after a vehement argument, never so young a captain. It is legendary that he was offered a place on a great professional team, but it is certain that his friends all knew Crane was going to be a writer. Writing, he said, over coffee and cigarettes in the restaurant, was a business like any other. One trained one's mind to observe and a man should be able to say something " worth while " about any event. American writers were not " sincere " and American magazines were " no good." As for college, it was a darned nuisance and he was glad to be done with all things academic in June of 1891.

II: *ROMANTIC MOVEMENTS*

THERE was an old house on Twelfth Street which belonged, in 1891, to a rowdy Italian merchant who had adorned its big spaces to please an Irish dancer, and the union of such talent had produced a wonderful, gay result of gilded chairs and flaming tapestries in a drawing-room that glowed, by night, under the jets of a monstrous chandelier. The flag of Ireland was effected in colored tiles above the fireplace, and elsewhere the house was quite as remarkable. But in September of 1891 this polychromatic paradise was rented to an invalid lady whose companion was an unsuccessful contralto, trained in Europe, a tall darkly pretty girl named Helen Trent.

Miss Trent left Avon, New Jersey, in the first week of September and came to rejoin the ailing Mrs. Potter. She found waiting a telegram from Avon: Stephen Crane was sorry that he had not seen Miss Trent to say good-by. Miss Trent had an idea that this might be a silent boy who played baseball on the beach at Avon, but she knew nothing of him and was busy, nursing her friend's asthma and slowly packing for a journey to Switzerland. Then on the 10th a servant brought word that Mr. Crane was calling and she went down to find a fair, untidy youth in black clothes, whose eyes seemed brown in the glory of the chandelier.

She thought him handsome, shy, and dull. The call went on for warm, indifferent hours while she tried to talk and he stared. Then he startled her. Had she seen Hamlin Garland, the new writer from the West, while he lectured at Avon? [1] She had not, but she asked what the Westerner looked like.

" Oh," Crane said, " like a nice Jesus Christ."

This was not in the conversational area of the year 1891. The next morning Miss Trent had from Crane a letter of a dozen sheets, written at the old Fifth Avenue Hôtel. He was suddenly informative; his brother Will had a baby named Helen; he was a reporter, himself; what was Miss Trent's favorite color? Did she like flowers and was she fond of dogs? He came, that night, to have these impor-

[1] See *A Son of the Middle Border*.

tant questions answered and kept coming, as the girl was pleased by his slow talk of camping trips in Sullivan County and of curious people met on the Jersey coast. Then, one evening, he brought a terribly bruised and plastered eye. He had been sitting in a saloon of the Bowery and a thrown bottle had landed on him. The accident did not amuse Miss Trent and she at once retired into the attitude of girls who find themselves comfortably older than admiring boys. Crane had already revealed some shocking opinions: a Negro could be handsome, even without the " classic profile " demanded by a world soaked in the art of Leighton and Poynter; American religion was " mildewed "; he found Buddhism interesting; he saw no reason why a young actress with a cottage at Avon couldn't go swimming at dawn, when the beach was empty, without a bathsuit. Miss Trent took the emphatic posture of American gentlewomen and forbade him to go near the Bowery. She had sung in charitable concerts there and it was a slum as vile as anything in Paris or Munich. It was not " nice " of Crane to go there. (The middle-aged lady who then was Helen Trent recalls her use of the word.) She spoke until Crane's lean body reared in his chair and he exploded with: " Hully gee! " The Bowery was the only interesting place in New York. Nobody had written anything " sincere " about its people. He was going to write a book some time soon about the Bowery and it was going to be a sincere book and he must see how these people lived and what they thought. Miss Trent broke in with protests. She was, for the hour, the composite portrait of all well-bred young women who have tried to explain proper art and letters to American artists. Why must he write any such book? Who wanted to read about such people? That Ferdinand Brunetière had lately stated: " The first temple of the young creative mind is the abyss " was not within her knowledge, nor within Crane's. So they wrangled unhappily and Crane walked out of the house, at last, leaving the word *hypocrite* in air. But he mailed a note, dated from the ferry to Jersey City: " I shall come back tomorrow night and we can start all over again. Yours sincerely, Stephen Crane."

So they argued and she sat playing Chopin for him at the black piano while he leaned on its side and sometimes hummed a barytone accompaniment to the wild bars. . . . He was enmeshed, one may guess, in an adventure that fell as fantastic on the mind of nineteen years spent in the lazy pleasantness of small towns and the placid medley of Asbury Park's crowded summer. The music pealed and chanted in this gaudy chamber where " great folds of lace swept down in orderly cascades . . . the colossal chandelier, gleaming like a Siamese head-dress . . . caught subtle flashes from the gilt and tempestuous silk." He had. seen handsome rooms, of course, in Newark and in Syracuse, but he had never seen Latin profusion joined to Celtic vulgarity with a lovely girl in the pooled lights and colors, singing songs in the French that he could not read or understand. He was not unconscious, though, of the theatrical base in all this, for when she took him up to her guardian's boudoir of shrieking velvets and enamels, he asked: " When will the stage hands take it away? "

There seemed to be no cause for mention of her betrothed young surgeon, studying at Guy's Hospital in London, and Miss Trent was not wearing an engagement ring while she drove with Crane in the warm night through Central Park or when he took her to a play at Wallack's Theater. They did not talk of books after a quarrel on the merits of Robert Louis Stevenson, but she sewed a button on his coat and tried to make him brush the fair, limp hair back from the width of his forehead and he lighted her cigarettes although he did not then approve of these for a lady. He was hoping for a place on the *Herald* and day after day he came to town and night after night he lounged on the piano, hearing the music of Chopin.

LAKEVIEW, N. J.
September 18, '91.

Dear Miss Trent:
I have found out something that you should know at once and will be up this evening to tell you.

Yours, S. C.

He came in solemnly excited. Did her guardian know that this house belonged to the very evil Mr. X and that the Italian had furnished it for a " person "? Well, Mrs. Potter should take her away at once; people might not understand that the house was merely rented. . . . Miss Trent woke up, honestly surprised and touched, with a lover on her hands. She thanked Crane and sent him away and next evening she was not at home. But the morning mail brought an undated scrawl on a leaf from a yellow notebook:

" Your window was lighted all last night but they said you were not in. I stood and looked at your window until a policeman came and made me go away. But I came back and looked until my head was just a sponge of lights.' Please do not treat me like this. Nothing else counts but that."

It frightened her. He came on the evening of September 20th while she was dressing to dine with friends in Sixtieth Street. Rain had fallen and Crane went out to find a hansom, then drove with her up the long channel of Fifth Avenue where white stone just patched the solid face of dim, chocolate buildings that rose above a pavement always blue under the lamps that sent, perhaps, jogging pulses of light on her bare arms. She remembers him quite silent as the hansom moved and when she came home late at night, he had left another note:

" You have the most beautiful arms I ever saw. You never should have to wear dresses with sleeves. If I could keep your arms nothing else would count. It would not matter if there was nothing else to hope for in the world or if there was no more world. In dreams, don't you ever fall and fall but not be afraid of anything because somebody safe is with you? I shall be here tomorrow. I must get back to Ed's house, now."

So he went off on the dreary trip to his brother Edmund's house at Lakeview, outside Paterson, where he was teaching lads of the neighborhood to play tearing football on Saturdays and writing furiously through nights in an attic turned to a study for his use. He came back, on September 21st, and Miss Trent strolled nervously into the florid drawing-room to tell him that she was to be married in London, soon. Crane gave a quick gasp and lifted both hands to his face. Then he spun and walked out of the house, permanently. In January of 1900, when an Englishman pointed out the celebrated Stephen Crane, she saw him across the flare of a London theater without knowing why he was celebrated. But in *The Black Riders*, on the eleventh page:

"Should the wide world roll away,
Leaving black terror,
Limitless night,
Nor God, nor man, nor place to stand,
Would be to me essential,
If thou and thy white arms were there,
And the fall to doom a long way."

2

Another romantic movement had accomplished itself while Crane grew up. Three days before he was born, sheriffs came to the house of William Marcy Tweed, in New York, and tenderly put under arrest the tall, obese stevedore who had stolen from the city one hundred and fifty million dollars. His fall was largely the act of a disgusted Irish gambler, and gelatinous grandees of New York sat in some confusion while the trial was forced along by a young Yankee lawyer. Many of the city's foremost men had privately done Tweed's bidding and had publicly shaken his gouty fingers while he lolled in his carriage at the curb of Wall Street. But Tweed's fall advertised radiantly the wealth and rascality of the plundered town's ruling strata, and tiny journals inland printed with due exaggeration the list of his pleasures and palaces. The tawdry seaport was suddenly Babylon in the mouths of rural preachers, and dealers in pornography now shifted the scene of revels from Boston or Philadelphia to New York. The city's population swelled between 1871 and 1873 by a hundred thousand and of this earned increment it was known that hundreds were people of means who now gazed in real awe at the stiff, timid native aristocrats. New York took on, in the nation's eye, the combined aspect of an eating-house and a gilded lupanar irresistible to the peasant mind. There followed a gradual welding of the parochial rich with a fresh plutocracy ready to outdo the pomps of the first Belmont, and soon the child of this match was a glittering amalgam which, toward 1890, complied with the custom of all adolescents and fell in love with itself.

Metropolitan society of the nineteenth century's last decade had a color of compound paradox. It was metropolitan only in location; it viewed with amazing disdain the aristocracies of other cities and instead of drawing in their wealth and fashion it ignored them. It was plainly a society of capital for it permitted family after family once eminent to sink from its midst unable to endure the monetary strain of entertainment. Yet it clung with ferocity to Washington Irving's pleasant myth of a Knickerbocker lordship while the descendants of the real patroons quietly took themselves elsewhere or fell into humdrum obscurity as the high world became a grocer's window filled with quarrelsome fruit. Money talked so loudly that small satirists of *Puck* and *Life* were not deceived by the grand gesticulations of the aged Ward McAllister and the younger Berry Wall. The man in the street knew that descent had the least possible part in this feckless, handsome show. But the whole movement was ruled by a sickly æstheticism: these vulgarians went laboring and stumbling after a dim ideal. They hunted grace.

This grace was altogether external and pictorial. A movement somewhat similar was afoot in France and England, the available models, where capitalism wooed a real aristocracy and wedded it effectively with all the blessings of journalism on the tinseled bed. In meek rapture from afar the ruling women of New York could observe the impatient gayeties of the Prince of Wales and might imitate with feeble discretion the balls of Madame de Sagan. " Anglomania " was nothing more than a rather wavering effort to improve the American picture. Now antiquaries found a market for chairs of stale oak and tapestries that might be Gobelins were carted to new country houses — some of which, strangely, were discovered to have long been owned by their possessors. Meanwhile gold service flashed at dinners given to successive French painters who pronounced American women the loveliest of earth. In 1896 it was seen with delight that eighty ladies appeared crowned with jewels in the boxes of the Opera and in 1897 one of them offered to remit the rents of certain cottagers beside her park on Long Island if they would let her replace the tin of roofs with English thatch. But the American winds blew the thatch away. . . .

Men were seldom powerful in this scented herd, but there did tower one commanding female shape. Documents well display the alert and vigorous Caroline, wife and then widow of William Astor, a woman truly charitable who could conceive a gay and

liberal grouping of her allies. She so far ruled the manifold fluc-
tuations of her tribe that when old McAllister mentioned " our
social leader " housewives of the midlands knew just who was
meant. If rivals did not concede that she was absolute, the baser
world did, and she addressed herself in the third person to editors
of newspapers. It was reported that she was subtle, wise in the mysteries of arts and crafts, and it is true that she would verbally singe
a committee for the stupid adornment of a public hall, but she
would not permit the same committee to consult John La Farge
because the colorist was a " professional painter." She liked to
laugh, but she made known her surprise that her son should go to
dine with Mark Twain. She was an admirer of Ouida and read
Moths five times, so she must have been literate, yet, hearing that
Miss Alice Duer had begun to publish poems, she cried: " But the
girl's not at all plain! " and seated in London beside Harold
Frederic she found the novelist amusing, so was moved to ask who
were his friends.

" Mostly writers and artists."

" Indeed," said Mrs. Astor, after a musing period, " that must
be very strange! "

She lived on until she could be described in a popular romance
as an old, old lady drowsing on a golden throne, but when she died
and appraisers were busy with her goods, an astonished public read
that the chairs of her ballroom might have been owned by anyone
and that the carpet of her famous, dreaded staircase, threadbare
and faded, had no more a value.

If all critical elements are carefully shorn from a society by the
will of its rulers, it can remain comfortably in love with its own
flesh, and it did. The smart world of New York's great decade
failed to discover in the patronage of its superiors the last flavor of
aristocratic contempt. In those bright rooms, agitated for weeks
by the assertion, without exhibition, of fresh rosebuds pinned to
the garters of young beauty, where were hung pictures by Rem-
brandt alongside the trash of Marcus Stone and Debat-Ponsin, the
native artists, the native critics had no place. It was understood
that they existed, probably somewhere in the shadowy void where
vague hordes were known to be crying out for the abolition of wine,
wealth, and unwedded love. But a great lady phrased the objection

of her group quite neatly in 1897 to a traveling Briton: " On the whole, Sir William, don't you think that reformers and writers always make things unpleasant? " And a little later William Dean Howells was driven to muse: " It sometimes seems to me that the wealthy class of New York fights shy of the writer and artist just as a schoolboy is timid before an older man. This was not true of Boston. Mrs. James Fields and a dozen other intelligent women were more than hospitable. . . . A young writer in New York may be given tea and a bun by his publisher's wife but the city is not hospitable to talents unless they come from Europe. Nor is the European artist always welcome. . . . You asked me last year what the rich New Yorker reads. He reads the newspapers." Precisely. If the Narcissus read anything, it read the newspapers, and its whole notion of things came from that unsubstantial, flashy medium. The paradox was perfect: a society bragged of its isolate refinement, and its ideas were those of the street. So in 1903 an acidulous Russian Ambassador noted that New York's high world was " *une servante qui porte assez gauchement les robes de sa dame* " and the same Count Cassini also wrote that the matrons of the city had not heard of the printing press save as an instrument to list " their stupid names."

Who doubts that such an attitude was profoundly influential? The wealthy class of the nation's largest city was a natural mark for imitation. The capital of arts and letters had no welcome for the artist, native or foreign, unless he had been stamped by the press, its guide, as an eminence. He was permitted to exist upon such terms as he could make with his environment, and a realm of cheap lodgings, cheap restaurants, and cheap journals lay ready to provide that environment unless he had cash in pocket to keep him elsewhere. For another romantic movement was afoot: the romance of journalism as the school of letters was well established now, and the delusion brought boys scurrying to the offices of the New York papers in droves. Had not Richard Harding Davis, Julian Ralph, Edward Townsend, and, more brilliantly still, Rudyard Kipling emerged from that battering apprenticeship? So journalism took hold of the national fiction and for a decade fiercely attuned it to the key of commonplace perceptions and to the flattery of an inferior city.

The tone of the press, in the decade of this history, was flattering to all things visible in New York save administration as contrived by the Democratic party. Spasmodically, in the cramped critical departments of the *Sun* or the *Herald*, a Mayo Hazeltine or Charles Meltzer might cry against some popular novel or deride the cult of suave goddesses shoved forward by the Frohmans and Palmers in banal rotation on the stages of Broadway. Everybody could see, though, that these were the gruntings of discontented and sour critics. The word *critic* itself was rather shunned. The word *reviewer* was brought into being; it was a milder, more pleasant generality. One reviewed the spectacle of the city's superb existence and was thrilled by such immensities of life and color. Manhattan became a crowned woman in the frescoes of new hotels and if James Huneker, in the pages of a perky monthly called *Mdlle. New York*, chose to hint that Manhattan really resembled a customs-house clerk, why, his magazine had its reward and did not live long. If the *Arena* kept insisting that the public schools were abominable and that the public libraries were maladministered antiques, the audience of Flower's dull ravings was mostly made up of school-teachers and reformers. Meanwhile the show was good. Victor Herbert's increased orchestras made silky melody in theaters where shoulders were naked at last, after the long discussion of a gentlewoman's right to dress as she pleased. Each autumn the groomed horses trotted in the New Madison Square Garden, after football games had filled New York with roarings and with the sight of youth pouring down to the festival with chrysanthemums in its coat of tawny English cloth. Each winter the Opera dazzled provincials and some people listened to the voices of the de Reszkés, of the soft-eyed Schalchi, of the patrician Emma Eames. These things were popular and therefore good and the newspapers reported them in affable detail never smirched by realism. The Sunday supplement was invented and suburban householders could see in hazy photographs the very bathrooms of the obliging rich who also let heaped gifts at the weddings of their daughters appear for the contemplation of brides who were not American beauties plucked by European noblemen from the profitable stem. All brides were ravishing and all weddings gorgeous in that strange decade, just as all parades of militia and all civic

ceremonies were " inspiring sights." The Narcissus tilted a mirror
to his visage and beamed with condescension on an envious land.

It is plain that this pervasive flattery must have been, in some
part, due to ignorance and to a lack of any valuing sense. But that
its root was the congenital cowardice of the educated American
there can be no doubt at all. A movement in counterpoint was
sounding in the magazines, new and old. The whole history of
the decade's mild revolt against the quality of American life is
bound for display in the slick paper of the *Century*, *Harper's*,
Scribner's, *McClure's*, and the *Cosmopolitan*, revived under John
Walker to startle editors by its mad varieties. Revolt showed first
in the illustrations which swung out of the inane traditional wood-
cuts and dreary imitations of Maclise into the stony veracities of
Howard Pyle and the smooth skill of Joseph Pennell and of Rad-
ford Brennan, Pennell's superior in draftsmanship, his inferior in
assemblage. People suddenly looked like people, it was said, and
if the general taste hung to the domestic pleasantness of Charles
Gibson and Howard Christy, there were other hands at work. Here
was Abbey's feathery line. Here were Low, Linson, Sonntag, Cas-
taigne, and the earlier Maxfield Parrish. Peter Newell and A. B.
Frost made farces of the respectable commoner's clothes, and his
face took on a satiric emptiness under their touch. Here, little
noticed, were the photographic exactitudes of Ernest Peixotto and
Jay Hambidge. Taste moved forward boldly and a children's
monthly, *St. Nicholas*, offered derivations from the art of Georges
Seurat to a public which, like that of his own country, had never
heard of him.

In this pictorial progress the *Century* had taken the lead and it
now led on in a new venture. There began to be a mild, most
courteous analysis of the American scene and Richard Gilder
bravely introduced, through his magazine, essayists and historians
whose work was not devised to flatter any element of the nation.
He had already made himself responsible for an impartial history
of the Civil War and he was a man of defined political tendencies.
The cloudy stir to be christened " the reform movement " found
an ally in him and he conciliated intellectual groups by critical
matter far outside the general taste. But the charming intelligence

of the man was haunted by some barren theory of good form. He would allow the honorable studies of Walter Wyckoff, those first visions of the American laborer, to pass from his desk to the office of *Scribner's* because *The Workers* seemed flamboyant and he shrank from Josiah Flynt's sketches in crime because their subjects were " sordid." It is uncanny that Gilder, first of the native editors, should have recognized the talent of Jack London, as he did. The success of *McClure's Magazine*, with its profanity, its bad poems, and its vivacity, passed his understanding, but he made of the *Century* a stable, enduring creature and its life is not yet spent.

These editorial powers, with their growing public, knew that eyes were turned to the artistic whirlpool of the European world. They saw that publishers found profit in translations of Zola. Some plane of the United States was soothed and saddened by Loti's wailing grace. There was an outcry against unwholesome foreign fiction, and even Rudyard Kipling, already sacred, was now and then attacked. But in the midst of these noises Howells and his local rival, Mayo Hazeltine, praised Russian writing and implored their admirers to read Thomas Hardy. Was there, then, something viable in the mode that Hazeltine had named " stark realism "? There might be and one can follow, in that decade, two parallel motions. There was the glib, smoothly moving fiction of the reportorial school and there was a minor realism by permission, under surveillance. This realism was hedged and neatly confined both by editorial policy and by the temper of its friends. Howells was its father and it stayed well within his orbit, daring little and effecting not much more than a break with the moralities and prettiness of that precedent fiction which has left the single name of Bret Harte, an artist of whom it has been surprisingly discovered since his death that he imitated Dickens, quite as though Harte's critics while he lived had not noticed the habit. Harte's influence, too, survived in this quasi-realism. The neat pattern of his product had stamped itself too heavily in the editorial brain, where it persists. But intermittently arrived in print stories of commonplace people, and the public welcomed this placid observation of sempstresses soured by age, of bored country women, of dirty stokers in Pennsylvania mills. The observation was commonplace as were the themes. Here were dignity and sincerity, with Hamlin Garland's Western sketches and Sarah Jewett's acid etchings to add some genuine, memorable achievements in brief narrative.

Yet here came a boy whose visual sense was unique in American writing and whose mind by some inner process had stripped itself of all respect for those prevalent theories which have cursed the national fiction. He was already an ironist, already able to plant his impressions with force, and reckless of the consequent shock to a public softened by long nursing at the hands of limited men. Upon what section of the visible scene would he commence his sardonic operations? Perhaps it was simple recoil from the lukewarm current of letters, or perhaps it was a deeper curiosity that took Stephen Crane headlong and resolute into the slums.

III: *MAGGIE: A GIRL OF THE STREETS*

NEW YORK was proud of the Bowery precisely as a child is proud of a burned thumb, and the fame of the long, tawdry street grew by rumors of incredible debauchery until in 1890 one Ahearn, a publican, found it worth his while to post youths in the Grand Central Station who offered arriving men to " Show you the Bowery for a dollar, mister? " with the understanding that trips through the glamorous sink would end in supper at Ahearn's saloon, where ruffians duly arranged battles among the tables and prizefighters were bred. But there was nothing fictitious in the poverty of the region, and the soberly industrious Continental Jews who would finally tame the quarter by mere numbers were still in a passive minority. The name " Bowery " had been made inclusive: all adjoining streets, alleys, and squares held Bowery boys and Bowery girls in popular report. The alleys, too, were plentiful and buildings of wood crazily leaned above fissures black by night, as part of the Democratic revenues rose from the profit of lighting and cleaning small lanes which were never lighted and so seldom cleaned that corpses often were unearthed in piles of rubbish months after their relatives had given up a hunt for some vanished entity. The Bowery's self had an honest average of three saloons to the block and its nightly glitter raked the eye with raw tones of green and red in the glazed doors of these solacing haunts. Laborious prostitutes strolled from sunset to dawn on selected beats and many moved westward from the economy of lodgings on Third Avenue to the public halls of Broadway and Fourteenth Street.

The Bowery, though, was funny. Comedians aped its dress on the stage of Koster and Bial's improper vaudeville and speakers at banquets recited Bowery jokes. There was no other slum in America so settled of speech and habit. It was supposed that the Bowery invented words. In 1890 the word *jay* was current as a Bowery coinage in contemptuous reference. The word was actually from the South, of course, and its original employment was the sentence: " Naked as a jaybird," much used by begging tramps who spent the warm season in the North. Patches of English slang floated in the talk of the district and blossomed as native when reporters drew on this reservoir of unchaste diction. Stephen Crane found " on the turf " a convenient evasion of " prostitute," for instance, and was accused of inventing a meaning known in London before 1870. But the Bowery language was humorous, as are a dozen dialects in which the fierce, defensive cynicism of the illiterate American takes on color and shape. There was a choppy rhythm in the speech from which the sound of *th* had been drawn away. Many vowels were washed over so briskly that it took experience to tell whether they had been pronounced at all by some hasty group of lads hanging for a breath together while the policeman's back was turned. For the Bowery was full of youth that lived without license to draw pay and the poor preyed comfortably on the poor.

In January of 1892 Wallis McHarg came to New York, ready to sail for Germany and the study of medicine. He found Crane's address by way of the *New York Herald's* office and invaded a house of far East 23rd Street where Crane was sharing the big bedroom of some young actor.[1] At once Wallis must be shown the Bowery, and Crane led his friend down its reaches with a happy air of proprietorship. Here was the saloon where he had got a black eye. This was the dance-hall wrecked by a gang of sailors from the Brooklyn Navy Yard who had been wrongfully expelled. There was a notorious procurer and that girl was supposed to be the daughter of a

[1] Probably William Riley Hatch.

wealthy family somewhere uptown who came here for the curious pleasure of attracting suitors and then making them quarrel while she went to refuge in the shadow of some policeman. Then Crane abruptly said: " I want you to read my book."

McHarg had no pretensions in letters. He was the very practical son of a roaming family, not much given to reading. He took the pile of manuscript to his room at the Gilsey House and looked through its neat, tall writing with bewilderment. No character had a name in the short story of a girl seduced by a bartender, and the use of " God damn! " struck him as impossibly accurate. Here was something strange, new, and outlandish. Next day he told Crane that nobody would print such a story and that the people should have names. And when had Crane written this?

" I wrote it in two days before Christmas," said Crane, coolly, and then admitted that his brother William also thought the people must have names. The lawyer had seen the defect of the experiment. These characters stirring in a stupid mist and almost without physical being would confuse readers. They were " the girl," " the girl's mother," her brother, her lover and out of this original framework something remains. The " woman of experience and audacity " was never thereafter christened.

McHarg went off to Germany appalled and thrilled. He had read the curt, compressed tales of the Wyoming Valley which Crane sent him in clippings from the New York Tribune, but he had never taken " Stevie " seriously as an author bound to be famous. Now the younger boy had done something that was at least extraordinary and would create noise if anybody published it. Late in February he had a note, dateless and without address. Brother William had named the book. It was now " Maggie: A Girl of the Street," and in a postscript: " The Herald fired me last week."

Crane's shadowy term with the New York Herald exactly prophesied his whole career as a journalist. He could not report. Apparently he did not even try to report. Of what use to any newspaper was an impression of impatient horses kicking " grey ice of the gutter into silvery angles that hurtled and clicked on frozen stone " when the boy had been sent to get the facts of a large and important fire? The stamping horses hitched to the engine and the stolid movement of a young fireman stepping back from a falling wall, these things took his eye and went on paper. The name of the building's owner, its number on the street, and the question of its insurance simply wafted from the brain behind the plunging blue eyes. Nor could a city editor accept an interview with a prominent alderman when that dignitary, under charges of corruption, " sat like a rural soup tureen in his chair and said, ' Aw! ' sadly whenever ash from his cigar bounced on his vest of blood and black." It is not now to be proved that the *Herald* discharged Crane. He was probably taken to task for some fantasy on an alderman or an actress and dismissed himself.

But a boy of twenty, loose in the world filled with improvident and hopeful other boys, would not much care, and *Maggie* was ready for high inspection. Crane got himself a note of introduction from his brother Townley and appeared at the offices of the *Century*. Richard Watson Gilder knew all the Cranes and knew that this must be young Stephen before he read the note. " He was thin and his blue eyes seemed enormous. He sat wrapped in a grey ulster much too big for him, talking very slowly about his family with whom I had lost touch," Gilder wrote, later. " I saw that his manuscript was not long and gave him an appointment for the next day."

Gilder had a bad evening with *Maggie*. The novel is almost unknown to Americans. It begins: " A very little boy stood upon a heap of gravel for the honour of Rum Alley. He was throwing stones at howling urchins from Devil's Row who were circling madly about the heap and pelting him. His small body was writhing in the delivery of great, crimson oaths. . . . From a window of an apartment house that upreared its form from amid squat, ignorant stables, there leaned a curious woman. . . . The engineer of a passive tugboat hung lazily to a railing and watched. Over on the Island, a worm of yellow convicts came from the shadow of a grey ominous building and crawled slowly along the river's brink. . . ." The calm world watches Jimmie Johnson fight and then he goes home to his drunken mother, with his drunken father. His sister Maggie upbraids him: " Yeh knows it puts mudder out when yehs comes home half dead, an' it's like we'll all get a poundin'." To this unsentimental address Jimmie answers: " Ah, what de hell! Shut up or I'll smack yer mout', see? "

These children grow up in the shade of fear. Their mother is an incessant drinker who bullies them. Jimmie becomes a truck-driver invested by habit with an awful contempt for everything, especially those strings of street cars that followed his truck " like intent bugs." He has some respect for heavy fire-engines: " They had been known to overturn street cars. Those leaping horses, striking sparks from the cobbles in their forward lunge, were creatures to be ineffably admired. The clang of the gong pierced his breast like a noise of remembered war." He attends meetings in missions where the hearers, hopeful only of free soup, confuse the preacher with Christ. He " menaced mankind at the intersection of streets . . . dreaming blood-red dreams at the passing of pretty women." He seduces a pair of women, himself, who " caused him considerable annoyance by breaking forth simultaneously, at fateful intervals, into wailings about support, marriage and infants. . . . Nevertheless, he had, on a certain starlit evening, said wonderingly and quite reverently: ' Deh moon looks like hell, don't it? ' "

His sister Maggie is a pretty girl — Crane did not describe her — who goes to work for a Jew in a collar factory at five dollars a week rather than go on the streets. She is wooed by Pete, an opulent young bartender who hasn't the slightest thought of marrying her and does not when he wearies of her stupid prettiness and goes back to a more experienced mistress. Jimmie has vague fancies that his own position should not permit him to be too stern with Maggie — there are his own informal brides — but all his ideas are cribbed by the conservatism of his breed. He allows his mother to turn Maggie out and in a chapter unforgettable the feeble child goes drifting across New York, trying to speak to busy men, and halts in the profound shadow of the river's edge. Word being brought that " Mag's dead " her mother finishes supper before breaking into due lamentations and, urged on by friends, concludes the story with the cry: " Oh, yes, I'll fergive her! I'll fergive her! " and the first ironic novel ever written by an American thus crisply ends.

On his own admission, made in 1904, this book gave Richard Gilder a fearful shock. It seemed to him daring and filled with good touches but it was " cruel." There was no visible sentiment. These creatures of an environment had no tenderness and no restraint of action to excuse their callosity, and next day Gilder sat pointing out excessive adjectives and slaughtered infinitives to the shy boy, who finally cut him short with an untactful question: " You mean that the story's too honest? "

Being a gentleman as well as an editor Gilder gave his courteous little nod and *Maggie* was carried away from him in a pocket of the gray ulster. It may have consoled Crane, on March 23, 1892, that Gilder saw nothing obscene in the story. There is no animal detail in the seduction of Maggie Johnson and the profanity of the novel was simply the " damns " and " curse yehs " of the Bowery's emotion lamely piling out. But Crane here had his first experience, without guessing, of a dualism which faces all American writers. In two years more Gilder would be bidding his friends to read the English Arthur Morrison's *Tales of Mean Streets* and would be aiding the Tenement Commission to clean up the slums of New York. But that a story of those slums, told without apology, should appear in the *Century* of 1892 was unthinkable. In 1904 he was asked why Morrison's " Child of the Jago " did not offend him when *Maggie* still seemed a breach of taste, and he made response: " But Mr. Morrison's an Englishman! " as if some permission of God rested on the Briton that his truculent realisms should be found inoffensive. The attitude might be comic if it were still not spinal in American editors of the year 1923.

Maggie roamed the offices of various magazines in March and April until Crane locked her up in a box at his brother Edmund's house in New Jersey and got to work on sketches which he might sell to the *New York Tribune*. He was now a freelance reporter, one of hundreds who haunted Park Row daily, trying to sell interviews with notables, articles investigatory and descriptive. The *Tribune* was a good market; he was known favorably in the office, and the paper had printed his work since 1888. Now he began to have a little reputation in all the offices, before summer. His adjectives were oddly placed and his brusque paragraphs stayed in the mind. To say that an injured street-sweeper " flattened his face toward heaven and sent up a jet of violet, fastidious curses," was certainly too elaborate for the journalism of 1892, but men buying material for the *Sun* and *Tribune* would remember even when they had chopped it from an account of an accident in Twenty-third Street.

Meanwhile the boy was engaged in a private game. He was being independent, as his mother had ordered him to be, and small pay, cheap rooms, casual food were part of the sport. If he sat by night on a bench in Union Square with John Northern Hilliard or Acton Davies wondering when a check might drop from somewhere, there was pleasure in that and Hilliard could tell him stories about the West. If the check was too long in coming, he could get on a train and go to Lakeview, where he spent aimless evenings with pretty girls singing popular songs around a piano. In May he wandered through Syracuse and glanced at the class of 1894, then spent a week at Port Jervis with William Crane. But on May 26th some check had been too long delayed and he wrote to Acton Davies that he must have five dollars before he went to Lakeview or Edmund Crane's front door and his baby would be his next meal. The baby and the door survived. In June he admitted that he had sat on his brother's back steps and compiled a mental dictionary of oaths. In July he was in Asbury Park once more, sending off sketches to the *Tribune* and helping Townley Crane gather notes of a very busy season.

The season was also busy in the *Tribune's* offices. Whitelaw Reid was candidate for Vice-president on the Republican ticket and the early campaign went badly although William McKinley had been brought east to speak on protection of industries from New Hampshire to Virginia. Reid's newspaper shows the strain of operation on behalf of a losing issue. Every meeting of workers that showed favor to the Republican party was reported in fullest detail. It was understood that the Grand Army of the Republic inclined toward Harrison and Reid and the Army's encampments fill page on page of the paper. Various societies of the laboring class, as it began to be called, had outings and holidays on the Jersey shore. Reports of these doings, then, were waited on eagerly in Park Row.

Meanwhile Crane lounged about Asbury and Avon and played baseball rather less than formerly. Some of his old friends thought he looked unwell that summer, and his silences were prolonged. He was a little criticized for an article on Asbury Park in which the respectable fathers of respectable families were sweepingly mentioned as beings " with a watch chain and about three children apiece." Then, one day, his brother went to a funeral in Newark and left the impressionist to chronicle a parade. These good men lugged banners praising Harrison and Reid, and Crane, looking at the motion of this spectacle, forgot that Reid owned the *New York Tribune*. He merely saw a number of sweating persons who mostly worked with their hands, marching on behalf of capital, and the thing amused him. All parades were silly, anyhow, and this was too silly. The men shambled in dust and sunlight for his eye. There was a doubled oversight both at the press bureau in Asbury and in the office of the paper on Park Row. Next week complaints arrived at the *Tribune's* door in every mail. The paragraph, printed obscurely and in only one edition, was too much read. Crane had fallen foul of the American commoner's inalienable right to be reported respectfully, no matter how tawdry or foolish his communal manifestations may appear. Somebody [1] in Park Row sent Townley Crane a heated message and Stephen retired to Port Jervis, to ride a horse in peace. The emotions of Townley Crane are now inscrutable.

But *Maggie* was haunting her maker. In November, Crane borrowed one thousand dollars from his brother William and went to New York with the revised manuscript. He had a definite scheme: cheap publishing houses then often put out paper-bound novels at the author's expense, and since the higher criticism would have none of *Maggie*, let her be seen on the news-stands. Few of his friends had read the manuscript and he knew, now, that Stephen Crane was nobody at all in the city of New York: " I hunted a long time for some perfectly commonplace name . . . I think that I asked [Post] Wheeler what he thought was the stupidest name in the world. He suggested Johnson or Smith and Johnston Smith went on the ugly yellow cover of the book by mistake. You see, I was going to wait until all the world was pyrotechnic about Johnston Smith's ' Maggie ' and then I was going to flop down like a trapeze performer from the wire and, coming forward with all the modest grace of a consumptive nun, say, I am he, friends! . . . The bill for printing eleven hundred copies was $869 and Appleton's tell me that the printer must have made about $700 out of me. . . . A firm of religious and medical printers did me the dirt. You may take this as proffered evidence of my imbecility. Will made me get the thing copyrighted. I had not even that much sense."

He was obliged to sign a statement that he was twenty-one years

---

[1] Whitelaw Reid was not responsible.

old before this vanished firm would take the contract. They refused their name for the title-page, in any case.[1] But *Maggie* was now born in mustard paper with the price "50 cents" on the right-hand upper corner of the cover and the talent of Johnston Smith might be seen by the world if Stephen Crane could get somebody to expose it for sale. So the book was offered to the shops which in that year were quietly selling flat, large copies of Émile Zola's *La Terre* and *Potbouillie* to schoolboys. But nobody would take *Maggie* save Brentano's, which took a dozen copies and returned ten of them. The news-stands didn't want such a book. By the end of January 1893 Crane had got rid of a hundred *Maggies* and on one of these, sold in 1922 for two hundred and fifty dollars, is the inscription: "Miss Wortzmann. This story will not edify or improve you and may not even interest you but I owe your papa $1.30 for tobacco. S. Crane." So *Maggie* lay in yellow piles in the corners of his room and Crane went into that period of starvation so much admired in the history of artists by comfortable critics, sure of next week's bread.

His family knew nothing about this. When he dropped down to Edmund's house at Lakeview he was as usual, ready to play games with his small nieces and likely to write all night, coming to breakfast when the small household was at lunch. The secrecy of a boy was heavy in him; he had the icy courage of a sensitive nature which has taught itself to be brave; Edmund was under orders never to lend him more than five cents at a time. But one night there was not enough in his pocket to get him to Lakeview and he tramped through the mud of a country road, dazed with emptiness, with the sense of a great bundle pressing on his back. Then some man said from frosty shadow: "You seem to be in a pretty bad way, boy," and took hold of his arm. Crane mumbled that he was ill and they tramped toward Lakeview together, the countryman drawling out some wandering yarn, until Crane saw the lamps of his brother's house. The farmer shook hands with him and trudged away, his face unseen, to become the twelfth chapter of *The Red Badge of Courage.*

Crane's courage afterwards seemed to him simple silliness. Two of his brothers believed in his talent, and their homes were his. He

[1] The name of this firm seems to be lost forever.

could have given himself quarters with William or Edmund and stayed as a pensioner until, somehow, he had established himself with a public. But Crane's independence had a bent almost savage and ungracious. He would not tell his family anything about gloomy days in the old building of the Art Students' League in East Twenty-third Street and there was a new biting horror; he could not write now. Not only could he not write enough wooden descriptions of fires and strikes in Brooklyn — temporarily the home of strikes — to pay his meals, but he could write nothing that pleased his own judgment. All words seemed false and awkward. One day in February he came to Edmund's office in New York and said, drearily: " I'll trouble you for five cents, Ed," and on the first of March he answered an advertisement in the *Herald* and became clerk in a wholesale house on Bleecker Street for one week, precisely.

The external Stephen Crane of this passage was a silent boy who might be spurred on to amuse the crowd in a lamentable restaurant of lowest Lexington Avenue. Here the waiters wiped spoons in the leather pockets of fouled aprons and here Crane might rouse himself to say that Mark Twain's *Yankee in King Arthur's Court* was " inappropriate as a drunken bride." The quality of his talk was tinctured always by adjectives strange and prolonged. His boarding-house was a respectable hypocrite of a place. An ancient egg had a " snarling smell." The feather on the Sunday hat of a pretty chambermaid was " quivering invitation."

This pretty chambermaid was named Jennie Creegan, and all the crew of hapless youths whose beds she made called her Bunny. She sat on trunks, chewing gum " like a slim, reminiscing cow " and told tales of the Bowery. Crane had borrowed of her some phrases of *Maggie* and she tried to read the book when he gave her a copy but the words were too hard. One day she collected an armful of *Maggies* from Crane's quarters and used them to light a fire. The ironist grinned and helped her to lug the dusty books downstairs.

Hamlin Garland appeared in this fog as the rescuing angel. Crane was surrounded by other boys, some younger than himself, who partly understood that *Maggie* was a rare performance. When anyone praised him with intelligence, he might flush and beam, but nobody in authority had yet said good words of *Maggie* and perhaps his confidence was slipping when Mr. Garland wrote to him inviting a call. The handsome Westerner was living not too comfortably in Harlem and Crane tramped the four miles between their rooms for the first visit. Mr. Garland was startled by the boy's admission that he would give away his literary future for thirty dollars and began work with an instant, practical kindness. So a copy of *Maggie* was sent to William Dean Howells. Sketches were mailed to O. B. Flower of the *Arena* and Flower promptly bought *An Omnibus Babe* for twenty-five dollars. The adviser understood something of markets. He recommended Crane to the *Press*, fed him beefsteak, and loaned him dollars. This was no springtide of fortune, but it was something solid after a winter of freezing doubts, and the *Press* had literary pretensions second just to those of the glittering and eclectic *Sun*. To Garland there was already a tragic vesture on this lean, sallow boy, who had played baseball with him at Avon eighteen months before. The palpitating eyes were somber; the tearing intensity of the brain was clear to his experience. He might laugh a little when Crane hummed tuneless anthems in praise of food but, to his scrutiny, Crane was a shape of pathos.

Crane's appearance misled people. He had heavy shoulders and a pair of meager hips that made clothes fit him badly even when he dressed with care. His eyes discolored easily and, after a night of work or indifferent poker, he seemed always ill. Women invariably thought him handsome; men, with some exceptions, thought his face too long and his mouth too flexible. But even in the summer of 1893 after weeks of good diet at Edmund Crane's house he left an impression of starved neglect on strangers. As this narrative must be, in part, the demolition of a romantic myth, it should be pointed out that Crane was actually muscular and his body was an enduring machine that could carry him through a good deal of fatigue, as long as he was given plenteous sleep. But his exterior was, somehow, fantastic and already, in March of 1893, he was pointed out to a Southerner, Ford Bemis, as an eccentric who spent all his time in dives of the Bowery and was the outcast son of an Episcopal bishop. It should be pointed out, too, that Crane had a degree of the grand innocence in his character. Walking across Union Square with Elbert Hubbard and Acton Davies, he would deliberately stop to talk to an interesting tramp or some elderly painted woman and would hold his circumspect, annoyed companions still until the wearisome string of lies had been rolled out. " He had," said Hubbard, " no sense of propriety." The publisher's own exterior was that of a professional Bohemian from the novels of Mürger, but he was circumspect in the highest degree and Crane's simmering curiosity frightened him.

Meanwhile William Dean Howells had gone sedately mad over *Maggie* and was trying to persuade Henry Harper to have the book issued with more dignity. Harper declined, but Howells asked Crane to dine with him and the impressionist appeared — in John Hilliard's best suit — to get a dose of praise administered by the first critic of the land. Howells happened to be master of a small art that is not forgotten: he could stand in a crowd and make compliments without embarrassing the beneficiary or annoying the witnesses. He presented Crane to his other guests with: " Here is a writer who has sprung into life fully armed," and followed that music by saying, while Mark Twain was under discussion: " Mr. Crane can do things that Clemens can't." Then, after dinner, he took down the volume of Emily Dickinson's poems and read some aloud. So it must have been an evening of amazements for Crane, in a borrowed suit of clothes. The one man in America who had properly praised Tolstoi had also praised him and he had heard a new sort of verse, better than *The Charge of the Light Brigade* and *The Burial of Moses*, but he did not stop to let his mind bask in all this; he walked over to the Bowery and spent the rest of the night watching drunken Negroes play poker in the rear room of a saloon.

Then he was suddenly absorbed in some kind of research. He raided piles of old magazines in the studio of Corwin Knapp Linson and complained to the illustrator that nobody had written anything worth reading about the Civil War. He dropped in, one Sunday, at the house of Mrs. Armstrong — once the Miss Brett who had spanked him for burying her nephew — and borrowed the *Century's* *Battles and Leaders* after her father had assured him that these were accurate. One afternoon he was idle in the rooms of William Dallgren, watching Dallgren sketch Acton Davies, when Davies tossed him Émile Zola's *La Débâcle*, in a translation. Davies was a round youth who doted on Zola and when Crane slung the book aside he was annoyed.

" I suppose you could have done it better? "

" Certainly," said Crane.

On April 2nd he sent back *Battles and Leaders of the Civil War* to Mrs. Armstrong with a note: " Thank you very much for letting me keep these so long. I have spent ten nights writing a story of the war on my own responsibility but I am not sure that my facts are real and the books won't tell me what I want to know so I must do it all over again, I guess." This is the birth notice of *The Red Badge of Courage*.

His mind had gone swinging back to war in the recoil from failure in realities. *Maggie* was not absolute reporting. He had invented its small plot, and only two incidents of the story were from the life — the fight in the saloon and the destruction of Maggie's lambrequin by her mother. But he was in full flight from the codes of natural-ism. . . . Flight took him inevitably to his first passion. He had made games of battle when he was a child. He was always playing mentally and all the force of imagination dragged at him in his very genuine despair of methods to release the hiding vigor of his brain. He could stand through nights in a blizzard of late March to write *Men in the Storm* or sleep in a Bowery shelter to get at the truth of *An Experiment in Misery*, but the emotions of a boy in battle he must find for himself, in himself, and the birth of the book was travail incomprehensible to men who have never hunted in them-selves passions and the flood of acts to which they are alien. How-ever, there had been a boy who went confidently off to make war on a world and a city. He had been beaten to shelter and had lurched up a lane in darkness on the arm of some stranger. He had been praised for his daring while his novel, like a retreating army, lay in unsold heaps and the maker of images was sure of his own clay.

But *Maggie* was riding his neck. Howells saw no reason why the book should not be sold. " To this hour," he said in 1913, " I cannot understand the attitude of the dealers. I saw several of them person-ally and tried to interest Mr. Brentano. If Crane had cared to try that trick he might have disposed of ' Maggie ' through certain stores which had the reputation of selling obscene paperbacks. I suppose that the profanity of his masterpiece would have appealed to High School boys. But he did not descend to the method and, on my suggestion, mailed copies to Dr. Parkhurst and another min-ister who were then interested in the condition of the slums.

Neither acknowledged the gift and Crane told me, afterwards, that a Roman Catholic notable wrote that ' Maggie ' was an insult to the Irish. I shall never understand what was found offensive in the little tragedy."

Howells might not understand, but as late as 1921 Maggie was described as " flippant and unfeeling " by a reviewer and it is plain that sardonic observation of seduction, drunkenness, and fatuous plebeians would not wash down the throats of booksellers in 1893. The book came headlong against an American mode in fiction. These characters were poor and so should have been treated more kindly. Even in the championship of Howells one sees a slanting attitude: the book was a " little tragedy " and the pity of Maggie's case appears more sharply in his three essays than any other feature of the story. But he was a champion and he shocked friends by his praise of this grimness. . . . The Howells of 1893 had altered somewhat from the nervous friend who scolded Mark Twain for writing " she combed me all to hell." He had emerged from the warm fogs of Bostonian eminence and was living among men whose theory of things possible differed broadly from that of his former group. He had been lightly bidden to sit still and talk while Saint-Gaudens finished the model of a quite naked woman who went on chewing gum as though she were fully clad. He was standing beside Stanford White on the deck of a ferry when some stoker fell from the stern of a tug and was smashed by its screw to pulp that left on the waters a lacquer of bloody oil. The architect yelled: " Oh, poor devil! " and then brought down both palms on the rail of the ferry with another cry: " My God! What color! " Thus, one sees in the realist's later novels a weak and brief concession of the absolute: a man might thrash another with a cowhide whip and then vomit in repugnance; the good and kindly might in New Leaf Mills come off second best in a peculiar world; his ethical optimism sometimes waned into admission of things senseless, chill, and real.

But neither Howells nor anybody else could sell Maggie. Edward Marshall of the Press tried to persuade his paper to make a serial of it and in May 1893 Crane had some hope of a hundred dollars and a chance to hear what " Men of Sense " would think. There existed a collection of humans who were " men of sense " as differing from mere men. They were people not shocked by trifles who were willing to believe that he meant what he said. Marshall, not much older than himself, was a man of sense and Crane took heed when the young editor told him that his adjectives were often too heavy and that his coined adverbs were frequently difficult. So a sketch to be called *The Reluctant Voyagers*, for which Corwin Linson made illustrations with Crane as a model, shows fewer adjectives, fewer adverbs, and greater ease. But nobody bought it. Nor did anybody buy, immediately, *The Pace of Youth*, which includes: " In the darkness stretched the vast purple expanse of the ocean, and the deep indigo sky above was peopled with yellow stars. Occasionally out upon the waters a whirling mass of froth suddenly flashed into view, like a great ghostly robe appearing, and then vanished, leaving the sea in its darkness, whence came those bass tones of the water's unknown emotion. . . . High in the sky soared an unassuming moon faintly silver." Not knowing that two eminent novelists of another land would at last honor his prose by adopting it, Crane had no consolation and no cash for *The Pace of Youth* in 1893.

In June he turned over three hundred copies of *Maggie* to Mrs. Armstrong for safekeeping: " Sometime or other somebody or other might buy some," and went to Edmund's house. He came downstairs often and read bits of his manuscript aloud to his brother. *The Red Badge of Courage* was being slowly examined and partly rewritten. Edmund Crane could write pure English and his young brother made test of a clear intelligence. The man of business objected frequently, to sentences without verbs and to adjectives that had got loose from all mooring, but he was excited by the battle, having himself started off to war at the age of seven.

Stephen Crane was not taking much advice. In September shooting had begun at Port Jervis and on the first of October he was feeling " bully. Am going camping in Sullivan [County] with some other bobcats." In that company he spent three weeks, but on some date of the month's last week he arrived in New York with a valise and a slight cold and the price of a pair of shoes in his pocket.

Having bought new shoes he used his last five-cent piece to descend on Edward Marshall in the office of the *Press* through a cold rainstorm that soaked his clothes. The two young men had a singular regard for each other. Marshall was a writer of some skill and not a flattering reporter of New York. His dismissal from the *Press* had been demanded more than once by annoyed and powerful men and he had not been dismissed, although no influence kept him in place. When Crane passed beyond the point of casual amity, his feeling became fixed and savage. He liked Marshall and trusted him as simply as he now asked for a job. Marshall sat on the corner of a desk, swinging his watch-chain around a finger for a minute, and then answered: " No. I'll take all the special articles you can do, Stevie, but you are made for better things. Don't waste your time."

Instead of asking for five dollars, Crane walked out of the office and started uptown through the rain. He tramped with two-thirds of *The Red Badge of Courage* in his valise from the tip of the city's tongue to East Twenty-third Street and stumbled into the rooms of Frederick Gordon in the Art Students' League building, a wildly fashioned barrack " which squatted, slumbering and old, between two exalted commercial structures which would have had to bend afar down to perceive it. . . . The northward march of the city's progress had happened not to overturn this aged structure, and it huddled there, lost and forgotten, while the cloud-veering towers strode on." Gordon, after a look at the shivering creature, got him out of his clothes and into bed. The artist's room was big enough for another cot and Crane stayed on after a week's violent illness. His cooking added infamy to his host's life and he placidly told an arriving Englishman, Holmes Bassett, that Mrs. Humphrey Ward must be an idiot. Her celebrated novel, *Robert Elsmere*, was a lot of higgling rubbish and so was most English writing.

Bassett had called on Gordon by mistake and was already embarrassed, talking to an utter stranger dressed in an undershirt who looked deplorably ill. This critical blast blew him from his feet, and as he had met Mrs. Ward in London, he was shocked. So he went off to the Holland House and then came back, after ten days, to hunt up this irreverent character and take him to a prizefight at Madison Square Garden. Corbett was to give an exhibition and all the world was going. . . . The occasion became historic, suddenly. Crane dined at the Holland House with a man wearing a monocle and sat beside Bassett near the ringside while the smoky height of the great oval cavern filled with men. Presently Mark Twain appeared in a box with Robert Reid and the ruddy Stanford White. There rose a considerable stir. Clemens was in the papers, fighting

ruin after the collapse of his printing scheme, and a comber of sentiment splashed toward the tall figure, sheathed in furs, while
the people of cheap seats whistled, here and there, recognizing the
clown of innumerable lectures with his whitened hair and the
beauty of his beginning age. Crane sat staring at "the divine amateur" in silence and on some question said: "I only like one of his
books." Which one? "*Life on the Mississippi.*"

Corbett boxed. Clemens was led in state by Stanford White to
the prizefighter's dressing-room. Crane went off to his borrowed
bed and a christening took place in a house near the Players' Club
on Gramercy Park. There was a Hungarian band playing. Mark
Twain came at 10.45 and Richard Harding Davis followed him.
Walter Damrosch made music on a piano while a tenor sang and
people began to discuss what names they would choose if they
could have the matter adjusted. Then Davis wanted to know what
name Clemens would have liked had he been a woman? The hu-
morist dallied with the matter, then decided on "Petunia Bloggs."
The joke went around the room. Queerly, Stanford White wanted
to be called Evelina. Then they began to christen famous people
who were elsewhere. The Prince of Wales became "Lily" by allu-
sive process. Ellen Terry was suddenly "Roderick Dhu" — it is
not remembered why — and Davis asked for a new name for Henry
James.

"Oh," said Clemens, "call him Henrietta Maria."

This jape was in London six months later, but Crane, a few
blocks to the north of its making, was far from well. He took more
cold and Gordon had to nurse him in the windy building of three
entrances where young fellows hunted each other with candles by
night to borrow twenty cents against the morning's breakfast. Bassett, no Bohemian, sometimes took Crane out to dine and was
pulled along the Bowery, with his monocle. This glass delighted
Crane and he liked to play with its round when there was nothing else for his fingers to caress. He must have something to fon-
dle or he wasn't comfortable. Smoking seemed to mean just an
object between his fingers and a dead cigarette was quite as good
as one burning until he noticed the extinction and threw the
thing away. He hated champagne because it made him dizzy after
two glasses, but a white German wine rather pleased him, and

meanwhile he told Bassett all about bears, horses, dogs, and sailing boats. His opinions squirted out in shocking jets on a conservative who was, at the time, devout. Marriage, Crane said, was a base trick on women, who were hunted animals anyhow. A wedding was a legal ceremony, if ceremony there must be, and of all sects the Episcopal Church was the biggest inanity. Men had been allowed to pervert the teachings of Christ and Buddha into formulas and there was no such thing as sin " except in Sunday schools." Bassett went off to see an uncle in Ottawa with an impression of wild radicalism afoot on East Twenty-third Street. But *Maggie* came to him by the next mail inscribed: " This work is a mud-puddle, I am told on the best authority. Wade in and have a swim." So he learned that his acquaintance was a writer for the first time.

In February Crane took *The Red Badge of Courage* to a typist and left it for copy, finished and ready for anybody to read. Typewriting then was still expensive, but thirty dollars seem heavy for the short book. Having paid fifteen of the fee, he got half the manuscript back and went up into Harlem to see Hamlin Garland. After one look Garland lent another fifteen dollars and the whole treasury was out of pawn. On the 24th of February Crane wrote to Bassett: " I have just sold another book and my friends think it is pretty good and that some publisher ought to bring it out when it has been shown as a serial. It is a war-story and the syndicate people think that several papers could use it." He had sold *The Red Badge of Courage* to Irving Bacheller's young syndicate for less than a hundred dollars.

IV: *FAME AND PREJUDICE*

STEPHEN CRANE's scarce letters are not often interesting. They have a formal running tone, now and then lifted by a phrase. Sometimes he exploded into an utterly informal and prolonged expression. These vital papers must have been dashed down at the end of a mood. They are seldom dated, seldom headed, and recipients say that they were usually addressed haphazard. Thus, on some date of late November 1894, and obviously from Port Jervis, comes:

" If you hear that I have been hanged by the neck till dead on the highest hill of Orange County you may as well know that it was for killing a man who is really a pug — No, by the legs of Jehovah! I will not insult any dog by comparing this damned woman to it. There is a feminine mule up here who has roused all the blood-thirst in me and I don't know where it will end. She has no more brain than a pig and all she does is to sit in her kitchen and grunt. But every when she grunts something dies howling. It may be a girl's reputation or a political party or the Baptist Church but it stops in its tracks and dies. Sunday I took a 13 yr. old child out driving in a buggy. Monday this mule addresses me in front of the barber's and says, 'You was drivin' Frances out yesterday' and grunted. At once all present knew that Frances and I should be hanged on twin gallows for red sins. No man is strong enough to attack this mummy because she is a nice woman. She looks like a dried bean and she has no sense, but she is a nice woman. Right now she is aiming all her artillery at Cornelia's [1] new hat. I have been deprived by heaven of any knowledge of hats but it seems to be a very kindly hat with some blue flowers on one side and a ribbon on the other. But we rustle in terror because this maggot goes to and fro grunting about it. If this woman lived in Hester Street some son or brother of a hat would go bulging up to her and say, 'Ah, wot deh hell!' and she would have no teeth any more, right there. She is just like those hunks of women who squat on porches of hotels in summer and wherever their eye lights there blood rises. Now, my friend, there is a big joke in all this. This lady in her righteousness is just the grave of a stale lust and every boy in town knows it. She accepted ruin at the hands of a farmer when we were all 10 or 11. But she is a nice woman and all her views of all things belong on the tables of Moses. No man has power to contradict her. We are all cowards anyhow. Bacheller thinks I had best start for Nevada as soon as possible, maybe before Christmas, but I should like to be with the family, of course." Then, in a postscript: "Somebody has written clean from California about The Red Badge."

The story, cut into lengths convenient for the *Philadelphia Press*, had surprised him by the number of letters that came showering

---

[1] Mrs. William Crane.

through the Bacheller Syndicate. Another surprise was less pleasing. Bacheller took him down to Philadelphia and the whole staff of the *Press* had swarmed up to congratulate him. There were old soldiers among the printers and their words had been very warm. Excitement or something more tangible gave him an attack of dyspepsia and this was new, painful, and lasting. He was used to colds, sore throats, and chilblains, but dyspepsia seemed unlawful, especially as it recurred. In 1894, too, the heat of New York's summer had suddenly been " fog, like a Turkish bath's steam chamber, with the whole dressed city panting and scratching in its weight." A trip to Scranton with Corwin Linson was a relief. They reported and sketched the mining town for Bacheller with a prospect of another article on deep-sea diving, but the sea change did not come and Crane was much at Port Jervis in the later summer. In Port Jervis he evolved a social theory that Elbert Hubbard bought for the *Philistine* together with an essay on charities in the New York slums. Hubbard lost these papers on a train and Crane never replaced them, but the social theory remains, in a letter of Hubbard.

The world was full of old, plain, and dull ladies who sat about on porches and were omnipotent. Nobody could argue with them; they ruled the universe; they blighted the scene. This bestial force came from the education of all Americans by female schoolteachers. Men were sent to school under the power of dull, limited women, and learned to cringe from them. The habit was so stamped in males that they never dared to argue with any woman and so there should be more male teachers. The article on the slums included some criticisms of Tolstoi, still Crane's literary god although *The Kreutzer Sonata* bored him so that he could not finish it — the thing was " an old maid's picnic." He seems to have distrusted any novel favored by elderly women, clergymen, or Frank R. Stockton, an author of the time, harmless, amusing, and much petted by the minor critics.

In 1894 he was enraged by Mrs. Frances Hodgson Burnett's *Little Lord Fauntleroy* and encountering two small boys who had been tricked out by their mothers in imitation of Reginald Birch's too faithful illustrations, in long curls and lace collars, he coolly gave the sufferers money to have their hair cut. This act of altruism took place about September 1st in the city of Albany and Crane carefully told his alarmed hostess what he thought of *Lord Fauntleroy*. His opinions of books never altered greatly. In 1899 he wrote: "No thanks. If the Whilomville stories seem like Little Lord Fauntleroy to you you are demented and I know that you are joking, besides. See here, my friend, no kid except a sick little girl would like Lord Fauntleroy unless to look at Birch's pictures for it. The pictures are all right."

This innocuous romance was printed in 1886 and its results sullied the lives of many small boys born in the decade following that date. Crane's rage was rooted in his dislike of sentimentalized children. Mrs. Burnett's shrewd bit of writing tells how one Cedric Errol, the grandson of an aged and gouty Earl, reformed his ancestor and soothed the life of an English countryside. Crane had heard, somewhere, Matthew Arnold's "sweetness and light" and he tacked the phrase to *Little Lord Fauntleroy*. As he seldom read books, an annoying novel left a scar in his mind, unhealed to his end. His impressions of Chicago in January of 1895 were stained by a procession of Lord Fauntleroys met on a corner beside a church. That any young male should be draped in lace and velvet and made to wear long curls!

Bacheller was sending him west to write sketches with a free hand, as long as he finished the trip in Mexico, and Crane's course is hard to follow. Most of his letters have been lost and the sketches appeared out of order. He had, though, three immediate wishes. He must see a cowboy ride. He wanted to be in a blizzard of the plains. He must look at the Mississippi because Elbert Hubbard had persuaded him to read *Huckleberry Finn* and 143 East Twenty-third Street had heard his grunt of disgust over the lame conclusion of Mark Twain's masterpiece. Didn't the genius know any better? A baby could have improved the end of *Huckleberry Finn*! The boys stopped being boys and were dolls. So, as in the mind of Arnold Bennet, *Life on the Mississippi* was always Twain's best book. It is not known that he saw much of the Mississippi, but he had his two other wishes. He saw cowboys ride and visited a ranch near the border of Nevada, where somebody gave him or sold him some silver spurs. He changed trains once at a dreary junction town where was a hotel of a dreadful blue that fascinated him. His thirst for blues ran to shades of cold electric tones and this

blue was a lugubrious, fainted tinge. In a hotel painted so loath-
somely, some dire action must take place and after four years he
made it seem so. But in Lincoln, Nebraska, on February 13th, he
pushed himself into an irony by trying to stop a fight in a drinking-
place. It appears that a very tall man was pounding a rather small
one and Crane shoved himself between them. " But thus I offended a local custom. These men fought each other every night.
Their friends expected it and I was a darned nuisance with my
Eastern scruples and all that. So first everybody cursed me fully
and then they took me off to a judge who told me that I was an
imbecile and let me go; it was very saddening. Whenever I try
to do right, it don't."

A blizzard was raging at Lincoln, but he found warm weather in
Little Rock, Arkansas, and hurried off to look at Hot Springs.
There he broke a tooth on a dried persimmon's stone and saw five
funerals. " It rained funerals on me. I was soaked with lamentations and the hope of widows." New Orleans was a pictorial disappointment, while Creole food gave him more dyspepsia, but
when he reached San Antonio, he fell in love with that maligned
city and with Texas. . . . All the adolescence in him frothed to
a head. His letters from San Antonio are almost childish. A wonderful Greek cook broiled pompano. Here was the monument to
the defenders of the Alamo with its legend: " Thermopylæ had
its messenger of defeat; the Alamo had none "; and that, he wrote
to Hilliard, boomed in his ears like the clashing of war-bronze.
Every night here was the blaze of East Houston Street, in spring,
with parading men in real sombreros and the lace of veils flung
across Mexican eyes. Persons with parenthetic mustaches sat in
saloons filled with antlers and lied about old duels. A red-haired
man swung his elbow against Crane's arm to get a revolver from
his belt and aim it at an enemy, before the bartender threw a seidel
and spoiled the show. He pulled a small girl out of the soapy little
river that wriggles through the town and she told him for his
trouble to go to hell.

One day he was lingering on the Alamo Plaza and distressed
sounds hit his ear. He saw a sixteen-year-old boy, as tall as himself, sitting on the edge of the gutter, sobbing. Young Edward
Grover had come southwest from Chicago to begin life freshly as

a cowboy with a birthday gift of sixty dollars in his pocket. Now the pocket was empty and the officers of Fort Sam Houston would not let him become a recruit. Crane marched this wretch into a restaurant, fed him thoroughly, and took him straight to the railroad station. At Saint Louis the home-going runaway met an uncle who could telegraph back funds to Crane. Six days later Grover had a note:

Dear Deadeye Dick:
    Thanks for sending back my money so fast. The hotel trun me out, as my friends of the Bowery say and I was living in the Mex diggings with a push of sheep men till my boss in New York wired me money.
    Now, old man, take some advice from a tough jay from back East. You say your family is all right and nobody bothers you. Well, it struck me that you are too young a kid [1] and too handsome to be free and easy around where a lot of bad boys and girls will take your pennies. So better stay home and grow a mustache before you rush out into the red universe any more.

Yours sincerely,
STEPHEN CRANE

    In that Mexican lodging-house he met a blushless rogue who, peddling illicit drink to the thirsty soldiery of Leon Springs in 1917, called himself Keenan. This man had charms; he was a Bowery boy who had wandered away from police and friends. He told Crane a tale of shooting down some Mexicans who tried to drive his sheep from a waterhole. The slaughter was a simple gesture of carelessness, for at once he sold his sheep to them and retired from the pass. Crane sent him, in 1897, a copy of the *Century Magazine* with *A Man and Some Others* and Keenan hated Crane ever after for spoiling the point of the story.
    The enchantment of Texas was partly equine. He rode a mule in the Painted Desert of Arizona, but again, in Mexico, there were all sorts of horses and a little bay that carried him through a real adventure faithfully reported in *Horses — One Dash*. . . . Crane and a Mexican guide, Miguel Itorbide, were benighted in a village suddenly invaded by a fashionable bandit, Ramon Colorado, and his followers. Diaz, the President-dictator of Mexico did not dis-

---

[1] Crane used the word long before it was popular in fiction.

courage a certain easy freedom in rural administration and small groups of banditry went cheerfully about their business within a hundred miles of the capital. Colorado heard that an American was lodged in the village and determined to absorb any money or luxuries that Crane might have with him. Then, exactly as in the story, a train of peripatetic harlots arrived on their way to some rejoicing in Mexico City and Colorado went to inspect. Crane and his guide crept from the hut and raced across the plain on their horses with Colorado's gang half a mile behind them. The pale uniforms of the rurales, the mounted constabulary of the district, came to solve the difficulty and a lieutenant sat cursing Colorado while the bandit tried to apologize for having annoyed a friend of the government. This business was delicious to Crane. . . . He had watched terrific brawls while, dressed in his worst clothes, he sat in Bowery dives and lodging-houses, but he had never been so closely threatened and the detail of his emotions pumps through *Horses — One Dash* in a clear ripple of self-examination, sardonic always.

Let it be stated that the mistress of this boy's mind was fear. His search in æsthetic was governed by terror as that of tamer men is governed by the desire of women. *Maggie* had represented the terror of an environment tinged by social judgment. In all the Mexican and Texan sketches appears, as in *The Red Badge of Courage*, a vision of man's identity faced by its end, by incomprehensible death. One gets the solid courage of the marshal of Yellow Sky who shoves annihilation from him by a simple statement; the rogue of *A Man and Some Others* dies easily because he is bound by contract to defend his flock. In the true story *Horses* and the fanciful *Five White Mice* one sees Crane himself, recording his own pulse before a shadow which he refused to kneel and worship. He could be afraid, and afraid with all the quivering imagination of an artist — here stood the great death and here, mentally or in flesh, stood he. But his recording of the state is never more than civilly sympathetic. The boy of *Five White Mice* stands with a drunkard on each hand and the cloudy group of Mexicans before him, speculating on his friend's attitude after the slaughter. " The other Kid would mourn his death. He would be preternaturally correct for some weeks, and recite the tale without swearing. But it would not bore him. For the sake of his dead comrade he would be glad to be preternaturally correct and to recite the tale without swearing." Then the tortured thought veers off to a memory of a summer hayfield and to the wonder of a distant crooning stream. And then he steps forward and the great death steps back. The Mexicans retire up the dim street. Nothing has happened. The emotion has projected its intensity against nonsense, against a posture of some loungers. It is the last point in futility, the hurtle of mighty chords on an unhearing ear. . . . That this work was outside the mood of his time and his nation everybody knows.

Notoriety now jumped on him while he tramped the streets of Mexico City with his waistcoat pockets filled with opals given him by Charles Gardner, an American engineer, invalid after smallpox in the brilliant, lazy town where Crane saw, for the first time, the Latin consent to public pleasures. " You can sit at a table in front of a Café — a real café — and drink cool drinks. Nobody comes up and says, Stop! The Yankees and the Englishmen get drunk sometimes and make noises at the circus but the Mexicans make noises just at the bullfights." The bullfights were disgusting to him because horses were killed there, an unthinkable sacrilege. Mr. Gardner, reading the *New York Herald*, saw that an absurd book of poems had appeared and asked across a table: " Is this poet Stephen Crane related to you? "

" I'm him," said Crane.

A fog rests on the birth of *Black Riders*, sold to Copeland and Day of Boston in 1894. Crane was careless about dates. His own judgment: " I wrote the things in February of 1893," cannot be true because he had not then dined with William Dean Howells and had not heard the critic read Emily Dickinson's verses aloud. The testimony of Hamlin Garland and John Northern Hilliard must be correct and the startling lines were written some time after the first of April 1893. Some of them were read by John Barry at a public meeting of literary persons in March of 1894, without applause. They came into Crane's head while he was depressed one night and it seemed, almost, that somebody dictated them to him. The whole manuscript was twice lost, once by Crane himself in an elevated railway car and once by a friend who left the shabby papers somewhere and had to ransack New York for them. They existed in the autumn of 1894 as proof sheets which Frederick Gordon had in his pocket while he helped Crane gather facts in the crowds watching bulletins of the mayoral election which temporarily took New York's affairs from the orderly pillage of Tammany Hall into the sloppy ineffectiveness of the Reform party's hands. Copeland and Day issued *Black Riders* with a clever design by Gordon for the cover of the handsome little book, which came out in April of 1895, and, with two favorable reviews in objection, the reading nation was told at once that Stephen Crane was mad.

The nation had been offered unrhymed sonnets of Anna Brackett and that Walt Whitman wrote long poems without rhymes was an established fact. The English even liked Whitman's concoctions. But *Black Riders and Other Lines* was the work of some pert maniac and opinions to the contrary in the *Bookman* and the *Lotos* had no weight. Here was simple insanity finely printed:

> Charity, thou art a lie,
> A toy of women,
> A pleasure of certain men.
> In the presence of justice,
> Lo, the walls of the temple
> Are visible
> Through thy form of sudden shadows.

That was rude and pretty bad. Worse came:

> I saw a man pursuing the horizon;
> Round and round they sped.
> I was disturbed at this:
> I accosted the man.
> " It is futile," I said,
> " You can never — "
> " You lie," he cried,
> And ran on."

> Two or three angels
> Came near to the earth.
> They saw a fat church.
> Little streams of black people

Came and went continually.
And the angels were puzzled
To know why the people went thus,
And why they stayed so long within.

If I should cast off this tattered coat,
And go free into the mighty sky;
If I should find nothing there
But a vast blue,
Echoless, ignorant, —
What then?

God lay dead in heaven;
Angels sang the hymn of the end;   .
Purple winds went moaning,
Their wings drip-dripping
With blood
That fell upon the earth.
It, groaning thing,
Turned black and sank.
Then from the far caverns
Of dead sins
Came monsters livid with desire.
They fought,
Wrangled over the world,
A morsel.
But of all the sadness this was sad, —
A woman's arms tried to shield
The head of a sleeping man
From the jaws of the final beast.

In the Bowery he had seen a young streetwalker cover the head
of a drunken procurer with her body while the fellow's assailants
were trying to stamp his face to pieces. Crane ran to bring help
and the police arrested the girl for cursing. (The exact morality of
the Irish police amused Crane considerably.)

A man feared that he might find an assassin;
Another that he might find a victim.
One was more wise than the other.

> I walked in a desert.
> And I cried,
> " Ah, God, take me from this place! "
> A voice said, " It is no desert."
> I cried, " Well, but —
> The sand, the heat, the vacant horizon."
> A voice said, " It is no desert."

A man's perception of beauty in disastrous circumstances should have been phrased with more prolix sentiment in 1895. But Richard Watson Gilder and others found pleasure in:

> Places among the stars,
> Soft gardens near the sun,
> Keep your distant beauty;
> Shed no beam upon my weak heart.
> Since she is here
> In a place of blackness,
> Not your golden days
> Nor your silver nights
> Can call me to you.
> Since she is here
> In a place of blackness,
> Here I stay and wait.

But the vision of the world as a rudderless ship " going ridiculous voyages, making quaint progress, turning as with serious purpose before stupid winds," had no claim on a public which was reading Fitzgerald's quatrains just then with a delighted sense of ethical exploration. Omar Khayyám might suit the awakened hedonism of a nation still taught to recite the stuff of Longfellow, but *Black Riders* suited nobody. The poems were bombast and drivel and obscene and that was completely all there was to the matter. But Crane was now somebody and he had expected this blast before he dedicated the book to Hamlin Garland. His friends, with some exceptions in the shapes of Hilliard, Gordon, Linson, and Hubbard, had openly told him he was an affected ass. So, arriving in New York in May, he took condolences serenely and said: " Some of the pills are pretty darned dumb, anyhow. But I meant what I said," and being asked if he admired Stéphane Mallarmé answered: " I don't know much about Irish authors."

He was made welcome at the new Lantern Club of journalists and editors in a crazy added story on the roof of an old building near Brooklyn Bridge. Irving Bacheller, Thomas Masson, Edward Marshall, Willis Hawkins, Richard Gilder, John Langdon Heaton — whose wife was " the most sensible woman in New York " to Crane — and some others lunched there almost daily. Crane shook hands with Richard Harding Davis for the first time, gave the best choice of his Mexican opals to Corwin Linson, then let the others vanish among " the Wild Indians " of the Art Students' League Building, save one kept carefully for his niece, Helen, his brother William's daughter, who lost it later at school in Switzerland. Then he went up with his silver spurs and some woven blankets to Hartwood, a hamlet of Sullivan County, easily reached from Port Jervis. There Edmund Crane had taken charge of some undeveloped property and had a simple house where Crane lay grinning over the reviews of *Black Riders* and taught his nieces to play fan-tan.

Ripley Hitchcock bought *The Red Badge of Courage* for Appleton's in December of 1894, but Crane's trip to Mexico had delayed correction of the proofs and the book did not appear until October 3, 1895. Hitchcock was a man of extraordinary shrewdness. He could see the merits of *The Red Badge of Courage* and of such transient dullness as the forgotten *David Harum* with equal speed. He nicely predicted the success of *The Red Badge* in August of 1895 and saw the prediction come off by the first of January. The success has become a legend in American publishing. It is still commonly stated that the book did not sell until the English reviews in January lifted it to notice. The facts, as taken from amalgamated statements, are these: All or nearly all the American reviews were enthusiastic and booksellers in New York bought large numbers of copies. But from Crane's hand on December 24, 1895: " Mr. Hitchcock tells me that the book does not sell much in New York. It has gone to about 4500, though, and many of them have been sent west." At one bookshop, Leggett's, only two copies had been sold by the 10th of January. . . . Then, in middle January, the city began to buy *The Red Badge of Courage* and the sale mounted so swiftly that Edgar Saltus, who in October wrote that Crane had outdone Zola, Tolstoi, and Kipling in a breath was now, on February 6th, moved to write to Charles Devlin: " A man sometimes yearns for the power to write vulgar inanity and sell it by the cart-load to fools. I hear that Stephen Crane has made twenty thousand dollars out of his trash." Devlin called the exquisite's attention to his former praise of the book and their interesting correspondence untimely ceased.

The history of a triumph is always dull. The unfavorable reaction to Crane's masterpiece is better worth study. Copies of *The Red Badge* were returned to Brentano's store in New York because the book held no "love-story" and it was sometimes returned because it was too grim. Two specimens of the first issue are scattered with bitter notes in the tremulous handwriting of some veteran who wrote: "Insulting," "unpatriotic," "damned nonsense" abreast of each sentence describing the young soldier's fears in the blank wildness of his flight from the first day's battle. A clergyman in Illinois, George Stephen Crane, who had served in a regiment at Chancellorsville, was assailed by letters from old friends either praising his memory or damning him for betraying confidences made at that less sentimental moment when his comrades were in retreat from the Southern army. Crane himself had letters profoundly pointing out that the boy's return to camp with his damaged head and his acceptance of his friend's belief that the bloodstains come from a wound taken in battle make up a nasty comment on the hero. Irony, says Carl Van Vechten, should always be carefully underlined in an American novel. And there is no notice, save that of William Dean Howells, printed in 1895, which mentions the ironies chasing themselves through *The Red Badge*. That critics of the day should note: "Mr. Crane's interesting novel contains no strictures on the cruel uselessness of war" was to be expected. Merely to expose is never enough for the prim intelligences posted as guides to the American public. Then, as now, their vision of the artist in letters is the cloudy image of a poet in solemn posture on some sanitary stage, dealing out commonplace evidence of man's imperfection and urging on the universal good.

The comedic element of *The Red Badge* probably had little notice at the time. But very soon certain episodes were imitated. Within a year the business of the lad who turns over his letter of farewell to Henry before the battle appeared in adaptation twice. The quarrels of the two boys could be fitted into other scenes and were, promptly. . . . The biographer has been reproached for pointing out, elsewhere, that Alan Seeger's graceful poem, still current, with its line: " I have a rendezvous with death," was suggested by the tenth chapter of Crane's novel, but Seeger's admiration of the book was known to his friends. The flowery advance of the banners has been precisely imitated in English and American war-tales to the number of three hundred and ten times. The finish of the tenth chapter, the finding of the dead man in the wood, the row between the regiment's commander and the disgusted general and the description of the fires by night have been used ceaselessly. Crane's effect on Anglo-American prose has never been questioned by critics of any competence and his clear departure from the traditions of written English startled his day. There were vigorous catcalls and brayings, of course. It was passionately urged that no decent youth should describe emotions in terms of colors, that his grammar was wildly molded to the needs of a point. But he was indisputably famous at the age of twenty-four, by reason of a book written, or designed, before his twenty-second birthday.

The act fell on academic culture as noisily as though a broken drumstick smote a plane of limp velvet. Crane had letters of praise from Bliss Perry, William Graham Sumner, and Brander Matthews, but recognition of living art had no place in the universities of the decade and Barrett Wendell, pausing in the consideration of Restoration comedy at Harvard, told one of his students that the book was sensational trash, then resumed his sour brilliance. So far as penetrable, smart society knew nothing of any such novel, for the Englishman already quoted in this history's second chapter vainly hunted in 1897 for somebody of New York's grandiose flock to make him known to Crane and at a dinner of forty found only one couple — the late Frederick Whitridge and his wife — who had ever heard of the author. But Boston rolled in its shrines and the new writer was asked swiftly to appear. He was pointed out to visitors at a football game in Cambridge, in latter November, and stood shyly for a few minutes in the famous drawing-room of Mrs. Fields.

Elbert Hubbard gave a dinner for him on December 19th in Buffalo and Crane stammered out something which, in the memory of Claude Bragdon, the dinner's master of ceremonies, was hardly a speech. Some of the guests took the party as an elaborate joke on Crane, who must be rather mad or a posturer, but excitement was

growing in the vague kingdom of arts and the blaze of the English
reviews lighted up January. Harold Frederic's letter to the *New
York Times* was carefully arranged so that Henry James might
know how little Frederic thought of his judgments — James having
recommended Heinemann's new publication in Frederic's presence
— but this war of two expatriates had no meaning in America and
Crane was pleased by a note from Frederic while he rode his new
horse, Peanuts, about Hartwood. The magazines were suddenly on
his track and to *McClure's* went the whole collection of Texan and
Mexican stories. Meanwhile Ripley Hitchcock was urging that *Maggie* be altered and published and Crane's old friend Harry Thompson wanted *George's Mother* for Edward Arnold as soon as it should
be finished. The crowd at the Lantern Club wanted him to write a
tale with a newspaperman as hero, of course, and people came driving compliments at him from every quarter. One of these was Richard Harding Davis, who did not particularly like Crane, but who
chose to make himself an agent of the younger man's reputation.
The air was full of projects: he should write a political novel; he
should write a play with Clyde Fitch. " It seems that I can do any
damn thing I want to but be let alone," he wrote in February, but
walking with a friend up Broadway, elation swelled. It was pleasant
to stroll to dinner at Mouquin's and to be a success.

2

WEIR MITCHELL was a practising, experienced neurologist as well as
a narrator of modest historical tales. He once put on paper a speculation: "The phenomena of envy are very much more marked
among artists than in other professions. Invariably or nearly so,
these take the form of gossiping stories about the personal character
of a successful writer and the stories always show the same trend:
the successful man is given to heavy indulgence in alcohol or to irregular use of drugs. The point is most interesting when one considers that artists are perpetually demanding for themselves the license of conduct which they deplore in print." These two methods
of subterranean attack were in full use against Crane before March
of 1896.

He had a trick of using small formulas in conversation and now,

when he was pressed to write some story which seemed too dull or
too fantastic he began to say: " Oh, I'd have to get too drunk to
write that." That this was hardly circumspect is plain and part of
Crane's legend became fixed: he was obliged to get drunk before he
could write at all. This had no currency among his friends, but it
was probably gospel in the bars of Mouquin's restaurant and of
Louis Martin's café. The fiction of a successful man aided in his
success by alcohol is very flattering to the less successful.

Here appears the shape of a forgotten and vanished being whose
name was Thomas McCumber. He was very tall, very handsome,
and usually very tipsy in the popular bars between the years 1895
and 1904, when he died in a hospital of paresis. His card bore the
word *Photographer* in one corner and he once lived at the old Gilsey House for some months of 1896. He also once lived at a boarding-house in East Nineteenth Street where James Huneker knew
him casually as a clever talker. It is faintly recalled that Crane had
a nodding acquaintance with this man and did not seem to like
him. He was described by O. Henry as " an infernal nuisance," but
he was genial and he talked, apparently, in an amusing fashion. On
a definite date, then, February 22, 1896, he made himself responsible for the statement that Crane took morphine.

In March of 1896 Crane seems to have been conscious that he
was under fire. His last note to Wallis McHarg, dated from Hartwood, says: " When people see a banker taking a glass of beer in a
café, they say, There is Smith. When they behold a writer taking
a glass of beer, they say, Send for the police! No great law of nature
can be proved from this but it pretty often hits me that people are
ingenious blockheads. I have been to Washington about a book on
political society for Mr. McClure but I came straight back." His further letters to McHarg are lost, but in another he mentioned that
some lying story had upset his friends and that a man hardly known
to him was to blame.

The rumor of morphine had already reached Ripley Hitchcock
and he diplomatically asked Crane's views on the taking of drugs.
Crane did not approve. His liberalism had certain inset features.
The ordinary prejudices of formal codes simply washed down from
his mind, but drug-taking was a habit of fools and he had seen the
dreary end of it on the East Side. A man of sense would not take

drugs, and two years later he repeated the opinion to James Huneker.

"As soon," said Harding Davis, " as Mr. Crane's success began there were ugly stories set in circulation about his private life. When he died his friends found it necessary to issue a denial that he took drugs. The yarn was absurd on its very face but it was told constantly. . . . I was never intimate with Crane but his best friends assured me that the story was false and they were not men to lie. He had a decided prejudice against drugtaking which I heard him express frequently at dinners and at the Lanthorn Club. But appearances were against him. He smoked constantly and he was very sallow and very thin. To see him through the smoke of a restaurant and to be told that he ate morphine would not have surprised me. But I know a great deal about the signs of the drug habit and Mr. Crane had none of them. Neither did it seem to me that he drank excessively. I remember that he disliked champagne, for instance, and as far as my memory serves me, he mostly stuck to dark beer. I know nothing about his relations with women and the story told about him in connection with some actress or artist's model was untrue to my knowledge."

The story yields up these facts. Crane was sitting with Acton Davies and Clyde Fitch in Mouquin's restaurant one night near the first of 1896 and a woman of some notoriety came up to ask Crane for a loan. This person had a number of titles and was sometimes married, informally or formally, but her actual name seems to have been Doris Watts. Crane had met her in 1895 as the titular wife of an acquaintance and she now appealed to him for a lone of fifty dollars. So he borrowed a blank check from Clyde Fitch and gave an amount not known. Acton Davies warned him that he would never be repaid. Crane's own statement of the sequel was dictated in November of 1899 and was also made orally to two friends. The woman, then known as Mrs. Bowen, began to worry him with letters asking for more funds on the plea that she was destitute and wanted to " reform." . . . He had a recklessly generous attitude toward women of all sorts and perhaps he was touched. He seems to have sent her several small checks which came to a total of a hundred and fifty dollars or thereabouts. But she wrote to him incessantly and at last threatened to come to Hartwood. This was a light variety of blackmail, of course, and Crane came to New York to have done with it. She was not sufficiently destitute to have dismissed her maid, a Negress, who let Crane into her rooms on West Forty-eighth Street. " I leaned on the door and told her to drop this nonsense. There was one of those horrors called Turkish corners in the room with a shield stuck full of knives. She lost her temper and grabbed a knife from the shield. It flew over my shoulder and stuck into the wood beside my ear and quivered so that I can still hear the noise." The disconsolate heroine then swooned, by rote, into the arms of her maid, and Crane went away, hatless. He borrowed a cap from a friend whose studio was in Thirtieth Street and retired to Hartwood.

The story was abroad by July and its general form was that Crane had seduced and then abandoned some girl of respectable parentage. The story naturally varied: she was a trusting artist's model; a country girl; a virgin actress. In July, Willis Clarke, a young fellow who was trying fiction, asked his brother, starting for New York, to make inquiries about Stephen Crane. In the old Cairo restaurant Clarke's brother was told that Crane was notoriously the father of a child by an unhappy girl who now was loose on the town. The Cairo was an excellent springboard for such information, as, with the exception of the Haymarket on Sixth Avenue, it was probably the rowdiest large night resort in New York at the time.

However, Crane was fair game for any legend. Hadn't he published a book of affected poems, one of which denied a Commandment? *Appleton's* had issued the slightly revised *Maggie* in June and it was plainly a shocking work although the reviews were civil. Besides, reporting for the *Press* the opening of a music-hall called the Broadway Gardens, he had already been published as the hero of a fight with a policeman who had bullied a girl about her business in the rear of the hall. . . . Crane was boyishly proud of the incident and discussed it with his brothers. He made a vehement attempt to destroy the policeman totally and was locked up all night but dismissed by some sensible judge in the morning. . . . A distinct flavor of *Maggie* mingled in the gossip and some of his admirers were seriously told that in order to write of her fate he had seduced a Bowery beauty and then thrown her to the wolves. All this compounded silliness was stirring, and in August the drown-

ing core of the fable herself appeared in the offices of a young attorney with four letters from Crane as evidence that he owed her
support. But all the letters began and ended formally and the checks
were described as "loans." The attorney refused the case. She then
attempted to have a warrant issued for Crane's arrest but was denied. A paragraph on August 23rd reports: "A young woman well
known to habitués of the gayer restaurants along Broadway yesterday applied for a bench warrant to right the 'wrongs' done her by a
prominent young writer of sensational fiction. The application was
denied as her evidence did not seem sufficient and the lady left the
court room on the arm of a gentleman whose buttonhole of lilies of
the valley had already interested onlookers."

It is impossible, now, to retrace the jigging route of this scandal.
It blew here and there fragrantly and entered the offices of the *Century*, where lay the manuscript of *A Man and Some Others*, sold to
the magazine by Paul Reynolds. In early autumn the literary agent
was hastily sent for by the editor, who demanded: "What does
Crane mean by getting into such a mess when he's sold a story
to us?"

The world of journals, though, had no space for the spite of a
pretty drab against an eccentric author. Front pages must be cleared
for the whirling news of a great duel between two voices — the barytone roar of William Jennings Bryan and the milder basso of William McKinley. It was now understood that some numerical incantation known as the silver standard would either make everybody
sixteen times richer or would ruin the United States. Few minds
were strong enough to comprehend the reasoning of this process,
but a plain case of the people against the wicked rich had been made
out, and as Mr. Bryan had already chosen the role of buffoon in the
arid comedy of American religion, he had the support of countless
women in the midland, where they have always been quietly powerful in our politics, so the Nebraskan was shown in posters as a
mailed knight spearing the fat dragon of plutocracy, and Democratic bankers were secretly heaving funds into the hands of Mark
Hanna, the fat dragon's visible jockey. It was the battle of a noise
against a timid, dully honorable man in hidden armor, but the nation shook in genuine hysteria until election day, when Ohio contributed another of her characteristic sons to the Presidential gallery

and Hanna, worn out by exertion, lighted his cigars in capitalistic peace. . . . Crane was shooting along the colored hills with his brother and the charming setter, Chester, and stopping to ask: " Will, isn't that cloud green? . . . But they wouldn't believe it if I put it in a book."

V: *FILIBUSTERING*

He loved babies, horses, oceans, or anything that offered an enigmatic surface to his thought. This comes strongly to view in a letter of 1895, when he was reading the criticism of Henry James: " What, though, does the man mean by disinterested contemplation? It won't wash. If you care enough about a thing to study it, you are interested and have stopped being disinterested. That's so, is it not? Well, Q.E.D. It clamours in my skull that there is no such thing as disinterested contemplation except that empty as a beerpail look that a babe turns on you and shrivels you to grass with. Does anybody know how a child thinks? The horrible thing about a kid is that it makes no excuses, none at all. They are much like breakers on a beach. They do something and that is all there is in it." So he put them under a detached observation and played with them by the hour. The detachment was so perfect that his tales of childhood in the town of Whilomville were called cruel when they appeared. But he had an absolute sentiment for children and on November 12, 1896, he wrote to a Miss Catherine Harris: " Thank you very much for your letter on Maggie. I will try to answer your questions properly and politely. Mrs. Howells was right in telling you that I have spent a great deal of time on the East Side and that I have no opinion of missions. That — to you — may not be a valid answer since perhaps you have been informed that I am not very friendly to Christianity as seen around town. I do not think that much can be done with the Bowery as long as the . . . [blurred] . . . are in their present state of conceit. A person who thinks himself superior to the rest of us because he has no job and no pride and no clean clothes is as badly conceited as Lillian Russell.[1] In a story of mine

[1] Crane singularly disliked this actress, for reasons unknown.

called 'An Experiment in Misery' I tried to make plain that the root of Bowery life is a sort of cowardice. Perhaps I mean a lack of ambition or to willingly be knocked flat and accept the licking. The missions for children are another thing and if you will have Mr. Rockefeller give me a hundred street cars and some money I will load all the babes off to some pink world where cows can lick their noses and they will never see their families any more. My good friend Edward Townsend — have you read his 'Daughter of the Tenements'? — has another opinion of the Bowery and it is certain to be better than mine. I had no other purpose in writing 'Maggie' than to show people to people as they seem to me.[1] If that be evil, make the most of it."

Then, on November 29th, writing from Jacksonville, Florida, to his brother William, a horse rises in the directions for his will and precedes the appointment of his literary executors — Howells, Garland, Willis Hawkins, and Ripley Hitchcock. William Crane was to be his sole executor and to receive a third of the estate, Edmund Crane was to have another third, and the remainder was divided between his two other brothers. But the horse, Peanuts: ". . . my saddle horse I would not like to have sold. I would prefer that he be kept in easy service at Hartwood and have him cared for as much as possible by Ed himself or by somebody whom it is absolutely certain would not maltreat him . . . and all I can add now is my love to you and Cornelia and all the babies."

Filibustering was much the fashion in the years 1895 and 1896. The condition of Cuba was now so acutely revolutionary that European papers were wondering why the Cleveland administration didn't interfere, just as in two years they would be indignant that the McKinley administration had interfered. A century of inartistic government tinted with sadism had wearied Cuba. Thirty thousand men were admittedly in revolt and thousands more were under suspicion. Enterprising ships passed carefully from the ragged coast of Florida, laden with cartridges and guns, to meet signals of the insurrectionists flashed from the rim of the tormented island. The Bacheller Syndicate had sent Crane in a hurry southward with a belt full of gold, and his ambition was to see real war. He also took

[1] "You abuse me for objectivity, calling it indifference to good and evil. . . . It's my task simply to show people as they are." — Anton Chekhov.

along for revision the manuscript of *The Third Violet*, which tells
how a young impressionist painter wooed a wealthy beauty, in dire
fear of her all the while, and won her in a drawing-room where a
colossal chandelier cast malign lights, as if a piece of prose could
fulfill a buried wish of his twentieth year. But Jacksonville bored
him, on first view, and he was alone who liked to have people always around him: "The town looks like soiled pasteboard that
some lunatic babies have been playing with. The same old women
are sitting on the hotel porches saying how well the climate suits
them and hurling the same lances with their eyes to begin bloodshed. . . . I went down the shore some distance yesterday and
watched the combers come counting in. Sometimes their addition
changes to multiplication and the music is confounded, like a war
of drummerboys." He had thrown a dinner-party into gay convulsions lately by insisting that music was "addition without pain,"
but the mathematical basis of music was not much discussed in
1896 and Crane could not quote Leibnitz in support of his view, as
he had never heard of Leibnitz, but the remark stuck in the memory of James Huneker, who thereafter insisted that Crane was an
intuitive natural philosopher. Meanwhile the "war of drummerboys" did not console him for the absence of friends and he desperately tried to finish *Peace and War*, as he called it. But Tolstoi's
endless panorama annoyed him. "He could have done the whole
business in one third of the time and made it just as wonderful. It
goes on and on like Texas."

Complete darkness covers him then until December 29th, when
the small and elderly steamer *Commodore* dropped down the river
from Jacksonville commanded by a strapping young Irish shipmas-
ter, Edward Murphy, and containing, besides cased guns and a ton
of cartridges, a large party of Cuban insurrectionists headed by one
Delgado. Crane's instinctive aversion to sheer theatrical points
would not let him believe that a plot had been arranged to frustrate
the cruise of the *Commodore*, but threats were shouted at her crew
in Spanish while she lay at the pier taking on coal, and a Cuban
student, Juan Broch, on his way northward, heard two men saying:
"It is all fixed. She will sink," in Castilian while he lingered on the
dock after bidding good-by to a friend. Jacksonville was a nest of
Cuban interests. Ralph D. Paine reports in *Roads of Adventure* the

location of the Cuban patriotic committee, and the Spanish secret service may well have been busy with the *Commodore*. The Spanish diplomatic powers at Washington had been protesting all autumn against the open sailing of filibustering ships from American ports. In a general embarrassment, the United States navy patrolled the coast, and Spanish gunboats were watchful. The *Commodore* went down-stream and met a squall as she passed from the St. John's River into pure salt water. Crane thought the ship no more seaworthy than an ice-house although she had been lately examined for reinsurance, and that she should begin to fill abreast of St. Augustine was not strange, but his last impression of the engine-room stayed deeply in his mind, with the fixity of all scenes in which the red he so loved was the commanding tone: " Water was swirling to and fro with the roll of the ship, fuming greasily around the half strangled machinery that still attempted to perform its duty. Steam arose from the water, and through its clouds shone the red glare of the dying fires. As for the stokers, death might have been with silence in this room. . . ."

The seasick Cubans lost their heads even before Captain Murphy turned the *Commodore* toward the shore. Their leader, Delgado, lost his temper and the jarring noise of quarrels rubbed on Crane's nerves. No one had slept for a day and a night and Crane was already ill before the ship began to founder. He watched her as she " shifted and settled as calmly as an animal curls down in the bush-grass " while he crouched beside the injured captain in a ten-foot dinghy, the last of the three boats to leave the heeling side of the steamer that disappeared noiselessly. " She might," he said, " have blown up to celebrate the New Year but she did not. She calmly left us orphans." The orphans were Captain Murphy, the ship's cook, Montgomery, an oiler, William Higgins, and Crane. Now, none of them knew the color of the sky.

The Open Boat is Crane's report of this wandering and Ralph Paine's statement shows that the sketch was corrected by Captain Murphy's memory. They rowed and the wind helped them toward their general aim, the point of Mosquito Inlet with its lighthouse and station. Murphy was helpless against the water-jar in the stern and Crane changed places with the oiler, Higgins, constantly. . . . They talked of food. " Canton flannel gulls flew near and far.

Sometimes they sat down on the sea, near patches of brown seaweed that rolled over the waves with a movement like carpets on a line in a gale. The birds sat comfortably in groups and were envied by some in the dinghy. . . . One came and evidently decided to alight on the top of the captain's head." Incorrigible, Crane's humor forbade him to neglect the absurd sight of Murphy timidly waving a hand to keep this gull from his soaked hair. Crests tumbled spray into the boat and the point of the lighthouse danced to view when the dinghy rose on the " jagged " waves. . . . A work of art progressed while his back ached with the work of the oar. Then followed woe; they were seen from the beach; men waved — then night came without rescue and a shark circled the drifting boat with a luminous wake. . . . " When it occurs to a man that nature does not regard him as important . . . he at first wishes to throw bricks at the temple and he hates deeply the fact that there are no bricks and no temples. Any visible expression of nature would surely be pelleted with his jeers. Then, if there be no tangible thing to hoot, he feels, perhaps, the desire to confront a personification and indulge in pleas . . . saying, ' Yes, but I love myself.' " . . . Dawn came and they turned the dinghy to the bobbing shore knowing they must swim after its inevitable upset. So they swam in a gripping current and Crane was flung clear across the floating boat by a comber. But even in that iced, stupendous motion he must see the water-flask bouncing gayly while he thrashed. They got ashore, somehow, and a wave smashed the spine of the oiler, Higgins, so that " a still and dripping shape was carried slowly up the beach and the land's welcome for it could be only the different and sinister hospitality of the grave."

He was not well, suffering from some intestinal trouble, when the *Commodore* sailed and now he had spent fifty hours almost sleepless, drenched with water, imperfectly fed on diluted whisky and biscuit. It is the opinion of his brother that health never returned and he certainly did himself no good by tramping and riding through the swamps below Jacksonville for weeks after the disaster. Rumors of very secret small expeditions kept the town wakeful and the navy was now most active off shore, sweeping plumes of searchlight across the skies at night. The tug *Three Friends* was the villain of the Spanish government now, and Crane might yearn for Cuba and wish that filibustering could be handed over to the adept management of a trust, but he could not get to the island, and the war between Greece and Turkey swung to view with all the promise of a fine testing-ground. " I am going to Greece for the *Journal*," he wrote, " and if the Red Badge is not all right I shall sell out my claim on literature and take up orange growing."

He was not without vanity and to be told, as he was constantly, that his book was mere fancy did not please him. To be told that he had imitated Zola's *La Débâcle* probably pleased him less, as he disliked most of Zola's work. Even *Nana*, that secret favorite of the American Puritan, bored him by its length although he found Nana herself amusing and, with his fatal lack of circumspection, informed a woman that " this girl in Zola is a real streetwalker. I mean, she does not fool around making excuses for her career. You must pardon me if I cannot agree that every painted woman on the streets of New York was brought there by some evil man. Nana, in the story, is honest. . . . Zola is a sincere writer but — is he much good? He hangs one thing to another and his story goes along but I find him pretty tiresome."

Effecting this irreverence casually he took orders from William Randolph Hearst and went off to England with a bad cold, having told Clyde Fitch that he would go on with their play when he came back from Greece. . . . The play had been a dozen times discussed and Fitch was impressed by the theme proposed. But the two brains fell from each other on an obvious point. There was to be this village in the Virginia of 1864 and the contentious armies would sweep in and out; a frightened young sentry would kill his best friend in the dark; a man would be afraid to touch a fallen body under orders to find papers in its pockets. Yes, said Fitch, but, now, about a heroine? Crane saw no woman concerned in this affair. They argued in the vapor of Mouquin's while men came up to borrow money from their generosity, helpless in the face of any claim by an old acquaintance, but the mind back of Fitch's rather wistful mask of a French dandy was conventional. A play without a " love interest " would never do. With all the playwright's atmospheric intelligence he was not daring outside small devices. His plays, alert, topical, and vivid ran always in due form. He consented to the usual and never shook off the habit of the theater even after success had piled about his anæmic body treasures of delicate furniture, of marmoreal surfaces shown against the lushness of purple velvet, of rare wines he could not use or relish in the slow starvation that rose from his earlier struggles to end his industry, his passions of gratitude, and his respectful service to lovely women with pallid golden hair. . . . A curious miasma seemed to flow on all these Americans of that century's last decade. Their lungs broke and slew them. They were slaughtered by their brothers or by crazy musicians. Fame had picked up a dagger and made use of it at random, but no bores died young.

Crane's sketch of his arrival in London shows his defect as an artist for popular use. He lacked the easy sentimentalism which so graces the notes of other American writers who get to London, but he saw a cab horse gravely slide down wet asphalt and was suddenly convinced that a man in a top hat might be human. He had silently distrusted top hats on Americans although their use was spreading and "there now exist many young men who consider that they could not successfully conduct their lives without this furniture. To speak generally I should say that the headgear then supplies them with a kind of ferocity of indifference. . . . Philosophy should always know that indifference is a militant thing." He also saw the newest novel of Hall Caine advertised on posters and startled William Heinemann by asking his English publisher if England read Hall Caine's works. Crane may have shared the purely American delusion that cheap novels are only read in the United States.

London contained, just then, dozens of American correspondents and he could at once meet Harold Frederic, principal agent of the *New York Times* in England and, in 1897, the author of *The Damnation of Theron Ware*, the sole courageous or truthful novel ever written by an American on the subject of religion. Frederic's fictions had changed, as their maker changed, from simple romanticism to a sort of shrewd, rough realistic tone and *Theron Ware* had for Crane the precise appeal of familiarity. He thought, privately, that " it could have been written a darned lot better," but he liked the story of the wavering young Methodist preacher who was bullied by sour old men of his stagnant church and learned to like pleasure at the hands of some crude hedonists who discharge their wisdom on Theron Ware as encyclopedic lumps, terribly prophesying the American novel of this moment. . . . Frederic's style suggests the man's diverse personality. He was shrewd, witty, and assertive to a degree. Even a dear friend would leave admissions that Frederic was not " finely fibred " and people who met him toward the end of a rather vexed life seldom much liked him, while his kindnesses to folk without importance and his desperate loyalties are as well remembered. He made many useful quips which survive in transmutations and borrowings. " Mr. Matthew Arnold plainly believes that Columbus should have been hanged in chains for the crime of discovering America. . . . In the United States it is considered sinful to drink champagne and eat lobster after midnight. Up to that hour it is a matter only of digestion. . . . Actresses are events which may take place in the most respectable family circles." His mind swung from balanced and liberal surveys to vehement prejudice, and the one letter available to this study displays: " Mr. Edward Garnett [1] would be an El Dorado to an American publisher of the superior class. He seems to be able to scent a new talent in fiction from a thousand miles and as a critic he possesses both sincerity and distinction of manner. He should be made known to Americans. . . . ' The Red Badge of Courage ' has probably been successful in the U. S. more because it is a Civil War story than because it is a brilliant study of an individual. . . . Henry James is an effeminate old donkey who lives with a herd of other donkeys around him and insists on being treated as if he were the Pope. He has licked dust from the floor of every third rate hostess in England. . . . Mr. James recommended Mr. Crane's novel before me in the house of our one mutual acquaintance and I was deterred from reading it for some days for that reason. With his usual lack of sense or generosity he described the book as an imitation of Zola's ' The Downfall ' which it resembles as much as I do Miss Ellen Terry." His encounters with Henry James were infrequent but dreadful to people who preferred that the older man's gauzy periphery of sentiments and perceptual tenderness should remain unbruised. In 1895, for instance, Frederic listened while the novelist outlined a charming tour of cathedral towns to an American lady and then advised her to look

---

[1] He had no personal acquaintance with Mr. Garnett.

through the slums of Liverpool and Manchester as well. . . . The
florid, tall man haunted Ireland in hope of seeing a revolution
start, but when a row began between peasants of his favorite fishing village and the British constabulary, he intervened. He abomi-
nated all the capacities of Oscar Wilde, but when the grand fakir
was on trial, at last, refused to allow exaggerations to be sent to
his newspaper and turned loudly on a group of gossips in a club
with: " Why do you sit and lie about the poor devil when he's
done for? " He had a war always threatening with any exquisite
and some of his rudenesses were wondrous. " Your new book held
me spellbound," he told a writer of thinly charming essays who
started to return thanks and was halted by: " Yes, I rode clear past
my station. The guard had to wake me up at the next one." Such
wit belongs in the snuffbox of Talleyrand. But Frederic had an
honest, quite unaffected admiration for Crane and led him into
the Savage on March 26th as though, says a witness, he had invented the boy.

They appeared together at a luncheon given for Crane by Richard Harding Davis on March 28th in the Savoy and there Crane
was presented to James Barrie, Justin McCarthy, Anthony Hope,
and some more. Frederic followed his new friend to Dover and
said good-by on April 1st, giving him into the keeping of Henry
Sanford Bennett, a Canadian, on his way to Greece also. Bennett
spoke French and guided Crane through Paris on April 2nd, making discoveries about the silent American that ended with a flash
of Crane's disgust in Notre Dame where some procession was passing toward the altar in color and music. Bennett was watching this
ceremony when Crane pulled his arm and broke out: " I can't
stand that nonsense! " Color, music, and the traditional pathos of
mass made no excuse to his nature for theatrical display. He looked
with indifference at a review of cavalry but made Bennett talk to
a trooper for him about horses in the French service and ask if the
man had been at Gravelotte in 1870. " He took," said Bennett,
" not the slightest interest in any of the show places except the
Luxembourg gardens and I had to help him talk to some French
children there."

Paris never properly impressed Crane, who spent his time on the
way to Greece trying to master some phrases of French, suddenly

worried because this war must be fought in strange tongues and he could speak only English. At Basel he mailed a letter: "I now know that I am an imbecile of rank. If nobody shoots me and I get back alive through those Indians in London I will stay home until there is a nice war in Mexico where it does not matter what you talk so long as you can curse immoderately. Willie Hearst has made a bad bargain." . . . He was right. Part of his prompt and flat failure as a war correspondent lay in his helplessness. He must rely on guides and interpreters throughout the brief campaign. The *New York Journal* and the *Westminster Gazette* had made a bad bargain. Even his sense of the comic straggled out under the blight and he could not well enjoy Athens with its masses of tourists who had come to see a real war comfortably. Notes of clear impression mingle with his reporting, but his whole raid into Greece was a series of irritations and he wrote: "I guess that I expected some sublime force to lift me in air and let me watch. Well, no! Like trying to see a bum vaudeville show from behind a fat man who wiggles. I have not been well either."

He was not well and, given a practical nature, he would have resigned his post in Paris. Perpetual indigestion bothered him and he found the Greek food abominable. Meanwhile the Crown Prince Constantine had begun practice of his specialty by running away from combat, to the disgust of all Greece, and Crane arrived at Velestinos eight hours after the beginning of the great engagement that finished the war. He had gone plunging along the line of emptied hilltowns and villages that lay between Velestinos and Volo and came hurrying back with other stragglers to find Richard Harding Davis and John Bass the only American correspondents on the scene of the long duel between the ill-officered Greek infantrymen and the agile Turkish force that peppered the trenches from an elevation. The war was lost, Davis accurately declared, in the cafés of Athens, and like Crane the expert raged at the command of the willing soldiers by dandies so ineffective. Davis went swiftly off to London, and Crane, worn out, suffering from attacks of bowel trouble, strolled about Athens with Julian Ralph, who marveled finding that the impressionists knew nothing of Greek architecture and could not distinguish types of columns on the Acropolis.

Crane had no sense of line. His few attempts to draw a human shape are not even in proportion and the whole mass of his impressions, transcribed so brilliantly from a visible scene, are truly " impressions " and not careful photographs. He seldom mentions contour in his quick passages of description. He saw the frenzied peasants rushing down the mountain into Volo: " It was a freshet that might sear the face of the tall, quiet mountain; it might draw a livid line across the land, this downpour of fear with a thousand homes adrift in the current — men, women, babes, animals. From it there arose a constant babble of tongues, shrill, broken, and sometimes choking, as from men drowning. Many made gestures, painting their agonies on the air with fingers that twirled swiftly. The blue bay with its pointed ships, and the white town lay below them, distant, flat, serene." The people of his tales have very seldom more than a suggestion of body. A man has " indomitable whiskers " or some clothes. The lad in *The Red Badge of Courage*, late in the book, has a bronzed throat. The pretty girl of *The Third Violet* is simply something the artist would like to paint — a trick of entry that Crane left to some thousands of writers. Since his art has lately been often likened to that of Anton Chekhov with inevitable comments by American critics as to his " able imitations " of the Russian, whose works were not, while Crane lived, known outside Russia, there is an interest in the parallel, but Crane never so elaborated his pictures of people as did Chekhov in *The Steppes*, and his fullest description of a being is that of his brother's setter, Chester, appearing as Stanley in *The Third Violet*. The contour of man had no particular spell for him and when he was asked to describe Gertrude Kingston, the English actress who was his choice as the prettiest woman on the London stage, he said: " Well, she's got black hair and a nose," which left James Huneker unenlightened.

These habits didn't prevent his enjoyment of prolix or exact art. He valiantly argued with Julian Ralph in Athens that *The Portrait of a Lady* was a masterpiece. Tolstoi's *Anna Karenina* was " too long because he has to stop and preach but it's a bully book." He adored Tolstoi the superb and ruthless artist, but for Tolstoi the emotional pedagogue, the pilgrim of redemption, he had no use. No fact so clearly sets Crane apart from Americans of his day and shows the course of his damnation by that criticism which still, for all the changing tone of these last years, most resembles a wavering lady in a dark crinoline, prudently girdled with chaste iron. Scratch an American critic, says the astute Julian Street, and you find a Yankee schoolmarm. To that instructive gentlewoman Crane appeared as a rowdy little boy who brought dead mice to school, a lurid and irregular child who upset the other children and then ran off before he could be taught on some filibustering game of his own making to leave a boy's cry trailing its shrill beauty against the stupid night.

In tumultuous Athens, though, Crane was ill of a mild dysentery and was nursed by a fair, affable woman, older than himself, Cora Taylor, who had fallen in love with him at Jacksonville and had come after him to Greece. So writing from Paris on September 2nd, he told Sanford Bennett: " Frederic and Mr. Heinemann have been urging me to stay in England for a time. So my wife — after practicing nine days I can write that without a jump — and I will be hunting a house or an attic in London pretty soon."

VI: *LONDON TO CUBA*

AN AMERICAN writer is safest abroad when he has somewhere left in storage his entire critical sense and has for the voyage replaced it by an emotional willingness comparable to the felicity of a noticed puppy. He may then roam in his destined character giving neither pleasure nor offense to men who will accept his admirations and hear his raptures as mature women might accept the flowers and phrases of some harmless schoolboy. On the Continent he will be, mostly, the child of the world's milch cow, but in England he must be wary as are boorish relations of whose manners something too much is known.

Crane's extreme dislike of Robert Louis Stevenson got him in trouble at William Heinemann's table early in October when he recklessly or absently assured two of the dead Scot's correspondents that Stevenson bored him. All through his first English winter he was forever meeting filaments of that monstrous reputation then being groomed for the American market by adoring hands. It had been well and naturally established in England that " R. L. S." was an American idol, and a transatlantic who didn't admire may have seemed vastly affected. On October 12th Crane wrote: " I believe in ghosts. Mr. Stevenson has not passed away far enough. He is all around town."

There was another spook, in better flesh, whose reputation was not, in 1897, amenable to grooming. Literary London was shaken or amused by the rumor of memoirs being written in Reading Gaol by Oscar Wilde, and Henry Harland, once an editor of the *Yellow Book*, assured Crane that terrible things might be expected to happen if the collapsed dandy found a publisher for his book of memories. Crane again was bored. Only some passages of Wilde's plays had any interest for him, and the poet in his view was just a sentimental neurotic who should be shipped for treatment to S. Weir Mitchell " or some other doctor who knows all about that kind of thing." He would later be shocked and nauseated by the sight of Wilde's blotched and powdered face bleating compliments at him in the smoke of the Café Procope, but now his refusal to discuss Oscar as a splendid sinner irritated Harland sharply. A pet criminal is always sacred, but Wilde had acquired a curious dignity because his case was restricted, in conversation, to small and liberal circles. In Crane's disgusted commentary: " Wilde was a mildewed chump. He has a disease and they all gas about him as though there was a hell and he came up out of it. . . . Mr. Yeats is the only man I have met who talks of Wilde with any sense. The others talk like a lot of little girls at a Sunday School party when a kid says a wicked word in a corner." Perhaps it was Crane's misfortune to be a little more modern in 1897 than was necessary. Or perhaps a young man who had sat in tramp's clothes by night in Union Square listening to darkened chatter of real tramps might not be so thrilled over the neurosis of an Irish poet. His indifference to the purple legend was disheartening. He failed of taking Oscar Wilde seriously or sadly and that, too, was held to be an affectation.

There was no tumult in the high world of letters English because Stephen Crane had rented a villa named Ravensbrook at Oxted in Surrey and proposed to make a stay. He was even snubbed with a vehemence that still bewilders the witnesses by George Meredith on the steps of a club before Crane had spoken to the celebrity. Algernon Charles Swinburne asked him to tea at Putney and, discovering that Crane neither read nor talked French, entertained the American by translating bits of a sixteenth-century manuscript to him. Extremely sensitive to courtesies of men older than himself, Crane was still somewhat wearied by this cultivated afternoon and spent the evening tramping with Robert Barr through a slum not then well advertised in fiction, the Limehouse now illustrious and now, as then, very dull indeed.

He was so sensitive to attentions of people more ancient than Stephen Crane that the trait lends itself to psychiatric description. Many of his letters were written to two ladies fifteen years ahead of him, on whom he lavished luncheons in his prosperous spring of 1896. . . . They were both dyspeptic. He would turn from the prettiest girl in a crowded room to chat with an elderly lady. Favors of middle-aged folk had some special meaning for the final child of a long family, used to petting and scolding from brothers and sisters who had been longer living. When he was seventeen he doted on a Canadian gentlewoman with seven infants. At twenty-six he was ordered by James Huneker to read Balzac and only the contrary opinion of another authority stopped him. And now he was ordered by Harold Frederic to write a novel about his trip to Greece and, in November of 1897, he began it. Mr. Frederic thought he should, so he would. But *Active Service* somehow began itself slowly and lagged on his desk at Oxted while he took up other tales and finished *The Monster* one day in early December, having spent a whole week of interrupted evenings on the long story, which shows every strength and every weakness of his armory. Harold Frederic strolled over from Robert Barr's house at Woldingham, within sight of the dank villa grown already detestable to Crane, and with Sanford Bennett made an audience for the reading aloud of the fantasy.

The Monster is a study of popular stupidity. The foremost doctor of Whilomville restores to life a vain Negro hostler who has rescued his small son from a burning house. Dr. Trescott's sentiment keeps alive this fellow, now an idiot and faceless. The sentimentality of Whilomville has acclaimed Henry Johnson a hero and a martyr while he was thought dying. Now the kindly and aimless monster terrifies first the Negroes who are paid to lodge him, then a children's party, then his former mistress, the belle of Watermelon Alley. The town swings against the surgeon who has kept Henry Johnson in being and the subject passes in vocal exhibition through the gossip of the barber's shop and through the kitchen wherein Martha Goodwin, a woman who was nothing but the mausoleum of a dead passion, gives judgment on the world's affairs and helps forward all local troubles by a series of sniffs. The sermon on useless pity completes itself with the picture of Dr. Trescott counting unused teacups on his wife's neglected table. Sentimentality has clubbed sentiment to death in Whilomville. *The Monster* suffers from a defect of exuberance; Crane's passion for recording fatuous conversations reaches a height twice in the narrative. The chatter in the barber's shop would not again be equaled for sheer emptiness until James Joyce wrote his *Portrait of the Artist as a Young Man,* but it is dangerous to lay emptiness before emptiness without pointing out the vacuum and Crane's satire is implicit. To the taste of 1897, *The Monster* was plainly a horrible tale of a man who had no face and, when Paul Reynolds offered it to the *Century* it was refused with speed, an editor explaining to the puzzled agent: " We couldn't publish that thing with half the expectant mothers in America on our subscription list! " Even to Harold Frederic the story was offensive and he told Crane to throw it away. The other half of the audience, Mr. Bennett, promptly gave proof of the power of impressionism, deftly handled, as a mode in fiction. He was for years troubled by a memory of the Negro's shattered visage and, picking up the tale after Crane died, was surprised to find that all his horror had been excited by the simple statement: " He had no face."

Crane thrashed up and down the room waiting for luncheon and arguing passionately while he tapped the butt of his Mexican revolver on furniture. What was wrong with people, anyhow? Here was a lot of ink on white paper and a story " with some sense in it." Why be frightened? His hopeless failure to catch the emotional viewpoint of average readers or, for that matter, of average writers came flashing up. " Men of sense " would not care if Henry Johnson had a face or no. The argument blazed. Mr. Bennett sat listening to the battle that lasted all through luncheon and ended in explosion. Frederic turned his guns on *The Nigger of the Narcissus,* and Crane, crashing down the revolver fatally on a dessert plate, yelled: " You and I and Kipling couldn't have written the Nigger! " Thus are these artists.

It has been worth while to detail this abstract quarrel since Crane was swiftly reported in New York as Harold Frederic's slave and subject. They were not seen so on November 30th by an American lawyer who called at Oxted. Next day he wrote to his wife: " Mr. [John] Stokes gave me a note of introduction to Mr. Crane and he was very pleasant in a quiet, boyish way when I got to his house. It surprised me how little he uses slang when his books are full of it and how young he is. Mrs. Crane asked me to stay for lunch. She is a southerner and very nice. I should imagine her to be six or seven years older than Mr. Crane with big blue eyes and reddish hair. Mr. Frederic, the *New York Times* correspondent came in the middle of the lunch with five other men and it was very embarrassing for Mrs. Crane as they were not expected. Mr. Frederic is not at all agreeable. He is funny in a sarcastic way about politics and people but he kept interrupting everybody else and was downright rude to Mr. Crane several times. They made Mr. Crane shoot with his revolver after lunch and he is a very fine shot. Some children came over from the next house to watch and Mrs. Crane made biscuit for tea. She is a wonderful cook."

By December a visible strain came on Crane's purse and Cora Crane's cookery. He wrote to Acton Davies: " Will you see if X and Y could let me have what they borrowed last May? I took X's note for $300 and Y owes me about $250. I hate to press nice fellows but it costs more to live over here than I was led to believe and some of these Comanche braves seem to think I am running a free lunch counter. Seven men have been staying over Sunday." So the plump little dramatic reporter ran Crane's errand in New York and failed to collect from men who hardly knew Crane and meanwhile parties of seven or, once, nine men came dropping down to convenient Oxted for Sundays of talk and poker. More game pies and claret must be sent for and, on December 3rd, he wrote: " I have been staying at this hotel " — it was Brown's, in Dover

Street — " two days so as to finish some work. Cora just now wires me that she has got rid of some people who have been boarding with us for three days, so I can go home."

He was, in short, pillaged by people who found his chromatic talk and his wife's biscuit admirable while his helpless good nature couldn't or didn't repel visitors scarcely agreeable. At tea in John Hay's house he told the Ambassador, after being congratulated on his success: " I wish success paid me a salary, sir," with a grin. In a few minutes the grin must have faded. A Countess asked him about his parents and when she heard that his father had been a Methodist pastor broke into laughter of some quality offensive to Hay and probably searing to Crane, who thereafter recorded that Lady Cardigan had no more manners than a streetwalker. This was, outside a small group of intimates, his last truthful statement as to his family in England and a few days later he told a lady dining beside him in the house of Hoyt De Fries that his father was a Presbyterian Cardinal.

" Oh," said she, " do Dissenters have cardinals in the States? "

The English unconsciousness of American habits and customs did not annoy him but it entertained him largely and he got an amusement out of wholesale lies: " They will believe anything wild or impossible you tell them and then if you say your brother has a bathtub in his house they — ever so politely — call you a perjured falsifier of facts. I told a seemingly sane man at Mrs. Garnett's that I got my artistic education on the Bowery and he said, ' Oh, really? So they have a school of fine arts there? ' I had, you see, just told Mrs. Garnett while this mummy listened all about the Bowery — in so far as I could tell a woman about the Bowery — but that made no difference to this John Bull. Now I am going to wave the starry flag of freedom a little " (he was writing to Huneker) " even if you contemn the practice in one who knows not Balzac and Dostoywhat'shisname. You Indians have been wasting wind in telling me how ' Unintrusive' and ' DELICATE ' I would find English manners. I don't. It has not been the habit of people to meet at Mr. Howells or Mr. Phillips or Mrs. Sonntages to let fall my hand and begin to quickly ask me how much money I make and from which French realist I shall steal my next book. For it has been proven to me fully and carefully by authority that all my books are stolen from the French. They stand me against walls with a teacup in my hand and tell me how I have stolen all my things from De Maupassant, Zola, Loti and the bloke who wrote — I forget the book. I find nothing ' unintrusive ' or ' delicate ' in these goings on. The simple rustic villagers of Port Jervis have as good manners as some of the flower of England's literary set."

It was not believed in England that he was truly ill informed in letters and he tired of explaining that some books of criticism and a few paper-backed copies of Flaubert and de Maupassant in translation were his acquaintances, casually made, with the French nineteenth century. He had never read Stendhal's *La Chartreuse de Parme*, and Henry Harland's insistence that he must have read it before writing *The Red Badge of Courage* finally angered him. The journalists at the Savage were willing to take him as an amusing companion and the taverns of London were more interesting than drawing-rooms where " everybody knows everybody else's business in the superlative degree and everybody reads everybody's books mainly — unless I am blind — to be at once able to tell everybody else how bad they are. Politics and literature have got wonderfully boiled into a kind of chowder. I feel like a clam."

Winter brought bad colds and a trip to Harold Frederic's pet Irish fishing village. On February 5th he dined with Frederic and Charles Griswold, an American tourist, at Richmond. To this matrix of a pleasant evening was suddenly added a nobleman then in alliance with a lady never certain as to her nationality, understood to be the honored subject of verses in the *Yellow Book* and reputed chaste though seldom sober. The party came back to Mr. Griswold's rooms in London and Madame Zipango (the name is certainly international) was imitating Yvette Guilbert when Henry James appeared to pay his young compatriot a call. The correct and the incorrect swam together in a frightful collision. Crane withdrew the elderly novelist to a corner and talked style until the fantastic woman poured champagne in the top hat of Henry James. Her noble lover had gone to sleep. Frederic was amused. The wretched host of this group was too young and too frightened to do anything preventive and Crane, coldly tactful, got the handsome creature out of the hotel, then came back to aid in the restoration of the abused hat.

Crane did not find this funny. In the next week he wrote: " I
agree with you that Mr. James has ridiculous traits and lately I have
seen him make a holy show of himself in a situation that — on my
honour — would have been simple to an ordinary man. But it seems
impossible to dislike him. He is so kind to everybody. . . ."

He was so kind. From the sacred fount of his self-adoration there
yet welled on gifted folk those pools of tender correspondence and
those courtesies a trifle tedious, one hears, but rendered with such
grace. Ada Rehan might vexedly call him " my dear snob " across
a luncheon-table, but she would repent for weeks that bit of unpremeditated, natural frankness. Another actress, in a forgetful
breath, assured him that she found his friend Paul Bourget's novels vulgar and then shook as the deep voice stammered: " Vul — "
to begin some sentence of pained expostulation that ended in mere
syllables of affront. He was no longer a man. Henry James was a
colored and complicated ritual that demanded of spectators a reverence unfailingly accorded. People who swooned under the burden of his final method sat and sat in pleasure while that astonishing egotism bared in slow phrases its detached and charming appreciation of its own singular skill. He had written plays incoherent
and banal in exquisite English for the simple and admitted purpose of making money " as much and as soon as possible," and his
votaries shuddered when the plebeians hooted *Guy Domville* from
the stage. He committed in reviews consummate silliness such as
his famous statement of tears shed over the butchered children of
Rudyard Kipling's *Drums of the Fore and Aft* with its added comment on the dreadful dirtiness of the dead drummers. The sob balanced the snobbery and nobody jeered, save one remote and logical
American. Critics mired themselves in verbal anguish over his successive novels. This plain and limited old bachelor commanded the
world to respect him and the world obeyed. He was so kind.

Life waned for this man in his absurd and wonderful position,
the patron of a cult. His books were so little read in America that
he could be mentioned as " the late Henry James " in 1898 at a
public banquet without exciting laughter. Americans invading England found, to their horror or secret relief, that nobody seemed to
read his books in the territory assigned to his renown. But to no
other writer in the Anglo-American field were attached such bris-

tling adherents! He was holy and impeccable to the gaze of innumerable talented folk. Mrs. Humphry Ward fell speechless and scarlet when it was said, in her presence, that Mr. James had derived his tale *Paste* from de Maupassant, and another votary still living ordered from his house a heretic who chose to argue that the Master's preoccupation with refinements was a vulgar habit. He was prim and circumspect, as befitted the child grown old who was ordered at the age of seven to compose a note of apology for appearing barefoot on the porch of a seaside villa before callers, and he was the pet of cynical voluptuaries. He was a provincial sentimentalist touted by worshippers as the last flower of European culture while he recoiled in amazement from the profound civilization of Havelock Ellis, who would and, " so successfully delicate in his attack on the matter of these abominations that one reads, I may say, almost painlessly," did write of sexual deflections and gross social phenomena without any sign of shock. This fading life of Henry James had passed in a series of recoils. Civilization, in his sight, seems to have been not the overthrow of empty inhibitions but an exaltation of limits. He had fled — and who blames him? — from a society that became, in his dreams, a tentacled beast ready always to overpower his individual trend, but he remained a Bostonian by every implication of his rare and scrupulous art. Even when in *The Turn of the Screw* he attempted to tell the story of " abominations " he must produce it with ghosts for sinners and the corrupted bodies must be those of children impossible and lovely as the babes of his predecessor Hawthorne. This master of groomed circumstance had found out a sunny garden where poisons blew as perfumes too heavy for a refined sense and crimes were shadows, not clouds, that swept across his shaved and watered turf.

Destiny now jolted the European sod beneath the feet of loitering transatlantics. On the night of February 15th the battleship *Maine* was blown up in the harbor of Havana and in two days it was known that treachery was suspected by the American government. The world's press went mad with all the brilliance of its eternal parochialism and any student in popular misinformation may gather material of delicious merits from the abiding files. Henry James was distressed by the " seeming inaccuracy of the Parisian, or indeed of all the Continental reports " and Stephen

Crane was bored at once to hear that "American troops always
run at the first shot and there is no such thing as the U. S. Navy.
These matters were clearly proven to me last night at the Savage
by a Mr. Wyndham who once met General Grant. I have vainly
tried to tell some good men and true that Cuba is not on friendly
terms with California but they will have it that one gets on a tug
at San Francisco to go to Havana."

He took the end of the *Maine* so calmly that some of his friends
were appalled. The quality of his nature forbade outcries after an
event and his "fatalism" seems rather to have been a severe reticence in the sight of disasters. The American colony in London
grew hysteric and John Stokes reproached Crane with his coolness
while the English press assumed an indignant tone and in Paris
La Patrie invented a formula of objections. Were the compatriots
of Cervantes and Velasquez to be accused of sinking a warship in
time of peace? Some emotional incantation, now unknown, summoned up Velasquez and Cervantes as the Castor and Pollux of
the moment in aid of Spain. These artists were invoked ceaselessly
and jumped the Channel. . . . All at once Americans discovered
themselves to be the dogs of the universe. The issue was confused
by the report of the commission which investigated the sinking of
the *Maine* and with a certainty neither graceful nor diplomatic
experts French, English, and German in the capitals of those lands
asserted that the commission lied in all its findings. Dislike of the
United States turned journals formerly loud in their insistence
that the United States should intervene on behalf of Cuba. Alternately Spain was a tottering lady to be defended from the assaults
of a brutal ruffian or a proud power capable of sweeping American
fleets and troops from the map with one gesture. The press of
America was silly in its brashness and the press of Europe was silly
from contempt long hoarded in its editorial brain. The spectacle
was repeated, of course, later, but its vividness in 1898 bewildered
the Yankee and roused the Southerner. In Europe the nose of the
golden calf was slapped with such violence that the poor beast began, not without primitive reasons, to turn and canter lowing
homeward. On March 10th landlords in Paris were quaintly worried by the flight of Americans from a city in which they were
daily insulted and the proprietors of hotels addressed themselves

in some agitation to the newspapers. Tinkling harshly, the dollar rolled away from the scene of its worship and cynics were diverted by the minatory sound. . . . The American's one value was in motion, and vulgar, acutely sensitive to that noise, Joseph Chamberlain advised: " Care should be taken that the American financial authorities do not take offence."

Another excitement shook London in the middle of March. Paying huge prices for stalls the smart world went in its best coat to see a benefit arranged for Nellie Farren, crippled and penniless in her discarded age. Magnificents who had refused to contribute a pound to her comfort now blubbered duly in boxes while the little paralytic was borne on the stage to croak her thanks. Henry Irving kindly recited *The Dream of Eugene Aram* and Ellen Terry loosed the enchantment of her voice as Ophelia. Marie Tempest sang a ballad from *The Geisha* and a whole train of celebrated actresses deployed their graces before Crane, whose evening dress was painfully tight, he wrote, but " Oscar Hammerstein couldn't get people to make bigger fools of themselves. Except Willie Hearst nobody understands the popular mind as well as Oscar. I see no difference between the *Journal* and Hammerstein's roofgarden. You get the blonde with the tincan in her gullet and the comic speaker and the song about mother's wayward boy in both shows. I must affiliate with Hammerstein. Mr. Conrad and I are writing a new kind of play."

But, in Washington, the Senator from Vermont had read his dry, emotionless report on the condition of Cuba and in a bar of Broadway some man lowered his glass with the wavering sentence: " Gentlemen, remember the *Maine!* " Imperfect history tells us only that he had a red mustache, but war was now inevitable and, for once, his court turned unbelieving eyes on Mark Hanna when he grunted that Spain could be licked in six months. The Assistant Secretary of the Navy paused before resigning his post to frustrate the revealed wish of some fifty Methodist and Baptist preachers in self-appointed committee that all Roman Catholic chaplains be withdrawn from ships sent to action, then went off to gather a regiment of cavalry. With parade and consequence promptly recorded in the social columns hundreds of well-washed New Yorkers offered their services to their country and bloody squadrons sailed

in print from Cadiz to ravage the American seaboard with guns of
a caliber not yet found. . . . Whether the nation was preparing
to avenge the *Maine* or to free Cuba was quite uncertain in the
nation's mind, but somebody was going to suffer and Crane wrote:
" This war will be fought in English. I can at least swear in Spanish and it will be more comfortable all around. But I have not decided on going yet."

He was ill. After a cerebral hemorrhage Harold Frederic was
dying, so consciously that he lifted aside a corner of the handkerchief partly veiling his distorted face to wink at callers who told
him he would soon be well again. And, dying, the hedonist accepted Christian Science treatment to please a devoted woman
who was made a scandal in the press with all the usual vulgarities
attendant on an erratic and published man's vanishing. He had
taken close hold on Crane's affection, though, and the younger
American lingered. Then, suddenly, he left a note at Sanford Bennett's rooms: " Sorry not to have seen you. I have raised the wind
and sail tomorrow. Nothing I can do for Harold. Barr will look
after him. Write me at Hartwood, N. Y., care of Edmund Crane.
Shall get myself taken in the Navy if possible." He was so swiftly
out of England that guests came down to Oxted and were surprised to find him gone. Only after he sailed the *World* cabled to
secure his services and he did not present himself at the office in
New York until a naval recruiting bureau had declined his body.
Then he was off to Key West, where Sampson's fleet pivoted on
the mangy little city filled with journalists, harlots, and mosquitoes,
who all found a nightly meeting-place in the gambling-hell. Thence
came to Robert Barr a letter postmarked May 23rd: " You should
see the jay who runs the table here. He is straight out of a dime
novel, moustache and all, with bunches of diamonds like cheap
chandeliers on each hand. Now I owe Harold an apology for laughing when he said they would tear me in pieces the minute my back
was turned. Hi, Harold! I apologize! Did you know me for a morphine eater? A man who has known me ten years tells me that all
my books are written while I am drenched with morphine. The
joke is on me."

But the gambling-hell was delightful and he took notes of its
owner's conversation. The man knew easily, he said, nine hun-

dred distinct oaths. When he told bawdy tales the ceiling changed
color and his sarcasm was so theatrically effective that it appears
too theatrical in *Moonlight on the Snow*. This character must be
made use of in the play and Crane's character was blighted more
deeply while he lounged, pointed out to strangers, in the smoky
rooms already hot with tropical spring. He missed the fleet's bombardment of Matanzas, but once the flagship carried him so closely
by the breakers lazily flapping crystal foam on the island's sands
that he could see a naked child tossing its hands in welcome from
the shore.

VII: CHANGE

THAT irrelevant baby becomes a convenient symbol of Crane's
doubled nature. He still wanted to push his growing frailty against
the random gestures of society's bad behavior. He would be in the
middle of matters with which, as an artist, he found himself concerned. Sense and the warnings of friends should have kept him
away from Cuba, but his curiosity took him there quite inevitably.
The man had not yet learned certain high values of posture: as a
superior writer he should have sentimentalized his position, retiring gravely into an attitude, but the elaborate fustian of his profession had no charm for him at the age of twenty-six and here
was this comprehensible war to be heard in English with many of
his comrades impatient at Key West or dodging in dispatch boats
after Sampson's fleet as it swept along the island's northern coast.
So he appeared and won three hundred dollars from the estimable
gambler in intervals of slow cruising on the tug *Three Friends* with
a bundle of manuscript and the worst equipment for a campaign
ever seen.

He was at once wonderfully disliked by some men who here saw
Stevie Crane for the first time. Travel and reputation had not made
him less reserved and he gave no proper account of his stay in England. England was all right. He had met some bully people. No, he
hadn't seen much of Rudyard Kipling and while he found James
Barrie a nice fellow he did not praise the new favorite's work. There

was a prompt impression of chilly listlessness and to a young gentleman who told him how greatly he resembled Robert Louis
Stevenson Crane straightway answered: " I hope I outgrow it," and
that, too, was not diplomatic. Old friends thought him little
changed and his poker was as bad as ever.

The war now halted while Europe took care to revise its opinion
of the American navy after Dewey massacred a feeble collection of
Spanish gunboats in Manila Bay. Lord Salisbury paraphrased for the
Primrose League, on May 4th, some ideas of Friedrich Nietzsche as
to dying states and the rights of the stronger nations. Crane grinned
a good deal over the new tone in dispatches from abroad and went
one day quickly to look at the sandy camping-place appointed for
troop gathering at Tampa in the rising temperature of May's last
weeks. There he cast an eye on volunteer regiments assembling and
disgusted correspondents by one of his usual failures in enthusiasm.
The volunteers had forsaken their business and already underwent
the hardships of the soldier without complaint. This was plainly
noble of the volunteers, but Crane affronted a group by asking:
" Don't the militia take an oath to defend the country anyhow? "
and only Frederic Remington joined him in this negative state of
mind while the woes of the militia were telegraphed daily to journals which either suppressed the details or began, as no battles occupied front pages, to make a cause against the laborious Alger,
Secretary of War, who was following the routine of his task and
giving proper orders never strictly obeyed. Crane gave a lad from
Wisconsin, discharged for heart trouble without any means of leaving Tampa, the necessary fifty dollars for his fare, then went back
to Key West and the dispatch boat's motion on a sea now troubled
by mythical Spanish keels. Admiral Cervera's swift squadron had
eluded Commodore Schley and lay serene in the harbor of Santiago,
but Admiral Camara's monstrous armament was roaming in the
sophisticated press of New York and old ladies of Nantucket Island
were agitated by glimpses of smoke on the horizon.

" The sailormen of Sampson's big canoe," Crane wrote from the
Three Friends on June 2nd, " ought to make us all ashamed of our
trade. The papers come aboard the flagship and who, I ask, want to
see this goulash of legendary lies and solemn rumours? We do, we
the cynics of Fleet Street and Park Row, the Rudyards, the lords of

the popular mind. The Jackies just look at all this manure and say, Well — and go on polishing brass. Davis and I tried to make them excited by donations of headlines and they said, Well — and peeled more onions. It is now the fashion of all hotel porches at Tampa and Key West to run Davis down because he has declined a captaincy in the army in order to keep his contract with his paper. The teaparty has to have a topic."

Other topics being scarce, he revised a story called *Vashti in the Dark* which tells how a young Methodist preacher from the South killed himself after discovering that his wife had been ravished by a Negro in a forest at night. To Acton Davies, who typed the manuscript, this was one of Crane's best tales, but no magazine ever bought it and Crane burned it in one of his rare fits of pique. Now he was struck by a title for a novel — "The Merry Go Round." This would be the adventures of a wandering carrousel in the Southwest and along the Atlantic shore. Projects boiled in him while the tug rocked and was nearly mangled by the U. S. S. *Machias* one hot night. James Pinker, his English agent, was paying forty pounds for each thousand words of his prose, so there might be a trip around the world, because "a Polish friend of mine who is an unancient mariner says I would be dippy over Polynesia." Meanwhile he lounged and wondered, with crescent boredom, how to make an end of *Active Service*, and out of that contemplation rose a remark on a postcard: "A reporter is no hero for a novel."

He came to the decision at the wrong second of journalistic history. In Tampa some reporters were doing the heroic thing. The process of vision had brought revolt, and offices in New York were bothered by facts, facts of all sorts, written and wired from the buzzing luxury of the hotel where ladies following chastely that odd camp danced under colored lights. Windy patriotism and romance were collapsing into hot veracity. The men of the press saw a willing army ill fed, badly dressed for a climate grown tormenting, and made ready for transport in ships hardly fitted to carry uncritical cattle. John Jacob Astor was offering to pay, since the government wouldn't, for a decent supply of water and many eyes saw the beginning of a crime on men rendered defenseless by discipline. The nation had engaged in a sentimental war and whooped at home for news of bloodshed. The symbol of Tampa was a rocking-chair in cartoons and already Major-General Shafter was complaining of his health to the attachés of Germany and Great Britain. Back from Florida spread a humming noise of discontent. The regular army was worthless. The war ought to be turned over to the volunteer officers directly. Everything was wrong. The papers said so.

On June 10th six hundred Marines landed from a bevy of gunboats on the eastern bank of Guantanamo's charming bay below Santiago, and the dispatch tug shed Crane with the force, enchanted by the glow of a burning village whence a fiery light was thrown upon some palms and " made them into enormous crimson feathers." The Marines in tawny linen uniforms camped on a flat plateau that interrupted this steep shore, and Crane talked all night long to a surgeon named Gibbs about consumptions while trenches were dug. Men were annoyed by the active Cuban land-crab's scuttling on their faces as they slept. Next afternoon, while they bathed in squads from the littered beach, firing began suddenly and Cuban scouts brought word that the guerrillas were the marksmen. Naked Marines and dressed Marines shot for an hour against the dense, lustrous green of the jungle and night came with vehemence while Crane lugged water up the hill, canteens rattling by the dozen from shoulders that already shivered. The surgeon gave him quinine and advised flight. The *Three Friends* had sailed to Jamaica, but Gibbs wanted the sick man to take shelter on the *Marblehead* or some other gunboat. . . . No. He had come to see this war and the correspondents of the dispatch boat had let him stay to see it. Volleys scattered on the plateau where men sprawled in hot blackness and Crane crouched part of the doleful time beside the signalman who waved slow lanterns sending word to the *Marblehead* how things went on this knob. The lights drew fire from the brush that on three sides flowed near the poor entrenchments and the guerrillas conversed between shots in the song of the local wood-dove. Then a ball struck the surgeon Gibbs and he began audibly to die in the crowded darkness while other wounded men cried out. Crane lay listening. . . . " Every wave, vibration, of his anguish beat upon my senses. He was long past groaning. There was only the bitter strife for air which pulsed out into the night in a clear, penetrating whistle with intervals of terrible silence in which I held my own breath in the common unconscious aspiration to help. I thought this man would never die. Ultimately he died." The next noon, when Ralph Paine landed from the returned tug with a flask of whisky, Crane had an illusion of his tall friend as Harold Frederic in a fur coat, and neither whisky nor fresh food cleared the thought from his brain for hours. Perhaps one does not jam the color of life on a feverish intelligence stoked with quinine harmlessly. He had no belief in ghosts and arguments on the immortality of the soul were dull to him as Presidential speeches, but now people began to remind him of the dead. Casper Whitney was like his father and he soon startled Harding Davis by telling the big man he was a corpse seen at Velestinos.

On June 14th the parties of Marines advanced into the jungle and swept the Spanish sharpshooters before them, burning a block-house and its heliograph with a water-tank named Cuzco from a village that had been. The *Dolphin* shelled the woods ahead of the column, and Crane was vexed by another illusion, transmuted in *War Memories* to a mere comparison. He was shooting with his brothers at Hartwood and the bursting shells were setters that roused birds. He ran errands for the lieutenant in charge of this fantastic sport and got official notice of his coolness under fire. Then the *Three Friends* carried him off from four days' piled strain to Port Antonio and, he hoped, to fine meals. But the resources of the small neutral port were scanty and the chemist had only one toothbrush in stock. "This town," he wrote, "is disgustingly ill appointed."

He made a tour around the Spanish outposts and saw, guided by half-clad Cuban scouts, the squadron of Cervera anchored in the round bay of Santiago as he cowered in the brush above the packed town wherein yellow fever had sprouted. It was a ride of almost forty miles, coming and going through danger, but " I did not discover my condition until we were well through the Spanish lines and . . . then I discovered I was a dead man. The nervous force having evaporated I was a mere corpse. My limbs were of dough and my spinal cord burned within me as if it were a red hot wire." But he must tramp the beach at Daiquiri and watch the troops land from transports commanded mostly by insolent or cowardly civilians who flouted the signals of General Shafter's orders and sailed tranquilly out to the supreme safety of open water with medicines and necessary equipment in the holds of the shipping hired at such colossal rates by the government. The tragedy of the Santiago campaign had well begun and confusions heaped themselves on heat while Crane investigated the American regular officers, those curios of a system which immured boys for four years in a military monastery, sent them to duties in petty forts and barren towns of the vanished frontier, and then produced their weariness for a public which at once expected of them diplomacies, social censorship, and the suave attitudes of a society that exiled and disregarded them until the instant of its need.

The commanding officer of this little army was a fat invalid who reposed on a cot and whined about his health. In gayer hours he told anecdotes that shocked both Richard Harding Davis and Acton Davies by the flavor of medical information contained in his style. Apparently the man was too sickly or too careless for any exercise of will and after the neatness of the landing Major General Shafter simply vanished from the beautiful beach while his veteran subordinates did what they could to make life better and brighter for twelve thousand men sweating in shirts of thick wool and in a temperature wavering between eighty and a hundred degrees. Dismounted cavalrymen and the hard infantrymen called sometimes "doughboys" bathed their mosquito-bites in salt water wondering why the commissariat was already short of tobacco. . . . From the camp of the First Volunteer Cavalry arose the pulsating voice of Theodore Roosevelt demanding food and clean drink for that amazing regiment of tramps, actors, cowboys, expert bartenders, millionaires, and football-players. From the camp of the journalists rose the anguish of the *World's* chief correspondent as Crane didn't turn in his highly paid prose for the cable to jerk in edited sentences to New York. The terrible infant was loose among the regiments delighted with so much to see and hear.

He saw almost nothing of the battle known at Las Guasimas on June 24th, a tortuous raid through two converging trails carried out by Wheeler's brigade. As usual, Richard Harding Davis had the best of that news. The thing envied as " the Davis luck " was rather a very swift, shrewd judgment of possibilities and Davis followed Roosevelt while unseen Spaniards in the metallic prettiness of the foliage killed some Rough Riders. Crane ran three miles to overtake Young's dismounted troopers on the other trail and presently ran back six miles to Siboney without stopping to survey the end of this action. His friend Edward Marshall had been shot through the body, so the war lost all charm while Crane tried to get help from the *Journal's* staff at the beach. Then he guided some sailors with a cot for the wounded man and walked beside this improvisation to Siboney again. That night he could not eat but he shocked Henry Carey and Acton Davies by saying it must be interesting to be shot. He had noticed that men struck in the chest ran ahead for a while before falling. Abdominal wounds crumpled the recipient. Davies was in the last miseries of sunburn. His rotundity always appeared to be coated with pink celluloid and he was now the tint of boiling lobster speckled by huge blisters. Crane stopped pouring linseed oil on the misplaced dramatic reporter's shoulders and mused: " You'd look bully if a shell hit you, ol' man. Like a squashed peony." The comparison was not kind and Davies took alarm. Crane seemed to want to be hit and talked academically of locations on his person for a bullet's entry.

He certainly went about the business of risking a wound with extraordinary and scientific zeal. Brigades pushed on in the riotous jungle and stretched thinly on July 1st before lizard-shaped crests upholding the villages of El Caney and San Juan. These hills were a necessity to the Spanish defense. Santiago could be shelled at leisure of the invaders if the range of steep slopes and delusive plateaus fell to the Americans. General Vara del Rey bravely commanded the force at El Caney and there he was killed in a ferocious little battle that lasted for nine hours. The San Juan fight was less venomous but more trying. Regiments sat in hollows or hasty trenches while the Spanish fire came sputtering downhill and the road rearward was a muddle of wounded men, advancing columns, and, for a while, of struggling horses as the few guns were brought up to shell the enemy's position. Intolerable heat, windless and constant, lay on this episode as Crane walked to and fro in a gray, conspicuous English waterproof, afraid to shed the coat because he might lose it. When he appeared with James Hare strolling along the line of Wheeler's brigade at noon, the cavalrymen lifted their heads and begged him to wear furs if he wasn't hot enough.

Crane brooded, staring up the hill, and stooped once or twice to look at the holes made by bullets landing near his feet in the bleached grass of the slope. He wandered close to a depression that didn't greatly shelter Leonard Wood and Richard Harding Davis. It seemed to Davis that the pale coat drew shots. Yellow sand flicked from the trench and soldiers called to Crane, swearing uncomfortably. His speculation became interminable and the Spanish officer who paraded the defending trenches with a walking-stick once visibly aimed it at the artist. This unknown' warrior pleased Crane immensely and many other reporters tried afterwards to find the man's rank or name. But his pleasure in the spectacle was interrupted by Davis, who yelled to him and bade him lie down. " Crane jumped," Davis reported, " as if he was waking from a nap and looked at me astonished by my voice, perhaps. He flattened out on the grass and crawled back behind a small hillock. But pretty soon he rose on his knees and then stood up once more, absorbed in watching. I called out as sarcastically as I could that Colonel Wood and I were not impressed by his courage and he blushed scarlet before he lay down. He did not stay long after that but helped a wounded man back to the battery at El Poso. . . ." The third point of the narrative was omitted by Davis. Colonel Wood moved away and Crane got up for the second time. Davis also rose, stepped over some prostrate soldiers, and caught Crane by the shoulders, forcing him down. A bullet knocked off Davis's hat and the leather of his field-glass was chipped by another ball. Then Crane went to play his game elsewhere and drank some coffee at the reporters' camp behind a battery that slung shells toward the Spanish blockhouse. He came back as the soldiers struggled up the hill and was seen trying to hammer back a loose heel of his shoe while the American flag was swung over the conquered village. Night and desolation smothered the battlefield while officers wrangled as to the safety of holding the crests and Leonard Wood reverted to his primary profession in the hospital, undermanned, packed with dying youth. Another step had been taken in the publicity of Theodore Roosevelt. Santiago was lost, although nobody quite understood so, and a corporal shot through both arms sat up in a corner of the stinking tent reserved to fevers, singing *The Star Spangled Banner* with irony, at the top of his voice.

Chill winds belied the date and rain fell in long showers on the camps now stretched twelve miles from the beach to the taken hills. Days passed and Crane found that life without doses of whisky and quinine was mere haze. He lurched off to see refugees from the city straggle into El Caney and to watch a surgeon operate on wounded Spanish soldiers in the chapel. He saw Richmond Hobson come between the regiments standing hatless in honor of his release and watched the hero of the *Merrimac* bow profusely as men pressed around him, but this welcome was his last sight of the idle army waiting outside Santiago. Crane was now a figure of irresponsible sickness. His friends tried to feed him and kept him sometimes quiet but he wandered on a pony from place to place in the lines and lamented that he had missed the destruction of Cervera's fleet on July 3rd. He had gone to Jamaica with the dispatch boat for a bath and some decent food. When the *Three Friends* brought him back, there were Sampson's gray ships in their usual place and the invincible Spanish squadron was already beginning to rust with tropical swiftness on the beach.

All sorts of fever had broken out in the American camp. Crane was apparently no more ill than were a dozen other reporters and photographers. People who spoke to him often thought him merely drunk. Then suddenly he was very plainly delirious all one night and Sylvester Scovel hauled him down to a ship loading with sick in Daiquiri. Crane was in a state of alternate vapor and lucidity. He sat on Scovel's pony chatting to Henry Carey and George Rhea gayly and then began to beg for pickles. Fever had dowered him with two yearnings — orange ice-cream soda and sour pickles. Rhea saw the wreck taken aboard the transport and Crane was ordered to isolate himself as a case of yellow fever. He lay on a rug, aft, and was fed casually on stewed tomatoes. Cuba vanished from him in an opalescent languor while wounded Negroes chanted jubilee as the ship sailed westward.

He had not yellow fever, actually, but the accumulated fatigue of twenty mad days had smitten him. It can only be a theory but Crane had long shown symptoms of intestinal consumption. Improperly or too coarsely fed, he was ill and in Cuba he had relied on stimulants from July 1st to July 7th. In order to meet the procession of the *Merrimac's* crew at San Juan Hill he swallowed half the content of Carey's brandy-flask, and as soon as his brain drank in the show, he let himself flop on the grass, asleep at once. Scovel and Rhea tried to feed him, but everything save soft fruit was an abomination. He could not even ride the Jamaican polo pony and men who had heard of his marvelous horsemanship saw the gaunt adventurer tumble from the saddle. Crane made his body a testing-ground for all sensations of living and for this most unliterary habit he paid, in the useful language of melodrama, the price.

A representative gathering of Americans now saw the physical bill of their emotional war. Cuba was freed. The transport floated to the pier at Old Point Comfort and Crane was allowed to go ashore directly. The hotels of the resort were jammed with women — wives of naval and military officers, fashionable ladies from New York, curious tourists, or anxious waiters. On the veranda of Chamberlain's Hotel he bowed to Mrs. Bolton Chaffee, who had dined at Oxted three months before. She did not know the wraith in soiled khaki, hatless and unshaven, and her small grandson was scared to tears, but after recognition she tried to get Crane to bed. No. He sat smoking on the arm of her chair and drawled sarcasms. Here is what he wanted to see: "The verandah was crowded with women in light, charming summer dresses and with spruce officers from the fortress. It was like a bank of flowers. It filled me with awe. . . . Across the narrow street on the verandah of another hotel was a similar bank of flowers. Two companies of volunteers dug a lane through the great crowd of the street and kept a way, and then through this lane there passed a curious procession. I had never known that they looked like that. Such a gang of dirty, ragged, emaciated, half starved and bandaged cripples I had never seen. . . . Then there were many stretchers, slow moving. When the crowd began to pass the hotel the banks of flowers made a noise which could make one tremble . . . something beyond either a moan or a sob. Anyhow the sound of women weeping was in it — The sound of women weeping."

Of course he went back to see the orderly, almost bloodless taking of Porto Rico and accepted the surrender of a rural village in which he was found the next morning drilling children on the principal street. Mrs. Chaffee was seen with him at Old Point, so naturally it was reported in New York that Crane had eloped with the wife of General Chaffee and was living in adulterous splendor at San Francisco. General Chaffee had no wife possible for this purpose, but Crane wrote to Mrs. Bolton Chaffee: "You must be careful about feeding runaway dogs. Mr. Bemis informs me that you and I are sinners and that we have flown to San Francisco. They have promoted you to the rank of Mrs. Brigadier General Chaffee. Perhaps it is not known to you — and it has not long been known to me — that my name in New York is synonymous with mud. Give my regards to your husband and tell him the cigars made many correspondents happier. My friends will pile a mountain of lies on me but they will smoke my cigars as freely as I smoke theirs. That is cynicism."

Accused promptly of cynical coldness as to the war, his real mood was the usual indifference to cheap sentiment tied with amazingly frank admission of his liking for certain exhibits. He was mute on Theodore Roosevelt's conduct as a commander in battle and positively lyric as to his care for the Rough Riders: "Say, this fellow worked for his troopers like a cider press. He tried to feed them. He helped build latrines. He cursed the quartermasters and the — 'dogs' — on the transports to get quinine and grub for them. Let him be a politician if he likes. He was a gentleman, down there." Admiral Sampson's coolness of manner did not distress him, as it did other correspondents. But the commanders had scant interest for him. The men, the utterly commonplace privates and recruits, absorbed him. "Yes, yes I know that it has been wonderfully proven how that the doughboys and the Jackies know nothing of manorial architecture and Pierre Loti. They care not if the journal of the sisters De Goncourt is never published at all. Velasquez? No. Cervantes? No. United intellects of superior lands bade them be licked to the glory of Cervantes and Velasquez. I don't know why. I shall never know why. But there is an excellence of human conduct independent of Cervantes and Velasquez. The Spaniards who lay dead in El Caney knew something of it. Our men knew something of it. Mob-courage? — mob-courage. The mob has no courage. That is the chatter of clubs and writers. Pray go stand with your back to deadly fire from a painted drop for a pantomime and wave signals for half an hour without wincing and then talk of mob-courage. Imperialism? All right. The White Man's Burden? What in hell did Private Jones and Seaman Smith know of

it? Stop being sarcastic. A year hasn't diminished by one inch my
respect for the men. I shall never see another war. I don't care if
Buller drives all the Boers up Egypt's fattest pyramid. The men
were all right."

His own posture in War Memories is that of a nervous and embarrassed spectator at an imbecile and ill-rehearsed show, but he
chooses no such attitude for the soldiers in The Price of the Harness or elsewhere in the sketches of the little campaign. There was
lacking in Crane that profound and diffused sentimentalism that
turns an individual reaction into a universal woe. It was impossible
for a being who had lived in the Bowery by night and watched the
ferocious diversions of San Antonio's Mexican quarter to whimper
over mud and sweat and pain. War was ridiculous but men went to
war. He accepts the visible with small protest. . . . "What were
we doing there at all? There was no definition. There was no use
in quoting Tolstoy. There was no Napoleon to say the right thing
and lend a gilded finish to the occasion. It galled one's mind at
times. But there we were." It seemed best to accept the situation
with calm raillery, to notice that a dying man could vex his friends
by peevishness, and that " the sun threw orange lances over enam-
elled, broad leaves."

He now fell in love with Havana and so sat writing there when
he should have gone back to England. Some shadowy person
named " Wells," not to be confused with H. G. Wells, had informed the woman anxious in Surrey of Crane's adultery with the
mythical general's lady. A theme had occurred to him. The past
was wooing Crane more vividly than it did in his first years.
Havana, lazy and filthy, suggested a tale of old days. Suppose that
a young sailor was cast up naked on the shore of Cuba and became the lover of a Spanish lady in the colored, lascivious city? But
he could get no clear account of Cuban history and Spanish was
unreadable. The story was abandoned and he finished Active Service before starting north, then threw the last chapters aside and
wrote them afresh. In October he got to New York after a stay in
Washington, where again he considered Congress from its gallery
and again it bewildered him. He was presented to some Senator
who told him gravely about the failures of the war and the discomforts undergone by a nephew in the Rough Riders. " I understand,

now, that Congressmen and Senators all rolled in august pain by night and sat weeping by day over our lot. This warhorse told me so. He told me that he visited the War Department hourly on July First. I asked him what good that did and he said it showed his interest in the campaign. Nobody would believe in him. I can't believe in him but it is true that I saw him."

New York received him with a faint but noted noise. His arrival was announced. Crane exposed himself in Cuba no more recklessly than did Edward Marshall, H. T. Whigham, or George Rhea, but he had been officially mentioned and Harding Davis had already before the public his article on the correspondents. Frederic Stokes was anxious for a novel and accepted another book of verses. Editors were offering higher rates. Paul Reynolds could sell *The Blue Hotel* for as much as three hundred dollars, a price almost as high as those accorded to Davis or Kipling. But Crane was off to Hartwood at once and his brothers were appalled by a condition suddenly manifest. The man was ill and restless. He rode and shot with vigor, but listlessness had come on him. People at Port Jervis crowded to hear him talk or to tell him stories he should write and he played long games with his nieces. Yet something had happened. The vitality of manner was gone; he slept endlessly; he put off necessary visits to New York. He was too tired to breathe, he wrote, and when William Dean Howells gave a luncheon for him at Delmonico's he sat silently respectful among older men, eating nothing, turning the stem of a wineglass in his yellow fingers. The grandees of criticism had been assembled — Mayo Hazeltine, probably the most powerful reviewer of the decade, and Marrion Wilcox, who was concluding an attempt to get facts from the war's beginning legend and soon rather shocked the world by his history's impartial discussion of the Spanish side. The luncheon was a failure and Crane fell asleep on a couch in his admirer's house that afternoon without apology. He was twenty-seven and had given up adding a year to his age while Howells was amused by his references to " my youth " and " when I was young." In the operation of his mind he was now an elderly, settled character of many responsibilities who needed a house in the country and had thoughts of buying a ranch in Texas. Once sensitively keen to hear what people were saying about his work, it left him cool to know that President McKinley had spoken favorably of *The Little Regiment*. But the President had been a soldier. " He would know if the stuff was real or not, even," Crane drawled, " if he can't write good English."

On November 23rd he strolled into Delmonico's bar with Huneker, and the critic nodded to Thomas McCumber, who was idle at a table. The pair drank cocktails and went off to dine somewhere, at the Everett House or in some German restaurant where talk might be unbridled and the frothing outpour of Huneker's conversation need not shock ladies. But at Delmonico's tongues were busy. Somebody knew Crane by sight and a discussion began. Was it true that he'd tried to get himself killed in Cuba? McCumber pulled himself into the chatter, uninvited. It was true, he said. Some incredulous stranger argued the point. Why should a famous young writer try to kill himself? The gigantic photographer grew noisy and men coming in for dinner stopped to listen. Crane was dying of nameless and disgusting diseases and everybody knew it. A reporter protested and the giant wanted to fight him. Richard Harding Davis had come in alone and was quietly ordering dinner in a corner of the room. After a moment he shouldered through the fringe at the bar and commanded McCumber to be still. McCumber didn't obey. He repeated his indictment with additions, towering and swaying above Davis's evening dress while an alarmed waiter pulled at his coat. The smaller man wearied and twenty or thirty people were witnesses of a suppression by force. Davis, blushing furiously, towed the big gossip out of the place and came back with his customary dignity and a cut lip to ask such men as he knew to forget the affair. . . . All penalties of the popular writer have now been paid by Davis. A general damnation has included his alert sketches of London and Paris and the satiric portrait of Captain Macklin, the military cad. The mind displayed was, perhaps, conventional but the man had a persisting quality most remarkable. He would praise and advertise his rivals and his betters with pen and voice. He lauded his successor, Gouverneur Morris, and distributed the first book of James Huneker to friends who didn't want to read it and could not understand what it meant. He called attention to Crane's reports of the Cuban war and afterwards, when he was obliged to explain who Crane had been, spent hours in description of the man who always, clearly, somehow shocked and puzzled him. Crane was " a strange genius " but that genius should not be neglected. This oddity of temperament got him into trouble when Stanford White was murdered by some inconsequent fellow in a quarrel over a trumpery woman who then was shown at the trial tricked out as a schoolgirl. The legal proceedings were so cynical in their appeal that the New York press recorded them with real unwillingness. The dead architect's mild sensualities were sprayed with slime so completely that the reviving courage of his friends has not yet established the hollowness of the attack. Here and there journalists and writers feebly denied that White was Nero recrudescent. He was a jolly, harmless pagan who possessed an enormous enthusiasm for art, art in all kinds. He was now reviled by men who had dined at his expense the week before his death and artists fled from the remains of their patron with that speed begotten in cowards by a scandal involving lust. Davis was not intimate with the monster but this strange sense of justice flashed out in a published praise of White. The man had been kind, talented, and generous, slain by a drunken fool. The brave reporter shouted against the world his outraged theory of fair play and his books were forthwith dumped from a public library in New Jersey while lads were warned by the headmaster of a famous school to beware *Soldiers of Fortune* and *The Princess Aline* as foul emanations of a depraved romancer. Only in an English-speaking country was such a folly possible and only an American could know the consequences of the act. It leaves him lonely in the tale of the national letters.

2

The alliance of Crane and James Huneker began casually and without much warmth on Crane's part but in the autumn of 1898 they walked and dined together frequently. A change was apparent in Crane. . . . His earlier friends were scattering. Corwin Linson went abroad in October and John Willard Raught, another young painter, was gone too. John Northern Hilliard had become an editor in Rochester. Hamlin Garland was much in the West and Edward Townsend was often traveling. The men of the

Lantern Club were bully fellows and he could entertain himself
with the garrulous wit of Acton Davies, but discontent had set in
and he found himself thinking of England while he hunted a house
in New York. Lounging at tea with a lady in December this came
to expression. " Englishmen aren't shocked as easily as we are. You
can have an idea in England without being sent to court for it."

His ideas and opinions had not given Edward Garnett, Harold
Frederic, or Ford Maddox Hueffer any moments of uneasiness. He
sometimes appalled Robert Barr, who was conservatively minded,
but Stephen Crane's cynicisms have by this year paled into common sense. His objection to the Mosaic deity, of course, did not
belong to his decade of careful avoidance. It is known that he
startled by an aristocratic habit of calling peasants in America
peasants. He derided the sacred petting of all Irishmen. His description of pity as " a virtue almost useless in ninety-nine cases
out of a hundred . . ." seemed affectation in 1896. His political
thinking is obscured but the violence of his rages with social and
religious limitation is recalled. He had no patience with doctrines
that sank individuals into the mass and defined their mental path.
" Frances Willard," he told Miss Harris, " is one of those wonderful people who can tell right from wrong for everybody from the
polar cap to the equator. Perhaps it never struck her that people
differ from her. I have loved myself passionately now and then but
Miss Willard's affair with Miss Willard should be stopped by the
police." At some time he " was a Socialist for two weeks but when
a couple of Socialists assured me I had no right to think differently
from any other Socialist and then quarreled with each other about
what Socialism meant, I ran away."

His views on women alarmed some of his friends. Against the
current of the nineties he was both chivalrous and realistic. He
had got himself in jail by protecting a streetwalker from a bullying
policeman but " most streetwalkers would be ' demimondianes ' "
— so spelled — " if they had money. Lots of women are just naturally unchaste and all you jays know it," yet the faint tinge of
Puritanism lay in him. He was perpetually nervous when gentlewomen smoked before him and a man who would accept a woman's
prolonged fidelity without offering her marriage was, in some way
not explained, censorable. He projected in *The Monster* and Ac-

tive Service finely compressed sketches of disagreeable middle-aged women, but a pretty girl was too much for his detachment and only a frantic admirer would join Elbert Hubbard in calling Crane a profound student of the female mind. The heiress of *The Third Violet* takes on rank life when she throws herself at the head of the timid, obtuse Hawker, but elsewhere, like the novel, she is something never quite finished. There was no androgynous streak in Crane and perhaps without that embarrassing trace no man writes well of women until age has calloused him to the wonder of a body unlike his own. However, some of his random annotations were disliked and he lightly expressed rather unusual thoughts, for his time. It was not circumspect in an American to suggest that women knew "the joys of cruelty." Margharita and her mother in *The Clan of No Name* were too frank for many readers. He once wrote the story of an artist's model who married into a small town, but the tale froze editors while it amused James Huneker and it has disappeared.

Crane was lingering, hesitant, with sour comment reaching him as to his habits and customs. "There must," said Huneker, "have been people who hated the boy monumentally. Three or four times when he had been spending the whole evening with Ryder and myself I would be told in the morning how drunk and disorderly he had been the night before by men who had not seen him. For a mild and melancholy kid he certainly had fallen completely into the garbage can of gossip. . . . The charm of his talk defies description. It was all adjectives and adverbs. He spoke of his friend Conrad as the devout speak of the B. V. M. Harold Frederic's case was dragging through the papers still and the bourgeois in Park Row used to bore Crane about it a good deal. He was a great individualist and he resented the twaddle about suicide intensely as he knew that Frederic could not have recovered anyhow. I saw him last about Christmas time. . . ." After Christmas he reached decision suddenly. He would go back to England and stay there. So he rode on the frosty highways around Hartwood with his brother and once his horse fell with him at a turn. Then he sailed on the *Manitou* in the first week of January. . . . Perhaps with some regrets. That New York, that acreage of brown stone and shoddy stucco was altering and imperial tones of marble shone everywhere as hotel after hotel opened to dazzle rustics with frescoes and satin chairs. Little pleasures faded in the crash of new display but he might recall long breakfasts in hot summer under the striped awning of the Vienna Bakery beside white Grace Church and the wet bodies of prizefighters lurching in the smoke of Harry Hill's queer restaurant where lightweights fought while men dined. . . . Music of that decade was the rolling of hansoms and he who so loved shimmering tones of light might remember the damp sheen of cabs on Broadway. There had been the young talk of the Hotel Griffon and the Bœuf à la Mode and the fresh voice of the Wild Indians in their barrack on Twenty-third Street. He would not forget a murmurous park with a pair of white arms beside him as he was driven around and around through warm night, and in an alien valley he would be sick again for the sight of tall towers and the noise of hurrying wheels.

VIII: *THE LAST*

WRITING to Edward Garnett on January 10, 1899, Cora Crane showed a knowledge of her husband's situation in two sentences: " His great difficulty is a lack of that machine-like application which makes a man work steadily. I hope that the perfect quiet of Brede Place and the freedom from a lot of dear good people, who take his mind from his work, will let him show the world a book that will live. . . ." Nine men, breathing or extinct, have claimed that they first mentioned Brede to Stephen Crane, but to Mr. Garnett belongs the credit of a sensible suggestion made in November of 1897. The critic advised Crane to find a house somewhere less easy of access. He talked of Brede as an available ruin and Mrs. Crane went to investigate while Crane enjoyed Cuba. So, on January 16th, they drove from Hastings through twilight and Crane saw his next home by the pleasing glow of lamps. The house, begun in the fourteenth century, was wonderfully dilapidated and an owl had built a nest on a beam of the paneled hall. He was charmed by the faint sound of water spilling under the bridge and by his wife's delight in this solidified romance: " It is a pretty fine affair," he wrote to Sanford Bennett, " and Cora believes that Sir Walter Scott designed it for her. They began one wing in 1378 and somebody kidded it with heavy artillery in Cromwell's time. We shall move in as soon as we can. I enclose 10 pounds. Do I owe you more than that?"

Brede was a relief after Oxted and Crane's stored goods were sent from Hartwood. Mexican blankets hung red and white on the walls of a little room above the gateway and furniture was somehow bought for ten chambers. The butler, Heather, appeared and undertook by stern discomposures to correct his master's habit of running downstairs coatless to meet guests. Maurice Hewlett was shocked on calling to find Crane in muddy boots when the ride that excused such articles had been taken before breakfast. Henry James came from Rye to inspect and was pained to hear Sanford Bennett call Crane " Baron Brede." An abrasion of tradition and privilege had occurred by no known intention. To Crane his manor was a playhouse and to some of his friends — or acquaintances — it was a sanctity invaded, carelessly, by an irreverent whose claret they would gladly still consume while they sighed in London over his bad form. A literary clergyman arriving to ask a hundred signed copies of *Bowery Tales* in the name of a charitable bazaar was peculiarly outraged by the sight of Crane in a gray flannel shirt rolling dice with strange adjurations on the hall's depressed floor. It is recorded that these dice were " not of the ordinary colour and must be American," and that, at tea, there were small, flat " hot rolls which Mrs. Crane insistently called biscuit although they were not biscuit but agreeable." Oh, England!

Crane worked and " the dear, good people " did not get at him unless they were summoned. He was reading a great deal. His individuality did not regard itself as a completed labor of God, at twenty-seven, and chance had dropped him among critical folk who knew things. His reverence, when one finds the quality coming to view, was latterly on the drift away from men who could do things and expending itself on men who knew things, on Huneker and on the Garnetts, whose progenitor " bossed the British Museum and talked about old man Caxton as if they had been at school together." The advantage of a little pedantry had been pointed out to Crane by Ripley Hitchcock and by Hamlin Garland, whose books he borrowed and probably never returned since his one absolute vice was a habit of not sending books back. He returned money when he thought of it with long apologies for his remissness but books he simply took and kept. So in one week of March 1899 he read a volume on Greek vases, Turgenev's *Smoke*, Du Maurier's *Peter Ibbetson* (he didn't like it), *Cashel Byron's Profession, Literature and Dogma, In the Cage*, presented to him by Henry James with an elaborate and almost affectionate inscription, in French. History, save as the background of battles, he had never much explored until now and its fascination was plain in Sussex with walls so ancient shedding dampness on him and the ghost of William the Conqueror troubling his wife's dreams. He even read May's constitutional history of England and survived without trouble the involuted dreariness of its manner. Huneker still wanted him to read Balzac, but Mr. Conrad had told him all about Balzac and he held himself excused.

With spring Brede was gayer. He had pledged a series of articles on great battles and fancied he would enjoy the work. *Harper's Magazine* wanted him to continue the stories of Whilomville. *Active Service* was finished and in print. Half a dozen tales had been sold and he could cheerfully lend a hundred pounds without taking a note. So he saw more people and the butler hired more servants to support his dignity properly. In April Crane discovered several housemaids washing the battalion of dogs necessary to life and wondered at Heather's ability. " My man," he wrote, " can hire me a pair of maids while I ride to Rye and back. If I went to Russia I should come home and find Parliament in buttons and Marie Corelli in the kitchen." But the maids were useful to wash Sponge and his consort Flannel and the solemn Russian poodles who were so indiscreet when they called on Henry James at Rye. Young ladies played absurd games in the hall with young authors after dinner and Crane watched nascent flirtations devotedly, although his wife refused him lamps with red shades.

He had come under scientific eyes and Mark Barr [1] caught his passion for red. The walls of the study must be made soothing by paint of a shade between vermilion and claret, the color of fresh sumach on the hills around Port Jervis. This red meant comfort,

---

[1] Mr. Barr is an American chemist.

thrilling excitement, or desire, according to the mood. When
some eventual psychologist has cleared from the investigation of
such manias the guesses now clinging to them, Crane's work will
be a chart of illustration. Writers in all degrees have indulged in
favorite colors. Grays and soft blues abound in the stanzas of Verlaine. Henry James had a positive, but not crude, affection for
clean floods of light and for brown dusks of interior. William
Morris would halt an address to stare at certain shades of orange
or dull green, a woman once noticed, and resume Socialism when
some memory was slaked in his brain. In Crane's work one sees
milder manias. Purple was sinister and repugnant. Grayish blue
and strong yellow were pleasant. Above everything comes the notice of lamps seen in the dark. . . . "Down an alley there were
sombre curtains of purple and black, on which the street lamps
dully glittered like embroidered flowers. . . ." When Mrs. Chaffee
played for him some phrases of Debussy the swift notes were " windows in a train at night going over the edge of a plain. . . ." A
kindness of Moreton Frewen was " a searchlight on a hungry boat
at sea . . ." and the foolish, persisting air whistled by American
troops in Cuba was " a jumble of Chinese lanterns in a fog." Half
Crane's achievement in letters was his astonishing ease of visual
description, and seemingly simple statements have a haunting effect of complete justice to a scene. Nothing could be better than
the two lights of *The Open Boat* which were the " furniture of
the world," to his racked eyes.

The Open Boat appeared in the autumn of 1898 and American
critics received these tales with the calm cordiality and the lack of
criticism that maddens. One review alone rises from the banal level
of the list. Rupert Hughes wrote of the new book with a sensitive
appreciation and a considerable analysis of the methods employed.
The other reviews were kind and flat. Crane exploded in a fluff of
angry words before the sympathetic Edward Garnett. Some day
he might make Americans forget *The Red Badge!* He wanted to
know what certain American reviewers would have to say, in the
next year, of *The Blue Hotel* but nobody said anything very dis-
criminating and Mark Twain thought it a grisly business. The Lincoln of our letters was never pleased by grimness in the fiction of
others writers and Crane, told of this censure, simply grinned.

American failure to recognize Crane's short stories was not so sweeping as it may have seemed to him. His nation's tribute to Crane has been the compliment of conscious or unconscious theft and if only the inferior war-time episodes of *The Little Regiment* were broadly popular, *The Blue Hotel, Death and the Child, A Desertion,* and *The Five White Mice* have been much honored in a ghostly fashion. He swayed clean from the national orbit. Where Ambrose Bierce failed by clinging to the tradition of Poe, Crane failed by a blank abandonment of the form still sacred with editors and critics, the truncated novel produced by Harte and de Maupassant. He was interested to sketch curtly colored cross-roads on the map of existence and that map had for him no sure or solacing pattern. His vision of the world is jabbed into *The Blue Hotel* by a symbol atrocious to the soft and, one supposes, distressing to the pious. A panicky and tipsy Swede is knifed in a Nebraskan saloon by a mild little gambler who, in Crane's speech, is merely the apex of a human movement, an adverb in the meaningless sentence. But the corpse of the Swede, "alone in the saloon, had its eyes fixed upon a dreadful legend that dwelt atop the cash-machine: 'This registers the amount of your purchase' . . ." and Crane, indifferent to his childish public, did not stop to brandish paragraphs of comment on the futility of such a bargain. Thus in *Wise Men* the two charming Kids back a fat old bartender against a trained runner in a footrace, for no reason, and their champion wins. Accident dominates an inchoate society. In the weaker *Twelve O'Clock* an idle argument about a cuckoo-clock brings death on two men and the cuckoo pokes out its inhuman head to squawk twelve times over the heaped slaughter. Once it begins, this human movement proceeds with all the vigor of a holy war but there is no cause to justify the hopes and terrors, the pompous stir of man's nonsensical activity under nature's bland survey. Rewards are as accidental as calamities. In *Active Service* the war-correspondent gets his sweetheart by merit of being the chance rescuer of her parents and through no virtue whatever. In *The Clan of No-Name*, one of Crane's poorest efforts, one still sees the dull Mr. Smith win Margharita simply because her lover is dead under the machete in Cuba. Even in *The Red Badge of Courage* the boy is allowed his moment of glory as the army staggers off the field in retreat. It needs no critical power to know that this perpetual refutation of endeavor is a thing disconcerting to the general, a caviar of pebbles. Edgar Saltus, setting forth in a polished and most literary style his derived philosophy of negations, was a figure more comfortable to the times, especially as he piled such a treasure of lewd facts in the lives of Czars and rowdy, luxurious Cæsars, a treat to housewives and that sort of critic for whom art is not art unless the toys of art be shown. Add to Crane's matter the manner described by Richard Gilder — privately — as grim flippancy, and the reason of his failure is plain enough. In *The Bride Comes to Yellow Sky*, his own favorite, he shows the drunken Wilson lurching through streets of barred and silent houses, death in his hand, then makes the man absurd in the universe by mention of his shirt from a Bowery sweatshop and of his boots with the red tops dear to little boys in snowy winter. He forbids primitive emotional relish to break out. The adobe house scarred by the cowboy's bullets rebukes his magnificence with its immobile dignity. The town is Wilson's plaything, but he, threshing his revolvers, is the plaything of a sardonic, casual fortune. Man is just man, even in the hour of courage when Crane lets him be, homely and awkward still, an image of endurance not without honor, not, in the end, without beauty. It should be remembered that in his decade's critical vocabulary "ironic" was a reproachful adjective.

One Cuban night Acton Davies [1] was moaning for his dear Broadway. He wanted such and such dishes at his pet restaurant, such wines, and a lustrous lady to sit across from him. Crane cut short the dream by saying: "Why don't you just say you want a good meal and a girl and be done with it?" That salvage, somewhat brutal, of the real from the sentimental obliquity was the right token of Crane's offense against the spirit of his day.

Brede Place warmed and Crane wrote through silent nights, lying abed until noon. Harold Frederic's lovely orphans played on the lawn and bruised their fingers in the old falconry. Mrs. Richie, from Kentucky, and her handsome daughters were privileged

---

[1] This is directly quoted from a letter of Mr. Davies dated July 2, 1898. The story was at once twisted to suit the mythology of Stephen Crane and has been printed as Crane's statement: "If I were on Broadway tonight all I'd want would be a bottle of whiskey and a woman." I regret the obligations of veracity in spoiling so neat an epigram.

guests. Robert Barr, H. G. Wells, A. E. W. Mason came and went. England was mildly concerned with the Boers but Crane heard that three regiments and some cavalry would chasten these yokels. This prophecy was made at Rye while Mrs. Humphry Ward poured tea for Henry James. Crane thought the lady pleasant but duller than a President and he had doubts as to the Boers. " People tell me that the South Africans and the Japanese can shoot like the devil and then tell me a couple of Guard regiments could whip them in a week. When a Yankee says such things he is bragging but I guess an Englishman is just lugging the truth from some dark cave."

A party escorted his niece Helen to Paris and there waited while Crane took the girl on to her school at Lausanne. Money still passed through his fingers without stopping and he had to borrow to get back to Paris. But now he was scared and working furiously: his wife must be secured for the future. He must try to repay his brothers the loans they had never mentioned. He would not live beyond thirty-one, he thought, and serenely drawled that guess to Karl Harriman when Robert Barr brought the young American down to Brede. " I never thought I'd live long," he said, " and I'm not much account any more." The mental tensity that had supported his first writing now was gone with health. Everything relaxed. He still rode Hengist or Horsa at a gallop along lanes and carried pots to the flower-show where Henry James helped Edith Richie to sell love-potions in a booth and enchanted Crane by a sentence that had easily thirty clauses and nine parentheses. He sometimes drove the trap whose wheels were painted in the somber colors of the Crane armor — although he wouldn't explain the choice when he was asked. Pride of race was one of his secrets and he shrank from snobbery as he shrank from talk of his health. . . . What did he think of death? With Robert Barr he had wasted a night in burlesque incantations to bring Harold Frederic back and, Barr wrote, " Stephen put me to bed about dawn but we did not evoke anything except one of his dogs." Brooding suited him less than did endless discussions of everything in the stone kitchen while July storms showed wet haycocks on the slope by flares of lightning and Mr. Mason's eyeglass was a violent round to catch his stare. Death? Here was humanity. Why bother? And he could dash off a tale about a haycock just to show Barr and Harriman how the thing was done.

His manners were not silken but he had always inoffensively gone through proper parties in New York or London. Lady Randolph Churchill thought him somewhat formal and other hostesses were surprised to hear that Crane was in any way Bohemian. He could be diplomatic when he chose; one of his guests recalls the nimbleness with which Crane manipulated conversations to spare the feelings of a man lately divorced. His natural informality was not a parade of what is called the artist's freedom as in England he found himself more at ease among intelligences than in America: " I once horrified Elbert Hubbard and his household by telling the story of an old negress in Minetta Lane I met when I was working for Ed Marshall on the *Press*. This old black devil was taking a bath in a wash-boiler when I walked into her flat and she called, ' Chile, I'se all disdressed.' That anecdote slew its thousands at Hubbard's and got me in much trouble. I shall never know why. They acted as though I had read one of Zola's loudest roars. Over here I have told it in front of seven or eight mothers of families and I assure you nothing happened. Nothing at all." He told the anecdote to Maurice Hewlett who responded: " Ah? She meant that she was distressed? I see," and the response possibly explains why no friendship ripened between Crane and the author of *Richard Yea and Nay*.

Crane liked people for obscure reasons and his open dislikes were so few that inevitably he collected both bores and boors. In moments of frightful tedium he occasionally rounded on someone with gibes too subtle for thick skins. A journalist appeared at Brede and paralyzed all present by his overbearing rudeness for three days. On the fourth morning he lodged a complaint about a servant who hadn't brought something to his room and Crane drawled: " Perhaps she has patrician instincts," but the journalist stayed on until, through James Pinker, Mrs. Crane managed to dismiss him. Once in July Crane broke out to his literary agent: " If you don't tell some of these lice that Cora and I aren't running a hotel I'll have to advertise the fact in the *Times*! " and then cleared his dwelling by taking off five youngsters to the Henley regatta. " How," he asked Sanford Bennett, " does it come to pass that anybody in

England thinks he can come and stay with me before I've asked him and patronize my wife's housekeeping? " He wrote to Elbert Hubbard: " I must have Egyptian blood in me. Mummies rise from the tomb and come to pay me calls that last for days."

Summer was pleasant, though, and he got slowly through the Whilomville series, but finding that the Great Battles wearied him, simply finished them off as he could in dry recitals of fact not anywhere florid but never enriched. One or two of the histories — such as Bunker Hill — have an interest but nothing went well with Crane when he wrenched his talent from its bent. In *Active Service* he had attempted a popular novel and had failed as he failed in popular reporting. The story lacks all the devices of its brand. Crane could not take his journalist seriously either in his professional aspect or as a lover. Fitfully the book glows — the lights of Broadway are jewels of a giantess, the poker game is a real game, the moment when the correspondent wanders in darkness beyond the Greek lines is wonderfully rendered, but *Active Service* dropped far below Crane's standard and some of his friends were indignant for the contemptuous portrait of a newspaperman. Some wrote to him their outrage with the poem in *War is Kind* when the verses were printed.

> A newspaper is a court
> Where every one is kindly and unfairly tried
> By a squalor of honest men.
> A newspaper is a market
> Where wisdom sells its freedom
> And melons are crowned by the crowd. . . .
> A newspaper is a symbol;
> It is fetless life's chronicle,
> A collection of loud tales
> Concentrating eternal stupidities,
> That in remote ages lived unhaltered,
> Roaming through a fenceless world.

The gray book of poems again bewildered reviewers. He was still writing unrhymed lines and his sentiments were still unusual. The first poem was somehow cryptic, or silly. They were not sure. " Mr. Crane's sense of humour," a Bostonian had to say, " is of a mystifying kind. He deliberately shows us the horrors of war and then entitles his work ' War is Kind.' " It wouldn't do.

> Do not weep, maiden, for war is kind.
> Because your lover threw wild hands towards the sky
> And the affrighted steed ran on alone,
> Do not weep.
> War is kind.

> Hoarse, booming drums of the regiment,
> Little souls who thirst for fight,
> These men were born to drill and die.
> The unexplained glory flies above them,
> Great is the battle-god, great, and his kingdom —
> A field where a thousand corpses lie. . . .

All the best poems of this second attack on formal versification are known to date from 1895, 1896, and 1897. Several were written while Crane and Captain Murphy lamented the *Commodore* in Jacksonville. Some experiments in rhythm go along excellently, but the love-poems are not fired by the spirit of the earlier work and only here and there is the tone of amusement memorable.

> " Have you ever made a just man? "
> " Oh, I have made three," answered God,
> " But two of them are dead,
> And the third —
> Listen! Listen!
> And you will hear the thud of his defeat."

> A man said to the universe:
> " Sir, I exist."
> " However," replied the universe,
> " The fact has not created in me
> A sense of obligation."

Very plainly rises his own patrician instinct before the spectacle of some triumphant vulgarian in a nest of spoils once the goods of better men.

> . . . The outcry of old beauty
> Whored by pimping merchants
> To submission before wine and chatter. . . .

If anything is to be gained by analysis of *War is Kind,* the book shows less agitation. The man of 1898 has got done with musing on sexual adventure as "sin" and his young quarrel with a Jewish tribal divinity is over. Sin had become for Crane any act of disloyalty to the given purpose. "Men have never much deserved Christ and Buddha," he wrote, "because they went to work and changed the teaching of generosity into a teaching of roars and threats. I can not be shown that God bends on us any definable stare, like a sergeant at muster, and his laughter would be bully to hear out in nothingness." As for his theory of love, one sees in the verses a knowledge of sentimentalized desire as a tumult not in proportion to the cause. He was an amorist and young. The interest was enormous, candid and not complex. One thinks of him as a thoroughly romantic lover who had not made many exactions in love and probably knew precious little of women. He could finely record the duel between the stupid George and his narrow, devoted mother, because he could coarsen his own figure and that of his parent, making Mary Crane a scolding woman of the tenements and himself a dull young workman, but the duel of desire was too tremulously moving for discernment and his erotic verse drops into the banal.

3

Crane seldom brought forth an opinion of a contemporary unless he was sure of his hearers but sometimes he was driven to expression and often he gave offense. The man was generous, almost crazily generous in his judgment up to a point, then out poured his distaste for the dramatized personality and those minor arts of exhibition so dear to most writers. Luckless in all things, he chose to say "an author is a man licensed by public opinion to act like a chorus girl at supper," when he was leaving the Savage Club after an evening with Mark Twain wooing adoration in the foreground. The retirement of Thomas Hardy struck him as "all right" and Mr. Kipling's notable absence from the drawing-rooms was "the man's own business." These views were harmless but, and before the wrong audience, he drawled that he could write in a circle all around Mariott Watson. Vastly pleased by the startling *McTeague* of Frank Norris he yet pronounced the book too moral and that sensible objection was whispered along as proof of his conceit. He also said there was too much " I " in W. E. Henley's *Invictus* and preferred the poet's less popular stanzas.

He was conceited in streaks. An eminent writer who is proud of mastering the revolver and publicly wishes he could write verse as well as he plays poker (Mr. William Crane denies that his brother could play poker even reasonably well) is courting comment. Now and then fits of pride came on Crane and in one of these he announced that *The Bride Comes to Yellow Sky* was a whole heap better than anybody had said in print. Sometimes he seemed to be drinking in flatteries from very trivial people and then he was coolly indifferent to pleasant words from beings in critical place. An air of ingratitude blew often in his drawl. His independence was dear to Crane and he exploded in August of 1899: " It seems that I am the only person who had nothing to do with bringing myself before the public! " Indeed, on his side of the question it should be said that too many gentlemen of the late nineties had " brought Stephen Crane before the public " and the manner of that production remains hopelessly dark after long investigation. He wrote: " I am, I think, sufficiently grateful to men who really did things for me and in particular to Mr. Garland who, as you know, gave me sound advice about ' The Red Badge.' But just what is it to the credit of A and B that they bought things from me? I mean, what is my obligation to them? They saw a profit to their papers in buying my stuff and we break even. If it comes to that sultry point, why shouldn't they be grateful to me? "

But the ingratitude of authors to publishers, critics, and editors is a notorious thing and safety lies in letting the balance tilt toward the appraising power. Crane further erred in writing: " Why should I be grateful for an utterly bad piece of criticism that leaves out everything good in ' George's Mother ' and mentions just the things I would like to write over again if that was honest? "

He would not rewrite. He was careless in reading proof and for some of his books he never read proof at all. Ripley Hitchcock begged him to think over *The Third Violet*, as Crane admitted many scenes were too compressed, but the story had appeared as a serial and it was " dishonest " to change the thing now that it had been offered to readers. He restored only a few paragraphs of

The Red Badge for its final form, so an opening description of the two armies as watchful beasts which so pleased Mr. Garland is forever lost. Sketches dashed off in a few hours were issued with all their imperfections just as first seen in the *Press* and the *World*. Enormous holes appear in his egotism, and his failure in grooming himself for the general gaze is a thing too curious.

> A little ink more or less!
> It surely can't matter?
> Even the sky and the opulent sea,
> The plains and the hills, aloof,
> Hear the uproar of all these books.
> But it is only a little ink more or less.

People came to Brede Place in the autumn of 1899 in numbers fatally large for the bank account. An insurrection occurred one morning in September and the household was cut down. By strenuous devices Crane swept the manor for a visit of Mr. and Mrs. Conrad and then was overwhelmed with guests invited or self-invited in the month's last week. Certain friends had license to come and go as they pleased. He was always glad to see Mrs. Richie and her daughters, Robert Barr, Mark Barr, H. G. Wells, and A. E. W. Mason. He wrote: " John Stokes and George Lynch have the kindness to let Cora know when they are coming but would to God that some of the other Indians would write and ask." . . . A paradox established itself. To some of his English friends Brede seemed a Bohemian stronghold while roaming Americans thought Stephen Crane in severe evening dress surrounded by formal gowns and black coats a most unhallowed spectacle, the Bohemian turned snob. Mark Barr suggested that hollows of the hall's flooring had once been filled with rushes and for a week or so rushes littered the place, painfully impressing Henry James as a parody of baronial state. A village blacksmith hammered iron holders for candles and the beams had their ancient light again. Its ghosts were invited back to Brede and its master of the moment, reading the Whilomville tales aloud to his young circle coughed gently as mists of October leaked through his ruinous dwelling in the most romantic way. Processions of dogs followed him when he rode Hengist or drove Horsa off to Rye, and the white Powder Puff got her tail caught under a door, on Crane's birthday. An offspring of Sponge and Flannel was selected for the use of Master Borys Conrad and the Russian poodles shed gloom by their presence at teas when literary ladies came to ask questions about Crane's ethics. . . . All this went on while Mr. Conrad and Mr. Garnett were wondering about the gaunt man's lungs and his wife spent afternoons guarding his privacy in the red study. He had read with appreciation Knut Hamsun's *Hunger* when Karl Harriman brought the book to Brede in summer, but appetite ceased and Mrs. Crane had agitated conferences with friends as to Switzerland and the Black Forest. He would not see doctors although he smoked less and less. Miss Edith Richie carefully poured doses of Scotch whisky into a sea of soda and is still indignant: " Cora and I would mix his highballs for Stephen. There would be about a tablespoonful of Scotch at the bottom of the glass and I have heard men who were drinking five times as much say, ' He is drinking himself to death.' He would light a cigarette and then let it go out in his fingers and, when he noticed that, light another and men said, ' He is smoking too much. . . .' " He sat so with that faintly colored beverage turning in his hand and listened to random talk. Now and then a rocket of adjectives mounted but he was becoming very silent and his voice went slowly while he praised the new Western sketches of Owen Wister and Alfred Henry Lewis.

He could still be excited by a discovery. Somebody urged him to read Anatole France and he went mad over *The Procurator of Judæa*, that picture of the aged Pilate trying to remember any such person as Jesus of Nazareth. He detailed his high opinion of Monsieur France to Henry James and to Edmund Gosse quite as though they had never heard of the Frenchman. He besought William Heinemann to buy the next novel of Frank Norris. Unliterary in his conduct, Crane was yet a man of letters although he chattered slang when talk became too exquisite of an evening at the Savage or in the waste spaces of the Reform Club. He had even critical views a little prophetic: " I should say that Mr. Wells will write better and better when he sticks to characters altogether and does not so much concern himself with narrative. I may be wrong but it seems to me that he has a genius for writing of underclass people more honestly than Charles Dickens. . . . I will bet all my marbles and my best top that Walter Besant is forgotten in twenty years. . . . Every one tells me that Mr. Stevenson was a fine fellow but nothing on earth could move me to change my belief that most of his work was insincere."

He would forgive all other crimes if a writer seemed to him honest in his scheme and for that reason he championed artists dead or living who were never important. His generosity gushed on half a dozen commonplace realists who "tried to write honestly about things." They did not get very far but they must care for their work and that was the point of honor. Æsthetic must be the application of emotional weight and to Crane it was plain enough that the arts were merely departments of the intelligent treasure in humanity. Once Mark Barr was talking of a research in higher mathematics and ended: "You see, I cared so much."

Crane broke out, "That's it, Mark! Now that you've said it always remember it. You can never do anything good æsthetically — and you can never do anything with anything that's any good except æsthetically — unless it has at one time meant something important to you."

In the same spirit he wrote to a youth who wasn't sure whether his genius would find better expression in sculpture or fiction: "You might be one of the people who have picked on a defenceless art as a means of telling how much certain things have meant, or mean to you, but did you ever think that this world is full of artists in alligator growing and the promulgation of mixed vegetables? Mr. James was recently quoting a piece from some French poet [1] who shows Narcissus seeing in himself the motion of all time. An artist, I think, is nothing but a powerful memory that can move itself at will through certain experiences sideways and every artist must be in some things powerless as a dead snake." Blessed in simile, did any writer ever limit the power of his vision by such a figure? Perhaps the secret of Crane's charm for many men lay in his rebuke of the artist's swollen vanity. He wrote to his intimate Hilliard: ". . . For I understand that a man is born into the world with his own pair of eyes, and he is not at all responsible for his vision — he is merely responsible for his quality

[1] Obviously André Gide.

of personal honesty. To keep close to this personal honesty is my supreme ambition. . . ."

Himself Crane recognized his lucklessness and lightly mentioned it to Willis Clarke when his admirer called at Brede in late November. Ripley Hitchcock had given the young fellow a note of introduction and Crane interrupted work to see him. Lamps were already lighted and Mr. Clarke's eye was caught by a photograph of Hall Caine framed on the wall with a legend below the familiar black cloak: " Christ on the Mountains of Man." Mr. Clarke wanted to write down their talk in shorthand and Crane was listlessly amused. He spoke of his parents at some length and then of *Maggie*, but his attention veered. He began to ask questions about Texas and about baseball teams in the Middle West. Mr. Clarke brought him round by saying: " It's hard luck that you and Mr. Kipling began to write at the same time."

" Yes. I'm just a dry twig on the edge of the bonfire," said Crane.

Chance had erected him as a slim, inscrutable statue before the running opal and fierce light of a talent then shimmering so changefully in the lettered air. It was just his luck.

4

Christmas must be gay. He was homesick. He filled Brede with youth and his wife cooked passionately. There were theatricals and the ghosts of Brede romped visibly. The dog Sponge became a father on New Year's Eve and Crane lifted his glass to the oncoming months with: " Let's drink to the twentieth century — in spite of your objection, Mark," he added to Mr. Barr, who had scientifically assured him that the century was not yet begun on January 1, 1900. But they danced through the night and guests trailed up to the rooms of the turret where C. Lewis Hind and other hardy souls had to sleep on cots. A man came back for a forgotten cigarette-case and saw Crane at one of his oddities, humming with his face close to the strings of a violin. His guest strolled up to speak to the dreamer and Crane fainted suddenly against his shoulder.

Alarm had commenced among his friends. Robert Barr was urging a voyage to South Africa in salt air. Some days after the New Year, Crane spoke of Texas to James Pinker. He had been very well down there and living was cheap. Moreton Frewen advised the south of France. People were not willing to say so, but they saw all signs of consumption. Crane listened to nothing and worked at highest speed, inviting folk to keep " Cora from seeing spooks." One night there was long poker and next afternoon he led a party of unshaven friends to a tavern in Rye where they idled under the stare of a most civilized person in a shadowy corner. Crane recalled his errand in the town as dusk fell. He must take back a manuscript to Henry James. The civilized being lifted from obscurity a voice of cultivated distress. Mr. James would not see a stranger save on appointment.

" Oh, sir," said Crane, " I know that the duel is not practiced in this country but I am prepared to waive that for your benefit."

The votary faded out and Crane was commanded to bring his friends into Lamb House, where ladies were dressed to dine. The Jamesian servants, so dreaded by the master, brushed off tweed coats and dinner went graciously forward. James played a joke on a matron who denounced prizefights. He had seen one, he said amid shudders, and slowly detailed the sweating muscles and the bestial faces of the crowd, all viewed, it turned out, on the decent screen of a crude moving-picture show. . . . Sometimes he seems to have stared with a strange wistfulness across the parapet of his seclusion. He must ask Mr. Hueffer's thoughts on the peasants about Rye and he must hear from Crane how cowboys lived and, if their livid emotion deserved that verb, loved. A little later he would weary an ailing millionaire at Hyères for the facts of his pauper boyhood. How did a person who so well knew French happen to have been a farmhand at thirteen? How was it allowed? Was — er — was there no resource? No, no grandfather had flourished in the Illinois of his friend's childhood to dispense millions among a dozen descendants and make it certain that nobody need worry about money or have to know coarse and humble people. " Oh," said the novelist of the finer grain, " horrible! Damnable! " . . . What did he think of the tired guest at his table who had " lived with violence " and was " so truly gifted " and " so very lovable " and " had the mannerisms of a Mile End Roader " and

" was of the most charming sensitiveness " in his somewhat diverse and troubled expressions? He sent to Stephen Crane, unasked, five manuscripts and invited an opinion, so he must have respected something in the weary impressionist. Being very old he said: " I loved him. . . ." and that, perhaps, was a convenient synthesis for a mind wanting to understand but not approving the vivid way-farer.

On January 20th Crane drifted into Mr. Pinker's office and re-claimed two tales mailed the day before from Brede. They weren't good enough, he said. His agent asked how the New Year's party had gone and Crane drawled: " I've heard it was a Babylonian orgy."

A confused impression followed. People were told that Crane had shut Brede and was gone to New York or to the Continent, and Robert Barr wrote, on January 24th, to an American: " Mrs. Crane is so incensed by the nonsense talked about the New Year party at Brede that Stevie is taking her home. England has been kind to Stevie in many ways but some of his cherished friends have said things too carelessly about his most generous but not too formal hospitality and I have heard some gossip that must wound him deeply. His skin is very thin and he is subject to a kind of jealousy that knows how to hurt him worst. His present plan is to take some land in Texas and live in the open air but, between our-selves, it is all over with the boy. He may last two years but I can not bring myself to hope for more than that. . . . He sails on the first of the month." He did not sail. The mood lasted an evening after his explosion of disgust. Only a few people knew that he had thought of quitting England. The rumor started and died. He had begun a fantastic novel, *The O'Ruddy*, and was sketching in the last somber flood of his prose as *War Memories*.

Meanwhile in America readers of *Harper's Magazine* were de-lighted and repelled by the Whilomville stories. For the first time since Mark Twain's demigod floated with his lazy slave on the Mis-sissippi, the national child stepped forward and yelped among the maples and swinging gates of a little town, unmoral, unadorned, and far from sweet. This creature lied and bragged and shocked ladies dreadfully. Crane's detachment wasted no loving words on Jimmie Trescott, Willie Dalzell, and the petted daughter of the

painter who blindly gave his brat five dollars and so desolated the
land. Midway in the series is a pure tragedy. Jimmie took his share
of picnic to the lake in a tin pail and all the children made him
suffer for no reason. He was hooted and cast out because 'of this
tin pail. It is the epic of democracies and Crane's enchantment
with the idiocy of communal thought had its last fling. But the
stories were not popular among mothers trained on Mrs. Burnett's
patent food, and male critics only were loud in praise. It was left
for Booth Tarkington to prove the justice of Crane's performance
and with gallantry to remind the public of his predecessor's exploit.
Crane handles the children as he handled mature beings. There is
the same gravity and the same lack of all respect for ordinary values.
As usual not one adventure of Jimmie Trescott is a success. Everything turns out badly, down to the frustration of the Christmas
tree for whose glittering sake he joins an alien Sunday school. So
biographical memory preserves soft female outcries against this
cruel raid in the pink and white realm of childhood. . . . He had
no luck at all. Surely in æsthetic mathematicians are most fortunate, raising their spells for the keen few in a tent of crystal fictions.
Painters and makers of sounds have prompt appeal to a single sense
and may thereby profit, but this written word must sink in a dark
water of all senses mingled, rousing strange brutes of some forgotten dream, brushing to nervous life old prejudice submerged and
shadowy in the mind that reads. Reward? No man of honor may
demand felicity buttressed on ease in a world so subject to mere
chance, but in the final dust vainglory cannot thrill.

Friends wanted to send him as a correspondent for the *Morning
Post* to Saint Helena but one day of March his mouth filled suddenly with blood while he petted a dog at luncheon and nobody
had much hope, after doctors had shaken their heads. He rallied
in April and was jubilant over the birth of twin nephews, one to
be named Stephen Crane and destined to short life. People must
come to Brede and amuse a frantic woman who paced the hall, trying to be affable still and bidding callers be sure to come again,
reproaching herself for so much entertainment. Henry James, full
of solicitudes, hurried to London when papers wrongly announced
that Dr. Trudeau, the famous specialist of Saranac, was lodged in
the city grown gloomy, as nothing went well with English armies

in South Africa. Terrific fevers of the malady swept the man's fancy back to bright sands of New Jersey and he lay reading bits of his father's sermons. Once he was worried because Sanford Bennett recalled some words of Ford Hueffer and he sent after the Canadian a last note: " You must not be offended by Mr. Hueffer's manner. He patronizes Mr. James. He patronizes Mr. Conrad. Of course he patronizes me and he will patronize Almighty God when they meet but God will get used to it, for Hueffer is all right. . . ."

Robert Barr must finish *The O'Ruddy*, and the Scotchman came to get orders for the jolly satire on old Ireland. Mrs. Crane thought of Germany after May entered Sussex and borrowed money broadcast for the useless journey. He was carried down to Dover and laughed when the dog Sponge clawed wallpaper in a room of the old Lord Warden. There Eugénie and the dead Prince Imperial had waited to welcome the last Napoleon into exile and, being told so, Crane stared at the Victorian adornments, whispering: " Hope she liked the carpet." Men came down out of a London surging with news of victories in South Africa. Ill himself, Joseph Conrad dragged to Dover and watched the blue eyes rove to a sail that fled above gray water outside the window. Grace of indifference thickened. He did not care which world held him or if the multicolored dice of a new being would flash beyond this towering shadow of the void. Out there? He didn't care, stroking his dog.

His niece joined him in hired chambers at Badenweiler and sun glowed in his wife's hair while he dictated orders for the gay novel and sometimes patted her white arms. On the fourth day of June he was very eager. Letters must go to his brothers and to John Hilliard. Sponge hopped around the bed and must be teased for a while. Then it was night and the tired woman fell asleep, to be wakened before dawn by the little dog's vain howling in the dark.

APPENDIX

Stephen Crane is buried at Elizabeth, New Jersey, and a tablet to his memory is now in the Free Library of Newark. Mr. Max Herzberg of the Newark *Evening News* was one of the movers for this memorial and to Mr. Herzberg I am much indebted for the use of certain papers collected by him in his personal researches as to Crane. I must at once acknowledge an even greater indebtedness to Mr. Willis Clarke for his generosity toward me. In 1903 Mr. Clarke began to collect copies of letters and facts for a life of Stephen Crane, but was so baffled by conflicting statements that he dropped the work. His shorthand report of an interview with Crane at Brede is quoted in Chapters i, iii, and iv and vii of this book. He was also the donor of letters from Mrs. Bolton Chaffee, Julian Ralph, Robert Barr, Acton Davies, and Henry Davies Hume, and of a passage in the diary of the late Charles Cary Griswold. The mythology encountered by Mr. Clarke may interest readers who have been struck by a note of apology in this most imperfect study. Mr. Clarke was informed by people who had met Crane and admired him that he was the illegitimate son of Grover Cleveland, the outcast child of an eminent family in New York, an Australian sailor, a German actor, and an ex-convict. He was gravely assured that the several published statements about Crane in journals, the *Bookman*, *Leslie's Weekly*, and *Scribner's Magazine*, were industrious camouflage devised by the late Ripley Hitchcock on behalf of Appleton's. My own contact with the legendary Crane revealed other jewels of rumor. I have, with regret, rejected the tales of Crane's love-affair with the lamented Sarah Bernhardt, of his duel in New Orleans, of his attempt to burn James Gordon Bennett's yacht, of his marriage to Australian, English, Spanish, and African dancers, of his ninety-thousand-dollar cablegram to the New York *Journal*, of his death of delirium tremens in Paris, and of his murder by an actress still living who happened at the time of his death to be in Chicago. With less pain I have rejected anecdotes of Crane which were in print during his childhood as anecdotes of Mark Twain, Thomas Hood, Abraham Lincoln, and Andrew Jackson.

There have also been visited upon me stories of his gayeties which
are, with probably as much truth, told in regard to Bill Nye,
Eugene Field, Clyde Fitch, and other celebrities still extant.

It was suggested to me by Mr. Huneker that Crane's picturesque
exterior offered a field for the imagination of some contemporaries
and that " they turned a little Flaubert into a big Verlaine." The
injustice of that romancing was great, however, and inevitably I
have concluded that a considerable spite followed him after his
success. Else why did three unsigned letters reach me when Mr.
Christopher Morley printed my wish for correspondence in the
New York *Evening Post?* All three votaries of romantic biography
had charges to make and the charges were couched in excellent
English.

Some of Crane's friends erred in their mention of him after
death. Elbert Hubbard's paper in the *Philistine* contained equivocal statements, and Robert Barr's " qualities that lent themselves
to misapprehension " is not a fortunate phrase. An article printed
as an obituary of Stephen Crane in a New York paper of June 6,
1900 took pains to clear him of the charge of drug-taking and probably settled that charge in the popular mind he so distrusted. Three
estimates likened him to Edgar Allan Poe, who is still, after scrupulous examination, held to have been a drunken madman by the
generality of readers. Without doubt I shall be accused of " white-
washing " Crane, and by choice I retort beforehand that a man is
entitled to his own identity, not to a cheap shell of gossip. If my
assumption that the reissue of *Maggie* roused silly conjectures is
incorrect, it is in one instance well supported. Mr. William Crane
tells me that after *Maggie* appeared in 1896 several ladies of Port
Jervis solemnly consulted him as to the propriety of receiving
Stephen Crane in their homes. . . . The American nineties present a singular mingling of poltroonery and bravado in the treatment of sexual and alcoholic matters public or private. You behold
young men singing Hovey's pretty " Stein Song " and you hear the
last despairing outcries of Frances Willard, who wanted her world
to be Christian and in loud addresses assured it that Christ's kindness to the woman taken in adultery was not an example to be
imitated " in our modern day." The author of *The Black Riders,*
Maggie, and *George's Mother* was plainly an object of suspicion,

and America never comes of age. A fellow who defends streetwalkers in night resorts and lends money to courtesans is naturally " immoral." His intimates took Crane for a man of honest and liberal views and their indignation with the figure created for him by fiction persists. . . . I take vast pleasure in issuing on behalf of a dead and generous man a firm denial of an attack on Crane in *The Derelict* by Richard Harding Davis. Illustrations of the story happened to resemble Crane somewhat and Mr. Davis suffered a deal of comment for which he was not responsible.

This book is probably filled with errors, but my variations from partial biographies have been made on the testimony of Crane's few letters. With genuine regret I have differed from Mr. Hamlin Garland's account of the birth of *The Red Badge*, which, in his recollection, was first shown to him in 1893 and in the month of February. Crane's own statement and the memory of other friends place the writing rather later. I can only suggest that the first rapid draft was the manuscript brought to Mr. Garland in Harlem and that the finished product was shown in the following winter. But Crane's carelessness was astonishing. Belonging to the vainest of professions, he took no trouble to annotate himself for history, and that carelessness remains a part of his charm for those who knew him. Many of his last letters were written in a singular blue ink that turned purple when dry and has now faded beyond process of revival. I have been unable to verify Crane's career as a reporter on the *Herald*, and some amusing episodes have been omitted for lack of proof. Also there have been removed from his letters some hasty estimates of living people in England and America. Crane himself had no great idea of his judgment as to character on first sight, as he took Mr. George Bernard Shaw for a " clerical person " and Mr. Frank Harris for an actor. It would have been pleasant to print his admiration of certain ladies who received him in England, but the wives of authors are entitled to such privacy as is left in the world.

For their kindness in aiding me this book should be dedicated to a number of people. If I have not effected a portrait of the Stephen Crane known to them, that is because, in his words, " an expression of life can always elude us." Excuse me a little. Another may do better. My thanks are offered, among the unconcerned dead, to:

James Gibbons Huneker, Charles Edward Devlin, Wallis McHarg, Clyde Fitch, James Pinker, Acton Davies, and to Edmund Crane, among the living to William Howe Crane, Edith Crane, Vera Sidmore, Hamlin Garland, Mark Barr, Edith Richie Jones, Corwin Knapp Linson, Frederic Gordon, Edward Garnett, Karl Edwin Harriman, Vincent Starrett,[1] Paul Reynolds, Richard Brett Armstrong, Sarah McHarg, Victoria Sonntag, John Langdon Heaton, Edward Sanford Bennett, Charles Gardner 2nd, Claude Bragdon, Irving Bacheller, Jesse Lynch Williams, Henry T. Carey, John Northern Hilliard, John Willard Raught, Helen Marie Campbell, Caroline Gunther, Eileen Bassett Dufriche, Joseph and Jessie Conrad.

[1] Mr. Starrett's *Bibliography* contains all my information as to Crane's unpublished work.

Three
Chinese Poets

OOD poems can be translated and often are. To say that they cannot be is only to say that some, or much, of the original magic must be lost in the change to another language. But a good poem has more magic than is heard in native vowels and consonants, in whatever beguiling order they reach the ear. There are the ideas, there are the images, which can be carried over. There is the beat of emotion which made the poem good in the first place. This is the real mystery of poetry: that the quickened and heightened pulse of the poet, in the midst of a true excitement, speaks in his words to the responding pulses of his readers. Nor is good poetry like simple sound, lost at a little distance and stopped by tangible barriers. Rather, it is like the waves of the ether which travel everywhere and through anything.

Take for example one poem by each of these three Chinese poets. Li Po's *Song of Ch'ang-kan* illustrates a convention of Chinese poetry, which has countless letters in verse from faithful women to their husbands or lovers away from home on military or official business. This poem is twelve hundred years old and, written by a man, it was merely dramatic to begin with. Yet the images are as bright and fresh as ever, and the resolute, anxious, eager devotion of the young wife throbs unmistakably in the alien words. Or *A Song of War-Chariots* by Tu Fu. Reading it, you not only see the conscripts dragged off to war but you feel the desolate mood of the village from which they go, you share with Tu Fu his bitter sense of their fate. Though the terse clang of the Chinese monosyllables has been lost, the rhythm of the passion and the thought survive translation. Po Chü-i in *Chu Ch'ēn Village* wrote in a rush of philosopher's homesickness for a quiet life, longed for in the midst of the crowding world. There is nothing new or old about this homesickness. It was felt in the first city, and it will be felt in the last. Of course it is not quite reasonable. The city men who hanker for villages would most of them be bored there. But the longing rises in spite of reason, rises in a kind of pulse of the mind. It rose in Po Chü-i, and it wakes its quick response across an intervening millennium. Good poems can be translated, and perhaps good poems only.

The body of Chinese poetry is so immense — from the T'ang dynasty of three hundred years nearly fifty thousand poems have been preserved — that the part of it known to English readers is very small. But the present century has seen, both in America and in England, several excellent translators, and it is now possible to read a good many Chinese poems in English with the simple natural pleasure with which the best poetry ought always to be read. Because the translations have often been anthologies, few Chinese poets are distinguished from their hundreds of rivals. I have here chosen three poets and have given enough poems by each of them, I hope, to make them seem interesting persons as well as moving voices. Kiang Kang-hu calls Li Po, perhaps better known to American readers than any other single Chinese poet, "the genie of poetry" and Tu Fu "the sage of poetry." I have myself an affectionate preference for Po Chü-i. I do not know any more touching poems about children than his two about Golden Bells, which may be compared with the first of the poems by John Crowe Ransom elsewhere in this volume. I know few poems humaner than Po Chü-i's *Flower Market* or *Watching the Reapers*, or more humorous than *Lazy Man's Song*, or more eloquent of friendship than the letter *To Li Chien*. I understand that the stricter schools of Chinese literary opinion do not value Po Chü-i and that he is left out of many anthologies. This seems to me like denying Burns his rank among English poets.

But the poems I have here selected do not need critical preliminaries. They may be read as they stand, as the record of ancient experiences of the mind which are also remarkably modern. The best Chinese poems are timeless. They are masculine in their concerns. They are seldom romantic about love between the sexes, but are more interested in friendship, wine, parents and children, landscapes, the details of the common life, and moral reflections. It must be remembered that the Chinese poets were most of them scholars and officials and that their poems spring from occasions which the poets found lovely or memorable.

C.V.D.

Li Po

Translated by

Witter Bynner and Kiang Kang-hu

IN THE QUIET NIGHT

So bright a gleam on the foot of my bed —
Could there have been a frost already?
Lifting myself to look, I found that it was moonlight.
Sinking back again, I thought suddenly of home.

A BITTER LOVE

How beautiful she looks, opening the pearly casement,
And how quiet she leans, and how troubled her brow is!
You may see the tears now, bright on her cheek,
But not the man she so bitterly loves.

A SONG OF PURE HAPPINESS

(Written to Music for Lady Yang)

I

Her robe is a cloud, her face a flower;
Her balcony, glimmering with the bright spring dew,
Is either the tip of earth's Jade Mountain
Or a moon-edged roof of paradise.

II

There's a perfume stealing moist from a shaft of red blossom,
And a mist, through the heart, from the magical Hill of Wu —
The palaces of China have never known such beauty —
Not even Flying Swallow with all her glittering garments.

III

Lovely now together, his lady and his flowers
Lighten forever the Emperor's eye,
As he listens to the sighing of the far spring wind
Where she leans on a railing in the Aloe Pavilion.

DOWN CHUNG–NAN MOUNTAIN

To the Kind Pillow and Bowl of Hu Ssü

Down the blue mountain in the evening,
Moonlight was my homeward escort.
Looking back, I saw my path
Lie in levels of deep shadow. . . .
I was passing the farmhouse of a friend,
When his children called from a gate of thorn
And led me twining through jade bamboos
Where green vines caught and held my clothes.
And I was glad of a chance to rest
And glad of a chance to drink with my friend. . . .
We sang to the tune of the wind in the pines;

And we finished our songs as the stars went down,
When, I being drunk and my friend more than happy,
Between us we forgot the world.

DRINKING ALONE WITH THE MOON

From a pot of wine among the flowers
I drank alone. There was no one with me —
Till, raising my cup, I asked the bright moon
To bring me my shadow and make us three.
Alas, the moon was unable to drink
And my shadow tagged me vacantly;
But still for a while I had these friends
To cheer me through the end of spring. . . .
I sang. The moon encouraged me.
I danced. My shadow tumbled after.
As long as I knew, we were boon companions.
And then I was drunk, and we lost one another.
. . . Shall goodwill ever be secure?
I watch the long road of the River of Stars.

IN SPRING

Your northern grasses are as blue as jade,
Our southern mulberries curve green-threaded branches;
And at last you think of returning home,
Now when my heart is almost broken. . . .
O breeze of the spring, since I dare not know you,
Why part the silk curtains by my bed?

THE MOON AT THE FORTIFIED PASS

(Written to Music)

The bright moon lifts from the Mountain of Heaven
In an infinite haze of cloud and sea,
And the wind, that has come a thousand miles,
Beats at the Jade Pass battlements. . . .
China marches its men down Po-têng Road

While Tartar troops peer across blue waters of the bay. . . .
And since not one battle famous in history
Sent all its fighters back again,
The soldiers turn round, looking toward the border,
And think of home, with wistful eyes,
And of those tonight in the upper chambers
Who toss and sigh and cannot rest.

A SONG OF CH'ANG–KAN

(Written to Music)

My hair had hardly covered my forehead.
I was picking flowers, playing by my door,
When you, my lover, on a bamboo horse,
Came trotting in circles and throwing green plums.
We lived near together on a lane in Ch'ang-kan,
Both of us young and happy-hearted.
. . . At fourteen I became your wife,
So bashful that I dared not smile,
And I lowered my head toward a dark corner
And would not turn to your thousand calls;
But at fifteen I straightened my brows and laughed,
Learning that no dust could ever seal our love,
That even unto death I would await you by my post
And would never lose heart in the tower of silent watching.
. . . Then when I was sixteen, you left on a long journey
Through the Gorges of Ch'ü-t'ang, of rock and whirling water.
And then came the Fifth-month, more than I could bear,
And I tried to hear the monkeys in your lofty far-off sky.
Your footprints by our door, where I had watched you go,
Were hidden, every one of them, under green moss,
Hidden under moss too deep to sweep away.
And the first autumn wind added fallen leaves.
And now, in the Eighth-month, yellowing butterflies
Hover, two by two, in our west-garden grasses. . . .
And, because of all this, my heart is breaking
And I fear for my bright cheeks, lest they fade.

. . . Oh, at last, when you return through the three Pa districts,
Send me a message home ahead!
And I will come and meet you and will never mind the distance,
All the way to Chang-fêng Sha.

A SONG OF LU MOUNTAIN

To Censor Lu Hsü-chou

I am the madman of the Ch'u country
Who sang a mad song disputing Confucius.
. . . Holding in my hand a staff of green jade,
I have crossed, since morning at the Yellow Crane Terrace,
All five Holy Mountains, without a thought of distance,
According to the one constant habit of my life.
. . . Lu Mountain stands beside the Southern Dipper
In clouds reaching silken like a nine-paneled screen,
With its shadows in a crystal lake deepening the green water.
The Golden Gate opens into two mountain ranges.
A silver stream is hanging down to three stone bridges
Within sight of the mighty Tripod Falls.
Ledges of cliff and winding trails lead to blue sky
And a flush of cloud in the morning sun,
When no flight of birds could be blown into Wu.
. . . I climb to the top. I survey the whole world.
I see the long river that runs beyond return,
Yellow clouds that winds have driven hundreds of miles
And a snow-peak whitely circled by the swirl of a ninefold stream.
And so I am singing a song of Lu Mountain,
A song that is born of the breath of Lu Mountain.
. . . Where the Stone Mirror makes the heart's purity purer
And green moss has buried the footsteps of Hsieh,
I have eaten the immortal pellet and, rid of the world's troubles,
Before the lute's third playing have achieved my element.
Far away I watch the angels riding colored clouds
Toward heaven's Jade City, with hibiscus in their hands.
And so, when I have traversed the nine sections of the world,
I will follow Saint Lu-ao up the Great Purity.

ENDLESS YEARNING

(Written to Music)

I

" I am endlessly yearning
To be in Ch'ang-an.
. . . Insects hum of autumn by the gold brim of the well;
A thin frost glistens like little mirrors on my cold mat;
The high lantern flickers; and deeper grows my longing.
I lift the shade and, with many a sigh, gaze upon the moon,
Single as a flower, centered from the clouds.
Above, I see the blueness and deepness of sky.
Below, I see the greenness and the restlessness of water. . . .
Heaven is high, earth wide; bitter between them flies my sorrow.
Can I dream through the gateway, over the mountain?.
Endless longing
Breaks my heart."

II

" The sun has set, and a mist is in the flowers;
And the moon grows very white and people sad and sleepless.
A Chao harp has just been laid mute on its phœnix-holder,
And a Shu lute begins to sounds its mandarin-duck strings. . . .
Since nobody can bear to you the burden of my song,
Would that it might follow the spring wind to Yen-jan Mountain.
I think of you far away, beyond the blue sky,
And my eyes that once were sparkling
Are now a well of tears.
. . . Oh, if ever you should doubt this aching of my heart,
Here in my bright mirror come back and look at me! "

BRINGING IN THE WINE

(Written to Music)

See how the Yellow River's waters move out of heaven.
Entering the ocean, never to return.
See how lovely locks in bright mirrors in high chambers,
Though silken-black at morning, have changed by night to snow.
. . . Oh, let a man of spirit venture where he pleases
And never tip his golden cup empty toward the moon!
Since heaven gave the talent, let it be employed!
Spin a thousand pieces of silver, all of them come back!
Cook a sheep, kill a cow, whet the appetite,
And make me, of three hundred bowls, one long drink!
. . . To the old master, Ts'ên,
And the young scholar, Tan-ch'iu,
Bring in the wine!
Let your cups never rest!
Let me sing you a song!
Let your ears attend!
What are bell and drum, rare dishes and treasure?
Let me be forever drunk and never come to reason!
Sober men of olden days and sages are forgotten,
And only the great drinkers are famous for all time.
. . . Prince Ch'ên paid at a banquet in the Palace of Perfection
Ten thousand coins for a cask of wine, with many a laugh and quip.
Why say, my host, that your money is gone?
Go and buy wine and we'll drink it together!
My flower-dappled horse,
My furs worth a thousand,
Hand them to the boy to exchange for good wine,
And we'll drown away the woes of ten thousand generations!

❄§ *Tu Fu* ❧

Translated by

Witter Bynner and Kiang Kang-hu

A HEARTY WELCOME

To Vice-Prefect Ts'uêi

North of me, south of me, spring is in flood,
Day after day I have seen only gulls. . . .
My path is full of petals — I have swept it for no others.
My thatch gate has been closed — but opens now for you.
It's a long way to the market, I can offer you little —
Yet here in my cottage there is old wine for our cups.
Shall we summon my elderly neighbor to join us,
Call him through the fence, and pour the jar dry?

STAYING AT THE GENERAL'S HEADQUARTERS

The autumn night is clear and cold in the lakka trees of this court-
    yard.
I am lying forlorn in the river-town. I watch my guttering candle.
I hear the lonely notes of a bugle sounding through the dark.
The moon is in mid-heaven, but there's no one to share it with me.

My messengers are scattered by whirls of rain and sand.
City gates are closed to a traveler; mountains are walls in my way —
Yet I, who have borne ten years of pitiable existence,
Find here a perch, a little branch, and am safe for this one night.

TO MY RETIRED FRIEND WÊI

It is almost as hard for friends to meet
As for the morning and evening stars.
Tonight then is a rare event,
Joining, in the candlelight,
Two men who were young not long ago
But now are turning gray at the temples.
. . . To find that half our friends are dead
Shocks us, burns our hearts with grief.
We little guessed it would be twenty years
Before I could visit you again.
When I went away, you were still unmarried;
But now these boys and girls in a row
Are very kind to their father's old friend.
They ask me where I have been on my journey;
And then, when we have talked awhile,
They bring and show me wines and dishes,
Spring chives cut in the night rain
And brown rice cooked freshly a special way.
. . . My host proclaims it a festival,
He urges me to drink ten cups —
But what ten cups could make me as drunk
As I always am with your love in my heart?
. . . Tomorrow the mountains will separate us;
After tomorrow — who can say?

ALONE IN HER BEAUTY

Who is lovelier than she?
Yet she lives alone in an empty valley.
She tells me she came from a good family
Which is humbled now into the dust.

. . . When trouble arose in the Huan district,
Her brothers and close kin were killed.
What use were their high offices,
Not even shielding their own lives? —
The world has but scorn for adversity;
Hope goes out, like the light of a candle.
Her husband, with a vagrant heart,
Seeks a new face like a new piece of jade;
And when morning-glories furl at night
And mandarin-ducks lie side by side,
All he can see is the smile of the new love,
While the old love weeps unheard.
The brook was pure in its mountain source,
But away from the mountain its waters darken.
. . . Waiting for her maid to come from selling pearls
For straw to cover the roof again,
She picks a few flowers, no longer for her hair,
And lets pine-needles fall through her fingers,
And, forgetting her thin silk sleeve and the cold,
She leans in the sunset by a tall bamboo.

SEEING LI PO IN A DREAM

I

There are sobs when death is the cause of parting;
But life has its partings again and again.
. . . From the poisonous damps of the southern river
You had sent me not one sign from your exile —
Till you came to me last night in a dream,
Because I am always thinking of you. . . .
I wondered if it were really you,
Venturing so long a journey.
You came to me through the green of a forest,
You disappeared by a shadowy fortress . . .
Yet out of the midmost mesh of your snare,
How could you lift your wings and use them?

, . . . I woke, and the low moon's glimmer on a rafter
Seemed to be your face, still floating in the air.
. . . There were waters to cross, they were wild and tossing;
If you fell, there were dragons and river-monsters.

II

This cloud, that has drifted all day through the sky,
May, like a wanderer, never come back. . . .
Three nights now I have dreamed of you —
As tender, intimate, and real as though I were awake.
And then, abruptly rising to go,
You told me the perils of adventure
By river and lake — the storms, the wrecks,
The fears that are borne on a little boat;
And, here in my doorway, you rubbed your white head
As if there were something puzzling you.
. . . Our capital teems with officious people,
While you are alone and helpless and poor.
Who says that the heavenly net never fails?
It has brought you ill fortune, old as you are.
. . . A thousand years' fame, ten thousand years' fame —
What good, when you are dead and gone?

A SONG OF AN OLD CYPRESS

Beside the Temple of the Great Premier stands an ancient cypress
With a trunk of green bronze and a root of stone.
The girth of its white bark would be the reach of forty men
And its tip of kingfisher-blue is two thousand feet in heaven.
Dating from the days of a great ruler's great statesman,
Their very tree is loved now and honored by the people.
Clouds come to it from far away, from the Wu cliffs,
And the cold moon glistens on its peak of snow.
. . . East of the Silk Pavilion yesterday I found
The ancient ruler and wise statesman both worshipped in one
    temple,
Whose tree, with curious branches, ages the whole landscape

In spite of the fresh colors of the windows and the doors.
And so firm is the deep root, so established underground,
That its lone lofty boughs can dare the weight of winds,
Its only protection the Heavenly Power,
Its only endurance the art of its Creator.
. . . When beams are required to restore a great house,
Though oxen sway ten thousand heads, they cannot move a mountain.
Though a tree writes no memorial, yet people understand
That not unless they fell it can use be made of it. . . .
Its bitter heart may be tenanted now by black and white ants,
But its odorous leaves were once the nest of phœnixes and pheasants.
. . . Let wise and hopeful men harbor no complaint.
The greater the timber, the tougher it is to use.

A SONG OF WAR–CHARIOTS

(Written to Music)

The war-chariots rattle,
The war-horses whinny.
Each man of you has a bow and a quiver at his belt.
Father, mother, son, wife, stare at you going,
Till dust shall have buried the bridge beyond Ch'ang-an.
They run with you, crying, they tug at your sleeves,
And the sound of their sorrow goes up to the clouds;
And every time a bystander asks you a question,
You can only say to him that you have to go.
. . . We remember others at fifteen sent north to guard the river
And at forty sent west to cultivate the camp-farms.
The mayor wound their turbans for them when they started out.
With their turbaned hair white now, they are still at the border,
At the border where the blood of men spills like the sea —
And still the heart of Emperor Wu is beating for war.
. . . Do you know that, east of China's mountains, in two hundred districts
And in thousands of villages, nothing grows but weeds,

And though strong women have bent to the plowing,
East and west the furrows all are broken down?
. . . Men of China are able to face the stiffest battle,
But their officers drive them like chickens and dogs.
Whatever is asked of them,
Dare they complain?
For example, this winter
Held west of the gate,
Challenged for taxes,
How could they pay?
. . . We have learned that to have a son is bad luck —
It is very much better to have a daughter
Who can marry and live in the house of a neighbor,
While under the sod we bury our boys.
. . . Go to the Blue Sea, look along the shore
At all the old white bones forsaken —
New ghosts are wailing there now with the old,
Loudest in the dark sky of a stormy day.

A SONG OF FAIR WOMEN

(Written to Music)

On the third day of the Third-month in the freshening weather
Many beauties take the air by the Ch'ang-an waterfront,
Receptive, aloof, sweet-mannered, sincere,
With soft fine skin and well-balanced bone.
Their embroidered silk robes in the spring sun are gleaming
With a mass of golden peacocks and silver unicorns.
And hanging far down from their temples
Are blue leaves of delicate kingfisher feathers.
And following behind them
Is a pearl-laden train, rhythmic with bearers.
Some of them are kindred to the royal house —
The titled Princesses Kuo and Ch'in.
Red camel-humps are brought them from jade broilers,
And sweet fish is offered them on crystal trays.
Though their food-sticks of unicorn-horn are lifted languidly

And the finely wrought phœnix carving-knife is very little used,
Fleet horses from the Yellow Gate, stirring no dust,
Bring precious dishes constantly from the Imperial kitchen.
. . . While a solemn sound of flutes and drums invokes gods and
     spirits,
Guests and courtiers gather, all of high rank;
And finally, riding slow, a dignified horseman
Dismounts at the pavilion on an embroidered rug.
In a snow of flying willow-cotton whitening the duckweed,
Bluebirds find their way with vermilion handkerchiefs —
But power can be as hot as flame and burn people's fingers.
Be wary of the Premier, watch for his frown.

Po Chü-i

Translated by Arthur Waley

GOLDEN BELLS

When I was almost forty
I had a daughter whose name was Golden Bells.
Now it is just a year since she was born;
She is learning to sit and cannot yet talk.
Ashamed — to find that I have not a sage's heart:
I cannot resist vulgar thoughts and feelings.
Henceforward I am tied to things outside myself:
My only reward — the pleasure I am getting now.
If I am spared the grief of her dying young,
Then I shall have the trouble of getting her married.
My plan for retiring and going back to the hills
Must now be postponed for fifteen years!

REMEMBERING GOLDEN BELLS

Ruined and ill — a man of twoscore;
Pretty and guileless — a girl of three.
Not a boy — but still better than nothing:

To soothe one's feelings — from time to time a kiss!
There came a day — they suddenly took her from me;
Her soul's shadow wandered I know not where.
And when I remember how just at the time she died
She lisped strange sounds, beginning to learn to talk,
Then I know that the ties of flesh and blood
Only bind us to a load of grief and sorrow.
At last, by thinking of the time before she was born,
By thought and reason I drove the pain away.
Since my heart forgot her, many days have passed
And three times winter has changed to spring.
This morning, for a little, the old grief came back,
Because, in the road, I met her foster-nurse.

THE FLOWER MARKET

In the Royal City spring is almost over:
Tinkle, tinkle — the coaches and horsemen pass.
We tell each other: " This is the peony season ";
And follow with the crowd that goes to the Flower Market.
" Cheap and dear — no uniform price:
The cost of the plant depends on the number of blossoms,
For the fine flower — a hundred pieces of damask:
For the cheap flower — five bits of silk.
Above is spread an awning to protect them;
Around is woven a wattle-fence to screen them.
If you sprinkle water and cover the roots with mud,
When they are transplanted, they will not lose their beauty."
Each household thoughtlessly follows the custom,
Man by man, no one realizing.
There happened to be an old farm laborer
          Who came by chance that way.
He bowed his head and sighed a deep sigh;
But this sigh nobody understood.
He was thinking: " A cluster of deep-red flowers
Would pay the taxes of ten poor houses."

PRUNING TREES

Trees growing — right in front of my window;
The trees are high and the leaves grow thick.
Sad, alas! the distant mountain view
Obscured by this, dimly shows between.
One morning I took knife and ax;
With my own hand I lopped the branches off.
Ten thousand leaves fall about my head;
A thousand hills come before my eyes.
Suddenly, as when clouds or mists break
And straight through, the blue sky appears;
Again, like the face of a friend one has loved
Seen at last after an age of parting.
First there came a gentle wind blowing;
One by one the birds flew back to the tree.
To ease my mind I gazed to the southeast;
As my eyes wandered, my thoughts went far away.
Of men there is none that has not some preference;
Of things there is none but mixes good with ill.
It was not that I did not love the tender branches;
But better still — to see the green hills!

AFTER GETTING DRUNK, BECOMING SOBER IN THE NIGHT

Our party scattered at yellow dusk and I came home to bed;
I woke at midnight and went for a walk, leaning heavily on a friend.
As I lay on my pillow my vinous complexion, soothed by sleep,
grew sober;
In front of the tower the ocean moon, accompanying the tide, had
risen.
The swallows, about to return to the beams, went back to roost
again;
The candle at my window, just going out, suddenly revived its
light.

All the time till dawn came, still my thoughts were muddled;
And in my ears something sounded like the music of flutes and
    strings.

ON BEING SIXTY

Between thirty and forty, one is distracted by the Five Lusts;
Between seventy and eighty, one is a prey to a hundred diseases.
But from fifty to sixty one is free from all ills;
Calm and still — the heart enjoys rest.
I have put behind me Love and Greed; I have done with Profit and
    Fame;
I am still short of illness and decay and far from decrepit age.
Strength of limb I still possess to seek the rivers and hills;
Still my heart has spirit enough to listen to flutes and strings.
At leisure I open new wine and taste several cups;
Drunken I recall old poems and sing a whole volume.
Mēng-tē has asked for a poem and herewith I exhort him
Not to complain of threescore, " the time of obedient ears."

WATCHING THE REAPERS

Tillers of the soil have few idle months;
In the fifth month their toil is double-fold.
A south wind visits the field at night:
Suddenly the hill is covered with yellow corn.
Wives and daughters shoulder baskets of rice;
Youths and boys carry the flasks of wine.
Following after they bring a wage of meat
To the strong reapers toiling on the southern hill,
Whose feet are burned by the hot earth they tread,
Whose backs are scorched by flames of the shining sky.
Tired they toil, caring nothing for the heat,
Grudging the shortness of the long summer day.
A poor woman follows at the reapers' side
With an infant child carried close at her breast.
With her right hand she gleans the fallen grain;
On her left arm a broken basket hangs.

And *I* today . . . by virtue of what right
Have I never once tended field or tree?
My government pay is three hundred tons;
At the year's end I have still grain in hand.
Thinking of this, secretly I grew ashamed;
And all day the thought lingered in my head.

TO LI CHIEN

Worldly matters again draw my steps;
Worldly things again seduce my heart.
Whenever for long I part from Li Chien
Gradually my thoughts grow narrow and covetous.
I remember how once I used to visit you;
I stopped my horse and tapped at the garden gate.
Often when I came you were still lying in bed;
Your little children were sent to let me in.
And you, laughing, ran to the front door
With coat-tails flying and cap all awry.
On the swept terrace, green patterns of moss;
On the dusted bench, clean shadows of leaves.
To gaze at the hills we sat in the eastern lodge;
To wait for the moon we walked to the southern moor.
At your quiet gate only birds spoke;
In your distant street few drums were heard.
Opposite each other all day we talked,
And never once spoke of profit or fame.
Since we parted hands, how long has passed?
Thrice and again the full moon has shone.
For when we parted, the last flowers were falling,
And today I hear new cicadas sing.
The scented year suddenly draws to its close,
Yet the sorrow of parting is still unsubdued.

CHU CH'ĒN VILLAGE

In Hsü-chou, in the District of Ku-fēng
There lies a village whose name is Chu-ch'ēn —
A hundred miles away from the county town,
Amid fields of hemp and green of mulberry trees.
Click, click goes the sound of the spinning-wheel;
Mules and oxen pack the village streets.
The girls go drawing water from the brook;
The men go gathering firewood on the hill.
So far from the town, government affairs are few;
So deep in the hills, man's ways are simple.
Though they have wealth, they do not traffic with it;
Though they reach the age, they do not enter the army.
Each family keeps to its village trade;
Gray-headed, they have never left the gates.

Alive, they are the people of Ch'ēn Village;
Dead, they become the dust of Ch'ēn Village.
Out in the fields old men and young
Gaze gladly, each in the other's face.
In the whole village there are only two clans;
Age after age Chus have married Ch'ēns.
Near or distant, they have kinsmen in every house;
Young or old, they have friends wherever they go.
On white wine and roasted fowl they fare
At joyful meetings more than " once a week."
While they are alive, they have no distant partings;
To choose a wife they go to a neighbor's house.
When they are dead — no distant burial;
Round the village graves lie thick.
They are not troubled either about life or death;
They have no anguish either of body or soul.
And so it happens that they live to a ripe age
And great-great-grandsons are often seen.

I was born in the Realms of Etiquette;
In early years, unprotected and poor.
Alone, I learnt to distinguish between Evil and Good;
Untutored, I toiled at bitter tasks.
The World's Law honors Learning and **Fame**;
Scholars prize marriages and Caps.
With these fetters I gyved my own hands;
Truly I became a much-deceived man.
At ten years old I learnt to read books;
At fifteen I knew how to write prose.
At twenty I was made a Bachelor of Arts;
At thirty I became a Censor at the court.
Above, the duty I owe to Prince and parents;
Below, the ties that bind me to wife and child.
The support of my family, the service of my country —
For these tasks my nature is not apt.
I reckon the time that I first left my home;
From then till now — fifteen springs!
My lonely boat has thrice sailed to Ch'u;
Four times through Ch'in my lean horse has passed.
I have walked in the morning with hunger in my face;
I have lain at night with a soul that could not rest.
East and west I have wandered without pause,
Hither and thither like a cloud astray in the sky.
In the civil war my old home was destroyed;
Of my flesh and blood many are scattered and lost.
        North of the river, and south of the river —
In both lands are the friends of all my life;
Life-friends whom I never see at all —
Whose deaths I hear of only after the lapse of years.
Sad at morning, I lie on my bed till dusk;
Weeping at night, I sit and wait for dawn.
The fire of sorrow has burnt my heart's core;
The frost of trouble has seized my hair's roots.
In such anguish has my whole life passed;
Long I have envied the people of Ch'ēn Village.

LAZY MAN'S SONG

I have got patronage, but am too lazy to use it;
I have got land, but am too lazy to farm it.
My house leaks; I am too lazy to mend it.
My clothes are torn; I am too lazy to darn them.
I have got wine, but am too lazy to drink;
So it's just the same as if my cellar were empty.
I have got a harp, but am too lazy to play;
So it's just the same as if it had no strings.
My wife tells me there is no more bread in the house;
I want to bake, but am too lazy to grind.
My friends and relatives write me long letters;
I should like to read them, but they're such a bother to open.
I have always been told that Chi Shu-yeh
Passed his whole life in absolute idleness.
But he played the harp and sometimes transmuted metals,
So even *he* was not so lazy as I.

THE BEGINNING OF SUMMER

At the rise of summer a hundred beasts and trees
Join in gladness that the Season bids them thrive.
Stags and does frolic in the deep woods;
Snakes and insects are pleased by the rank grass.
Wingèd birds love the thick leaves;
Scaly fish enjoy the fresh weeds.
But to one place Summer forgot to come;
I alone am left like a withered straw . . .
        Banished to the world's end;
Flesh and bone all in distant ways.
From my native place no tidings come;
Rebel troops flood the land with war.
Sullen grief, in the end, what will it bring?
I am only wearing my own heart away.
Better far to let both body and mind
Blindly yield to the fate that Heaven made.

Hsün-yang abounds in good wine;
I will fill my cup and never let it be dry.
On Pēn River fish are cheap as mud;
Early and late I will eat them, boiled and fried.
With morning rice at the temple under the hill,
And evening wine at the island in the lake . . .
Why should my thoughts turn to my native land?
For in this place one could well end one's age.

AFTER COLLECTING THE AUTUMN TAXES

From my high castle I look at the town below
Where the natives of Pa cluster like a swarm of flies.
How can I govern these people and lead them aright?
I cannot even understand what they say.
But at least I am glad, now that the taxes are in,
To learn that in my province there is no discontent.
I fear its prosperity is not due to me
And was only caused by the year's abundant crops.
The papers that lie on my desk are simple and few;
My house by the moat is leisurely and still.
In the autumn rains the berries fall from the eaves;
At the evening bell the birds return to the wood.
A broken sunlight quavers over the southern porch
Where I lie on my couch abandoned to idleness.

LODGING WITH THE OLD MAN OF
THE STREAM

Men's hearts love gold and jade;
Men's mouths covet wine and flesh.
Not so the old man of the stream;
He drinks from his gourd and asks nothing more.
South of the stream he cuts firewood and grass;
North of the stream he has built wall and roof.
Yearly he sows a single acre of land;
In spring he drives two yellow calves.

In these things he finds great repose;
Beyond these he has no wish or care.
By chance I met him walking by the water-side;
He took me home and lodged me in his thatched hut.
When I parted from him, to seek market and court,
The old man asked my rank and pay.
Doubting my tale, he laughed loud and long:
" Privy councillors do not sleep in barns."

TITLES AND SOURCES